560-80

ANNUAL REVIEW OF PHYSIOLOGY

ANNUAL REVIEW OF PHYSIOLOGY

VICTOR E. HALL, *Editor*
University of California at Los Angeles

FREDERICK A. FUHRMAN, *Associate Editor*
Stanford University

ARTHUR C. GIESE, *Associate Editor*
Stanford University

VOLUME 24

1962

PUBLISHED BY
ANNUAL REVIEWS, INC.
IN COOPERATION WITH THE
AMERICAN PHYSIOLOGICAL SOCIETY

———————

ON SALE BY
ANNUAL REVIEWS, INC.
PALO ALTO, CALIFORNIA, U.S.A.

ANNUAL REVIEWS, INC.
PALO ALTO, CALIFORNIA, U.S.A.

Library of Congress Catalogue Card Number: 39-15404

FOREIGN AGENCY

Maruzen Company, Limited
6, Tori-Nichome, Nihonbashi
Tokyo

PRINTED AND BOUND IN THE UNITED STATES OF AMERICA
BY GEORGE BANTA COMPANY, INC.

PREFACE

The Annual Review of Physiology has selected its contributors because they could write good reviews. A glance at their names, however, is enough to show that they are almost invariably leaders in the development of their fields. It may thus be of interest to learn where they work. A count made in fourteen volumes scattered from 1939 to 1961 shows that, in round numbers, 31 per cent belonged to departments of physiology, almost all in medical schools, 17 per cent to other basic medical science departments (anatomy, biochemistry, etc.), 14 per cent to biological science departments outside medical schools, 20 per cent to clinical departments or hospital staffs, and 18 per cent to other organizations. A look at the figures before and after 1950 shows, surprisingly, no clear differences in the distribution of affiliations. Accepting our conviction that these figures relate to leadership in physiological research, we are reminded again of the great extent to which physiology transcends departments of physiology. However, in spite of the enormous proliferation of new institutions practicing physiology which have come into being since 1939 unaccompanied by similar increases in the number of university departments of physiology, the latter have continued to provide their original share of leadership. How—we leave to our readers.

To the newest group of contributors, most but not all of whom are new to our fellowship, we extend our deep appreciation and gratitude for their labors. Our intrepid and invaluable Assistant Editor, Joann Huddleston, continues to carry the main load of administration with relish and efficiency. To the George Banta Company, our printers, again our appreciation.

R.S.A.	H.H.
F.F.	R.L.R.
A.C.G.	C.M.S.
R.G.	V.E.H.

ERRATUM

Volume 22

Page 425, third paragraph, next to the last line. For "insolubility" please read "solubility".

CONTENTS

WALLACE O. FENN

BORN FIFTY YEARS TOO SOON

By Wallace O. Fenn

School of Medicine and Dentistry, University of Rochester, Rochester, New York

It is probably impossible to look back fifty years with what passes for the wisdom of age to make a valid comparison with the contemporary scene. In the mad rush of these turbulent days, however, man needs time for quiet contemplation—and time to decide whether he was born too soon or born too late; and for better or for worse, I propose to discuss the matter in this introductory chapter. It might help us in planning for the next half-century.

A retired physiologist visiting a laboratory today may be excused for feeling that he was born too soon. The most obvious transformation is in the instrumentation now available to those who are just beginning their careers.

I recall an article published in England in 1878 from the Harvard Department of Physiology and written by twenty-six-year-old Charles Sedgewick Minot, later professor of Anatomy at Harvard. In the discussion of his experiments concerning fatigue in frog muscle, the author wrote: "This is the first time, as far as I am aware, that so extended a physiological research requiring the use of physical methods has been carried out in America—and we may anticipate a future distinguished by more numerous investigations." He could boast then of his physical equipment which consisted of a kymograph and an inductorium, but what would he say to the physical instrumentation available in our laboratories of physiology today? The four- to six-channel oscillographs are the present symbols of progress and now they are almost standard equipment in physiology departments for every group of two to four students. They serve to record almost any change in blood or tissue that a student needs to measure. When one considers the efforts spent in years gone by putting together all sorts of makeshift apparatus for these various purposes, and the high percentage of failures achieved, one develops an overpowering sense of the futility of human endeavor. By waiting a few years the results of a month of effort might have been obtained in a day by turning the right dials on a gleaming instrument panel. A modern flame photometer calls dismally to mind the years wasted in precipitating and titrating those hundreds of sodium and potassium samples. More time might well have been spent in technical advances before trying to work with inadequate equipment. The manpower working in the physiology of electrolytes today could finish in one year all the work done by their relatively few predecessors between 1900 and 1940—and the results would be better.

The same is true for many other (but not all) fields. All that we learned about hemodynamics by the old clumsy mechanical methods could have been clarified by present-day personnel and equipment in short order. It is particularly discouraging to see one of the modern electronic cell counters which counts one by one all the cells in a half milliliter of solution in little over a minute and provides at the same time a frequency distribution curve of their sizes. One remembers with real anguish the many hours wasted clicking a

1

hand counter over a hemocytometer. Therefore many of us feel that we were born fifty years too soon, even though perhaps in our sober moments we sometimes hope that the progress of science depends upon such pioneer experiments carried out with any apparatus that can be improvised for the purpose.

In addition to the elegant equipment now available for research there is more money. There has to be if only to make the fancy equipment available. Anyone with big ideas, if they are reasonably good ones, can manage sooner or later to find financial support for them and can thereby become more or less independent of his local university administration. This in itself is indeed a most extraordinary situation which has both good and bad points. It certainly provides ample encouragement for anyone who has, or thinks he has, the urge for research, and thereby more people are brought into scientific laboratories. For a nation which produces more goods than it can use and simultaneously suffers from the curse of unemployment, this indeed is a fortunate circumstance. There is always room for more men in research if the money is available, because the unknown is without limit and any increase in knowledge is an advantage to society.

When a government increases its support of research it is in effect saying that more of its citizens should be engaged in expanding our intellectual horizons and fewer should be receiving unemployment benefits or trying to maintain themselves in various ways of relatively less value to society. Research has become fashionable and even important in the eyes of the nation. The United States by mechanizing its agricultural and industrial operations has freed a large fraction of its population for "unproductive" work, i.e., work which does not produce a marketable product in spite of its intrinsic value to society. What better use is there for this excess manpower than to put it to use in research even though it must be supported directly or indirectly by taxes? Even if it is supported by industry or by philanthropy, the money came originally from the work of others. The choice is between more knowledge of life and our environment or a still higher standard of living for everyone regardless of his real contribution to society. Considering also that knowledge is power the choice seems clear, provided that undeserved poverty is eliminated. And new knowledge has a more enduring value than new buildings, gadgets, or consumer goods in general.

Along with more money in recent years there is more of everything that money can buy. Living is softer, life is easier, security is greater, and the demands on the individual are less. Marriage is possible during the predoctoral years and an $1800 stipend is said to be "disgracefully low". Real hardship is rare. We are no longer accustomed to "roughing it". We expect to find all the amenities of civilization freely available at all times including complete health insurance, tuition scholarships, and old age benefits.

Many of us wonder indeed whether this country is not in danger of being weakened by over-indulgence. We have a higher standard of living than any other country in the world, and, as a result, no one loves us. We can be more generous than most countries because of our wealth even though we may be less generous relative to our wealth. We never win the respect which the poor widow wins with her farthing. The evidence seems to be that all our wealth has done us no good internationally. Within our own country, however, the situation in general is much better and our older citizens might well say that they were born fifty years too soon.

More financial support also means that productive scientists can accomplish more because they do not have to spend their time building their own equipment in an amateurish way and doing menial or routine tasks which could be done equally well or even better by less highly trained personnel, or by personnel trained in a more appropriate specialty. Thus the investigator has time to explore the broader implications of his projects and to make certain that a proper orientation in the field as a whole is maintained. Probably the greatest cause of mediocrity in scientific work is a failure to make full use of the existing knowledge in adjacent fields. No project is better than the man who directs it, and that is where high quality is essential and deserving of financial support.

In view of the generous finances now available for research, those of us who experienced the early days of "making do" without much money may well feel that we were born too soon. My own first research grant came in 1941 after I had been chairman of a physiology department for seventeen years. Then I timidly obtained a grant of $500 but I built a low-pressure chamber for about $1000 out of the departmental budget. It was surely the worst high-altitude chamber in the country but a rare atmosphere is the same wherever you find it and we managed to do a lot of work in it throughout the war with a squad of conscientious objectors and ourselves as subjects. Indeed this experience suggests that perhaps most of the changes under discussion have occurred in the last twenty years. Certainly our ideas of the requirements for research have become much more grandiose since that time.

It must be admitted, however, that there are dangers in this easy money regime which must be recognized and guarded against. When research becomes a big business it is not easy to maintain the standard of excellence which is desired. The more generous the supply of money, the lower the average quality of the work performed. Some of it becomes perfunctory—a mere collection of vast amounts of data in the hope that it may be possible to make some sense out of it when the report is written. A job that requires many technicians and quantities of supplies and apparatus is often far inferior to a simpler project built around a single brilliant new idea. In the past the big discoveries and the classical papers have come often from men working in cellars in their spare time with home-made equipment and little help. Then there was not much money and what there was went to the few who were truly elite, and then only to their most promising projects.

It is possibly true that the average level of professorship (or quality of the professors) is higher now in European countries than it is in the United States. This is almost axiomatic if there are fewer such positions available in proportion to the population. As a consequence the average level of European research papers may also be higher, although I am not convinced that this is really true. Even if it were true, however, that does not mean necessarily that the financial support available in the United States for research is excessive. Mopping-up operations are as important in an assault upon the unknown as they are in warfare, and new clues often turn up in most unexpected places. The progress of science is slow, and new discoveries must be repeated endlessly in laboratories all over the world and even in classrooms before they are thoroughly established and accepted. And in the process the wide ramifications of the subject are brought to life and new leads are opened up.

From my own observations, I am convinced that there is need in science for all kinds of people—for the routine confirmatory workers as well as the geniuses who are truly creative. Somewhere of course it is necessary to draw the line but I do not think we have reached the cut-off point yet. On the whole I think that the money spent for research in this country is well spent. Not every researcher finds gold, of course, but the money keeps him trying and sooner or later he may well surprise us. No one wants to spend his life dipping buckets into empty wells and he will soon give up an unproductive project voluntarily or be cut off by some committee when its gamble fails to pay off.

It has been estimated that the number of biological serials doubles every eighteen years [Conrad (1)]. In that case there must be nearly eight times as much annual literature to read now as there was fifty years ago. This might be regarded either as a great educational asset or as an extra difficulty imposed upon the scientist who tries to obtain a broad up-to-date orientation in his subject. Either way the vast and expanding literature is certainly a sign that physiology and the biological sciences are flourishing as they never have before.

The exploding biological literature remains a serious practical problem which urgently demands some action. The number of biological journals is now at least 6000 and some have estimated as many as 20,000. If each journal averages 50 articles per year this means 300,000 to 1,000,000 articles per year. Of these *Biological Abstracts* now abstracts 80,000 per year and the British *International Abstracts of Biological Sciences* about 24,000. The *Biological Abstracts* annual volume now occupies a foot and a half of shelf space not counting the index of three to four inches. Obviously it is impractical to abstract all the biological articles which are published, for this would require six to twenty-two feet of shelf space per year. Some practical plan for the retrieval of all this expanding literature has therefore become imperative.

Many societies have committees now at work studying this problem. As a first step the committee of the American Institute of Biological Sciences is trying to make sure how many biological journals there really are and where they may be obtained in this country. If the task of abstracting so many articles is impossible, then an index of title and perhaps key words selected by the author, but not included in the title, might be a feasible next step. Abstract journals for special subjects might then select from this list certain of the more important articles for abstracting. Punch card systems for machine retrieval in specialized information centers are also under consideration by many groups. All of these services are expensive and can be realized at the present time only for specialized areas on an experimental basis. Studies of this problem, however, show clearly how serious the situation is. Perhaps we shall have to settle for a very incomplete coverage of the literature with the hopeful thought that the rest of it is not worth reading anyway and that it is better not to read too much before starting an investigation because it prejudices our interpretations and stultifies creativity. Some one else, we may hope, will read the literature not available to us and will bring the important results to our attention in due time, perhaps in the pages of the *Annual Review of Physiology*. The life of a biologist was less frustrating, however, when it seemed possible to read all the pertinent articles soon after they were published. When scientific papers are being printed faster than they can be read and digested there is real danger of intellectual indigestion.

Physiology in Europe has always been more competitive than it is in the United States. Now it is more competitive even in this country than it was fifty years ago. The American Physiological Society had only 176 members in 1911 compared to 1920 today. To be sure, there must be correspondingly more jobs today, but the competition for the top level "hard money" tenure jobs is pretty severe. With the present large university departments not many can hope to obtain a chairmanship or a full professorship or an opportunity to direct a research unit. Nevertheless, most physiologists can look forward to a comfortable livelihood and they need not struggle in poverty in the shadow of a professor who seems to endure forever. Moreover, a department chairmanship is a mixed blessing and usually interferes seriously with scholarly work which alone brings national or international recognition. Under present conditions, indeed, with so many generous grants available many prefer the independence and freedom of a subordinate or nonadministrative post and thereby achieve more satisfying and sometimes more distinguished careers. These considerations are more important and critical today than they were fifty years ago, because departments are larger and the problems of space and dollars are much more urgent and time-consuming. We can all think of individuals who gave up promising research careers for the sake of some important administrative post. But this is an age when a high degree of specialization seems to be required for real progress and it has become increasingly difficult for any one man to achieve distinction in both teaching and research, to say nothing of administration. Nevertheless, physiology is still expanding as new medical schools are established and new industrial or government laboratories are opened up, and the opportunities for advancement and for productive work are infinitely better now than in times past.

Under present conditions few scientists run their own lathes in the laboratory or blow their own glass, but at home they must be their own plumbers, carpenters, electricians, and handy men. Some laboratories make a brave show of trying to teach the manual arts to graduate students but mostly these are learned at home, mending the children's toys or repairing the home gadgets and the house. Formerly the reverse was the case with more help at home than in the laboratory; but always the American scientist, unlike his much honored professional counterpart in Europe, has been a "do-it-yourself" artist either at home or in the laboratory and he has been proud of it. Perhaps this is why America has excelled in applied science while most of the great theoretical advances have come from European countries. Likewise, in medical schools our students have tended to learn more by actually doing things with their hands in the laboratory or the clinic while foreign students have tended to specialize in book learning. Medicine is becoming increasingly dependent upon the specialists in physics, chemistry, electronics, computer analysis, and mathematics; and few physiologists now-adays are capable of repairing, much less constructing, the apparatus which they use. But the wide variety of apparatus available in the market keeps the collection of data surprisingly broad and this is a compensating advantage peculiar to modern times. Few people mend their own automobiles in this complicated society of specialists, and it is no disgrace for a physiologist to avail himself of the mysterious "black box" technique provided he can check the reliability of the results.

In comparing physiology then and now some comment may appropri-ately be made concerning the role of the doctoral degree in medical school physiology, for such appointments are more common now than they were then. This is also a comparison of physiology "here" and "there" because it is chiefly in America that a physiologist with only a Ph.D. degree can so easily gain acceptance in a medical faculty. The reasons for this situation are perhaps not hard to discern, and at least some possible explanations suggest themselves. This trend probably began with the renaissance of medical education following the Flexner report in 1910. At that time there developed a strong move to encourage scientific research in medical schools. But almost all of the young men with the M.D. degree were trained for clinical practice, and nothing else would satisfy their desires. Some could be found who would perhaps take time to lecture to medical students about physiology in spare time squeezed out of a busy practice, but they had no research background to offer. To obtain the needed men willing to devote full time to the science of physiology, it became necessary to admit men with the Ph.D. to the medical faculties. The rather strict limitations in the size of medical school classes did not ease the situation because there were plenty of opportunities in medical practice for all the Doctors of Medicine that could be produced.

In some respects this was probably a fortunate attitude for the progress of medicine in this country, for the Ph.D. students brought a fresh point of view into medical school—a single-minded devotion to physiology for its own sake—quite apart from its applications to the practice of medicine. Unlike the medical graduates they also had special training in chemistry, biology, physics, or mathematics and so could attack problems of medicine with new and potent tools. There was of course some tendency to regard the Ph.D. holders as outsiders who knew much about little and nothing at all about medicine and this attitude was not altogether unjustified. Neverthe-less, the scientific level of the basic science departments was raised by the

advent of men with Ph.D. degrees not because they were intrinsically better—for they were not—but because their objective was different. The
newcomers themselves were given excellent facilities and every effort was
made to make them feel at home in this medical environment. Nevertheless,
they could not escape altogether the feeling that they were playing on
another team as indeed they were. Many doors were closed to them in the
world of medicine and most of their honors would come from outside. They
were what Emerson called "river barks on an ocean brine" and often felt
like the weary poet who exclaimed at last in desperation, "Goodbye, proud
world, I'm going home."

There have been many instances of men with Ph.D. degrees who have
attained high places in medical schools and have even served effectively as
deans. One of the most distinguished of them remarked to the writer that
"a Ph.D. could get along in a medical school but he had to work twice as
hard for everything he achieved". I consider it, however, a great tribute to
the American medical schools that they have been so willing to accept such
men on their faculties and have recognized no distinction between the two
degrees except in the legal requirements for dealing with patients. In the
future this attitude may well change slowly because great efforts are being
made to educate medical students in the ways of research, and a progressively larger fraction of them are likely to remain after graduation in academic medicine where they will devote their lives to the progress of the basic
medical sciences. Thus there should be plenty of medical graduates available
to staff departments of physiology and it must be admitted that a teacher in
a medical school feels much more comfortable with a standard M.D. degree
and all the prestige pertaining thereto. It will still be true, however, that the
ordinary medical school course even with the addition of some summer research projects is hardly adequate as a training for research in the basic
sciences. Indeed biological science is no longer the "easy" subject it once
was, but it is becoming regularly more and more sophisticated and requires
more physics, chemistry, and mathematics and, in short, more specialization. To be sure, these subjects are not beyond the reach of medical students
who are mostly highly qualified, but life is short and after graduation from
medical school it is not easy to find time or motivation for further formal
courses. So it seems likely that there will be places for Ph.D. holders in
medical schools for a long time to come.

Even the American Medical Association has recently taken notice of
the Ph.D. problem in medical schools by appointing a committee to study
the relation between medicine and the allied sciences. The resulting report
commented that there are now two and a half times as many staff members
with Ph.D. degrees as there are with M.D. degrees teaching the basic sciences
in medical schools and urged mutual respect and cooperation. The report
recognized also that the former had their own rules for their own education
and qualifications with which the latter had no reason to interfere. It insisted
only that final decisions concerning welfare of patients be reserved for the
medical doctors.

Thus, physiology has been drastically changed in the last fifty years.

Of the typical laboratory experiments in a course in medical physiology of that period hardly a single one remains—perhaps only the technique of recording heart rate and arterial pressure in man by the usual clinical method. And for research purposes even these quantities are usually measured today by more automatic and accurate electronic equipment.

In addition physiology has been fragmented. It used to include the application of chemistry to the cell but now the biochemists have hauled up a "back to the cell" banner and lay claim to what was once cell physiology. Other parts of cell physiology are claimed by biophysicists who also have appropriated many physical aspects of physiology such as electrophysiology, hemodynamics, and muscle mechanics. Sense organs, brain function, and behavior all belong to a large extent to psychology now; and endocrinology belongs either to anatomy, in correlation with morphological changes in the glands, or to pharmacologists because the active principles can be put into syringes like any artificial "drug". Even nutrition is now a subject by itself which is neither biochemistry nor physiology. Little remains indeed that is distinctively or exclusively physiological. Just as for the last fifty years the anatomists have mostly worked in physiology, so for the next fifty years the physiologists will be mostly working in biochemistry or biophysics. What physiologists will teach in the next fifty years will depend upon the particular personalities involved and how the medical schools organize their departments and their curricula. There might even be a medical school without any physiology department at all because there is so little material which cannot be handled as well by people who prefer some more specific designation. Under any name, however, the subject continues to advance rapidly and still forms a large fraction of the scientific basis for the practice of medicine. From this point of view it makes no difference when you were born or what you call the subject. The physiological science will always be a great and exciting discipline.

Complaints are often heard nowadays that the present crop of medical students is more demanding and less willing to take orders and work hard than its predecessors fifty years ago. There is probably some truth in this observation but, if so, it is a sign of the times rather than a deficiency of character. Many medical students are married and have responsibilities to their families. With more accessories and fringe benefits available it is inevitable that more will be requested. Those of us who used to heat our rooms in the college dormitory by a coal fire in an open grate would certainly demand steam heat today. We would also insist on electric lights in place of gas jets. There is also much more to learn in medical schools, so students object to memorizing an excessive amount of anatomical or biochemical detail and they resist a vast amount of routine cell counts and urine analyses in the clinic and demand more time for reading, conferences, and study. Similarly there is some truth in the accusation of the "flabby Americans". To be sure, we seldom walk if we can ride more quickly but we accomplish thereby much more in a day and I wonder if young men today are any more flabby in character and enterprise where it really counts than their predecessors were. Indeed it seems to me that the present life is much more demanding of the student than the student is demanding of life.

In our daily lives it is easy to overlook the drastic changes wrought by time in the circumstances of our work—the modern electronic equipment, the insecurity of the grant-in-aid system, the ever-present threat of a nuclear rocket, the constant nagging bitterness of the cold war, the avalanche of new books, journals, reprints, abstracts, symposia, and meetings. Man can adapt to all these things after a fashion. What remains is no different from what it was fifty years ago. *Plus ça change, plus c'est la même chose.* Life is still a long series of severe personal trials to be faced with such resources of skill and courage as one can muster. The examinations to be passed as a student represent only a feeble adumbration of the great challenges that lie ahead, the sum of which will spell failure, survival, or distinction according to one's own innate capacities.

As we grow older the pace grows faster and if ever a time comes when the next challenge does not seem greater than the last then it is probably time to retire. For any task is what you make it. When it seems to be routine, this is a sign that ambition is dead and the spirit of progress is languishing. Success is in the striving not in the arriving and no job is ever done so well that it could not be done better in a new effort.

The accomplishments of the nineteenth century in science were reviewed and summarized by John Fiske (2), the distinguished Harvard philosopher and historian of science. He viewed the accomplishments of that period in science with great elation as proof that man had indeed inherited the earth and had great promise for the future. The chief theme of the century according to him was the idea of evolution, not alone in biology but also in astronomy, geology, physics, and chemistry. Man had at last come to realize that we live in a slowly changing or evolving world.

One could view the developments of the last sixty years with no less elation but it is hard to know what the general theme would be unless it were the discoveries of the structure of the atomic nucleus. All these developments have been exciting indeed and it is sad to think how much the scientists of the last century would have enjoyed subsequent developments in their several fields, if they could have lived long enough to see them. Likewise those of us who are retiring today look forward eagerly to the developments of the immediate future in the hope that we might yet live to see something of their nature. From this point of view we were indeed born too soon. We have seen the revolution in physics but some of us feel that a revolution in biology is next on the agenda and we hate to leave the meeting prematurely. The recent brilliant discoveries in nucleic acid structure, protein synthesis, virology, and genetics seem to foretell even greater understandings to come. Perhaps then we shall really be in a position to create life and to control some of the subtle biological processes of inheritance and development, all of which might have such tremendous practical consequences for human life and welfare. All this it would be fun to see but we have probably had our full share of that kind of joy and have no cause for complaint.

What then is the proper conclusion to the general question under discussion? Professionally I believe that we older physiologists were born too soon. In that field, at least, the future will be much more exciting than the past and the opportunities for an interesting and rewarding career in the physiological sciences are incomparably greater than they were fifty years ago. The same is true for the population in general because the discrepancies between the wealthy and the impoverished classes have become progressively less. Decent and reasonably comfortable homes are now available for almost anyone willing and able to work and the opportunities for a good education are within reach of anyone who really wants them. Most of our older people were born too soon.

Granted all this, for many older people there is still a nostalgic yearning for the peace and quiet of a day that is gone. Amid the grind of traffic and the rude braying of the radios there has developed an unhappy imbalance between sensory input and motor output and a vague feeling that something is wrong with the world. At least in days of yore there was no cause to worry about the future of the world. No one then ever suggested in all seriousness that our most important text books ought to be carved on stone tablets and stored in caves to ensure their survival in case of some catastrophic holocaust that might destroy civilization and deprive posterity (if any) of all our hard-won gains. Before the atom bomb there was complete confidence that human civilization if not perfect was at least on the path of progress which would lead us onward and upward forever into the glorious and Utopian future. Life was much simpler and it was good. Nor was it static. And those of us who are old today have probably seen more revolutionary and exciting changes in daily living than any generation before and perhaps more than any generation yet to come. When will there be another generation that can see in one lifetime anything as dramatic as the beginning of telephones, electric lights, automobiles, airplanes, radio, movies, television, and nuclear power, to say nothing of the new synthetic products of the chemical industry, and space travel? To be sure, we have also lived through two terrible world wars but who can say that there may not be worse to come? Fortunately our children seem to be undaunted by the possibility of future catastrophe and we can only hope that indeed they were not born too late.

As spokesman for the older physiologists who have had their day and are preparing to pass the torch to others, I must conclude, however, that the best is yet to come. We were born too soon, all things considered. The challenges and stresses are much greater now with the space age, the population explosion, and the dire threat of an ideology of tyranny under communism. But the opportunities and resources are also greater and mankind has a richer store of knowledge, experience, and wisdom, with which the future can be made even brighter than the past.

LITERATURE CITED

1. Conrad, M., *Biol. Abstr.*, **36**, No. 7, p. xx (1961)
2. Fiske, J., *A Century of Science* (Houghton Mifflin and Co., Boston, Mass., 1899)

GROWTH AND DIFFERENTIATION[1]

By Rita Levi-Montalcini and Pietro U. Angeletti[2]
Washington University, St. Louis, Missouri

The convergent trend in biological sciences already apparent in the past few years recently became more pronounced. Fields which used to be the privileged property of a restricted group are now claimed by students of different disciplines. As a consequence, in 1961, the embryo no longer belongs to the embryologist nor the microbe to the microbiologist. Barely had the fences between different biological sciences been removed when new concepts developed and old concepts appeared in a new light. Possibly no concepts profited more from this invasive trend than the old concepts of growth and differentiation. Only a few decades ago, these words conveyed mainly the idea of the developing embryo and of the laborious and intricate processes which mold it into a complete and self-supporting organism. Today, many of the biologists preoccupied with these concepts are not familiar with the embryo and, for that matter, would not be able to identify one if they were confronted with it. At present the words "growth and differentiation" have acquired such a broad significance as to encompass almost all biological sciences. Faced with the problem of delimiting the field to be discussed, the reviewers found their assignment difficult. Although one of the two would label herself an embryologist, the embryo did not benefit from her admittedly modest and one-sided knowledge of this object, not so much because of awe or the fear of not doing it justice, as because of persuasion that the embryo, as a whole, has contributed less in recent years to our understanding of growth and differentiation than simpler objects such as isolated cells or cell groups.

Our presentation is divided into two parts. In the first, we review some of the work in the field of primitive organisms, isolated cells, and cell populations, and we discuss recent advances in the field of embryonic induction. In the second, the chemical aspects of growth and differentiation are presented.

The Cellular Slime Molds

A revival of interest in these forms is documented by the number of review articles and original contributions which appeared in these last years. This is justified by the privileged position of slime molds which share properties with unicellular and multicellular organisms, and by the extensive pre-existing literature and the ready availability of the object. Of the four developmental stages which characterize the life cycle in this organism— vegetation, aggregation, migration, and formation of the fruiting body—the

[1] The survey of literature pertaining to this review was concluded June 30, 1961.

[2] The authors wish to express their appreciation to Dr. F. Moog for her critical reading of the manuscript. Grateful acknowledgement is made to Mrs. E. Stanbery for secretarial help.

11

last three were the most thoroughly investigated. Recent work in these areas will be briefly presented.

Analysis of the aggregation pattern.—Shaffer (1) reviewed his own extensive contributions and those of others in this field. The production and mode of action of "acrasin", the diffusible substance responsible for the aggregation of myxamoebae, are discussed; a "relay" hypothesis proposed by the author explains satisfactorily many previously unexplained aspects of cell aggregation and center formation in slime molds (1, 2). This theory proposes that the center, acting as a pacemaker, emits acrasin; the adjacent amoebae are oriented and in turn stimulated to produce the same substance. Since acrasin is inactivated as soon as it is produced, the first pulse emitted by the center is obliterated, but a new pulse produced by the activated amoebae spreads to the adjacent cells and a new gradient is thus established. The relay theory has the advantage of explaining how acrasin can be carried at a distance through intermediate cells which receive and, in turn, convey the message. The same theory also submits that the center emits acrasin rhythmically and that in this way, by conveying subsequent pulses, the center retains its dominant position as a pacemaker. Other aspects of the mechanisms of aggregation, such as the variety of aggregative patterns, the orientation and polarity of cell movements, and the size-control of the aggregates, are analyzed in the lucid and informative book by Bonner (3) who contributed to the understanding of all these problems as well as to the knowledge of other aspects of the life cycle of slime molds. The sorting out of cells during aggregation, the rate of movement and compatibility of cells of different species and strains, and the morphogenetic effects obtained by mixing, in various ways, cells belonging to different species are the object of recent investigations by the same author (4, 5). The rate of locomotion of amoebae as related to their developmental stage, size, position, and physicochemical environmental conditions was studied by Samuel (6). Sussman and his group (7, 8, 9), in a brilliant and extensive series of investigations, analyzed synergistic relations between morphogenetically deficient mutants and the dependence of center formation on cell number and on special cells of large size which they consider to be center initiators. The existence of initiator cells (I cells) and their morphological and physiological differentials from the remaining cells (R cells) has not yet received general acceptance (3, 5). However, new evidence in favor of this hypothesis was recently submitted by the same group (10), who extend the previous list of differences between I and R cells to include: genetic stability, nuclear size, number, and mode of cell division. The possible occurrence of syngamic processes among myxamoebae—a long-debated question—received confirmation by Kerr (11) who described a technique to isolate fusing pairs. The evidence in favor of sexuality in Acrasiales was previously presented by Wilson and co-workers (12) while Bonner (5) considered it at best doubtful.

The mechanism of cell aggregation was investigated with different techniques. DeHaan (13) studied the effects of a chelating agent in preventing aggregation. The results bear close resemblance to those obtained with chelating agents on metazoan cells. Gregg & Trygstad (14), using serological techniques, tested the hypothesis that cell adhesiveness during the aggregation phase might be caused by an antigen-antibody reaction. Immunological experiments revealed surface antigen aberrances in aggregateless variants; these results agree with the working hypothesis that surface changes may account for the failure of these ultraviolet-induced variants to aggregate. In his more recent work, Gregg (15) used the same technique to study a new surface antigen which is found in spores but not in early aggregates or in migrating slugs. The recovery of this antigen from the surface washings of spores suggests the hypothesis of antigen ejection from the spore surface. The weak adhesiveness of spores in contrast to the strong adhesiveness of cells at the onset of aggregation (2) correlates with the finding that antigenic material can be easily removed from the spore surface by washing. The poor agglutination capacity of spores may be explained as a consequence of the inability of the antigen to remain attached to the cell surface.

Analysis of migratory and differentiative patterns.—Investigations of the effects of environmental factors such as light and temperature showed a positive tropism of the migrating slug toward light and temperature gradients (16), whereas a slight decrease in humidity causes migration to stop and spore differentiation to start (17). Mixing of cells of different species and strains showed varying degrees of compatibility among the combinations which resulted in the formation of separate fruiting bodies, of double fruiting bodies, or of a single sorus containing two distinct, separate patches of spores of the two strains (18). These results indicate that the cells "showed no specificity in their regrouping with respect to the species but only with respect to the tissue" (18).

The independence of growth and morphogenetic processes in slime molds was shown by R. and M. Sussman (19); in these experiments an increase in cell number was prevented by transfer of small cell groups at the aggregative stage on washed agar. Under such conditions, differentiation and formation of the fruiting bodies occurred in cell populations with no numerical increase from the aggregating to the fruiting stage.

THE EMBRYONIC CELL

Cell contact.—Under the heading "Cell Contact", P. Weiss (20) analyzes many aspects of cell-surface properties in the static and dynamic embryonic cells explanted *in vitro*. These properties were investigated intensively in recent years in reference to problems of cell differentiation, cell interaction, and morphogenetic processes. Some of the pertinent literature is reviewed here. Most of it deals with observations of embryonic vertebrate cells *in vitro;* only a few investigations deal with invertebrate cells *in vivo* during cleavage or subsequent stages. The electron microscope, in revealing submicroscopic and molecular dimensions, made necessary a revision of previous concepts of surface contact. P. Weiss suggests that "we shall consider a cell in contact with another body not only if the two surfaces are in direct apposition, but also if they are separated by a narrow space occupied by a molecular population whose free mobility is restrained" (20). All observations are consistent with the notion that an intercellular space varying in width between 100 and 200 A is interposed between contacting cells (21). The electron microscope gave evidence for the existence of intercellular contact bodies bridging this space. They were designated in accordance with their shape as "bobbins" (20), "membrane knotting" (22), or "interdigitating cell processes" (23). According to some authors, the existence of cementing material between adjacent cells, while not precluded, does not seem required to account for cell adhesion (24). Cells of like surfaces conform to the Verwey-Overbeek model which predicts that stable adhesion occurs when two like surfaces are 100 to 200 A apart. In proposing this theory of specific adhesion of like cell types, Curtis (24) objects to the adhesion theory advanced by Steinberg (25), which is based on the concept of adhesion of adjacent cells through calcium ions cross-linking the opposite surfaces. This linkage apparently takes place only when adjacent surfaces are at a distance of 10 A or less, while, as mentioned above, a separation of 100 to 200 A is usually interposed between cells in contact.

The role of calcium in cellular adhesion is generally acknowledged (26). However, in the opinion of L. Weiss, "the mode and site of action of calcium are still largely conjectural" (27). The hypothesis that seems to him more plausible is that calcium (and magnesium) might play a part in the coacervate formation between negatively charged mucopolysaccharides and amphoteric proteins. In this way, inorganic cations would exert a stabilizing effect on intercellular matrices and cement (26).

Cell-to-cell adhesion and adhesion of cells to substratum change according to cell types (20), stage and differentiation (27), culture media (28), and other conditions such as glass surface (29, 30). The significance of cell adhesion to the substratum as a directing force of cell movements on solid surfaces was explored by P. Weiss who proposed the term "contact guidance" to define the effect exerted by an oriented matrix in directing cells and nerve fiber movements (20). While contact guidance may be defined as the positive thigmotactic effect of the substratum, a negative thigmotatic effect was described by Abercrombie and his associates (31) under the name of "contact inhibition". Contact inhibition, first described in fibroblast cultures, gives a satisfactory explanation of the radial movements of cells away from the explant. A cell reacts to contact with other cells by moving away from the point of collision. At variance with normal cells, sarcoma cells are not inhibited by contact with fibroblasts, as proved by their free movement over and through sheets of these cells. Movements of fibroblasts and sarcoma cells and interactions between these two cell types were studied with the interference microscope which revealed new aspects of the phenomenon (32). Recently, a sedimentation technique was developed which permits a quantative evaluation of the adhesiveness of neoplastic and normal cells to a glass surface (33). L.

Weiss comments: "It is tempting to generalize, and to relate invasive properties of malignant cells to a modification in their surfaces which has altered their adhesive potential in such a way that contact inhibition no longer acts as a check on their movements" (27). A similar concept is expressed by P. Weiss (20).

Amoeboid movements in cells *in vitro* and in nerve fibers growing in semisolid or liquid media were the object of a detailed analysis by Levi and his associates (34, 35). These authors pursued in these last years the pioneer investigations on cell growth and behavior *in vitro* which were started by Levi in the early twenties. Motion picture observations gave evidence of the formation of extremely thin and expanded membranes at the tip of the growing fibers. Similar "filopodia" are described by Japanese workers (36, 37) and other authors.

Morphogenetic movements.—This developmental process consists of movements of entire cell layers in which each unit maintains a relatively stable juxtaposition with adjacent units. A detailed analysis of these movements and of their morphogenetic importance is given in an investigation by Townes & Holtfreter (38). This work represents a fundamental contribution of this and other problems of morphogenesis. The forces underlying cell movements were recently explored and analyzed in the chick blastoderm explanted *in vitro* (39, 40). Of considerable interest are two lucid investigations by Spratt who, in collaboration with Haas, studied morphogenetic movements in the hypoblast of unincubated and early chick blastoderms explanted on an albumen agar clot in upside-down position (41). Carbon or carmine particles were applied to the surface of small cell groups and the movements recorded by means of camera lucida outline drawings at close time intervals. The analysis revealed that the hypoblast movements precede and are largely independent of those in the epiblast surfaces. A major feature is "the radial and fountain-like outward streaming of cells from a center in the pellucid area located near its prospective posterior junction with the opaque area" (41). In a subsequent investigation the same authors succeeded, through mechanical devices, in blocking either all the movements or various components of the hypoblast of unincubated blastoderms (42). The results of these experiments reveal the unitary nature of these movements and their importance for the embryonic axis formation. They also show the independence of developmental processes such as expansive growth of the blastoderm, formation of the junction zone ring, and formation of the embryonic axial system. A detailed analysis of cell movements in reference to morphogenetic events was also performed by DeHaan in the same material used by previous investigators. He was able to observe and follow discrete cell clusters of mesodermal cells by means of time-lapse photography. Morphogenetic processes in the heart-forming regions, and movements of the anterior intestinal portal, somites, and Hensen's node, were the object of this interesting analysis which is still in progress (43).

The elucidation of the mechanisms underlying morphogenetic movements represents one of the main goals of chemical embryology. Brachet (44),

Ranzi (45), and their associates contributed largely to the investigation of this problem. The hypothesis that changes in the proportion of—SH and —SS proteinic groups might alter the structural configuration of the proteins and that such changes may play a role in morphogenetic events such as the folding and closure of the neural plate, was recently tested by Brachet and Delange-Cornil (46). The authors investigated the effect of beta-mercapto-ethanol, a reducing agent introduced by Mazia (47), and of dithiodiglycol (an oxidizing agent) on the closure of the neural plate in amphibians. In both groups of experiments the neural plate failed to close. The authors submit the hypothesis that a block of the—SH groups is responsible in both instances for the observed effects. The opposite result, precocious closure of the medullary plate, was obtained by Ambellan (48) who treated amphibian embryos with ATP, adenosine-monophosphate-3, and ADP. It was suggested that "the mechanism by which these materials are utilized to advance neurulation may more closely resemble normal synthetic mechanisms of the embryo than utilization of ATP or AMP-3" (48). Brachet (46) agrees with this hypothesis.

   Cell differentiation in vitro.—Improved tissue culture techniques offered a most valuable tool for investigating problems of cell differentiation, morphogenesis, and tissue interaction. Recent investigations in these areas will be reviewed in the following pages. At first, we shall consider some of the work in the field of cell differentiation.

   In an elegant series of experiments, Niu (49) gave evidence of inductive effects exerted *in vitro* by the dorsal lip of the blastopore of *Triturus* embryos on the presumptive ectoderm of the same embryos at the early gastrula stage. The reacting tissue which, in the absence of other cells, would differentiate into epithelium, differentiated, when combined *in vitro* with the inductor, into pigment cells, nerve cells, and occasionally myoblasts. The latter differentiated in large numbers when cultured for a longer time in the presence of inductor cells. Since no contact was established between the inductor and the induced tissues, it was assumed that these effects were ascribable to a diffusible substance released by the inductor into the culture medium. This hypothesis received strong support when the above results could be repeated by simply culturing the ectoderm alone in a medium previously conditioned by the inductor. The inductor or "transforming agent" was identified in a nucleoprotein fraction isolated from the conditioned medium.

   In a subsequent investigation (50) it was reported that extracts of calf thymus, added to the culture medium, transformed presumptive ectoderm of *Amblystoma Tigrinum* into neural and nonneural tissue. A specificity for RNA isolated from different sources was also claimed (51). Niu suggests that the role of RNA in embryonic induction might be "similar to DNA in microbial transformation and to RNA in the production of tobacco mosaic virus" (51). The same reasoning prompted other workers to investigate the effects *in vitro* of whole ribosomes extracted from rat liver or kidney, or of purified RNA from rat liver and yeast. These ribosomes were tested on fibroblasts derived from the subcutaneous tissue of adult rats (52). Heteromorphic changes in the fibroblasts occurred in both groups of experiments. The formation of fiber-like prolongations was observed in fibroblasts, and the effect is described as a "neutralization effect". Although it was not possible to obtain conclusive evidence that these cells are in fact nerve cells, the statement was made that "the term neutralization is used provisionally and for the sake of brevity" (52).

Using a somewhat different technique, Ebert (53) tested the effect of the inoculation of a mixture of cardiac microsomes and Rous sarcoma virus into the chorioallantoic membrane of 11-day-old chick embryos. In 27 per cent of a total of hundreds of experiments, muscle fibers were identified in the tumorous masses formed at the site of the inoculum, whereas no muscle fibers were detected in control experiments consisting of the inoculation of the Rous sarcoma virus alone. The results are discussed in the light of the concept of epigenetic recombination. While the above experiments were aimed at the investigation of the effects of nucleic acids in cell differentiation, Wilde studied the effects of amino acids and of amino acid analogues on the differentiation of neural crest derivatives. The results of this extensive series of experiments were recently reviewed by this author (54, 55). The working hypothesis was proposed that an amino acid, phenylalanine, plays an essential role in the differentiation of pigment cells and ectomesenchyme: the addition to the culture medium of a series of structural analogues of phenylalanine produced inhibitory effects on one or the other of the neural crest derivatives. Thus, by a sort of "molecular dissection" (54) one can alter at will the configuration of the amino acid molecule and obtain predictable changes in cell differentiation (55). Cells can be forced into atypical and new differentiation channels. The addition of phenylalanine (the normal amino acid) to the medium induces "pigment cells, pigmentation and a strange mesenchyme from ventral ectoderm," which in normal condition would not form pigment cells (55).

A most interesting investigation by Barth & Barth (56) raises questions as to the specificity of the above effect. These authors traced the effects of environmental conditions on cell differentiation in amphibians. The material used was the presumptive epidermis and chordamesoderm of *Rana pipiens* at the early gastrula stage. The presumptive epidermis was cultured in a normal medium to which lithium chloride was added at the final concentration of 0.1 M. As reported by Barth & Barth, "the appearance of cells after brief lithium treatment bears a striking resemblance to that pictured and described by Wilde for ventral ectoderm and neural crest cultures of amblystoma to which phenylalanine or tyrosine has been added" (56). In the same series they also report having obtained histological and functional differentiation of nerve, muscle, and pigment cells as well as the differentiation of ciliated, mucus-secreting, and notochord cells in unconditioned media. A metaplastic transformation of keratinizing squamous epithelium of chick embryos into mucus-secreting cells was observed when vitamin A was added to the culture medium (57, 58, 59). A large number of control experiments supported the hypothesis of a specific vitamin-induced effect. Recently, however, various types of metaplastic changes, including secretory metaplasia, were obtained by Moscona (60, 61) in the epithelium of the chorioallantoic membrane, by the simple procedure of incubating graft-bearing eggs in air with a high carbon dioxide content. Keratogenic metaplasia was also obtained in the chorionic epithelium cultured *in vitro* upon a plasma clot "without further experimental interference" (61). Evidence of morphological transformations in epithelial explants *in vitro* is also reported by Matoltsy, who transplanted epidermal fragments stripped from the underlying mesoderm from the neck region of 14-day chick embryos, and cultured such fragments in a liquid medium consisting of Earle's solution and 20 per cent horse serum. Forty-eight hours later, aggregate tubules were formed in some parts of the tissue. "These results indicate that the epidermis in the absence of dermis diverts from its normal course of development and its cells, instead of forming keratin, assemble into tubes" (62). The multiple potentalities of epithelial tissues of the upper external sheath of the hair follicle in response to variations in tissue environment were discussed by Chase (63).

An analysis of the concept of tissue and cellular metaplasia is presented by Grobstein (64) in his lucid article on the differentiation of vertebrate cells. In considering these results in reference to the more general problem of cell differentiation one should not forget that, in this respect, "different cell types may, in fact, vary widely, from extreme lability to complete fixity" (65). The lability of epithelial cells, already well-known to old pathologists, is well documented by the above work and warns against the temptation of generalizing from one cell type to another.

An interesting instance of cell transformation through environmental factors is described by Shelton & Rice (66). They report on the transformation of mouse lymphocytes to fibroblasts when cultured in Algire chambers in the mouse peritoneal cavity. The evidence is based on (a) observed morphological changes in cell type from lymphocytic to the fibroblastic type and concomitant change in growth pattern: the cells at first separated from each other and then gave origin to cohesive sheets: (b) the identification by electron microscope studies of collagen in the culture chambers: (c) the chemical determination of hydroxyproline in long-time cultures, whereas hydroxyproline was not detected from the cells before their transplantation. Shelton & Rice describe this observation as "a study in cell modulation", thus leaving open the possibility that the same cells may revert to the original cell type, upon return to previous environmental conditions. This occurrence does not seem likely and for this reason the term "transformation" would perhaps be more appropriate.

Hormonal effects on cell differentiation and growth.—Space considerations force us to limit this sector to an outline of some work on hormonal effects on cells and to omit references to the extensive literature on the effects of hormones *in vitro* and *in vivo* on growth and differentiative processes in tissues and organs. The effects *in vitro* are reviewed in comprehensive review articles (67, 68). The important work by Et. Wolff and his associates (69) on hormonal effects on differentiation of sex glands *in vitro*, and by Gallien (70) and Gaillard (71) on effects of the parathyroid hormone on bone formation *in vitro*, should be consulted. The role of fetal hormones in prenatal development was the object of a systematic series of investigations by Jost and co-workers (72). The development of the function of the adrenal cortex and other endocrine glands was studied by Moog (73). Her basic contribution to understanding the mode of action of hormones in enzyme synthesis is presented in the second part of this review. The extensive work by Williams, Schneiderman, and others on hormones in insects is reviewed by Schneiderman & Gilbert (74) in a recent publication.

A direct tissue-specific action of thyroxine on nerve cell differentiation was proved by implanting pellets soaked in the hormone in proximity to developing brain centers in amphibian larvae. Nerve cells adjacent to the hormonal pellet underwent precocious maturation and size increases (75). A specific effect called forth by thyroxine is described by Wilt (76) in a system which proved particularly suitable for investigation of this effect: the visual pigment of bullfrog tadpoles. The author gave evidence of a direct hormonal effect in the conversion of porphyropsin to rhodopsin. The suggested mechanism underlying this conversion is the loss of an enzyme-forming system concerned with vitamin A_2 synthesis. As the biosynthesis of vitamin A_2 (this vitamin is the chromophore of porphyropsin) ceases, vitamin A_1 (vitamin A_1 aldehyde is the chromophore of rhodopsin) would enter the eye from surrounding tissues in which it is already present in larval stages.

A specific nerve growth factor.—A proteinic nerve growth factor was discovered in recent years in mouse sarcomas, snake venom, and mouse submaxillary salivary glands (77, 78). Upon injection into the chick embryo it evokes a striking growth response of the sensory and sympathetic nerve cells. Daily injections into newborn mammals evoke a similar growth response of the sympathetic nerve cells (79). The analysis *in vitro* and *in vivo* of the nerve growth factor and of the response elicited in the receptive nerve cells revealed similarities between these and hormonal effects. A classification of this growth factor must, however, await further analysis. It was also reported that an antiserum to the purified nerve growth factor selectively destroys almost totally the sympathetic nerve cells in newborn mammals (80, 81, 82). This factor was recently isolated from the serum of a variety of mammals, man included, from the sympathetic nerve cells (83), and from embryonic material (84). While these and results reported above (75, 76) indicate that nerve cells are receptive to diffusible agents, it should not be concluded that these are the only agents to control growth and differentiative processes in nerve cells. Previous work by Hamburger and his associates (85) gave evidence of the importance of the peripheral field of innervation as a regulative factor in the size of a given population. The importance of these factors was again stressed in recent work (86).

Morphogenetic processes in vitro.—A review article by Nicholas (87) in the *Annual Review of Physiology* (1960) covers part of the work performed in this field during the preceding years. The present review will therefore center on some aspects not dealt with in the previous article and on the more recent contributions in this sector.

The analysis of selective cell adhesion and recombination entered a new phase with the shifting of emphasis from the cellular to the intercellular phase and the exploitation of new techniques. Although the importance of the ground substance in morphogenetic processes has been acknowledged for a long time and has been the object of attention by leading investigators in the field (88, 89), it is only recently that its role has been submitted to a more close and detailed inspection. The structural and chemical characteristics of the extracellular material produced by cell aggregates *in vitro* were the object of an interesting analysis by Moscona (90). The tenuous mucous substance which shares many properties with the intercellular substance of intact tissues and forms the microenvironment of the cell is considered as "a cell-integrating system, endowed with specific cell-directing activities that affect movements and association of cells" (90). Ingenious experiments were devised to test this hypothesis. Dissociated embryonic cells were cultured in a liquid medium in rotating flasks. Under these conditions they reaggregated in a three-dimensional extracellular material and cell entity. When dissociated cells are forced instead to grow in monolayers and thus exposed individually to the culture medium, they gradually lose the capacity to produce the extracellular material, as shown by their failure to aggregate and to cohere. A striking documentation of the parallelism between the capacity to produce the extracellular material and the capacity to undergo differentiation is shown in two sets of experiments. In the first series, shaker-flask aggregates of freshly dissociated mouse embryonic skin cells, when transferred to plasma clots, formed skin sheets and hair rudiments. In the second series, the same type of cells grown for 10 days in a monolayer "became rapidly dissipated into an outgrowth of epithelial and fibrocytic cells" (90) when piled up on plasma clots. They regained the morphogenetic potentialities upon coaggregation with freshly dissociated embryonic cells. The capacity of producing the intercellular matrix as one important aspect of cell differentiation is also emphasized in two other interesting investigations: Holtzer and associates (91) showed that chondrocytes, liberated from embryonic cartilage by the standard dissociation procedures, continue to synthetize chondroitin sulfate *in vitro* and to incorporate inorganic S^{35} into ester-bound sulfate. This property is lost when the same cells are grown for 10 to 15 days in Carrel flasks. Under these conditions they fail to produce extracellular metachromatic material and "when organ-cultured fail to differentiate into recognizable chondrocytes" (91). Another investigation along this line was performed by T. Okada (92), who studied the production *in vitro* of the intercellular matrix from precartilaginous cell clusters using tracer techniques. He was able to show that S^{35} that is taken up by dissociated precartilaginous cells can accumulate in the intercellular matrix following reaggregation of these cells. These results are taken as evidence that the isotope picked up at first by the dissociated cells can be utilized for the synthesis of the intercellular substance.

The loss of differentiative traits in cells cultured in monolayers is discussed also by Eagle (93), who was impressed by the basic similarities in the nutritional requirements and metabolic activities of normal and malignant human cells in culture. This similarity finds an explanation if one considers that "the metabolism of dispersed cell cultures is: primarily the metabolism of growth, and not that of function." Eagle concludes with the statement that "only when we have learned the conditions necessary for the preservation of function can we reasonably hope that the biochemical factors which underlie cellular differentiation, inherited metabolic disorders, and malignancy will become amenable to analysis in cell cultures" (93).

The biochemical aspects of cell growth *in vitro* and the observations of the frequent spontaneous transformation of normal into malignant cells were the object of extensive investigation by different groups. Earle, Evans, Sanford, and associates were the first to describe spontaneous transformation of normal into malignant cells *in vitro*. Results of this work are presented in recent articles (94, 95). The nutritional requirements of different cell lines were investigated by Eagle and co-workers (93, 96), by Em. Wolff (97), Lieberman (98), Puck (99), and others.

Another factor in cell differentiation and morphogenesis is indicated by Loomis (100) and Trinkaus & Drake (101) who studied the role of carbon dioxide tension. Loomis investigated the effect of the pCO_2 in *Hydra* differentiation and reported that sexual differentiation in this coelenterate occurs as the pCO_2 increases. After discussing other instances of the effect of carbon dioxide tension on growth and differentiation in embryonic tissues, Loomis concludes: "In general it appears that the level of pCO_2 in the environment of a living cell is one of the most labile and neglected of all biological variables, yet one that is capable of regulating both the rate of cell division and the process of cellular differentiation" (100). Trinkaus & Drake came to a similar conclusion on the basis of studies *in vitro* of morphogenesis of blastoderms of the teleost *Fundulus*. The enhanced differentiation of fused blastoderms, as compared to single blastoderm cultures, is correlated with the increase of pCO_2 in crowded cultures.

The capacity of individual cells to reaggregate and build complete organs from single-cell suspension is shown in an impressive series of experiments by Weiss & Taylor (102). Isolated cells from kidney, liver, or skin of 8-to-14-day chicks, recompacted and transplanted to the chorioallantoic membrane of 8-day embryos, gave rise to "remarkably complete and morphologically well organized organs of the respective kinds, with the various tissue components in their normal mutual relations and functional activity." These results, while attesting to the extraordinary property for self-organization built into the individual cells, do not answer the questions if, when, and how this property was first acquired. Since the cells came from organs in an already advanced stage of differentiation, they apparently carried along a property impressed on them in an early differentiative stage. Another interesting instance of self-organization is presented by Boterenbrood (103), who dissociated the prosencephalic area of the early neural plate of *Triturus alpes-*

tris, together with adjacent neural fold and ectoderm. The cells reaggregated *in vitro*, and well-organized eye structures and telencephalic and diencephalic units were formed from the central neural mass.

Two investigations which differ from those discussed above in the technical procedure as well as in the material used are of considerable interest. Both concern reaggregation in primitive forms. Scott (104) studied tissue affinities and reaggregative capacities in a tunicate *Amaroecium constellatum*, the tadpoles of which were subjected to fragmentation of their organs by cutting with surgical instruments until reduced to clumps of tissues. The epidermis covering the dissociated organs was only partly ruptured and the tunic was left intact. The tadpoles were then lodged into host tunics evacuated of their owners. The reconstitution of the fragmented forms was practically completed in 24 hours. Cell clusters of different organs succeeded in locating, identifying, and adhering to tissues of the same kind for the purpose of rebuilding the integrity of the organs. The tissues also oriented themselves in accord with the former axial gradient. The ordered pattern of tissue reaggregation and re-establishment of organ integrity proved two properties in the dissociated tissues: recognition of affinities and inherent axiation. It is suggested that diffusible substances might convey information as to the proper position and orientation to cells of minced tissues.

Reconstitution of a unicellular form: *Stentor*, after dissociation into as many as 40 fragments, was the object of a series of investigations by Tartar (105), who found that reconstitution is accomplished not by dedifferentiation but by "parallel and generally homopolar realignment of the patches, joining of stripes into continuous runs and selective resorption of minor parts which do not fit." The interesting conclusion is reached that "cells, like cellular tissues and organisms, can reconstitute and develop from disaggregated parts without guidance of a pre-existing wholeness" (105).

Pertinent to the problem of cell reassociation *in vitro* is an analysis of dissociated and reaggregated retinal cells *in vitro* by Stefanelli and associates (106).

Tissue interaction in vitro.—The analysis of tissue interaction *in vitro* represents another highly successful approach to the problem of dependent and autonomous tissue organization. This line of investigation was initiated with the penetrating analysis by Grobstein (107) of the mesenchymal-epithelial interrelationship in kidney and mouse salivary glands, and was extended in recent years to other systems and to the core of the problem—the mechanism of such interactions.

Sobel (108) reported that the anterior lobe of the pituitary of eight-day chick embryos reaggregates *in vitro* upon cell dissociation, forming quiescent clusters of epithelial cells. The addition of perichondrial connective tissue to the aggregate results in the differentiation of the epithelial aggregate into typical anterior lobe tissue. Auerbach & Grobstein (109) tested the ability of an inducing system such as the dorsal spinal cord and the metanephrogenic mesenchyme to react after dissociation and reaggregation of the two tissues. The results showed that "the dissociation of either reactant does not destroy its ability to participate in induction" (109). Other aspects of this inducing system, such as the realization of the morphogenetic effect across a thin millipore filter and the persistence of the effect when the inducer is removed after 30 hours, are discussed by Auerbach in a subsequent paper (110). He analyzed the interaction between mesenchymes isolated from a variety of embryonic rudiments and the epithelial component of mouse embryo thymus. The combined techniques of tissue culture and transplantation to the anterior eye chamber and onto the chorioallantoic membrane were used to investigate many problems of thymus morphogenesis. Of particular interest is the contribution of these studies to the solution of a long-debated problem, the origin of the lymphoid population in the thymus. A series of rigorous tests, including the production of chimeric organs from chick mesenchyme and mouse thymus epithelial component, gives strong support to the hypothesis of the epithelial origin of thymus lymphocytes (111).

The effects of notochord and embryonic spinal cord as cartilage inducers from somites were reinvestigated by Holtzer and associates (112). Chondrogenesis occurs also from dissociated somite cells. Loss of competence in somite cells from older embryos (stage 24) is correlated with the incipient myoblastic differentiation of these cells. Once embryonic somite cells mobilize their intracellular machinery to synthesize contractile proteins, they lose their capacity to respond to the cartilage inductors. Instances of osteogenic induction through millipore filters *in vivo* were reported by Goldhaber (113), while lens induction through an agar barrier about 20 microns thick was the object of an investigation by McKeehan (114). Benoit (115) reports on the formation of cartilage from the head mesenchyme under the inductive influence of extract of pooled epithelial otic vesicles from five-day chick embryos. Induction of cartilage from somite material by a spinal cord and notochord extract had been previously described by Strudel (116). Extracts of embryonic and adult chick brain induce skin and feather formation *in vitro*, according to Sengel (117). The chemical analysis of the inductive agent isolated from the nervous tissue indicates that it is thermostable; the possibility that it might be a protein molecule of low molecular weight is not excluded (117).

The mechanism of tissue interactions and the identification of the inductive agents are the main object of investigation in the recent work by Grobstein. The inductive tissue was incubated in tritiated amino acids; the two reactants, spinal cord and metanephrogenic tissues, were then placed on the two opposite sides of a millipore filter. The spatial distribution pattern of the radioactive material in the filter and in the induced metanephrogenic mesenchyme was found to coincide to a considerable degree with the area of induction (118). Radioactivity and induction fall off sharply with increasing distance from the tissue source; both show definite correlation with the size of the pores and the thickness of the filters. Grobstein presents these results as indicative of the degree of mobility and transport across the filter of large molecules synthesized by the inductor, but he clearly states that they do not necessarily identify the inductive material (119). Of no less interest is the analysis, also by Grobstein, of the concept of cell contact in relation to embryonic induction (120). He agrees with the definition of contact as proposed by P. Weiss (20) and comes to the conclusion that "close association (between inductive interactants) rather than contact in the physical sense is a general requirement" (120).

In closing this section, we should like to mention a new concept in tissue interaction which may have considerable impact on future work in morphogenesis. The electronmicroscopic analysis of the development of the basement lamella of larval skin of Anura (121, 122) strongly suggests that the complex and highly organized orthogonal arrangement of collagen fibers in this membrane is the result of the synergistic action of the mesenchyme and of the skin epithelium. Analysis of the process of wound repairing brought additional evidence in favor of this concept (123). A biochemical interaction between adjacent tissues is indicated in the analysis by Herrmann of the corneal stroma of the developing chick embryo. Considerations presented in previous work (120) led him to suggest that the cornea mesoderm is dependent for protein formation on a factor supplied by the corneal epithelium. In searching for an explanation of the apparent loss of autonomy of mesenchymal cells once they have differentiated into corneal mesoderm, Herrmann suggests the possibility that this might be due to the loss of some enzyme system during development (124). The strict interaction between ectodermal and mesodermal derivatives during development, as exemplified in the above material, will be considered again in the following two sections.

INDUCTION

"The ancient and hoary subject of the normal embryonic induction in the amphibia, which has been worked on now for so long that we know more about it than about any other case of tissue interaction, but which still remains so obscure" (54) has not lost its fascination in spite of the truth of the above statement by Waddington. On the contrary, it is clear from the extensive and remarkable contributions of the last few years that the concept of embryonic induction and its fundamental importance in morphogenesis are perhaps better realized today than a decade ago when frustration and scepticism set in after the enthusiasm raised by the early discoveries had faded away. For this revival of interest we are indebted to a few leading figures who have established active centers in Japan, Europe, and the United States, entirely devoted to the analysis of this problem. We will limit this review to the most recent contributions since previous work has been presented in the article by Nicholas (87).

In commenting on the present status of the concept of embryonic induction, Brachet makes some relevant remarks as to the approaches to the biochemical mechanism of induction and discusses some of the recent results. Of the two main goals, the isolation and purification of the inducing agent and the elucidation of the mechanisms underlying induction, the former is far more advanced than the latter. Data emerging from investigations pursued in different laboratories agree in the recognition that the inductive action displayed by many adult tissues is bound to a protein rather than to a ribonucleoprotein fraction (54). In the same informative book (54) Nieuwkoop and Toivonen present their theories of embryonic induction. Nieuwkoop summarizes the results of a series of experiments performed in the intact amphibian embryo with the "fold implantation technique". This technique, described in detail in a previous investigation (125), consists of the excision of presumptive cranioventral ectoderm from gastrula to neurula stages. Fragments of the excised ectoderm are then folded and implanted in the presumptive rhombencephalic region of host neurula. A comparison of the structures formed in different implanted fragments and in isolated fragments gives information on the competence of the ectoderm. This competence varies according to the origin, the stage, and the influences played upon the implant by the inductive system. Neural induction consists for Nieuwkoop of two processes, activation and transformation, the former preceding the latter. The two processes spread in a decremental way into the implanted tissue. While activation can be brought about by a number of agents, the process of transformation is more specific in character (54). Other aspects of induction such as the establishment of the regionalities in the nervous system, the species-specific relationship between the temporal extension of the competence, and the reactivity of the ectoderm for activation are discussed in the quoted article (54). That anterior brain structures (archencephalon) precede the spinocaudal structures in their appearance has been generally accepted ever since the two-gradient concept was first proposed by Yamada, while to Holtfreter goes the merit of the distinction between mesodermalizing and neuralizing agents (126). At variance with Nieuwkoop, Toivonen considers the neuralizing and mesodermalizing actions to be caused by two different inductive principles. Using bone marrow as an inductor, he studied its action *in vitro* with the "sandwich technique" (devised by Holtfreter) which consists of implanting the inductive system *in vitro* between two pieces of presumptive neurectoderm. Under these conditions, mesodermic structures formed prior to neural structures. The results of these and more recent experiments by Toivonen and his associates (54, 127, 128) are taken as evidence of the existence of two principles: the N (neuralizing) and the M (mesodermalizing) principles which can act independently from each other. The M/N gradient also received support from two other interesting series of experiments, in which HeLa and amniotic cell lines grown *in vitro* were tested for changes in their inductive properties upon implantation in *Triturus vulgaris*. It was found that while the HeLa cells grown in untreated pooled human serum are strong deuterencephalic-spinocaudal inductors, they lose both properties after heating of the cells for 30 minutes at 65 C but still induce archencephalic structures. Cultivation of the cells in serum heated at 56 C almost completely destroys the spinocaudal inductive effects. The results of these and other similar experiments "may be explained as a weakening of the mesodermalizing (M) principle in the cells while the neuralizing (N) principle remains the same" (129). The results obtained with the amniotic cell line are in agreement with the ones presented above (130).

The extensive work of the Japanese group has centered on two main objects: (*a*) the analysis of the developmental potentialities of the three germ layers when cultured alone, in combination, or under the effect of various inductors; and (*b*) the chemical nature of the inductors. The hitherto much neglected problem of endoderm determination has been elucidated by Japanese investigators who discovered significant inductive interactions. According to Okada (131) the regional differentiation of the early neurula endoderm from *Triturus pyrrhogaster* is controlled by two factors; one resides in the explanted endoderm and the other in the mesenchyme combined in culture with the endoderm. The technique consisted of explanting the endoderm between the neurula and the tail-bud stages, together with the ventral half of the lateral mesoderm within an ectodermal envelope (V-L test). Endodermal fragments alone or combined with the cranial neural crest were used in another experimental set. In control experiments, the endoderm was explanted alone (E-C control) or the anterior quarter of the neural fold was transplanted with the adjacent medullary plate (AN-control). In the E-C control, the explant developed as an amorphous assemblage of undifferentiated cells with yolk granules, while a pharynx with a typical morphological pattern developed from AN-controls. An analysis of the results obtained in the "V-L test" series indicates that the branchial material gradually loses its pluripotency from the late neurula stage onwards. The loss of pluripotency occurs also if the branchial endoderm is kept in isolated condition from the early neurula stage; hence the determination of branchial endoderm appears to be an autonomous process. The results are in agreement with the principle of "autonomous regionalisation" proposed by Waddington (132). The role of the mesenchyme is viewed as not indispensable for the regionalization of the branchial endoderm *in situ*, but as an accelerator of its differentiation. It is confirmed by these experiments that the mesenchyme factor causes the future middle or posterior region of the gut to develop into more anterior structures (131). The presence of the mesenchyme seems, furthermore, to be indispensable for the completion of regionalization of the pharynx; in mesenchyme-free environment the pharynx cannot shape itself and it forms a "pharyngoid". The epitheliomesenchymal relationships in the regional differentiation of the digestive tract in the same material were the object of another investigation by the same author (133).

The anteriorization factor ("A" factor), which causes the cephalad shift in the development of the explanted endodermal fragment, varies in its effects according to its site of origin; the mesenchyme derived from the anterodorsal area has the greatest effect, whereas the whole mesenchyme from more posterior regions has the least. The "A" factor seems, therefore, to be distributed throughout the whole mesenchymal region with a gradient of efficiency. The conclusion that "the development of epithelial structures is very much controlled by a morphogenetic active property of the mesenchyme" (133) is in agreement with the results reported in the previous section on the role of the mesenchyme in morphogenetic processes. It is gratifying to see the convergence of different techniques and experimental appróaches in the analysis of exceedingly complex problems, of morphogenesis. It is even more gratifying to see the concordance of opinions in some basic problem of induction when, only a few years ago, disagreement seemed to be the rule and the elucidation of inductive mechanisms a hopeless goal.

A recent investigation by Takata (134) deals also with the same problem of the influence of the mesoderm in the differentiation *in vitro* of isolated endoderm regions; her results confirm and extend the results reported by Okada. She found that the anterolateral mesoderm promotes the differentiation of the liver, whereas the ventrolateral mesoderm promotes the differentiation of the intestine and the presumptive somites promote both the liver and the intestine differentiation. The addition of the notochord in all the above experiments enhances the frequency of pharynx formation and reduces in most cases the frequency of the liver formation. At variance with Okada, Takata believes that the relation between endodermal and mesodermal structures might be mutual rather than one-sided and that soluble agents might play a role in these tissue interactions.

In another investigation, Takata (135) studied the differentiation *in vitro* of the isolated endoderm in the presence of the neural fold of the same species. The neural crest elicits the differentiation of pharynx, oesophagus, stomach, liver, intestine, and pancreas. Differentiation of cartilage from the neural fold was observed only when the neural fold was combined with anterior endoderm, thus indicating that the endoderm, in turn, exerts an inductive influence on the neural fold. To this same line of investigations on tissue interactions belongs an interesting analysis by Jacobson (136) of the influence of ectoderm and endoderm on heart differentiation in the newt. In isolation, the presumptive heart mesoderm, which was explanted at an early neurula stage, formed a heart in 14 per cent of a total of 44 experiments; when combined with anterior presumptive epidermis, beating hearts formed in one-third of the cases, whereas the heart formed in all explants of presumptive heart mesoderm when it was combined with anterior presumptive epidermis and endoderm from the future heart region. The formative influence of the endoderm is also present in endoderm from more dorsal or posterior regions; however, the results of this group of experiments are less consistent. Of particular interest is the observation that a heart always failed to form when the anterior neural plate and fold, as well as the anterior presumptive epidermis, were included. The inhibitory influence of neural tissue on heart formation is further stressed by the observation that "endodermless animals fail to produce heart, but endodermless animals also deprived of their neural plate and fold did produce hearts" (136). A suppressive influence of future brain tissue on the differentiation of striated muscle from somite mesoderm was previously described by Muchmore (137).

The inductive agent.—The chemical approach to the problems of embryonic induction was considerably enhanced by the discovery that some adult tissues contain potent inductive agents; among those intensively investigated in these last years were the bone-marrow factor and inductive factors isolated from malignant cells and from the chick embryo.

The substance reponsible for mesodermal induction by bone marrow was identified by Yamada in a nondialyzable, acid-precipitable fraction, obtained through standard biochemical procedures for protein isolation. An active component which causes intensive mesodermization of the isolated gastrula ectoderm was isolated through electrophoresis (138). Induction of endodermal tissues from the ectoderm was the object of an extensive subsequent investigation (139). Heat treatment of bone marrow, which was obtained by steaming thin layers of this material for different lengths of time, changed the type of induced structures according to the following sequence: trunk mesoderm—spinocaudal—deuterencephalic—archencephalic structures. These results elaborated and extended in another investigation provided additional evidence in favor of the proteinic nature of the mesodermalizing agent (140). The heat treatment for periods of 25, 40, 60, and 150 seconds causes the appearance of a new regional type of induction for each step; a new type replaces the type dominating at an earlier phase of heat treatment. Of considerable interest is the observation that "perhaps it is not an exaggeration to state that most of the principal organ rudiments of the three germ layers may be induced from the presumptive ectoderm by the guinea-pig marrow during the whole course of its regional transformation" (140). The results of this investigation raise the question "whether each regional type is caused by an agent specific for it, or one and the same agent causes various types of induction in various phases of its progressive transformation" (140). Yamada considers the second alternative more likely, whereas Toivonen favors the first alternative (128). A parallel investigation by Hayashi (141) centered on the chemical analysis of the inductive factor isolated from guinea-pig liver; the results show that the activity resides in the pentose nucleoprotein fraction. The possibility that the activity might be bound to the only protein component is not considered.

The question whether the shift in inductive effects called forth by denaturation procedures is due to the presence in the bone marrow of multiple inducing agents or is caused by the degradation of one agent was recently reinvestigated by Kuusi (142), who had already made substantial contributions to the field of induction. She used urea as the denaturating agent of the bone marrow. The results of an extensive series of experiments favor the hypothesis that the bone marrow contains two inducing principles, a mesodermal and a neural principle. Denaturation with diluted urea, at variance with the effects called forth by heat treatment, does not destroy the mesodermalizing effect; a slight decrease in both the mesodermal and the neural inductions was observed "but the mesodermal component was definitely still present, although the urea denaturation of the protein was complete and irreversible" (142). She explains the discrepancies between her results and those of Yamada on the basis of differences in the denaturing agents used in the two sets of experiments. Heat treatment would alter the physical status of the inductive agent in such a way as to prevent its resorption from the reactant tissue, whereas neither alcohol nor urea treatment results in such effects. The hypothesis submitted by Kuusi that induction can be affected by the physical properties of the inductor calls the attention to one aspect of the problem which deserves attention and is well worth further investigation.

The chemical characterization of inducing substances isolated from chick embryos was pursued by Tiedemann and co-workers. In 1959, Tiedemann reported (143) on the isolation and partial purification through column chromatography of a mesoderm-inducing substance identified as a protein. Posterior head- and anterior head-inducing substances were identified in nucleoprotein fractions. Since these fractions were inactivated by trypsin and pepsin but not by ribonuclease, it was suggested that the inducing effects could probably be ascribed to a protein fraction as in the case of the mesoderm-inducing substance. A further purification of the spinocaudal-mesodermal factor was recently reported: an effective deuterencephalic factor was also isolated from ribosomes of chick embryos and chicken liver (144).

Serological evidence for the transfer of proteins in an inductive system was obtained in different laboratories. The serological technique applied to a system consisting of *Rana pipiens* and *Taricha torosa* ectoderm "suggests the passage of antigenic substances from the mesoderm to the ectoderm" (145). A passage of a small amount of nucleoprotein from adjacent labeled meso derm is also indicated in the same material from experiments for which the inductor tissues were made radioactive by incubation in a saline solution containing $NA_2C^{14}O_3$ (145). These results reported by Flickinger & Rounds were extended by the same group in a subsequent investigation (146); cytological examination of chimeric explants did not reveal any passage of cells from the inductor to the induced system and confirmed the previous findings indicating a protein passage in the inductive system. The fluorescent antibody technique was used by Clayton & Romanowsky (147) in Waddington's laboratory to study the possible transfer of antigenic material from guinea-pig marrow and liver inductors to *Triturus alpestris* ectoderm. Evidence was presented that antigenic material may be found in yolk platelets of the ectoderm. Experiments performed at the same time by the Finnish group who used serological and fluorescent techniques in an inductive system *in vitro* are also in agreement with the conclusions presented above (148). The hypothesis of the protein nature of the inductor therefore receives support from these experiments.

MORPHOGENETIC FIELDS

The morphogenetic field most thoroughly investigated in recent years is undoubtedly the limb field in the chick embryo. We will therefore limit this sector to a brief review of the extensive work devoted to the analysis of this process. The background and early experimental work in this field are presented by Zwilling (149) in a lucid and comprehensive article on limb morphogenesis. Two different theories have been proposed to account for the development of limb in tetrapode vertebrates: one considers the ectoderm apical ridge that caps the early limb buds as a major element in limb morphogenesis, whereas the other considers the apical ridge unimportant and confers the major formative role on the mesoderm instead. The main proponents of the former theory are Saunders, Zwilling, and Hampé; the main proponents of the latter hypothesis are Amprino & Camosso, and Bell and his associates. The position of the first group is presented by Zwilling in the quoted review article (149). On the basis of his own work as well as that of Saunders and co-workers, of Tschumi, and of Hampé, he presents the arguments concerning the postulated major role of the apical ridge in limb morphogenesis. Briefly they are as follows. (a) The very existence of an apical ridge as a constant feature in early limb buds in tetrapods. (b) The failure of limb elements to continue their growth and differentiation upon extirpation of the ectodermal ridge. If at the time of the extirpation, some limb parts have already initiated their differentiation, only the distal parts will be missing whereas the proximal parts will instead be normal. (c) The reciprocal dependence of the apical ridge from a "maintenance factor" which is provided by the underlying mesoderm. In the absence of this factor the apical ridge undergoes regression. Limb properties (forelimb versus hindlimb) originate in the limb mesoderm.

Additional arguments are based on extensive work on limbless mutants. The study of early developmental stages of these mutants showed that the ectodermal ridge regresses during the third day and is missing by the end of the fourth (150). A procedure was devised by Zwilling to separate the ectodermal ridge from the mesoderm by versene treatment and to reunite the two components in various combinations, including chimeric limbs of chick- and duck-parts. An extensive series of ingenious experiments by Saunders and co-workers (151 to 154) led this group to restate the above points in an even less compromising way. They state that "the apical ridge, or material intimately associated with it and the subjacent mesoblast, can induce outgrowth in limb-bud mesoderm" (154). The morphogenetic role of the apical ridge is also claimed by Tschumi (155) who investigated the process of limb morphogenesis in *Xenopus*. A detailed analysis by Hampé (156) of limb morphogenesis in the chick embryo under normal and experimental conditions led him to confirm Saunders and Zwilling's work and to accept the above points.

Kieny (157) reports that limb buds, when deprived by versene action of the apical ridge and transplanted in the flank of host embryos, develop normal limbs even if the transplanted mesoderm is fragmented into small pieces before transplantation. The mesoderm becomes covered by the flank epithelium. It is concluded that the limb mesoderm is the primary inductor of the limb, but at the same time it is stated that the flank ectoderm undergoes transformation into an apical ridge which in turn exerts an inductive influence on the underlying mesoderm. The author does not submit evidence in support of the claimed morphological transformation of normal flank epidermis into an ectodermal thickening.

The morphogenetic role of the apical ridge is questioned by Bell *et al*. (158) and denied by Amprino & Camosso (159). The former group used the technique of focusing ultrasounds to obtain the separation of the ectoderm from the mesoderm. The denuded limb mesoblast, grafted into the flank of host chick embryos, developed into complete limbs. Bell *et al.* conclude that these experiments, although they "do not contradict the contention that the apical ridge possesses inductive activity, and is capable of reorganizing mesodermal processes, do not support it" (158). Amprino & Camosso, on the basis of an extensive and penetrating analysis of their experimental results, arrived at the conclusion that "the apical epidermal ridge proper seems not to play an inductive role (in limb morphogenesis)" (160). While denying morphogenetic potencies to this ridge. Amprino & Camosso submit the hypothesis that the distal limb structures form under the influence of more proximally located mesenchymal territories of the limb bud. Their viewpoint is based essentially on: (*a*) the observation that normal limbs can form from limb buds deprived of the ectodermal ridge and of part of the underlying mesoderm; (*b*) the detailed analysis by carbon-marking experiments of the respective position during development of the ectodermal ridge and the underlying mesoderm (160). This analysis showed that the apical ridge is not a static structure but is formed by a proximodistal shifting of the lateral ectoderm from the sides to the free extremity of the limb bud. It is first in contact with the mesoderm which will give origin to the stylopod (upper arm) and then, in subsequent stages, with the mesoderm which gives origin to the zygopod (forearm) and finally with the territory which forms the autopod (hand) (161).

One cannot but be impressed by the valiant efforts and the extensive analysis of this problem by proponents of the two opposite theories on limb morphogenesis. While the evidence in favor of their viewpoints is equally convincing on both sides, the burden of explaining how a limb deprived of its apical ridge can form, under given experimental conditions, remains to the group which claims the all-importance of the ectodermal ridge.

NUCLEIC ACIDS

In the following pages we review some of the work done during these recent years on growth and differentiation at the biochemical level. From the extensive literature we have omitted some pertinent topics because space is limited and some of them had already been reviewed in a very competent way by authorities in these matters. In particular, for a fundamental chapter on nucleocytoplasmatic relationships, we refer the reader to the extensive and illuminating reviews by Briggs & King (162) and by Prescott (163).

Deoxyribonucleic acid.—There is much evidence that in normal plant and animal cells, the amount of DNA in the nuclei of any given species is directly proportional to the number of chromatids present. The accepted evidence of DNA constancy implies, as a direct consequence, that new synthesis of DNA must occur whenever a process of cell division takes place in growing tissue. In view of the genetic importance of DNA, the mechanism of its synthesis during embryonic development has become a major problem. It is generally accepted that DNA synthesis occurs in the cell nucleus. However, incorporation of tritiated thymidine in the cytoplasm of the amoeba has been observed recently (164, 165), but there are difficulties in interpretation because ingested organisms in the food vacuoles may contribute to synthesis (166, 167). The observation that egg cytoplasm may contain some reserve of DNA-like substances has received further experimental support; this reserve seems to be well demonstrated in insect eggs (168, 169) and in amphibian eggs (170, 171), and it has been interpreted as a storage mechanism related to the need for rapid cell division at early stages of development. According to Grant (172), early cleavage would be characterized by the utilization of this store of DNA or DNA precursors in the cytoplasm, which, together with a pool of soluble deoxyriboside precursors, could account for development to a mid-blastula stage. After this stage, when cell division decreases and the cytoplasmic reserves have been exhausted, the synthesis of DNA follows pathways *de novo* (173). Investigations with folic acid analogues, which are known to inhibit the incorporation of formate and glycine into purines and pyrimidines of nucleic acids, gave evidence that synthesis *de novo* of DNA becomes a limiting factor for further growth and differentiation at the end of the cleavage (173). That appreciable DNA synthesis begins at the onset of gastrulation is also indicated by the work of Chen (174), who assayed the nucleic acid content of urodele eggs at different developmental stages. Autoradiographic studies with labeled adenine also indicate that noticeable incorporation into nuclei of sea urchin eggs begins at an early blastula stage and progressively increases in later stages (175). Likewise, incorporation of tritiated uridine into amphibian eggs (176) indicates an active DNA synthesis occurring during segmentation. At the blastula and young gastrula stages the incorporation is exclusively nuclear, and treatment of sections with deoxyribonuclease completely removes the radioactivity, thus showing that uridine is incorporated into the DNA moiety; after gastrulation the incorporation occurs also in ribonucleic acid, both nuclear and cytoplasmic.

In a recent interesting paper, Simmel & Karnofsky (177) gave clear evidence that DNA synthesis is already initiated in the haploid nuclei soon after fertilization in sand dollar embryos. In this study, incorporation of tritiated thymidine was observed by autoradiography: the uptake of the labeled precursor already begins within 15 minutes after fertilization in both male and female pronuclei, and the labeled pronuclei fuse about 30 to 40 minutes later. At cleavage, the labeled nuclear material is distributed to both daughter cells. Unfertilized eggs and sperm exposed to tritiated thymidine did not show any appreciable incorporation; this fact suggests that fertilization is associated with some cytoplasmic change which initiates the synthesis of DNA in the pronuclei (177). The close relationship of DNA synthesis to chromosome synthesis correlates well with the evidence that most of the genetic material is constituted of DNA (178). The incorporation of the labeled precursors into DNA occurs at a rapid rate in actively dividing tissues whereas it is low or practically absent in nondividing tissues; it is generally assumed that such uptake is coincident with DNA duplication and reflects therefore the synthesis of new chromosome material (179). There is some evidence, however, that some part of the DNA is not inert and may

be turned over in nondividing tissues (180, 181, 182). This evidence, however, is not conclusive and there are reports in the literature which deny
the existence of special metabolic DNA; thus, studies of incorporation of
tritiated thymidine in epithelial nuclei of mouse seminal vesicle indicate
that the uptake of thymidine is clearly associated with DNA synthesis
preceding the mitosis, and there seems to be no reason to postulate the
presence of metabolic DNA in nondividing cells (183). Much of the recent
interest in the metabolic activity of DNA has centered in study of giant
polytene chromosomes of *Dipteran larvae* and of the Lampbrush chromosomes
of amphibian oocytes (184, 185). They belong to actively synthesizing cells
and present, in certain stages, special protrusions into the nuclear sap called
"loops" in the former case, and "Balbiani rings" in the latter; the situation
in the polytene chromosomes is characterized by a heavy incorporation of
thymidine at the time of "Balbiani ring" formation interpreted as a genic
hyperactivity in these bands associated with synthesis of DNA and of new
proteins. As Gall & Johnson point out, these findings "are of utmost interest,
since puffing may be a cytological expression of gene activity. If similar
phenomena occur in other organisms, we may expect to find DNA synthesis
as a regular nuclear feature, independent of mitosis or polyploidization" (183).

Several time studies of DNA synthesis as a function of the cell cycle
have in general confirmed the earlier works; all the investigators agree that
there is no synthesis during the mitosis; the synthesis of DNA takes place
during some fraction of the interphase and, actually, at different times of
the interphase, depending on the cell type (186, 187, 188). The interesting
work in Mazia's laboratory indicates that initiation of DNA synthesis prior
to cell division is independent of the mechanisms which produce focal centers
for the organization of the mitotic apparatus. Fertilized eggs of the sea
urchin were exposed to beta-mercaptoethanol at various intervals during
development; this substance, introduced at the proper time, blocks the
mitosis and prevents duplication of centers (189, 190). Incorporation of
tritiated thymidine into DNA, as demonstrated by autoradiography, showed
that DNA synthesis takes place during the mercaptoethanol block, regardless of whether or not the centers have already duplicated (191). With
respect to the mechanism of DNA replication, the extraordinarily successful
approach made by Kornberg and his colleagues (192, 193) resulted in remarkable progress in our knowledge in this area. Synthesis of DNA *in vitro*
has been obtained by this group in a relatively simple cell-free system which
requires the presence of deoxyriboside triphosphates, a polymerizing enzyme
preparation, and DNA as primer or starter. The immediate precursors of
DNA synthesis are deoxyribonucleoside triphosphates, and there is some
evidence that limited control of DNA can be achieved in a population of
growing cells in a medium deprived of thymidine or deoxyriboside (194).

The periodic production of deoxyribosidic compounds associated with
chromosome reproduction has been described by Stern in developing anthers
(195); in a later work, the same author found that such pulselike production
of DNA precursors is matched by a corresponding pattern in DNase activity;

whenever a pool of deoxyribosides appears *in situ*, it is preceded by the appearance of DNase (196). The principal conclusion drawn by Stern on the basis of these studies is that periodic induction of enzyme activity over a brief period in the life span of a cell may be a mechanism for its morphogenetic development.

The experiments of Friedkin indicate that a critical step in the synthesis of DNA during development is the synthesis of thymidine from uracil-deoxyriboside (197). In chick embryo, the synthesis of deoxyuridine does not imply the reaction uridine-cyclouridine-deoxyuridine, but requires the presence of vitamin B_{12} in the reaction connected with methylation of uracil (198). Addition of fluorodeoxyuridine to sea urchin embryos, soon after fertilization, results in an impairment in DNA synthesis and causes cytolysis at the eight-blastomere stage (199). The synthesis of nucleotides from glycine has been found to occur during all the development of these embryos; thus, the enzyme system responsible for purine biosynthesis must be present at all times (172); in agreement with this finding is the evidence for the existence, in the early stage of development, of some precursor pools necessary for DNA synthesis (172, 200). One of the major sources of the deoxyribonucleoside precursor is represented by the ribonucleotide pool, and it has been shown that this conversion occurs in chick embryos (201). The enzyme which incorporates ribonucleotides into the DNA moiety has recently been isolated and purified from calf thymus nuclei (202).

Among other limiting factors for the synthesis of DNA during development are ribose (203) and the folic acid coenzyme system, necessary for the synthesis of precursors (173). Although the existence of a deoxyribonucleoside triphosphate has not been demonstrated in embryonic tissue, it is conceivable that the nucleus, after the early stages, has a mechanism for forming triphosphorylated nucleotides. As Mirsky (204) points out, our knowledge of nuclear enzymes is so far relatively poor; but there is hope that in a near future, other enzymatic processes of importance in the nucleus, concerned with DNA synthesis, will be brought to light. Of particular interest with regard to DNA synthesis and development is the observation that, in some experimental conditions, these two processes may be dissociated to a certain extent; this contention recently has received experimental support: DNA synthesis may proceed when development has stopped (205) and, conversely, DNA synthesis can be inhibited without effect on protein, RNA synthesis, and growth. In microorganisms, dissociation of the nucleic acid synthesis from the synthesis of proteins may be produced by means of purine analogues (206); likewise, mustard gas blocks DNA synthesis in *Escherichia Coli* but permits protein, RNA, and enzyme synthesis to proceed (207). In avian embryos, synthesis of specific protein may be dissociated from DNA synthesis; the use of base analogues will block hemoglobin formation before but not after a period in which some part of the synthetic mechanisms or perhaps some RNA-associated structure is formed; this period in avian embryos was calculated to be of approximately two to three hours before stage nine (208). Mustard gas blocks synthesis in growing muscle tissue but does not affect the development of multinuclearity, indicating that multinuclearity of muscle cells arises through successive cell fusion rather than through amitotic nuclear multiplication (209).

Ribonucleic acid.—RNA, in the form of soluble RNA or of ribonucleo-protein particles (ribosomes), is considered to be actively involved in protein synthesis during growth and differentiation (210); the hypothesis that it plays a role as an intermediate carrier of genetic information between DNA and proteins is today strongly supported by several lines of evidence.

Recent studies give further support to the assumption that the nucleus is the main site of RNA synthesis; as we shall see, however, there is still a discrepancy in the results presented and there is a divergence of opinions among different authors as to whether or not independent synthesis of RNA takes place in the cytoplasm. In plant cells (*Vicia faba*), Woods & Taylor (211) observed that nuclei are the first to incorporate tritiated cytidine; if at this time the cells are transferred to a nonradioactive medium, cytoplasmic RNA begins to be labeled despite the dilution of the radioactive precursor pool and gradually increases while the radioactivity of the nucleus is decreasing; on the basis of these findings, Woods & Taylor conclude that cytoplasmic RNA is nuclear in origin. Similar results were later reported by Woodard *et al.* (212), who used H_3-uridine as the RNA precursor, but they reached different conclusions, stating that "in presence of radioactive precursor pool it is impossible to determine whether cytoplasmic RNA is nucleolar in origin or whether it is synthesized *in situ* from precursors of the labeled pool." Recent studies in microorganisms indicate that RNA is synthesized for the most part in the nuclear region and is subsequently transported into various parts of the cell (213, 214). An ingenious system was devised by Zalokar (215) to investigate the problem of RNA synthesis in nucleated cells, making use of centrifuged *Neurospora* cells fed for a short period with tritiated uridine and then transferred to a nonradioactive medium; the results presented indicate that at least 99 per cent of the cellular RNA is synthesized in the nuclei and that it then migrates into the cytoplasm where the major part of the proteins is made (216). Studies on incorporation of radioactive precursors into mammalian cells grown in tissue culture also gave evidence of a nuclear origin of cytoplasmic RNA (217, 218, 219). Experiments *in vitro* by Schneider (220) indicate that intact nuclear RNA is released from nuclei to the microsomal and supernatant fraction of the cytoplasm during incubation of reconstituted homogenates. The earlier findings by Ficq that rapid incorporation of RNA precursors occurs mainly in the nucleolus were confirmed in more recent investigations (221 to 225). The evidence presented appears as yet undecisive as to whether the cytoplasmic RNA would come from both nucleolus and chromatin (222, 224), or from the chromatin after passing through the nucleolus (226), or conversely from the nucleolus through the chromatin (225).

Amano & Leblond (227), on the basis of their results, propose that synthesis of RNA takes place in both chromatin and nucleolus but only nucleolar RNA would migrate into the cytoplasm. The main fact which emerges from these reports is that the problem is intricate and the hope to obtain a definite answer from studies on enucleated cells not yet fulfilled. Reviewing the experimental work done with enucleated *Amoeba proteus*, Plaut (228) suggests the hypothesis that RNA is synthesized in both nucleus and cytoplasm, that there is some transfer of RNA from nucleus to cytoplasm during interphase but the amount of RNA transferred to the cytoplasm is likely to be small as compared with the amount synthesized there. These conclusions, however, are strongly questioned by Prescott (166, 229) who presented evidence that uptake of radioactive precursors into RNA of enucleated *Amoeba proteus* is caused by organisms ingested in food vacuoles and that, when enucleated cells (*Acanth-Amoeba*) are cultured aseptically, no incorporation of RNA precursors occurs; thus it is indicated that both cytoplasmic and nuclear RNA are assembled in the nucleus. There is no doubt that the presence of infective organisms in the cytoplasm of such cells as *Amoeba* or *Acetabularia*, and the difficulty of growing these cells in aseptic conditions, represent the main shortcomings of this system, otherwise so well suited for studies of synthetic processes after enucleation. Recent evidence indicates that infection of amoeba cytoplasm is rather widespread (230, 231, 167) and re-emphasizes, therefore, the need for demonstration that no infection is present prior to incorporation studies. In *Acetabularia*, the problem is further complicated because accurate estimations of RNA are difficult to carry out; in these cells, the earlier finding by Brachet that enucleate halves are still capable of synthesizing RNA was not confirmed by Richter (232) and by Naora, Richter & Naora (233) who found that there is little or no change in the RNA content of enucleate fragments during the first week after operation. While the German group, headed by Hammerling (234), does not express a definite conclusion and states that the problem of cytoplasmic synthesis of RNA must be left open for further studies, Brachet and his collaborators re-examined the problem in later investigations and found that the total content of RNA in enucleated fragments does not markedly change, but there is a net synthesis of chloroplast-RNA at the expense of RNA present in the other cell fractions (235, 236). On the basis of these findings, confirmed by others (237, 238, 239), Brachet concludes that chloroplasts in *Acetabularia* have a high degree of independence and can synthesize RNA in complete absence of the nucleus whereas microsomal and soluble ribonucleic acids, in *Acetabularia* as well as in the amoeba, are under close control of the nucleus. As Prescott comments (229), there may be a basic difference between cell types with respect to cytoplasmic synthesis of RNA, especially between plant and animal cells. It is important, however, to state that the integrity of RNA of nuclear origin is required for growth, morphogenesis, and protein synthesis as indicated by the experiments of Stich & Plaut (240) which were later confirmed by Brachet (241).

With respect to the mechanisms of RNA synthesis, after the discovery of polynucleotide phosphorylase by Ochoa and his group (242), a search was started in different laboratories for other enzymes which may be concerned with RNA synthesis. As Ochoa points out (243), the main reason for this was that the polynucleotide phosphorylase system did not appear to provide a mechanism for nucleic acid replication; furthermore, if all the evidence suggests for RNA the role of a carrier of genetic information from DNA to protein, a system for RNA replication should be in some way dependent on DNA for its activity. Reports appearing in recent literature seem to support this hypothesis; bacterial cells as well as animal cells (244 to 247) were found to contain enzymes which bring about DNA-dependent incorporation of nucleotides from ribonucleoside triphosphates into RNA. In these systems the effect of DNA is not due to inhibition of nucleases in the enzyme preparation and appears to be of a more direct nature (243). Although little can be said, at present, about the mode of action of DNA, "the fact that it is required as well as all four nucleoside triphosphates are required for incorporation of one of them, would be in line with a mechanism for imprinting genetic information in DNA on to RNA, analogs to that of DNA polymerase whereby DNA would act as template for determining the order of ribonucleotides in RNA" (243).

To establish a chemical basis for the study of ribonucleic acid function in amphibian embryonic development, Finamore & Voklin (248) examined the chemical nature of the RNA obtained from mature ovarian frog eggs; at least two fractions of ribonucleic acid can be isolated differing from one another and from RNA of differentiated mammalian tissues; it is not known whether or not the two forms of RNA correspond to different locations within the cell. Quantitatively measurable (174) RNA synthesis during amphibian development begins at gastrulation; earlier findings that RNA synthesis is very low or absent during cleavage were confirmed by the work of Grant (172) and Rounds & Flickinger (145). Regional differences in isotopic labeling of RNA and proteins in early sea-urchin development were described by Markman (175): incorporation of C^{14}-labeled adenine becomes noticeable at blastula stage and is stronger in the animal region; in the course of development the vegetal incorporation increases relative to the animal one and becomes predominant in later stages. Similar conclusions were reached by Immers by injecting labeled precursors into the body cavity of the female sea-urchin and observing the distribution of radioactivity in the eggs (249); the animal-vegetal gradient in the synthesis of RNA parallels a similar gradient in the synthesis of proteins. The existence of well-defined gradients of distribution for RNA during early development of fishes, reptiles, birds, amphibians, and mammals is indicated by several cytochemical data recently reviewed and critically evaluated in the excellent monograph by Brachet (44).

PROTEIN

Fraser states that "we can account for cytodifferentiation on the basis of protein synthesis; in the maturing cells, this must imply an evolution of protein types in conformity with, and, indeed, guiding the direction of the path taken by the cell" (250). Comprehensive surveys of the general problem of protein biosynthesis are presented by several workers in this field (251,

252). Here we shall outline only some problems of protein formation in the course of growth and development. Studies of proteins in the very early stage of development, with regard to the onset of synthetic processes in vertebrate and invertebrate eggs, have been reviewed by Brachet (44).

In experiments in which S_{35} methionine was injected into sea urchin eggs while still in the ovary, Monroy and his group (253, 254) were able to demonstrate that an active uptake or radioactivity begins a few minutes after fertilization; fractionation of egg-soluble proteins by column chromatography and starch gel electrophoresis indicated that new synthesis of at least one protein component starts immediately after fertilization (255).

Went investigated the antigenic composition of the mitotic apparatus in the sea urchin by means of double diffusion in agar gel and found only two antigens present in both fertilized and unfertilized eggs; in the latter, however, the precursor-1-component was present both as a soluble protein and as an insoluble form associated with intracellular structures (256). Further studies support the hypothesis that the mitotic apparatus is assembled from materials already present in the cell at the time of division (257).

During early development of the sea urchin, Immers (258) observed an increased incorporation of C^{14}-labeled algal protein in advanced blastulae and correlated this finding with the second wave of protein synthesis described in the embryo by Kavanau. Autoradiographic patterns of incorporation of labeled leucine and adenine during development of sea urchins indicate that leucine incorporation becomes noticeable in the cytoplasm of the early blastula and increases in later stages (175). In an interesting experiment, Hulting & Bergstrond (259) studied the incorporation of C^{14}-labeled leucine into proteins in cell-free extracts from sea urchin eggs and embryos and showed a gradual increase of incorporation during development; they correlated this increase with a parallel increase in the content of active ribonucleoprotein particles. Extensive investigations on the development of sea urchin hybrids were carried out by Baltzer and his associates (260); specific differences in the patterns of free amino acids and peptides of the hybrids of different species were found. That qualitative differences accompany quantitative changes in protein synthesis during development is indicated by Bloch & Hew (261) who worked out a method for characterization *in situ* of nuclear histones. In *Helix aspersa*, during cleavage, faintly basic histones make their appearance; these cleavage histones differ from the adult type by their ability to bind fast green, and during gastrulation they revert to a type as yet indistinguishable from that of adult somatic cells.

Analysis of ascidian development was pursued by Reverberi and his group (262), using radioisotopes; it was found that labeled amino acids are taken up by the eggs from the stage preceding fertilization, whereas uptake of nuclei acid precursors begins in fertilized eggs a few minutes before segmentation. In amphibians, protein synthesis and RNA synthesis are not detectable during cleavage and seem to begin at gastrulation to become more marked as development proceeds (44).

In mouse tissues, incorporation of radioactive isotopes does not become appreciable till the ninth day and increases steadily thereafter (263). Protein changes during development of *Rana pipiens* were investigated by Spiegel by comparing the electrophoretic patterns of soluble proteins extracted at different developmental stages; the results obtained "were interpreted in terms of the hypothesis that differentiation involves, in part, the loss of ability to synthesize a particular protein and/or changes in the solubility of pre-existing proteins" (264). In a series of investigations, Collier (265, 266) studied the effects of removing the polar lobe in the protein synthesis of molluscan embryos; the period of maximal protein synthesis, as indicated by the incorporation data, preceded in normal embryos the onset of visible differentiation. It was demonstrated that the lobeless embryos have a reduced capacity to synthesize proteins, which indicates that the polar lobe cytoplasm plays an important role in normal development.

The effects of several natural and synthetic media were tested in the glycine incorporation during growth of chick explants; under conditions of slow growth a much greater increase of incorporation of labeled glycine into proteins occurs than in conditions of rapid growth, thus indicating that tissues may utilize different types of precursors for protein formation, depending on the condition of growth (267). In discussing the quantitative aspects of protein synthesis during development, Herrmann points out that enzymatic and immunological methods should be completed by other quantitative analyses which may give an estimate of the relationship between synthesis and breakdown of the protein investigated (268). Analysis of incorporation of labeled amino acids is suggested by Herrmann as the most appropriate approach to the problem; thus incorporation of radioactive glycine into the glycine moiety of actomyosin and collagen of leg muscle of chick embryos at various developmental stages indicates that a large part of the increase in specific activity in these proteins is a measure of the actual net synthesis (269). The relationship between synthesis of specific proteins and tissue differentiation was investigated by Lash & Holtzer, who studied the uptake of radioactive sulfate during cartilage induction (270). The synthesis of acid mucopolysaccarides was found to begin within the three-to-four–day interval between the cartilage induction and the matrix formation. Chondroitin sulfate is found to appear only when a discernible matrix is present; thus the biochemical differentiation of the tissue seems to parallel its morphological differentiation.

The serological approach.—That synthesis of specific proteins accompanies or immediately precedes the appearance of new morphological structure is also indicated by immunological experiments. These have been widely used to investigate the first appearance of specific proteins during embryonic organogenesis and to establish the possible existence of stage-specific antigens whose appearance or disappearance could be correlated with morphological or functional aspects of differentiation. Most of the work along these lines was concentrated on definite organs, like the lens, the heart, and the skeletal muscle, chosen for having some characteristic components that are relatively easier to isolate and to purify. The gradual appearance of seven distinct antigens during development of the chick lens was reinvestigated and confirmed by Maisel & Langman (271) who grouped the antigens in three main fractions according to their electrophoretic mobility; fraction 1 appears to be identical with the protein alpha crystallin, fraction 2 is identical with the beta crystallin, and fraction 3 is identified with the gamma crystallin; this is the last antigen to appear during development. Fraction 2 is characterized by at least four antigenic subfractions which appear at the onset of differentiation and growth of nuclear lens fibers. Fraction 1 is detected in the epithelial cells of the lens placode before the appearance of any other lens antigen and is thus considered to be the first lens protein to appear during organogenesis.

This protein (fraction 1) is also important because it is found in the lens of representative species of the vertebrate series and is present in the iris and cornea (272). Since these tissues in urodeles have the property of regenerating the lens upon removal of the original lens, the data presented suggest a relationship between lens regenerating capacity and the presence of identical antigens. A minimum of four distinct antigens was found by Beloff (273) in the adult chick lens, and a sequence of appearance was found for these antigens in the developing lens. Parallel studies of morphogenesis and developing lens antigens in the hen by Konyukhov (274, 275) show that antigen synthesis of the definitive lens begins in the lens ectoderm in embryos of 16 to 18 somites. One antigen of the definitive lens was revealed in the lens placode (23 to 25 somites), three antigens were found in the lens vesicle (three-day embryo), six antigens in lens of the four-day embryo, and seven antigens in later stages as well as in the adult lens. Morphological differentiation of the lens is closely related to its antigenic structure modifications, the latter preceding the former. A relationship between the appearance of lens antigens and its differentiation was also found by Flickinger & Stone (276); however, their results do not support the contention that the number of lens antigens increases in the early stage of lens determination. The presence of an antigen with lens-specific determinate groups, revealed in immature occytes, in neurulae, and probably in retina and iris, by the same authors, is considered as a reflection of lens-forming capacity, since the antigen is no longer found in tissues which have lost lens competence; this hypothesis is further supported by the observation that the lens-inducing capacity of the optic vesicle can be inhibited by the anti-adult-lens sera (277). Other attempts to obtain inhibition of lens development by using specific antisera were reported. While Flickinger et al. (278) were not able to produce eye abnormalities in frogs, rats, and chickens by using antilens sera, Wood (279) observed eye abnormality after passive or active immunization of pregnant female rabbits; in his experiments the time of exposure of the fetuses to antibodies appears to be critical, since positive results are obtained only in the early part of gestation.

Similar results are reported by Langman (280), who obtained localized eye defects by use of antilens and anticrystallin sera in liquid cultures of optic cups of chicken embryos; also, in these experiments the appearance of eye abnormalities appeared to be dependent on the antiserum action on primordia at early developmental stages. The same authors, in a later work, did not succeed in producing inhibition *in vivo* of lens development since the results, if present, are obscured by the widespread cytotoxic effects elicited by the antiserum in the embryo (281). On the other hand, Vyazov & Bocharov (282) reported clear-cut growth inhibition of the chick lens by injection of specific serum into developing embryos.

The location of lens antigens by means of fluorescent antibodies has also been the subject of investigations. Nace & Clarke (283), using fluorescent antibodies to explants of tail bud, were able to demonstrate lens antigens in the optic cups and lens of frog embryos at stage 19–20. The reaction was negative at earlier and later stages, thus suggesting the existence of stage-specific or transitory antigens—a possibility also suggested by Langman's (280) study. On the other hand, van Doorenmaalen (284) found that in 5- to 16-day embryos only the lens was stained specifically by the fluorescent antiserum; a lack of specificity was observed in earlier stages. So, while the lens antigens can be detected by the precipitin method after 58 hours of incubation, the fluorescent localization is negative before the fifth day. The apparent discrepancy may be explained by the varying sensitivity of the methods employed. It must be noted as Tyler (285) points out that the failure to detect an antigen does not prove its absence; the increase in number of lens antigens during development may represent an epigenetic formation of new proteins or, alternatively, may be due to a differential increase of pre-existing molecules to detectable levels (273, 286). In this latter case, only quantitative variation in the relative amounts of different proteins in different developmental stages would explain the sequence of their appearance as well as the finding of transitory antigens.

A better characterization of the lens antigens with respect to both their immunological and physicochemical properties is now in progress as is evident from the work of Maisel & Langman (271) and the work in Ebert's laboratory (287). In this latter case, four alpha-crystallin proteins were isolated from the adult bovine lens upon column chromatography and a series of studies on the physicochemical nature of the purified adult alpha-crystallin were carried out; it has been shown that one of the alpha crystallins occurs as a dimer and under definite conditions may be converted into its monomer (288). Of the four molecular species of alpha crystallin found in the adult bovine lens, two were found in the lens at the third month of development and a third component appeared after the fifth month; in the calf lens all the four components are present. It was also observed that the cortical fibers of developing lens show progressively less gamma crystallin, whereas a large amount of these proteins are retained in the nuclear fibers, thus suggesting that the synthesis of gamma crystallin may be suppressed in the cortical region as the lens develops, while it is retained in the nuclear fibers (287). In the case of cardiac myogenesis, Ebert was first able to show that a positive precipitin reaction takes place when antiadult heart serum is confronted with extracts of embryo even before the heart is formed.

Later studies were then carried out with purified muscle components like myosin and actin; they have been reviewed and discussed by Ebert (289). In the chicken embryo, cardiac myosin is already synthesized in the later headfold stage; the antigen reactive groups of myosin appear to be localized in the heart-forming area while the ability to synthesize myosin from the other parts of the embryo disappears. Actin formation begins at the head-process stage, but at variance with myosin it is restricted after the first appearance in the heart-forming area (289).

The work of Ogawa (290), however, indicates that the order of appearance of contractile proteins during myogenesis may differ in various species; in the skeletal muscle of the newt embryo, actin always precedes myosin in the course of myogenesis. That myosin is synthesized in very early stages is also indicated by the interesting work of Holtzer and associates (291 to 294) who used fluorescent antibodies to localize contractile proteins in differentiating muscle. In a very early stage a diffuse staining of the embryo tissues is obtained, and only in later stages does a specific staining by anti-myosin occur in the myoblast. It is of particular interest in this work that slender fluorescent filaments of fibrils are detected before any appearance of cross striation and that in the heart, the presence of myofibrils is observable by means of the fluorescent staining before the heart starts beating. These findings are further supported by the study of Laufer (295) on the regeneration of the forelimb of *Triturus;* the agar diffusion technique showed immunological reactivity to specific muscle antibodies before cross striation is visible in the regenerate.

The enzymatic approach.—The synthesis of enzymes, as specific proteins closely related to the cellular function, represents one of the main features of growth and differentiation. In recent years, the hope that we might establish a casual relationship between enzyme formation and differentiative events has been disappointed and, as Moog states, "emphasis has shifted from enzymes as agents to enzymes as objects of differentiation" (296). Histochemical methods have been widely used to investigate changes in enzyme patterns accompanying morphological and functional modifications in developing tissues.

Spratt studies the organizer center in the early chick embryo with regard to reducing enzyme activities; the evidence presented supports the conclusion that the developmental activites of the node center cells are associated with a marked increase of dehydrogenase activity which appears when the node is fully formed and begins its axial-organ–forming function (297). Alkaline phosphatase increase in the cervical nervous system has been correlated with a pattern of differential distribution which takes place with the differentiation of the nervous system (298, 299). Histochemical studies of aliesterase in the adrenal cortex of the developing mouse have provided new information concerning the activity of the X zone (300). This work indicated that the enzyme activity in the X zone reaches a maximum in the second week after birth and drops down at a low level after the third week. The time course of development of diphosphopyridine nucleotide diaphorase activity in the adrenal gland showed a similar pattern, thus indicating that the X zone at this stage is performing a function as yet unknown which is later taken over by the cells of the permanent cortex (301). In continuing his study on cholinesterase during development, Shen (302) offers an interesting example of a specific relation between enzyme and cytological structure. The evidence is based on studies of cholinesterase distribution in the central nervous system, the neuroretina, and the myoneural junction; in this last focus it has been shown by Shen that muscular differentiation *in vitro* is accompanied by a significant accumulation of cholinesterase; furthermore, the synthesis of the enzyme occurs prior to the innervation and may be, therefore, a determining factor in the site of motor nerve termination in the muscle.

That cholinesterase activity and muscle differentiation appear to go hand-in-hand is also suggested by the work of Singer on the regenerating forelimb of the adult newt *Triturus;* the activity of the enzyme is found to be low in the early formative phases of development, then increases gradually, and reaches a maximum in the stage just preceding the differentiation of the muscle. The variation in cholinesterase activity correlates well with the cycle of acetylcholine production during regeneration (303, 304). In apparent contrast to these findings however, are the results obtained by Buznikov *et al.* (305) who studied the cholinesterase activity in the embryogenesis of mollusks and found that the development of the motor pattern is not directly related to the acetylcholine-cholinesterase system.

Close relationship between tissue differentiation and changes in enzymatic pattern is also shown in the valuable work by Rudnick (306): the author found that growth and differentiation of the retina in chick eyes is accompanied by an increase of glutamotransferase activity; appreciable increase of this enzyme is also observed when the retina has been transplanted in a heteroptic position in early optic cup stages. The damage of transplantation is limited to the ganglion cells, whereas the external layers of retina differentiate in a normal regular fashion. Study of β-galactosidase activity in the developing intestinal tract (307) shows that the enzyme activity increases rapidly at the end of fetal life, parallel to the very fast histodifferentiation of the organ; at time of weaning the activity decreases abruptly to the low adult level. Similarly associated with the sex differentiation of the tissue is the increase of glycosidase in the epididymis (308). The elegant work of Moog (309, 310, 311), centered in the development of the alkaline phosphatase in the intestine of a variety of animals, deals with the patterns of enzymes in differentiating tissues and with some of the factors which may regulate the synthesis and the accumulation of enzymes in some particular stages of development. The alterations in enzyme activity are related to changes in the functional activity of the tissue, and thus "differential enzyme growth in the embryonic and fetal stages may be regarded as a reflection of metabolic adaptation to the changing needs of the developing organism" (309). That alkaline phosphatase accumulation in the intestines of birds, mammals (309, 311), and **amphibians (312)** may be hastened by the experimental application of corticosteroids or of specific substrates makes such a hypothesis a probable one. Metabolic adaptions in adult tissue are by now well known, and very likely they play a role of great importance in the regulation of metabolism (313 to 318).

Some examples of induced enzyme synthesis during development have appeared although some have been a matter of controversy in different laboratories. By administration of arginine to incubating chick embryos, Roeder (319) could delay the decline in arginase activity which normally occurs after the sixth day; in the experiment of Gordon & Roeder (320), injection of adenosine induced a striking increase in adenosine deaminase synthesis in chick embryos; Palmer & Solomon (321), however, failed to confirm that result. The addition of acetylcholine to explants of chick embryo resulted in an increase of cholinesterase activity (322). As Moog (309) points out, in none of these cases has an actual increase of enzyme protein been demonstrated. That this point is a critical one in the interpretation of the enzyme-substrate relationships during biochemical differentiation is indicated by the recent work of Wright (323). Processes not involving alterations in enzyme concentration could account for metabolic changes during development as well as for the increase of enzyme activity that is induced by substrate administration. Changes of enzyme activity revealed by assay *in vitro* may simply reflect differential enzyme stability as a function of the stage of development, and the substrate effect may consist of a protection of the enzyme against inactivation, thus simulating induced synthesis of new enzyme proteins. Furthermore, the enzyme activity *in vivo* may be altered although the enzyme concentration remains constant, depending on the rate at which the endogenous substrate becomes available or on the presence of inhibitors or activators of preformed protein. Induction of α-ketoglutarate transaminase in rat liver (324) and the loss of arginase activity in developing chick embryos (325) are examples in which this type of mechanism seems to be involved. In the light of this consideration, Wright re-examines the observed changes of enzyme activities during development of slime molds and finds that they are not associated with changes of the relative enzyme concentrations; the conclusion she draws is that "sequential substrate utilization (and inhibition) could account for some metabolic changes occurring during differentiation of *Dityostelium discoideum*" (323). There are examples, however, of substrate induction in which differences in enzyme activities are associated with differences in content of specific enzyme proteins in developing tissues, and such changes occur by net synthesis rather than by stabilization of pre-existing enzyme protein. The evidence reported for alkaline phosphatase makes it clear that the substrate induces synthesis of new enzyme-molecules and that the effect may be regarded as a direct influence of substrate on enzyme formation (309). It is interesting that experimental induction of this enzyme in various organs in chick embryo is dissociable to a considerable extent from the morphological differentiation of the tissue (326). In experiments performed by Stearns & Kostellow (327) in dissociated embryonic cells of *Rana pipiens* induced synthesis of tryptophan-peroxidase, formylase, and β-galactosidase was obtained from the respective substrates. In a later study (328) it was reported that typtophan peroxidase can be synthesized from cells from each layer during the blastula stage; as gastrulation proceeds, the cell ability to respond to the induction becomes progressively restricted to endoderm cells. If, however, cells from other layers have been induced while in the blastula stage, they continue to synthesize the enzyme for several weeks if cultured in a proper medium. This provocative work of Stearns & Kostellow is of great interest because it suggests the possibility of enzyme induction in dissociated cells well in advance of the time when the spontaneous enzyme activities can be detected in normal embryos and furthermore indicates that under these conditions, sequential enzyme induction can also be obtained similar to that now known to occur in bacteria. However, Ebert (287) reports that several attempts made by Kato in his laboratory failed to confirm these findings. Ebert comments that the many variables in such culture techniques may perhaps account for the different results obtained and "in view of the significant and far-reaching nature of the previous report (327) it remains desirable to repeat these experiments."

Other examples of the enzyme induction in cell systems cultured *in vitro* have been reported in the literature; DeMars was able to obtain induction of glutamyl transferase by addition of glutamic acid to the culture medium of HeLa cells (329). In recent investigations, Klein (330) studied the substrate effect on several enzyme activities of various cell strains and freshly isolated embryonic cells cultured *in vitro*. It was not possible to induce formation of any of the enzymes tested in established cells strains grown either in Eagle or Parker-199 medium; on the other hand, the addition of arginine to embryonic chick cells resulted in a significant increase of arginase activity: upon addition of RNA to the culture medium the increase of arginase activity was about seven to ten times that in the controls.

In a recent interesting work, Nemeth gives evidence that mechanisms other than substrate induction may operate enzyme formation in developing tissues (331). Tryptophan peroxidase shows a characteristic pattern of changes during tissue development: it is absent or very low in fetal liver, then very suddenly, within 24 hours, reaches the adult level; this occurs soon after birth in the rabbit and guinea pig and after the fifteenth postnatal day in rats. Enhancement of the enzyme activity can be obtained at this stage by injection of substrate or by adrenocortical hormones; no response whatsoever is evoked when the enzyme has not reached the adult level of activity. The lack of response of the fetal liver to L-tryptophan as well as to hormones indicates that, in this case, these are not the mechanisms which directly control the increase of enzyme synthesis during development. In rabbits, premature delivery results in an immediate and rapid increase in the enzyme activity while prolongation of the gestation times prevents enzyme formation until after delivery, thus suggesting that some factor in the uterine environment represses the synthesis of the enzyme (332). Finally, we should like to mention another interesting aspect of enzyme ontogenesis during tissue development which has come quite recently to the attention of the chemical embryologist from the increasing evidence of the molecular heterogeneity of enzymes in living tissue. It has been, in fact, ascertained that several enzymes exist in multiple molecular forms not only within a single organism but even within a single tissue. By means of various techniques, these proteins with the same enzymatic properties, or isozymes, as proposed by Markert & Møller (333), can be separated and identified (333, 334). The pattern of distribution of these separable forms of enzymes is species and tissue specific (335, 336) and presents some characteristic changes during the neoplastic growth (337). Markert and colleagues (333, 335) have shown that the pattern of distribution of isozymes changes during development of tissue by the disappearance of isozymes, the appearance of new isozymes, and, most commonly, by the change in the relative titer of various forms. Thus, the ontogenesis of heart esterase activity is characterized by the successive addition of new forms and by a total increase of esterase activity as the cardiac tissue matures. Using cellulose ion exchanger and starch gel electrophoresis. Flexner *et al.* (338) found four components of lactic dehydrogenase (LDH) in the cerebral cortex of mouse and guinea pig; the several components tested were also different for their ratios of reduction of nicotine-adenine dinucleotide and two of its analogues; these components apparently contribute to different degrees to the increase of LDH in the cortex during development. On the contrary, maturation of the liver was found to be accompanied by a reduction in the number of LDH components. Heterogeneity of LDH in newborn and adult rat hearts was investigated by Kaplan *et al.* (339), using coenzyme analogues, and distinct differences between newborn and adult LDH were found. Evidence for the existence of multiple forms of alkaline phosphatase in the small intestine has been recently given by Moog (340). Kinetic studies suggest that the preweaning increase in activity in the duodenum represents the synthesis of a new form of enzyme not previously present in significant quantity. The existence of multiple form enzymes and their pattern of distribution, characteristic of specific developmental stages, is, indeed, an interesting phenomenon; and in Markert's opinion, "in view of the genetic control of protein structure, it is conceivable that each molecular form of enzyme owes its existence to a separate gene and, if so, the pattern of isozymes may reflect the pattern of activated genes during the developmental process" (341).

BIOLOGICAL SPECIFICITY AND DEVELOPMENT

The acquisition of biological specificity of species, individuals, and tissues represents nowadays a quite well-established epiphenomenon of growth and differentiation. In dealing with problems of development, it appears mandatory that mention, at least, should be made of this newly defined chapter of modern embryology, for it has contributed so much to the progress of our knowledge in developmental biology. Extensive and critical reviews of these topics have recently been given by Ebert (289), Ebert & DeLanney (342), and Ebert & Wilt (343). We have already mentioned the usefulness of serological tools in the study of proteins during development; the emergence of intraspecific differences in the protein antigens during development has been also a matter of intensive investigation: the application of physico-chemical techniques (344), as well as the immunological approach, has contributed a great deal to our understanding of the processes which bring about the individualization of organisms. Intraspecific variations in the serological specificity of serum proteins have been demonstrated by Goodman & Schwimmer (345), Dray & Young (346), and Dubinski *et al.* (347), among several others. Some of these variations have a genetic basis. It appears from these studies that antigenic specificities in the organism continue to evolve for a long time after birth, their appearance is under control of late-acting genes (348), and the full expression of the genetic information in the form of proteins occurs only after the mature stage of ontogeny is reached. An important implication of this postulate is that a retarded epigenesis of some protein types would cause the organism to have imperfect immunological tolerance to its own proteins which could be, in turn, the cause of degenerative processes. Another powerful tool to detect antigenic differences or similarities is represented by the phenomenon of actively acquired tolerance, namely the suppression of immunological reactivity as the result of exposure of embryos to antigenic stimuli before the maturation of their immunological responsiveness (349). The mechanism of establishment of immunological tolerance is itself a subject of great importance, for it implies the possibility of specific inhibition of protein synthesis and may give insight into the problem of differentiation at molecular level (289).

Although the possibility that tolerance represents an adaption of the graft to the host has not definitely been ruled out, most of the experimental evidence favors the hypothesis that changes in the mechanism of antibody formation in the host are involved (343). On the basis of recent data appearing in the literature, Ebert *et al.* (342) suggests that tolerance to homografts and unresponsiveness to heterografts and noncellular antigens may all be expressions of the same phenomenon. Of particular interest in this connection are the results reported by Wittembach (350) of induced tolerance in rabbits injected with protein extracts of chicken liver and spleen. Whether or not the presence of nuclear components in the antigenic stimulus is necessary for the production of acquired tolerance has not been definitely established. As for the optimal time for the induction of tolerance, there seems not to be a rigid correlation with the time of hatching or birth, but a state of immunological tolerance will be induced whenever antigen stimuli (structural groupings of proteins or protein-like substances) have been in systemic contact with the host immunological systems prior to the initial activation of the mechanisms for antibody synthesis.

Ebert *et al.* (342) recently re-investigated the problem of growth-promoting activity of transplants or extracts of homologous organs in the corresponding embryonic tissues, in the light of new immunological findings. The evidence presented strongly suggests an immunological basis for the stimulation of host embryonic spleen by an adult spleen graft, and the effects elicited are more than a graft-versus-host reaction. Studies with radioactively labeled transplants showed that the growth stimulation in the embryonic tissue does not result from a massive transfer of intact cells of the donor, although the transfer of a few viable cells can not be ruled out; further studies with labeled subcellular fractions confirmed a selective uptake by the homologous embryonic organs, which is associated with a significant increase in the weight of the host organ (342). Whether or not the growth response to grafting of homologous spleen and that to injections of cell-free extracts are elicited through the same mechanism can not be decided at present. The problem of maturation of immune response during development has itself been largely investigated, and comprehensive surveys of the pertinent literature have been given by Lawrence (351) and Ebert & DeLanney (342). Synthesis of gamma globulin in the embryos appears late in development, probably near birth, and increases gradually to the adult level; incorporation of S_{35} sulfate into gamma globulins of newborn rabbits has been investigated by Deichmiller & Dixon (352), who confirmed previous findings. While much experimental evidence indicates that the synthesis of most gamma globulins follows antigenic stimulation, the question whether or not the animal may form any gamma globulins in the absence of antigens can not be answered now (343). That embryonic environment is suitable for antibody formation has been indicated by the fact that adult chicken spleen cells pre-immunized *in vivo* and then transplanted into chick embryos continue to synthesize antibodies (353); antibody formation also occurs when adult spleen cells are inoculated simultaneously with the antigen into the embryo (354).

In recent exciting papers, Szilard (355, 356) discussed the molecular basis of antibody formation in the light of a new model of cellular differentiation. In reviewing all the valuable data on the phenomenon of enzyme repressions in bacteria, he suggests that similar mechanisms may play a major role in certain types of cellular differentiation in higher organisms; his model would in particular apply to later stages of embryonic development when specific organizers (or antigens in the case of antibody formation) are involved; in either case, "we may assume that the event is triggered by a transient reduction of the concentration of specific repressor." While we refer the reader to Szilard's papers for the detailed description of his postulates, we would like to point out the interesting fact that similar conclusions are reached by Ebert & Wilt, who independently approached the problem from different viewpoints (343). As Szilard points out, "it has to be expected that our assumption will have to be modified later on in the light of future experimental data." Nevertheless, his postulates maintain a great value and significance for they offer new investigative approaches and represent stimulus for further study. More importantly, here the trend to unify and synchronize all the efforts of students in different disciplines to reach a final common goal appears clear and already fruitful. It is being proven that microorganisms no less than embryos may contribute to our understanding of developmental mechanisms in higher forms. The reviewers fully agree with Nanney's conclusive remark in his interesting paper (357) that "broad comparative studies on a variety of forms, selected for their suitability in exploring particular problems, should cross-illuminate each other and provide eventually the foundation for a *synthetic* biology."

SUPPLEMENTARY REFERENCES

* In the reference list, articles included in recent publications on growth and differentiation are quoted. Here we give a list of other books dealing with the subject matter.

Hamburger, V., *A Manual of Experimental Embryology*, revised ed. (Univ. of Chicago Press, Chicago, Ill., 220 pp., 1960)

Berrill, N. J., *Growth, Development and Pattern* (W. H. Freeman & Co., San Francisco and London, 555 pp., 1961)

Sussman, M., *Animal Growth & Development* (Prentice Hall, Inc., Englewood, N. J., 114 pp., 1960); *Growth Symposia*, **16–20** (1958, 1960)

Davies, J., *Survey of Research in Gestation and the Developmental Sciences* (Williams & Wilkins Co., Baltimore, Md., 203 pp., 1960)

Brachet, J., *The Biochemistry of Development* (Pergamon Press, New York, N. Y., 1960)

Romanoff, A. L., *The Avian Embryo, Structural and Functional Development* (Macmillan Co., New York, N. Y., 1960)

Bulankin, I. N., and Nikitin, V. I., *Problemi Vozractnoy Fiziologi I Bioximi* (Problems of Age Physiology and Biochemistry) (Karkov Univ., Karkov, USSR, 1960); *Glands of Internal Secretion in the Embryonic Development of Birds and Mammals* (Mitskevich, M. S., Ed., Acad. Sci., Moscow, Engl. Transl. publ. for the Natl. Sci. Foundation by the Israel Program for Sci. Transl., 1959)

LITERATURE CITED

1. Shaffer, B. M., *Am. Naturalist,* **91:** 19–35 (1957)
2. Shaffer, B. M., *Quart. J. Microscop. Sci.,* **99,** 113–21 (1958)
3. Bonner, J. T., *The Cellular Slime Molds* (Princeton Univ. Press, Princeton, N. J., 150 pp., 1959)
4. Bonner, J. T., *Proc. Natl. Acad. Sci. US,* **45,** 379 84 (1958)
5. Bonner, J. T., *Symposium Soc. Study Develop. Growth, 18th,* 1–20 (1960)
6. Samuel, E. W., *Develop. Biol.,* **3,** 317–35 (1961)
7. Sussman, M., *Symposium on Chem. Basis Develop., Johns Hopkins Univ.,* 264–95 (1958)
8. Ennis, H. L., and Sussman, M., *Proc. Natl. Acad. Sci. US,* **44,** 401–11 (1958)
9. Sussman, M., and Ennis, H. L., *Biol. Bull.,* **116,** 304–17 (1959)
10. Sussman, R. R., Sussman, M., and Ennis, H. L., *Develop. Biol.,* **2,** 367–92 (1960)
11. Kerr, N. S., *Exptl. Cell Research,* **23,** 603–11 (1961)
12. Wilson, C. M., and Ross, I. K., *Am. J. Botany,* **44,** 345–50 (1957)
13. DeHaan, R. L., *J. Embryol. Exptl. Morphol.,* **7,** 335–43 (1959)
14. Gregg, J. H., and Trygstad, C. W., *Exptl. Cell Research,* **15,** 358–69 (1958)
15. Gregg, J. H., *Biol. Bull.,* **118,** 70–78 (1960)
16. Whittingham, W. F., and Raper, K. B., *Am. J. Botany,* **43,** 619–27 (1957)
17. Bonner, J. T., and Shaw, M. J., *J. Cellular Comp. Physiol.,* **50,** 145–54 (1957)
18. Bonner, J. T., *J. Embryol. Exptl. Morphol.,* **6,** 346–56 (1958)
19. Sussman, R. R., and Sussman, M., *J. Gen. Microbiol.,* **23,** 287–93 (1960)
20. Weiss, P., *Intern. Rev. Cytol.,* 391–423 (1958)
21. Fawcett, D. W., in *Frontiers in Cytology,* 19–41 (Palay, S. F., Ed., Yale Univ. Press, New Haven, Conn., 529 pp., 1958)
22. Waddington, C. H., Perry, M. M., and Okada, E., *Exptl. Cell Research,* **23,** 631–33 (1961)
23. Balinsky, B. I., *Exptl. Cell Research,* **16,** 429–33 (1959)
24. Curtis, A. S. G., *Am. Naturalist,* **94,** 37–56 (1960)
25. Steinberg, M. S., *Am. Naturalist,* **92,** 65–81 (1958)
26. Rinaldini, L. M. J., *Intern. Rev. Cytol.,* **7,** 587–647 (1958)
27. Weiss, L., *Intern. Rev. Cytol.,* **9,** 187–225 (1960)
28. Fisher, M. W., Puck, T. T., and Sato, G., *Proc. Natl. Acad. Sci. US,* **44,** 4–10 (1958)
29. Rappaport, C., *Exptl. Cell Research,* **20,** 479–94 (1960)
30. Rappaport, C., Poole, J. P., and Rappaport, H. P., *Exptl. Cell Research,* **20,** 465–79 (1960)
31. Abercrombie, M., Heaysman, J. E. M., and Karthauer, H. M., *Exptl. Cell Research,* **13,** 276–92 (1957)
32. Abercrombie, M., and Ambrose, E. J.,

Exptl. Cell Research, **15**, 332–45 (1958)

33. Easty, G. C., Easty, D. M., and Ambrose, E. J., *Exptl. Cell Research*, **19**, 539–48 (1960)

34. Levi, G., and Godina, G., *Atti accad. nazl. Lincei*, **8**, 734–47 (1959)

35. Levi, G., and Godina, G., *Boll. Soc. piemont. Chir.*, **26**, 3–12 (1956)

36. Nakai, J., and Kawasaki, Y., *Z. Zellforsch.*, **51**, 108–22 (1959)

37. Nakai, J., *Z. Zellforsch.*, **52**, 427–59 (1960)

38. Townes, P. L., and Holtfreter, J., *J. Exptl. Zool.*, **128**, 53–120 (1955)

39. Bellairs, R., *J. Embryol. Exptl. Morphol.*, **5**, 340–50 (1957)

40. DeHaan, R. L., *Symposium on Chem. Basis Develop.*, *Johns Hopkins Univ.*, 339–74 (1958)

41. Spratt, N. T., and Haas, H., *J. Exptl. Zool.*, **144**, 139–57 (1960)

42. Spratt, N. T., and Haas, H., *J. Exptl. Zool.*, **144**, 257–75 (1960)

43. DeHaan, R. L., in *Ann. Rept. Director Dept. Embryol.*, **59**, 366–70 (Carnegie Inst. Wash. Year Book, 1959–1960)

44. Brachet, J., *The Biochemistry of Development* (Pergamon Press, New York, 324 pp., 1960)

45. Ranzi, S., in *The Beginning of Embronic Development*, 291–318 (Am. Assoc. Advance Sci., Washington, D. C., 1957)

46. Brachet, J., and Delange-Cornil, M., *Develop. Biol.*, **1**, 79–100 (1959)

47. Mazia, D., *Biol. Bull.*, **114**, 247–54 (1958)

48. Ambellan E., *J. Embryol. Exptl. Morphol.*, **6**, 86–93 (1958)

49. Niu, M. C., in *Cellular Mechanisms in Differentiation and Growth*, 155–71 (Fourteenth Growth Symposium, Rudnick, D., Ed., Princeton Univ. Press, Princeton, N. J., 236 pp., 1956)

50. Niu, M. C., *Proc. Natl. Acad. Sci. US*, **44**, 1264–74 (1958)

51. Niu, M. C., in *Evolution of Nervous Control from Primitive Organisms to Man* (Bass, A. D., Ed., Publ. 52, Am. Assoc. Advance Sci., Washington, D. C., 231 pp., 1959)

52. Benitez, H. H., Murray, M. R., and Charfaff, E., *J. Biophys. Biochem. Cytol.*, **5**, 25–34 (1959)

53. Ebert, J. D., *J. Exptl. Zool.*, **142**, 587–622 (1959)

54. Wilde, C. E., in *Biological Organisation Cellular and Subcellular* (Proc. Symposium organized on behalf of UNESCO, by Waddington, C. H., Pergamon Press, New York, 328 pp., 1959)

55. Wilde, C. E., in *Cell Organism and Milieu*, 3–34 (Seventeenth Growth Symposium, Rudnick, D., Ed., Ronald Press Co., New York, 326 pp., 1958)

56. Barth, L. G., and Barth L. J., *Embryol. Exptl. Morphol.*, **7**, 218–22 (1959)

57. Fell, H. B., and Mellanby, E. J., *J. Physiol. (London)*, **119**, 470–88 (1953)

58. Fell, H. B., in *Decennial Rev. Conf. Tissue Culture*, *J. Natl. Cancer Inst.*, **19**, 643–50 (1957)

59. Weiss, P., and James, R., *Exptl. Cell Research*, Suppl. 3, 381–94 (1955)

60. Moscona, A., *Transplant. Bull.*, **20** 120–24 (1960)

61. Moscona, A., *Develop. Biol.*, **1**, 1–23 (1959)

62. Matoltsy, A. G., *Intern. Rev. Cytol.*, **10**, 315–51 (1960)

63. Chase, H. B., *Brit. J. Radiol.*, **31**, 65–69 (1958)

64. Grobstein, C., in *The Cell*, **I**, 437–91 (Brachet, J., and Mirsky, A. E., Eds., 816 pp., Academic Press, New York, London, 1959)

65. Trinkaus, J. P., *Am. Naturalist*, **90**, 273–89 (1956)

66. Shelton, E., and Rice, M. E., *Am. J. Anat.*, **105**, 283–341 (1960)

67. Borghese, E., *Symposium on Chem. Basis Develop.*, *Johns Hopkins Univ.*, 704–73 (1958)

68. Lasnitzki, I., *Intern. Rev. Cytol.*, **7**, 79–121 (1958)

69. Wolff, Et., and Wolff, Em., *Acta 11, Congr. Intern. Ornithol.*, 86–103 (1955)

70. Gallien, L., *Arch. anat. microscop. morph. exptl.*, **48**, 83–100 (1959)

71. Gaillard, P. J., *Develop. Biol.*, **1**, 152–181 (1959)

72. Jost, A., *Harvey Lectures, Ser.* 55, 201–26 (1961)

73. Moog, F., *Symposium on Comparative Endocrinology*, 624–38 (Gorbman, A., Ed., John Wiley & Sons, Inc., New York, 746 pp., 1959)

74. Schneiderman, H. A., and Gilbert, L. I., in *Cell, Organism Milieu*, 157–87 (Ronald Press Co., New York, 326 pp., 1959)

75. Pesetsky, I., and Kollross, J. J., *J. Exptl. Cell Research*, **11**, 477–82 (1956)

76. Wilt, F. H., *J. Embryol. Exptl. Morphol.*, **7**, 556–63 (1959)

77. Levi-Montalcini, R., *Symposium on Chem. Basis Develop., Johns Hopkins Univ.*, 646–64 (1958)
78. Cohen, S., *Symposium on Chem. Basis Develop., Johns Hopkins Univ.*, 665–76 (1958)
79. Levi-Montalcini, R., *Proc. Natl. Acad. Sci. US*, 46, 373–84 (1960)
80. Cohen, S., *Proc. Natl. Acad. Sci. US*, 46, 302–11 (1960)
81. Levi-Montalcini, R., and Cohen, S., *Ann. N. Y. Acad. Sci.*, 85, 324–41 (1960)
82. Levi-Montalcini, R., and Angeletti, P. U., *Regional Neurochemistry, Proc. Intern. Neurochem. Symposium, 4th*, 362–71 (Kety, S. S., and Elkes, J., Eds., Pergamon Press, New York, 1960)
83. Levi-Montalcini, R., and Angeletti, P. U., *Quart. Rev. Biol.* (In press)
84. Bueker, E. D., Schenkein, I., and Bane, J. L., *Cancer Research*, 20, 1220–28 (1960)
85. Hamburger, V., *Am. Scientist*, 45, 263 77 (1957)
86. Hamburger, V., *Am. J. Anatomy*, 102, 365–410 (1958)
87. Nicholas, J. S., *Ann. Rev. Physiol.*, 22, 95–110 (1960)
88. Weiss, P., *J. Exptl. Zool.*, 100, 353–86 (1945)
89. Holtfreter, J., *J. Morphol.*, 80, 25–56 (1947)
90. Moscona, A., in *Developing Cell Systems and Their Control*, 45–70 (Eighteenth Growth Symposium, Rudnick, D., Ed., Ronald Press Co. New York, 1960)
91. Holtzer, H., Abbott, J., Lash, G., and Holtzer, S., *Proc. Natl. Acad. Sci. US*, 46, 1533–42 (1960)
92. Okada, T. S., *Exptl. Cell Research*, 16, 437–40 (1959)
93. Eagle, H., *Harvey Lectures, Ser. 54*, 156–75 (1959)
94. Evans, V. J., Earle, W. R., and Stevenson, R. E., *Am. J. Hygiene*, 73, 96–104 (1961)
95. Sanford, K. K., Dunn, T. B., Covalesky, A. B., Dupree, L. T., and Earle, W. R., *J. Natl. Cancer Inst.*, 26, 331–57 (1961)
96. Eagle, H., *Proc. Natl. Acad. Sci. US*, 46, 427–32 (1960)
97. Wolff, Em., *Bull. Biol.*, 91, 271–82 (1957)
98. Lieberman, I., Lanny, F., and Ove, P., *Science*, 129–43 (1959)
99. Puck, T. T., *Harvey Lectures, Ser. 55*, 1–12 (1961)
100. Loomis, W. L., in *Cell Organism and Milieu*, 253–76 (Seventeenth Growth Symposium, Rudnick, E., Ed., Ronald Press Co., New York, 326 pp., 1959)
101. Trinkaus, J. P., and Drake, J. W., *Develop. Biol.*, 1, 377–95 (1959)
102. Weiss, P., and Taylor, A. C., *Proc. Natl. Acad. Sci. US*, 46, 1177–85 (1960)
103. Boterenbrood, E. C., *Proc. Koninkl. Ned. Akad. Wetenschap., Ser. C*, 61, 470–81 (1958)
104. Scott, F. M., *Acta Embryol. Morphol. Exptl.*, 2, 209–26 (1959)
105. Tartar, V., *J. Exptl. Zool.*, 144, 187–207 (1960)
106. Stefanelli, A., Zacchei, A. M., and Ceccherini, V., *Acta Embryol. Morphol. Exptl.*, 4, 47–55 (1961)
107. Grobstein, C., in *Aspects of Synthesis and Order in Growth* (Thirteenth Growth Symposium, Rudnick, D., Ed., Princeton Univ. Press, Princeton, N. J., 274 pp., 1954)
108. Sobel, H. J., *J. Embryol. Exptl. Morphol.*, 6, 518–26 (1958)
109. Auerbach, R., and Grobstein, C., *Exptl. Cell Research*, 15, 384–97 (1959)
110. Auerbach, R., in *Self-Organizing Systems*, 101–7 (Pergamon Press, Oxford, 1960)
111. Auerbach, R., *Develop. Biol.*, 2, 271–84 (1960)
112. Stockdale, F., Holtzer, M., and Lash, J., *Acta Embryol. Morphol. Exptl.*, 4, 40–46 (1961)
113. Goldhaber, P., *Science*, 113, 2065–67 (1961)
114. McKeehan, M. S., *Anat. Record*, 132, 297–305 (1958)
115. Benoit, J., *J. Embryol. Exptl. Morphol.*, 8, 33–38 (1960)
116. Strudel, G., *Compt. rend. acad. sci.*, 249, 470–71 (1959)
117. Sengel, P., *La Colloq. intern. centre natl. recherche sci. (Paris)*, 95–13 (1961)
118. Grobstein, C., *J. Exptl. Zool.*, 142, 203–21 (1959)
119. Grobstein, C., *Colloq. intern. centre natl. recherche sci. (Paris)* (1961)
120. Grobstein, C., *Exptl. Cell Research*, Suppl. 8, 234–45 (1961)
121. Kemp, N. E., *Develop. Biol.*, 1, 459–76 (1959)
122. Weiss, P., and Ferris, W., *Proc. Natl. Acad. Sci. US*, 40, 528–40 (1954)
123. Weiss, P., *Harvey Lectures, Ser. 55*, 13–42 (1961)
124. Herrmann, H., *Science*, 132, 529–32 (1960)

125. Nieuwkoop, P. D., *Acta Embryol. Morphol. Exptl.*, **2**, 13–53 (1958)
126. Holtfreter, J., and Hamburger, V., in *Analysis of Development*, 230–96 (Willier, B. H., Weiss, P. A., and Hamburger, V., Eds., W. B. Saunders, Co., Philadelphia and London, 735 pp., 1955)
127. Toivonen, S., Saxen, L., and Vainio, T., *Experientia*, **17**, 86–87 (1961)
128. Toivonen, S., *Experientia*, **17**, 87–88 (1961)
129. Saxen, L., and Toivonen, S., *J. Embryol. Exptl. Morphol.*, **6**, 616–32 (1958)
130. Toivonen, S., Saxen, L., and Vainio, T., *Acta Embryol. Morphol. Exptl.*, **3**, 23–34 (1960)
131. Okada, T. S., *Wilhelm Roux' Arch. Entwicklungsmech. Organ.*, **151**, 559–71 (1960)
132. Waddington, C. H., *Principles of Embryology* (Allen, G., Unwin Ltd., London, 510 pp., 1956)
133. Okada, T. S., *Wilhelm Roux' Arch. Entwicklungsmech. Organ*, **152**, 1–21 (1960)
134. Takata, C., *Embryologia*, **5**, 38–70 (1960)
135. Takata, C., *Embryologia*, **5**, 194–205 (1960)
136. Jacobson, A. G., *Develop. Biol.*, **2**, 138–54 (1960)
137. Muchmore, W. B., *J. Exptl. Zool.*, **139**, 181–88 (1958)
138. Yamada, T., *Symposium on Chem. Basis Develop., Johns Hopkins Univ.*, 217–38 (1958)
139. Takata, C., and Yamada, T., *Embryologia*, **5**, 8–20 (1960)
140. Yamada, T., *Embryologia*, **4**, 175–90 (1959)
141. Hayashi, Y., *Develop. Biol.*, **1**, 343–63 (1959)
142. Kuusi, T., *Acta Embryol. Morphol. Exptl.*, **4**, 18–39 (1961)
143. Tiedemann, H., *Naturwissenschaften*, **46**, 613–23 (1959)
144. Tiedemann, H., Kesselring, K., Becker, U., and Tiedemann, H., *Biochim. et Biophys. Acta*, **49**, 603–5 (1961)
145. Rounds, D. E., and Flickinger, R. A., *J. Exptl. Zool.*, **137**, 479–99 (1958)
146. Flickinger, R. A., Hatton, E., and Rounds, D. E., *Exptl. Cell Research*, **17**, 30–34 (1959)
147. Clayton, R. M., and Romanowsky, A., *Exptl. Cell Research*, **18**, 410–12 (1959)
148. Vainio, T., Saxen, L., and Toivonen, S., *Experientia*, **16**, 27–28 (1960)
149. Zwilling, E., in *Advances in Morphogenesis*, **1**, 301–30 (Abercrombie, M., and Brachet, J., Eds., Academic Press, New York, 460 pp., 1960)
150. Zwilling, E. J., *Exptl. Zool.*, **132**, 173–87 (1956)
151. Saunders, J. W., Jr., Cairns, J. M., and Gasseling, M. T., *J. Morphol.*, **101**, 57–88 (1957)
152. Saunders, J. W., Jr., Gasseling, M. T., and Cairns, J. M., *Develop. Biol.*, **1**, 281–301 (1959)
153. Saunders, J. W., Jr., Gasseling, M. T., and Gfeller, M. D., Sr., *Exptl. Zool.*, **136**, 39–74 (1958)
154. Gasseling, M. T., and Saunders, J. W., Jr., *Develop. Biol.*, **3**, 1–25 (1961)
155. Tschumi, P. A., *J. Anat.*, **91**, 149–73 (1957)
156. Hampé, A., *Arch. Anat. Microbiol. Exptl.*, **48**, 345–478 (1959)
157. Kieny, M., *J. Embryol. Exptl. Morphol.*, **8**, 457–67 (1960)
158. Bell, E., Kaighn, M. E., and Fessenden, L. M., *Develop. Biol.*, **1**, 101–24 (1959)
159. Amprino, R., and Camosso, M., *Acta Anat.*, **38**, 280–88 (1955)
160. Amprino, R., and Camosso, M., *Arch. Anat. Morphol. Exptl.*, **48**, 261–306 (1959)
161. Amprino, R., and Camosso, M., *Experientia*, **17**, 92–93 (1961)
162. Briggs, R., and King, T. J., in *The Cell*, 537–617 (Brachet, J., and Mirsky, A., Eds., Academic Press, Inc., New York, 1959)
163. Prescott, D. M., *Ann. Rev. Physiol.*, **22**, 17–44 (1960)
164. Plaut, W., and Sagan, L. A., *J. Biophys. Biochem. Cytol.*, **4**, 843–46 (1958)
165. Plaut, W., *Biochem. Pharmacol.*, **4**, 73–85 (1960)
166. Prescott, D. M. J., *Biophys. Biochem. Cytol.*, **6**, 203–6 (1959)
167. Roth, J. E., and Daniels, E. W., *J. Biophys. Biochem. Cytol.*, **9**, 317–23 (1961)
168. Nigon, V., and Daillie, J., *Biochim. et Biophys. Acta*, **29**, 246–55 (1958)
169. Durand, M. C., *Exptl. Cell Research*, **15**, 257–59 (1958)
170. Finamore, F., J., and Volkin, E., *Exptl. Cell Research*, **15**, 405–11 (1958)
171. Bieber, S., Spence, J. A., and Hitchinger, G. H., *Exptl. Cell Research*, **16**, 202–14 (1959)
172. Grant, P., *J. Cellular Comp. Physiol.*, **52**, 227–48 (1958)

173. Grant, P., *Develop. Biol.*, **2**, 197–251 (1960)
174. Chen, P. S., *Exptl. Cell Research*, **21**, 523–34 (1960)
175. Markman, B., *Exptl. Cell Research*, **23**, 118–29 (1961)
176. Bieliavsky, N., and Tencer, R., *Nature*, **185**, 401–6 (1960)
177. Simmel, E. B., and Karnofsky, D. A., *J. Biophys. Biochem. Cytol.*, **10**, 59–65 (1961)
178. Beadle, G. W., *Ann. Rev. Physiol.*, **22**, 45–74 (1960)
179. Stern, H., in *Developing Cell Systems and their Control*, 135–65 (Rudnick, D., Ed., Ronald Press Co., New York, 240 pp., 1960)
180. Chayen, S., *Exptl. Cell Research*, Suppl. 6, 115–31 (1959)
181. Koenig, H., *J. Biophys. Biochem. Cytol.*, **4**, 785–92 (1958)
182. Pelc, S. R., and LaCour, L. F., *Experientia*, **15**, 131–33 (1959)
183. Gall, J. G., and Johnson, W. W., *J. Biophys. Biochem. Cytol.*, **7**, 657–66 (1960)
184. Rudkin, G. T., and Corlette, S. L., *Proc. Natl. Acad. Sci. US*, **43**, 964–71 (1957)
185. Ficq, A., Pavan, C., and Brachet, J. *Exptl. Cell Research*, Suppl. 6, 105–14 (1959)
186. Newton, A. A., and Wildy, P., *Exptl. Cell Research*, **16**, 426–35 (1959)
187. Firket, H., *Arch. biol. (Liège)*, **69**, 1–7 (1958)
188. Walcker, P. M. B., and Mitchinson, J. M., *Exptl. Cell Research*, **13**, 167–70 (1959)
189. Mazia, D., and Zimmerman, A. M., *Exptl. Cell Research*, **15**, 138–53 (1958)
190. Mazia, D., and Harris, P. *J. Biophys. Biochem. Cytol.*, **7**, 1–20 (1960)
191. Bucher, H. C. R., and Mazia, D., *J. Biophys. Biochem. Cytol.*, **7**, 651–55 (1960)
192. Kornberg, A., *Stanford Med. Bull.*, **18**, 66–75 (1960)
193. Kornberg, A., *Science*, **131**, 1503–8 (1960)
194. Burns, V. W., *Science*, **129**, 566–67 (1959)
195. Stern, H., *Ann. N. Y. Acad. Sci.*, **90**, 440–54 (1960)
196. Stern, H., *J. Biophys. Biochem. Cytol.*, **9**, 271–77 (1961)
197. Friedkin, M., in *Kinetics of Cellular Proliferation*, 97 (Stohlman, F., Ed., Grune & Stratton, New York, 1959)
198. Reichard, P., *J. Biol. Chem.*, **234**, 2719–22 (1959)
199. Nemer, M., *Federation Proc.*, **20**, 360 (1961)
200. Finamore, F. J., and Crouse, G. T., *Exptl. Cell Research*, **14**, 160–65 (1958)
201. Reichard, P., *J. Biol. Chem.*, **234**, 1244–48 (1959)
202. Krakov, J. S., *Federation Proc.*, **20**, 360 (1961)
203. Peabody, R. A., and Hurwitz, C., *Federation Proc.*, **20**, 351 (1961)
204. Mirsky, A., in *The Cell Nucleus*, 167–69 (Butterworth, London, 1960)
205. Brachet, J., in *Fundamental Aspects of Normal and Malignant Growth* (Nowinski, W. W., Ed., Elsevier Co., Amsterdam, 1960)
206. Chartrenne, H., and Devreux, S., *Exptl. Cell Research*, Suppl. 6, 152–60 (1959)
207. Pardee, A. B., *Exptl. Cell Research*, Suppl. 6, 142–51 (1959)
208. O'Brien, B. R. A., *Nature*, **184**, 376–84 (1959)
209. Konigsberg, I. R., McElvain, N., Tootle, M., and Hermann, H., *J. Biophys. Biochem. Cytol.*, **8**, 333–43 (1960)
210. Brachet, J., *The Biological Role of Ribonucleic Acids* (Elsevier Co., Amsterdam, 144 pp., 1960)
211. Woods, P., and Taylor, J., *Lab. Invest.*, **8**, 309–18 (1959)
212. Woodard, J., Rasch, E., and Swift, H., *J. Biophys. Biochem. Cytol.*, **9**, 445–62 (1961)
213. Caro, L. C., and Forro, F., *J. Biophys. Biochem. Cytol.*, **9**, 555–65 (1961)
214. Ezekiel, D. H., *J. Bacteriol.*, **80**, 119–30 (1960)
215. Zalokar, M., *Exptl. Cell Research*, **19**, 559–76 (1960)
216. Zalokar, M., *Exptl. Cell Research*, **19**, 184–86 (1960)
217. Taylor, J. II., *Ann. N. Y. Acad. Sci.*, **90**, 409–21 (1960)
218. Goldstein, L., and Micou, J., *J. Biophys. Biochem. Cytol.*, **6**, 1–5 (1959)
219. Goldstein, L. and Micou, J., *J. Biophys. Biochem. Cytol.*, **6**, 301–3 (1959)
220. Schneider, J. H., *Biochim. et Biophys. Acta*, **47**, 107–13 (1961)
221. Perry, R. P., Hell, A., and Errea, M., *Biochim. et Biophys. Acta*, **49**, 47–57 (1961)

222. Perry, R. P., *Exptl. Cell Research*, **20**, 216–20 (1960)

223. Sirlin, J. L., *Exptl. Cell Research*, **19**, 177–80 (1960)

224. Sirlin, J. L., Kato, K., and Jones, K. W., *Biochim. et Biophys. Acta*, **48**, 421–23 (1961)

225. Fitzgerald, P. J., and Vinijchaikul, K., *Lab. Invest.*, **8**, 319–29 (1959)

226. Pelling, G., *Nature*, **184**, 655–56 (1959)

227. Amano, M., and Leblond, C. P., *Exptl. Cell Research*, **20**, 250–56 (1960)

228. Plaut, W., *Exptl. Cell Research*, Suppl. 6, 69–77 (1959)

229. Prescott, D. M., *Exptl. Cell Research*, **19**, 29–34 (1960)

230. Mercer, E. H., *Proc. Roy. Soc. (London), B*, 150–232 (1959)

231. Daniels, E. W., and Roth, L. E., *Radiation Research*, **14**, 66–82 (1961)

232. Richter, G., *Biochim. et Biophys. Acta*, **34**, 407–19 (1959)

233. Naora, H., Richter, G., and Naora, H., *Exptl. Cell Research*, **16**, 434–36 (1959)

234. Hammerling, J., Clauss, H., Keck, K., Richter, G., and Werz, G., *Exptl. Cell Research*, Suppl. 6, 210–26 (1959)

235. Brachet, J., *Nature*, **186**, 194–99 (1960)

236. Naora, H., Naora, H., and Brachet, J., *J. Gen. Physiol.*, **43**, 1083–1102 (1960)

237. Sutter, R. P., Whitman, S. L., and Webster, G., *Biochim. et Biophys. Acta*, **49**, 233–35 (1961)

238. Braverman, G., and Konigsberg, N., *Biochim. et Biophys. Acta*, **48**, 418–20 (1961)

239. Braverman, G., and Konigsberg, N., *Biochim. et Biophys. Acta*, **43**, 374–81 (1960)

240. Stich, H., and Plaut, W., *J. Biophys. Biochem. Cytol.*, **4**, 119–21 (1958)

241. Brachet, J., *Exptl. Cell Research*, Suppl. 6, 78–96 (1959)

242. Ochoa, S., *Angew. Chem.*, **72**, 225 (1960)

243. Ochoa, S., Burma, D. P., Kroger, H., and Weill, J. D., *Proc. Natl. Acad. Sci. US*, **47**, 670–79 (1961)

244. Weiss, S. B., *Proc. Natl. Acad. Sci. US*, **46**, 1020–26 (1960)

245. Weiss, S. B., and Tokumasa, N., *Proc. Natl. Acad. Sci. US*, **47**, 694–97 (1961)

246. Hurwitz, J., Bresler, A., and Diringer, R., *Biochem. Biophys. Research Communs.*, **3**, 15–18 (1960)

247. Steven, A., *Biochem. Biophys. Research Communs.* **3**, 92–94 (1960)

248. Finamore, F. J., and Volkin, E., *J. Biol. Chem.*, **236**, 443–47 (1961)

249. Immers, J., *Exptl. Cell Research*, **18**, 585–88 (1959)

250. Fraser, R. C., *Am. Naturalist*, **93**, 47–80 (1959)

251. Work, T. S., in *Developing Cell Systems in their Control*, 205–35 (Rudnick, D., Ed., Ronald Press Co., New York, 240 pp., 1960)

252. Campbell, P. N., *Biol. Revs. Cambridge Phil. Soc.*, **35**, 413–58 (1960)

253. Monroy, A., and Nakano, E., *Pubbl. staz. zool. Napoli*, **31**, 95–99 (1959)

254. Monroy, A., *Experientia*, **16**, 114–16 (1960)

255. Monroy, A., Vittorelli, M. L., and Guarneri, R., *Acta Embryol. Morphol. Exptl.*, **4**, 77–95 (1961)

256. Went, H. A., *J. Biophys. Biochem. Cytol.*, **5**, 447–55 (1959)

257. Went, H. A., and Mazia, D., *Exptl. Cell Research*, Suppl. 7, 200–18 (1959)

258. Immers, J., *Exptl. Cell Research*, **18**, 585–88 (1959)

259. Hulting, T., and Bergstrond, A., *Develop. Biol.*, **2**, 61 (1960)

260. Baltzer, F., Chen, P. S., and Whiteley, A. H., *Exptl. Cell Research*, Suppl. 6, 192–209 (1959)

261. Bloch, D. P., and Hew, H. Y. C., *J. Biophys. Biochem. Cytol.*, **8**, 69 (1960)

262. Reverberi, G., Verly, W. G., Mansueto, C., and Di Anna, T., *Acta Embryol. Morphol. Exptl.*, **2**, 202–12 (1960)

263. Atlas, M., Bond, V. P., and Cronkite, E. P., *J. Histochem. Cytol.*, **8**, 171 (1960)

264. Spiegel, M., *Biol. Bull.*, **118**, 451–62 (1960)

265. Collier, J. R., *Exptl. Cell Research*, **21**, 126–36 (1960)

266. Collier, J. R., *Acta Embryol. Morphol. Exptl.*, **4**, 70–76 (1961)

267. Britt, L. G., and Herrmann, H., *J. Embryol. Exptl. Morphol.*, **7**, 66 (1959)

268. Herrmann, H., in *Fundamental Aspects of Normal and Malignant Growth* (Nowinski, W. W., Ed., Elsevier Co., Amsterdam, 1960)

269. Herrmann, H., Lerman, L., and White, B. N., *Biochim. et Biophys. Acta* **27**, 161–66 (1958)

270. Lash, J. W., Holtzer, H., and White-

house, M. W., *Develop. Biol.*, **2**, 76–89 (1960)

271. Maisel, H., and Langman, J., *J. Embryol. Exptl. Morphol.*, **9**, 191–201 (1961)

272. Langman, J., *J. Embryol. Exptl. Morphol.*, **7**, 264–74 (1959)

273. Beloff, R. H., *J. Exptl. Zool.*, **140**, 493–518 (1959)

274. Konyukhov, B. V., and Lishtvan, L. L., *Arch. Anat. Embryol.*, **8**, 32–39 (1959)

275. Konyukhov, B. V., *Zhur. Obschei Biol.*, **20**, 299–306 (1959)*

276. Flickinger, R. A., and Stone, G., *Exptl. Cell Research*, **21**, 541–47 (1960)

277. Clarke, I., and Fowler, I., *Develop. Biol.*, **2**, 155–72 (1960)

278. Flickinger, R. A., Levi, E., and Smith, A. E., *Physiol. Zool.*, **28**, 79 85 (1955)

279. Wood, D. C., *Ross Pediatric Research Congr., 23rd*, 77 pp. (Ross Lab., Columbus, Ohio, 1957)

280. Langman, J., Schalekamp, M. A., Kukyen, M. P., and Veen, R., *Acta Morphol. Neerl.-Scand*, **2**, 142–54 (1957)

281. Langman, J., *Anat. Record*, **137**, 135 (1960)

282. Vyazov, O. E., and Bocharov, Yu. S., *Bull. Exptl. Biol. Med.*, (*USSR*) (*Engl. Transl.*), **47**, 87–90 (1959)

283. Nace, G. W., and Clarke, W. M., *Symposium on Chem. Basis Develop., Johns Hopkins Univ.*, 546–61 (1958)

284. Doorenmallen, W. J. van, *Acta Morphol. Neerl.-Scand.*, **2**, 1–12 (1958)

285. Tyler, A., in *The Beginning of Embryonic Development* (Am. Assoc. Advance Sci., Washington, D. C., 1957)

286. Perlmann, P., and DeVincentis, M., *Exptl. Cell Research*, **23**, 612–16 (1961)

287. Ebert, J., in *The Year Book No. 59*, 386 pp. (Carnegie Inst., Washington, D. C., 1960)

288. Resnik, R., and Papaconstantinou, J., *Federation Proc.*, **19**, 340 (1960)

289. Ebert, J., in *The Cell*, **I**, 619–93 (Brachet, J., and Mirsky, A., Eds., Academic Press, New York, 816 pp., 1959)

290. Ogawa, Y., *Nature*, **182**, 1312–13 (1958)

291. Holtzer, H., Marshall, J. M., Fink, H., Pepe, F., *Exptl. Cell Research*, Suppl. 3, 705–11 (1957)

292. Marshall, J. M., Holtzer, H., Fink, H., and Pepe, F., *Exptl. Cell Research*, Suppl. 7, 219–33 (1959)

293. Fink, H., and Holtzer, H., *Exptl. Cell Research*, **23**, 251–57 (1961)

294. Holtzer, H., Abbott, J., and Cavanaugh, M., *Exptl. Cell Research*, **16**, 595–62 (1959)

295. Laufer, H., *J. Embryol. Exptl. Morphol.*, **7**, 431–58 (1959)

296. Moog, F., in *Embryonic Nutrition*, 87–113 (Rudnick, D., Ed., Univ. of Chicago Press, Chicago, Ill., 1958)

297. Spratt, N. T., *J. Exptl. Zool.*, **138**, 51–80 (1958)

298. Rogers, K. T., De Vries, L., Kepler, J. A., Kepler, C. R., and Speidel, E. R., *J. Exptl. Zool.*, **142**, 89–103 (1960)

299. Rogers, K. T., *Exptl. Zool.*, **145**, 49–60 (1960)

300. Allen, J. M., *Anat. Record*, **134**, 385–94 (1959)

301. Allen, J. M., *Anat. Record*, **132**, 195–208 (1958)

302. Shen, S. C., *Symposium on Chem. Basis Develop., Johns Hopkins Univ.*, 416–32 (1958)

303. Singer, M., Davis, M. H., and Arkowitz, E. S., *J. Embryol. Exptl. Morphol.*, **8**, 98–111 (1960)

304. Singer, M., *Develop. Biol.*, **1**, 603–20 (1959)

305. Buznikov, G. A., *Doklady Akad. Nauk SSSR*, **3**, 723–25 (1960)*

306. Rudnick, D., *J. Exptl. Zool.*, **142**, 643 (1959)

307. Alvarez, A., and Sas, J., *Nature*, **190**, 4778–79 (1961)

308. Conchie, J., Findlay, J., and Levvi, G. A., *Biochem. J.*, **71**, 318–25 (1960)

309. Moog, F., in *Cell Organism and Milieu*, 121–55 (Rudnick, D., Ed., Ronald Press Co., New York, 240 pp., 1959)

310. Kato, Y., and Moog, F., *Science*, **127**, 812–13 (1958)

311. Moog, F., and Ortiz, E., *J. Embryol. Exptl. Morphol.*, **8**, 182–94 (1960)

312. Chieffi, G., and Carfagna, M., *Acta Embryol. Morphol. Exptl.*, **3**, 213–20 (1960)

313. Knox, W. E., in *Proc. Intern. Symposium Enzyme Chem., Tokyo and Kyoto, 1957*, 414–18 (1958)

314. Knox, W. E., *Acta Union Intern. contra Cancrum*, **16**, 1018–21 (1960)

315. Schimke, R. T., *Federation Proc.*, **20**, 226 (1961)

316. Walker, J., *J. Biol. Chem.*, **235**, 2357–61 (1960)

317. Rosen, F., Milholland, R. J., and Solomon, D., *Federation Proc.*, **20**, 225 (1961)
318. Ono, T., and Potter, Van R., *Federation Proc.*, **20**, 224 (1961)
319. Roeder, M., *J. Cellular Comp. Physiol.*, **50**, 241–48 (1957)
320. Gordon, M. W., and Roeder, M., *J. Biol. Chem.*, **200**, 859–66 (1953)
321. Palmer, D. E., and Solomon, J. B., *Proc. Biochem. Soc.*, *J. Biochem.*, **72**, 28 pp. (1953)
322. Burkhalter, A., Featherstone, R. M., Schuller, F. W., and Jones, M., *Proc. Soc. Exptl. Biol. Med.*, **96**, 747–50 (1957)
323. Wright, B., *Proc. Natl. Acad. Sci. US*, **46**, 798–803 (1960)
324. Kennedy, F. T., *Federation Proc.*, **19**, 4 (1960)
325. Ceska, M., and Fisher, J. R., *Biol. Bull.*, **117**, 611–25 (1959)
326. Kato, Y., *Develop. Biol.*, **1**, 477–510 (1959)
327. Stearns, R. N., and Kostellow, A. B., *Symposium on Chem. Basis Develop.*, *Johns Hopkins Univ.*, 448–53 (1958)
328. Kostellow, A. B., *Federation Proc.*, **20**, 222 (1961)
329. DeMars, R., *Biochim. et Biophys. Acta*, **27**, 435–36 (1958)
330. Klein, E., *Exptl. Cell Research*, **22**, 226–32 (1961)
331. Nemeth, A. M., *J. Biol. Chem.*, **234**, 2921–24 (1959)
332. Nemeth, A. M., *Science*, **132**, 1497 (1960)
333. Markert, C. L., and Møller, F., *Proc. Natl. Acad. Sci. US*, **45**, 753–63 (1959)
334. Wieland, T. H., and Pfleiderer, G., *Ann. N. Y. Acad. Sci. US*, 16 (1961) (In press.)
335. Markert, C. L., and Hunter, R. L., *Histochem. & Cytochem.*, **7**, 42 (1959)
336. Kaplan, N. O., Ciotti, M. M., Hamolsky, M., and Bieber, R. E., *Science*, **131**, 392 (1960)
337. Angeletti, P. U., Suntzeff, V., and Moore, B. W., *Cancer Research*, **20**, 1229–34 (1960)
338. Flexner, L. B., Flexner, J. B., Roberts, R. B., and de la Haba, G., *Develop. Biol.*, **2** (1960)
339. Kaplan, N. O., and Ciotti, M. M., *Biochim. et Biophys. Acta*, **43**, 425–26 (1961)
340. Moog, F., *Develop. Biol.*, **3**, 153–74 (1961)
341. Market, C. L., in *Symposium on Normal and Abnormal Differentiation and Development*, 3 (Kaliss, N., Ed., Natl. Cancer Inst. Monograph No. 2, 187 pp., 1960)
342. Ebert, J. D., and DeLanney, L. E., in *Symposium on Normal & Abnormal Differentiation and Development*, 73–111 (Kaliss, N., Ed., Natl. Cancer Inst. Monograph No. 2, 187 pp. 1960)
343. Ebert, J. D., and Wilt, F. H., *Quart. Rev. Biol.*, **35**, 261–312 (1960)
344. Allison, A. C., *Am. Naturalist*, **94**, 5–16 (1959)
345. Goodman, M., and Schwimmer, B., *Federation Proc.*, **18**, 570 (1959)
346. Dray, S., and Young, G. O., *Science*, **129**, 1023 (1959)
347. Dubinsky, S., Dudziak, Z., and Skalba, D., *Immunology*, **2**, (1959)
348. Goodman, M., *Am. Naturalist*, **94**, 153–66 (1960)
349. Billingham, R. E., *Symposium on Chem. Basis Develop.*, *Johns Hopkins Univ.*, 575–91 (1958)
350. Wittembach, C. R., *Develop. Biol.*, **2**, 173–95 (1960)
351. Lawrence, H. S., *Physiol. Revs.*, **39**, 811–59 (1959)
352. Deichmiller, M. P., and Dixon, F. J., *J. Gen. Physiol.*, **43** 1047–59 (1960)
353. Sibal, L. R., and Olson, V. H., *Proc. Soc. Exptl. Biol. Med.*, **97**, 575–79 (1958)
354. Papermaster, B. W., Bradley, S. G., Watson, D. V., and Good, R. A., *Proc. Soc. Exptl. Biol. Med.*, **102** 260–64 (1959)
355. Szilard, L., *Proc. Natl. Acad. Sci. US*, **46**, 277–92 (1960)
356. Szilard, L., *Proc. Natl. Acad. Sci. US*, **46**, 293–302 (1960)
357. Nanney, D., *Am. Naturalist*, **94**, 167–79 (1960)

* English translation will be announced in *Technical Translations*, issued by the Office of Technical Services, US Department of Commerce, and will be made available by the Photoduplication Service, Library of Congress, and by the SLA Translation Center at the John Crerar Library, Chicago, Illinois.

REPRODUCTION[1,2]

By Gregory Pincus

The Worcester Foundation for Experimental Biology, Shrewsbury, Massachusetts

Introduction

Reproductive physiology is concerned with: (a) the genesis of the germ cells, (b) the factors involved in their maturation, safeguarding, and release, (c) the mechanisms ensuring their transport and union, (d) the maintenance of embryogenesis and fetal life, (e) the delivery of young and the means of ensuring their immediate survival. Inquiry into the literature on these five apparently simple problems discloses a multiplicity of approaches, an extraordinary diversity of tangential data the relevance of which to any central problem is often unjudgable, and an amassing of information so voluminous that its orderly classification requires computing machine techniques rather than the mind of a reviewer. Therefore, what follows is not a review but an essay, an attempt to pose the meaningful questions facing the experimentalist interested in the physiology of reproduction, to indicate the methods being used to answer these questions, and perhaps to find some answers to them. Such assessment inevitably reflects to a greater or lesser extent the personal interests and biases of the reviewer, who hereby apologizes for his predilections and is comforted that in other years other reviewers will offer other facets of judgment.

Gametogenesis

A curious deficit of investigation into ovogenesis may exist because of the major and perhaps exclusive formation of oocytes in mammalian embryos. The once active controversy as to neogenesis in postnatal life [see Hartman (1)] seems to have left Sir Solly Zuckerman as the triumphant protagonist of an unrenewable stock of oocytes at birth. Recent studies of orthotopic ovarian transplants (2, 3, 4) confirm the linear decline of ovum number with the logarithm of advancing age, with no evidence of new ovum formation from either fresh or deep-frozen transplants. Similarly, the factors determining the sex of the gamete are in desuetude despite the finding of a genetic human female producing sperm (5).

Spermatogenesis has been the subject of more active study, with a careful timed study of its time onset in adolescent animals (6), the finding that its inhibition by estrogen may be overcome by intratesticular androgen implants (7) in rats, and the retardation of secondary spermatogonia formation by testosterone administered to frogs (8). Tissue oxidations occurring

---

[1] The survey of literature pertaining to this review was concluded in June 1961.

[2] Among the abbreviations used in this chapter are: FSH (follicle-stimulating hormone); HCG (human chorionic gonadotropin); LH (luteinizing hormone); and PMS (pregnant mare's serum).

in the developing testis have been correlated with emerging stages of spermatogenesis, with the finding of fructose oxidation coincident with the onset
of spermatid and sperm production (9). The search for inhibitors of spermatogenesis has continued, with testis tubule necrosis caused by cadmium salts
(10) which unfortunately also cause marked interstitial cell destruction,
nitrofurazone inhibiting spermatocyte and subsequent development and
leaving spermatogonia and interstitial cells intact (11), bis (dichloroacetyl)
diamines suppressing only spermatogenesis in man (12), and aspermato-
genesis in guinea pigs developing with the administration of homologous
testicular homogenate (13).

Gamete Maturation and Release and Attendant Phenomena

The experimental induction of ovulation by gonadotropic hormones continues to offer a means of studying: (a) the timing of ovum discharge, as
after intravenous luteinizing hormone (LH) given rabbits (14), and (b)
the production of ova from immature ovaries as in mice primed with pregnant mare's serum (PMS) and then ovulated by human chorionic gonadotropin (HCG) (15). Eggs so produced appear to be fully fertilizable and may
be carried to term by feeding progesterone (16). In lactating ewes, ova produced by PMS and progesterone treatment are not fertilized, but ova produced by altered light:dark exposures are (17). Although administration of
sheep or horse pituitary extract, i.e., for one to four days, followed by
HCG has been shown to cause ovulation in 58 per cent of 50 anovulatory
women (18), follicle-stimulating hormone (FSH) priming and subsequent
administration of estrogen, progestin, or combinations thereof lead to infrequent ovulation in anovulatory or oligo-ovulatory women (19). Since the
administration of gonadotropin of animal origin soon leads to refractoriness
(18), human pituitary gonadotropin has been tested as offering a more reliable method for follicle stimulation. Human FSH clearly stimulates estrogen
production in anovulators and when it is followed by HCG, progesterone
secretion is demonstrable (20). Indeed, Gemzell (20) has reported successful
pregnancies as a result of this human FSH-HCG regime.

The study of ovulation indices in the cow (21) and the woman (22) for
rapid detection finds the nature of the cervical mucus change at ovulation
time the easiest to follow, with basal body temperature changes next in
dependability. A number of other suggested indices, e.g., the rat ovary
hyperemia test and the glucose concentration in the cervical mucus, are
found to be even less reliable. A highly accurate, easily performed method
for predicting the time of ovulation in women would be of inestimable value.

Research in numerous phases of pituitary-gonad relationships awaits
the accurate chemical description and preparation of extremely pure gonadotropins. Recent advances include a notable purification of pituitary FSH
(23) and of human menopausal gonadotropin (HMG) (24). Some indication
of significant active groups in HMG has also been obtained by enzymic
degradation studies, inactivation being rapidly accomplished by carboxy-

peptidase and receptor-destroying enzyme and much more slowly by chymotrypsin, papain, trypsin, and glucosidase (25).

Studies of patterns of pituitary gonadotropin production indicate the
establishment of a sex pattern in FSH:LH activities very early in postnatal life (26). In human pituitaries, age and ovariectomy increase gonadotropic activity and cortisone treatment decreases it, whereas prolactin
activity is increased by age and cortisone treatment and decreased by ovariectomy (27). The renal clearance rate for HMG in women has been statistically evaluated as well as the blood concentrations (28).

Methods for the accurate assay of gonadotropins continue to be sought.
For FSH the augmentation reaction with LH (or HCG) in immature or
hypophysectomized rats has not been seriously challenged, but new methods
for LH determination are under active investigation. Ovarian ascorbic acid
depletion in the hypophysectomized rat is quite sensitive to LH, but lysine
and arginine vasopressin are more active than LH (29), so their absence
must be assured. Sensitivity to LH in this test may be maintained by
pituitary autografting in the test animals (30). Gunn et al. (31) obtain an
excellent dose:response relationship for LH in the hypophysectomized
male rat using Zn^{65} uptake by the prostate (31). A senstive quantitative passive hemagglutination assay for HCG, which includes the use of a rabbit
antiserum, has been described (32) and its use for a rapid and accurate
pregnancy diagnosis confirmed (33). The fact that urinary HCG may be
separated by a fairly simple procedure ($HgCl_2$ treatment and ethanol fractionation followed by cysteine treatment for "reactivation") into two fractions, one of which appears to be FSH-like (34), should stimulate further
assay development.

The neurohumoral control of ovulation has been the subject of intensive
continuing study. Papers by Harris (35), Sawyer & Kawakami (36), and
Everett (37) in a recent conference offer excellent summaries of central
nervous system–pituitary relationships. Much of what they have to say
was reviewed in this publication last year (38). In rabbits, a center in the
paraventricular region of the hypothalamus appears to exert a tonic inhibitory effect on FSH release and one in the tuber cinereum is responsible
for LH release and ovulation. Infusion of extracts of the median eminence
directly into the anterior pituitary causes ovulation and increased circulating
LH; this effect is not observed with extracts of the cerebral cortex or other
hypothalamic extracts (35). In rats, LH release appears to be controlled
by a neurohumor produced in the preoptic region (37). The plasma LH
elevation in ovariectomized rats is inhibited by median eminence lesions,
indicating that this is one site of sex hormone inhibition (39). Rats in constant estrus because of rostral hypothalamic lesions do not exhibit compensatory hypertrophy but do show diestrus smears; it is concluded that
ovarian estrogen before unilateral ovariectomy is adequate to prevent LH
release presumably from the median eminence (40). Median eminence extracts infused directly into pituitaries of rats in "nembutal-blocked" pro-

estrus cause ovulation (35); and in ten minutes following the injection of such an extract into estrogen-treated (LH-suppressed) castrate rats, LH activity may be detected in the plasma (41). Barraclough has analyzed the constant estrus state eventually resulting from testosterone propionate administered to infantile (2 to 5 day old, but not 10 day old) rats (42, 43). Apparently the androgen acts as a lesion to the anterior preoptic hypothalamus region but does not affect a second region in the median eminence (arcuate-ventromedial complex) which controls ovarian estrogenesis. A region in the median eminence which inhibits luteotropin release has been demonstrated; if these lesions are made in proestrus or estrus in rats, deciduoma formation may be induced. Furthermore, lobular alveolar development has been observed in the mammary glands of 50 per cent of such lesioned animals, and lactating rats with median eminence lesions exhibit a retarded mammary gland involution (44). Critchlow (45) has described certain amygdaloid lesions which affect the inhibition of gonadotropin secretion in immature rats (45). Problems which undoubtedly will receive much attention are: (a) the chemical nature of the gonadotropin stimulating and inhibiting neurohumors, and (b) the total complex of central nervous mechanisms which control neurohumor release. Extension of such studies to the male also would seem to be called for, cf. the effects of androgen on hypothalamic factors controlling spermatogenesis and interstitial cell activity (46).

The investigation particularly of nonnervous factors which may affect the activity of the ovulation-controlling mechanism has been notably stimulated in recent years by the need for a simple means of contraception. It has been interesting that the president of the Endocrine Society took the world population problem and fertility control as the theme of his presidential address (47) and that an ex-president and his colleagues reported on a successful method of oral contraception (48). The method is based on the ovulation-inhibition exerted by ovarian steroids and was developed from animal experiments indicating a high oral potency in rabbits of certain 19-nor steroid gestagens. These compounds are especially useful since they may be used both to prevent ovulation and to control menstrual periodicity, particularly when administered cyclically in combination with a small amount of estrogen (49, 50). Of 200 tested, about 60 steroids have exhibited some degree of ovulation inhibition in the mated rabbit *post partum*. The most potent have been gestagens, and the oral ovulation-inhibiting potency has paralleled the oral:subcutaneous ratio of progestational activity shown by these same compounds in the carbonic anhydrase assay in Clauberg rabbits (49, 51). Steroid pituitary gonadotropin inhibitors have been studied by investigators using various methods of assay including inhibition of the castration increase in gonadotropin potency exhibited by rats (52, 53), inhibition of ovarian and testicular growth in immature rats and mice (54 to 57). In contrast to rabbits, estrogens appear to be particularly active antigonadotropins in rats and mice (53). Nonetheless, certain synthetic gestagens are demonstrably potent in these animals (54, 55, 57). Among nongestagens, 2α-fluoro-17α-ethinyltestosterone and 17α-methyl-17β-hydroxyandrostane-3-one are reported as especially potent (57), as well as adrenal androgens (55). In the rabbit, androgens appear to be poor ovulation inhibitors (51), but a potent gestagen is quite active when fed to bitches (58). In woman, pregnancy occurring in cases of virilizing congenital hyperplasia suggests endogenous androgen is not ovulation inhibiting (59), but administered testosterone propionate causes a 50 per cent reduction in castrate or menopausal women's urinary gonadotropin with five times the dose of estrogen required to effect a similar reduction (60). However, large doses of methyltestosterone (5 to 100 mg per day) did not reduce postmenopausal urinary gonadotropin excretion, conjugated estrogens did, estrone sulfate did not, and the synthetic gestagen norethisterone at high (20 mg per day) but not at low dose did suppress HMG output (61). Since HMG seems chiefly to reflect pituitary FSH and contains little LH, the possibility of a differential effect of the compounds studied is not determined by these studies.

Nonsteroidal gonadotropin inhibitors have been reported, including proniazid dichloride as a transient LH inhibitor in rats (62). Other amine oxidase inhibitors and 5-hydroxytryptamine inhibit the onset of sexual maturity, reproductive organ growth, and ovarian activity in mice (63). Chloramiphene is antigonadotropic in immature and parabiotic rats (64) None of these compounds inhibits responsivity to gonadotropin, so a central nervous system locus of action is postulated. Naturally occurring and probably nonsteroidal antigonadotropins have been found in: (a) fetal serum, which contains a suppressor (not found in normal human serum) of the effect of HCG on frog ovaries (65); (b) urine of male and female children under six years of age, which contains an inhibitor of pituitary gonadotropin (66); and (c) crude pituitary extracts of both FSH and LH, which contain material antagonizing HCG activity in immature female rats and PMS activity in hypophysectomized female rats (67). The antigonadotropic activity of Lithospermum ruderale extracts in vitro and in vivo has again been demonstrated using a chick testis response to FSH and LH; a polypeptidase is suggested by its inactivation of oxytocin (68). Both HCG and sheep pituitary FSH have been employed as antigens to yield very potent antisera; gel-diffusion tests disclose the presence of several antigens in each of these purified gonadotropin preparations (69, 70, 71).

The stimulation of gonadotropin secretion has been sought and found in the reserpine-induced production of LTH in rats (72) and the increased content of FSH in blood and of FSH and LH induced in pituitaries of ovariectomized rats by a protein-deficient diet (73). Cortisol augments the rise in pituitary gonadotropin content in ovariectomized rats and counteracts the suppressive effect of estrogen in such animals (55). Whatever the mechanism of this cortisol effect, it may operate in people since small doses given to infertile women with irregular menses or amenorrhea have led to a rather high incidence of conception (74, 75). Six of eighteen women with

secondary amenorrhea given an anti-estrogen (MER-25) gave evidence of
ovulation, but no pregnancies occurred (76), and following a course of ovulation suppression with 19-nor steroids sixteen of thirty-nine anovulatory
women ovulated (77).

Evidence that ovarian hormones may act directly as gonadotropins or
antigonadotropins has been brought forth by Bradbury (78) who finds that
estrogens applied locally to one ovary of immature rats cause unilateral
weight increase, corpus luteum formation, and increased responsiveness to
exogenous gonadotropins; by Wright (79) who finds frog ovaries *in vitro*
ovulate under the influence of progesterone alone, which also enhances the
ovulating activity of pituitary gonadotropin; and by Croes-Buth *et al.* (80)
who find that estrogen induces similar decrease in the amount of interstitial
tissue in immature rats and hypophysectomized rats. Estrogen also inhibits
pituitary-extract-induced ovulation of frog ovaries *in vitro* (79). The maintenance of testicular activity by intratesticular testosterone pellets in hypophysectomized males also illustrates direct steroid action (81). A gonadotropic activity of 2,3-bis-(p-hydroxyphenyl)-proprionitrile is suggested by
the marked uterine and ovarian enlargement seen following its administration to hypophysectomized rats (82).

The gonads have not been ignored as steroid producers. A much-needed
reinvestigation of testis steroid content has resulted in the isolation of eight
steroids, several hitherto suspected as the result of our knowledge of the
course of steroidogenesis, e.g. 17α-hydroxyprogesterone, others indicating
hitherto unsuspected transformations, e.g. 15α-hydroxytestosterone, 6β
hydroxytestosterone (83). Follicular fluid steroid analysis in the mare dis
closes estradiol-17β as the major component in ten of twelve samples, but
significant amounts of its presumable precursors, progesterone, 17α-hydroxy-
progesterone, Δ^4-androstene-3,17-dione, 19-nor-Δ^4-androstenedione, and es
trone; in mare corpus luteum tissue, progesterone, as expected, is the predominant steroid (84). In human follicular fluids taken during the prolifera-
tive phase of the menstrual cycle, estrone and estradiol have been identical
in amounts, accounting for 40 per cent of the biological activity; luteal phase
follicular fluid contains in addition estriol which, with estrone and estradiol,
accounts for all of the biological activity (85). A number of unidentified
phenols were seen in extracts of both types of follicular fluid. Zander *et al.*
(86) extracted human corpora lutea, identified estrone and estradiol, found
no estriol nor 16-17 ketols, but observed six unidentified phenols. In human
fetal gonads, steroidogenesis occurs much as in adult gonads, but the 17-
hydroxyprogesterone desmolase is absent or ineffective (87). Studies with
perfused dog testes *in vitro* (88) and mouse testes in tissue culture (89) disclose a stimulation of androgen production by HCG, and no steroidogenic
action of LTH on the mouse testis.

Factors Affecting the Transport and Union of Gametes

The complexities attendant on the safe delivery of gametes for fertilization involve phenomena as varied as the formation and delivery of an

ejaculate, estrus and mating, oviduct activity affecting gamete transport. Sperm may reside in the vas deferens for long periods of time before discharge; indeed, the organs ordinarily contributing to the ejaculate may atrophy (after castration) but vas deferens sperm survive (90). The secondary organs of the reproductive tract have long ago been shown not to be essential to sperm as fertilizing agents, but their ready responsiveness to gonad steroids has made them the subject of much investigation. We shall consider them later as tools for the study of the mechanism of action of steroid hormones. Here we report that their physiological activities have been much neglected; for example, although excellent investigations of their chemical contributions to the seminal plasma have been made (91), how they function in ejaculation is largely unknown except that estrogen and androgen exert some effect on contractility (92).

The transport of spermatozoa in the female reproductive tract of the hamster somewhat resembles that of other rodents in that, following mating, sperm are found in the ampulla in less than two minutes as the result of antiperistaltic action (93); variations in the speed of transport appear to be a function of the age of the female. Harvey (94, 95) has studied the speed of human spermatozoa and their movement through cervical mucus of varying consistency, and Guard (96) has described a simple method of quantitating the rate of penetration into cervical mucus with some interesting indications of the effects of progestins and husband-wife incompatibilities. Unknown fertility factors, perhaps related to sperm movement and survival in the female tract, have been indicated by increased fertility of mixed semen in the rabbit (97).

The movement of ova through the fallopian tubes of rabbits has been duplicated by anionic resin spheres 120 microns in diameter and impregnated with Au^{128} to make possible their ready location at any time. Following ovulation these spheres take eight hours to traverse the upper half of the tubes, require an additional forty hours to traverse an additional 30 per cent of the tubes, and enter the uterus between the fifty-sixth and sixty-fourth hours (98). Greenwald (99) finds that rabbit ova traverse the upper half of the tubes in two hours with very slow progression thereafter; estrogens at low dose speed ovum descent into the uterus, but various dosages of progesterone leave the rate of traverse relatively unaffected. Studies of spontaneous and electrically induced fallopian tube contractions have been reported (100, 101). An ingenious method for collecting oviducal secretions in the intact conscious rabbit has been described. The rate of fluid secretion is highest in estrus and declines by the third day after mating to a level 50 per cent of that of estrus, with some decline in sodium content (102). By 67 hours after ovariectomy, a plateau of secretion is reached equal to one-third of the estrus rate; restoration to estrus levels is accomplished by estrogen administration, and progesterone inhibits this estrogen effect as well as the normal secretion rate in estrus rabbits (103).

Fertilization in mammals requires sperm capacitation in the female reproductive tract (104). Austin (105) believes that capacitation involves acrosome removal and consequent increased release of hyaluronidase which allows penetration through follicle cells surrounding the ovum. He has studied rabbit, rat, and hamster sperm and found that, following formaldehyde treatment which preserves the acrosome, sperm supernatant fluid contains one-tenth of the hyaluronidase activity seen in supernatant fluid from sperm treated with acrosome-removing digitonin. On the basis of a statistical study of 1000 couples, it has been found that the minimum number of sperm necessary for a fertile insemination is 1,000,000 (106). Shettles (107) reports two types of spermatozoa in normal human semen distinguished by head size, shape, and length; large-headed sperm which accumulate blebs of volatile oil of anise *in vitro* may be X chromosome containing.

Pertinent to successful insemination and fertilization are factors influencing female reproductive function at the time of estrus and fertilization. Thus the condition of the cervical mucus may severely limit sperm access. Variations in mucus consistency occur throughout estrus cycles and a careful description has been made of these variations in cattle, sheep, horses, and pigs (108). In mice, cervical mucus has been found to concentrate administered I^{131} to a considerable extent; its uptake therein is decreased by ovariectomy, restored by estrogen, and progesterone antagonizes the estrogen effect. In women I^{131} uptake by cervical mucus may be observed in five minutes after administration, and the rate of uptake is not affected by the degree of thyroid activity. Furthermore, such concentration disappears in old age (109). Estriol appears especially effective as a stimulant of vaginal and cervical function (110). The increased and rather lasting flow of cervical mucus commencing within a few minutes of insemination suggests a seminal stimulating factor meriting further investigation (111). Sperm entering the uterus live in a fluid that seems to be a plasma ultrafiltrate containing specific uterine secretions (112). Its further analysis also is inviting. The control of uterine function by estrogen has led to an interest in anti-estrogens as possible antifertility agents. 19-Norsteroids have proven potent anti-estrogens in rats (113) and in mice (114, 115) both by parenteral and by oral routes. Certain diethyl stilbestrol derivatives are also active especially on local application (116). MER-25, undoubtedly active in rats, must be given in rather massive dose to exert its full effect (116a). In women, butyl diiodohydroxybenzoate taken in 0.25 mg dose four times daily for six days regularly inhibited the effect of a depot estrogen on the vaginal smear (117).

PREGNANCY

The cleaving tubal ovum in mammals appears to be relatively autonomous. It may readily be explanted and develop in various culture media, but blastocyst development both *in vivo* and *in vitro* is highly dependent on exogenous factors (118). Lutwak-Mann and her collaborators have continued their valuable studies of rabbit blastocyst biochemistry, describing developmental changes in bicarbonate, glucose, and lactic acid concentrations and the nature of radioactive ion uptake (119, 120). Energy systems operating in developing rabbit ova have been analyzed and a rather remarkable concentration of glycine in six-day blastocysts discovered (121). Considerable blastocyst mortality occurs in normal and superovulated rabbit ova; but in the latter, postimplantation losses may be quite high (122, 123). When large numbers of eggs are transplanted to pseudopregnant recipients, postimplantation mortality occurs in over 50 per cent of the eggs (123). Similarly, in sheep maximum mortality of transplanted ova occurs in early embryos, fetal mortality after the eighteenth day being negligible (124). The ovicidal factor in the uterus is undetermined but its sharp emergence is indicated because ova transferred into a pseudopregnant uterus, one day older than the eggs, develop normally for five days and then degenerate; if the uterus is one day younger than the eggs, a delay of ovum development occurs until a five-day uterus appears allowing implantation (125).

Ovariectomy following fertilization has been a practically universal means of preventing implantation. In the guinea pig if this operation is performed on the second day after mating, the usual effect is observed. Ovariectomy on the third to seventh day does not, however, prevent implantation. Progesterone administration to day-two operated animals ensures implantation and it is effective in preventing the postimplantation degeneration occurring on day fourteen in three- to seven-day operated animals (126). Either prolonged action of progestin from three-day ovaries is involved, or a hitherto unsuspected implantation factor is produced. Implantation in mice does not occur when the pituitary removed during the first to the fifth day of pregnancy is autografted to the kidney unless daily injections of estrogen are made (127). Again, what is the estrogen-stimulated implantation factor? Implantation in rats may be delayed by reserpine administration and this effect too is overcome by administering small doses of estradiol (128). The delay of implantation occurring in the uterus of lactating rats may be overcome by local injection of estradiol or progesterone into adipose tissue near the uterine artery. If the steroid dose is low, a single implant will occur adjacent to the injection site; if it is higher a "spread" of implants is seen (129). Implantation and pregnancy maintenance by synthetic gestagens have been studied in rats and rabbits. 17α-Ethinyl- and 17α-methylnortestosterone have been reported as active by Marois (130), but others have found the norethisterone inactive (131). Complete maintenance has been had with 6α-methyl-17-hydroxyprogesterone acetate (132) and an acetophenone derivative of $16\alpha,17\alpha$-dihydroxyprogesterone (131). Full maintenance by 17α-hydroxyprogesterone acetate or caproate occurs only if small amounts of androgen or estrogen are added (133). Certain steroidal androgens inhibit fetal development on administration to rats, e.g. testosterone proprionate and androstenedione; but others do not, e.g. methyl testosterone and isoandrosterone. Ovarian malfunction is induced by the former (134). Estrogens have long been known to inhibit pregnancy in mice. Now diethylstilbestrol derivatives which are anti-estrogens have also been shown to have the same effect (135). The presence of strange males prevents pregnancy in

recently mated female mice. Apparently the strange males' odor is responsible for reactions leading to LTH suppression (136, 137). This interesting
phenomenon has led Parkes to speculate about the role of odors in reproductive processes (138). The embryocidal effect of ethionine in rats is inhibited
by simultaneous administration of progesterone (139). Thyroid extract does
not completely correct the pregnancy-inhibiting and embryocidal effect of
thyroidectomy, nor does thyroxine or triiodothyronine (140). Fetal deaths in
uteri crowded with implantations of superovulated mouse eggs appear to
result from reductions in the pressure of blood supplied to the placenta rather
than from competition for nutrition (141). Fetal death rates in people appear to correlate with the age of the fathers, increasing with advancing age
(142).

The effects of ovarian hormones on uterine functions other than direct
pregnancy maintenance involve studies on uterine and endometrial growth
and on uterine enzyme systems and their products. Several studies have
been reported on the effects of replacement therapy on uterine growth in
castrated animals by ovarian hormones in various combinations. Wada &
Turner (143) find the three major ovarian hormones, estrogen, progesterone,
and relaxin, essential for complete growth of the uterus in the rat, but Yochim
& Zarrow (144) find that optimal uterine growth in the ovariectomized rat
may be secured by a proper ratio of progesterone to estrogen and that
relaxin may indeed antagonize this progestin:estrogen optimum; when the
progestin:estrogen ratio is suboptimal, concomitant relaxin administration
will enhance uterine growth. Several studies of steroid interactions on rat
and rabbit uteri have been published by Edgren and his associates (145,
146, 147). Augmentation of estrone stimulation may be obtained with
testosterone proprionate or estriol, and inhibition by proper dosages of
progesterone and 11-deoxycorticosterone. A number of synthetic progestins
induce similar interactions. Brody & Westman (148, 149) find that rabbit
uterine hypertrophy along with increased DNase concentrations is induced
by estrogen and that estrogen, plus progesterone, induces hyperplasia as
evidenced by significant increases in DNA concentrations. In immature
hypophysectomized rats the uterine growth response to synthetic progestins
and related steroids is not correlated with progestational activity measured
by Clauberg assay (150). The steroidal spirolactones exhibit uterine growth
effects and endometrial progestational action which does not correlate with
their aldosterone antagonistic effects (151). The uterotropic, vaginal-
cornifying, pregnancy-preventing, and pituitary-inhibiting effects of a new
plant estrogen, mirestrol (152), derived from *Pueraria mirifica* have been
found to parallel similar effects of natural and synthetic estrogens (153, 154).

The normal cellular pattern of uterine epithelial cells is not restored in
hypophysectomized rats by an estrogen:androgen administration regime
although normal growth rate is obtained; growth hormone administered with
the steroids restores the normal cellular pattern (155). A highly polar substance extracted from human and rabbit plasma, which stimulates mouse

uterine epithelium in the Hooker-Forbes test, has no effect on the rabbit endometrium (156). Progestational proliferation of rabbit endometria by certain $9\beta:10\alpha$ steroids (retrosteroids) is paralleled by their effects on human endometrium, with 6-dehydro-17α-hydroxyretroprogesterone as the most active of a series in both species (157, 158). An extremely sensitive indication of estrogen action in castrate rats is the increase following intrauterine administration of Golgi material of the uterine epithelial cells accompanied by depletion of basal phospholipid and increase in peripheral phospholipid (159). Thioglycoll or mercaptanol-ethanol inactivated relaxin reverses the antidecidual effect of relaxin in rat uteri (160).

Studies of uterine tissue enzyme systems give curious evidence of the individuality of response of each system to ovarian hormones. Thus in rat uteri following estrogen administration, dipeptidase activity increase (which peaks in two hours) is dose proportional, whereas a tripeptidase activity increase is not; progesterone administration also increased dipeptidase but not tripeptidase activity (161). Uterine phosphorylase alpha activity is stimulated by estrogen and relaxin but not by progestin (162). Physiological doses of estrogen and progesterone given to castrate rats both depress uterine phosphamidase activity; but in progesterone-conditioned deciduoma, phosphamidase concentrations rise to five times that seen in nondeciduomatous tissue (163). In contrast, the carbonic anhydrase content of rat uterine deciduoma is not increased, and progesterone does not decrease uterine carbonic anhydrase (164). As previously reported, progesterone inhibits the estrogen-induced reduction of carbonic anhydrase concentration in rat uteri. Finally, guaiacol peroxidase, which appears in significant concentration in mouse uterine tissue following estrogen administration, is not present when progesterone is simultaneously administered. Mesidine peroxidase is not produced by the administration of either estrogen, progesterone, relaxin, or combinations thereof; but it is found in the uterine tissue of pregnant mice and even in a sterile uterine horn in pregnancy (165). In mice, relaxin augments the stimulating action of estradiol on myometrial glycogen and alkaline phosphatase and on stromal edema; relaxin partially prevents progesterone-induced depression of alkaline phosphatase activity (166). The control of intrauterine *E. coli* infection in rabbit uteri by estrogens is inhibited by concomitant progesterone administration; apparently this does not involve a direct effect of steroids or steroid-induced uterine products but an estrogen stimulation of leucocyte activity antagonized by progesterone (167).

An excellent review of mammalian sex determination and developmental sex anomalies has been published (168). That the sex hormones may affect the genesis of reproductive tract organs is abundantly evident. However, in mammals the gonads appear to be relatively insulated from sex hormone influence whereas the development of Mullerian duct and Wolffian duct-derived structures is clearly hormone labile. Recent experimental studies have been concerned with the masculinizing effects of androgens and of certain synthetic progestins (169, 170, 171). A variety of substances administered during pregnancy affect the nature of the external genitalia in rats. Androgens administered to women during pregnancy have in some instances caused a female pseudohermaphroditism characterized by the presence of ovaries and female ducts but with varying degrees of masculinization of the urogenital sinus and external genitalia (172). There is no progressive virilization following birth and the condition is correctible (173, 174). A survey of 650 pregnancies in which 17-ethinyltestosterone or its 19-nor derivative was administered disclosed two cases of such masculinization of female infants (175). Treatment for habitual abortion by oral 17-ethinyltestosterone apparently has been involved in most of the cases reported (168, 173). Grumbach (168) states, "In rare cases progesterone and diethylstilbestrol have been suggested as possible fetal masculinizing agents, but the evidence implicating them is inconclusive." Judging by Jones & Wilkins' data, so is the evidence for steroids other than 17-ethinyltestosterone since in their 27 cases, 63 per cent had been born of mothers treated with this agent, 11 per cent came from untreated mothers, 15 per cent from 17-ethinyl-19-nortestosterone treated mothers, and smaller percentages from women having other steroid medication. That the ethinyl-19-nortestosterone is in fact androgenic in humans is suggested by a sebaceous gland enlargement seen following its administration to three prepuberal males (176).

The metabolism of ovarian hormones during pregnancy is in part reviewed in "Hormones in Human Plasma" (177). We shall later consider over-all problems related to steroid metabolism. Here we note studies specific to pregnancy. Thus, placental estrogenesis and transport have been investigated in the guinea pig (178); and cortisone, cortisol, progesterone, and four unidentified ultraviolet-absorbing steroids have been isolated from minced human placenta incubated *in vitro* (179). Estrogen and pregnanediol excretion were depressed in a 10-day administration of ethinylnortestosterone in three of five women (180), but in menopausal women the administration of this compound as well as four other 19-nortestosterone derivatives was followed by a marked increase in the output of estrone, a lesser increase in estradiol and a depression of estriol (181). Since estriol is the major estrogen excreted in human pregnancy, is there indicated a specific blocking action on processes leading to estriol formation? The levels of estrogen excretion in women with uterine myoma are like those of women in the last seven weeks of gestation; estriol output is particularly elevated and the amounts excreted appear to be proportional to myoma size (182). The increased output of unconjugated 6β-hydroxycortisol in normal pregnancy and its further elevation in urines from toxemic patents suggest a "stress" secretion by the adrenal cortex rather than an indication of sex hormone effects (183). From human meconium, estriol glucosiduronate (184) and dehydroepiandrosterone (but not androsterone or etiocholanolone) (185) have been isolated.

THE DELIVERY AND NURTURE OF YOUNG

Experimental studies with animals rather uniformly indicate that the myometrium is "progesterone-dominated" until just before term and that it then becomes "estrogen-dominated". The estrogen influence is such that it increases spontaneous myometrial contraction and its irritability. This transition has been demonstrated in rats and rabbits by membrane potential changes in parturient uteri; and the contrasting actions of administered progesterone and estrogen, by the suppressive action of progesterone on contraction propagation which involves a suspension of membrane and myoplasmic activity (186, 187). Twenty-four hours before parturition in the rabbit, the progesterone type of myometrial activity disappears and an estrogen-induced activity supervenes; this is evident also in data from sheep and human myometria (188, 189). In mice the extrauterine weight gain which has been shown to be progesterone-induced rises to a maximum on days fifteen to seventeen and declines sharply two days before parturition, suggesting that effective levels of progesterone decline (190).

Although in the rabbit the ovarian vein content of progesterone diminishes at the end of pregnancy (191), a thorough study of blood levels of progesterone determined by a chemical method in pregnant mares, cows, ewes, and sows disclosed preparturient rises and falls and no single variation that could account significantly for the initiation of labor (192). The rather inconsistent data on variations of blood progesterone and related gestagens with advancing pregnancy have been reviewed by Pearlman (193) who points out the discrepancy between chemical determinations and biological assay by the Hooker-Forbes method. The lack of significant systematic change in pregnanediol excretion by women preceding or even during labor has been known for many years and cited as evidence against diminished progesterone production as a causal factor in labor initiation. A possible explanation of the discrepancy between the data on myometrial activity and the findings related to progesterone maintenance has been adduced by the data on estrogen and especially estriol concentration changes in blood and urine preceding and during labor. Blood estrogen concentrations in women show a rather steep rise before labor with a further increase at term (194). Furthermore, after the thirty-second week of pregnancy a rather abrupt increase in urinary estriol occurs which extends to term and contrasts with a plateauing or limited increase in pregnanediol excretion (195). This estriol output increase is not seen when uterine death has occurred, and a decrease may precede fetal death (196, 197). There appears to be some evidence that exogenous estriol will precipitate labor in late pregnancy (195). An estrogen-dominated uterus may therefore be attributable to increased estriologenesis in the face of high progesterone production.

Pubic separation in ovariectomized guinea pigs is induced by estrogen, not affected by progesterone, but the estrogen effect is increased with simultaneous progesterone administration. Interestingly enough, neither 17α-methyl nor 17α-ethinyltestosterone shows similar enhancement, but allylestrenol and 6α-methyl-17α-acetoxyprogesterone do (198). In the castrate rat, estrogen alone causes growth of the circle of connective tissue about the cervix, and relaxin in estrogen-primed animals increases extensibility by causing a reduction in collagen and an increase in noncollagenous connective tissue substance (199). This relaxin-induced softening and increased dilatability of the cervix are seen in cows, pigs, rats, mice, monkeys, and women. When pregnancy is maintained in ovariectomized rats and mice by progesterone or a progesterone-estrogen combination, relaxin appears to be necessary for the induction of parturition by oxytocin administration or by progesterone withdrawal (200, 201). The obstetrical indications for relaxin, however, are still not too clear although its most frequent use is to "soften" the cervix before labor (202). Whether it affects labor directly is doubtful since intravenous relaxin administered to women in labor did not at any dose used affect uterine contraction significantly (203). An excellent symposium on oxytocin (204) indicates the specific measurable role that this hormone plays in labor.

For the full development of the mammary gland and active lactation a number of hormones appear to be required (205). This has been re-emphasized by the finding that in male or nonpregnant female mice optimal combinations of estrogen and progestin produce, as judged by mammary DNA content, tissue at 50 per cent of the level seen in pregnancy (206). In hypophysectomized female rats a combination of PMS, thyroxin, cortisone, and insulin led to maximal mammary development (207). In adrenogonadectomized male rats carrying mammotropic tumors which secrete both prolactin and growth hormone, extensive alveolar development occurs but milk production occurs only when cortisol is administered (208). Cortisol acts as an excellent stimulant to increased milk secretion in lactating rats (209). Chlorpromazine in rats involuting *post partum* maintains milk secretion apparently by stimulating ACTH and prolactin secretion since in animals hypophysectomized *post partum* it does not maintain milk secretion nor demonstrate the adrenal weight increase it stimulates in intact animals (210). In hypophysectomized lactating rats, the adequate maintenance of a good alveolar structure and milk secretion occurs with the combined administration of ACTH, prolactin, and oxytocin; cortisone may replace ACTH (211). The induction of mammary growth and lactation in rabbits by pharmacological doses of epinephrine, acetylcholine, and serotonin probably involves activation of pituitary hormone secretion perhaps as a "stress" effect (212). Although progesterone administered under certain conditions to lactating rats may inhibit milk secretion (213), a synthetic progestin (17-methyl-19-nortestosterone) did not prevent lactation in women although, judging by accompanying vaginal atrophy and uterine involution, endogenous estrogen secretion (or action) was inhibited (214). Since LH production seems to be inhibited during lactation (215), a relative deficit of ovarian hormones presumably should be expected. Rat mammary glands taken during pregnancy and incubated with prolactin *in vitro* exhibit a stimulation of carbon dioxide production from C-1 and C-6 labeled glucose and an increased incorporation of glucose carbon into lipid. This effect of prolactin *in vitro* is not seen when lactating glands are used (216). Prolactin has no clear effect as an inducer or enhancer of lactation in cows or women;

however, it is found in the blood of lactating women but not in the blood of children, men, or women in the follicular phase of the menstrual cycle (217).

At this point we have concluded our discussion of topics strictly relevant to reproductive processes. Nonetheless, we should like to discuss certain investigations based on phenomena: (a) ancillary to reproductive processes, or (b) basic to the understanding of certain mechanisms involved in reproduction. To the former belong tumorigenesis, particularly in reproductive tract organs, and certain miscellaneous effects of sex hormones. To the latter belong aspects of hormone metabolism, and studies of the mechanism of hormone action.

SEX HORMONES AND TUMORS

Estrogens as cancer-inducing agents have been extensively studied over the years. Certain recent experiences with pure-line mice have been summarized by Muhlbock (218, 219), who reports: (a) mammary and cervical tissue as the prime target organs, (b) high spontaneous incidence of mammary cancer (as in the DBA strain of mice) associated with a larger endogenous estrogen production than in a low tumor strain (C57B1), (c) the induction of mammary tumors in practically all animals of certain mouse strains by continuous exogenous estrogen administration and a fivefold reduction in such incidence with intermittent administration. Because castrated Bittner strain female mice kept in lactation by an estrogen-progestin-prolactin-cortisone combination after a first litter had a higher breast tumor incidence than castrates receiving estrogen alone (or estrogen plus any other one of the other three hormones), Huseby (220) considers the development of a lactating gland a potentiating influence in carcinogenesis. Nandi et al. (221) report that the presumed precancerous nodules transplanted from the breast to fat pads in $C_3H/Crgl$-strain mice developed more tumors than normal lobule transplants. When the nodules were kept in a lactating condition by the administration of cortisol plus prolactin (or plus growth hormone), no tumors developed, contradicting the above-mentioned results with the Bittner strain. Furthermore, tumors could be developed from nodule transplants in hypophysectomized mice when one steroid (not necessarily an estrogen) and one pituitary hormone were administered. Lacassagne (222) has reported that small doses of reserpine increased the incidence of mammary cancer in certain strains receiving estrogen treatment. He attributes the effect of reserpine to its induction of prolactin release via suppression of the hypothalamic inhibitor of prolactin release. The mammary glands of senile nulliparous rats exhibit a strikingly high incidence of mammary hyperplasia and tumors accompanied by high incidences of pituitary enlargement and excessively large corpora lutea, with tendencies to have large ovaries and adrenal glands in contrast to low tumor incidence and lower incidences of accompanying phenomena in multipara (223). The foregoing phenomena suggest greater ovarian and adrenal steroid production plus pituitary hyperactivity as the prime factors in nullipara, not lactation.

The striking demonstration by Huggins *et al.* (224, 225) of a rapid development of mammary cancer in 100 per cent of treated female rats following a single feeding of 3-methylcholanthrene has been confirmed (226). The hormone-dependence of such tumor development has been demonstrated by their nonoccurrence in males, their reduced incidence in pregnant and progesterone-treated animals. Furthermore, low estrogen dosages are permissive of tumor development, high estrogen dosages blocking, and estrogen-progestin combinations most effectively inhibitory (227). In contrast, weekly paintings of 20-methylcholanthrene resulted in a higher incidence of breast tumors in breeding and pseudopregnant mice than in virgins (228). Here luteal activity would appear to promote carcinogenesis. That mouse breast tumor growth is responsive to hormonal steroids generally quite different from those affecting rat breast tumor growth is abundantly evident from the investigations of Glenn (229).

Estrogen-induced testicular tumors in mice are, however, retarded in development under progestin influence, and complete resistance to their induction in certain strains may have a hormonal basis (230, 230a). Estrogen-induced and -dependent testicular interstitial cell tumors show characteristic chromosome stem lines with the increased chromosome numbers tending to stabilize on serial transplantation (231). The indicated mutagenic effect of steroid treatment has fascinating implications. In hamsters diethylstilbestrol induction of kidney tumors is inhibited by 11-deoxycorticosterone (232). This may be the result of a nephrotoxic action of 11-deoxycorticosterone or of its progestational properties.

Possible relationships between sex hormones and tumorigenesis in humans continue to be anomalous. Thus although some evidence of hyperestrinism is seen in women with cancer of the cervix (233), no differences in the output of urinary estrogens between normal pre- and postmenopausal women and those with cancer of the cervix are found (234). Nor did urinary estrogen levels before ovariectomy or adrenalectomy or following operation correlate with the postoperative clinical course of breast cancer (235). In a limited number of postmenopausal cases studied, a high estradiol:estriol ratio (as seen in normal women or women with benign breast lesions) appeared to be prognostic of a favorable response to estrogen therapy (236). The responsiveness of inoperable breast cancer to testosterone proprionate treatment has been analyzed statistically with the finding that the proportion of objective remissions increases with increasing postmenopausal age (237). The effects of treatment with a number of newer steroids having greater or lesser hormonal effects have been detailed in a conference on hormone-tumor relationships (238). Considering its usual antitumor effect in animals, the singular inability of progesterone (given by mouth, however) to induce objective remissions in breast cancer cases is curious. A weak androgen, 2α-methyldihydrotestosterone, and a substance, Δ^1-testololactone, which has no direct hormonal action but which augments the activity of certain androgens at low dose and inhibits at high doses (239), are both reported to have induced rather high remission rates. A speculative discussion of steroids and tumor incidence in man suggests that the age-conditioned decline in the genesis of certain steroids may have etiologic relationships (240).

EFFECTS OF SEX HORMONES

The catalogue of diverse effects of sex hormones continues to increase. Thus, estrogens: (a) act upon the bile duct of rabbits to cause an abnormal proliferation not seen in estrogen-treated rabbits made cirrhotic by carbon tetrachloride administration (241); (b) usually cause regression of coronary artery atheroma in cholesterol-fed chicks, but estrogenic doses of doisynolic acid and epiestradiol are not effective (242); (c) stimulate the activity of the reticuloendothelial system (243); (d) given intravenously to hamsters, monkeys, and people, cause in connective tissue (especially that adjacent to small blood vessels) a rapid increase in acid mucopolysaccharides with a lengthening of their polymers and a shift in the sol-gel equilibrium toward the gel phase (244); (e) administered continuously to rabbits for a year, produce persistent adrenal enlargement with initial hyperplasia and adenomata formation and later a zona glomerulosa atrophy and some focal cortical fatty dystrophy (245); (f) protect mice against the effects of whole-body irradiation, particularly on pretreatment (246, 247); (g) appear to act directly on the thyroid of rabbits as inhibitors of TSH stimulation of I^{131} uptake (248); (h) enhance histamine-induced peptic ulceration in the dog (249); (i) in guinea pigs, restore melanocytes which shrink on ovariectomy and cause a large increase in skin melanin at various sites, an action opposed by progesterone (250); (j) elevate protein-bound iodine in men and women with ischemic heart disease (251).

Androgens: (a) stimulate sebaceous activity measured in prepuberal humans by forehead secretions collected on filter paper (252); (b) have a hypertensive effect on animals of either sex with unilateral nephrectomy and a ligature around the remaining kidney (253); (c) stimulate amino acid incorporation into the mouse kidney (254); (d) inhibit the development of the bursa Fabricii of chick embryos with ring-A reduced androgens being more active than the ring-A unsaturated 19-carbon steroids (255); (e) inhibit the hepatic necrosis induced in female rats by ethionine (256); (f) fail to stimulate reticuloendothelial phagocytosis stimulated by other sex hormones (257).

Progestins: (a) protect vitamin A-deficient rats against weight loss and ocular degeneration and prolong survival times (258); (b) inhibit the estrogen-induced melanin increase in guinea pig skin (250); (c) cause (when they are of certain structure, e.g. 6α-methyl-17-acetoxyprogesterone) adrenal atrophy, perhaps by direct action since posthypophysectomy adrenal atrophy is accelerated (259); (d) stimulate reticuloendothelial phagocytosis (257).

A number of steroids inhibit the confusion states induced in rats by the administration of lysergic acid diethylamide. Estrogens alone are ineffective in this test (260).

The Metabolism of Sex Hormones

New methods have been described for the determination of estrogens in blood (261, 262). The use of a sensitive double isotope method permits the quantitative determination of estrone and estradiol-17β in human plasma, and some plasma concentration values for normal, amenorrheic, and pregnant women are given; a large increase in pregnancy is indicated (263). A method for the quantitative measurement of four 17-ketosteroids in human plasma has been developed (264), and a novel method involving its enzymatic conversion to estrogen makes possible the measurement of plasma testosterone (265). Application of 17-ketosteroid analysis to peripheral and ovarian venous blood of twenty women demonstrated a consistently higher concentration in the ovarian vein samples (266). A comparative study of the Ittrich and Brown methods for urinary estrogen analysis has led to the conclusion that the former is the less sensitive (267). A new method, involving spread layer chromatography on alumina, allows the separation of individual urinary pregnanetriols and of pregnanediol (268). For the first time, testosterone has been isolated from human urine (269) and the isolation of etiocholane-3:11:17-trione has been accomplished (270).

Ryan & Smith (271, 272) have studied steroidogenesis *in vitro* in human ovary tissue taken after ovine FSH treatment. From incubations with acetate-1-C^{14}, radioactive estrone, estradiol, and cholesterol have been identified. Using isotope dilution methods, no estriol or epiestriol could be found, but unknown highly polar phenols are present. Following incubation with progesterone-C^{14}, radioactive estrone, estradiol, and estriol were identified. Recent advances in estrogen metabolism have been reviewed by Engel (273) and Marrian (274). 2-Hydroxyestrone, a new metabolite of estradiol-17β, has been isolated from human urine (275); and the central position of estrone in human estrogen metabolism has been demonstrated by the finding chiefly of C^{14}-containing transformation products following administration to women of a mixture of estrone-C^{14} and estradiol-H^3. Estrone-H^3 is formed slowly (276). The action of rat liver 6β- and 6α-hydroxylases on estrogen substrates has been described; the former acts on both estrone and estradiol, the latter on estradiol only (277, 278).

Steroid metabolism in endocrine tumors has been reviewed (279). Savard *et al.* (280) report a remarkably complete analytical study of steroidogenesis in an interstitial cell virilizing tumor taken from a $5\frac{1}{2}$-year-old boy; 11-deoxy and 11-oxygenated androgens and 17-hydroxyprogesterone were synthesized *in vitro*, but estrogenic products could not be identified. Only 17-hydroxyprogesterone synthesis could be demonstrated in a similar testicular tumor (281).

The metabolic fate in women of progesterone-4-C^{14} has been described and compared with that of 17-hydroxyprogesterone caproate. The former is absorbed more rapidly and is stored in fat tissue; neither concentrates very much in uterine tissue (282). Pregnanetriolone has been found in the urine of 16 consecutive Stein-Leventhal syndrome patients and is therefore considered pathognomic; all other neutral steroids were found to be at normal levels (283). In contrast, Lanthier (284) finds a urinary 17-ketosteroid elevation, mostly because of androsterone and etiocholanolone increase, in the Stein-Leventhal syndrome.

An effect of sex steroids on corticosteroid metabolism is indicated by a shorter half life of corticosterone in female rat blood compared with male and a calculated secretion rate of corticosterone twice that of males (285). Also, a higher blood corticosterone level is seen in female rats following stress or ACTH administration, and in etherized animals an adrenal vein concentration $2\frac{1}{2}$ times that of males is observed in females (286). The effect of estrogen on the protein binding of corticosteroids, now well established in humans (287, 288), may be responsible for these sex differences. Certainly estrogen administered to men causes a prompt increase in free plasma 17-hydroxy-corticosteroids (289). The rate of reduction of ring A of hormonal corticosteroids may be involved; the presence in rat liver microsomes of five different Δ^4-3-keto reductases (290) raises the problem of rate-limiting substances for such reductions.

THE MECHANISM OF SEX STEROID ACTION

There seem to be three schools of thought regarding the fundamental mechanism of estrogen action. The first is that advanced by Talalay and his collaborators (291, 292), which states that the primary role of the estrogens is the enzymatic transport of hydrogen or electrons at physiological concentrations in several systems significant for energy production and certain organic syntheses. The second is that of Villee and collaborators (293, 294, 295), which finds that an estrogen-sensitive transhydrogenase present in the nonparticulate fractions of estrogen target organs reduces TPN to TPNH. There follows, therefore, an increase in energy-rich phosphates as donors of energy for the synthesis of lipids, proteins, and nucleic acids. The third is represented by the work of Mueller and collaborators (296, 297, 298), who find that early estrogen action in the rat uterus is dependent on a puromycin-sensitive protein synthetic system which may or may not be independent of an estrogen-sensitive uterine lipid-synthesizing system. Mueller *et al.* (297) believe that their data rule out the possibility that estrogen acts to increase the permeability of uterine tissues to substrates for these systems, and indeed Hechter & Lester (299) have been unable to find evidence for estrogen facilitation of the early entry of glucose or amino acid. In the reviewer's opinion, the hypotheses presented above are not necessarily mutually exclusive, but they all (with the possible exception of Mueller's) scarcely account for specific estrogen effects, probably because of the difficulties of the unraveling of the pathways from not-yet-securely-established initial effects to end results that we denominate as specifically estrogenic.

Similar studies of the effects of testosterone on prostate enzymatic systems disclose: (a) a puromycin-inhibited testosterone-stimulated protein synthesis (300); (b) citric and fatty acid and protein synthesis stimulation by catalytic amounts of testosterone, indicating it "facilitates activation of acyl residues by ATP, the first step in all three biosynthetic activities"—this notion is partially confirmed by the finding that fatty acid synthesized by prostatic tissue from pyruvate which does not require ATP is not testosterone sensitive (301); (c) stimulation by testosterone (but not progesterone) of cytochrome-c reductase which may lead to increased ATP activity (302). Butenandt (303) also finds increased leucine incorporation into seminal vesicle protein as a primary effect of testosterone. In rats a stimulation by testosterone proprionate on isocitric dehydrogenase of brain and on succinic dehydrogenase of brain and liver has been shown. It is claimed that this is a direct action (303a). No comparable studies on the mode of action of progesterone on tissues have been reported.

Having lived and fought for some time with the material of this paper, the reviewer cannot forbear from delivering himself of certain outcomes of this experience. Like our predecessors, we found ourself faced with an awesome number of publications. In this mass of material the culling of that pertinent to certain central themes in reproductive physiology was an almost herculean task, for clearly the mosaic character of additions to scientific knowledge is a long-established affair. To find the pattern inherent in often sadly incomplete mosaics requires a skill we would like to have. Therefore we have often wistfully left unmentioned a number of ingenious and provocative contributions. Mindful of the injunction "Treasure your exceptions" we have wondered about: (a) the sex difference in the rates of liver mitochondrial oxidations of cholesterol and pyruvic acid and in cholesterol biosynthesis (304), (b) the finding that a 19-carbon hydrocarbon, 5α-androstane, is androgenic in chicks both on injection and on inunction (305), (c) the nature of the processes occurring in pure lines of mice demonstrating a genetically determined diminution of libido and pituitary hypofunction (306), (d) the uterine factor presumably promoting luteolysis, which is lost by hysterectomy (307), (e) why all the blood changes in spawning salmon lead to a diagnosis of Cushing's syndrome (308), and so on.

More significant, perhaps, is the appreciation of certain hiatuses in our knowledge of certain central processes. Thus, the study of gonad differentiation has been long pursued by experimental embryologists; its morphological basis in cortical vs. medullary dominance has been established in practically all species studied, but we still await the identification of the sex organizers and even an approximate biochemical description of their action. It is no good saying genes act as templates in molding such differentiation, for we know that complete or partial sex reversal may be induced by steroid hormones. Again, our knowledge of the natural history of the fertilized ovum is marvellously detailed, but we still search for an intimate understanding of the fertilization process, for the synthetic mechanisms responsible for ovum growth; even for the energetics involved. When it comes to mechanisms for safeguarding the product of conception, we are faced with more questions than answers, particularly in the mammals. What are the biochemical processes of implantation? What are the placental safeguards? I recall the more-than-30-years-old observation of Nicholas that, following rat ovum transplantation to a sterile gut horn, an almost gigantic fetal growth ensues. These questions could be many times multiplied. And that is why we can be sure of a continuous, accelerating accumulation of investigation in reproductive physiology.

LITERATURE CITED

1. Hartman, C. G., *Fertility and Sterility*, **12**, 1–19 (1961)
2. Jones, E. C., and Krohn, P. L., *J. Endocrinol.*, **20**, 135–46 (1960)
3. Mussett, M. V., and Parrott, D. M. V., *J. Reproduction and Fertility*, **2**, 80–97 (1961)
4. Parrott, D. M. V., *J. Reproduction and Fertility*, **1**, 230–41 (1960)
5. Raboch, J., and Bleha, O., *Endocrinology*, **39**, 534–53 (1960)
6. Clegy, E. J., *J. Reproduction and Fertility*, **1**, 119–20 (1960)
7. Hohlweg, W., Doerner, G., and Kopp, P., *Acta Endocrinol.*, **36**, 299–309 (1961)
8. Van Oordt, P. G. W. J., and Schouten, S. C. M., *J. Reproduction and Fertility*, **2**, 61–67 (1961)
9. Joshi, M., and Macleod, J., *J. Reproduction and Fertility*, **2**, 198–99 (1961)
10. Parizek, J., *J. Reproduction and Fertility*, **1**, 294–309 (1960)
11. Fierlafijn, E., *Rev. méd. Louvain*, **10**, 252–57 (1960)
12. Heller, C. G., Moore, D. J., and Paulsen, C. A., *Toxicol. and Appl. Pharmacol.*, **3**, 1–11 (1961)
13. Bishop, D. W., *Proc. Soc. Exptl. Biol. Med.*, **107**, 116–21 (1961)
14. Harper, M. J. K., *J. Endocrinol.*, **22**, 147–52 (1961)
15. Lamond, D. R., *J. Endocrinol.*, **20**, 277–87 (1960)
16. Aziuk, P. J., and Runner, M. N., *J. Reproduction and Fertility*, **1**, 321–32 (1960)
17. Allen, D. M., and Lanning, G. E., *J. Reproduction and Fertility*, **1**, 213–222 (1960)
18. Jones, G. S., Aziz, Z., and Urbina, G., *Fertility and Sterility*, **12**, 217–35 (1961)
19. Garcia, C. R., Harrigan, J. T., Mulligan, W. S., and Rock, J., *Fertility and Sterility*, **11**, 303–10 (1960)
20. Gemzell, C. A., in *Control of Ovulation*, 192–209 (Pergamon Press, New York, N. Y., 251 pp., 1961)
21. Bane, A., and Rajakoski, E., *Cornell Vet.*, **51**, 77–95 (1961)
22. Cohen, M. R., and Hankin, H., *Fertility and Sterility*, **11**, 497–507 (1960)
23. Li, C. H., *Postgrad. Med.*, **29**, 13–25 (1961)
24. Albert, A., Kobi, J., Leiferman, J., and Deiner, I., *J. Clin. Endocrinol.*, **21**, 1–20 (1961)
25. Got, R., and Bourrillon, R., *Experientia*, **16**, 495–561 (1960)
26. Yazaki, I., *Annotationes Zool. Japon.*, **33**, 217–25 (1960)
27. Currie, A. R., *Acta Endocrinol.*, **36**, 185–96 (1961)
28. Apostolakis, M., and Loraine, J. A., *J. Clin. Endocrinol.*, **20**, 1437–44 (1960)
29. McCann, S. M., and Taleisnik, S., *Am. J. Physiol.*, **199**, 847–50 (1960)
30. Baird, J. M., Wolf, R. O., and Rennels, E. G., *Proc. Soc. Exptl. Biol. Med.*, **106**, 362–65 (1961)
31. Gunn, S. A., Gould, T. C., and Anderson, W. A. D., *Proc. Soc. Exptl. Biol. Med.*, **105**, 433–35 (1960)
32. Wide, L., and Gemzell, C. A., *Acta Endocrinol.*, **35**, 261–67 (1960)
33. McKean, C. M., *Am. J. Obstet. Gynecol.*, **80**, 596–600 (1960)
34. Banik, U. K., and Barna, A., *Ann. Biochem. and Exptl. Med. (Calcutta)*, **20**, 217–20 (1960)
35. Harris, G. W., in *Control of Ovulation*, 56–78 (Pergamon Press, New York, N. Y., 251 pp., 1961)
36. Sawyer, C. H., and Kawakami, M., in *Control of Ovulation*, 79–100 (Pergamon Press, New York, N. Y., 251 pp., 1961)
37. Everett, J. W., in *Control of Ovulation*, 101–21 (Pergamon Press, New York, N. Y., 251 pp., 1961)
38. Velardo, J. T., *Ann. Rev. Physiol.*, **23**, 196 (1961)
39. Taleisnik, S., and McCann, S., *Endocrinology*, **68**, 263–72 (1961)
40. Flerko, B., and Bardos, V., *Acta Endocrinol.*, **36**, 180–84 (1961)
41. McCann, S. M., and Taleisnik, S., *Endocrinology*, **68**, 1071–73 (1961)
42. Barraclough, C. A., *Endocrinology*, **68**, 62–67 (1961)
43. Barraclough, C. A., and Gorbski, R. A., *Endocrinology*, **68**, 68–79 (1961)
44. McCann, S. M., and Friedman, H. M., *Endocrinology*, **67**, 597–608 (1960)
45. Critchlow, V., in *Control of Ovulation*, 75–78 (Pergamon Press, New York, N. Y., 251 pp., 1961)
46. Davidson, J. M., and Sawyer, C. H., *Proc. Soc. Exptl. Biol. Med.*, **107**, 4–7 (1961)
47. Nelson, W., *Endocrinology*, **59**, 140–52 (1956)
48. Pincus, G., Garcia, C. R., Rock, J., Paniagua, M., Pendleton, A., Laraque, F., Nicolas, R., Borno, R.,

and Pean, V., *Science*, **130**, 81–83 (1959)

49. Pincus, G., in *Modern Trends in Endocrinology, 2nd Series*, 231–45 (Butterworth & Co., Ltd., London, Engl., 1961)

50. Rock, J., in *Control of Ovulation*, 222–41 (Pergamon Press, New York, N. Y., 241 pp., 1961)

51. Pincus, G., and Merrill, A. P., in *Control of Ovulation*, 37–55 (Pergamon Press, New York, N. Y., 251 pp., 1961)

52. Cozens, D. A., and Nelson, M. M., *Endocrinology*, **68**, 767–72 (1961)

53. Martin, J., and Endroczi, E., *Acta Physiol. Acad. Sci. Hung.*, **17**, 317–20 (1960)

54. Logothetopoulos, J., Sharma, B. B., and Kraicor, S., *Endocrinology*, **68**, 417–30 (1961)

55. Varon, H. H., and Christian, J. J., *Federation Proc.*, **20**, 181 (1961)

56. Matscher, R., and Lupo, C., *Arch. sci. biol.* (*Bologna*), **44**, 350–58 (1960)

57. Kincl, F. A., Ringold, H. J., and Dorfman, R. I., *Acta Endocrinol.*, **36**, 83–86 (1961)

58. Bryan, H. S., *Proc. Soc. Exptl. Biol. Med.*, **105**, 23–26 (1960)

59. Southren, A. L., Saito, A., Laufer, A., and Soffer, L. J., *J. Clin. Endocrinol. and Metabolism*, **21**, 675–83 (1961)

60. Buchholz, R., *Geburtsh. u. Frauenheilk.*, **19**, 851 (1959)

61. Rosemberg, E., *J. Clin. Endocrinol.*, **20**, 1576–86 (1960)

62. Setnikar, I., Murmann, W., and Magistretti, M. J., *Endocrinology*, **67**, 511–20 (1960)

63. Robson, J. M., and Botros, M., *J. Endocrinol.*, **22**, 165–75 (1961)

64. Holtkamp, D. E., Greslin, J. G., Root, C. A., and Lerner, L., *Proc. Soc. Exptl. Biol. Med.*, **105**, 197–201 (1960)

65. Casaglia, G., and Faggioli, A., *Boll. soc. ital. biol. sper.*, **37**, 60–63 (1961)

66. Landau, B., Schwartz, H. S., and Soffer, L. J., *Metabolism, Clin. and Exptl.*, **9**, 85–87 (1960)

67. Woods, M. C., and Simpson, M. E., *Endocrinology*, **68**, 647–61 (1961)

68. Breneman, W. R., Carmack, M., Overack, D. E., Creek, R. D., and Shaw, R., *Endocrinology*, **67**, 583–96 (1960)

69. Rao, S. S., and Shahani, S. K., *Immunology*, **4**, 1–12 (1961)

70. Rao, S. S., and Shahani, S. K., *J. Reproduction and Fertility*, **2**, 203–4 (1961)

71. Hakim, S. A., and Segal, S. J., *J. Reproduction and Fertility*, **2**, 198 (1961)

72. Feyel-Cabanes, T., *Ann. Endocrinol.*, **21**, 217–22 (1960)

73. Srebnik, H. H., Nelson, M. M., and Simpson, M. E., *Endocrinology*, **68**, 317–26 (1961)

74. Jefferies, W. McK., *Fertility and Sterility*, **11**, 100–8 (1960)

75. Kotz, H. L., and Herrmann, W., *Fertility and Sterility*, **12**, 299–308 (1961)

76. Olson, H. J., and Gotlib, M. H., *Intern. J. Fertility*, **4**, 429–32 (1960)

77. Smith, J. J., and Romney, S. L., *Intern. J. Fertility*, **5**, 8–18 (1960)

78. Bradbury, J. T., *Endocrinology*, **68**, 115–20 (1961)

79. Wright, P. A., *Gen. and Comp. Endocrinol.*, **1**, 20–23 (1961)

80. Croes-Buth, S., De Jongh, S. E., and Paesi, F. J. A., *Acta Physiol. Pharmacol. Néerl.*, **9**, 303–14 (1960)

81. Jaggard, J., and Bradbury, J. T., *Endocrinology*, **79**, 759–66 (1961)

82. Pittman, J. A., Brown, R. W., and Martindale, W. E., *Proc. Soc. Exptl. Biol. Med.*, **105**, 435–38 (1960)

83. Neher, R., and Wettstein, A., *Helv. Chim. Acta*, **43**, 1626–39 (1960)

84. Short, R. V., *J. Endocrinol.*, **22**, 153–63 (1961)

85. Smith, O. W., *Endocrinology*, **67**, 698–707 (1960)

86. Zander, J. V., Brendle, E., Münstermann, A. M., Diczfalusy, E., Martinsen, B., and Tillinger, K. G., *Acta Obstet. Gynecol. Scand.*, **38**, 724–36 (1959)

87. Villee, D. B., *Am. J. Diseases of Children*, **100**, 489–90 (1960)

88. Mason, N. R., and Samuels, L. T., *Endocrinology*, **68**, 899–907 (1961)

89. Lostroh, A. J., *Proc. Soc. Exptl. Biol. Med.*, **103**, 25–27 (1960)

90. Bobkov, A. G., *Bull. Exptl. Biol. Med.*, **59**, 609–11 (1960)

91. Mann, T., *Biochemistry of Semen* (John Wiley & Sons, New York, N. Y., 240 pp., 1954)

92. Grunt, J. A., Walker, J. E., and Huggins, J. T., Jr., *Am. J. Physiol.*, **198**, 754–56 (1960)

93. Yamanaka, H. S., and Soderwall, A. L., *Fertility and Sterility*, **11**, 470–74 (1960)

94. Harvey, C., *J. Reproduction and Fertility*, **1**, 84–89 (1960)
95. Harvey, C., *J. Reproduction and Fertility*, **1**, 111–12 (1960)
96. Guard, H. R., *Fertility and Sterility*, **11**, 392–98 (1960)
97. Beatty, R. A., *J. Reproduction and Fertility*, **1**, 52–60 (1960)
98. Harper, M. J. K., Bennett, J. P., Boursnell, J. C., and Rowson, L. E. A., *J. Reproduction and Fertility*, **1**, 244–67 (1960)
99. Greenwald, G. S., *Fertility and Sterility*, **12**, 80–95 (1961)
100. Ichijo, M., *Tôhoku J. Exptl. Med.*, **72**, 211–19 (1960)
101. Ichijo, M., *Tôhoku J. Exptl. Med.*, **72**, 219–28 (1960)
102. Mastroianni, L., Jr., and Wallach, R. C., *Am. J. Physiol.*, **200**, 815–18 (1961)
103. Mastroianni, L., Jr., Beer, F., Shah, U., and Clewe, T. H., *Endocrinology*, **68**, 92–100 (1961)
104. Chang, M. C., *Nature*, **175**, 1036–37 (1955)
105. Austin, C. R., *J. Reproduction and Fertility*, **1**, 310–11 (1960)
106. Zanartu, J., and Hamblen, E. C., *Fertility and Sterility*, **11**, 248–54 (1960)
107. Shettles, L. B., *Fertility and Sterility*, **12**, 20–24 (1961)
108. Polge, C., *J. Reproduction and Fertility*, **1**, 113–14 (1960)
109. Kawaishi, T., *Hiroshima J. Med. Sci.*, **9**, 97–102 (1960)
110. Puck, A., *Geburtsh. u. Frauenheilk.*, **20**, 775–79 (1960)
111. Barton, M., *J. Reproduction and Fertility*, **1**, 317–18 (1960)
112. Ringler, I., *Endocrinology*, **68**, 281–91 (1961)
113. Edgren, R. A., *Proc. Soc. Exptl. Biol. Med.*, **105**, 252–54 (1960)
114. Dorfman, R. I., Kincl, F. A., and Ringold, H. J., *Endocrinology*, **68**, 17–24 (1961)
115. Dorfman, R. I., Kincl, F. A., and Ringold, H. J., *Endocrinology*, **68**, 43–49 (1961)
116. Martin, L., Cox, R. I., and Emmens, C. W., *J. Endocrinol.*, **22**, 129–32 (1961)
116a. Cutler, A., Epstein, J. A., and Kupperman, H. S., *Acta Endocrinol.*, **51**, 897 (1960)
117. De la Pena Regidor, P., *Rev. ibérica endocrinol.*, **7**, 551–58 (1960)
118. Purshottam, N., and Pincus, G., *Anat. Record*, **140**, 51–55 (1961)
119. Lutwak-Mann, C., *J. Reproduction and Fertility*, **1**, 316–17 (1960)
120. Lutwak-Mann, C., Boursnell, J. P., and Bennett, J. P., *J. Reproduction and Fertility*, **1**, 169–85 (1960)
121. Fridhandler, L., *Exptl. Cell Research*, **22**, 303–16 (1961)
122. Adams, C. E., *J. Reproduction and Fertility*, **1**, 315–16 (1960)
123. Adams, C. E., *J. Reproduction and Fertility*, **1**, 36–44 (1960)
124. Moore, N. W., and Rowson, L. E. A., *J. Reproduction and Fertility*, **1**, 332–49 (1960)
125. Dickmann, Z., and Noyes, R. W., *J. Reproduction and Fertility*, **1**, 197–212 (1960)
126. Deansley, R., *J. Reproduction and Fertility*, **1**, 242–48 (1960)
127. Meunier, J.-M., and Mayer, G., *Compt. rend. acad. sci.*, **251**, 1043–45 (1960)
128. Mayer, G., Meunier, J.-M., and Thevenot-Duluc, A. J., *Ann. Endocrinol.*, **21**, 1–13 (1960)
129. Yoshinaga, K., *J. Reproduction and Fertility*, **2**, 35–41 (1961)
130. Marois, M., *Bull. acad. natl. méd. (Paris)*, **144**, 511–18 (1960)
131. Lerner, L. J., Brennan, D. M., De Phillipo, M., and Yiacas, E., *Federation Proc.*, **20**, 200 (1961)
132. Wu, D. H., *Fertility and Sterility*, **12**, 236–44 (1961)
133. Stucki, J. C., *Acta Endocrinol.*, **33**, 73–80 (1960)
134. Marois, H., *Compt. rend. soc. biol.*, **154**, 1361–66 (1961)
135. Martin, L., Emmens, C. W., and Cox, R. I., *J. Endocrinol.*, **20**, 299–306 (1960)
136. Bruce, H. M., *J. Reproduction and Fertility*, **1**, 96–103 (1960)
137. Bruce H. M., *J. Reproduction and Fertility*, **1**, 311–12 (1960)
138. Parkes, A. S., *J. Reproduction and Fertility*, **1**, 312–14 (1960)
139. Schultz, R. L., Schultz, P. W., and Conn, A. A., *Proc. Soc. Exptl. Biol. Med.*, **105**, 88–91 (1960)
140. Parrott, M. W., Johnston, M. E., and Durbin, P. W., *Endocrinology*, **67**, 467–83 (1960)
141. Healy, M. J. R., McLaren, A., and Michie, D., *Proc. Roy. Soc. (London)*, B, **153**, 367–79 (1960)
142. Sonneborn, T. M., *Publ. Am. Inst. Biol. Sci.*, **6**, 288 (1960)
143. Wada, H., and Turner, C. W., *Endocrinology*, **68**, 1059–63 (1961)
144. Yochim, J., and Zarrow, M. X., *Fertility and Sterility*, **12**, 263–76 (1961)

145. Edgren, R. A., *Experientia*, 16, 544–46 (1960)
146. Edgren, R. A., and Calhoun, D. W., *Endocrinology*, 68, 633–38 (1961)
147. Edgren, R. A., Elton, R. L., and Calhoun, D. W., *J. Reproduction and Fertility*, 2, 98–105 (1961)
148. Brody, S., and Westman, A., *Acta Obstet. Gynecol. Scand.*, 39, 557–65 (1960)
149. Brody, S., and Westman, A., *Acta Obstet. Gynecol. Scand.*, 39, 566–74 (1960)
150. Miyake, T., and Kobayashi, F., *Endocrinol. Japon.*, 7, 215–24 (1960)
151. Edgren, R. A., and Elton, R. L., *Proc. Soc. Exptl. Biol. Med.*, 104, 664–65 (1960)
152. Taylor, N. E., Hodgkin, D., and Rollett, J. S., *J. Chem. Soc.*, 3685 (1960)
153. Jones, H. E., and Pope, G. S., *J. Endocrinol.*, 22, 303–12 (1961)
154. Jones, H. E., Wayforth, H. B., and Pope, G. S., *J. Endocrinol.*, 22, 293–302 (1961)
155. Grattarola, R., *Acta Endocrinol.*, 34, 242–55 (1960)
156. Maeyama, M., Veda, H., Nakano, Y., and Negoro, T., *Wakayama Med. Repts.*, 5, 85–91 (1960)
157. Schöler, H. F. L., *Acta Endocrinol.*, 35, 188–96 (1960)
158. Tillinger, K. G., and Diczfalusy, E., *Acta Endocrinol.*, 35, 197–203 (1960)
159. Elftman, H., *Proc. Soc. Exptl. Biol. Med.*, 105, 19–21 (1960)
160. Frieden, E. H., and Velardo, J. T., *Acta Endocrinol.*, 34, 312–16 (1970)
161. Fuhrmann, K., *Z. Geburtshilfe u. Gynäkol.*, 155, 12–26 (1960)
162. Schmidt, J. E., and Leonard, S. L., *Endocrinology*, 67, 663–67 (1960)
163. Herbener, G. H., and Atkinson, W. B., *Proc. Soc. Exptl. Biol. Med.*, 106, 348–50 (1961)
164. Bialy, G., and Pincus, G., *Endocrinology*, 67, 728–29 (1960)
165. Paul, K. G., and Wiquist, N., *Experientia*, 16, 421 (1960)
166. Hall, K., *J. Endocrinol.*, 20, 355–64 (1960)
167. Turner, G. D., and Sykes, J. F., *Am. J. Vet. Research*, 21, 644–48 (1960)
168. Grumbach, M., in *Clinical Endocrinology*, 407–36 (Grune & Stratton, New York, N. Y., 724 pp., 1960)
169. Marois, M., *Bull. acad. natl. méd.* (*Paris*), 144, 506–11 (1960)
170. Revesz, C., Chappel, C. I., and Gaudry, R., *Endocrinology*, 66, 140–44 (1960)
171. Suchowsky, G. K., and Junkmann, K., *Endocrinology*, 68, 341–49 (1961)
172. Grumbach, M. M., and Ducharme, J. R., *Fertility and Sterility*, 11, 157–80 (1960)
173. Jones, H. W., Jr., and Wilkins, L., *Fertility and Sterility*, 11, 148–56 (1960)
174. Magnus, E. M., *Tidsskr. Norske Laegeforen.*, 80, 92–93 (1960)
175. Bongiovanni, M., and McPadden, A. S., *Fertility and Sterility*, 11, 181–86 (1960)
176. Strauss, J. S.. and Kligman, A. M., *J. Clin. Endocrinol. and Metabolism*, 21, 215–19 (1961)
177. Antoniades, H. N., *Hormones in Human Plasma* (Little, Brown & Co., Boston, Mass., 667 pp., 1960)
178. Levitz, M., Condon, G. P., Money, W. L., and Dancis, J., *J. Biol. Chem.*, 235, 973–77 (1960)
179. Sybulski, S., and Venning, E. H., *Can. J. Biochem.*, 39, 203–14 (1961)
180. Napp. J. H., *Geburtsh. u. Frauenheilk.*, 20, 794–800 (1960)
181. Kaiser, R., *Deut. Med. Wochschr.*, 85, 1457–60 (1960)
182. Foltnyowicz - Mankowa, J., and Smoczkiewicza, A., *Ginekol. Polska*, 31, 35–44 (1960)
183. Frautz, A. G., Katz, F. H., and Jailer, J. W., *Proc. Soc. Exptl. Biol. Med.*, 105, 41–43 (1960)
184. Menini, E., and Diczfalusy, E., *Endocrinology*, 67, 500–10 (1960)
185. Francis, F. E., Chang Shen, N.-H., and Kinsella, R. A., Jr., *J. Biol. Chem.*, 235, 1957–59 (1960)
186. Kurujama, H., and Csapo, A., *Endocrinology*, 68, 1010–25 (1961)
187. Marshall, J. M., and Csapo, A., *Endocrinology*, 68, 1026–35 (1961)
188. Schofield, B. M., *J. Endocrinol.*, 22, xi–xiii (1961)
189. Bengtsson, L. P., and Schofield, B. M., *J. Reproduction and Fertility*, 1, 402–9 (1960)
190. Dewar, A. D., *J. Endocrinol.*, 22, ix–x (1961)
191. Mikhail, G., Noall, W. M., and Allen, W. M., *Endocrinology* (In press, 1961)
192. Short, R. V., *J. Reproduction and Fertility*, 1, 61–70 (1960)
193. Pearlman, W. H., in *Hormones in Human Plasma*, 415–54 (Little, Brown & Co., Boston, Mass., 667 pp., 1960)
194. Ittrich, G., Jakobovitz, A., and Igel,

H., *Zentr. Gynäkol.*, **82**, 1772–74, 1960

195. Klopper, A., MacNaughton, M. C., and Michie, E. A., *J. Endocrinol.*, **22**, xiv–xv (1961)

196. Cartlidge, K., Spencer, P. M., Swyer, G. I. M., and Woolf, A. J., *J. Endocrinol.*, **22**, xvi–xvii (1961)

197. Coyle, M. G., *J. Endocrinol.*, **22**, xvii–xviii (1961)

198. Madjerek, Z., *Arch. intern. pharmacodynamie*, **130**, 473–76 (1961)

199. Cullen, B. M., and Harkness, D. R., *J. Physiol. (London)*, **152**, 419–36 (1960)

200. Hall, K., *J. Reproduction and Fertility*, **1**, 368–84 (1960)

201. Hall, K., *J. Endocrinol.*, **22**, xxii–xxiii (1961)

202. Frieden, E. H., and Kasdon, S. C., in *Clinical Endocrinology*, 542–50 (Grune & Stratton, New York, N. Y., 724 pp., 1960)

203. Emberg, M. P., *J. Endocrinol.*, **22**, xxiii–xxiv (1961)

204. Caldeyro-Barcia, R., and Heller, H., *Oxytocin* (Pergamon Press, London, Engl., 475 pp., 1961)

205. Lyons, W. R., Li, C. H., and Johnson, R. E., *Recent Progr. in Hormone Research*, **14**, 219–54 (1958)

206. Anderson, R. R., Brookreson, A. D., and Turner, C. W., *Proc. Soc. Exptl. Biol. Med.*, **106**, 567–70 (1961)

207. Donovan, B. T., and Jacobsohn, D., *Acta Endocrinol.*, **33**, 197–213 (1960)

208. Clifton, K. H., and Furth, J., *Endocrinology*, **66**, 893 (1960)

209. Talwalker, P. K., Meites, J., and Nicoll, C. S., *Am. J. Physiol.*, **199**, 1070–72 (1960)

210. Talwalker, P. K., and Hopkins, T. F., *Am. J. Physiol.*, **199**, 1073–76 (1960)

211. Meites, J., and Hopkins, T. F., *J. Endocrinol.*, **22**, 207–13 (1961)

212. Meites, J., Talwalker, P. K., and Nicoll, C. S., *Proc. Soc. Exptl. Biol. Med.*, **104**, 192–94 (1960)

213. Persson, B. H., *Acta Soc. Med. Upsaliensis*, **65**, 100–15 (1960)

214. Ferin, J., Van Campenhout, J., and Charles, J., *Ann. Endocrinol.*, **21**, 129–48 (1960)

215. Sadler, W. A., and Browning, H. C., *Proc. Soc. Exptl. Biol. Med.*, **106**, 558–62 (1961)

216. McLean, P., *Biochim. et Biophys. Acta*, **42**, 166–67 (1960)

217. Simkin, B., and Goodart, D., *J. Clin. Endocrinol. and Metabolism*, **20**, 1095–1106 (1960)

218. Muhlbock, O., *Mem. Soc. Endocrinol.*, **10**, 108–11 (1961)

219. Muhlbock, O., in *Biological Activities of Steroids in Relation to Cancer*, 331–38 (Academic Press, New York, N. Y., 530 pp., 1960)

220. Huseby, R. A., *Proc. Am. Assoc. Cancer Research*, **3**, 237 (1961)

221. Nandi, S., Bern, H. A., and De Ome, K. B., *Mem. Soc. Endocrinol.*, **10**, 129–32 (1961)

222. Lacassagne, A., *Acta Unio Intern. contra Cancrum*, **17**, 96–104 (1961)

223. Howell, J. S., and Mande, A. M., *J. Endocrinol.*, **22**, 241–55 (1961)

224. Huggins, C., in *Biological Activities of Steroids in Relation to Cancer*, 1–6 (Academic Press, New York, N. Y., 530 pp., 1960)

225. Huggins, C., Grand, L. C., and Brillantes, F. P., *Nature*, **189**, 204–7 (1961)

226. Dao, L. T., Bock, F. G., and Greiner, M. J., *J. Natl. Cancer Inst.*, **25**, 991–1003 (1960)

227. Huggins, C., *Can. Cancer Conf.*, **4**, 81–88 (Academic Press, New York, N. Y., 435 pp., 1961)

228. Ranadive, K. J., Hakim, S. A., and Kharkar, K. R., *Brit. J. Cancer*, **14**, 508–13 (1960)

229. Glenn, E. M., Richardson, S. L., Bowman, B. S., and Lyster, S. C., in *Biological Activities of Steroids in Relation to Cancer*, 257–306 (Academic Press, New York, N. Y., 530 pp., 1960)

230. Andervont, H. B., Shimkin, M. B., and Canter, H. Y., *J. Natl. Cancer Inst.*, **25**, 1069–81 (1960)

230a. Andervont, H. B., Shimkin, M. B., and Canter, H. Y., *J. Natl. Cancer Inst.*, **25**, 1083–96 (1960)

231. Hellstrom, K. E., *J. Natl. Cancer Inst.*, **26**, 707–17 (1961)

232. Riviere, M. R., Chouroulinkov, I., and Guerin, M., *Compt. rend. soc. biol.*, **154**, 1415–18 (1960)

233. Koga, K., Yamada, M., and Suginoro, H., *Kyushu. J. Med. Sci.*, **11**, 207–15 (1960)

234. Murata, H., *Hirosaki Med. J.*, **11**, 602–19 (1960)

235. Swyer, G. I. M., Lee, A. E., and Masterson, J. P., *Brit. Med. J.*, 617–19 (1961)

236. Kushinsky, S., Demetriou, J. A., Macdonald, I., Crowley, L. G., and Wu, J., *Acta Endocrinol.*, **51**, 745 (1960)

237. Segaloff, A., in *Biological Activities of*

Steroids in Relation to Cancer, 355–62 (Academic Press, New York, N. Y., 530 pp. 1960)

238. Pincus, G., and Vollmer, E., Eds., *Biological Activities of Steroids in Relation to Cancer* (Academic Press, New York, N. Y., 530 pp., 1960)

239. Lerner, L. J., Bianchi, A., and Borman, A., *Cancer*, 13, 1201–5 (1960)

240. Pincus, G., *Can. Cancer Conf.*, 4, 29–42 (Academic Press, New York, N. Y., 435 pp., 1961)

241. Cuppage, F. E., and Bloodworth, J. M. B., Jr., *Proc. Soc. Exptl. Biol. Med.*, 105, 506–8 (1960)

242. Campbell, R. S. F., Lawrie, T. D. V., Pirrie, R., MacLauren, J. C., and Moran, F., *Acta Endocrinol.*, 34, 207–12 (1960)

243. Juhlin, L., and Miguel, J. F., *Acta Endocrinol.*, 36, 87–97 (1961)

244. Schiff, M. V., and Burn, H. F., *Arch. Oto-laryngol.*, 73, 63–71 (1961)

245. Podilchak, M. D., and Kalynyuk, P. P., *Folia Biol. (Warsaw)*, 6, 365–69 (1960)

246. Gligore, V., Stein, S., Abel, S., Bacin, Z., and Teodicescu, I., *Stud. Cercitari Med.*, 9, 95–100 (1958)

247. Rooks, W. H., and Dorfman, R. I., *Endocrinology*, 68, 838–43 (1961)

248. Beckers, C., and De Visscher, M., *Acta Endocrinol.*, 36, 343–49 (1961)

249. Griffen, W. O., Nicoloff, D. M., Stone, N. H., and Wangensteen, O. H., *Proc. Soc. Exptl. Biol. Med.*, 106, 101–4 (1961)

250. Snell, R. S., and Bischitz, P. G., *J. Invest. Dermatol.*, 35, 73–82 (1960)

251. Alexander, R. W., and Marmorston, J., *J. Clin. Endocrinol. and Metabolism*, 21, 243–51 (1961)

252. Strauss, J. S., and Kligman, A. M., *J. Clin. Endocrinol. and Metabolism*, 21, 215–19 (1961)

253. Braun-Menendez, E., and Penhos, J. C., *Acta Physiol. Latinoam.*, 10, 52–57 (1960)

254. Frieden, E. H., Cohen, E. H., and Harper, A. A., *Endocrinology*, 68, 862–66 (1961)

255. Aspinall, R. L., Meyer, R. K., and Rao, M. A., *Endocrinology*, 68, 944–49 (1961)

256. Canal, N., *Atti soc. lombarda sci. med. biol.*, 14, 424–26 (1960)

257. Juhlin, L., *Acta Endocrinol.*, 36, 87–97 (1961)

258. Graugand, R., Conquy, T., and Nicol, M., *Compt. rend. soc. biol.*, 154, 115–18 (1960)

259. Holub, D. A., Katz, F. H., and Jailer,

J. W., *Endocrinology*, 68, 173–77 (1961)

260. Bergen, J. R., Krus, D., and Pincus, G., *Proc. Soc. Exptl. Biol. Med.*, 105, 254–56 (1960)

261. Ittrich, G., *Z. physiol. Chem.*, 320, 103–10 (1960)

262. Roy, E. J., and Brown, J. B., *J. Endocrinol.*, 21, 9–23 (1960)

263. Svendsen, R., *Acta Endocrinol.*, 35, 161–87 (1960)

264. Oertel, G. W., and Eik-Nes, K. B., *Arch. Biochem. Biophys.*, 92, 150–53 (1961)

265. Finkelstein, M., Forchielli, E., and Dorfman, R. I., *J. Clin. Endocrinol. and Metabolism*, 21, 98–101 (1961)

266. Seeman, A., *Compt. rend. soc. biol.*, 153, 1968–71 (1960)

267. Rutzmann, L., and Würterle, A., *Clin. Chim. Acta*, 5, 727–31 (1960)

268. Stark, L., and Malikova, J., *J. Endocrinol.*, 22, 215–19 (1961)

269. Schubert, K., and Wehrberger, K., *Naturwissenschaften*, 47, 281 (1960)

270. Schubert, K., and Wehrberger, K., *Naturwissenschaften*, 47, 397–98 (1960)

271. Ryan, K. J., and Smith, O. W., *J. Biol. Chem.*, 236, 705–9 (1961)

272. Ryan, K. J., and Smith, O. W., *J. Biol. Chem.*, 236, 710–14 (1961)

273. Engel, L. L., in *Biological Activities of Steroids in Relation to Cancer*, 111–23 (Academic Press, New York, N. Y., 530 pp., 1960)

274. Marrian, G. F., *Mem. Soc. Endocrinol.*, 10, 1–11 (1961)

275. Fishman, J., Cox, R. I., and Gallagher, T. F., *Arch. Biochem. Biophys.*, 90, 318–19 (1960)

276. Fishman, J., Bradlow, H. I., and Gallagher, T. F., *J. Biol. Chem.*, 235, 3104–7 (1960)

277. Breuer, H., Knuppen, R., and Schriefers, H., *Z. physiol. Chem.*, 319 136–42 (1960)

278. Breuer, H., Nocke, L., and Pangels, C., *Acta Endocrinol.*, 34, 359–65 (1960)

279. Dorfman, R. I., in *Biological Activities of Steroids in Relation to Cancer*, 445–56 (Academic Press, New York, N. Y., 530 pp., 1960)

280. Savard, K., Dorfman, R. I., Baggett, B., Fielding, L. L., Engel, L. L., McPherson, H. T., Lister, L. M., Johnson, D. S., Hamblen, E. C., and Engel, F. L., *J. Clin. Invest.*, 39, 534–53 (1961)

281. Dominguez, O. V., *J. Clin. Endo-*

crinol. and Metabolism, **21**, 663–74 (1961)

282. Davis, M. E., Plotz, E. S., Lupu, C. I., and Ejarque, P. M., *Fertility and Sterility*, **11**, 18–48 (1960)

283. Shearman, R. P., Cox, R. I., and Gannon, A., *Lancet*, **I**, 260–61 (1961)

284. Lanthier, A., *J. Clin. Endocrinol. and Metabolism*, **20**, 1587–1600 (1960)

285. Glenister, D. W., and Yates, F. E., *Endocrinology*, **68**, 747–58 (1961)

286. Kitay, J. I., *Endocrinology*, **68**, 818–24 (1961)

287. Daughaday, W. H., *Hormones in Human Plasma*, 495–514 (Little, Brown & Co., Boston, Mass., 667 pp., 1960)

288. Daughaday, W. H., Holloszy, J., and Mariz, I. K., *J. Clin. Endocrinol. and Metabolism*, **21**, 53–61 (1961)

289. Marks, L. J., *J. Lab. Clin. Med.*, **57**, 47–53 (1961)

290. McGuire, J. S., Jr., and Tomkins, G. M., *J. Biol. Chem.*, **235**, 1634–38 (1960)

291. Talalay, P., and Williams-Ashman, H. G., *Recent Progr. in Hormone Research*, **16**, 1–47 (1960)

292. Williams-Ashman, H. G., Liao, S., and Talalay, P., in *Biological Activities of Steroids in Relation to Cancer*, 147–56 (Academic Press, NewYork, N. Y., 530 pp., 1960)

293. Villee, C. A., Hagerman, D. D., and Joel, P. B., *Recent Progr. in Hormone Research*, **16**, 49–78 (1960)

294. Villee, C. A., in *Developing Cell Systems and Their Control*, 93–113 (Roland Press, New York, N. Y., 1960)

295. Glass, R., Loring, J., Spencer, J., and Villee, C., *Endocrinology*, **68**, 327–33 (1961)

296. Mueller, G. C., in *Biological Activities of Steroids in Relation to Cancer*, 129–42 (Academic Press, New York, N. Y., 530 pp., 1960)

297. Mueller, G. C., Gorski, J., and Sizawo, Y., *Proc. Natl. Acad. Sci. US*, **47**, 164–69 (1961)

298. Aizawa, Y., and Mueller, G. C., *J. Biol. Chem.*, **236**, 381–86 (1961)

299. Hechter, O., and Lester, G., *Recent Progr. in Hormone Research*, **16**, 139–86 (1960)

300. Wilson, J. D., *Clin. Research*, **9**, 54 (1961)

301. Farnsworth, W. E., and Brown, J. R., *Endocrinology*, **68**, 978–86 (1961)

302. Loring, J., Spencer, J., and Villee, C., *Endocrinology*, **68**, 501–6 (1961)

303. Butenandt, A., *Z. physiol. Chem.*, **322**, 28–37 (1960)

303a. Eckstein, B., Kahan, D., Bornt, A., Eshkol, Z., and Sobel, H., *Bull. Research Council Israel* (*Exptl. Med.*), **8**, 141–46 (1960)

304. Kritchevsky, D., Staple, E., Rabinowitz, J. L., and Whitehouse, M. W., *Am. J. Physiol.*, **200**, 519–22 (1961)

305. Segaloff, A., and Gabbard, R. B., *Endocrinology*, **67**, 887–89 (1960)

306. Fowler, R. E., and Edwards, R. G., *Genet. Research*, **1**, 393–407 (1960)

307. Silbiger, M., and Rothchild, I., *Federation Proc.*, **20**, 186 (1961)

308. Robertson, O. H., Krupp, M. A., Favour, C. B., Hane, S., and Thomas, S. F., *Endocrinology*, **68**, 733–46 (1961)

TEMPERATURE[1]

By Loren D. Carlson

Department of Physiology, University of Kentucky, Lexington, Kentucky

A review seems a static thing in the dynamic scientific world of continual increase in the wealth of facts and the vicissitudes in the interpretation of these facts. This review is challenged by the excellence of the previous review (138) and aided by a number of published symposia and reviews (15, 46, 62, 122, 128, 155, 210, 241, 276, 280, 285, 316). During the year 1961, The Fourth Symposium on Temperature, Its Measurement and Control in Science and Industry, the second of these to devote sessions to biological problems, was held.[2]

A challenge to conventional views of temperature regulation has been espoused during the period and calls to question the use of rectal temperature as a reference temperature in the studies of thermal regulation. This will undoubtedly stimulate interest and further activity in the study of temperature regulation.

TEMPERATURE REGULATION

It is necessary in discussion of temperature regulation to be explicit as to what is regulated as well as what is regulating. The major regulated mechanisms in man are heat production, changes in circulation, and sweating. Heat production by shivering is experimentally indicated by the electromyogram or reflected in increases in metabolism. Nonshivering thermogenesis is reflected only by an increase in metabolism in the absence of muscle activity (electromyographic or tension). Change in circulation to the periphery is usually indicated by skin temperature or by heat flow rather than direct measurements of blood flow. Sweating is measured as a weight loss or by change in moisture content of air. In man, as well as in other animals, change in circulation changes tissue insulation. In fur-bearing animals piloerection is an added mechanism for changing insulation; panting replaces sweating, perhaps involving different neural pathways. Calorimetric heat loss reflects the skin temperature as well as the conditions of the environment. The sweat rate (moisture loss) involves the assumption that all calories are involved in surface cooling. Direct measures of what is regulated

[1] The survey of literature pertaining to this review was concluded May 31, 1961. The author acknowledges support from AF contract 41(657)-335 administered by the Arctic Aeromedical Laboratory.

[2] Symposium on Temperature, Its Measurement and Control in Science and Industry. March 27–31, 1961. In addition to the broad coverage of temperature problems six sessions were devoted to biology: temperature instrumentation in biophysics and medicine, physiological responses to cold, physiological responses to heat, tissue heating and thermal sensation, temperature in biophysics, physiological temperature regulations. To be published as *Temperature, Its Measurement and Control in Science and Industry*, III (Hardy, James D., Ed., Am. Inst. Phys., New York, 1962.)

are measures of metabolism (preferably localized to a tissue), of circulation (an abrupt change in circulation to the skin will be reflected in an exponential change in skin temperature and in heat loss), of piloerection (change in insulation), and of evaporative cooling.

With an initial paper in *Proceedings of the National Academy of Science of the United States* (24), Benzinger has reported calorimetric experiments on temperature regulation in man which have been extended in succeeding reports[3] (22, 23, 25, 26). Benzinger's findings are that in a nonsteady state at high evaporative loss, total heat loss follows an "internal" temperature (sphenoid or tympanum) rather than skin temperature (24). In water bath and ice ingestion experiments, internal temperature (sphenoid or tympanum) deviates from rectal temperature (24), and heat loss more closely follows "internal" temperature. At steady state, sweat rate and calculated conductance do not coincide when data of heat loss, resulting from different work loads, are plotted against skin temperature. A best fit is obtained using "internal" temperature.

Benzinger's conclusions are sweeping albeit drawn from elegant instrumentation. He states that afferent impulses from the skin are not a prerequisite to the thermoregulatory response of the preoptico-supraoptic region of the hypothalamus; that no pathway connecting the thermoreceptor cells of the skin via the thalamus with the hypothalamic thermoregulatory system seems to be required to account for human temperature regulation in a warm environment; that as far as this task is concerned the preoptic-supraoptic receptor cells are terminal sensory organs; that the skin seems not to have one main function hitherto ascribed to it—to serve as a sensory component in the autonomic system of human temperature control by sudomotor and vasomotor action; that skin receptors are involved in a Pavlovian response involving behavior and posture. Benzinger states further that since rectal temperatures do not permit conclusions on stimulus response relations, there are no contradictions whatsoever between any pertinent observations of classical authors (21) and the results of gradient calorimetry. The comparison with results in which rectal temperature is used as indicative of internal temperature is forbidden although it does not seem definitely demonstrated that it is invalid in the steady state. The inference is that in Robinson's (237) now classical data, rectal temperature varied from the sensor ("internal") temperature, though reduced skin temperature could inhibit sweating.

The Benzinger concept may be summarized as postulating a thermally sensitive (anterior) area of the hypothalamus from which heat loss responses originate. That this center is not influenced by afferent impulses from warmth receptors is deduced from the fact that sweating and conductivity changes are not related to skin temperature but to internal temperature. A heat

[3] The author is indebted to Dr. Benzinger for the privilege of reading the report presented at the American Institute of Physics Temperature Symposium.

maintenance center (posterior), that is insensitive to the stimulus of temperature, relays cold receptor impulses, transducing these into shivering and increased heat production. An interrelation exists between the two centers—anterior inhibiting posterior.

Although the validity of sphenoid or tympanic temperature as indicative of the critical hypthalamic temperature is not definitely demonstrated at all environmental temperatures, the marked correlation with regulated events gives reason for generalization. The vasculature of the hypothalamus is anatomically complex (52) and warrants reservations concerning any single temperature as the "sensor" or center temperature. It may be significant that hypothalamic blood flow serves to cool the hypothalamus (217). A heat-sensitive region in the medulla has been described (153). The idea that the temperature-regulating center is thermal sensitive is not new (138) and it may be premature to name it a terminal sensory organ, analogous to the eye, without histologic evidence. Ström (280) suggests that it is thermodetector rather than thermoreceptor. There are many parallels of sensor mechanisms in the hypothalamus such as the postulated osmoreceptors and the glucose-sensitive receptors, and in the sensitivity of the respiratory center to carbon dioxide. The point at issue is whether sensory input from the skin via cold or warmth receptors modifies or controls sudomotor and vasomotor action mediated via the center—in addition to possible local and spinal reflex mechanisms. Another controversial point is whether sphenoid or tympanic temperatures are measures of the temperature of the hypothalamic regulatory center.

Experimental demonstrations of the involvement of the hypothalamic areas in temperature regulation in various animals continue with a variety of techniques. Keller (179 to 182) has reviewed ablation experiments. Fever reactions may involve a functional state, thus indicating a relationship of the hypothalamus to higher centers (113). In the rat, the temperature-regulating center is localized to the preoptic area and partially overlaps the thyroid-stimulating hormone regulating area which lies between the paraventricular nucleus and the median eminence (256). This impairment does not involve regulation against cold (120). Ventromedial lesions do not disturb regulation (121). By heating and cooling the carotid blood and controlling air temperature around the body, Lim (205) has extended his work with the dog. The thermal dissociation technique leads to the conclusion that shivering may be initiated or inhibited by either central or peripheral control. Earlier work led to a similar result with respect to heating (204). Contrary evidence is offered by Brendel (45) from perfusion experiments. Lowered blood temperature causes a fall in oxygen consumption; lowered skin temperature causes a rise in oxygen consumption. Newman (239) has described blood pressure response to perfusing the head of anesthetized cats. If the brain temperature rises to 41 or 42°C there is a sudden fall of blood pressure.

Thermodes to heat or cool the hypothalamus have been the tools of several thermoregulatory physiologists (35, 63, 64, 70, 85, 94, 100, 106, 119, 258). The dog has received intensive calorimetric study in the range 8 to 36°C (118) in Hardy's laboratory. This group studied hypothalamic cooling in unanesthetized dogs and concluded that thermoregulatory responses result from the summing of two drives, central and peripheral. Local temperature change of the hypothalamus affects heat production in the rat (85), heat production in the cat (219), muscular activity in the dog (63, 64), and ear blood flow (258). In the ox, thermal polypnea is controlled by stimulation from the periphery until a body (brain) temperature of 40°C is reached (94).

Bligh (35) measured temperature below the point of bifurcation of the bicarotid trunk in sheep. Ambient temperature was changed from 20 to 42°C in conjunction with or independent of a head mask temperature. Bligh concludes that the panting response to an abrupt rise in ambient temperature need not be preceded by a change in deep body temperature. Carotid blood can exchange heat with the jugular vein if the face is cool (262). When temperature regulation is established in the lamb (70), it apparently involves the dual system of regulation with respect to shivering. When oxygen content was reduced to 10 to 15 per cent, shivering was suppressed. Shivering seems oxygen tension dependent; the high oxygen tension suppression of shivering has been confirmed (216).

Stimulation of the "preoptic" heat loss center causes polypnea and vasodilatation. The preoptic thermal control is inhibited reflexly from surface cold receptors and more directly by lowering internal temperature. When an adequate stimulus is applied to the "heat loss center", polypnea and vasodilation continue for several minutes after stimulation. Post-stimulatory electrical activity was recorded from the "heat loss center" for periods up to four minutes. Exposure to cold or reduction of body temperature depresses the persistent thermoregulatory response as well as the post-stimulatory electrical activity (5). Thermal stress changes catecholamine concentration in certain areas of the brain; these areas are medullary and hypothalamic. The authors infer that thermal stress switches off some neurons in the lower brain (189).

Further elucidation of properties of thermal receptors and their relation to mechanoreceptors has come from Hensel's laboratory (140, 309). Repetition of earlier experiments (139) removed the objection (303) that the temperature displacement was from a temperature where cold receptor discharge is nearly zero and established that the conclusion that cold receptors are stimulated simply by cooling and not by slope or direction of any intracutaneous spatial temperature gradient is still valid. Cold receptors have representation in the cortex (66). Apparently the inguinal region and the udder are well endowed with thermoreceptors (206, 293). Discharge of other receptors (muscle spindle) is temperature dependent (207).

While the neural path from the peripheral receptors to the hypothalamus has not been demonstrated, the deduction seems valid that peripheral temperature *per se* has a role in temperature regulation. This seems most clearly indicated in the case of cold exposure. Whether the center is thermosensitive in the sense of a receptor organ or whether temperature changes the threshold or response level to incoming impulses lies in the realm of interpretation.

A perplexing adjunct to the interpretation of the regulating system is the diurnal variation in body temperature which parallels the sleep-wakefulness pattern (274).

The sensory intensity of warmth and cold increases as the difference from a neutral point increases as a power function. The exponent for warmth is 1.6, that for cold 1.0 (277).

Following a flavorful introduction, Renbourne reports on a study of temperature and pulse rate before athletic events. The emotional hyperthermia is not accompanied by an elevated pulse rate (257). Emotional hyperthermia may be due to change in muscle tension or release of epinephrine (194). Emotional reactions and skin temperature (dorsum of hand) responses in children show high normal skin temperature related to comfort, need, satisfaction, and objective mastery over environment. Increasing skin temperature correlates with threats productive of resentment for which adaptive reactions were not taken; decreasing skin temperature is associated with anxiety, fear, and anger. Moderate reductions in skin temperature resulted from preparation for appropriate action while large falls resulted from concerted efforts (286). The dorsum of the hand was perhaps a convenient place for temperature but the finger might reflect emotional effects more dramatically. The use of finger plethysmographs would have measured the system of direct interest.

Measurement of energy exchange in one- to two-day-old premature infants (790 to 2170 g) established that thermoregulation was present (50).

Effects of Heat

In addition to thermoregulatory influences, heat has received attention in areas of assessment of environments and protection, assessment of the strain produced by heat stress, mechanisms of effects, and circulatory and sweating responses.

Billingham & Kerslake (32) present a theoretical analysis of the ways in which various environmental parameters may be combined to produce a state of thermal comfort in man. Where requirements for comfort are not met, the discrepancy can be expressed as a deficiency or an excess in rate of removal of body heat. The equations are represented graphically. Some experimental evidence supports the theoretical evaluation (33), and a specification for thermal comfort in aircraft is proposed (31). Theoretical analyses have been extended to thermal considerations for space suits in orbit, evaluating three major aspects; orbit considerations, body geometry, and suit properties (69).

The study of ventilated suits has emphasized many of the critical problems of initial thermal state and the temporal relationships of change from one steady state to another (296). The emphasis on extended temperature ranges, defining tolerance time in terms of survival and in terms of performance, exposes gaps in our knowledge and emphasizes the specific need for development of fabrics and special construction of gloves, boots, and closure devices. Various aspects of the problem, for example, techniques of measuring heat flow through clothing under dynamic conditions to determine local effects of body movement (312), need extended analysis.

Prior body-cooling influences tolerance time in the heat (291a). Mean body temperature is a discriminating criterion for prediction (291a). Hall & Polte (116) found a correlation between the Craig strain index and body heat storage and made a careful study of the variability. Gold (110) proposes a unified system for selection of heat-stress candidates based on effective heat storage and an index of strain; these two factors appear to be correlated. Craig's index of strain is modified by incorporating the initial heart rate. In the hot environment, heat storage reflects the ineffectiveness of sweat rate and circulation (108). A method for predicting sweat rates (39) is another means of estimating work time. Minard (224) stresses the role of fitness in prevention of heat casualties.

Gold (109) tackled the problem of the mechanism of collapse from heat which is characterized by its precipitous nature. It is his thesis that cessation of sweating is the result of rising venous pressure and the primary event is high output cardiac failure. Body temperatures above 100°F produce a kyperkinetic circulation as characterized from the ballistocardiogram (231). The "heat stroke" syndrome may include erosions of stomach and duodenum and brain lesions (157).

The increase in blood flow to the forearm following arterial occlusion is related to muscle temperature while the hyperemia of exercise is not (67). Of the multiple factors controlling cutaneous flow to the forearm, temperature is the most important (273). Muscle flow follows temperature when heating is accomplished by diathermy (1). Finger blood flow does not always correlate with forearm cutaneous flow. Bradykinin formation in human sweat glands is a factor in heat vasodilatation (98) as well as in periglandular (sweat) vasodilatation. Vasomotor fibers to skin of the upper arm, calf, and thigh have been demonstrated by nerve block techniques (36). The minute pattern of human perspiration has been observed with a sensitive resistance hygrometer (234). A periodic cycle of a few seconds is reminiscent of the cycling in skin flow. Circulation reactions (174) and heart rate changes (41) with rapid changes in temperature are of interest in light of the non-steady-state studies for which there is need.

The physical performance of a group of men and women was studied under three environmental conditions: 25°C, 43 per cent RH; 37.2°C, 25 per cent RH; 32.2°C, 82 per cent RH. The five females were younger than the six males studied. During exercise, heart rate in the women was higher in the hot humid environment (49). Physical performance has received attention by other workers (212, 315).

While acclimation to heat is accepted phenomenologically, the mechanism has not been defined. Streeten et al. (279) reported that the process by which man acclimatizes to heat involves a great increase in the elaboration of aldosterone which effects the responsiveness of sweat glands to sodium retention. Rats adapt to heat with a lowered metabolism (53, 59).

In the dog, thermal panting leads to acapnia (193) and the increase in pH is responsible for the hypophosphatemia (173). Hypoglycemia is also related to the degree of involvement of the respiratory apparatus (172). Hyperthermia leads to loss of potential young in the ewe as well as to a change in concentration, motility, and fertility of sperm in the ram (4).

Increased temperature as a stress caused biochemical changes *per se* as well as through regulative mechanisms. Hale & Mefferd (114, 115) investigated some of these changes in detail by urinalysis of electrolytes and nitrogen compounds and most recently by testing the effect of somatotropin in rats acutely exposed to heat and acclimated. In acute exposures, somatotropin contributes to homeostasis; in acclimated rats, somatotropin had some effects which were heat (or altitude) mimetic. Heat stress (33°C) does not alter the hormone content of the pars nervosa (71).

The results of C. P. Yaglou's arduous research on requirements for shelters were published after his death (313, 314). In a study of the limits for cold, heat, and humidity, barracks temperatures of 50 and 70°F were not particularly different; at a barracks temperature of 35°F the men suffered from severe shivering in the first few days, which tended to moderate (314). Geographical origin affects response to heat; southerners (Floridians) have a more efficient heat regulation than northerners (New England) as judged by sweat rate, rectal temperature change, and heart rate (313).

Protection against high temperature can be affected by chlorpromazine in the rat (171) and in the pig (169). Ascorbic acid is also protective. Reserpine is less effective (170). Methimazole reduces survival at high temperature (168).

Extreme warmth results in a growing inattentiveness and general deterioration (246). Warmth is different from lack of sleep, reducing accuracy rather than activity (245).

EFFECTS OF COLD

The effects of exposure to cold have been the object of extensive research, especially at the biochemical level. It is in reference to cold exposure that the question of acclimatization or adaptation is still vigorously argued both as to whether it exists and as to what criteria should be used as indices of the existence of acclimatization.[4] Edholm (88) advanced the negative hypothesis, indicating that the complete failure to find any adaptation makes this approach more sensible. Carlson & Thursh (60) in a selected bibliog-

[4] Two laboratories confine their research activity to the field of this review. For a comprehensive bibliography, the reader may write: Commander, Arctic Aeromedical Laboratory, Ft. Wainwright, Alaska; Director, Biology Division, National Research Council, Ottawa, Canada.

raphy indicate the broad range of physiological responses that have been considered indicative of a response to cold, a change in response presumably being acceptable as indication of acclimatization.

The physiological interest centers around the basic response patterns of man and animal to continued or intermittent exposure to low environmental temperatures; a teleological urge ascribes an adaptive function.

Human tolerance to cold presents interesting physiological problems (58), but knowledge of how to live in the cold and an ability to adapt sociologically are more important practical items (272). Actual exposure in the cold is minimized by many factors (259). In fact, exposure to cold seems the least important aspect of polar physiology (88). Polar activities during the International Geophysical Year, as well as studies in natural climatic situations elsewhere, have led to a number of observations on men in cold environments. The adaptive range of the polytypic, polymorphic species of modern man has been described as "nothing short of tremendous" (238). Irving's summary (162) of field studies of cold adaptation provides the basis for succeeding work. Under conditions of exploration of the Antarctic, Siple (275, 276) and Taylor (283) give accounts of personal observations indicating the intense extremes of exposure and the day-to-day medical problems. Psychological and social aspects of polar life have been considered by Mullin (233) and Willis (304). The British group found that body weights and skin-fold thickness reached maximum values in the cold months because of reduced activity; the increase in fat was of trivial benefit as insulation (202, 305). There was a voluntary reduction in the clothing worn (number of layers) during prolonged cold stress (111) and an increase in fat consumption (112). Milan (220, 221) and Milan and co-workers (222) evaluated the thermal stress in man in the Antarctic region and found seasonal differences in energy expenditure and consumption: fall, winter, and spring: 3775, 3370, and 4175 kcal expended and 3400, 4396, and 4285 kcal consumed, respectively. Metabolic rates and thermal responses to cold exposure also showed seasonal changes. Similar results have been reported for dogs in Alaska—whether Husky or poorly insulated beagle (86a).

Pace studied many physiological parameters in an attempt to establish a pattern of response related to particular stresses. These metabolic patterns or profiles from blood and urine constituents were more indicative of the physical work stress in the Antarctic than cold *per se* (242, 243). Plasma electrolytes change in man exposed to cold when his food intake is restricted: magnesium increases and calcium decreases in the first day, then there are slight decreases in phosphate, sodium, chloride, hemoglobin, and packed cell volume (126).

When man is exposed to falling ambient temperatures he may meet the situation by increasing the body insulation (peripheral cooling) and later by increasing his metabolic rate (8). The extent to which the body cools without increase in metabolic rate varies. The Arctic Indian has been compared with Caucasians in the same locale. In a cold environment the Indians slept more (0.51 versus 0.31 from EEG evidence) (163). There was no seasonal difference in metabolic rate. The Indians responded to cooling with lower skin temperatures on the thigh (91). In a cold bath (4 to 5°C) the hands of the Indians transfer more heat whether the body is warm (room temperature 22 to 24°C) or cool (17 to 19°C) (92). With the evidence of the effect of physical fitness on skin temperatures (135) in mind, these authors tested the Indians and classified them as intermediate between sedentary and athletic individuals (6). Nomadic Lapps were compared to a control group under moderate cold exposure. The Lapps slept well at 0°C; the metabolic rate was close to basal; skin temperature was higher and rectal temperature change greater (7). The Bushmen of the Kalahari Desert do not follow the pattern of the Australian aborigene. When compared with Europeans the Bushmen sleeping at temperatures from 27 to 2°C have an elevated oxygen consumption and less change in skin and rectal temperature (295). Sleep in cold is influenced by food intake (190), the caloric content being more important than composition. Food intake is linked with temperature regulation (47).

The hands of fishermen who work in cold water differ from those who lack this experience. Gaspé fishermen's hands in 10°C water were warmer, gave less pressor response, less pain, and a greater heat dissipation than those of their controls. They did not differ in a Y-test for two-edge discrimination. Skin biopsies showed an increase in mast cells (198). The levels of hand blood flow at 40, 20, and 10°C of North Norwegian fishermen were not different from those of habituated noncontrol subjects. Cold vasodilatation at 0°C was more rapid in the fishermen (5.6 min contrasted with 8.8 min) (191). Heat output from the hands of Norwegian fishermen is not different from that of nonhabituated controls (136). The differences found in hand blood flows and heat loss may be due to the temperatures employed; the differences may appear only when the subject is partially vasoconstricted. Heat output and blood flow are correlated in the finger (89). Two members of a religious group who commonly wear only a cotton robe were students at the University of Alaska. When compared with one Air Force airman, these two exhibited a marked reduction in shivering and maintained hand and foot temperatures duirng cold stress (164). The differences in response of Negroes and Caucasians to cooling previously noted in their extremities are not marked for the whole body (159).

In a simulated environment, lightly clothed men were studied in a temperature of 15.6°C for 12 days (18). There was a marked increase in turnover of food and of energy expenditure without a catabolic effect. The thyroid increases the uptake, rate of formation, and rate of release of thyroxin. Peripheral utilization of thyroxin is increased (18). Energy balance in cold environments meets the requirement whether it is because of work or the increased metabolism to combat cold (137, 212). Heat production from shivering in nude subjects was measured over a temperature range of 90 to 20°F with wind velocities of 1, 5, and 10 mph. The relationship of metabolism to temperature and to wind velocity is nonlinear. Metabolism as high as 350 kcal per hr was recorded (291) during shivering.

Nonshivering thermogenesis has been demonstrated in man (73, 74) and had been implied earlier (57). While the mean rectal temperature and mean surface temperature during a standard cold exposure of 14°C for 1 hour showed no seasonal variation, the mean time to onset of shivering changed from 16 minutes to longer than 60 minutes when the same men were compared in October and February at Fort Knox, Kentucky. The heat production at the end of the exposure was reduced to 50 per cent. There is a significant increase in the catecholamine secretion in the cold in man (6.5°C–1 hr), most marked for epinephrine (10). This may be involved in nonshivering thermogenesis (57). Work and deprivation from sleep also influence excretion of catecholamines (134).

Local cooling in man affects blood flow, movement of muscles, joints, and tendons, and nerves (97). Temperatures in the lower saphenous vein were 29.1 and 30.2°C, and antecubital temperatures of 34.2 to 34.6°C and a deep gastrocnemius temperature of 34.6°C were recorded, while blood clotting mechanisms were being tested. In the range 22 to 37°C, one-stage prothrombin time and clotting time increased as temperature decreased. Blood viscosity approximately doubled (261). Edwards & Burton (90) mapped the temperature on the human head and provided isothermal maps. An average decrease in skin temperature was 12°C when ambient temperature changed from 24 to 0°C; the range was 8 to 20°C. An earlier paper from the same laboratory (103) indicated that the insulation of the head did not change with temperature. Peripheral cooling (withdrawal of circulation) adds to body insulation. In immersion studies (15°C stirred water) Keatinge (176) found that the rectal temperature change with time was inversely related to mean skin-fold thickness (subcutaneous fat) and that even in thin men fat provides the major part of insulation. The critical temperature for increase in metabolism did not differ with the extent of fat, but the magnitude of the increase with decreasing temperature was less for fatter men (55). This would indicate that skin cooling signals an increase in metabolic rate but that subcutaneous fat serves as insulation. A skin temperature of 33 to 34°C is the point of vasoconstriction on several areas of the body (55). Both warm and cold water markedly stimulate respiratory rate and pulse rate (177). Work has little effect on the fall of surface and rectal temperatures on immersion in cold water. Clothing substantially reduced this fall in temperature; this protective effect was reduced by work (178). English Channel swimmers are not necessarily fat; they have a high mesomorphy (253) and can supply a high energy output from fat.

In a cold environment (60°F) blood volume decreases in the first five hours and remains at the lower level for two weeks of exposure; capillary fragility decreases (240). Distensibility of digital blood vessels decreases in cold, involving high pressure vessels more than low (158). The pressor response resulting from immersion of a limb is not related to the magnitude or direction of change in either cardiac output or total peripheral resistance (42).

Animal experimentation in cold environments extends the range of temperatures and the nature of measurements that can be made. Physiological effects of cold on animals illustrate specific ecological effects as well as phenomenological effects related to size, shape, and natural protection (131, 133). The response of the whole animal involves behavior as well as physiological and biochemical changes. Oxygen consumption and behavior of unanesthetized dogs at environmental temperatures of -10 to 35°C yield a minimal metabolism at 24°C with a rise in metabolism on either side of this temperature (117). This type of curve is reminiscent of those presented by Brody (48) and supplemented by the Scholander type of analysis (132, 268). It seems more reasonable to speak of minimal metabolism rather than critical temperature in this type of study. The Vo_2 of rats increases linearly with temperature from 30 to 5°C and the ventilation ratio remains constant (16). Exposure to cold or injection with thyroxine increases food consumption in rats. The digestion coefficient does not change markedly. Injections of thyroxine in rats kept at 4°C did not increase food intake (156). Thyroidectomy effects a change in cooling rate during acute exposure of rats to cold, through a failure of heat conservation (102). A similar response is observed in cats with the additional observation that the thyroid plays a role in maintaining body fluids (37). Hypothalamic lesions which permit adequate trophic hormone secretions at normal temperatures drastically curtail thyroidal and ovarian function and selectively limit adrenal responses in the cold (72). If the colonic cooling rate is used as a screening test, the requirement for the restrained rat cooled at 5°C is 5 μg per day of thyroxine and 2 to 2.5 mg of cortisone (101). Absence of the thyroid impairs adaptive changes to cold; absence of adrenals does not (247). Reduction in thyroid activity also modifies the rewarming rate following hypothermia (292).

There are differences in response of animals continually exposed to cold and those intermittently exposed (143, 145, 146, 147, 149). Rats exposed intermittently are similar in cold resistance and in metabolic adjustments but dissimilar in endocrine response and isolated liver Qo_2 (150). Animals may also adapt topically (87).

Electrical activity of muscles is usually coupled with chemical thermoregulation (shivering). Rubner's terminology suggested that chemical regulation was not dependent on muscle activity. There is a "tone" at rest which is at a minimum at the minimum temperature (161). In a study on rats exposed to cold, the electromyogram coincided with an increase in muscle electrical activity (165) after the animals were 11 days of age. The electromyographic response was not present in the two-day-old rat.

In rats, exposure to 4°C causes a marked decrease in plasma albumin and an increase in plasma volume and thyocyanate space; hematocrit and muscle water are unchanged (269). The decrease in albumin and the fall in A/G ratio are similar to the responses to ionizing radiations. The stresses are additive (43). Serum magnesium is elevated acutely with cold exposure (decreasing in peripheral tissues) and then declines but does not return to pre-exposure level (236). Cold-acclimated rats have a smaller muscle mass than controls (142). The pelt, fat, skeleton, spleen, and thymus are reduced in size while the liver, intestine, kidney, heart, and adrenals hypertrophy (141). In cats, tissue-slice water and electrolyte distribution shift with cold exposure; circulating thyroid hormone is depleted. Restoration of equilibrium follows replenished hormone production (38). The reaction of rats to drugs changes with cold exposure and cold adaptation (44, 199). Age has an effect on the response in cold to pentobarbital (299). Cold exposure increases the resistance to hemorrhage in dogs (192).

Urinary excretion of norepinephrine is fifteen times that of epinephrine in the rat; there is a fivefold increase in the cold-adapted rat (197, 200). Tissue catecholamines are increased in the adrenal and decreased in the heart (228). Nuclear dry weight of the adrenal medulla increases 58 per cent after cold exposure—an indication of increased cell activity (260). Norepinephrine is implicated in the nonshivering thermogenesis that develops during cold adaptation of the rat. Norepinephrine may be involved in thermal regulation of the neonate in the cat, rat, mouse, and rabbit (229). The liver could not be directly implicated by liver blood flow studies (175) and seemed to be ruled out by studies on functionally eviscerated animals (81). Hannon & Larson (125) have evidence that the liver is involved and that the calorigenic effect is attributable to the mobilization and oxidation of nonesterified fatty acids. Nonshivering thermogenesis does occur in the functionally eviscerated animal (77, 81); infusion of norepinephrine mimics this response (80).

Cold reduces the average length of life of rats (152) (59). There are skin changes in rats and goats exposed to cold (196). Mitotic rate is reduced at the lower temperature (148). Exposure to cold increases the incidence and severity of coronary lesions in rats (271). Truly adaptive changes with exposure to cold may occur in mice (17). The comparative aspects of thermal regulation have been extended to the armadillo (166) and fish (185). The armadillo (166) has a rather large diurnal cycle and a rather marked resistance to cooling.

Intermediary metabolism has received considerable emphasis in the study of prolonged exposure to cold. Tissue slice Qo_2 data are still equivocal. In general, liver Qo_2 is increased with cold exposure depending on the age of the animal (299) and varies with its phylogenetic status (263). Exposure to cold modifies metabolism of mouse liver (287). There are interdependent effects of diet, temperature, and duration of exposure on the major constituents of rat livers (290).

Seventeen enzyme systems have been studied in liver and in muscle of rats (84), yet identification of the tissues involved in cold acclimation and the mechanism of action hormones involved await elucidation. In the rat, liver metabolic acclimation involves three overlapping phases concerned with liver mass and enzyme concentration: an increase in the capacity of the liver to form sugar, an elevated heat-producing capacity, and an increase in liver mass (124). After two weeks or more, oxidative phosphorylation is depressed and the mitochondria of liver are more susceptible to "aging" (203). Adenosine triphosphatase activity is unchanged (123). The depression of lipogenesis induced by cold stress is accompanied by a low rate of triphosphopyridine nucleotide regeneration via hexose monophosphate pathways; this may be a low enzyme effect or an unfavorable co-factor environment (213). Cold exposure increases the turnover of albumin-bound palmitate in rats, not necessarily sparing glucose (79, 82, 83, 214). Liver tissue has increased capacity to oxidize albumin-palmitate in the acclimated rat (125). Plasma glucose turnover is increased in the warm-adapted rat only with cold exposure (78). Glucose uptake and insulin sensitivity of epididymal fat of the rat seem to fluctuate, defying a functional interpretation (54a). Adipose tissue from cold-acclimated rats synthesizes three to five times as much long-chain fatty acid per milligram of tissue protein (244). Metabolically the shivering response to cold exposure does not pose unusual biochemical problems except that shivering metabolism involves no oxygen debt. It is the nonshivering thermogenesis which seems to involve the production of a proper substrate of enzymes and co-factors to allow the rapid response to norepinephrine and a possible interaction with thyroxin (151).

Habituation to cold has been demonstrated experimentally (107). Habituation is defined as the process of forming into a habit or accustoming. The implication is that the process depends on the mind and that it may mean diminution of normal responses or sensations. The physiological basis may be the same as that of learning or a conditioned reflex but habituation differs in being a decrease in a response. The sensations which accompany a 60-second immersion of the human hand at 47 and 4°C were abolished or greatly diminished after repetition of immersions several times daily for 9 to 15 days. The indices used were blood pressure and heart rate. There is a gradual diminution in one day. The habituated response was abolished by 75 mg of chlorpromazine. Anxiety or interest may inhibit the response. It is inferred from calorimetric measurements that there is no change in the blood flow response with time.

Provins & Clarke provided an excellent review of the effects of cold on reaction time, tracking efficiency, tactile discrimination, and muscle strength (252). Tactile discrimination is related to skin temperature. The two-edge threshold deteriorates below 8°C and shows marked impairment below 4°C skin temperature (230, 251). Manual performance (knot tying) decrements increased as the rate of cooling decreased and persisted after rewarming (65).

Behavioral thermoregulation has been studied in rats taught to press a bar to obtain heat. The behavioral response results in maintenance of a fairly constant ($\pm 2°C$) peripheral temperature (300, 301). After acclimation, the bar pressing response for heat is delayed (195).

ANALOGUE STUDIES

Notable contributions toward analogue study of heat transfer in dynamic situations have appeared (127, 128, 311). These may serve to solve problems, to illustrate the magnitude of certain environmental changes, and to point toward specific functional characteristics of the entire system. Iberall (160) extends the model concept, discussing the physiological physics of the human as a potential heat source. The large heat capacity of the system and estimates of thermal resistances suggest that a period of time of the order of three hours may be required for thermal equilibrium. This is a factor often neglected in environmental experiments. Experimental measurements indicate a considerable number of important sustained thermal and thermal power oscillations with periods as short as 90 seconds. These oscillatory phenomena deserve more attention and require a combination of direct and indirect calorimetry to obtain adequate data for analysis. Wissler (306, 307, 308) directed attention to the transient and steady-state temperature distribution in the human. A mathematical model for human heat transfer in the steady state and in the transient state was developed which considers man as a six-element system. The model includes: (a) distribution of metabolic heat generation; (b) the conduction of heat in the tissue; (c) the conviction of heat by flowing blood; (d) the loss of heat by radiation, conduction, and evaporation; (e) the loss of heat through the respiratory tract; (f) the storage of heat in tissue and blood; (g) countercurrent heat exchange between large arteries and veins; (h) sweating; (i) shivering; and (j) the conditions of the environment. Computed values compare favorably with experimental results. Aschoff & Wever (11) follow a similar line of reasoning in developing schematic isotherms at high and low room temperature to illustrate the participation of the core in cooling. This article also includes a summary of the relative density of cold points, and of the heat production of various organs at rest and during work expressed in calories per gram as well as per cent of the total. These same authors (14) produced model experiments in countercurrent heat exchange for a human extremity and compared model cooling (Newtonian) with actual experiments (12). Transport of heat through the skin is anisotropic (13). The respiratory tract is an important part of calculations of heat exchange and serves to conserve heat and water based on principles of heat and water exchange (294).

Molnar evaluated wind chill equations (227), and Lentz & Hart (201) reviewed the question of heat transfer in reporting on the effect of wind and moisture on heat loss through the fur of newborn caribou. Our knowledge of principles for clothing in various climates is empirical in nature (288).

HYPOTHERMIA

Several aspects of hypothermia were reviewed in a recent British symposium: technique of induced hypothermia (218); experimental deep hypothermia (183); profound hypothermia in cardiac surgery (86); circulation in hypothermia (68); metabolism in hypothermia (93); hormones in hypothermia (30); central nervous system in hypothermia (208); temperature effects on response to drugs (54, 105); and temperature effects on sensitivity to irradiation (302). Reports of work on hypothermia divide roughly into those describing successful surgical ventures (29, 235), techniques, and studies of the physiological parameters. The first two have had phenomenal success in light of the dearth of information on the third. Parenthetically, skeletal, esophageal, rectal, and muscle temperatures decrease during conventional surgery (310). The rationale of hypothermia is simply stated as a reduction of stress (34). Accidental hypothermia (75° to 90°F) results in a number of complications during recovery (104). Pulmonary edema and ateletasis are found in dogs cooled to termination (56). Pulmonary hemorrhages have been found in cold-injured neonates (40). A single case of transient pulmonary insufficiency caused by cold has been reported (154). Carbon dioxide acts as an anesthetic agent preventing increase in oxygen uptake with cooling (281), but as the percentage of carbon dioxide increases to 20 per cent, desaturation of blood occurs. Carbon dioxide is a factor that contributes to successful reanimation (223, 282). Beaton (19) reports that a relative hypoxia exists in hypothermic rats: that is, available oxygen is insufficient to meet even the reduced metabolic activity.

During hypothermia, glucose tolerance tests in rabbits give evidence of failure to metabolize glucose although the respiratory quotient indicated that some glucose was oxidized (20). There is a hyperglycemia during hypothermia which may be due to intrinsic epinephrine release (184). Other workers report a decrease in adrenomedullary function during artificial hypothermia, eliminating epinephrine as a possible agent causing fibrillation (188). Kidney function changes with temperature. Creatinine clearance and para-aminohippuric acid clearance fall as a function of temperature between 38 and 22°C (28).

In dogs subjected to blood stream cooling, the temperature of midesophagus, heart, liver, and kidney fell rapidly while muscle cooled more slowly. Brain temperature can be estimated as the mean of muscle and midesophageal temperature, and midesophageal temperature may be predicted (96). Temperature variations of 10°C have been observed in the heart (95). Total oxygen consumption falls in an exponential fashion when plotted against muscle temperature (129). The cerebral oxygen consumption of the monkey varies logarithmically in a linear fashion with the reciprocal of the absolute temperature (27). Cerebral oxygen consumption studies in man showed a progressive rise in respiratory quotient, associated with a lack of uptake of glucose (3), when blood flow was occluded.

Anesthetics influence cardiac activity as well as hypothermia. Frances et al. (99) found retrograde V-A conduction in 13 of 22 dogs at normal temperature with pentobarbital. After cooling, 8 of the 9 remaining developed V-A conduction. Artificial hypothermia lowers circulating blood volume without a change in plasma protein (187). On rewarming, the surviving dogs showed increased blood volume. Therapeutic measures (atropine, hexonium, dimedrol) and addition of glucose, vitamin C, and vitamin B_1 to perfusing blood are of aid in restoring phosphorus and phosphate compounds of brain and heart during and after hypothermia (254).

Vagal inhibition of the heart sharply decreases heart rate at all frequencies to a body temperature of 12°C (2) [the relative effect seems greater as temperature is lowered (211)] and disappears reversibly between 12 and 8°C. At low temperatures (24 to 27°C) there is a reduction in threshold to square wave pulses and a prolongation of the minimal gradient requirement (289).

Hypothermia (27 to 28°C) potentiates the pressor response to epinephrine and norepinephrine (265). The hypothermic dog retains reflex action to hypoxic or carotid occlusion stimuli at a level below normal (265). According to Stevenson et al. (278), conduction of nerve is affected more than synaptic transmission between 37 and 27°C. There is an augmentation of the evoked potential in the dorsal column between 33 and 25°C. At 23°C the evoked potentials from the posteroventral lateral nucleus of the thalamus and the periaqueductile midbrain reticular formation are depressed, the midbrain reticular formation being most sensitive (278). A transient increase in cortical excitability develops between 34 and 28°C in the cat and rabbit (the EEG shows convulsive patterns). The primary spikes of the direct cortical response and of the visual cortical response increase in amplitude (298). Spontaneous EEG activity in the monkey disappears at 23°C with pentobarbital anesthesia and at 19°C with ether anesthesia; heart rate and respiratory rate decrease similarly regardless of anesthetic. Bemegride activated the EEG in hypothermia (51).

There is an increased potassium in the heart in hypothermia (248), and the lethal level of potassium is lowered (75). Hypothermia inhibits potassium influx and efflux equally between 30 and 20°C; as temperatures approach 10°C, the effect on influx increases (186). Plasma magnesium concentration increases in hypothemia (232). The upper limit of tolerable ischemia for the deeply hypothermic heart is about one hour. Defibrillation is best attempted at 28°C (270).

HIBERNATION

Hibernation has received exhaustive review (209, 210, 215). It is of interest also that poikilothermic animals resist cold (264). The critical factors in initiation of hibernation and arousal are still elusive. Hibernators are of considerable experimental interest in the study of comparative effects of cold exposure with and without hibernation. The highly significant increase in clotting time during hibernation probably arises from decreased prothrombin synthesis and appearance of a heparinoid substance (76). Hepatic function is not impaired by lowered body temperature (130). Young and old rats differ from ground squirrels in response to cooling. The ratio of metabolic rate is 1:3:6 and the ratio of survival at 10°C is 1:4:14 when the comparison is adult rat: young rat: ground squirrel (249). Cooled hibernators differ from the hibernation state in respect to metabolic rate, blood pressure, and pulse rate (250).

During arousal a tiny hibernator (7 to 16 g birchmouse) can increase metabolism 25-fold in 30 minutes, increasing body temperatures 1°C per minute (167). The EEG of this animal shows a burst of activity below 10°C (9).

Adenosine triphosphatase is insufficient to maintain homeothermy in the hibernating hamster near 0°C. Acylphosphatase may provide for thermogenesis both at low temperature and during the early part of arousal (225). During arousal, release of energy from phosphate compounds provides heat to a point where glycolysis and respiration become important in thermogenesis (226). Knowledge of the regulative processes of the hibernant would be increased by the combination of direct and indirect calorimetry particularly during arousal.

COLD INJURY

Cold injury literature has been summarized by Carlson & Thursh (61)· Trauma and vascular diseases from cold injury continue to be studied (284), and experimental immersion foot has received extensive study and description in Montgomery's laboratory. Immersion of the leg at 3°C for three hours leads to neurological and vascular damage on rewarming (267); immersion at 2°C results in an immediate decrease in blood flow to chilled muscle. Transient movement increases blood flow (266). Prior arteriosclerotic disease increases susceptibility to cold injury (284). There is histological evidence for cellular adaptation to cold injury (144).

LITERATURE CITED

1. Abramson, D. J., Bell, Y., Rejal, H. T., Burnett, C., Fleischer, C. J., and Tuck, S., Jr., *Am. J. Phys. Med.*, 39, 87–95 (1960)
2. Adolph, E. F., and Nail, R. L., *J. Appl. Physiol.*, 15, 911–13 (1960)
3. Adams, J. E., *J. Neurosurg.*, 18, 168–74 (1961)
4. Alleston, C. W., Egli, G. E., and Ulberg, L. C., *J. Appl. Physiol.*, 16, 253–56 (1961)
5. Anderson, B., Persson, N., and Ström, L. *Acta Physiol. Scand.*, 50, 54–61 (1960)
6. Andersen, K. L., Bolstad, A., Loyning, Y., and Irving, L., *J. Appl. Physiol.*, 15, 645–48 (1960)
7. Andersen, K. L., Loyning, Y., Nelms, J. D., Wilson, O., Fox, R. H., and Bolstad, A., *J. Appl. Physiol.*, 15, 649–53 (1960)
8. Andersen, K. L., and Hellstrom, B., *Acta Physiol. Scand.*, 50, 88–94 (1960)
9. Andersen, P., Johansen, K., and Krog, J., *Am. J. Physiol.*, 199, 535–38 (1960)
10. Arnett, E. L., and Watts, D. T., *J. Appl. Physiol.*, 15, 499–500 (1960)
11. Aschoff, J., and Wever, R., *Naturwissenschaften*, 45, 477 (1958)
12. Aschoff, J., and Wever, R., *Arch. ges. Physiol.*, 269, 207–13 (1959)
13. Aschoff, J., and Wever, R., *Arch. ges. Physiol.*, 269, 130–34 (1959)
14. Aschoff, J., and Wever, R., *Z. ges. exptl. Med.*, 130, 385 (1958)
15. Aschoff, J., *Klin. Wochschr.*, 36, 193–202 (1958)
16. Bargeton, D., and Chassain, A., *J. physiol. (Paris)*, 52, 16–17 (1960)
17. Barnett, S. A., *Nature*, 188, 500–1 (1960)
18. Bass, D. E., in *Conf. on Cold Injury, Trans. 6th*, 317–39 (1960)
19. Beaton, J. R., *Can. J. Biochem. and Physiol.*, 39, 1–8 (1962)
20. Beckford, A. F., and Mottram, R. F., *Clin. Sci.*, 19, 345–59 (1960)
21. Benzinger, T. H., in *Symposium on Temperature, Its Measurement and Control in Science and Industry, III* (Hardy, J. O., Ed., *Am. Inst. Phys., New York*, 1961)
22. Benzinger, T. H., *Federation Proc.*, 19, Suppl. 5, 32–41 (1960)
23. Benzinger, T. H., *Federation Proc.*, 20, 213 (1961)
24. Benzinger, T. H., *Proc. Natl. Acad. Sci. US*, 45, 645–59 (1959)
25. Benzinger, T. H., *Sci. Am.*, 204, 134–47 (1961)
26. Benzinger, T. H., Pratt, A. W., and Kitzinger, C., *Proc. Natl. Acad. Sci. US*, 47, 730 (1961)
27. Bering, E. A., Jr., *Am. J. Physiol.*, 200, 417–20 (1961)
28. Bettge, S., Voss, R., Rothange, C. F., and L'Allemand, H., *Klin. Wochschr.*, 38, 1182–86 (1960)
29. Bigelow, W. G., and Heimbecker, R. O., *Can. J. Surg.*, 4, 50–55 (1960)
30. Bigelow, W. G., and Sidlofsky, S., *Brit. Med. Bull.*, 17, 56–60 (1960)
31. Billingham, J., and Kerslake, D. McK., *Flying Personnel Research Committee Memo 133, Air Ministry, Great Britain* (1960)
32. Billingham, J., and Kerslake, D. McK., *Flying Personnel Research Committee Memo 134, Air Ministry, Great Britain* (1960)
33. Billingham, J., and Hughes, T. L., *Flying Personnel Research Committee 1109, Air Ministry, Great Britain* (1960)
34. Blair, E., *Clin. Pharmacol. Therap.*, 1, 758–68 (1960)
35. Bligh, J., *J. Physiol. (London)*, 146, 142–51 (1953)
36. Blair, D. A., Glover, W. E., and Roddie, I. C., *J. Physiol. (London)*, 153, 232–38 (1960)
37. Boatman, J. B., *Am. J. Physiol.*, 196, 983–86 (1959)
38. Boatman, J. R., Pisarcik, P. A., and Rabinovitz, M. J., *Am. J. Physiol.*, 199, 256–60 (1960)
39. Bognar, A., Hamar, N., Molnar, B., and Tizavolgyi, G., *Acta Med. Acad. Sci. Hung.*, 16, 19–23 (1960)
40. Bower, B. D., Jones, L. F., and Weeks, M. M., *Brit. Med. J.*, No. 5169, 303–9 (1960)
41. Bowman, K., *Am. Med. Exptl. Fenn.*, 38, 39–44 (1960)
42. Boyer, J. T., Fraser, J. R., and Doyle, D. E., *Clin. Sci.* 19, 539–50 (1960)
43. Brailovski, S. A., and Ledintsov, Y. K., *Bull. Exptl. Biol. Med. (USSR) (Engl. Transl.)*, 48, 1365–68 (1959)
44. Braun, H. A., and Lusky, L. M., *Toxicol. Appl. Pharmacol.*, 2, 458–63 (1960)
45. Brendel, W., *Arch. ges. Physiol.*, 270, 607–47 (1960)
46. *Brit. Med. Bull.*, 17, 1–78 (1961)
47. Brobeck, J. R., *Recent Progr. in Hormone Research*, 16, 439–66 (1960)

48. Brody, S., *Bioenergetics and Growth* (Reinhold Publishing Co., New York, 1945)
49. Brouha, L., Smith, P. E., Delanne, R., and Maxfield, M. E., *J. Appl. Physiol.*, **16**, 133–40 (1961)
50. Brück, K., and Brück, M., *Klin. Wochschr.*, **38**, 1125–60 (1960)
51. Bryce-Smith, R., Epstein, H. G., and Glees, P., *J. Appl. Physiol.*, **15**, 440–44 (1960)
52. Buchanan, A. R., *Functional Neuro—Anatomy*, 215 (Lea & Febiger, Philadelphia, Pa., 1948)
53. Bulzakov, R., and Andjus, R. K., *J. physiol.* (*Paris*), **52**, 40–41 (1960)
54. Burns, J. H., *Brit. Med. Bull.*, **17**, 66–69 (1961)
54a. Candela, J. L. R., *Med. Exptl.*, **3**, 84–87 (1960)
55. Cannon, P., and Keatinge, W. R., *J. Physiol.* (*London*), **154**, 329–44 (1961)
56. Caranna, L. J., Neustein, H. B., and Swan, H., *Arch. Surg.*, **82**, 147–52 (1961)
57. Carlson, L. D., *Federation Proc.*, **19** (II), Suppl. 5, 25–29 (1960)
58. Carlson, L. D., *J. Occupational Med.*, **2**, 129–31 (1960)
59. Carlson, L. D., and Jackson, B. H., *Radiation Research*, **11**, 509–19 (1959)
60. Carlson, L. D., and Thursh, H., *Tech. Rept. 59-18* (Arctic Aeromed. Lab., Ladd Air Force Base, Alaska, 1960)
61. Carlson, L. D., and Thursh, H., *Tech. Rept. 59-20* (Arctic Aeromed. Lab., Fort Wainwright, Alaska, 1960)
62. Chatonnet, J., *J. physiol.* (*Paris*), **51**, 319–78 (1959)
63. Chatonnet, J., Tanche, M., and Cabanac, J. L., *J. physiol.* (*Paris*), **52**, 48–49 (1960)
64. Chatonnet, J., and Tanche, M., *J. physiol.* (*Paris*), **52**, 48–49 (1960)
65. Clark, R. E., and Cohen, A., *J. Appl. Physiol.*, **15**, 496–98 (1960)
66. Cohen, M. J., Landgren, S., Ström, L., and Zotterman, Y., *Acta Physiol. Scand.*, **40**, 202, 210 (1950)
67. Coles, D. R., and Cooper, K. E., *J. Physiol.* (*London*), **145**, 241–50 (1959)
68. Cooper, K. E., *Brit. Med. Bull.*, **17**, 48–51 (1960)
69. Cramer, K. R., Divine, T. F., Ohm, A. F. B., and Patterson, W., *WADC Tech. Note 60-145* (1960)
70. Cross, K. W., Dawes, G. S., and Mott, J. C., *J. Physiol.* (*London*), **146**, 316–43 (1949)
71. Cullingham, P. J., *J. Anat.*, **94**, 363–74 (1960)
72. D'Angelo, S. A., *Am. J. Physiol.*, **199**, 701–6 (1960)
73. Davis, T. R. A., in *Conf. on Cold Injury, Trans. 6th*, 223–70 (1960)
74. Davis, T. R. A., and Johnston, D. R., *J. Appl. Physiol.*, **16**, 231–35 (1961)
75. Deavers, E. S., Huggins, R. A., and Hoff, H. E., *J. Appl. Physiol.*, **16**, 250–53 (1961)
76. Deynes, A., and Carter, J. D., *Nature*, **190**, 450–52 (1961)
77. Depocas, F., *Can. J. Biochem. and Physiol.*, **36**, 691–99 (1958)
78. Depocas, F., *Can. J. Biochem. and Physiol.*, **37**, 175–81 (1959)
79. Depocas, F., *Can. J. Biochem. and Physiol.*, **37**, 285–95 (1959)
80. Depocas, F., *Can. J. Biochem. and Physiol.*, **38**, 107–14 (1960)
81. Depocas, F., *Federation Proc.*, **19**, 19–24 (1960)
82. Depocas, F., *Federation Proc.*, **19**, 106–9 (1960)
83. Depocas, F., and Masseroni, R., *Am. J. Physiol.*, **199**, 1051–55 (1960)
84. Depocas, F., *Brit. Med. Bull.*, **17**, 25–31 (1960)
85. Donhoffer, S., Farkas, M., Hang-Laslo, A., Jarai, I., and Szegvári, G., *Arch. ges. Physiol.*, **268**, 273–80 (1959)
86. Drew, C. E., *Brit. Med. Bull.*, **17**, 37–42 (1960)
86a. Durrer, J. L., and Hannon, J. P., *Proc. XII Alaska Sci. Conf.* (1960)
87. Eagan, C. J., *Federation Proc.*, **20**(I), 210 (1961)
88. Edholm, O. G., *Federation Proc.*, **19**(II), Suppl. 5, 3–8 (1960)
89. Edwards, M., and Burton, A. C., *J. Appl. Physiol.*, **15**, 201–8 (1960)
90. Edwards, M., and Burton, A. C., *J. Appl. Physiol.*, **15**, 209–11 (1960)
91. Elsner, R. W., Andersen, K. L., and Nermansen, L., *J. Appl. Physiol.*, **15**, 659–61 (1960)
92. Elsner, R. W., Nelms, J. D., and Irving, L., *J. Appl. Physiol.*, **15**, 662–66 (1960)
93. Fairley, H. B., *Brit. Med. Bull.*, **17**, 52–55 (1960)
94. Findlay, J. D., and Ingram, D. L., *J. Physiol.* (*London*), **155**, 72–85 (1961)
95. Fisher, B., and Fedor, E. J., *Proc. Soc. Exptl. Biol. Med.*, **106**, 275–77 (1961)

96. Forrester, A. C., and Brown, J., *Anesthesia*, **16**(II), 129 (1961)

97. Fox, R. H., *Brit. Med. Bull.*, **17**, 14–18 (1960)

98. Fox, R. H., and Hilton, S. M., *J. Physiol.* (*London*), **142**, 219–31 (1958)

99. Francis, C. K., Campbell, C. A., and Hoff, H. E., *J. Appl. Physiol.*, **15**, 1035–40 (1960)

100. Freeman, W. J., and Davis, D. D., *Am. J. Physiol.*, **197**, 145–48 (1958)

101. Fregley, M. J., *Am. J. Physiol.*, **199**, 437–44 (1960)

102. Fregley, M. J., Iampietro, P. F., and Otis, A. B., *J. Appl. Physiol.*, **16**, 127–32 (1961)

103. Froese, G., and Burton, A. C., *J. Appl. Physiol.*, **10**, 235–41 (1957)

104. Fruchan, A. E., *Arch. Internal Med.*, **106**, 218–29 (1960)

105. Fuhrman, G. J., and Fuhrman, F. A., *Ann. Rev. Pharmacol.*, **1**, 65–78 (1961)

106. Fusco, M., Hardy, J. D., and Hammel, H. T., *Am. J. Physiol.*, **200**, 572–80 (1961)

107. Glaser, E. M., Hall, M. S., and Whittow, G. C., *J. Physiol.* (*London*), **146**, 152–64 (1959)

108. Gold, J., *Aerospace Med.*, **31**, 933–40 (1960)

109. Gold, J., *J. Am. Med. Assoc.*, **173**, 1175–82 (1958)

110. Gold, J., *J. Appl. Physiol.*, **16**, 144–52 (1961)

111. Goldsmith, R., *J. Appl. Physiol.*, **15**, 776–80 (1960)

112. Goldsmith, R., and Lewis, H. E., *J. Occupational Med.*, **2**, 118–22 (1960)

113. Gorbatsevich, L. I., *Pavlov J. Higher Nervous Activity*, **9**, 95–102 (1959)*

114. Hale, H. B., and Mefferd, R. B., Jr., *J. Appl. Physiol.*, **16**, 123–26 (1961)

115. Hale, H. B., and Mefferd, R. B., Jr., *J. Appl. Physiol.*, **16**, 243–47 (1961)

116. Hall, J. F., and Polte, J. W., *J. Appl. Physiol.*, **15**, 1027–30 (1960)

117. Hallwachs, O., *Arch ges. Physiol.*, **271**, 748–60 (1960)

118. Hammel, H. T., Wyndam, C. H., and Hardy, J. D., *Am. J. Physiol.*, **194**, 99–108 (1958)

119. Hammel, H. T., Hardy, J. D., and Fusco, M. M., *Am. J. Physiol.*, **198**, 481 (1960)

120. Han, P. W., and Brobeck, J. R., *Am. J. Physiol.*, **200**, 707–10 (1961)

121. Han, P. W., and Brobeck, J. R., *Am. J. Physiol.*, **200**, 703–6 (1961)

122. Hannon, J. P., and Viereck, E. G., *Symposia on Arctic Biol. and Med.,*

I Neural Factors, II Temperature Regulation, Arctic Aeromed. Lab. USAF (AAC), APO 731 (Seattle, Wash., 1960)

123. Hannon, J. P., *Am. J. Physiol.*, **196**, 890–92 (1959)

124. Hannon, J. P., and Vaughan, D. A., *Am. J. Physiol.*, **200**, 94–98 (1961)

125. Hannon, J. P., and Larson, A., *Federation Proc.*, **20**,(I), 209 (1961)

126. Hannon, J. P., Larson, A. M., Drury, H. F., Vaughan, D. A., and Vaughan, L. N., *US Armed Forces Med. J.*, **11**, 676–81 (1960)

127. Hardy, J. D., *NADC-MA-5413* (US Naval Air Development Center Johnsville, Pa., 1954)

128. Hardy, J. D., *NADC-MA-6015* (US Naval Air Development Center, Johnsville, Pa., 1960)

129. Harper, A. M., Bain, W. H., Glass, H. I., Glover, M. M., and Mackay, W. A., *Surg., Gynecol. Obstet.*, **112**, 519–25 (1961)

130. Harrington, J. P., and Nordonne, R. M., *Am. J. Physiol.*, **196**, 910–12 (1959)

131. Hart, J. S., *Brit. Med. Bull.*, **17**, 19–24 (1960)

132. Hart, J. S., in *Conf. on Cold Injury, Trans. 6th*, 271–303 (1960)

133. Hart, J. S., *Rev. can. biol.*, **16**, 133–74 (1957)

134. Hasselman, M., Schaff, G., and Metz, B., *Compt. rend. soc. biol.*, **154**, 197–201 (1960)

135. Heberling, E. J., and Adams, T., *J. Appl. Physiol.*, **16**, 226–31 (1961)

136. Hellstrom, B., and Andersen, K. L., *J. Appl. Physiol.*, **15**, 771–75 (1960)

137. Henschel, A., in *Conf. on Cold Injury, Trans. 6th*, 303–17 (1960)

138. Hensel, H., *Ann. Rev. Physiol.*, **21**, 91–116 (1959)

139. Hensel, H., and Zotterman, Y., *J. Physiol.* (*London*), **115**, 16–24 (1951)

140. Hensel, H., and Witt, I., *J. Physiol.* (*London*), **148**, 180–87 (1959)

141. Héroux, O., and Gridgeman, N. T., *Can. J. Biochem. and Physiol.*, **36**, 209–16 (1958)

142. Héroux, O., *Can. J. Biochem. and Physiol.*, **36**, 289–93 (1958)

143. Héroux, O., Depocas, F., and Hart, J. S., *Can. J. Biochem. and Physiol.*, **37**, 473–78 (1959)

144. Héroux, O., *Can. J. Biochem. and Physiol.*, **37**, 811–19 (1959)

145. Héroux, O., *Can. J. Biochem. and Physiol.*, **37**, 1247–53 (1959)

146. Héroux, O., and Schonbaum, E., *Can.*

J. Biochem. and Physiol., **37**, 1255–61 (1959)

147. Héroux, O., and Campbell, J. S., *Can. J. Biochem. and Physiol.*, **37**, 1263–69 (1959)

148. Héroux, O., *Can. J. Biochem. and Physiol.*, **38**, 135–42 (1960)

149. Héroux, O., *Can. J. Biochem. and Physiol.*, **38**, 518–21 (1960)

150. Héroux, O., and Willmer, J., *Can. J. Biochem. and Physiol.*, **38**, 1215–16 (1960)

151. Héroux, O., *Federation Proc.*, **19**, 82–85 (1960)

152. Héroux, O., and Campbell, J. S., *Lab. Invest.*, **9**, 305–15 (1960)

153. Holmes, R. L., Newman, P. P., and Wolstencroft, J. H., *J. Physiol. (London)*, **152**, 93–98 (1960)

154. Houk, V. N., *US Armed Forces Med. J.*, **10**, 1354–57 (1959)

155. Horvath, S. M., Ed., *Conf. on Cold Injury, Trans. 6th* (1960)

156. Hsieh, A. C., and Ti, K. W., *J. Nutrition*, **72**, 283–88 (1960)

157. Hunter, J. C., *Military Med.*, **126**, 273–81 (1961)

158. Hyman, C., Arthur, J. D., Trotter, A. D., Jr., Humphreys, P. C., and Winsor, T., *J. Appl. Physiol.*, **16**, 257–61 (1961)

159. Iampietro, P. F., Goldman, R. F., Buskirk, E. R., and Bass, D. E., *J. Appl. Physiol.*, **14**, 798–800 (1959)

160. Iberall, A. S., *J. Basic Engineering (Trans ASME)*, 96–102, 103–12 (March 1960)

161. Ivanov, K. P., *Sechenov Fiziol. Zhur. SSSR*, **46**, 639–47 (1960)*

162. Irving, L., in *Conf. on Cold Injury, Trans. 6th*, 339–61 (1960)

163. Irving, L. Andersen, K. L., Bolstad, A., Elsner. R., Hildes, J. A., Loyning, Y., Nelms, J. D., Peyton, L. J., and Whaley, R. D., *J. Appl. Physiol.*, **15**, 635–44 (1960)

164. Irving, L., *Nature*, **185**, 572–74 (1960)

165. Ivanov, K. P., and Den Su, *Sechenov Physiol. J. USSR (Engl. Transl.)*, **46**, 76–84 (1960)

166. Johansen, K., *Physiol. Zoöl.*, **34**, 126–44 (1961)

167. Johansen, K., and Krog, J., *Am. J. Physiol.*, **196**, 1200–4 (1959)

168. Juszkiewicz, T., *Am. J. Vet. Research*, **22**, 549–52 (1961)

169. Juszkiewicz, T., and Jones, L. M., *Am. J. Vet. Research*, **22**, 553–57 (1961)

170. Juszkiewicz, T., *Am. J. Vet. Research*, **22**, 537–43 (1961)

171. Juszkiewicz, T., and Jones, L. M., *Am. J. Vet. Research*, **22**, 544–48 (1961)

172. Kanter, G. S., *Am. J. Physiol.*, **196**, 619–24 (1959)

173. Kanter, G. S., *Am. J. Physiol.*, **199**, 261–64 (1960)

174. Kaufmann, W., Betz, E., Hundeshagen, H., Marx, H. H., Schlitter, J. G., Stein, E., and Schochmeich, P., *Verhandl. deut. Ges. Kreislaufforsch.*, **25**, 271–77 (1959)

175. Kawahata, A., and Carlson, L. D., *Proc. Soc. Exptl. Biol. Med.*, **101**, 303–6 (1959)

176. Keatinge, W. R., *J. Physiol. (London)*, **153**, 166–78 (1960)

177. Keatinge, W. R., and Evans, M., *Quart. J. Exptl. Physiol.*, **46**, 83–94 (1961)

178. Keatinge, W. R., *Quart. J. Exptl. Physiol.*, **46**, 69–82 (1961)

179. Keller, A. D., *Ann. N. Y. Acad. Sci.*, **80**, 457–74 (1959)

180. Keller, A. D., *Federation Proc.*, **19**, Suppl. 5, 30–32 (1960)

181. Keller, A. D., in *Conf. on Cold Injury, Trans. 6th*, 13–54 (1960)

182. Keller, A. D., *Physiol. Revs.*, **40**, Suppl. 4, 116–35 (1960)

183. Kenyon, J. R., *Brit. Med. Bull.*, **17**, 43–47 (1960)

184. Kilburn, K. H., *Am. J. Physiol.*, **199**, 955–58 (1960)

185. Kinne, O., *Physiol. Zoöl.*, **33**, 288–317 (1960)

186. Klein, R. L., and Evans, M. L., *Am. J. Physiol.*, **200**, 735–40 (1961)

187. Klussmann, F. W., Luetcke, A., and Koenig, W., *Arch. ges. Physiol.*, **268**, 515–29 (1959)

188. Korostovtseva, N. V., *Fiziol. Zhur. SSSR*, **45**, 1118–23 (1959)*

189. Krause, M., and Strzoda, L., *Arch. Internal Physiol.*, **68**, 623–32 (1960)

190. Kreider, M. B., *J. Appl. Physiol.*, **16**, 239–43 (1961)

191. Krog, J., Folkow, B., Fox, R. H., and Andersen, K. L., *J. Appl. Physiol.*, **15**, 654–58 (1960)

192. Kuhn, L. A., Page, L. B., Turner, J. K., and Frieden, J., *Am. J. Physiol.*, **196**, 715–18 (1959)

193. Kumar, S., and Sinha, A. S. *Indian J. Physiol. Pharmacol.*, **4**, 179–81 (1960)

194. *Lancet*, **II**, 475–76 (1960)

195. Laties, U. G., and Weiss, B., *Science*, **131**, 1891–92 (1960)

196. LeBlanc, J., *Am. J. Physiol.*, **196**, 1042–44 (1959)

197. LeBlanc, J. A., and Nadean, G., *Can.*

J. Biochem. and Physiol., **39**, 215–17 (1961)

198. LeBlanc, J., Hildes, J. A., and Héroux, O., *J. Appl. Physiol.*, **15**, 1031–34 (1960)

199. LeBlanc, J., *Proc. Soc. Exptl. Biol. Med.*, **105**, 109–11 (1960)

200. Leduc, J., *Acta Physiol. Scand.*, **51**, 94–95 (1961)

201. Lentz, C. P., and Hart, J. S., *Can. J. Zool.*, **38**, 679–87 (1960)

202. Lewis, H. E., Masterson, J. P., and Rosenbaum, S., *Clin. Sci.*, **15**, 551–62 (1960)

203. Lianides, S. P., and Beyer, R. E., *Am. J. Physiol.*, **199**, 836–40 (1960)

204. Lim, T. P. K., and Gordins, F. S., *Am. J. Physiol.*, **180**, 445 (1955)

205. Lim, T. P. K., *J. Appl. Physiol.*, **15**, 567–74 (1960)

206. Linzell, J. L., and Bligh, J., *Nature*, **190**, 173 (1961)

207. Lippold, O. C., Nicholls, J. G., and Redfearn, J. W., *J. Physiol. (London)*, **153**, 218–31 (1960)

208. Lougheed, W. M., *Brit. Med. Bull.*, **17**, 61–65 (1960)

209. Lyman, C. P., in *Conf. on Cold Injury, Trans. 6th*, 57–89 (1960)

210. Lyman, C. P., and Dawe, A. R., *Bull. Mus. Comp. Zool.*, **124**, 1–549 (1960)

211. Mainwood, G. W., *J. Physiol. (London)*, **146**, 205–16 (1959)

212. Malhotra, M. S., Ramaswamy, S. S., and Ray, S. N., *J. Appl. Physiol.*, 769–70 (1960)

213. Masoro, E. J., *Am. J. Physiol.*, **199**, 449–52 (1960)

214. Masironi, R., and Depocas, F., *Can. J. Biochem. and Physiol.*, **39**, 219–24 (1961)

215. Matthewes, L. H., *Brit. Med. Bull*, **17**, 9–13 (1960)

216. MacCannon, D. M., and Fitzman, D. D., *Federation Proc.*, **20**, Pt. 1., 213 (1961)

217. McCook, R. D., Peiss, C. N., and Randall, W. C., *Federation Proc.*, **20**, 213 (1961)

218. McMillan, I. K. R., and Machill, E. S., *Brit. Med. Bull.*, **17**, 32–36 (1960)

219. Mestian, G., Jarai, I., Szegvári, G., and Farkas, M., *Acta Physiol. Acad. Sci. Hung.*, **17**, 69–73 (1960)

220. Milan, F. A., and Rodahl, K., *AAL Tech. Rept. 60-11* (Arctic Aeromed. Lab., Fort Wainwright, Alaska, 1961)

221. Milan, F. A., *AAL Tech. Rept. 60-10* (Arctic Aeromed. Lab., Fort Wainwright, Alaska, 1961)

222. Milan, F. A., Elsner, R. W., and

223. Miller, J. A., and Miller, F. S., *Am. J. Physiol.*, **196**, 1218–23 (1958)

224. Minard, D., *Military Med.*, **126**, 261–72 (1961)

225. Mokrasch, L. C., *Am. J. Physiol.*, **199**, 950–54 (1960)

226. Mokrasch, L. C., *Experientia*, **16**, 318 (1960)

227. Molnar, G. W., in *Conf. on Cold Injury Trans. 6th*, 175–223 (1960)

228. Moore, K. E., Calvert, D. N., and Brody, T. M., *Proc. Soc. Exptl. Biol. Med.*, **106**, 816–18 (1961)

229. Moore, R. E., and Underwood, M. C., *Lancet*, **I**, 1277–78 (1960)

230. Morton, R., and Provins, K. A., *J. Appl. Physiol.*, **15**, 149–54 (1960)

231. Moss, A. J., and Bradley, B. E., *J. Appl. Physiol.*, **15**, 445–48 (1960)

232. Moussa, S. L., and Boba, A., *Am. J. Physiol.*, **199**, 1090–92 (1960)

233. Mullin, C. S., *Am. J. Psychiat.*, **117**, 323–25 (1960)

234. Nakayama, T., and Takagi, K., *Japan. J. Physiol.*, **9**, 359–64 (1959)

235. Negovski, V. A., Soboleva, V. I., Gurvich, N. L., Kiseleva, K. S., and Machivariani, S. S., *Bull. Exptl. Biol. Med. (USSR) (Engl. Transl.)*, **48**, 1338–41 (1959)

236. Neubeiser, R. E., Platner, W. S., and Shields, J. L., *J. Appl. Physiol.*, **16**, 247–50 (1961)

237. Newburg, L. H., *Physiology of Heat Regulation*, Chap. 5 (W. B. Saunders & Co., Philadelphia, Pa., 1949)

238. Newman, M. T., *Ann. N.Y. Acad. Sci.*, **91**, 617–33 (1961)

239. Newman, P. P., and Walsencraft, J. H., *J. Physiol. (London)*, **152**, 87–92 (1960)

240. Norman, P. S., Kreider, M. B., and Iampietro, P. F., *J. Appl. Physiol.*, **15**, 261–64 (1960)

241. *Nutrition Rev.*, **18**, 179–81 (1960)

242. Pace, N., *Am. Soc. Heating & Vent. Engrs.*, *65th Ann. Meeting* (1959)

243. Pace, N., in *Conf. on Cold Injury, Trans. 6th*, 141–75 (1960)

244. Patkin, J. K., and Masoro, E. J., *Am. J. Physiol.*, **200**, 847–50 (1961)

245. Pepler, R. D., *APU 286/58, Appl. Psychol. Research Unit, Med. Research Council* (Cambridge, Engl., 1958)

246. Pepler, R. D., *Appl. Psychol. Research Unit, Med. Research Council* (Cambridge, Engl., 1958)

247. Petrovic, V. M., and Andjus, R. K,. *J. physiol. (Paris)*, **52**, 191–92 (1960)

248. Pogosova, A. V., *Doklady—Biol. Sci. Sect.* (Engl. Transl.), **128**, 886–88 (1960)

249. Popovic, V., *Am. J. Physiol.*, **199**, 463–66 (1960)

250. Popovic, V., *Am. J. Physiol.*, **199**, 467–71 (1960)

251. Provins, K. A., and Morton, R., *J. Appl. Physiol.*, **15**, 155–60 (1960)

252. Provins, K. A., and Clarke, R. S. J., *J. Occupational Med.*, **2**, 169–76 (1960)

253. Pugh, L. G. C. E., Edholm, O. G., Fox, R. H., Wolff, H. S., Hervey, G. R. Hammond, W. H., Tanner, J. M., and Whitehouse, R. H., *Clin. Sci.*, **19**, 257–73 (1960)

254. Raiko, Z. A., Petrov, I. R., and Kudritskaia, T. E., *Fiziol. Zhur. SSSR*, **45**, 1489–96 (1959)*

256. Reichlin, S., *Endocrinology*, **66**, 340–54 (1960)

257. Reubourn, E. T., *J. Psychosomatic Research*, **4**, 149–75 (1960)

258. Ringer, F. J., Kundt, H. W., Hensel, H., and Brück, K., *Arch. ges. Physiol.*, **269**, 240–47 (1959)

259. Rodahl, K., *J. Occupational Med.*, **2**, 177–82 (1960)

260. Roels, H., and Lagasse, A., *Exptl. Cell Research*, **23**, 408–9 (1961)

261. Rubenstein, E., and Lack, A., *J. Appl. Physiol.*, **15**, 598–602 (1960)

262. Rubenstein, E., Meub, D. W., and Eldridge, F., *J. Appl. Physiol.*, **15**, 603–4 (1960)

263. Sadhu, D. P., *Nature*, **188**, 672 (1960)

264. Salt, R. W., *Brit. Med. Bull.*, **17**, 5–8 (1960)

265. Salzano, J., and Hall, F. G., *Proc. Soc. Exptl. Biol. Med.*, **106**, 199–204 (1961)

266. Sayen, A., and Boland, C., *Clin. Sci.*, **20**, 217–21 (1961)

267. Sayen, A., Meloche, B. R., Redeshi, G. C., and Montgomery, H., *Clin. Sci.*, **19**, 243–56 (1960)

268. Scholander, P. F., Hock. R., Walters, V., and Johnson, F., *Biol. Bull.*, **99**, 225–36 (1950)

269. Shields, J. L., Platner, W. S., and Neubeiser, R. E., *Am. J. Physiol.*, **199**, 942–44 (1960)

270. Sealy, W. C., Young, W. G., Jr., Lesage, A. M., and Brown, I. W., *Ann. Surg.*, **153**, 797–810 (1961)

271. Sellars, E. A., and Baker, D. G., *Can. Med. Assoc. J.*, **83**, 6–13 (1960)

272. Sellars, E. A., *J. Occupational Med.*, **2**, 115–17 (1960)

273. Senay, L. C., Jr., Christensen, M., and Hertzman, A. B., *J. Appl. Physiol.*, **15**, 611–18 (1960)

274. Sharp. G. W. G., *Nature*, **190**, 146–48 (1961)

275. Siple, P. A., in *Conf. on Cold Injury, Trans. 6th*, 89–117 (1960)

276. Smith, R. E., *Federation Proc.*, **19**, Suppl. 5 (1960)

277. Stevens, J. C., and Stevens, S. S., *J. Exptl. Psychol.*, **60**, 183–92 (1960)

278. Stevenson, G. C., Collins, W. F., Randt, C. T., and Saurwein, T. D., *Am. J. Physiol.*, **194**, 423–26 (1958)

279. Streeten, D. H. P., Conn, J. W., Lewis, L. H., Fagans, S. S., Seltzer, H. S., Johnson, R. D., Guttler, R. D., and Dube, A. H., *Metabolism, Clin. and Exptl.*, **9**, 1071–92 (1960)

280. Ström, G., in *Handbook of Physiology, Sect. I. Neurophysiology*, **II**, 1173–96, 1960.

281. Stupfel, M., *J. physiol. (Paris)*, **52**, 575–606 (1960)

282. Stupfel, M., *J. physiol. (Paris)*, **52**, 673–725 (1960)

283. Taylor, I. M., in *Conf. on Cold Injury, Trans. 6th*, 117–41 (1960)

284. Tebrock, H. E., and Fisher, M. M., *Ind. Med. and Surg.*, **29**, 334–37 (1960)

285. Thauer, R., *Klin. Wochschr.*, **36**, 989–98 (1958)

286. Tjossem, T. D., Leider, A. R., Dersher, R. W., Holmes, T. H., and Ripley, H. S., *J. Psychosomatic Research*, **4**, 32–43 (1960)

287. Turchini, J. P., Bonhomme, C., and Pourhadi, R., *Compt. rend. soc. biol.*, **154**, 158–60 (1960)

288. Turl, L. H., *J. Occupational Med.*, **2**, 123–28 (1960)

289. Ushiyama, J., and Brooks, C. McC., *Am. J. Physiol.*, **200**, 718–22 (1961)

290. Vaughan, D. A., Hannon, J. P., and Vaughan, L. N., *Am. J. Physiol.*, **194**, 441–45 (1958)

291. Vaughan, J. A., Goldman, R. F., Iampietro, P. F., Kreider, M. B. Masucci, F., and Bass, D. E., *J. Appl. Physiol.*, **15**, 632–34 (1960)

291a. Vechte, J. H., and Webb, P., *J. Appl. Physiol.*, **16**, 235–39 (1961)

292. Voss, R., L'Allemand, H., Eisenreich, F. X., and Fetzer, S., *Klin. Wochschr.*, **38**, 1139–42 (1960)

293. Waites, G. M. H., *Nature*, **190**, 172–73 (1961)

294. Walker, J. E. C., and Wells, R. E., Jr., *Am. J. Med.*, **30**, 259–67 (1961)

295. Ward, J. S., Bredell, G. A., and Werzell, H. G., *J. Appl. Physiol.*, **15**, 667–70 (1960)
296. Webb, P., *Ann. N.Y. Acad. Sci.*, **82**, 714–23 (1959)
298. Weinstein, W., Kendig, J. H., Goldring, S., O'Leary, J. L., and Lourie, H., *Arch. Neurol.*, **4**, 441–48 (1961)
299. Weiss, A. K., *Am. J. Physiol.*, **196**, 913–16 (1959)
300. Weiss, B., and Laties, U. G., *J. Comp. and Physiol. Psychol.*, **53**, 603–8 (1960)
301. Weiss, B., and Laties, U. G., *Science*, **133**, 1338–44 (1961)
302. Weiss, L., *Brit. Med. Bull.*, **17**, 70–73 (1960)
303. Williams, C. M., *Air Univ. School of Aviation Med. USAF Randolph AFB Texas Publ.* 58–53 (1–16)
304. Willis, J. S., *Med. Serv. J., Can.*, **16**, 689–720 (1960)
305. Wilson, O., *Brit. J. Nutrition*, **14**, 391–401 (1960)
306. Wissler, E. H., *Mathematical Studies in Thermal Physiology* (Univ. of Texas, Austin, Texas, Rept. #1, 1959)
307. Wissler, E. H., *Mathematical Studies in Thermal Physiology* (Univ. of Texas,
308. Wissler, E. H., *Mathematical Studies in Thermal Physiology* (Univ. of Texas, Austin, Texas, Rept. #4, 1961)
309. Witt, I., and Hensel, H., *Arch. ges. Physiol.*, **268**, 582–96 (1959)
310. Wollman, H., and Connard, T. H., *Anesthesiology*, **21**, 476–81 (1960)
311. Woodcock, A. H., Thwaites, H. L., and Breckenridge, J. R., *HQ Quartermaster R&D Command, Natick, Mass., Tech. Rept. EP-86* (1958)
312. Woodcock, A. H., and Goldman, R. F., *Quartermaster Research & Eng. Center, Natick, Mass., Rept. EP-137* (1960)
313. Yaglou, C. P., *Arch. Environmental Health*, **2**, 1–8 (1961)
314. Yaglou, C. P., *Arch. Environmental Health*, **2**, 110–15 (1961)
315. Yang, T. L., and Lissak, K., *Acta Physiol. Acad. Sci. Hung.*, **17**, 63–68 (1960)
316. Yoshimura, H., Ogata, K., and Itoh, S., *Essential Problems in Climatic Physiology* (Nankodo Publishing Co. Ltd., Kyoto, Japan, 1960)

* English translation will be announced in *Technical Translations*, issued by the Office of Technical Services, US Department of Commerce, and will be made available by the Photoduplication Service, Library of Congress, and by the SLA Translation Center at the John Crerar Library, Chicago, Illinois.

THE DIGESTIVE SYSTEM[1]

By N. C. HIGHTOWER, Jr.

Department of Clinical Research, Scott and White Clinic, Temple, Texas

The pursuit of knowledge related to the physiology of the digestive system usually has two objectives: one is to seek an understanding of basic mechanisms concerned with motor activity, secretion, absorption, and associated processes; the other is to apply clinically the information obtained in the laboratory to disease states of the alimentary canal. The boundaries of the gastrointestinal physiologist, like the universe, are ever expanding. Thus, if he pursues a topic far enough he well may find himself in the domain of the physical chemist, geneticist, or enzymologist. As in medicine, the gastrointestinal physiologist has become specialized, for it is no longer possible to be expert in all areas, even within the confines of a single organ system.

The reviewer, thus having rationalized sufficiently his own limitations, will proceed with the task at hand.

APPETITE, HUNGER, AND THIRST

Interest in the regulation of food intake, appetite, hunger, and thirst is manifest in the increased number of publications related to these topics. Techniques have been improved and great ingenuity demonstrated in the experimental methods used. Of interest to students of this area of physiology will be the recent publication of Andersson & Larsson (1) in *Pharmacological Reviews*.

In experimental animals, the role of the hypothalamus in regulating food intake, appetite, hunger, and thirst has continued to receive considerable attention. The presence of a "satiety" center in the ventromedial hypothalamus and a "feeding" or "hunger" center in the lateral hypothalamus has been demonstrated in a number of species.

Wyrwicka & Dobrzecka (2) produced a conditioned reflex in goats, associated with feeding, that consisted of placing the left foreleg on the food tray. Electrodes then were implanted into the ventromedial and lateral hypothalamus. Electrical stimulation of the ventromedial hypothalamus inhibited the conditioned movements and food intake in hungry goats. Stimulation of the lateral hypothalamus elicited the conditioned movements and eating. It was noted that stimulation of the ventromedial hypothalamus could inhibit the responses elicited by lateral hypothalamic stimulation, suggesting the dominance of the satiety center.

In the cat, Morgane & Kosman (3) reported that stereotactic lesions in

[1] The survey of literature pertaining to this review was completed in June 1961. A few abstracts have been cited, but no reference has been made to papers presented at meetings.

the lateral hypothalamus at the level of the tuberal region did not alter food intake or body weight from preoperative control levels. Lesions restricted to the ventromedial hypothalamus resulted in hyperphagia and obesity. The authors concluded that the lateral hypothalamus does not function as a feeding center in the cat.

To demonstrate the neural organization of the feeding centers in the rat, Morgane (4) devised an elegant experiment that required the animal to cross an electrified grill and press a lever to obtain food. After electrodes were implanted in various parts of the hypothalamus, stimulation of the far-lateral hypothalamus resulted not only in a feeding response in sated animals, but also in their crossing the electrified grill to obtain food. Stimulation of the midlateral hypothalamus produced a feeding response but did not "motivate" the animal to cross the grill to obtain food. Simultaneous stimulation of the satiety center and the far-lateral hypothalamus gave similar results. After lesions had been placed in the medial forebrain bundle, a feeding response could still be obtained in sated animals by far-lateral hypothalamic stimulation, but the animals would not cross the grill to obtain food.

These results suggest that the medial forebrain bundle is important in "hunger motivation" since overcoming a barrier to obtain food apparently depends upon the integrity of this bundle. With this bundle interrupted, basic feeding responses could still be elicited, but the animal would not "work" for his food. The satiety center apparently is capable of selectively supervising this "hunger drive". Morgane concludes that the feeding center in the rat probably is composed of both basic feeding (midlateral hypothalamus) and "hunger drive" (far-lateral hypothalamus) elements and that only the latter is depressed by the satiety mechanism.

Grossman (5) used an ingenious method of stimulating areas of the hypothalamus of the rat. By means of a double cannula system into which are placed minute amounts of crystalline chemicals, he obtained repeated stimulation of central structures. Both adrenergic and cholinergic stimulation of the "feeding" and "drinking" mechanisms in the lateral hypothalamus were studied. Cell concentrations exerting control over feeding and drinking appeared to be highly localized in the lateral hypothalamus but clearly separate from each other. The feeding mechanism was selectively activated by adrenergic stimulation, while the drinking mechanism responded selectively to cholinergic stimulation.

The satisfaction of thirst in dogs was studied by Holmes & Montgomery (6). To induce a standard drinking pattern, 20 per cent sodium chloride was administered intravenously. The amount of water consumed in response to the intravenous saline stimulus was taken as the control. Various drinking solutions were then substituted for water, and it was found that 5 per cent sodium sulfate, 0.9 per cent sodium bicarbonate, 0.85 per cent ammonium chloride, 1.15 per cent sodium acetate, and 0.9 per cent magnesium chloride did not alter the total fluid intake significantly. When 0.9 per cent sodium chloride was given as the drinking solution, the intake averaged 2.4 times that observed for water. The introduction of 0.9 per cent sodium chloride, 5 per cent glucose, 1.8 per cent urea, and water into the stomach 40 minutes prior to the intravenous injection of 20 per cent sodium chloride inhibited the drinking response. However, when similar solutions were given intravenously, no inhibition occurred. Thus, it appears that intravenous administration of fluids cannot substitute for drinking in satiation of thirst.

Herxheimer & Woodbury (7) demonstrated a decrease in the taste preference threshold for salt in rats treated with deoxycorticosterone. Before this treatment, the animals could select solutions of salt at concentrations between 0.09 and 0.016 per cent. After this treatment, the animals could select concentrations between 0.003 and 0.0005 per cent. Similar studies with various concentrations of sucrose did not show significant differences after deoxycorticosterone treatment. It is of interest that the total fluid intake became progressively less as the preference threshold was approached.

The taste threshold for sodium has been studied by Bell & Williams (8) in the calf. Sodium depletion of the animals was produced by exteriorizing a parotid duct. The salivary sodium to potassium ratio progressively fell after the operation, but could be restored to normal when the animal was allowed access to either 1 per cent sodium chloride or 2 per cent sodium bicarbonate. The sodium-depleted calf is able to self-select salt solution from a variety of other sapid solutions.

In similar experiments with sheep, Denton & Sabine (9) found that from one to four liters of alkaline saliva containing 180 to 700 meq of sodium ion, mainly as sodium bicarbonate, may be lost per day from a unilateral parotid duct fistula. If the animals had daily access to solutions of sodium chloride and sodium bicarbonate, even for limited periods of time (15 to 60 min), they were able to maintain sodium balance. It is of interest that there was a preference for sodium bicarbonate over sodium chloride. More remarkably, most of the sodium in the drinking solutions was consumed within five minutes, before more than a small fraction could be absorbed.

Beilharz & Kay (10) have extended these observations by studying the effect of introducing sodium bicarbonate or water into the rumen or by giving sodium chloride or glucose intravenously shortly before the animals were offered water or sodium bicarbonate solution to drink. They found that placing 25 to 50 g of sodium bicarbonate in the rumen did not alter the sheep's appetite for the sodium bicarbonate offered in the drinking water. Infusion of 300 to 400 meq of sodium, roughly half the sodium deficit, usually reduced the subsequent intake of sodium by a similar amount.

Obesity in man continues to attract considerable attention, and recent reviews of the problem have appeared in the literature (11, 12). Although various physiologic and psychiatric theories exist, little has been added to our basic knowledge of obesity in man. No known metabolic derangement has been found in the obese. The mechanisms of regulation of food intake and appetite control in man are extremely difficult to study. Unfortunately, it has not been possible to apply clinically, with any degree of success, the knowledge of hypothalamic function obtained experimentally in animals. Clinical experience with pharmacologic agents that suppress appetite have, in general, been disappointing. It appears that man must accept "the inevitability of calories", as recently discussed on the editorial pages of *Lancet* (13).

The recent report of Chalmers *et al.* (14) is encouraging, for it describes a fat-mobilizing and ketogenic substance in the urine of human beings who are actively mobilizing and utilizing fat. In mice this polypeptide-like substance causes transient hypoglycemia, ketonemia, and increased mobilization of fat. As little as 1 μg per ml will cause the release of free fatty acids from rat adipose tissue *in vitro*. Apparently this is neither growth hormone nor corticotropin.

The "high fat" diet recently in vogue and advocated for weight reduction seems to be losing ground and justifiably so (13). In a recent study, Pilkington *et al.* (15) have demonstrated that over prolonged periods, the rate of weight loss on a diet consisting mainly of fat does not differ significantly from an isocaloric diet consisting mainly of carbohydrate.

MOTOR ACTIVITY

This past year more reports related to motor activity of the alimentary canal appeared than in any previous year. In the *Annual Reviews of Physiology* published in the past decade, this topic has frequently been mentioned only in a cursory manner, undoubtedly because of insufficient data.

STUDIES *In Vitro*

In a study of the relationship of conduction in smooth muscle to cell length, cell diameter, and extracellular space, Prosser *et al.* (16) reported a decrease in rate of conduction with decreasing cell length and increasing extracellular space. Diameter of muscle fibers does not vary. For example, in the esophagus of the guinea pig the average muscle fiber was 220 μ in length and 6 μ in diameter, and extracellular space amounted to 4.4 per cent; the rate of conduction was 15 cm per second. In the longitudinal muscle of the small intestine of the cat, the average muscle fiber length was 120 μ, cell diameter was 6 μ, and extracellular space amounted to 12.5 per cent; the rate of conduction was 3 cm per second. It is of interest that the rate of conduction reported for the guinea pig esophagus is similar to the rate reported for the propagation of the primary peristaltic contraction in the upper esophagus of man (17). In isolated muscle strips of esophageal muscularis muscosae (guinea pig), intestinal muscles (cat), and taenia coli (guinea pig), Burnstock & Prosser (18) recorded electrical activity with the sucrose gap electrode. They report slow waves of low potentials of 5 mv and spikes of 25 to 45 mv. Gillespie (19) measured the membrane potential of individual smooth muscle cells of the isolated, doubly innervated rabbit colon preparation. In the absence of nerve stimulation the membrane potential of the smooth muscle cells was not stable. Regular slow potential waves lasting serveral seconds were observed. The depolarization phase of these waves initiated short-lived bursts of action-potential spikes followed by repolarization; associated with each burst there was a contraction of the longitudinal muscle. Single stimuli to the parasympathetic nerves produced both a mechanical and an electrical response, which was either a slow depolarization lasting some 600 msec or an action potential.

Use of the isolated gut strip continues to be a popular technique for studying the effects of various drugs. The relationship of catecholamines to motor activity has engaged a number of investigators recently. Sjostrand (20) found that small doses (0.5 to 5.0 mg per 15 ml bath) of catecholamines generally produced a contraction of the guinea pig ileum, whereas large doses (5.0 to 10.0 mg per 15 ml bath) produced relaxation. The stimulating action of catecholamine was abolished by atropine and nicotine, and the author concluded that catecholamines stimulate the intestine through liberation of acetylcholine. The inhibitory action of large doses of catecholamines could be demonstrated after contraction was induced by histamine, acetylcholine, and substance P. Thus, the inhibitory action appears to be nonspecific and of a general type. In the isolated guinea pig and rabbit colon, Lee (21) found that sympathetic nerve stimulation reduced the amount of 5-hydroxytryptamine (5-HT) released by colonic gut segments of the guinea pig and rabbit on the average of 30 per cent. Pelvic nerve stimulation caused no significant change. As a result of studies on the effect of nicotine on the isolated rabbit colon, Gillespie & Mackenna (22) concluded that small doses of nicotine ($<10^{-5}$M) produce inhibition by liberating a catecholamine, basing their conclusion on the evidence that after prior daily intravenous injections of reserpine the inhibitory effects of nicotine virtually disappeared. It is presumed that the reserpine caused a depletion of catecholamines. After degenerative section of the sympathetic nerves to the segment, the effect of nicotine was reduced or lost. Also, removal of the mucosa, where the only chromaffin cells in the colon are located, did not abolish the inhibition produced by nicotine. Thus, these authors believe that the release of catecholamines by nicotine occurs either at the endings of the extrinsic sympathetic nerves or at some structure associated with them.

The action of morphine and other drugs on the isolated guinea pig jejunum has been studied by Szerb (23). Lewis (24) studied the ability of morphine to inhibit the action of smooth muscle stimulants in the isolated guinea pig ileum. As morphine is capable of suppressing the action of stimulants that act on nervous structures, as well as the action of stimulants that act directly on smooth muscle, it probably accomplishes its effect by inhibition of a metabolic process common to both nervous and muscle structures. For a long time, clinical gastroenterologists have been seeking a drug with action similar to morphine but without its tendency to cause addiction. Such a preparation would be a valuable adjunct in the control of hypermotility and diarrheal states.

Two interesting papers (25, 26) appeared that shed new light on the effects of gluten on the bowel. It has been found that an aqueous extract of gluten and its ultrafiltrate depress the peristaltic reflex of the rat jejunum. Peptic-tryptic digestion did not abolish the effect, but acid hydrolysis did. The output of acetylcholine at rest and from cholinergic nerve stimulation was depressed by the gluten fraction. Thus, the inhibition of motility by gluten is thought to be caused by suppression of acetylcholine release. These findings might offer an explanation of the segmental dilatation, atony, and slow transient time in the small bowel of patients with sprue.

Unidirectional fluxes of K^{42} in the longitudinal smooth muscle of the guinea pig ileum were studied by Weiss *et al.* (27). It is reported that acetylcholine and pilocarpine produce an increase in potassium efflux and a decrease in the influx of potassium ion. Cocaine was found to block the contractile response and to depress K^{42} efflux. It was presumed that cocaine acting at the membrane impedes ion fluxes important to smooth muscle contraction.

STUDIES *In Vivo*

In this part of the review an anatomical division of data will be used because motor activity of the various parts of the alimentary canal varies considerably.

Pharyngeal motility.—Dutta & Basmajian (28) made a detailed anatomical study of the pharyngeal constrictors in rabbits and found that the motor units of these muscles contained only two to six muscle fibers each. The smallness of the motor units is characteristic of muscles capable of very rapid, but delicate movements. In electromyographic studies these same authors (29) report that the entire second stage of active deglutition lasts only 316 ± 47 msec in the rabbit with rapid sequential contraction of the constrictors from above downwards. In electromyographic studies of the pharyngeal constrictors of man (30), the activity of the superior, middle, and inferior constrictor each lasted approximately one-half second. Unfortunately, only one muscle could be studied at a time in the human subjects, and it was impossible to obtain sequential data. The activity of the pharyngeal constrictors in man, as determined by measurements of intraluminal pressure (17), suggests that the sequence of events is similar to that reported for the rabbit.

Esophageal motility.—Smith & Brizzee (31), using methods of motion analysis of cineradiographic films, have shown that the role of the esophagus, as well as that of the stomach, is a passive one during the act of vomiting in the cat. External pressures and forces apparently account for expulsion of the vomitus. In adult cows, Stevens & Sellers (32) recorded the velocity of esophageal peristalsis after swallowing saliva and found it to average about 42 cm per sec.

Propulsive motor activity of the human esophagus stimulated by a small balloon was found by Flood & Fink (33) to be inhibited by methantheline (Banthine), propantheline (Pro-Banthine), atropine, valethamate (Murel), and trimethaphan camphorsulfonate (Arfonad). Large doses of barbiturates, glyceryl trinitrate, and isoproterenol (Isuprel) had no effect on esophageal motility under the conditions of the study. In the cat, Schenk & Frederickson (34) report that epinephrine constricts the lower segment of the esophagus, whereas acetylcholine and vagal stimulation cause relaxation in a localized and discrete manner. This they consider to be pharmacologic evidence of a "cardiac" sphincter in the cat.

In an attempt to produce achalasia of the esophagus experimentally, Harris *et al.* (35) administered an anticholinesterase agent, diisopropylfluorophosphate, to dogs for prolonged periods. Aperistalsis and failure of the lower esophageal sphincter to relax in response to swallowing developed, but the characteristic response of the esophagus to methacholine (Mecholyl), which occurs in human beings with esophageal achalasia, could not be elicited in the dogs.

Manometric exploration of the sphincteric mechanism of the esophagogastric junction of man in health and disease continues to be popular. Monges' (36) report of intraluminal pressures in the esophagus and esophagogastric junction of normal individuals is similar to data previously published by this reviewer (37) and others. Kelly *et al.* (38) made a detailed investigation of the pressure changes within the esophagogastric junction during deglutition and demonstrated a caudad progression of relaxation followed by contraction through the esophagogastric sphincteric zone. This finding accounts for the necessary pressure gradients for normal esophageal evacuation. Tuttle *et al.* (39) were unable to find any significant difference in the height and length of the esophagogastric high pressure zone of patients with hiatal hernia when compared to those without hernia. One would expect a decrease in the gastric-esophageal pressure barrier in patients with hiatal hernia to account for acid reflux. Code *et al.* (40) report that 90 per cent of 502 patients examined had maximal resting pressure within the esophagogastric junction of less than 30 cm of water. Resting pressure in excess of 40 cm of water was found in 22 patients and termed a "hypertensive gastroesophageal sphincter". In 14 of these patients an associated diagnosis of diffuse spasm of the esophagus had been made.

Gastric motility.—In the decerebrate ruminant (41), stretch of the reticulum and reticulorumenal fold was found to be the best stimulus of contractions in the rumen and reticulum. Atropine abolished this response. Prior to eructation in sheep (42), motor activity begins in the posterior ventral sac a few seconds before contractions appear in the rumen. The abdominal muscles then contract and eructation begins and is completed by a strong contraction of the main ventral sac of the rumen.

By varying the duration (0.01 to 10 msec) and potential (1 to 10 v) of stimuli applied to the distal end of the sectioned vagus of the cat, Martinsson

& Muren (43) have apparently demonstrated a stimulation threshold at which inhibition of gastric motility occurs. The findings suggest that there are two groups of efferent fibers in the vagus that influence motility: one group of cholinergic excitatory fibers with a low threshold of stimulation, and one group of inhibitory fibers with a higher stimulation threshold which are not cholinergic. Perret & Hesser (44, 45) have made elaborate investigations of central neural control and associated pathways concerned with gastric motility in the cat. The reader should consult these papers for the details of the intricate pathways involved in excitatory and inhibitory control of central structures on gastric motility.

Louckes *et al.* (46, 47) continued to use the inductograph for studying motor activity of the antrum and pylorus of the dog. The inherent rhythm of the pyloric sphincter (4 to 6 contractions per minute) of the dog is almost impossible to alter with various cholinergic and adrenergic agents. This is similar to man's antrum and pylorus (48) in which it has been found that disease, surgical procedures, and pharmacological agents have little effect on "basic rhythm".

In simple, but beautifully designed experiments, Menguy (49) demonstrated that biliary and pancreatic secretions are essential to inhibition of gastric motility by fat in the duodenum of the rat. These results raise the interesting point that the mechanism of inhibition of gastric motility, as well as that of secretion, may be increased osmolarity of intestinal contents produced by fat emulsions rather than fat *per se* in contact with the mucosa. Hunt (50, 51) continued to study gastric emptying time by dilution techniques, using test meals. He offers convincing evidence that gastric emptying can be regulated by osmotic receptors located in the upper small bowel.

Small bowel motility.—Transport through the duodenum of goats and sheep has been determined with an ingenious electromagnetic method by Singleton (52, 53). The method is based on the flowmeter principle of Wetterer. Duodenal flow, which was intermittent, ranged from 400 to 1300 ml per hr for different animals. In man, Sprung & Roisch (54) have reported pressure patterns recorded from the small intestine. Farrar *et al.* (55) described an improved radiotelemetering capsule that is energized from outside the body. It is claimed that base line drift and sensitivity to temperature are much less than with battery powered capsules. Unfortunately, the angle of coupling between the capsule and antenna is extremely critical, so for satisfactory recording of intraluminal pressures, the subject must assume positions that bring the capsule into proper orientation with the antenna.

A better understanding of the relationship of electrical activity of the small bowel to motility has been provided by recent publications of Daniel *et al.* (56, 57). Electrical phenomena, as recorded from the small intestine of the dog, consist of slow waves of potential change, amounting to 1.5 to 3.5 mv, and bursts of action potentials. Both types of electrical activity are thought to originate in the muscle layers of the gut wall. The slow wave activity occurs in a rhythmic manner at rates of 17 to 22 per minute in the duodenum and 9 to 12 per minute in the terminal ileum of the dog. These rates are similar to those of rhythmic contraction reported by Douglas & Mann (58). In two human subjects with iliac stomas the rhythmic rate of slow wave electrical activity was 7.6 and 7.25 per minute. Again, this is similar to rates of 8.1 and 8.6 reported by Code *et al.* (59) for rhythmic contractions recorded from the terminal ileum of two patients with iliac stomas. Electrophysiology of the small bowel and its relation to motor activity is an area in need of further investigation.

Colonic motility.—In a series of papers (60 to 62) Chaudhary & Truelove report their results from an investigation of colonic motility in normal individuals, patients with the irritable bowel syndrome, and patients with chronic ulcerative colitis. When patients with irritable colon with active symptoms (pain) and patients with colitis had diarrhea, an increase in the number of pressure waves, as compared to normals, was found. When both groups of patients were symptom free, the patterns of colonic motility were essentially normal. The administration of prostigmine and the eliciting of certain emotions by psychiatric interview increased colonic pressure waves in all groups.

The role of serotonin in regulating motor activity of the gut continues to intrigue investigators. In isolated preparations it can cause strong contractions and, in patients with the carcinoid syndrome, diarrhea is a frequent feature. Although obviously a stimulator of motility, the mechanism of action is not clear. The anatomical location of the major body depot of serotonin in the enterochromaffin cells of the gastrointestinal mucosa may imply an intimate relationship. Sleisenger *et al.* (63) concluded that serotonin does not act via a cholinergic pathway, but concede that it may modulate the cholinergic system.

Miscellaneous observations.—Of interest to physiologists will be Harper's (64) recent critical review of evidence for a vagovagal reflex in man. Few data are available except in the Russian literature. The Pavlovian school strongly believes that a vagovagal mechanism is of fundamental importance in the regulation of motility and secretion. In a detailed study of reflex inhibition of motility, Kock (65) presents evidence that centrally induced inhibition (stimulation of afferent somatic nerves) is dependent on an intact sympathoadrenal system. The number of nerve fibers at various levels of the vagus nerves in man has been tabulated by Hoffman & Schnitzlein (66).

SALIVARY SECRETION

Investigations related to salivary secretion continue to be concentrated in three general areas: (*a*) the composition of saliva, particularly its ionic componenets; (*b*) innervation of salivary glands; and (*c*) the effects of various drugs and hormones on salivary secretion. Not only does saliva differ from gland to gland in the same animals, but also there is considerable species variation. For this reason, many data do not lend themselves easily to interpretation of mechanisms. Thus, the report by Langley & Brown (67) is indeed refreshing. By application of the "stop-flow" technique for analysis of ionic transfer in the dog parotid gland, they were able to obtain convincing evidence that ionic transfer is the exclusive function of the duct cells. In addition, they were able to show that along the duct there appear to be specific areas for the transfer of K, Na, I, Ca, and P. During flow stoppage, sodium and chloride concentration in the ducts decreased while potassium, calcium, iodine, and phosphorus concentrations increased. The authors postulate a recirculation of sodium and chloride between plasma and saliva. For many years the concept has existed that salivation is analogous to urine formation in that saliva is a product of alveolar tissue and is modified in its passage through the ducts. The findings of Langley & Brown cast doubt on such an analogy.

Composition of saliva.—The effects of flow rate on electrolyte composition of saliva continue to interest some workers. Schneyer & Schneyer (68) found in the rat that with high flow rates the parotid saliva is usually isotonic or slightly hypertonic to serum and has a high concentration of sodium and a low concentration of potassium. The reverse was found true for the submaxillary gland. Sublingual saliva was also hypotonic. Thus, rat submaxillary and sublingual saliva is like parotid saliva of man and dog in tonicity. Kay (69) reported on the volume, ionic concentrations, and tonicity of saliva in sheep and goats under various conditions and flow rates. He established that the adult pattern of parotid salivary secretion does not develop in young goats until about the age of three months (70). Physiologic maturity is closely associated with evidence of histologic maturity. Schneyer & Schneyer (71) examined electrolyte (Na, K, and Cl) and inulin spaces in submaxillary and parotid glands of rats and concluded that parotid saliva could be formed from a small fraction (approximately 10 per cent) of unmodified intracellular fluid to which a solution having the electrolyte composition of extracellular fluid is added. Blix & Lindberg (72) isolated five sialic acids from mucins of the bovine submaxillary gland and one from mucins of the equine submaxillary gland.

Innervation of salivary glands.—Since the time of Claude Bernand it has been assumed that specific secretory fibers to the submaxillary gland were located in the cervical sympathetic trunk, although doubt has been cast upon this concept by histological studies. Emmelin & Engstrom (73) reviewed the problem recently, and concluded from experiments in the cat that the cervical sympathetic trunk does indeed contain specific secretory fibers for the submaxillary gland. Innervation of lingual salivary glands determined by histological methods in man and the cat (74) demonstrated the presence of a perialveolar plexus formed by autonomic fibers. In forming such an arrangement, two fibers run together, each closely duplicating the other's course and branching. It is suggested that such pairs of fibers consist of one sympathetic fiber and one parasympathetic fiber.

From Emmelin's laboratory come continued reports (75, 76, 77) of the effect of various denervating procedures (surgical and chemical) on salivary secretion in the cat. Salivary responses to cortical and sciatic stimulation were reported by Velo & Hoff (78). It appears to this reviewer that pre- and postganglionic denervating procedures, as well as ablative surgery of the spinal cord, midbrain, and various ganglia combined with pharmacologic agents that affect the autonomic nervous system, offer almost unlimited combinations to determine effects on salivary secretion. For this reason, numerous reports related to this aspect of salivary secretion probably will continue to appear.

GASTRIC SECRETION

If judged on the basis of number of publications as an indication of interest in a particular area of gastrointestinal physiology, gastric secretion would probably win the contest hands down. Data relating to certain aspects of gastric secretion have become so voluminous that reviews of rather isolated topics are now commonplace. As space is limited and this assignment includes all the alimentary canal, the topic of gastric secretion cannot be covered completely.

Although the precise mechanism for secretion of HCl by the stomach has not been found, Hogben (79) clearly defined the issues involved. Solutions to the intriguing problems of whether there are separate "pumps" for hydrogen or chloride ions or a single "pump" for hydrochloric acid, and what the location of these processes within the mucosa may be, must await further investigation.

Of clinical interest is the report by Segal (80) wherein he outlines the rationale, indications, and limitations of measurement of gastric secretory activity in man. Because of their clinical implications, two papers (81, 82) from Code's laboratory will be of interest to those who have responsibility for selecting diets, particularly for the ulcer patient. The relative stimulating effects of different foods were determined in dogs with vagally innervated pouches. Foods that produced the highest secretory response included meat, fish, and eggs. Foods that stimulated the least production of acid were fruits, white bread, butter, and some dry cereals. A close correlation was found between the protein content of the foods and their ability to stimulate acid.

Electrolytes in gastric juice.—A detailed report giving values for volume, acid, sodium, potassium, chloride, and pepsin in gastric juice of man in the basal state and following stimulation with histamine has been published recently by Hirschowitz (83). On the basis of these and other data (84), Hirschowitz calculated the theoretical clearance of sodium by the gastric mucosa and postulated a mechanism for secretion of the hydrogen ion by an exchange for sodium. The role of potassium in gastric juice has not been settled. Werther *et al.* (85) present evidence that potassium is not an integral part of primary acid secretion, as no consistent correlation between acid and potassium concentration could be found after histamine stimulation. Blair *et al.* (86), however, report a highly significant positive correlation between total outputs of potassium and hydrogen ion secretion in cats. The significance of sodium and potassium in gastric secretion is the subject of a recent review by Hollander (87). The composition of abomasal secretion in sheep was studied by Hill (88) and found to be similar to that in other animals. Gastric secretion in spider monkeys, equipped with chronic gastric fistulae, has been studied in Brooks' laboratory (89, 90). Contents from the fistula during fasting showed total acid concentrations of 99 to 127 meq per liter with the animal in its cage, and less with it restrained in a chair. The maximal total acid concentration after histamine stimulation was 130 to 141 meq per liter and after insulin hypoglycemia 98 to 138 meq per liter. Wright (91) reports that hydrochloric acid first appears in the rabbit fetal stomach at the twenty-third day of gestation. It had been shown previously by histological methods that the oxyntic cells made their appearance in the rabbit fetal gastric mucosa at this time.

Pepsin.—As indicated in the last *Annual Review of Physiology* (92), accumulating data concerning the mechanism of pepsin secretion indicate it probably will prove to be as complicated as the secretion of acid. In man, at least, evidence continues to appear indicating that histamine is capable of stimulating pepsin secretion (83, 93). That histamine stimulation of pepsin cannot be demonstrated in the dog has been explained as a species difference (93). The transient rise in pepsin output in dogs following histamine stimulation is considered a "washout" effect. The role of sympathetic innervation on pepsin secretion may prove important. Altamirano *et al.* (94) demonstrated that stimulation of sympathetic fibers innervating a segment of resting gastric mucosa of the dog causes high pepsinogen output when the rate of stimulation exceeds 15 per second. Intravenous phenoxybenzamine (Dibenzyline) inhibited this response. Acid secretion was not produced. When secretion was stimulated by histamine, a transient rise in pepsinogen occurred. Following histamine stimulation, rates of stimulation below 10 per second caused high outputs of pepsinogen. The sulfated galactosan, carrageenin, as well as other sulfated polysaccharides from seaweed, can inhibit proteolytic activity of pepsin acting upon serum albumin. Houck *et al.* (95) demonstrated that carrageenin is also capable of protecting from ulcer the rat whose pylorus has been ligated. The measurement of uropepsin in the urine continues to be popular, although its relationship to gastric secretion of pepsinogen has not been established completely. Cummins (96) suggests that the two-hour uropepsin determination is of value in separating patients with gastrointestinal bleeding into those who have duodenal ulcers and those with variceal bleeding. Of interest to some will be the study of Greenberg & Lester (97) who measured uropepsin output in human subjects before, during, and after drinking intoxicating amounts of a strong alcoholic beverage (dry martini). They found a marked increase in uropepsin output that continued into the hangover period. An antacid administered after drinking decreased uropepsin output.

Histamine.—An interesting paper by Harries (98) establishes a point worthy of note. Discontinuous infusions of histamine in the dog produced a significantly greater secretion of acid in response to the second infusion as compared to the first or subsequent tests. In view of the popularity of the "double" histamine test for assessing inhibition of gastric secretion in the dog and in man, these data are important. From results of a comparison of the augmented histamine test and insulin hypoglycemia, Clark *et al.* (99) concluded that the action of histamine on the parietal cell is neither specific nor direct; they suggest that it acts, at least in part, through neural structures. Marks *et al.* (100) have continued their studies of the parietal cell mass and its relation to secretion of acid. By administering histamine subcutaneously and intravenously in graded doses to dogs, they were able to construct dose-response curves. The animals were later sacrificed, and a linear relationship was established for maximum histamine response and parietal cell mass. Of interest to those who use the cat as an experimental animal will be the observations of Read & Johnstone (101) who tabulated the distribution of parietal cells in the cat gastric mucosa and found a pattern similar to that in man.

Steroids.—Although Gray (102) continues to propose the hypothesis that corticotropin and adrenal steroids stimulate gastric secretion, the results of three careful studies recently published (103, 104, 105) dispute his claims. Adrenal steroids have also been implicated in the pathogenesis of peptic ulcer; a close examination of available data indicates that such an implication is based more on theory than fact. Bowen *et al.* (106) found that although the incidence of peptic ulcer in patients with rheumatoid arthritis was three to four times as great (8.1 per cent for 877 patients) as it was in the general population of patients observed, the administration of systemic steroids did not change the incidence (7.5 per cent for 1237 patients). If adrenal steroids have any significant effect upon gastric secretion, such an effect is difficult to prove. Sun & Shay (107) suggest that the late phase (third to fifth hour) of the gastric secretory response to insulin hypoglycemia is dependent upon intact adrenals and that a synergestic action of the adrenals with vagal mechanisms occurs.

Glucagon.—The recognition of the Zollinger-Ellison syndrome has stimulated a search in the pancreas for a substance that is apparently responsible for the hypersecretion observed in this condition. As the pancreatic tumors associated with the Zollinger-Ellison syndrome do not produce insulin, glucagon was considered as the possible agent stimulating gastric secretion and has been investigated extensively in the past few years. It is now obvious that glucagon is not responsible for the hypersecretion. Recent evidence (108, 109) confirms previous studies that showed glucagon does not stimulate gastric secretion significantly; in fact, a transient inhibition of histamine-stimulated gastric secretion has been demonstrated in man (108). With extremely large doses of glucagon, the pylorus-ligated rat does show a significant increase in hydrochloric acid output (109). This effect was not diminished by vagotomy. Thus, the secondary hypoglycemia that results from extremely large doses of glucagon is apparently not the cause of the increased secretion. Although no correlation was noted between the degree of inhibition of histamine-stimulated gastric secretion in man and the level of blood sugar (108), Dotevall & Muren (110) reported that 30 per cent glucose infused intravenously in the dog will inhibit the secretion of a Pavlov pouch stimulated by insulin or sham feeding.

Pyloric gland area and gastrin.—The pyloric gland area (antrum), with its elaboration of gastrin, is undoubtedly the most active area of the gut in terms of stimulating investigations on gastric secretion. It is significant that results of experimental work, obtained in the past few years, are finding application in clinical surgery (111, 112, 113). The importance of the rapid developments occurring in this phase of gastric secretion is emphasized by the recent appearance of Woodward & Dragstedt's article (113) in *Physiological Reviews* and Schofield's editorial (114) in *Gastroenterology.*

Gregory & Tracy (115) continued their important work on the purification of gastrin, and report the gastric secretory response of a human subject to subcutaneous, intramuscular, and intravenous administration of their preparation. Amounts corresponding to 200 g of hog antral mucosa were given. After subcutaneous and intramuscular injections, secretion commenced within 15 minutes and lasted for over three hours. After intravenous injections the response was much smaller and lasted only about two hours. A method for biologic assay of gastrin, proposed by Emas & Uvnäs (116, 117), compares the secretory response of gastrin to histamine in the unanesthetized cat.

The review of recent evidence for the role of the pyloric gland area in gastrin secretion (113, 114) indicates that the antrum is, indeed, a true endocrine organ capable of releasing into the circulation its hormone, gastrin, which regulates the gastric phase of gastric secretion. This homeostatic mechanism operates in response to a number of stimuli: nervous (vagal excitation), mechanical (local distention), and chemical (alcohol, liver extract, and protein products of digestion). An acid medium (usually pH of 1.5 or less) inhibits gastrin release. Recent contributions (118, 119, 120) confirm these observations. The exact site of origin of gastrin is not known, but probably is related to intramural cholinergic plexuses. The degree to which vagal excitation contributes to gastrin release apparently is much greater than previously supposed (119, 120). In view of these recent findings, Nyhus *et al.* (119) proposed a new classification of the phases of gastric secretion consisting of: (*a*) direct vagal, (*b*) vagal-antral, (*c*) local antral, and (*d*) intestinal. There appears to be considerable merit in this suggestion.

The agent(s) responsible for hypersecretion following portacaval transposition is not known, but gastrin has been implicated. From an analysis of the data of Gregory (121), Janowitz (92) stated the stimulating substance could not be gastrin. Now, Olbe (122) confirms this by reporting that antral resection does not abolish the increase of the secretory response to insulin hypoglycemia caused by portacaval transposition. He further demonstrated that gastrin produced the same secretory response whether injected into the foreleg or hindleg of dog which has undergone portacaval transposition.

Whether acid in the antrum simply inhibits the release of gastrin or causes the liberation of a humoral inhibitory agent, or both, has not been answered. The recent evidence presented by DuVal & Price (123, 124) is some of the best in support of the hypothesis that a second inhibitory hormone is released from the antrum by acid. They have overcome tremendous technical difficulties in cross-circulation experiments with dogs to show that acid in the antrum of one dog is capable of inhibiting gastric secretion in its parabiotic mate stimulated by a balloon distending the antrum. Shapira *et al.* (125) reported that they were unable to inhibit histamine-stimulated gastric secretion by perfusing the antrum with hydrochloric acid; thus, they were unable to confirm the earlier work of Woodward *et al.* (126). Shapira and co-workers interpreted their results as raising doubts that the antrum was capable of producing an antisecretory hormone. Andersson (127 to 132) reported the effects of perfusing with acid an excluded antral-duodenal pouch in Pavlov and Heidenhain-pouch dogs under a variety of stimulating conditions. It is difficult to interpret some of these results and to make a clear separation between antral inhibitory and duodenal inhibitory influences. There are obviously many conflicting data in the literature, and many problems must await clarification.

PANCREATIC EXOCRINE FUNCTION

Current reviews of pancreatic physiology, presented in broad, general terms, continue to appear (133). Laboratory methods for detecting and evaluating pancreatic exocrine function in man (134, 135, 136) are also popular. More attention has been placed on malfunction of the pancreas and its various disease states than on the normal function of this organ. Little new information has been accumulated since the last *Annual Review*.

Dreiling & Janowitz (137) presented new evidence in support of their hypothesis that the pancreatic secretory cells produce a bicarbonate solution iso-osmolar to plasma and that the secretion, as it passes down the ductal system, undergoes a bicarbonate-chloride equilibration. The observations of Dumont & Mulholland (138) on concentrations of lipase and amylase in thoracic duct lymph of man are interesting. They found that secretin administered intravenously produced a marked rise in the concentration of amylase and lipase in thoracic duct lymph without significant changes in the serum levels of these enzymes. If morphine was given before secretin, the rise in levels of these enzymes in thoracic duct lymph was even greater. Though not surprising, the evidence indicates a direct functional lymphatic pathway from pancreatic cell to thoracic duct.

The electrophoretic behavior of trypsin from beef, sheep, and pig has been studied by Vithayathil *et al.* (139). Porcine trypsin was found to differ from its bovine and ovine counterparts in that it had a lower electrophoretic mobility at pH 4.8 and a higher stability in alkaline media. The differences were attributed to structural variations of the porcine trypsin and were consistent with earlier observations that porcine and bovine trypsin have different immunological properties. Liener (140) reports a chromatographic method whereby trypsinogen and trypsin may be separated, on a large scale, on carboxymethyl cellulose at pH 3.2. The electrophoretic characteristics of pancreozymin and uropancreozym (a substance extracted from urine that, when given intravenously, stimulates the pancreas to secrete amylase, lipase, and trypsinogen) have been studied by Svatos & Queisnerova (141) and found to be similar. Each ninhydrin-reactive spot of the electrophoreogram was eluted and freeze-dried; the dissolved residues were titrated on dog's pancreas *in situ*. The eluates from the first spot, which migrated most slowly from the anode, for both pancreozymin and the native urine caused an elevation of pancreatic enzymes. The eluates of other spots did not influence the level of pancreatic enzymes.

Radioactively labeled fats, mainly in the form of I^{131} triolein, have been used extensively as a clinical means of detecting pancreatic exocrine insufficiency in man. Thus, the results of gas chromatographic, infrared spectrographic, and chemical analysis of commercial I^{131} triolein (Abbott) by Lakshminarayana *et al.* (142) are of interest. They found that I^{131}-labeled triolein contained methyl esters and tri-, di-, and monoglycerides of labeled oleic acid. When I^{131} triolein and I^{131} oleic acid were administered to normal individuals, the chromatographic fractionation of serum lipids showed that 90 per cent of the radioactivity was in the triglyceride fraction and the remainder was mostly in the diglyceride and nonesterified fatty acid fractions.

Exocrine function of the pancreas in patients with fibrocystic disease continues to attract more attention (143, 144), and it is now evident that this disease may account for a significant proportion of chronic nontuberculous lung disease in adults (145). At the National Institutes of Health, diSant'Agnese and his co-workers found that certain fractions of mucopolysaccharides in the mucus obtained by duodenal aspiration in patients with fibrocystic disease are characterized by low sialic acid and high fucose content (143). These quantitative differences in the carbohydrate components may account for the abnormal viscosity of the mucus observed in fibrocystic disease.

The abundant reserve of pancreatic exocrine function is demonstrated in the study of Uram *et al.* (146) who found that the rat is capable of normal or near normal digestion with only 1 per cent, or less, of its exocrine pancreas.

BILE FORMATION

As data accumulate, one appreciates more and more that bile formation is indeed a complicated process. Determinants of flow rate and composition of bile have been reviewed recently by Wheeler (147). It is suggested that bile salts, as organic anions, are actively transported into the biliary canaliculi and that water may move in the bile passively. That bile is isotonic with respect to plasma is used as an argument in favor of water moving along the osmotic gradient created by the active transport of the organic anions. These anions have the ability to form large aggregates or micelles, thus reducing their contribution to the total osmotic pressure of the bile. However, the sum of sodium, potassium, chloride, and bicarbonate concentrations correlates well with the observed osmolarity.

Bile flow is dependent upon adequate availability of bile salts, and it is estimated that 80 to 90 per cent of the bile salt excreted in the bile is reabsorbed and returned to the liver. The effects of back-pressure upon bile flow rate have been studied by Richards & Thomson (148, 149). They suggest an interesting hypothesis that relates the "load" of bile salts within the liver cells to secretory rates. It is assumed that at "resting" secretory rates the presentation of bile salts to and secretion from the cells are in equilibrium. When a back-pressure is applied, secretion is immediately reduced, and with presentation remaining the same, an increased "load" of bile salts accumulates within the cell. This increased "load" causes increased secretion to reestablish equilibrium. The authors outline interesting experiments using vertical tubes of different diameter connected to the cannulated common bile duct of the dog. Harrison & Hill (150) recorded the rate of flow and total solids in sheep with biliary fistulae. Effects of temperature and perfusion pressure on volume and flow rate of bile in the isolated liver of the rat have been studied by Morris (151). Maximal production of bile occurred at 38°C. Significant reductions in flow were observed at 32 and 42°C.

As previously mentioned by Hogben (152), the appearance of large inert molecules in bile suggests an unusual degree of porosity for the relatively free exchange of large uncharged particles, probably at the parenchymal cell-bile capillary interface. In support of this is the study of Juhlin (153) in which he found that spherical particles of methyl methacrylate, marked with a fluorescent color and less than 0.1 micron in diameter, passed readily into the bile whereas larger particles did not.

In a recent publication from Bollman's laboratory, Hoffman et al. (154) summarized present knowledge of bile pigments, particularly as they relate to clinical jaundice. Their work shows that the diglucuronide of bilirubin (direct-reacting) is of hepatic origin. Their findings do not support the concept that an absent or defective glucuronyl transferase activity exists in patients with constitutional hepatic dysfunction. Hartiala et al. (155) pointed out that the presence of β-glucuronidase activity in a tissue does not mean that glucuronide-conjugating capacity exists.

The presence of a number of organic constituents in bile has been reported. An analysis of human bile for lipids by Blomstrand (156) demonstrated that lecithin is the predominant phospholipid and that palmitic, stearic, oleic, and linolenic acids are the major fatty acids in bile. In the bile of rats and rabbits, Nakayama & Blomstrand (157) demonstrated the presence of at least six phospholipid components which include cephalin, sphingomyelin, and lysolecithin, in addition to lecithin. A carbohydrate complex found in human gallbladder bile is reported by Giles et al. (158) to contain predominantly glucosamine, galactosamine, and galactose with smaller amounts of glucose, arabinose, fucose, and ribose.

Interest continues in sulfobromophthalein (BSP) secretion by the liver cells of man and other species (159 to 165). Species differences have been noted. Hepatic cells have the ability to "store" BSP and to continue to secrete it into the bile after its disappearance from the plasma (159). It has been noted that the rate of uptake by liver is greater in the dog than in man (160). A number of substances are capable of inhibiting uptake of BSP by liver cells, such as probenecid (in dog but not rat) and biligrafin (in rat and dog), presumably by competing for the same mechanism (163). Acute or chronic biliary tract obstruction (165) and toxic agents that produce hepatocellular damage (162) also inhibit BSP uptake and storage by the hepatic cells. The "storage capacity" of the hepatic cell can apparently be saturated by BSP, for its secretion into bile becomes constant when plasma concentration of BSP exceeds 3 mg per 100 ml (161). In the dog it has been demonstrated that BSP and glutathione combined intrahepatically to yield a variety of ninhydrin-positive conjugates (164).

The germ-free animal (166, 167) undoubtedly will become extremely useful for the study of effects of intestinal microbial flora on the host. By use of the germ-free rat, Gustafsson & Lanke (166) demonstrated that the site of origin of urobilins is the small intestine and that it is produced by the reduction of bilirubin by organisms that were isolated from the intestinal contents of conventional animals. The action of intestinal microorganisms on bile acids has been studied by Norman & Bergman (168). It was found that 7-ketodeoxycolic acid was the main metabolite formed in aerobic cultures.

INTESTINAL ABSORPTION

The transfer of many materials across the epithelial boundary of the gut has become relatively easy to measure, particularly with the use of isotopes. The everted, isolated, intestinal segment appears to be maintaining its popularity as the method of choice for studies *in vitro*. These circumstances have resulted in the publication of data for the intestinal absorption of almost every conceivable substance that might, at one time or another, be found within the lumen of the gut. Although data are easy to collect and not too difficult to publish, the interpretation of such data is extremely difficult. It is not surprising that views expressed are frequently in conflict. In a consideration of intestinal absorption, certain fundamentals like pH and electrochemical potential gradient must be taken into account. The reader is referred to a recent paper by Ussing (169) for an excellent discussion of the relationship of electrical potential to sodium and chloride ion transport. Hogben again pointed out the importance of considering the pH at the site of absorption (170) and suggested a classification of mechanisms concerned with movement of material across cell membranes (171).

From a clinical standpoint, recent considerations of the malabsorptive states that occur in man and the evaluation of laboratory procedures used to detect them (172, 173, 174) may be of interest.

Water and electrolyte movement.—Substrate requirements for ion transport by rat intestine *in vitro* have been determined by Gilman & Koelle (175). The rate of aerobic glycolysis was higher for the jejunum than for the ileum. When glucose in the mucosal fluid was replaced by citrate or pyruvate, transport practically ceased in the jejunum but was little affected in the ileum. It was concluded that glycolysis provides an obligatory source of energy for ion transport by the jejunum. In isolated jejunal and ileal segments of rat intestine, water movement was found to be passive, following the osmotic forces set up by net solute transport (176, 177). Experiments *in vivo* with Thiry-Vella loops in dogs (178) and in cats (179) demonstrated that water movement occurs in the absence of, or against high osmotic gradients, suggesting an active transport mechanism for water. These differences may be accounted for by the techniques used and the increased permeability of the isolated gut segment. Annegers (180) measured water absorption from intestinal loops of unanesthetized dogs and found that net water absorption at given osmolar perfusate concentrations was greater from salt than from glucose or sorbose solutions. Code *et al.* (181) found that acidification of the contents of duodenal and ileal segments of dogs will decrease absorption of water. Increases in portal pressure apparently have little effect on absorption of water from the small intestine (182).

The principles underlying the exchanges of potassium and sodium ions across cell membranes have been reviewed by Conway (183). The movement of sodium, potassium, chloride, and other ions across the intestinal mucosa has been studied in preparations *in vitro* (176, 177, 184) and *in vivo* (178 to 182, 185, 186, 187).

Sodium is actively transported across the intestinal mucosa against an electrochemical gradient and apparently is dependent upon the presence of glucose as a substrate (175, 176). Net absorption from lumen to plasma occurs at all levels above 32 meq per liter for concentrations of perfusate, and the rate of transfer is proportional to the concentration of perfusate (178). In man (186) and dog (181), the absorption rate of sodium from the intestine is exponential. In a recent study, effects of motility on sodium absorption were inconclusive, but an organomercurial, mercaptomerin, had no effect on the transport of sodium from lumen to plasma when a mercurial effect on the kidney was observed (186). Acidification of the intestinal contents decreases the absorption of sodium (181). An increase in portal vein pressure does not affect the sodium absorption from lumen to plasma in the dog, but does increase plasma to lumen transfer (182). Deoxycorticosterone increased the unidirectional flux rate from lumen to plasma in the colon of the dog, but no effect was noted in the small bowel.

Clarkson *et al.* (184) reported that chloride, bromide, iodide, nitrate, and thiocyanate ions moved at approximately the same rates in isolated jejunal and ileal segments of the rat. Bicarbonate, acetate, propionate, and phosphate moved preferentially in the jejunum. Transfer of chloride from plasma to lumen in the dog against a concentration and electrochemical gradient has been considered as evidence of "active" transfer by Tidball (187). Net chloride secretion rates were found to be greater in the jejunum than in the ileum (180).

Calcium and strontium in concentrations below one millimolar increased sodium and water absorption *in vivo* from the intestine of the rat (188); concentrations above this had an inhibitory effect. Studies *in vivo* have also demonstrated that calcium is actively transported against a concentration and potential gradient by the duodenum of the rat (189). Active transport, as well as diffusion of calcium, is enhanced by vitamin D (190). Lysine also has been found to increase the absorption of calcium and of strontium from the small intestine of the rat (191). Radiophosphorus is absorbed at all levels of the rat's small intestine, but most effectively from the ileum (192).

The amount of iron within the body stores in some manner regulates the absorption of iron from the intestinal tract. The role of ferritin in the transport of iron is still obscure. It has been repeatedly demonstrated that iron absorption increases when body stores of iron are depleted and decreases when total body iron is in excess of normal amounts. These observations have been confirmed recently in rat (193) and man (194). A search for humoral factors that might regulate iron absorption in plasma and crude extracts of liver, spleen, kidney, and bone marrow of rats was not rewarding (195).

Fat absorption.—Ingested fat is rapidly, but incompletely, hydrolyzed in the upper small bowel by the action of pancreatic lipase in the presence of bile salts. Free fatty acids are absorbed directly through the lipoid membrane of the intestinal cells. It is estimated that approximately 30 per cent of the fatty acids pass into the mucosal cells as glycerides (196). Studies *in vitro* have suggested the presence in the intestinal mucosa of a lipase that appears to be somewhat specific for the hydrolysis of monoglycerides (197). Within the mucosal cell, the long-chain fatty acids are synthesized into triglycerides, while the short fatty acids pass unchanged into the portal blood. In cell-free homogenates of rat and human intestinal mucosa, a very active enzyme system has been demonstrated which incorporates palmatate-1-C^{14} into neutral fat (198). The esterification of the fatty acid is dependent upon coenzyme A, adenosinetriphosphate, and magnesium ions. Homogenates prepared from the duodenum and jejunum, the usual sites of fat absorption, were four to five times as active as those from the ileum or colon. The triglycerides within the mucosal cell are incorporated into chylomicrons and appear in lymph as neutral fat. About 10 to 15 per cent of fat in lymph is in the form of phospholipids. Apparently this fraction is independent of the type of lipid absorbed from the intestine (199, 200). Palmitic acid-C^{14} or $NaH_2P^{32}O_4$ is incorporated into phosphatidic acids when incubated with intestinal segments of the hamster and, if fatty acids are added, the process is increased two- to threefold (201). Although this might suggest that phospholipids represent an important aspect of fat transport, their exact role is not understood.

An interesting report by Jimenez-Diaz *et al.* (202) points out that individuals with steatorrhea, as well as normal persons, frequently excrete more fat in the stool than is taken in with their diets. Their data seem to show that much of the fat in the stool is endogenous in origin and poses the interesting question of secretion of fat by the intestine. The usual site of absorption of fat is generally considered to be the upper small bowel (196); however, rapid transport through, or inadequate mixing in, this area may allow a greater quantity of fat to be absorbed from the lower small bowel (203, 204).

The data of Fedor & Fisher (205) are indeed welcome for they clearly refute the strong clinical impression that an impairment of fat absorption exists after cholecystectomy. The radioactivity appearing in the blood after ingesting I^{131} triolein has been separated into two fractions by George *et al.* (206). The "alpha" fraction, which comprises about 5 per cent of the radioactivity, is cleared slowly over approximately nine hours, whereas the "beta" fraction, which comprises about 95 per cent, is cleared in five to ten minutes. Straight peptide chains that will produce steatorrhea in patients sensitive to gluten have been isolated from gliadin (207). Continued progress in this area seems to offer promise of a biochemical explanation of the malabsorption state in sprue.

Reports accompanied by beautiful electronmicrographs demonstrating particulate fat in the microvilli and other areas of intestinal epithelial cells continued to appear (208, 209). The significance of this mode of fat transport is still obscure.

Protein absorption.—In the normal course of events, ingested proteins are reduced to amino acids by digestive processes and absorbed as such. In the past it has been commonplace to consider (*a*) that L-amino acids were actively transported by stereochemical specific mechanisms, and (*b*) that the D-amino acids were absorbed by passive diffusion. These concepts were based on the fact that L-amino acids will disappear from the lumen of the intestine at a faster rate than their corresponding D-isomers. However, recent investigations showed that neither of these concepts is entirely correct. The active transport of an amino acid may be inhibited by the presence of one or more other amino acids. This mutual inhibition suggests that tyrosine, phenylalanine, methionine, tryptophan, and histidine share at least one common step in their absorption, and it casts doubt on the specificity of a stereochemical mechanism (210, 211). Jervis & Smyth (212) demonstrated that D-methionine can be absorbed against a concentration gradient and that such absorption is susceptible to metabolic inhibition and the presence of L-methionine. These observations suggest that D-methionine can utilize the transfer mechanism of L-methionine, but has a lower affinity for it than does L-methionine. Other D- and L-amino acids are known to share the same transfer mechanism. Once across the epithelial boundary, the mucosal cell has the ability to concentrate and store amino acids without apparent degradation. The mucosal concentration may be as high as nine times that in the bathing medium (210). Mucosal concentration has been demonstrated for L-tyrosine (210), L-tryptophan (211), and L-phenylalanine (213). Spencer & Samiy (214) demonstrated that the net amount of L-phenylalanine transported is a function of the mucosal concentration. It has been suggested that intramural accumulation is the "active" process in absorption of amino acids and that outward diffusion from wall to serosa is a passive event (213). The kinetics of carrier-mediated, active transport mechanisms for amino acids was discussed by Jacquez (215). In isolated intestinal sacs of hamster intestine, it has been demonstrated that absorption rates of L-tryptophan (211) and L-phenylalanine (214) are greater in segments of gut from the midintestine. An interesting study by Guggenheim *et al.* (216) showed that the biological availability of certain amino acids (lysine and methionine) is not necessarily related to the content of these amino acids in various proteins.

There is no doubt that molecular protein can pass intact through the intestinal mucosa. The mechanism of transport is obscure, although pinocytosis has been suggested. Type-A botulinum toxin with size range comparable of S_{20} values of 4.4 to 11.4 has been identified in intestinal lymph after being placed in the small intestine of the rat (217). Bovine gamma globulin has been found in the blood after oral administration to the young rat (218). In the first 36 hours of the pig's life (219), the protein absorption mechanisms are qualitatively nonselective and permit the absorption of many nonporcine proteins, as well as polyvinylpyrrolidone.

Carbohydrate absorption.—Crane's excellent, recent review (220) should be consulted for the present status of our knowledge of the intestinal absorption of sugars. Some 14 monosaccharides have now beeen found that are actively absorbed against a concentration gradient. The specific requirement for a hydroxyl group at the carbon-two position continues to hold for all sugars actively transported by the gut. Like amino acids, the phenomenon of mutual inhibition can be demonstrated (221), and suggests that all actively absorbed sugars share a common pathway, at least at one step, which exhibits Michaelis-Menten kinetics (220). Crane lists some 35 other sugars that have been tested and found not to be absorbed against a concentration gradient. The rates of absorption of substances in this group are nearly proportional to increasing concentrations and suggest passive diffusion as the mechanism of transport, although it is doubtful that the process is this simple.

The sodium ion and the "sodium pump" are apparently essential for the active transport of sugars. Replacing the sodium ion with lithium or magnesium *in vivo* (222) or *in vitro* (223) abolishes active sugar transport. Digitalis and similar drugs inhibit the active transport of 3-methylglucose (224). Such drugs probably act by preventing sodium ion transport, with the resultant effect on sugar transport being a secondary one. The electrical potential has been measured across the isolated intestinal segment of the rat and found to be about 8 mv (225). This potential difference is related to sodium transport and, thus, to active absorption of sugars.

The absorption of sucrose, maltose, and oligosaccharides from starch hydrolysis was studied by Chain *et al.* (226). When the isolated rat intestinal segment was perfused with sucrose, a higher concentration of fructose was obtained on the serosal side than after perfusion with fructose. It was concluded that sucrose, after being absorbed, was broken down into glucose and fructose within the cell and these products then appeared in the serosal fluid. Only glucose appeared on the serosal side after starch hydrolysate perfusion.

The site of absorption in the small bowel has been determined for a number of sugars in various species. The demonstration that glucose is readily absorbed from segments of the upper parts of the small bowel of the rat but not from the lower ileum (227) is in keeping with the general concept that a gradient, from the pylorus downward, exists for the active absorption of sugars (220). There is limited absorption in the stomach and little, if any, in the colon. Active transport has been demonstrated for glucose, 6-deoxy-D-glucose, and galactose in the small intestine of fetal and newborn rabbits (228). Glucagon does not influence absorption of glucose by rat and hamster small intestine (229). Semistarvation (230) increases the rate of absorption of glucose and alcohol depresses (231) absorption of xylose from rat small intestine.

Vitamin B_{12} absorption.—As a result of studies with gastrectomized rats, Cooper & Castle (232) proposed an interesting hypothesis to explain observed differences in activity of different species of intrinsic factor on absorption of B_{12} by the rat. They considered the mechanism of absorption to consist of three phases. The first phase is a non-species-related competitive binding of dietary B_{12} by intrinsic factor. The second phase is a non-energy-requiring absorption by the intestinal mucosa of the intrinsic factor-bound B_{12}. This phase is dependent upon the presence of a divalent cation, preferentially calcium. The third phase is a species-related conversion of the Ca^{++}-dependent bond and release of free vitamin B_{12} at the surface of or within the mucosal cell, possibly as a result of enzymic action. The freed B_{12} would then be accepted by an appropriate transport mechanism or would simply diffuse passively into the blood vessels of the intestine.

The principal site of absorption of vitamin B_{12} in the rat is the upper and mid portion of the ileum (233, 234). In man, however, evidence suggesting that the lower ileum is the primary site of absorption continues to appear (235, 236). In patients who have had partial gastrectomy, absorption of B_{12} is enhanced when administered with food (237). It has been reported that intrinsic factor-bound vitamin B_{12} is not absorbed as well as free crystalline B_{12} in patients with the idiopathic malabsorption syndrome (238). These observations are diametrically opposed to those in normal individuals and patients with pernicious anemia.

Cholesterol absorption.—Borgstrom (239) used C^{14} cholesterol to study cholesterol absorption in man and found that absorption rates are higher in the upper small bowel than lower in the intestine. The incomplete absorption of cholesterol (40 to 60 per cent) as opposed to the absorption of dietary fat, which is normally about 95 per cent, is not well understood. Although previously considered not to be absorbed, coprostanol, the *cis*-isomer of cholestanol (dihydrocholesterol), has now been shown to be absorbed from the small intestine of the rat (240). Setty & Ivy (240) reviewed the stereochemical structure of compounds related to cholesterol and known to be absorbed by the rat intestine, and found they all have a "chair" conformation. In the rat, cholesterol is absorbed to an extent of about 65 per cent, cholestanol 22 per cent, and coprostanol 50 per cent. Hellman *et al.* (241), by means of cannulation of the thoracic duct in man and the administration of labeled cholesterol, found that dietary cholesterol is largely transported through the lympatics after absorption and that the major portion is esterified during the absorptive process.

VISCERAL CIRCULATION

The topic of visceral circulation, particularly as it pertains to the digestive tract, has not been commented upon in recent *Annual Reviews of Physiology*. This subject has become increasingly important in the past few years and is an area with which physiologists interested in the digestive system will become more and more concerned. With methods now available it is possible to determine blood flow to a number of organs of the digestive tract and to relate vascular factors to other functions. Clearance methods employing the indirect principle of Fick are commonly used for studies in the intact animal. Other techniques include calorimetry and flowmeters of various types to determine local blood flow to an organ. Henning *et al.* (242) reviewed a number of methods currently in use for determining blood flow of digestive organs in the intact animal. Examples of indicators recently used to determine hepatic blood flow include sulfobromophthalein (243, 244), I^{131}-labeled rose bengal (245), indocyanine green (246), radioactive colloid chromic phosphate (247), and colloidal aggregates of heat-denatured human serum albumin labeled with I^{131} (248).

In man, hepatic blood flow during surgical anesthesia was found to decrease from a mean value of 829 to 539 ml per min (247). There was no difference between patients with cirrhosis and those with normal livers. Recent measurements of hepatic blood flow in patients with portal hypertension seem to indicate that they are not significantly different from normal subjects (248). This is of interest in view of the findings of Shaldon *et al.* (249) that high levels of epinephrine and norepinephrine can be recovered from the portal venous blood of patients with portal hypertension. A method for estimating the amount of collateral blood flow in portal hypertension was reported by Iber *et al.* (250). In dogs with partial or complete occlusion of the supradiaphragmatic vena cava, flow in the portal vein and the hepatic artery was measured by the square-wave electromagnetic flowmeter (251). No significant difference in flow was found between these animals and normal dogs which had a hepatic flow of 39 ml/kg/min. The portal vein to hepatic artery flow ratio was usually 2:1.

The gut seems to share with the brain and heart a preferential blood flow during total body perfusion (252). In dogs (253), flow rate for the duodenum has been reported as 1.39 ml per minute per gram wet tissue, jejunum 0.98, ileum 0.83, and colon 0.73 in the fasted state. This suggests a decreasing gradient. The regulation of intestinal blood flow in the dog has been studied by Johnson (254). He reports that a reduction in arterial pressure from 120 mm Hg to 400 mm Hg resulted in a decrease in vascular resistance of the terminal ileum in 72 per cent of the experiments. When the pancreas is stimulated with secretin an increase in blood flow, as well as blood content, has been demonstrated (255, 256). Improved techniques for isolating and perfusing the liver *in situ* have been described recently (257, 258).

LITERATURE CITED

1. Andersson, B., and Larsson, S., *Pharmacol. Revs.*, **13**, 1–16 (1961)
2. Wyrwicka, W., and Dobrzecka, C., *Science*, **132**, 805–6 (1960)
3. Morgane, P. J., and Kosman, A. J., *Am. J. Physiol.*, **198**, 1315–18 (1960)
4. Morgane, P. J., *Science*, **133**, 887–88 (1961)
5. Grossman, S. P., *Science*, **132**, 301–2 (1960)
6. Holmes, J. H., and Montgomery, V., *Am. J. Physiol.*, **199**, 907–11 (1960)
7. Herxheimer, A., and Woodbury, D. M., *J. Physiol. (London)*, **151**, 253–60 (1960)
8. Bell, F. R., and Williams, H. L., *J. Physiol. (London)*, **151**, 42P-3P (1960)
9. Denton, D. A., and Sabine, J. R., *J. Physiol. (London)*, **154**, 51P (1960)
10. Beilharz, S., and Kay, R. N. B., *J. Physiol. (London)*, **155**, 60P-1P (1961)
11. Gastineau, C. F., Franklin, R. E. Rynearson, E. H., and Rome, H. P., *Proc. Staff Meetings Mayo Clinic*, **35**, 119–42 (1960)
12. Editorial, *Lancet*, **I**, 1281–82 (1960)
13. Yudkin, J., and Carey, M., *Lancet*, **II**, 939–41 (1960)
14. Chalmers, T. M., Pawan, G. L. S., and Kekwick, A., *Lancet*, **II**, 6–9 (1960)
15. Pilkington, T. R. E., Gainsborough, H., Rosenoer, V. M., and Carey, M., *Lancet*, **I**, 856–58 (1960)
16. Prosser, C. L., Burnstock, G., and Kahn, J., *Am. J. Physiol.*, **199**, 545–52 (1960)
17. Hightower, N. C., and Salem, M. E., *J. Lab. Clin. Med.*, **52**, 820 (1958)
18. Burnstock, G., and Prosser, C. L., *Am. J. Physiol.*, **199**, 553–59 (1960)
19. Gillespie, J. S., *J. Physiol. (London)*, **155**, 59P (1961)
20. Sjostrand, N., *Acta Physiol. Scand.*, **49**, 57–61 (1960)
21. Lee, C. Y., *J. Physiol. (London)*, **153**, 405–18 (1960)
22. Gillespie, J. S., and Mackenna, B. R., *J. Physiol. (London)*, **152**, 191–205 (1960)
23. Szerb, J. C., *Brit. J. Pharmacol.*, **16**, 23–31 (1961)
24. Lewis, G. P., *Brit. J. Pharmacol.*, **15**, 425–31 (1960)
25. Schneider, R., Bishop, H., and Shaw, B., *Brit. J. Pharmacol.*, **15**, 219–23 (1960)
26. Schneider, R., and Bishop, H., *Brit. J. Pharmacol.*, **15**, 575–77 (1960)
27. Weiss, G. B., Coalson, R. E., and Hurwitz, L., *Am. J. Physiol.*, **200**, 789–93 (1961)
28. Dutta, C. R., and Basmajian, J. V., *Anat. Record*, **37**, 127–34 (1960)
29. Basmajian, J. V., and Dutta, C. R., *Anat. Record*, **139**, 443–49 (1961)
30. Basmajian, J. V., and Dutta, C. R., *Anat. Record*, **139**, 561–63 (1961)
31. Smith, C. C., and Brizzee, K. R., *Gastroenterology*, **40**, 654–64 (1961)
32. Stevens, C. E., and Sellers, A. F., *Am. J. Physiol.*, **199**, 598–602 (1960)
33. Flood, C. A., and Fink, S., *Gastroenterology*, **38**, 582–86 (1960)
34. Schenk, E. A., and Frederickson, E. L., *Gastroenterology*, **40**, 75–80 (1961)
35. Harris, L. D., Ashworth, W. D., and Ingelfinger, F. J., *J. Clin. Invest.*, **39**, 1744–50 (1960)
36. Monges, P. H., *Gastroenterologia*, **93**, 46–55 (1960)
37. Hightower, N. C., Jr., *Am. J. Digestive Diseases*, **3**, 562–83 (1958)
38. Kelley, M. L., Jr., Wilbur, D. L. III, Schlegel, J. F., and Code, C. F., *J. Appl. Physiol.*, **15**, 483–88 (1960)
39. Tuttle, S. G., Bettarello, A., and Grossman, M. I., *Gastroenterology*, **38**, 861–72 (1960)
40. Code, C. F., Kelley, M. L., Jr., Olsen, A.M., Ellis, F. H., Jr., and Schlegel, J. F., *Proc. Staff Meetings Mayo Clinic*, **35**, 391–99 (1960)
41. Titchen, D. A., *J. Physiol. (London)*, **151**, 139–53 (1960)
42. Reid, C. S. W., *J. Physiol. (London)*, **153**, 39P–40P (1960)

43. Martinsson, J., and Muren, A., *Acta Physiol. Scand.*, **50**, 103–4 (1960)

44. Perret, G. E., and Hesser, F. H., *Gastroenterology*, **38**, 219–30 (1960)

45. Hesser, F. H., and Perret, G. E., *Gastroenterology*, **38**, 231–46 (1960)

46. Louckes, H. S., Quigley, J. P., and Kersey, J., *Am. J. Physiol.*, **199**, 301–10 (1960)

47. Louckes, H. S., and Quigley, J. P., *Am. J. Physiol.*, **198**, 1329–32 (1960)

48. Code, C. F., Hightower, N. C., Jr., and Morelock, C. G., *Am. J. Med.*, **8**, 328–51 (1952)

49. Menguy, R., *Am. J. Digestive Diseases*, **5**, 792–800 (1960)

50. Hunt, J. N., and Pathak, J. D., *J. Physiol. (London)*, **154**, 254–69 (1960)

51. Hunt, J. N., *J. Physiol. (London)*, **154**, 270–76 (1960)

52. Singleton, A. G., *J. Physiol. (London)* **154**, 55P–6P (1960)

53. Singleton, A. G., *J. Physiol. (London)*, **155**, 134–47 (1961)

54. Sprung, V. H. B., and Roisch, R., *Gastroenterologia*, **93**, 145–56 (1960)

55. Farrar, J. T., Berkley, C., and Zworykin, V. K., *Science*, **131**, 1814 (1960)

56. Daniel, E. E., Wachter, B. T., Honour, A. J., and Bogoch, A., *Can. J. Biochem. and Physiol.*, **38**, 777–802 (1960)

57. Daniel, E. E., Honour, A. J., and Bogoch, A., *Gastroenterology*, **39**, 62–73 (1960)

58. Douglas, D. M., and Mann, F. C., *Am. J. Digestive Diseases*, **6**, 318–22 (1939)

59. Code, C. F., Rogers, A. G., Schlegel, J., Hightower, N. C., Jr., and Bargen, J. A., *Gastroenterology*, **32**, 651–65 (1957)

60. Chaudhary, N. A., and Truelove, S. C., *Gastroenterology*, **40**, 1–17 (1961)

61. Chaudhary, N. A., and Truelove, S. C., *Gastroenterology*, **40**, 18–26 (1961)

62. Chaudhary, N. A., and Truelove, S. G., *Gastroenterology*, **40**, 27–36 (1961)

63. Sleisenger, M. H., Law, D. H., Smith, F. W., Pert, J. H., and Lewis, C. M. *J. Clin. Invest.*, **38**, 2119–29 (1959)

64. Harper, A. A., *Gastroenterology*, **39**, 639–41 (1960)

65. Kock, N. G., *Acta Physiol. Scand.*, **47**, 5–54 (1959)

66. Hoffman, H. H., and Schnitzlein, H. N., *Anat. Record*, **139**, 429–35 (1961)

67. Langley, L. L., and Brown, R. S., *Am. J. Physiol.*, **199**, 59–62 (1960)

68. Schneyer, C. A., and Schneyer, L. H., *Am. J. Physiol.*, **199**, 55–58 (1960)

69. Kay, R. N. B., *J. Physiol. (London)*, **150**, 515–37 (1960)

70. Kay, R. N. B., *J. Physiol. (London)*, **150**, 538–45 (1960)

71. Schneyer, L. H., and Schneyer, C. A., *Am. J. Physiol.*, **199**, 649–52 (1960)

72. Blix, G., and Lindberg, E., *Acta Chem. Scand.*, **14**, 1809–14 (1960)

73. Emmelin, N., and Engstrom, J., *J. Physiol. (London)*, **153**, 1–8 (1960)

74. Gomez, H., *Anat. Record*, **139**, 69–73 (1961)

75. Emmelin, N., *Brit. J. Pharmacol.*, **15**, 356–60 (1960)

76. Emmelin, N., and Engstrom, J., *J. Physiol. (London)*, **153**, 9–16 (1960)

77. Emmelin, N., Malm, L., and Stromblad, B. C. R., *Quart. J. Exptl. Physiol.*, **45**, 349–51 (1960)

78. Velo, A. G., and Hoff, E. C., *Am. J. Physiol.*, **200**, 46–50 (1961)

79. Hogben, C. A. M., *Am. J. Med.*, **29**, 726–31 (1960)

80. Segal, H. L., *Ann. Internal Med.*, **53**, 445–61 (1960)

81. Saint-Hilaire, S., Lavers, M. J., Kennedy, J., and Code, C. F., *Gastroenterology*, **39**, 1–11 (1960)

82. Code, C. F., *Am. J. Digestive Diseases*, **6**, 50–55 (1961)

83. Hirschowitz, B. I., *Am. J. Digestive Diseases*, **6**, 199–228 (1961)

84. Hirschowitz, B. I., *J. Appl. Physiol.*, **15**, 933–38 (1960)

85. Werther, J. L., Parker, J. G., and Hollander, F., *Gastroenterology*, **38**, 368–73 (1960)

86. Blair, E. L., Harper, A. A., Harris, D., Reed, J. D., and Wilkinson, R., *J Physiol. (London)*, **154**, 68P–69P (1960)

87. Hollander, F., *Gastroenterology*, **40**, 477–90 (1961)

88. Hill, K. J., *J. Physiol. (London)*, **154**, 115–32 (1960)

89. Brooks, F. P., *Science*, **132**, 1489 (1960)

90. Smith, G. P., Brooks, F. P., Davis, R. A., and Rothman, S. S., *Am. J. Physiol.*, **199**, 889–92 (1960)

91. Wright, G. H., *J. Physiol. (London)*, **155**, 24P–25P (1961)

92. Janowitz, H. D., *Ann. Rev. Physiol.*, **23**, 153–82 (1960)

93. Piper, D. W., *Am. J. Digestive Diseases*, **5**, 880–88 (1960)

94. Altamirano, M., Chiang, L., and Bravo, I., *Am. J. Physiol.*, **199**, 131–35 (1960)

95. Houck, J. C., Bhayana, J., and Lee, T., *Gastroenterology*, **39**, 196–200 (1960)

96. Cummins, A. J., *Ann. Internal Med.*, **52**, 1213–20 (1960)

97. Greenberg, L. A., and Lester, D., *J. Appl. Physiol.*, **15**, 995–98 (1960)

98. Harries, E. H. L., *J. Physiol. (London)*, **152**, 73P–74P (1960)

99. Clark, C. G., Curnow, V. J., Murray, J. G., Stephens, F. O., and Wyllie, J. H., *J. Physiol. (London)*, **153**, 61P–62P (1960)

100. Marks, I. N., Komarov, S. A., and Shay, H., *Am. J. Physiol.*, **199**, 579–88 (1960)

101. Read, A. M., and Johnstone, F. R. C., *Anat. Record*, **139**, 525–29 (1961)

102. Gray, S. J., *Am. J. Digestive Diseases*, **6**, 355–71 (1961)

103. Trethewie, E. R., *Australian J. Exptl. Biol. Med. Sci.*, **37**, 573–80 (1959)

104. Beck, I, T., Fletcher, H. W. McKenna, R. D., and Griff, H., *Gastroenterology*, **38**, 740–49 (1960)

105. Wiederanders, R. E., Classen, K. L., Gobbel, W. G., Jr., and Doyle, M. W., *Ann. Surg.*, **152**, 119–28 (1960)

106. Bowen, R., Jr., Mayne, J. G., Cain, J. C., and Bartholomew, L. G., *Proc. Staff Meetings Mayo Clinic*, **35**, 537–44 (1960)

107. Sun, D. C. H., and Shay, H., *J. Appl. Physiol.*, **15**, 697–703 (1960)

108. Cohen, N., Mazure, P., Dreiling, D. A., and Janowitz, H. D., *Gastroenterology*, **39**, 48–54 (1960)

109. Jow, E., Webster, D. R., and Skoryna, S. C., *Gastroenterology*, **38**, 732–39 (1960)

110. Dotevall, G., and Muren, A., *J. Physiol. (London)*, **154**, 4P–5P (1960)

111. Thompson, J. C., and Peskin, G. W., *Surg., Gynecol. Obstet.*, **112**, 205–27 (1961)

112. Retzer, O., Morrison, M., and Harrison, R. C., *Surg., Gynecol. Obstet.*, **111**, 285–88 (1960)

113. Woodward, E. R., and Dragstedt, L. R., *Physiol. Revs.*, **40**, 490–504 (1960)

114. Schofield, B., *Gastroenterology*, **39**, 511–14 (1960)

115. Gregory, R. A., and Tracy, H. J., *J. Physiol. (London)*, **154**, 52P (1960)

116. Emas, S., *Gastroenterology*, **39**, 771–82 (1960)

117. Uvnäs, B., and Emas, S., *Gastroenterology*, **40**, 644–48 (1961)

118. Irvine, W. T., Watkin, D. B., and Williams, E. J., *Gastroenterology*, **39**, 41–47 (1960)

119. Nyhus, L. M., Chapman, N. D., DeVito, R. V., and Harkins, H. N., *Gastroenterology*, **39**, 582–89 (1960)

120. Thein, M. P., and Schofield, B. M., *J. Physiol. (London)*, **154**, 53P–54P (1960)

121. Gregory, R. A., *J. Physiol. (London)*, **144**, 123–37 (1958)

122. Olbe, L., *Acta Physiol. Scand.*, **50**, 110–11 (1960)

123. DuVal, M. K., Jr., and Price, W. E., *Ann. Surg.*, **152**, 410–15 (1960)

124. DuVal, M. K., Jr., and Price, W. E., *Ann. Surg.*, **153**, 581–84 (1961)

125. Shapira, D., Morgenstern, L., and State, D., *Am. J. Physiol.*, **199**, 593–97 (1960)

126. Woodward, E. R., Turnbull, W. E., Schapiro, H., and Towne, L., *Am. J. Digestive Diseases*, **3**, 204–13 (1958)

127. Andersson, S., *Acta Physiol. Scand.*, **49**, 42–56 (1960)

128. Andersson, S., *Acta Physiol. Scand.*, **49**, 231–41 (1960)

129. Andersson, S., *Acta Physiol. Scand.*, **50**, 23–31 (1960)

130. Andersson, S., *Acta Physiol. Scand.*, **50**, 105–12 (1960)

131. Andersson, S., *Acta Physiol. Scand.*, **50**, 186–96 (1960)

132. Andersson, S., *Acta Physiol. Scand.*, **50**, 12–13 (1960)

133. Warren, S., *Science*, **132**, 564–66 (1960)

134. Janowitz, H. D., *Am. J. Digestive Diseases*, **6**, 441–46 (1961)

135. Sun, D. C. H., and Shay, H., *Gastroenterology*, **40**, 379–82 (1961)

136. Polachek, A. A., and Williard, R. W., *Ann. Internal Med.*, **52**, 1195–1200 (1960)

137. Dreiling, D. A., and Janowitz, H. D., *Am. J. Digestive Diseases*, **5**, 639–54 (1960)

138. Dumont, A. E., and Mulholland, J. H., *Gastroenterology*, **38**, 954–56 (1960)

139. Vithayathil, A. J., Buck, F., Bier, M., and Nord, F. F., *Arch. Biochem. Biophys.*, **92**, 532–40 (1961)

140. Liener, I. E., *Arch. Biochem. Biophys.*, **88**, 216–21 (1960)

141. Svatos, A., and Queisnerova, M., *Gastroenterologia*, **94**, 290–94 (1960)

142. Lakshminarayana, G., Kruger, F. A., Cornwell, D. G., and Brown, J. B., *Arch. Biochem. Biophys.*, **88**, 318–27 (1960)

143. diSant'Agnese, P. A., Jones, W. O., and Dische, Z., *Ann. Internal Med.*, **54**, 482-2 (1961)

144. Best, E. B., Hightower, N. C., Jr., Williams, B. H., and Carabasi, R. J., *Southern Med. J.*, **53**, 1091-95 (1960)

145. Karlish, A. J., and Tarnoky, A. L., *Lancet*, **II**, 514-15 (1960)

146. Uram, J. A., Friedman, L., and Kline, O. L., *Am. J. Physiol.*, **199**, 387-94 (1960)

147. Wheeler, H. O., *Gastroenterology*, **40**, 584-86 (1961)

148. Richards, T. G., and Thomson, J. Y., *J. Physiol. (London)*, **154**, 60P-1P (1960)

149. Richards, T. G., and Thomson, J. Y., *Gastroenterology*, **40**, 705-7 (1961)

150. Harrison, F. A., and Hill, K. J., *J. Physiol. (London)*, **154**, 61P-62P (1960)

151. Morris, B., *Australian J. Exptl. Biol. Med. Sci.*, **38**, 99-110 (1960)

152. Hogben, C. A. M., *Ann. Rev. Physiol.*, **22**, 381-406 (1960)

153. Juhlin, L., *Acta Physiol. Scand.*, **49**, 224-30 (1960)

154. Hoffman, H. N. II, Whitcomb, F. F., Jr., Butt, H. R., and Bollman, J. L., *J. Clin. Invest.*, **39**, 132-42 (1960)

155. Hartiala, K., Nanto, V., Rinne, U. K., and Savola, P., *Acta Physiol. Scand.*, **49**, 65-73 (1960)

156. Blomstrand, R., *Acta Chem. Scand.*, **14**, 1006-10 (1960)

157. Nakayama, F., and Blomstrand, R., *Acta Chem. Scand.*, **14**, 1211-12 (1960)

158. Giles, R. B., Jr., Smith, J. E., Crowley, G., and Michael, M., *J. Lab. Clin. Med.*, **55**, 38-45 (1960)

159. Wheeler, H. O., Epstein, R. M., Robinson, R. R., and Snell, E. S., *J. Clin. Invest.*, **39**, 236-47 (1960)

160. Barber-Riley, G., Goetzee, A. E., Richards, T. G., and Thomson, J. Y., *J. Physiol. (London)*, **151**, 37P-39P (1960)

161. Wheeler, H. O., Meltzer, J. I., and Bradley, S. E., *J. Clin. Invest.*, **39**, 1131-44 (1960)

162. Heikel, T., Knight, B. C., Rimington, C., Ritchie, H. D., and Williams, E. J., *Proc. Roy. Soc. (London)*, **153**, 47-79 (1960)

163. Barber-Riley, G., *J. Physiol. (London)*, **153**, 22P-23P (1960)

164. Javitt, N. B., Wheeler, H. O., Baker, K. J., Ramos, O. L., and Bradley, S. E., *J. Clin. Invest.*, **39**, 1570-77 (1960)

165. Andrews, W. H. H., and Lozano, I. D. R., *J. Physiol. (London)*, **154**, 59P-60P (1960)

166. Gustafsson, B. E., and Lanke, L. S., *J. Exptl. Med.*, **112**, 975-81 (1960)

167. Gordon, H. A., *Am. J. Digestive Diseases*, **5**, 841-67 (1960)

168. Norman, A., and Bergman, S., *Acta Chem. Scand.*, **14**, 1781-89 (1960)

169. Ussing, H. H., *J. Gen. Physiol.*, **43**, 135-47 (1960)

170. Hogben, C. A. M., *Federation Proc.*, **19**, 864-69 (1960)

171. Hogben, C. A. M., *The Physiologist*, **3**, 56-62 (1960)

172. Ringelhann, B., *Gastroenterologia*, **94**, 20-29 (1960)

173. Frazer, A. C., *Gastroenterology*, **38**, 389-98 (1960)

174. Rinaldo, J. A., Jr., *Gastroenterology*, **40**, 86-93 (1961)

175. Gilman, A., and Koelle, E. S., *Am. J. Physiol.*, **199**, 1025-29 (1960)

176. Curran, P. F., *J. Gen. Physiol.*, **43**, 1137-48 (1960)

177. Clarkson, T. W., and Rothstein, A., *Am. J. Physiol.*, **199**, 898-906 (1960)

178. Vaughan, B. E., *Am. J. Physiol.*, **198**, 1235-44 (1960)

179. Ullmann, T. D., Dikstein, S., Bergmann, F., and Birnbaum, D., *Am. J. Physiol.*, **198**, 1319-22 (1960)

180. Annegers, J. H., *Am. J. Physiol.*, **200**, 107-10 (1961)

181. Code, C. F., Bass, P., McClary, G. B., Jr., Newnum, R. L., and Orvis, A. L., *Am. J. Physiol.*, **199**, 281-88 (1960)

182. Shields, R., and Code, C. F., *Am. J. Physiol.*, **200**, 775-80 (1961)

183. Conway, E. J., *J. Gen. Physiol.*, **43**, 17-41 (1960)

184. Clarkson, T. W., Rothstein, A., and Cross, A. *Am. J. Physiol.*, **200**, 781-88 (1961)

185. Berger, E. Y., Kanzaki, G., and Steele, J. M., *J. Physiol. (London)*, **151**, 352-62 (1960)

186. Groisser, V. W., and Farrar, J. T., *J. Clin. Invest.*, **39**, 1607-18 (1960)

187. Tidball, C. S., *Am. J. Physiol.*, **200**, 309-12 (1961)

188. Dumont, P. A., Curran, P. F., and Solomon, A. K., *J. Gen. Physiol.*, **43**, 1119-36 (1960)

189. Wasserman, R. H., Kallfelz, F. A., and Comar, C. L., *Science*, **133**, 883-84 (1961)

190. Harrison, H. E., and Harrison, H. C., *Am. J. Physiol.*, **199**, 265-71 (1960)

191. Raven, A. M., Lengemann, F. W., and Wasserman, R. H., *J. Nutrition*, **72**, 29–36 (1960)

192. Cramer, C. F., *Can. J. Biochem. and Physiol.*, **39**, 499–503 (1961)

193. Field, M., Seki, M., Mitchell, M. L., and Chalmers, T. C., *J. Lab. Clin. Med.*, **55**, 929–35 (1960)

194. Pirzio-Biroli, G., and Finch, C. A., *J. Lab. Clin. Med.*, **55**, 216–20 (1960)

195. Beutler, E., and Buttenwieser, E., *J. Lab. Clin. Med.*, **55**, 274–80 (1960)

196. Dawson, A. M., and Isselbacher, K. J., *Arch. Internal Med.*, **107**, 305–8 (1961)

197. Tidwell, H. C., and Johnston, J. M., *Arch. Biochem. Biophys.*, **89**, 79–82 (1960)

198. Dawson, A. M., and Isselbacher, K. J., *J. Clin. Invest.*, **39**, 150–60 (1960)

199. Blomstrand, R., and Dahlback, O., *J. Clin. Invest.*, **39**, 1185–91 (1960)

200. Rampone, A. J., *Am. J. Physiol.*, **199**, 1015–20 (1960)

201. Johnston, J. M., and Bearden, J. H., *Arch. Biochem. Biophys.*, **90**, 57–62 (1960)

202. Jimenez-Diaz, C., Linazasoro, J. M., Marina, C., and Romero, J. M., *Gastroenterologia*, **93**, 228–35 (1960)

203. Aberdeen, V., Shepherd, P. A., and Simmonds, W. J., *Quart. J. Exptl. Physiol.*, **45**, 265 (1960)

204. Janssen, B., Jr., Tyor, M. P., Owen, E. E., and Ruffin, J. M., *Gastroenterology*, **38**, 211–16 (1960)

205. Fedor, E. J., and Fisher, B., *Surg., Gynecol. Obstet.*, **111**, 206–10 (1960)

206. George, E. P., Farkas, G. S., and Sollich, W., *J. Lab. Clin. Med.*, **57**, 167–81 (1961)

207. van Roon, J. H., Haex, A. J. C., Seeder, W. A., and deJong, J., *Gastroenterologia*, **94**, 227–35 (1960)

208. Lacy, D., and Taylor, A. B., *J. Physiol. (London)*, **151**, 47P (1960)

209. Ashworth, C. T., Stembridge, V. D., and Sanders, E., *Am. J. Physiol.*, **198**, 1326–28 (1960)

210. Llu, E. C. C., and Wilson, T. H., *Am. J. Physiol.*, **199**, 127–30 (1960)

211. Spencer, R. P., and Samiy, A. H., *Am. J. Physiol.*, **199**, 1033–36 (1960)

212. Jervis, E. L., and Smyth, D. H., *J. Physiol. (London)*, **151**, 51–58 (1960)

213. Samiy, A. H., and Spencer, R. P., *Am. J. Physiol.*, **200**, 505–7 (1961)

214. Spencer, R. P., and Samiy, A. H., *Am. J. Physiol.*, **200**, 501–4 (1961)

215. Jacquez, J. A., *Proc. Natl. Acad. Sci. US*, **47**, 153–63 (1961)

216. Guggenheim, K., Halevy, S., and Friedmann, N., *Arch. Biochem. Biophys.*, **91**, 6–10 (1960)

217. Heckly, R. J., Hildebrand, G. J., and Lamanna, C., *J. Exptl. Med.*, **111**, 745–59 (1960)

218. Brambell, F. W. R., Halliday, R., and Hemmings, W. A., *Proc. Roy. Soc. (London)*, **153**, 477 (1961)

219. Lecce, J. G., Matrone, G., and Morgan, D. O., *J. Nutrition*, **73**, 158–66 (1961)

220. Crane, R. K., *Physiol. Revs.*, **40**, 789–825 (1960)

221. Jorgensen, C. R., Landau, B. R., and Wilson, T. H., *Am. J. Physiol.*, **200**, 111–16 (1961)

222. Csaky, T. Z., and Zollicoffer, L., *Am. J. Physiol.*, **198**, 1056–58 (1960)

223. Csaky, T. Z., and Thale, M., *J. Physiol. (London)*, **151**, 59–65 (1960)

224. Csaky, T. Z., Hartzog, H. G. III, and Fernald, G. W., *Am. J. Physiol.*, **200**, 459–60 (1961)

225. Barry, R. J. C., Dikstein, S., Matthews, J., and Smyth, D. H., *J. Physiol. (London)*, **155**, 17P–18P (1961)

226. Chain, E. B., Mansford, K. R. L., and Pocchiari, F., *J. Physiol. (London)*, **154**, 39–51 (1960)

227. Baker, R. D., Searle, G. W., and Nunn, A. S., *Am. J. Physiol.*, **200**, 301–4 (1961)

228. Wilson, T. H., and Linn, E. C. C., *Am. J. Physiol.*, **199**, 1030–32 (1960)

229. Nagler, R., Forrest, W., and Spiro, H. M., *Am. J. Physiol.*, **198**, 1323–25 (1960)

230. Kershaw, T. G., Neame, K. D., and Wiseman, G., *J. Physiol. (London)*, **152**, 182–90 (1960)

231. Small, M. D., Gershoff, S. N., Broitman, S. A., Colon, P. L., Cavanagh, R. C., and Zamcheck, N., *Am. J. Digestive Diseases*, **5**, 801–6 (1060)

232. Cooper, B. A., and Castle, W. B., *J. Clin. Invest.*, **39**, 199–214 (1960)

233. Okuda, K., *Am. J. Physiol.*, **199**, 84–90 (1960)

234. Moertel, C. G., Scudamore, H. H., Owen, C. A., Jr., and Bollman, J. L., *Am. J. Physiol.*, **199**, 289–91 (1960)

235. Clark, A. C. L., and Booth, C. C., *Arch. Disease Childhood*, **35**, 595–99 (1960)

236. Allcock, E., *Gastroenterology*, **40**, 81–88 (1961)

237. Deller, D. J., Germar, H., and Witts, L. J., *Lancet*, **I**, 575–77 (1961)

238. Reizenstein, P. G., *Am. J. Digestive Diseases*, **5**, 917–22 (1960)
239. Borgstrom, B., *J. Clin. Invest.*, **39**, 809–15 (1960)
240. Setty, C. S., and Ivy, A. C., *Am. J. Physiol.*, **199**, 1008–10 (1960)
241. Hellman, L., Frazell, E. L., and Rosenfeld, R. S., *J. Clin. Invest.*, **39**, 1288–93 (1960)
242. Henning, N., Demling, L., and Gromotka, R., *Am. J. Digestive Diseases*, **5**, 655–68 (1960)
243. Shoemaker, W. C., *J. Appl. Physiol.*, **15**, 473–78 (1960)
244. Castenfors, H., Hultman, E., and Josephson, B., *J. Clin. Invest.*, **39**, 776–81 (1960)
245. Combes, B., *J. Lab. Clin. Med.*, **56**, 537–43 (1960)
246. Ketterer, S. G., Wiegand, B. D., and Rapaport, E., *Am. J. Physiol.*, **199**, 481–84 (1960)
247. Levy, M. L., Palazzi, H. M., Nardi, G. L., and Bunker, J. P., *Surg., Gynecol. Obstet.*, **112**, 289–94 (1961)
248. Moreno, A. H., Rousselot, L. M., Panke, W. F., and Burke, M. L., *Surg., Gynecol. Obstet.*, **111**, 443–50 (1960)
249. Shaldon, C., Peacock, J. H., Walker, R. M., Palmer, D. B., and Badrick, F. E., *Lancet*, **I**, 957–61 (1961)
250. Iber, F. L., Kerr, D. N. S., Dolle, W., and Sherlock, S., *J. Clin. Invest.*, **39**, 1201–6 (1960)
251. Drapanas, T., Schenk, W. G., Jr., Pollack, E. L., and Stewart, J. D., *Ann. Surg.*, **152**, 705–16 (1960)
252. Johnson, J. A., Gott, V., and Welland, F., *Am. J. Physiol.*, **200**, 551–56 (1961)
253. Geber, W. F., *Am. J. Physiol.*, **198**, 985–86 (1960)
254. Johnson, P. C., *Am. J. Physiol.*, **199**, 311–18 (1960)
255. Holton, P., and Jones, M., *J. Physiol. (London)*, **150**, 479–88 (1960)
256. Jones, M., *J. Physiol. (London)*, **151**, 49P–50P (1960)
257. Shoemaker, W. C., Panico, F. G., Walker, W. F., and Elwyn, D. H., *J. Appl. Physiol.*, **15**, 687–90 (1960)
258. Healey, J. E., Jr., *Am. J. Gastroenterol.* **35**, 9–22 (1961)

THE PERIPHERAL CIRCULATION[1]

By Keith E. Cooper

*Medical Research Council, Body Temperature Research Unit, Department
of the Regius Professor of Medicine, Radcliffe Infirmary, and
Fellow of St. Peter's College, Oxford*

This year there is the usual enormous literature on the peripheral circulation and no attempt has been made to quote it all. Sufficient references have been chosen to indicate either the trends of new thought or the current controversies. Fervent arguments are going on in the field of the pulmonary circulation and exciting new advances have occurred in the study of the muscle and skin blood flows; the renal circulation still provides a good basis for argument, as does the cerebral circulation.

Perhaps too much is written, and a large number of papers seemed to have appeared too early in the course of the work, which, to your reviewer, is a reflection on the system of financing research in so many places.

My apologies are offered to those who are not mentioned, but space made it necessary to be selective and frequently this selection was all too arbitrary.

The award for enterprise in the study of the more exotic aspects of vascular physiology should be shared by Goetz *et al.* (84) for a very nice study of haemodynamics in the giraffe, and Senft & Kanwisher (189) for their studies of the heart rate and electrocardiogram of the finback whale.

Cardiac output, central blood volume, and the pulmonary circulation.—Cardiac index, i.e., the cardiac output per unit of surface area, is widely used as a comparative standard. This index may be unsound for several reasons, particularly because the cardiac output is influenced by metabolic rate and the metabolic rate is not in all circumstances a linear function of surface area. The relation between cardiac output, oxygen uptake, arteriovenous oxygen difference, and body surface area has been reassessed in fifty normal subjects by Reeves *et al.* (170). They found, as others have, a good linear relationship between body oxygen uptake and cardiac output, and the arteriovenous oxygen difference was relatively constant. The surface area relationship with cardiac output left a lot to be desired both mathematically and philosophically. Furthermore, when exercise in the supine posture is undertaken, the cardiac output-to-oxygen uptake relationship becomes nonlinear, and the cardiac output is lower during walking than during supine exercise involving similar oxygen uptakes [Reeves *et al.* (171, 172)].

The measurement of central blood volume from dye-dilution curves has come in for some criticism because of the errors involved in estimating the mean transit time under the different conditions which may obtain distal to a peripheral arterial sampling site. As Marshall & Shepherd (141) point out, the "central blood volume" has two components, i.e., the volume in the

[1] The survey of literature pertaining to this review was concluded in June 1961.

heart and lungs and a systemic volume bounded by all vessels equidistant in time with the sampling site; and this latter volume is large in comparison with the true central blood volume. A simultaneous measurement with sampling from both brachial arteries, after reactive hyperaemia had been induced in one arm, gave markedly different central blood volumes but the same measure of cardiac output. The central blood volume difference was related to the difference in flow velocity in the two arteries, giving different linear dispersals of the dye. Exercise, or any condition which markedly alters the flow velocity in peripheral arteries, will therefore alter the so-called central blood volume evaluated by this method. A high aortic sample would be less fallacious, but more traumatic. An ingenious approach to obtaining a central, or pulmonary, blood volume is that of Dock et al. (61). They simultaneously injected Evans blue into the pulmonary artery and ^{131}I-labelled albumin into the aortic root, and sampled from the brachial artery, calculating the cardiac output from the Evans blue dilution curve, but having two mean transit times—one from the pulmonary artery and the other the systemic component from the left heart. The cardiac output times the difference between these mean transit times gave the pulmonary blood volume. This method has the advantage of eliminating the variable systemic volume component but entails aortic catheterization. The values of Dock et al. for pulmonary blood volume were smaller than those obtained by most previous workers; and, in the absence of pulmonary vascular disease, this volume was proportional to the pulmonary venous pressure. This relationship was altered by vasoconstriction or obstruction of the pulmonary vessels, and Dock and co-workers suggest that a number of factors operate to maintain the pulmonary blood volume within a narrow range.

Differences in the estimated cardiac output, obtained by the radioactive indicator dilution method, have been described according to the site of injection of the indicator and whether the counting is done on arterial samples or by external counting over the chest [Gunnells & Gorten (91)]. The same authors (86), using a model circulation, have analysed the errors ascribable to external counting and showed that the mixing factors were the most important. Evidence for the validity of the thermal dilution technique for cardiac output has been presented, by comparison with the more conventional indicator dilution method, by Evonuk et al. (71).

The cardiac output (total body blood flow) and the lower body blood flow have been measured in man by a multiple dye injection technique [Marshall et al. (140)]. The exercise was done on a bicycle ergometer with one leg only, and this raised the cardiac output from nearly six to twelve litres per minute. Of this rise in output, the lower body blood flow contributed ten to eleven litres per minute.

The relationship between pressure and flow in the pulmonary bed has been discussed from a biophysical standpoint by Burton (36). He draws attention to the confusion in the parameters which have been used to define the driving pressure in the calculation of resistance in the pulmonary bed and points out that if the pulmonary arteriovenous pressure gradient, and not the transmural pressure, is used as the measure of driving pressure, the 'cold war' on the changes in pulmonary vascular resistance during respiration can be resolved. This resistance, he found, fell in inspiration and rose in expiration. There was also evidence of vasomotor activity in the pulmonary resistance vessels [Burton (36); Burton & Patel (37)]. Finally, Burton makes the interesting suggestion, backed up by observations on a piece of thin rubber tubing cemented to a balloon, that collapse of the lung will be associated with kinking of alveolar blood vessels and a consequent rise in vascular resistance.

Pulmonary vascular resistance in the dog was usually found to be slightly higher in the collapsed lung than at moderate levels of inflation, and in a few cases more markedly so, by Whittenberger *et al.* (211). These findings are out of line with those of Burton & Patel (37) in the isolated perfused lung. High levels of positive pressure inflation lead to progressively more marked elevations of vascular resistance, apparently caused by transpulmonary pressure on the vessels surrounding the alveloi. Burton & Patel consider the increase in transmural pressure of the 'intrathoracic' extrapulmonary vascular segments to be the cause of the fall in vascular resistance during negative pressure inflation. This concept, which is hotly denied by Roos *et al.* (176), is difficult to hold if, as they say, the resistance of these vessels is of the order of 1 per cent of the total resistance. Roos *et al.* point out that four pressure parameters—namely, pulmonary arterial, left atrial, pleural, and intrapulmonary pressures—are concerned in a complex interrelationship in determining the pulmonary vascular resistance. In their dogs, positive pressure inflation produced a rise, and negative pressure inflation a fall, with a supervening rise in vascular resistance if the inflation was carried further. Elevation of the pulmonary arterial or left atrial pressures led to a decrease in resistance.

Pulmonary vascular resistance in dogs was found by Simmons *et al.* (193) to be increased with either a decrease or an increase in lung volume; in fact, the variation reflected a U-shaped curve of resistance versus lung volume, with a minimum at the normal resting volume.

In excised lungs from dogs, Permutt *et al.* (159) and Howell *et al.* (105) determined the vascular volume of the lung under positive and negative pressure inflation. The hypothesis is advanced that the vascular system of the lung can be considered as made up of two compartments, one being 'compressed' and the other 'expanded' when the transpulmonary pressure is raised. It is suggested that the compressed compartment contains a small amount of fluid at low intravascular pressures and a relatively large proportion of the vascular capacity at high intravascular pressures. The different static pressure volume curves obtained with dextran and kerosene in the vessels support this idea; and, without exact anatomical detail, it is suggested that the site of the compressed compartment is in minute vessels, with the expanded portion in large vessels.

Inequality in vascular perfusion of the lung in man in the upright posture has been determined by clearance of radioactive carbon dioxide [West & Dollery (209)] and was found to be highest at the base of the lung and diminishing towards the apex. This conclusion gains support from carbon monoxide (O^{15}-labeled) clearance studies by Dollery et al. (63), who believe their results imply that at rest the basal capillaries are open and that the number of open capillaries diminishes towards the lung apex. In exercise the apical capillaries open up.

Perfusion of different parts of the lung measured by $C^{15}O_2$ uptake was measured, and either high flow with normal pulmonary arterial pressure or normal flow with high pressure gave a high perfusion in the upper zone [Dollery et al. (64)]. Clearance was related to the ratio of pulmonary to systemic flows. This method may prove a sensitive detector of left to right shunts.

Defares et al. (55) presented evidence to indicate a shift of blood from a hypoxic lung to an air-breathing lung in man in the supine position. This shift does not occur if the hypoxic lung is the lower in the lateral position [Arborelius et al. (5)], which is taken to indicate that the hypoxic stimulus is too weak to counter quite small hydrostatic effects.

The consequences of underwater swimming with a snorkel breathing apparatus are illustrated in a study of the cardiovascular effects of negative pressure breathing in man by Ting et al. (201). It is suggested that the veins coming into the thoracic cavity collapse, leaving a low-pressure thoracic circulation, while the extrathoracic circulation is mantained at normal pressure. The maintenance of these pressure differences falls on the left ventricle.

An indirect method for estimating bronchial arterial blood flow has been developed in dogs, using an indicator dilution technique with ^{131}I-serum albumin as the indicator [Cudkowicz et al. (49)], which has been modified for use in man. The errors are clearly described. In normal human subjects the bronchial arterial blood flow is less than 2 per cent of the left ventricular output, and four of six patients with clubbing of the fingers had increased bronchial arterial flow. In isolated dog lung preparations, when the blood flows normally through the pulmonary capillaries, blood from the bronchial circulation enters the pulmonary veins directly via the bronchopulmonary veins. In the absence of a normal pulmonary blood flow, the bronchopulmonary blood flows through the pulmonary capillaries [Aviado et al. (9)].

Auld and co-workers (8) studied bronchial collateral flow in dogs and described and authenticated both forward and reverse flows, using ^{131}I-albumin studies. Two bronchial circulations are postulated, one draining into the pulmonary arterial system and the other into the pulmonary venous system. Venous admixture caused by "shunt" flow in the pulmonary circulation was estimated by Finley et al. (73) to average 5 per cent of the total flow, in anaesthetized dogs; a reduction to 1 per cent during positive pressure breathing is ascribed to opening of lung areas which had collapsed during anaesthesia.

Occlusion of the pulmonary artery in the dog did not cause significant transpulmonary pressure differences or elasticity changes [Verstraeten & Leusen (204)]. Intravenous injection of 20 per cent sodium chloride in the dog provoked a transitory pulmonary arterial hypertension and a small decrease in the left atrial pressure [Brutsaert et al. (34)], and a transient constriction of the small pulmonary veins may possibly be implicated. Similar experiments by Eliakim et al. (69) showed a rise in pulmonary arterial pressure after a 20 per cent sodium chloride solution was injected intravenously. There were differences in the responses in the superior and inferior main vessels, and the site of vascular constriction was thought to be in the veins close to the left atrium and also at the pulmonary arteriolar level.

Using ^{131}I-serum albumin and ^{51}Cr-labeled red cells, Parrish et al. (157) measured the mean transit times of plasma and red cells in open-chest experiments on anaesthetized dogs. The ratio of the cell to plasma transit times was 0.91 ± 0.05. Although these authors obtained indications from their transfer characteristic curves that a proportion of the transit time was made via slow-moving circuits or intermittent flow channels, there was no evidence of a preferential cell-shunting mechanism in the lung.

The average time spent by the red cells in the pulmonary capillaries was estimated at 0.79 second in the human subject at rest, and this decreased to about 0.5 second in treadmill exercise sufficiently severe to triple the volume flow through the pulmonary capillary bed [Johnson et al. (113)]. The exercise mean transit time of red cells through the pulmonary capillaries deviated from the predicted rectangular hyperbola, which would obtain if the capillary blood volume had not changed from its resting value, in such a way as to suggest that the capacity of the capillaries in the lung increases with exercise. Johnson et al. also point out that if the pulmonary capillary volume is equal to or greater than the right ventricular output, the red cells will occupy at least one cardiac cycle in the lung capillary bed, and this will help to obviate the effect of pulsatile flow on the red cell transit time.

An ingenious method for measuring the right ventricular output in man, involving a continuous infusion of [85]Kr in solution into the right atrium and sampling from the pulmonary artery, has been described by Rochester et al. (174). Its value is in obtaining multiple observations at short time intervals. The values obtained agree within 10 per cent with the conventional direct Fick measurement and indicate that the cardiac output rises well within the first minute of exercise.

Exercising dogs violently on a treadmill caused a threefold rise in cardiac output and a continued fall in pulmonary vascular resistance (pulmonary artery pressure minus pulmonary wedge pressure divided by flow); in two dogs the lung plus left heart volume did not change, whereas it rose by 18 per cent in the third [Marshall et al. (142)]. Ligation of the left pulmonary artery had surprisingly little effect on the haemodynamic factors previously mentioned despite the fact that the whole of the increase in cardiac output passed through one lung.

Rosenberg & Forster (177) obtained evidence, from measurement of carbon monoxide diffusing capacity during manoeuvres designed to vary the mean intravascular pressure-flow relationships, that the pressure across the walls of the pulmonary vessels determines the size of the pulmonary capillary bed in the cat. Whether the increase in the pulmonary vascular bed consequent on raising the intravascular pressure is caused by rerouting some blood through previously closed capillaries or by dilating already open vessels cannot be settled by the evidence.

Harasawa & Rodbard (94) have investigated the effects of tetraethylammonium chloride and aminophylline on the pulmonary circulation; the former reduced pulmonary arterial pressure and pulmonary blood flow and the latter elevated both. No change in resistance occurred, and the view that active vasodilatation occurs with these drugs is challenged.

Bradykinin causes a fall in pulmonary vascular resistance in the isolated, perfused lobe of the dog lung, and this change is not affected by atropine [Waaler (205)].

Central control of peripheral blood flow.—The role of the hypothalamic "flight or fight" reaction in the control of muscle blood flow is discussed under a separate section [see Muscle circulation, p. 151].

The relation between skin blood flow and the control of body temperature in man remains a complex matter. Benzinger (19, 20, 21) and his colleagues have, in a series of papers, rekindled what promises to be a sharp and interesting controversy. He has measured the heat loss parameters from the skin, relating them to three cranial temperatures all measured outside the cranial cavity, but where they would reflect internal carotid blood temperature without this being subjected to further venous precooling before the blood enters the brain. He rejects the rectal temperature, as have many previous workers, e.g. Gerbrandy *et al.* (81), for the measurement of quick changes in arterial blood temperature. The site of the receptors (on whose existence and importance most workers are agreed) which mediate the efferent response to these blood temperature alterations is predicted to be in the anterior hypothalamus on the basis of extrapolation from animal experiments and by analogy with the energy-sensitive receptors of the retina. On Benzinger's own evidence they could be at any point isothermal with the temperature of the arterial blood in his measuring sites. The site in man is, however, unproven, and this reviewer feels chary of accepting the thermoregulatory organization of animals as an exact model for man in view of many features apparently unique to man. Benzinger rejects the skin as a source of sensory information for autonomic regulation of cutaneous blood vessels in body temperature adjustment; he relegates them to the "cortical" regulation of clothing, activity, and choice of environment. It is difficult to accept this view in its entirety in the face of previous evidence that (*a*) thermal radiation causes reflex vasodilatation at a variety of environmental temperatures and in the face of a sharp drop in sublingual and oesophageal temperatures [Kerslake & Cooper (119)]; (*b*) this reflex response is a quantitative reflection of the radiant heat load [Cooper *et al.* (46)]; and (*c*) it is abolished by sympathectomy of the heated area although cutaneous temperature sensation there appears to be intact [Cooper & Kerslake (45)]. Even if this reflex effect is only a short-term adaptive response to a rapidly altering thermal environment, it remains outside the 'cortical' regulation classification.

It might then be argued that the nervous reflex vasodilatation has been measured only in the hand and perhaps that part of the forearm which behaves as hand in a vascular sense, and that it may subserve reactions only in those areas where vasoconstrictor tone is the predominant control. These areas would be hand, feet, nose, and ears; and in other areas where vasodilator nerves are predominant, the reflex mechanism might operate only at low ambient temperatures. In these latter areas where the vasodilator mechanism may be linked to sweating, the argument will center around the peripheral or central control of sweating. Again, Benzinger claims evidence for the sole participation of central control, and Kerslake & Brebner (118) cite evidence for a neuronal pathway from the trunk which induces sweating in the forearm. In either case, the peripheral reflex aspects of temperature regulation have been widely quoted in the older literature as temporarily overriding the central receptor mechanism. The precision of Benzinger's method of gradient calorimetry has, however, enabled him to add powerful evidence of the delicate sensitivity of the central receptor in man.

Further evidence for thermosensitive regions in the medulla of the cat is reported by Newman & Wolstencroft (149). These regions were observed under sodium pentobarbital anaesthesia and consisted of a fall in arterial pressure if the brain temperature rose to 40–41°C. The devastating effect of anaesthesia on normal temperature regulation is well known, and the responses of the medulla to such high temperatures under these conditions are difficult to fit into the thermoregulation schema as it is at present. The significance of this effect is suggested in relation to heat exhaustion and collapse.

Electrical stimulation of various parts of the brain shows that peripheral vasomotor responses can be elicited from a number of areas. Sawyer *et al.* (184) obtained a rise in arterial pressure in cats and an arousal EEG on stimulating the anterior lobe of the cerebellar vermis, and often a fall in arterial pressure on stimulating the posterior lobe. Cerebral cortex stimulation could cause phasic changes in the calibre of the hindlimb blood vessels of the dog, the motor "analyser" having a closer connection than the parietal cortex with these vasomotor mechanisms [Orlov (153)]. A hypothalamic site has been located which on stimulation causes constriction of large arteries [Weckman (208)]. Lindgren (132) has studied the medullary vasomotor centers of cats surviving decerebration for 4 to 9 days. The vasomotor activity of the dorsal medulla is much the same as in intact aniamls, acting as a tonic and reflex center even after degeneration of pathways from higher centers. The functional significance of the vasomotor changes elicited by electrical stimulation in anaesthetized animals is often obscure, but the widespread and complex integration of vasomotor control by the brain is becoming more evident. The range of autonomic control of blood vessels has been clearly reviewed recently by Folkow (74), and the characterization by electrical stimulation of the autonomic outflow to the vessels of the hindlimb of the dog has been reported by Rawson & Randall (168).

A beautiful study of the adrenergic neurohumoral control of resistance and capacitance vessels in the cat has been made by Mellander (144). At low or moderate rates of stimulation of vasoconstrictor fibres, the effects were relatively more pronounced on the capacity than on the resistance vessels. In the latter the resistance changes were greater in the precapillary than in the postcapillary vessels. Catecholamines infused in physiological amounts, or stimulation of adrenal medullary nerves, gave weaker effects on resistance and capacity vessels than did graded stimulation of vasoconstrictor fibres.

One interesting observation by Black et al. (25) has shown that hypnotic suggestion does not mimic the cutaneous vascular responses to body heating or modify the response to thermal stimuli to any significant extent; but as we know little of the neurophysiological basis of hypnosis, the interpretation of this finding is not clear.

The participation of the cholinergic innervation of the limb blood vessels in posthaemorrhagic shock has received support from the work of Trzebski (203).

Baroreceptor and chemoreceptor activity.—The controversy over the existence and significance of baroreceptors in the mesenteric circulation has been kept alive [Selkurt & Rothe (186); Heymans et al. (103); Boyer & Scher (33)]. Selkurt & Rothe perfused the superior mesenteric artery in dogs and found only minimal changes in arterial pressure with large variations in superior mesenteric intraluminal pressure. Similarly, only small changes in systemic arterial pressure followed partial occlusion of the superior mesenteric artery or coeliac axis, separately or together, in the dog. Larger responses to this manoeuvre were observed in cats (average 74% rise in systemic arterial pressure), and in this species the response to simultaneous occlusion of the coeliac axis and superior mesenteric artery was the arithmetical sum of the effects of separate occlusions. The responses in the dog were increased by carotid sinus denervation. The dog results were thought to be suggestive of the existence of abdominal baroreceptors whose influence on the systemic blood pressure is of minor importance. In the cat, the role of these structures appeared to be more important. The anaesthetic used was chloralose in both species.

Boyer & Scher (33) perfused the abdominal aorta and found that neither sudden variation in perfusing pressure in cats nor sine wave changes in perfusion pressure in dogs produced any reflex alteration of systemic arterial pressure above the diaphragm. Similarly, occlusion of the mesenteric artery or coeliac axis, or both, during perfusion did not cause reflexly induced systemic arterial pressure responses. The vascular reactivity of the animals was established by control observations on carotid sinus pressure variations.

The anaesthetic used was chloralose, but barbiturate anaesthesia was also tried and did not modify the results. The systemic arterial pressure was considerably raised when the splanchnic arteries were occluded in nonperfusion experiments. This response was not altered by spinal cord transection at the first cervical level or by massive thiopental infusions—procedures which eliminate the carotid sinus baroreceptor responses and therefore seem to reflect a hydrodynamic effect arising from elimination of a large flow area from the circulation. Heymans *et al.* (103), using dogs under chloralose and morphine anaesthesia, were unable to demonstrate any changes in the systemic blood pressure resulting from manipulations of the various splanchnic vessels which could not be explained on a passive hydrodynamic basis. Such changes as they observed were unaltered by doses of hexamethonium sufficient to abolish the carotid sinus mechanism, or by spinal cord transection combined with hexamethonium. There seems then to be a fair measure of agreement that splanchnic baroreceptors if they exist have little functional significance in the dog. The results of experiments on cats are open to more argument with the onus of proof still resting on those who postulate visceral baroreceptors affecting the systemic arterial pressure.

Heymans *et al.* (103) found no evidence of chemoreceptors in the dog's splanchnic vascular bed which would respond to potassium cyanide, lobeline, and nicotine in doses adequate to stimulate carotid body receptors; larger doses produced transient respiratory effects which were considered as nonspecific products of irritant substances. These results contrast with a report by Kulaev (123) that, in cats whose intestinal circulation was isolated except for its nervous connections and perfused with Ringer-Locke solution, both acetylcholine and nicotine produced changes in systemic arterial pressure, giving a fall in pressure in doses of 0.01 to 1.0 μg and a rise with 5 to 100 μg. The possible effects of perfusing the gut with a nonphysiological fluid on the many afferent nerve endings contained in this area need further exploration; the nature of the receptors involved is not evident.

Other areas of the circulation have been investigated for the presence of baroreceptors and chemoreceptors. Intracardiac baroreceptors have been described by Ross *et al.* (180). They respond to a rise in intracardiac pressure, causing a rise in systemic blood volume and a fall in systemic vascular resistance. The most important site appears to be the left side of the heart, and there is some doubt as to whether part of these responses could originate in coronary baroreceptors. These receptors, one could speculate, might be of value in adjusting the capacity of the circulation to the cardiac output. Reflex pressor responses to acetylcholine injected into the femoral vein and depressor or pressor responses to epinephrine injected into the same site are reported by Rokotova & Gorbunova (175). Entry into the general circulation was prevented by clamping the inferior vena cava.

In dogs, peripheral osmoreceptors explain the results obtained by Lasser *et al.* (128). These receptors were located in the distribution of the femoral and brachial arteries, and their stimulation by hypertonic solutions—salt, glucose, and urea—caused a rise in arterial blood pressure, heart rate, and respiratory rate. The afferent nerves concerned were somatic and the responses mediated by sympathetic efferent fibres. Pericardial chemoreceptors have also been studied by Kulaev (124).

Denervation of the carotid bifurcation and cutting the vagus nerve had remarkably little effect on the haemodynamics of exercise in the dog [Leusen & Lacroix (129)]. Cardiac output changes were normal, and it is possible that higher levels of arterial pressure were obtained than in the normal animal.

Using dogs anaesthetized with morphine, chloralose, and urethane, Ross et al. (181) were able to demonstrate venoconstriction, a decreased vascular volume, and an increased venous return when the pressure was reduced in the isolated carotid sinuses. This effect was apparent after administration of catecholamines or acetylcholine. The reverse effects obtained with a raised carotid sinus pressure and trimethaphan. The baroreceptor mechanism, then, has an important role in the control of both capacity and venous return as well as in arteriolar tone.

A detailed study of the anatomical distribution and histological appearance of baroreceptors in the pulmonary artery has been made, by Coleridge et al. (41). The majority of endings—fine coiled fibres in connective tissue and supplied with thick myelinated nerve fibres—were located in the right pulmonary or in the left branch but not in the main trunk.

Skin.—Until recent years, the control of the cutaneous circulation, other than in the hand and forearm, has received little attention. It has been a habit among physiologists to infer the behaviour of blood vessels in all skin areas from observations on a few easily measurable sites, a clearly erroneous inference in the light of recent work. Investigations have shown some areas of the skin circulation to be under the control of vasoconstrictor nerve fibres, while in others the vasomotor control is effected predominantly by an active vasodilator system, possibly associated with the sweat gland activity and consequent release of bradykinin-forming enzyme. The distribution of the mechanisms over different skin regions is indicated in Table I. These results indicate vasodilator activity in response to indirect body heating, and readers should note that both mechanisms may be present with one or the other clearly predominating. It would be interesting to know where, in a vascular control sense, the forearm ends and the hand begins. The facial and upper chest regions mentioned are frequently included in the blush area; but this type of vasodilatation has not been explained. A concise analysis of the sympathetic control of skin blood vessels in the hand and forearm can be found in a review by Barcroft (12). Changes in the skin temperature over the head on going from a room temperature of 24°C to one at 0°C have been mapped by Edwards & Burton (68), and the isothermal map at 0°C room temperature correlates closely with the anatomical arrangement of the arterial blood supply.

Some evidence has come to light that the onset of vasodilatation in the arm and leg on exposure to heat may not always be correlated with the onset

TABLE I

DOMINANT MECHANISM FOR RAISING BLOOD FLOW

Skin area	Active vasodilator	Release of vaso-constrictor tone	Thermal sweating	Gustatory sweating
HEAD				
Forehead	+	−	Marked	Yes
Nose	−	+	Not conspicuous	
Cheek	+	−	Marked	Yes
Lip (glabrous)	−	+		
Chin*	+	−	Marked	Yes
Ear	−	+	Not conspicuous	
UPPER CHEST	+	−	Marked	
LIMBS				
Hand	−	+	Not great	
Forearm*	+	−	Marked	
Upper arm	+	−		
Thigh*	+	−		
Calf*	+	−		

* Vasoconstrictor fibres are known to take part in the reduction of regional blood flow during body cooling. Data obtained for Fox et al. (75, 76); Blair et al. (30, 31).

of thermal sweating [Senay et al. (188)], nor is there always a close correspondence between the extent of the vasodilatation and the sweat production. These observations do not fit neatly into the bradykinin-mechanism explanation of vasodilatation in the forearm and leg. Love & Shanks (134) invariably found sweating to precede active vasodilatation, whereas a dissociation between sweating and vasodilation was observed by Senay et al. (187) (using the photoelectric plethysmograph to estimate blood flow in the forearm) when the ambient temperature was slowly raised and cycled. They emphasize the meagre vasoconstrictor fibre activity in this area, but draw attention to the possible multifactorial control of active vasodilatation, one factor in which may be the local skin temperature.

Cold vasodilatation continues to excite interest. Using a surface calorimeter designed to estimate heat flow from a small, cooled area of skin, Fox & Wyatt (77) estimated the relative intensity of the cold vasodilatation in differing skin areas. Such results might indicate the areas in which cold vasodilatation is most active; but if the response is largely ascribable to the effect of cold on blood vessels, as Keatinge (116) suggested, it could reflect in part the vascular density of these areas. Similarly, if an axon reflex is involved, the density of nerve receptors would determine the response which might vary if different sized areas of skin were cooled.

The extent of cold vasodilatation in the hands of cold-adapted and un-adapted men has been studied [Krog *et al.* (121); Hellström & Andersen (99)] in Norwegian Lapps and North Norwegian fisherman (cold-adapted) and in scientific personnel (unadapted). With the subjects comfortably warm, the hand heat elimination to water at 0°C was not greater in the cold-adapted subjects although its onset was more rapid in them than in the unadapted men [Krog *et al.* (121)]. According to the other study by Hellström & Andersen (99), neither in comfortable warmth nor at low ambient tempera-tures was there a significant difference in the extent of cold vasodilatation between adapted and control groups. These reports conflict with previous literature. There may be an added racial factor as yet not determined.

During total immersion in water below 12°C, fat men are thought to have a more marked skin cold vasodilatation than thin men [Cannon & Keatinge (39)].

One means of raising the skin temperature locally is by the use of radiant heat, which if confined to a small area does not induce widespread reflex vasodilatation in other limbs. The response to this type of thermal stimulus has been further studied in the forearm skin by Crockford *et al.* (48). There is a vasodilatation which extends to the distal unheated part of the forearm skin; such a centrifugal spread of vasodilatation occurs after the application of rubefacients and ultraviolet irradiation. Nerve block proximal to the stimulus does not prevent the spread of vasodilation distally, but distal-ring block with lignocaine or epinephrine given subcutaneously does. The evi-dence favours a spread of vasodilatation by direct conduction in the smooth muscle of the subcutaneous plexus.

Reactive hyperaemia in the hand was found by Wisheart (212) to be greater after a three-minute arterial occlusion high in the upper arm than it was after a similar period of occlusion at the wrist. A lower intravascular pressure was found during shoulder occlusion than during wrist occlusion. This work supports a vascular myogenic stimulus as a major contributory cause of reactive hyperaemia.

Muscle circulation.—A considerable confusion has evolved around the differences in apparent blood flow which, under some circumstances, result from simultaneous measurement of ^{24}Na depot clearance and venous occlu-sion plethysmography, thermal conductivity, or venous outflow recordings. These differences have led to the suggestion that preferential channels exist in muscle which do not subserve any nutritive or ion-exchange requirements. An extensive study by Hyman *et al.* (108) showed that, in anaesthetized cats, intra-arterial infusion of Compound 48/80 (a condensation product of paramethoxyphenethylmethylamine with formaldehyde) or methacholine and sciatic nerve stimulation increased the gastrocnemius muscle flow and ^{24}Na clearance proportionately. Clamping the femoral artery reduced the flow and clearance proportionately, but sympathetic stimulation decreased total flow more than ^{24}Na clearance. Stimulation of hypothalamic vasomotor pathways raised the blood flow without consistent changes in clearance.

While pointing out difficulties in interpreting ²⁴Na clearance data, Hyman *et al.* conclude that most procedures alter nutritional and shunt circulations, but that hypothalamic stimulation is restricted to shunt flow effects.

A careful and unsuccessful search for typical arteriovenous shunts in muscle was previously reported by Barlow *et al.* (14), and subsequent studies by Barlow and co-workers (15, 16) have led to a reappraisal of the ²⁴Na clearance technique. The effect of epinephrine infusion on this clearance of ²⁴Na and other measures of "flow" from cat skeletal muscle was measured. As with human muscle, there was a failure of correspondence in the ²⁴Na clearance and venous outflow, Hensel needle flowmeter data, or direct observation of flow. The clearance consisted of two components, a fast phase with a half-time of 1.63 ± 0.14 min and a slow phase of half-time of 44.07 ± 4.09 min. These two clearance rates represent the ²⁴Na removal from muscle and intermuscular septa and tendons respectively. The effect of epinephrine differs in the two sets of vessels. Other factors such as a possible specific effect of epinephrine on the movement of sodium ions, capillary permeability, and pH were excluded. It seems that the dual circulation in muscle must be redefined as muscle blood flow and intermuscular septal and tendon blood flows. The clearance of ²⁴Na from muscle is so fast that it will be excluded from all but the first one to three minutes of measurements made in the cat (and six to twelve minutes in man) after the injection of a depot.

An important and detailed study has been made of the hypothalamic and brainstem vasodilator pathways to skeletal muscle in the cat by Abrahams *et al.* (1). They have defined with some accuracy the regions in the hypothalamus, mesencephalic tegmentum, and central grey matter from which atropine-sensitive skeletal muscle vasodilatation can be elicited by electrical stimulation. This muscle vasodilatation was found to be accompanied by other autonomic effects such as occur in the 'defence' or 'flight or fight' reactions. Stimulating these regions via implanted electrodes in the conscious cat evoked coordinated defence reactions. The evoked vasodilator response did not occur on its own, but as an integral part of a coordinated defence reaction preparing the animal for a period of intense activity. This coordinated activity, including muscle vasodilatation, could be produced by cutaneous stimulation in cats following high decerebration. A limited area just dorsal to the cerebral peduncles produced, on electrical stimulation, a muscle vasodilatation without the organized defence reaction. The nerve pathways involved are described in detail.

The responses of human forearm muscle blood vessels to emotional stimuli have been established by employing fright or mental arithmetic as the stressing stimulus [Barcroft *et al.* (11); Blair *et al.* (27); Glover (83)]. These authors agree that cholinergic vasodilator fibres mediate the greater part of the vasodilator response and that this response is peculiar to the muscles. Barcroft *et al.* (11) adduce evidence which points to an additional humoral component, which is probably circulating epinephrine. Both groups agree that this response is a part of the effects of the emotional experiences of everyday life and draw attention to the possible comparison with the effects of stimulating hypothalamic vasomotor pathways in animals.

The effects of walking and running on the calf blood flow have been investigated. Black (26) thought that the postexercise hyperaemia was caused by a "debt" built up in exercise which is paid off partly during exercise and partly after, the hyperaemia after exercise being small at speeds below three to four miles per hour and increasing progressively with speed thereafter. Halliday (93) extended these observations to the effects of prolonged walking in substantial agreement with Black's results. Leg exercise causes a small fall in forearm blood flow and a rise in systemic arterial pressure, the fall in flow being caused apparently by a rise in vasoconstrictor tone in the muscle vessels [Blair *et al.* (32)].

The effect on the forearm blood flow of releasing the circulation to the leg, after a period of arterial occlusion, has supplied evidence for a stable vasodilator substance emanating from the previously ischaemic tissue [Freeburg & Hyman (79)].

Cooling the hindlimb of the rabbit reduced the muscle blood flow, except for occasions when the limb moves and causes transient rises in the limb temperature and blood flow [Sayen & Boland (185)].

Liver and splanchnic vascular beds.—After a critical analysis of the errors involved in the conventional bromsulphalein (BSP) method for estimating hepatic blood flow, Shoemaker (192) describes a modification of the technique in dogs which gets round many difficulties. Chronically implanted portal and hepatic vein catheters give constant site sampling and enable a direct Fick calculation to be carried out on the portal-hepatic venous BSP gradient—without complications caused by extrahepatic clearance of the dye. Improved analytical methods give a greater accuracy because the measurement may be carried out with lower plasma BSP levels, at which the greater extraction ratio leads to relatively greater portal-hepatic vein concentration differences.

The nervous control of hepatic blood vessels seems to reside in the sympathetic fibres accompanying the hepatic artery. The effect of a given dose of acetylcholine is considerably less when injected into the portal vein than when infused into the hepatic artery in animals with an intact sympathetic nerve supply. The difference was not so marked with epinephrine and norepinephrine, although it followed the same pattern [Andrews & Riolozano (4)]. Iriuchijima (111) has demonstrated periodic changes in splanchnic blood flow after stimulating the splanchnic nerve or the central end of the carotid sinus nerve, or after asphyxia. These fluctuations had a 10 to 25-sec period and could be sufficient to alter the systemic blood pressure.

The portal collateral circulation, in some cases, can be measured by injecting ^{131}I-labelled albumen into the spleen and observing the concentration in the hepatic vein and the peripheral circulation [Iber *et al.* (110)].

Estimates of functional perfusion rates in various parts of the gut have been made in fasting anaesthetized rats by a rubidium fractionation technique. The highest value was that of the duodenum with the stomach next and a progressive decrease down the intestinal tract [Steiner & Mueller (196)].

Rayner *et al.* (169) present evidence for a reduction in mucosal, submucosal, and muscular blood flow in the ileum in endotoxin shock. Using an isotope technique Bacaner & Pollycove (10) estimated the colonic blood together with cardiac output. Acetylcholine raised the regional blood volume, decreased the colon blood flow, and raised the cardiac output. Norepinephrine reduced the colon blood flow and raised the cardiac output; pitressin and haemorrhage reduced both. Infusion of saline or stimulation of the pelvic ganglion reduced the flow but did not alter cardiac output.

Small doses (0.01 to 5 μg) of acetylcholine increased the spleen volume and decreased splenic vascular resistance, these effects being abolished by atropine [Daly & Scott (51)]. This was a passive response to dilatation of the splenic blood vessels. Larger doses (5 to 100 μg) caused splenic contraction, one aspect of which was caused by the nicotine-like action of acetylcholine. The authors discuss the possibility that this contraction may be the result of release of norepinephrine. The effects of catecholamines, acetylcholine, and vasopressin on hindquarter, renal artery, and superior mesenteric artery blood flow have been measured in the conscious dog with implanted ultrasonic flowmeters by Rushmer *et al.* (183). The flow in these vessels was also found to be reduced by tilting but unchanged by mild exercise on a treadmill. Electrical stimulation of the Forel H_2 field caused a rise in hindquarter flow and a fall of flow in renal and mesenteric arteries.

The problem of autoregulation in the kidney has been relegated to the study of abnormal organs by Langston *et al.* (126), who claim that if the dog's kidney was perfused *in situ* without surgical trauma, by an ingenious technique which obviated any interruption of the renal arterial blood flow, then no autoregulation occurred. Temporary renal ischaemia or perirenal damage caused autoregulation to occur. The authors tentatively suggest that either interruption of the blood supply to the renal vessel walls or blocking the renal lymphatic drainage may be concerned with the development of autoregulation. In the reported experiments the steps in arterial pressure were maintained for two minutes, and the consequences of longer intervals between pressure alterations with this technique remain to be elicited.

Waugh & Shanks (207) do not agree that renal autoregulation is an artefact, and suggest that the results of Langston, Guyton & Gillespie (126) may be ascribed to renal vasoconstriction induced by an aortic catheter as reflected by the rather low flows of less than 2 ml per min per g kidney. They postulate a myogenic response with the "myocytes" of the juxtaglomerular apparatus involved in its control.

Renal blood flow has long been known to increase in pyrogen-induced fever. The effect is clearly not mediated by a nervous pathway for it occurs in the autotransplanted kidney; it also happens when the pyrogen is given intrathecally and consequently is not apparently caused by circulating pyrogen [Cooper *et al.* (47)].

The effects of carbon dioxide on the circulation.—Recently, the circulatory responses to alterations in arterial blood carbon dioxide tension have received attention. Studies have been made on the blood vessel responses to raised pCO_2 or to topically applied CO_2 both in the intact subject and in the denervated limb; also, the vasodilatation following carbon dioxide inhalation has been studied. Vasodilatation occurs in a hand immersed in water saturated with CO_2, and the blood flow is about 40 per cent greater than that in a hand similarly immersed in water saturated with N_2O [Diji (59); Glover & Greenfield (82)]. Subcutaneous injection of CO_2, or a mixture of CO_2 and N_2O, caused a rise in skin temperature which far exceeded that produced by injecting N_2O alone, or air [Diji & Greenfield (60)]. This rise in skin temperature with CO_2 injection was interpreted as a local dilator effect of the gas on the resistance vessels. The possible contribution of humoral factors has also been mentioned by McArdle *et al.* (139). Breathing 5 to 7 per cent CO_2 in air for 5 to 10 minutes does not alter the forearm blood flow [Richardson *et al.* (173)]. These authors found, however, that breathing 5 to 7 per cent CO_2 in air raised the blood flow and lowered the vascular resistance in the forearm which had its sympathetic nerves blocked by intra-arterial injection of phenoxybenzamine. A low arterial pCO_2, induced by voluntary hyperventilation, raised the blood flow in the intact forearm by 20 per cent. Changes in arterial blood pH, produced by intravenous infusion of sodium bicarbonate, ammonium chloride, or lactic acid solutions, did not alter the blood flow in the intact forearm; but both acidosis and alkalosis increased the forearm blood flow when the vasoconstrictor nerves were blocked with phenoxybenzamine, alkalosis producing the greater response. With higher concentrations of CO_2 inhaled—12 to 30 per cent CO_2 in oxygen—vasoconstriction occurs in the intact forearm [Blair *et al.* (28); McArdle & Roddie (139)]. During general anaesthesia, inhalation of high concentrations of CO_2 either caused no alteration in forearm blood flow or an increase [McArdle & Roddie (139)], and after local anaesthetic infiltration of the nerves to the forearm there was usually a rise in forearm blood flow when CO_2 was breathed [Blair *et al.* (28)].

The hand blood flow decreases, if anything, when 5 per cent CO_2 in air is breathed, according to Downey & Mottram (67). The effect of raising the alveolar pCO_2 on the splanchnic circulation in patients lightly anaesthetized with thiopentone (for induction) and N_2O was measured by Epstein *et al.* (70). There was a significant rise in splanchnic vascular resistance, and a fall in the circulating splanchnic blood volume; and the estimated hepatic blood flow (by the BSP clearance method) varied according to the changes in systemic arterial pressure. The arterial pressure tended to rise; and, curiously, flushing of the skin of the face and torso was observed. Arteriolar and venous constriction in the splanchnic bed were postulated to explain the findings which, in the carefully controlled experiments, were effects of CO_2 and not artefacts caused by anaesthetic or respiratory techniques. How the limb skin and muscle blood vessels reacted under this light anaesthetic is not known. These findings support the early contentions of a dual action of CO_2 on the peripheral circulation, i.e., a central action leading to increased vasoconstrictor tone and a direct vasodilator action on the resistance vessels, with the former predominant in the conscious subject.

Richardson et al. (173) found that breathing 7 per cent CO_2 in air for seven minutes caused a 45 per cent rise in cardiac output, accompanied by a small rise in arterial pressure and heart rate. These changes were a consequence of the arterial CO_2 tension and not of the mechanical effects of hyperpnoea. If the vascular beds of limb skin, muscle, and the splanchnic organs constrict and the cerebral flow increases by 300 to 800 ml per min, it would be interesting to know the distribution of this considerable rise in cardiac output.

The events following a period of hypercapnia in man have been extensively studied by Blair et al. (27). A vasodilatation occurs in the forearm after breathing 5 to 30 per cent CO_2 which lasts from one to twenty minutes. This response is diminished or absent if the CO_2 concentration in the inspired air is reduced gradually. Their evidence supports the theory that this post-hypercapnia vasodilatation is caused by CO_2 remaining in the tissues when the arterial pCO_2 has returned to normal and the central vasoconstrictor response has ceased. These findings, as has been previously suggested, could be of some consequence to the patient undergoing anaesthesia with a closed circuit system.

Cerebral blood flow.—An opportunity to measure the blood flow in the human internal carotid artery with an electromagnetic flowmeter during necessary neck dissection has been taken with interesting results by Hardesty et al. (95). The measurements were made under differing types of anaesthesia, without control of CO_2 tension being possible, and usually after ligation of the internal jugular vein. The mean internal carotid flow was 364 ml per min with a range of 286 to 494 ml per min. Occlusion of the common carotid artery led to either a forward flow of up to 75 ml per min or a retrograde flow of up to 85 ml per min in the internal carotid artery. About 50 per cent of observations fell into each type of response, and the factors which determine whether forward or retrograde flow occurs are not clear. Turning the head away from the side on which the measurement was made consistently reduced the internal carotid blood flow. Again the internal carotid artery blood flow increased when the opposite common carotid artery was compressed so as to occlude it. The possible errors in the indirect cerebral blood flow measurements are well known, but it is interesting to note that contamination of jugular bulb blood with extracerebral blood occurs in a fair proportion of people, according to Lassen & Lane (127), who noted this contamination in 5 out of 67 observations.

In a short report, Rapela et al. (167) describe a technique for measuring the cerebral blood flow in animals, by collecting the venous outflow from the confluence of the sagittal and transverse sinuses, and suggest that there may be evidence for cerebral autoregulation. Novack *et al.* (150) report that in dogs under pentobarbital anaesthesia there was a better statistical correlation between arterial blood pH and cerebral blood flow than was the case with pCO_2 and brain blood flows ranging from 24 to 100 ml per 100 g per min and pH 7.05 to 7.50.

The pressure pulse wave has been recorded simultaneously at multiple points in the closed cranial cavity, and appeared simultaneously at all points, with an interval of 57 to 63 msec after ventricular ejection [Belek-hova & Naumenko (18)]. Their evidence favours the view that the cerebrospinal fluid transmits the pulse wave through the cranial cavity, attenuating its amplitude in proportion to the cerebrospinal fluid pressure.

The intracerebral blood content, measured by Rosomoff (179) with a technique involving freezing the dog's head in liquid nitrogen 15 to 30 min after an injection of ^{131}I-albumin, averaged 2.26 per cent of the total intracerebral contents.

The central vasomotor effects of serotonin, norepinephrine, and reserpine may be attributed to the local action of these substances on cerebral blood flow. Cooling and warming the fluid in the lateral ventricles produced responses which could also have a similar explanation [Kaneko *et al.* (115)].

The effects of intravenous insulin and glucose on the brain circulation have been studied in the monkey, with a heated thermocouple device [Grayson & Mendel (87)]. Insulin caused a marked rise in the thalamic blood flow, but only small and variable effects on the cortical circulation; in the thalamus, a marked rise in heat production occurred, and a small rise in heat production in the cortex. Glucose had little effect on cortical blood flow or heat production but produced a marked fall in heat production in the thalamus and a variable blood flow response. Apart from the metabolic aspects, the role of blood sugar in the distribution of brain blood flow is an important new factor which will require further inquiry.

An investigation of transport of various substances from the cerebrospinal fluid to the blood in goats showed an active transport system for low concentrations of iodopyracet (Diodrast) and phenolsulfonphthalein possibly via the choroid plexus of the fourth ventricle [Pappenheimer *et al.* (155)]. Transfer of creatinine, fructose, and insulin takes place passively by diffusion and absorption in bulk at sites other than the fourth ventricle, and there is a passive transfer component in iodopyracet removal.

Coronary blood flow.—The factors controlling the coronary blood flow continue to excite interest. Juhász-Nagy & Szentiványi (114) assert that the vagus nerve has no part in the innervation of the dog's coronary vessels and that the vasomotor impulses are derived from sympathetic preganglionic 'B' fibres which synapse with intracardiac adrenergic and cholinergic neurons. The vasodilator fibres were found to be cholinergic.

Other evidence for a nervous factor in the control of the dog's coronary blood flow has been obtained by use of a heated thermistor at the tip of a catheter in the coronary venous sinus. The flow under normal resting conditions was a direct function of the intra-aortic pressure. This simple relation failed during visceral stimulation or stimulation of the carotid sinus, as it also did when epinephrine or isopropylnorepinephrine were given [De Caro *et al.* (54)].

A new approach to the resistance of the coronary capillary bed was made by Stubbs & Widdas (197, 198), who draw attention to the support given to the capillaries by the myocardial interstitial fluid. If the interstitial fluid pressure rises in systole, as for example in the more forceful and rapid heart beat after adding epinephrine to the perfusing fluid, then some of this fluid will pass into the capillaries and the diastolic support will be less. Until the extravascular fluid compartment has been refilled, the capillaries will therefore dilate and the over-all coronary resistance will fall. That loss in interstitial fluid occurred during epinephrine stimulation of the isolated perfused heart was proven.

Douglas *et al.* (65) and Douglas & Talesnik (66) also draw attention to the mechanical as well as metabolic factors in the control of coronary blood flow in papers in which an increase in coronary blood flow is described as accompanying cardiac acceleration. This latter was produced by drugs, or by warming the pacemaker. The effect on coronary flow was inversely proportional to the red cell concentration. They postulate a servo-mechanism, the details of which are not yet available. Their results would in the main be explicable in terms of the Widdas & Stubbs hypothesis. As in the study of reactive hyperaemia, the term "vasodilator metabolites"—a useful hypothesis on occasions—can become a cliché which stifles further enquiry, and it is refreshing to see new explanations being subjected to experimental test.

If metabolic products are implicated in some conditions, adenosine, which is known to dilate coronary vessels, should be considered. Berne (24) finds inosine and hypoxanthine in the effluent from the perfused heart in hypoxic conditions. These substances are known metabolic derivatives of adenosine; also, adenosine added to the perfusion does not come out in the effluent but these two breakdown products do. Lewis *et al.* (131) also demonstrated a fall in intravascular resistance in the coronary vessels with cardiac acceleration and with similar drugs; and in the stopped heart, where the effect of myocardial contraction is absent, there was a fall in resistance when intracoronary isoproterenol, norepinephrine, and epinephrine were given. This adds a further factor still to be explained on the "cardiac support" theory of Widdas.

Rosenblueth *et al.* (178) found that, over a wide range, the cardiac work did not determine the coronary blood flow. There was a margin of safety in the coronary flow within which the heart could raise its work without wanting or getting an increased coronary flow. The work was done in dogs with an electrically determined heart rate.

The coronary blood flow, measured in man by the nitrous oxide saturation method, was normal in hypertensives; but the coronary vascular resistance was therefore raised [Rowe *et al.* (182)]. Local hypothermia decreased

vascular resistance in the dog coronary vessels, despite the relative increase
in time spent in systole. In part this could have been a direct effect of low
temperature on the coronary vessel smooth muscle [Hardin *et al.* (96)].

The left ventricle was found to have a uniform distribution of its circulation in the various parts measured, as estimated by the 20-second uptake of
^{86}Rb [Levy & Oliveira (130)]. A study of the blood supply of the myocardium
which is of some clinical value and a method of coronary angiography has
been described by Sloman & Hare (195).

Reproductive organs, foetal and neonatal circulation.—The uterine blood
flow has been measured in the pregnant goat by means of the Fick principle,
using the arteriovenous concentration differences of injected 4-aminoantipy-
rine [Huckabee & Barron (106); Huckabee *et al.* (107)]. The flow was high in
nonpregnant animals and early pregnancy, falling to a plateau of about
277 ml per kg at midpregnancy. Dawes *et al.* (52) found that the foetal
arterial blood pressure in monkeys rose to reach about 55 mmHg at birth
and that carotid sinus and vagal responses were present. The circulatory
changes occurring at birth and the arterial pressure regulation of the newborn
have been the subject of two excellent recent reviews by Dawes (53) and
Young (216).

Mammary blood flow in the goat gave mean values of 28 ml per 100 g
per min in dry goats and 45 ml per 100 g secreting per min in lactating animals giving 100 ml milk per 100 g tissue per day. The figures are higher
than those from previous observations because measurements were made
with the animal standing [Linzell (133)].

Arteries, capillaries, and veins.—The measurement of 'active tension' in
the smooth muscle of blood vessels has been a problem. Burton & Stinson
(38) devised a method applicable to the rabbit's ear, by means of which they
demonstrate that the rise in driving pressure at a constant rate of infusion is a
good linear measure of the increase in active tension, except for minute
pressure rises. The changes in resistance measured at constant perfusion
pressure are not related linearly to active tension. A mathematical argument
presented suggests that this constant flow perfusion technique may be applicable to other vascular beds.

The static and dynamic elastic properties of the aorta, the carotid, and
the femoral arteries in the dog have been measured by Bergel (22, 23).
Values are given for the static elastic modulus of these vessels and for resting
vascular smooth muscle, the latter value being over ten times that given in
some earlier reports. It is suggested that the elastic, collagenous, and
muscular elements are arranged in parallel, each taking some of the load at
all pressures. The dynamic elastic modulus increases abruptly between zero
and two cycles per sec and the magnitude of this change is related to the
amount of muscle in the vessel wall. At higher frequencies up to twenty
cycles per sec, the modulus remains constant. The relative contribution
of the various component tissues in the arterial wall to the elastic modulus
has also been discussed by Peterson *et al.* (160), who give the results of a

computer analysis of the mechanical properties of these tissues. They present evidence that the concept of arteries acting as "peripheral hearts" is unjustified. Heyman (102), studying the intra-arterial pressure and the movement of the brachial artery with a proximal cuff obstructing the circulation, presents evidence for movements of the artery linked to the pulse and to the atrial activity. These movements he believes to be mediated by nervous influences on the tone of the arterial wall with each pulse cycle. Patel *et al.* (158) have measured with electrical calipers the diameter and length of different aortic segments in the thoracotomized dog. They describe lengthening of the thoracic and shortening of the abdominal aorta during inspiration and during systole. The contour curve of diameter—as a function of time— usually resembled the pressure curve, but aortic wall velocities were small in comparison with the flow velocity. Figures for distensibility are given.

The biophysical aspects of oscillatory pressure and flow in the arterial tree have been extensively discussed by McDonald (143) in a recent monograph. The movement away from the Windkessel theory to a consideration of the circulation as a system in a steady state oscillation is ably described.

Harmonic analysis of the aortic pressure pulses adds support to the concept of reflected waves as discrete and definable quantities with the origin of reflection. Evidence for this view was obtained in the peripheral one-third of the dog's thigh by Farrow & Stacy (72).

The rheological problems involved in the flow of blood through small vessels are again the subject of papers, e.g. Haynes (97). The behaviour of resistance vessels when subjected to an increased transmural pressure was discussed by Greenfield (89). In this paper, he points out that a myogenic response could obtain or a detector linked to the resistance vessel by nervous or humoral pathways could also be present. Because it is not possible to subject the resistance vessels to a change in transmural pressure without also doing the same to other vessels, the separation of these mechanisms is difficult on the basis of available evidence.

The behaviour of the venous side of the circulation has been studied under different climatic conditions. Wood & Bass (214) describe experiments in which forearm venoconstriction was observed in people walking on a treadmill at a normal environmental temperature of 77°F. This constriction also occurred when they were walking in a hot environment and was maximal on the third and fourth days of exposure to the heat. It is interesting that the minimal symptoms of heat exhaustion with exercise occurred at the time of maximal venoconstriction as did the minimal forearm arteriolar dilatation. The distensibility of the finger tip blood vessels was found to decrease in a cold environment [Hyman *et al.* (109)], and this change was thought to occur in both high and low pressure vessels. The distensibility of the capacity vessels of the forearm is reduced by hyperventilation, and it seems that neither blood pCO_2 nor cyclical pressure changes in the thorax are responsible, but stretch receptors in the lungs remain a possible motivating factor [Lyttle (137, 138)].

Inflation of an antigravity suit so as to reduce the transmural pressure in the lower-limb veins to zero causes a shift of the expiratory end-tidal position measured on a spirometer. This shift is said to be proportional to the volume of blood displaced and is modified by the initial venous pressure and tone [Shephard (190)]; it has been used in the assessment of the pressure-to-volume relationship of the leg veins.

Blood haematocrit in dogs was found to be a determinant of the venous return, the latter varying inversely as the blood viscosity. A measure of the minute volume of red cells transported through the tissues—haematocrit times venous return—reached a maximum with a haematocrit of 40. This minute volume of cell transport was low in anaemia because of the paucity of cells and in polycythermia because of sluggish venous return [Guyton & Richardson (92)]. The whole problem of the role of veins in control of venous return has been carefully reviewed recently by Bartelstone (17).

Dokukin (62) described an ingenious method for measuring the vascular permeability of capillaries in an isolated subcutaneous urinary bladder pouch. A general increase in capillary permeability in haemorrhagic shock, estimated with labelled phosphate, was also described by Neiko (148).

Circulation in hypothermia.—Portal blood flow was found to decrease in moderate hypothermia to about 70 per cent of the control level, but it represented a greater proportion of the cardiac output in the cooled dog. Gastric cooling in the normothermic dog did not alter portal blood flow, and neither gastric cooling nor general hypothermia altered the portal oxygen saturation according to Heimburger *et al.* (98).

On the other hand, gastric cooling in an otherwise normothermic dog reduced estimated hepatic blood flow (BSP method) to 34 per cent of normal, leaving splanchnic blood volume constant. In the mildly hypothermic dog, the fall in estimated hepatic blood flow was greater (51%), with a decrease (21%) in splanchnic blood volume and a rise in splanchnic resistance [Wangensteen *et al.* (206)]. The factors altering the blood cerebrospinal fluid barrier permeability in hypothermia have been reported by Takács *et al.* (199). Other aspects of the circulation in hypothermia have been the subject of full reviews recently, written by Cooper (44), Fox (78), and Kenyon (117).

The effect of hypoxia has been compared in normal and "chemoreceptorless" dogs. In both groups, arterial pressure and heart rate fell and pulse pressure rose within two minutes of breathing 10 per cent oxygen in nitrogen; these responses were reduced in hypothermia. Interestingly, in hypothermia the normal dogs developed acidosis whereas the "chemoreceptorless" dogs did not [Terzioǧlu *et al.* (200)].

Hypertension.—A separate review would be required to cover the literature on the clinical aspects of the circulation. Mention must be made, however, of a controversy which has continued and another which has just started. Oldham *et al.* (151) and Pickering (161) published further evidence to support the hypothesis that essential hypertension represents a quantitative deviation from the norm, with a multifactorial or polygenic mode of inheritance. This view is challenged by Platt (163, 164) and Morrison & Morris (147), whose interpretation of the evidence is that it favours a qualitative deviation from normality inherited as a dominant characteristic. The other concept which has started controversy is that of "neurogenic hypertension", the cause of which is said to be restriction of the cerebral blood flow by atheromatous narrowing of the arteries [Dickinson & Thomson (57), Dickinson (58)]. The hypothesis is that during sleep the medullary blood flow is maintained just adequate by arterial pressure regulation. In conditions where the fluid-carrying capacity is reduced because of arterial narrowing, the pressure would have to rise to maintain the same adequate medullary blood flow. The evidence is derived from measurement *post mortem* of the fluid-carrying capacity of arterial specimens which correlates with the known arterial pressure *ante mortem*. The hypothesis has been challenged by Lowe (136) and Mitchell & Schwartz (146). Lowe points out the difficulty in comparing flow rates in the cadaver with those occurring in life, and the predicted alterations in pressure gradient between the aorta and the circle of Willis were not in line with his observations. Mitchell & Schwartz simply point out that deductions from the difference in slope of the fluid-carrying capacity–to–pressure *ante mortem* lines between arteries going to the head and to other regions reflect the pressure-to-flow characteristics of different sized vessels rather than any special properties of the cerebral vessels. It should be said that Dickinson & Thomson do not claim to have proved their hypothesis, and the hope is that it will stimulate further enquiry.

Apart from the renal causes of hypertension, there have been other claims for new methods of inducing it. Golitsynskaia (85) claims that simultaneous application of an indifferent stimulus with intravenous epinephrine injection could lead to a conditioned reflex rise in arterial pressure in rabbits. Asagoe & Saneshige (6) claimed that ligation of the testicular arteries gave rise to persistent hypertension in rats and that a lipoid fraction of extracts of the atrophic testes could cause hypertension in castrated male rats. Daily administration of gonadotropin, testosterone, and estradiol did not affect arterial pressure, nor did castration. Areas of infarction in one kidney, in the rabbit, produced by injection of a variety of particulate substances, usually produced a temporary rise in arterial pressure whether or not the opposite kidney was removed [Alexander *et al.* (3)]. The cause of the rise in arterial pressure could have been either the presence of necrotic material or ischaemia at the periphery of the infarcts. Some further evidence for a humoral anti-hypertensive agent derived from the kidney has been obtained from studies on parabiotic rats by Tóth & Bártfai (202). Critical closing pressure in the finger blood vessels was found to rise with increasing arterial pressure in "uncomplicated" hypertension, but, in the same arterial pressure range, those patients with retinopathy and malignant hypertension had lower critical closing pressures [Coles & Gough (42)].

Any population survey of arterial pressure will be of value in establishing adequate data to resolve the arguments over the inheritance of hypertension. One such study has appeared, by Lovell *et al.* (135), in which the arterial pressures of Fijians and Indians in Fiji have been measured. The over-all figures are similar in the two groups, but the Indians' arterial pressure rises more steeply with age than the Fijians'. Up to the sixth decade the values are similar to those obtained for Londoners, and thereafter fall below.

Lacroix & Leusen (125) have found that the oxygen uptake per unit mass of heart tissue is unaltered in the cardiac hypertrophy of renal hypertension in rats.

Miscellaneous clinical findings.—The assessment of the degree of impairment of the blood flow to the foot continues to be of clinical importance, and Horwitz & Abramson (104) have described a modified vasodilatation test for this purpose.

Vasovagal reactions have occurred during right heart catheterization [Greene *et al.* (88)], and the central haemodynamic changes have been observed. The arterial hypotension was said to be a consequence of a fall in cardiac output caused by decreased stroke output. Atropine did not restore the haemodynamic *status quo*. The peripheral resistance changes as calculated do not suggest, as one would expect, the large changes in muscle blood flow which have so frequently been described in previous literature on fainting.

Pharmacology and the circulation.—A most interesting hypothesis concerning the working of adrenergic nerve fibres has been put forward by Burn (35). It is that the nerve fibre may first release acetylcholine which then causes the release of norepinephrine. This property of acetylcholine falls into the 'nicotine-like' category and hence is not abolished by atropine. The evidence for such a view, as Burn says, is "weighty but cannot be regarded as complete." The hypothesis would go a long way to explaining the actions of reserpine, bretylium, and guanethidine. Another view on the action of reserpine in dilating forearm vessels has been advanced by Parks *et al.* (156), who found that intra-arterial infusion of the drug caused vasodilatation which was abolished by previous general "reserpinisation" but was unaffected by sympathectomy, antihistamines, or atropine. The vasodilatation could be caused by depletion of norepinephrine stores provided that it is allowed that these stores exert a tonic influence on the vessels independently of the sympathetic fibres. Actions of many of the hypotensive agents have been discussed in detail in a recent book on the treatment of hypertension by Pickering *et al.* (162).

Much work has been done on the pharmacology of angiotensin both in man and animals, and this has been fully reviewed recently by Page & Bumpus (154). To this have been added a number of recent papers on regional circulatory effects of angiotensin by Assali & Westersten (7), Barer (13), Daly & Duff (50), and Gross *et al.* (90).

A useful study by Cobbold *et al.* (40) has compared a wide variety of responses to isopropyl norepinephrine in man to the responses obtained with norepinephrine and epinephrine. The participation of isopropyl norepinephrine in physiological responses in man awaits confirmation of its production in the body.

Space allotment limits this section severely, and with new vasoactive drugs appearing at a rate with which the pharmacologist cannot cope, the subject becomes so vast that it can only be mentioned in this review.

Methods.—Numerous devices, based on a wide variety of physical principles, have been added to the armament of the would-be measurer of blood flow [Wolter & Menke (213), electrolyte dilution; Wretlind (215), differential pressure; Hensel (100) and Hensel & Doerr (101), thermal conductivity; Singer (194), paramagnetic relaxation; Westersten *et al.* (210) and Olmsted & Aldrich (152), electromagnetic effects; Mellander (144), venous flow with heated thermistor; Polzer *et al.* (165), conductivity; and Kudravcev & Bowman (122), nuclear magnetic resonance]. Many of these methods require close comparison with standard techniques, while for some the accuracy appears to be greater than available methods. The venous occlusion plethysmograph and the electromagnetic flowmeter have been compared in work on the amputated forepaw of the dog, with no significant difference found between them—mainly because of self-cancelling artefacts in the plethysmographic method [Conrad & Green (43)]. Shephard (190), using the nitrous oxide technique, has applied the Fick principle to the lower limbs in man with useful results.

Arterial pressure measurement in an orbiting space ship is a problem, an intra-arterial needle being out of the question, and Adams *et al.* (2) have introduced a cuffless continuous recording device not requiring a cannula the limitations of which are clearly discussed. Other methods applicable to dogs and rats are described by Deriabin (56) and Kogan (120). Permanent arterial cannulation has been achieved in rats and ground squirrels by Popovic & Popovic (166). A new photoelectric device for use as an ear-detecting unit in measuring dye-dilution curves is described by Gabe & Shillingford (80).

Finally, an artefact in left atrial pressure measurement has been described which is caused by the catheter's entering the atrial appendage where the muscle contracts over the catheter tip [Johansson & Ohlsson (112)].

The author wishes to thank Miss G. Riggott for all her help in the preparation of the manuscript of this article.

LITERATURE CITED

1. Abrahams, V. C., Hilton, S. M., and Zbrożyna, A., *J. Physiol. (London)*, **154**, 491–513 (1960)
2. Adams, R., Corell, R. W., and Wolfeboro, N. H., *Surgery*, **47**, 46–54 (1960)
3. Alexander, N., Heptinstall, R. H., and Pickering, G. W., *J. Pathol. Bacteriol.*, **81**, 225–37 (1961)
4. Andrews, W. H. H., and Riolozano, I. del., *J. Physiol. (London)*, **153**, 31–32P (1960)
5. Arborelius, M., Jr., Lundin, G., Svanberg, L., and Defares, J. G., *J. Appl. Physiol.*, **15**, 595–97 (1960)
6. Asagoe, Y., and Saneshige, T., *Yonago Acta Med.*, **4**, 117–23 (1960)
7. Assali, N. S., and Westersten, E. E., *Circulation Research*, **9**, 189–93 (1961)
8. Auld, P. A. M., Rudolph, A. M., and Golinko, R. J., *Am. J. Physiol.*, **198**, 1166–70 (1960)
9. Aviado, D. M., Daly, M. de B., Lee, C. Y., and Schmidt, C. F., *J. Physiol. (London)*, **155**, 602–22 (1961)
10. Bacaner, M., and Pollycove, M., *Federation Proc.*, **20**, 98 (1961)
11. Barcroft, H., Brod, J., Hejl, Z., Hirsjärvi, E. A., and Kitchin, A. H., *Clin. Sci.*, **19**, 577–86 (1960)
12. Barcroft, H., *Physiol. Revs.*, **40**, Suppl. 4, 81–91 (1960)
13. Barer, G. R., *J. Physiol. (London)*, **156**, 49–66 (1961)
14. Barlow, T. E., Haigh, A. L., and Walder, D. N., *J. Physiol. (London)* **143**, 80–81P (1958)
15. Barlow, T. E., Haigh, A. L., and Walder, D. N., *J. Physiol. (London)*, **149**, 18–19P (1959)
16. Barlow, T. E., Haigh, A. L., and Walder, D. N., *Clin. Sci.*, **20**, 367–85 (1961)
17. Bartelstone, H. J., *Circulation Research*, **8**, 1059–76 (1960)
18. Belekhova, M. G., and Naumenko, A. I., *Bull. biol. méd. exptl. URSS*, **48**, 1454–57 (1959)
19. Benzinger, T. H., *Proc. Natl. Acad. Sci. US*, **45**, 645–59 (1959)
20. Benzinger, T. H., *Federation Proc.*, **19**, 32–41 (1960)
21. Benzinger, T. H., *Ann. Intern. Med.*, **54**, 685–99 (1961)
22. Bergel, D. H., *J. Physiol. (London)*, **156**, 445–57 (1961)
23. Bergel, D. H., *J. Physiol. (London)*, **156**, 458–69 (1961)
24. Berne, R. M., *Federation Proc.*, **20**, 101 (1961)
25. Black, S., Edholm, O. G., Fox, R. H., and Kidd, D. J., *J. Physiol. (London)*, **151**, 29–30P (1960)
26. Black, J. E., *Clin. Sci.*, **18**, 90–93 (1959)
27. Blair, D. A., Glover, W. E., Greenfield, A. D. M., and Roddie, I. C., *J. Physiol. (London)*, **148**, 633–46 (1959)
28. Blair, D. A., Glover, W. E., McArdle, L., and Roddie, I. C., *Clin. Sci.*, **19**, 407–23 (1960)
29. Blair, D. A., Glover, W. E., and Roddie, I. C., *J. Physiol. (London)*, **152**, 17–18P (1960)
30. Blair, D. A., Glover, W. E., and Roddie, I. C., *J. Physiol. (London)*, **153**, 232–38 (1960)
31. Blair, D. A., Glover, W. E., and Roddie, I. C., *J. Appl. Physiol.*, **16**, 119–22 (1961)
32. Blair, D. A., Glover, W. E., and Roddie, I. C., *Circulation Research*, **9**, 264–74 (1961)
33. Boyer, G. O., and Scher, A. M., *Circulation Research*, **8**, 845–48 (1960)
34. Brutsaert, D., Lacroix, E., and Leusen, I., *Acta Cardiol.*, **15**, 273–80 (1960)
35. Burn, J. H., *Brit. Med. J.*, *I*, 1623–27 (1961)
36. Burton, A. C., *Pulmonary Circulation* (Adams, W. R., and Veith, I., Eds., Grune & Stratton, New York, N. Y., 1959)
37. Burton, A. C., and Patel, D. J., *J. Appl. Physiol.*, **12**, 239–46 (1958)
38. Burton, A. C., and Stinson, R. H., *J. Physiol. (London)*, **153**, 290–305 (1960)
39. Cannon, P., and Keatinge, W. R., *J. Physiol. (London)*, **154**, 329–44 (1960)
40. Cobbold, A. F., Ginsburg, J., and Paton, A., *J. Physiol. (London)*, **151**, 539–50 (1960)
41. Coleridge, J. C. G., Kidd, C., and Sharp, J. A., *J. Physiol. (London)*, **156**, 591–602 (1961)
42. Coles, D. R., and Gough, K. R., *Clin. Sci.*, **19**, 587–94 (1960)
43. Conrad, M. C., and Green, H. D., *J. Appl. Physiol.*, **16**, 289–92 (1961)
44. Cooper, K. E., *Brit. Med. Bull.*, **17**(1), 48–51 (1961)
45. Cooper, K. E., and Kerslake, D. Mc. K., *J. Physiol. (London)*, **119**, 18–29 (1953)

46. Cooper, K. E., Ferres, H. M., and Mottram, R. F., *J. Physiol.* (*London*), **131**, 29P (1956)

47. Cooper, K. E., Cranston, W. I., Dempster, W. J., and Mottram, R. F., *J. Physiol.* (*London*), **155**, 21–22P (1960)

48. Crockford, G. W., Hellon, R. F., Heyman, A., and Parkhouse, J., *J. Physiol.* (*London*), Proc., 28th–29th July (1961)

49. Cudkowicz, L., Abelmann, W. H., Levinson, G. E., Katznelson, G., and Jreissaty, R. M., *Clin. Sci.*, **19**, 1–15 (1960)

50. Daly, J. J., and Duff, R. S., *Clin. Sci.*, **19**, 457–63 (1960)

51. Daly, M. de B., and Scott, M. J., *J. Physiol.* (*London*), **156**, 246–59 (1961)

52. Dawes, G. S., Jacobson, H. N., Mott, J. C., and Shelley, H. J., *J. Physiol.* (*London*), **152**, 271–98 (1960)

53. Dawes, G. S., *Brit. Med. Bull.*, **17**, 148–53 (1961)

54. De Caro, L. G., Baldright, J., and Casella, C., *Arch. fisiol.*, **60**, 110–59 (1960)

55. Defares, J. G., Lundin, G., Arborelius, M., Strömblad, R., and Svanberg, L., *J. Appl. Physiol.*, **15**, 169–74 (1960)

56. Deriabin, L. N., *Sechenov Physiol. J. USSR.* (*Engl. Transl.*), **45**, 113–15 (1959)

57. Dickinson, C. J., and Thomson, A. D., *Clin. Sci.*, **19**, 513–38 (1960)

58. Dickinson, C. J., *Lancet*, **I**, 1167–68 (1961)

59. Diji, A., *J. Appl. Physiol.*, **14**, 414–16 (1959)

60. Diji, A., and Greenfield, A. D. M., *J. Physiol.* (*London*), **140**, 42P (1957)

61. Dock, D. S., Kraus, W. L., McGuire, L. B., Hyland, J. W., Haynes, F. W., and Dexter, L., *J. Clin. Invest.*, **40**, 317–28 (1961)

62. Dokukin, A. V., *Bull. biol. méd. exptl. URSS*, **48**, 1297–98 (1959)

63. Dollery, C. T., Dyson, N. A., and Sinclair, J. D., *J. Appl. Physiol.*, **15**, 411–17 (1960)

64. Dollery, C. T., West, J. B., Wilcken, D. E. L., Goodwin, J. F., and Hugh-Jones, P., *Brit. Heart J.*, **23**, 225–35 (1961)

65. Douglas, R. C., Armengol, V., and Talesnik, J., *Acta Physiol. Latinoam.*, **10**, 205–17 (1960)

66. Douglas, R. C., and Talesnik, J., *Acta Physiol. Latinoam.*, **10**, 21727– (1960)

67. Downey, J., and Mottram, R. F., *J. Physiol.* (*London*), Proc., 28th–29th July (1961)

68. Edwards, M., and Burton, A. C., *J. Appl. Physiol.*, **15**, 209–11 (1960)

69. Eliakim, M., Stern, S., and Nathan, H., *Circulation Research*, **9**, 327–32 (1961)

70. Epstein, R. M., Wheeler, H. O., Frumin, M. J., Habif, D. V., Papper, E. M., and Bradley, S. E., *J. Clin. Invest.*, **40**, 592–98 (1961)

71. Evonuk, E., Imig, C. J., Greenfield, W., and Eckstein, J. W., *J. Appl. Physiol.*, **16**, 271–75 (1961)

72. Farrow, R. L., and Stacy, R. W., *Circulation Research*, **9**, 395–401 (1961)

73. Finley, T. N., Lenfant, C., Haab, P., Piiper, J., and Rahn, H., *J. Appl. Physiol.*, **15**, 418–24 (1960)

74. Folkow, B., *Physiol. Revs.*, **40**, 93–99 (1960)

75. Fox, R. H., Goldsmith, R., and Kidd, D. J., *J. Physiol.* (*London*), **150**, 12–13P (1959)

76. Fox, R. H., Goldsmith, R., and Kidd, D. J., *J. Physiol.* (*London*), **150**, 22–23P (1960)

77. Fox, R. H., and Wyatt, H. T., *J. Physiol.* (*London*), **151**, 30–31P (1960)

78. Fox, R. H., *Brit. Med. Bull.*, **17**(1), 14–18 (1961)

79. Freeburg, B. R., and Hyman, C., *J. Appl. Physiol.*, **15**, 1041–45 (1960)

80. Gabe, I., and Shillingford, J., *Brit. Heart J.*, **23**, 271–80 (1961)

81. Gerbrandy, J., Snell, E. S., and Cranston, W. I., *Clin. Sci.*, **13**, 615–24 (1954)

82. Glover, W. E., and Greenfield, A. D. M., *J. Physiol.* (*London*), **143**, 67P (1958)

83. Glover, W. E., *Am. Heart J.*, **60**, 321–23 (1960)

84. Goetz, R. H., Warren, J. W., Gauer, O. H., Patterson, J. L., Jr., Doyle, J. T., Keen, M. D., and McGregor, M., *Circulation Research*, **8**, 1049–58 (1960)

85. Golitsynskaia, M. T., *Sechenov Physiol. J. USSR*, **45**, 82–89 (1959)*

86. Gorten, R., and Gunnells, J. C., *J. Appl. Physiol.*, **16**, 266–70 (1961)

87. Grayson, J., and Mendel, D., *J. Physiol.* (*London*), **154**, 26–38 (1960)

88. Greene, M. A., Boltax, A. J., and Ulberg, R. J., *Circulation Research*, **9**, 12–17 (1961)

89. Greenfield, A. D. M., *Am. Heart J.*, 59, 476–78 (1960)

90. Gross, von F., Bock, K. D., and Turrian, H., *Helv. Physiol. et Pharmacol. Acta*, 19, 42–57 (1961)

91. Gunnells, J. C., and Gorten, R., *J. Appl. Physiol.*, 16, 261–65 (1961)

92. Guyton, A. C., and Richardson, T. Q., *Circulation Research*, 9, 157–64 (1961)

93. Halliday, J. A., *Am. Heart J.*, 60, 110–15 (1960)

94. Harasawa, M., and Rodbard, S., *Am. J. Physiol.*, 200, 287–91 (1961)

95. Hardesty, W. H., Roberts, B., Toole, J. F., and Royster, H. P., *Surgery*, 49, 251–56 (1961)

96. Hardin, R. A., Scott, J. B., and Haddy, F. J., *Am. J. Physiol.*, 199, 163–66 (1960)

97. Haynes, R. H., *Nature*, 185, 679–80 (1960)

98. Heimburger, I., Teramoto, S., and Shumacker, H. B., Jr., *Surgery*, 47, 534–41 (1960)

99. Hellström, B., and Andersen, K. L., *J. Appl. Physiol.*, 15, 771–75 (1960)

100. Hensel, H., *Naturwissenschaften*, 46, 1–2 (1959)

101. Hensel, H., and Doerr, F. F., *Arch. ges. Physiol.*, 270, 78 (1959)

102. Heyman, F., *Acta Med. Scand.*, 169, 87–93 (1961)

103. Heymans, C., Schaepdryver, A. F. de, and Vleeschhouwer, G. R. de, *Circulation Research*, 8, 347–52 (1960)

104. Horwitz, O., and Abramson, D. G., *Am. J. Cardiol.*, 6, 663–66 (1960)

105. Howell, J. B. L., Permutt, S., Proctor, D. F., and Riley, R. L., *J. Appl. Physiol.*, 16, 71–76 (1961)

106. Huckabee, W. E., and Barron, D. H., *Circulation Research*, 9, 312–18 (1961)

107. Huckabee, W. E., Metcalfe, J., Prystowsky, H., and Barron, D. H., *Am. J. Physiol.*, 200, 274–78 (1961)

108. Hyman, C., Rosell, S., Rosén, A., Sonnenschein, R., and Uvnäs, B., *Acta Physiol. Scand.*, 46, 358–74 (1959)

109. Hyman, C., Arthur, J. D., Trotter, A. D., Jr., Humphreys, P. C., and Winsor, T., *J. Appl. Physiol.*, 16, 257–60 (1961)

110. Iber, F. L., Kerr, D. N. S., Dölle, W., and Sherlock, S., *J. Clin. Invest.*, 39, 1201–7 (1960)

111. Iriuchijima, J., *Federation Proc.*, 20, 97 (1961)

112. Johansson, B. W., and Ohlsson, N. M., *Brit. Heart J.*, 23, 281–84 (1961)

113. Johnson, R. L., Jr., Spicer, W. S., Bishop, J. M., and Forster, R. E., *J. Appl. Physiol.*, 15, 893–902 (1960)

114. Juhász-Nagy, A., and Szentiványi, M., *Am. J. Physiol.*, 200, 125 (1961)

115. Kaneko, Y., McCubbin, J. W., and Page, I. H., *Circulation Research*, 8, 1229–34 (1960)

116. Keatinge, W. R., *J. Physiol. (London)*, 142, 395–405 (1958)

117. Kenyon, J. R., *Brit. Med. Bull.*, 17(1), 43–47 (1961)

118. Kerslake, D. McK., and Brebner, D. F., *J. Physiol. (London)*, 156, 4–5P (1961)

119. Kerslake, D. McK., and Cooper, K. E., *Clin. Sci.*, 9, 31–47 (1950)

120. Kogan, A. Kh., *Bull. biol. méd. exptl. URSS*, 48, 1300–4 (1959)

121. Krog, J., Folkow, B., Fox, R. H., and Andersen, K. L., *J. Appl. Physiol.*, 15, 654–58 (1960)

122. Kudravcev, V., and Bowman, R. L., *13th Ann. Conf. on Electrical Techniques in Medicine and Biology, Digest of Technical Papers*, p. 21 (Lewis Winner, New York, N. Y., 1960)

123. Kulaev, B. S., *Bull. biol. méd. exptl. URSS*, 48, 1311–15 (1959)

124. Kulaev, B. S., *Bull. biol. méd. exptl. URSS*, 48, 1449–53 (1959)

125. Lacroix, E., and Leusen, I., *Arch. intern. physiol. et biochim.*, 69, 114–16 (1961)

126. Langston, J. B., Guyton, A. C., and Gillespie, W. J., *Am. J. Physiol.*, 199, 495–98 (1960)

127. Lassen, N. A., and Lane, M. H., *J. Appl. Physiol.*, 16, 313–20 (1961)

128. Lasser, R. P., Schoenfeld, M., Allen, D. F., and Friedberg, C. K., *Circulation Research*, 8, 913–19 (1960)

129. Leusen, I., and Lacroix, E., *Arch. intern. pharmacodynamie*, 130, 470–72 (1961)

130. Levy, M. N., and Oliveira, J. M. de, *Circulation Research*, 9, 96–98 (1961)

131. Lewis, F. B., Coffman, J. D., and Gregg, D. E., *Circulation Research*, 9, 89–95 (1961)

132. Lindgren, P., *Circulation Research*, 9, 250–55 (1961)

133. Linzell, J. L., *J. Physiol. (London)*, 153, 492–509 (1960)

134. Love, A. H. G., and Shanks, R. G.,

J. Physiol. (London), **156**, 42–43P (1961)

135. Lovell, R. R. H., Maddocks, I., and Rogerson, G. W., *Australasian Ann. Med.*, **9**, 4–17 (1960)
136. Lowe, R., *Brit. Med. J.*, **I**, 1109 (1961)
137. Lyttle, D., *J. Physiol. (London)*, **152**, 16P (1960)
138. Lyttle, D., *J. Physiol. (London)*, **156**, 238–45 (1961)
139. McArdle, L., and Roddie, I. C., *Brit. J. Anaesthesia*, **30**, 358–66 (1958)
140. Marshall, H. W., Fox, I. J., Rodich, F. S., and Wood, E. H., *Proc. Staff Meetings Mayo Clin.*, **35**, 774–82 (1960)
141. Marshall, R. J., and Shepherd, J. T., *J. Clin. Invest.*, **40**, 375–85 (1961)
142. Marshall, R. J., Wang, Y., Semler, H. J., and Shepherd, J. T., *Circulation Research*, **9**, 53–59 (1961)
143. McDonald, D. A., *Blood Flow in Arteries* (Edward Arnold, London, Engl., 1960)
144. Mellander, S., *Acta Physiol. Scand.*, **50**, Suppl. 176 (1960)
145. Mellander, S., and Rushmer, R. F., *Acta Physiol. Scand.*, **48**, 13–19 (1960)
146. Mitchell, J. R. A., and Schwartz, C. J., *Lancet*, **I**, 1003–4 (1961)
147. Morrison, S. L., and Morris, J. N., *Lancet*, **II**, 864 (1959)
148. Neiko, E. M., *Bull. biol. méd. exptl. URSS*, **48**, 1209–11 (1959)
149. Newman, P. P., and Wolstencroft, J. H., *J. Physiol. (London)*, **152**, 87–92 (1960)
150. Novack, P. Ariza-Mendoza, F., De-Armas, D., Bartolucci, G., Faust, J., and Usman, A., *Federation Proc.*, **20**, 100 (1961)
151. Oldham, P. D., Pickering, G. W., Fraser Roberts, J. A., and Sowry, G. S. C., *Lancet*, **I**, 1085–93 (1960)
152. Olmsted, F., and Aldrich, F. D., *J. Appl. Physiol.*, **16**, 197–201 (1961)
153. Orlov, V. V., *Pavlov J. Higher Nervous Activity*, **9**, 625–34 (1959)*
154. Page, I. H., and Bumpus, F. M., *Physiol. Revs.*, **41**, 331–90 (1961)
155. Pappenheimer, J. R., Heisey, S. R., and Jordan, E. F., *Am. J. Physiol.*, **200**, 1–10 (1961)
156. Parks, V. J., Sandison, A. G., Skinner, S. L., and Whelan, R. F., *Clin. Sci.*, **20**, 289–95 (1961)
157. Parrish, D., Strandness, D. E., Jr., and Bell, J. W., *Am. J. Physiol.*, **200**, 619–21 (1961)
158. Patel, D. J., Mallos, A. J., and Fry,

D. L., *J. Appl. Physiol.*, **16**, 293–99 (1961)
159. Permutt, S., Howell, J. B. L., Proctor, D. F., and Riley, R. L., *J. Appl. Physiol.*, **16**, 64–70 (1961)
160. Peterson, L. H., Jensen, R. E., and Parnell, J., *Circulation Research*, **8**, 622–39 (1960)
161. Pickering, G. W., *Essential Hypertension* (Symposium, Bock and Cottier, Eds., Springer-Verlag, Berlin, Germany, 1960)
162. Pickering, G. W., Cranston, W. I., and Pears, M. A., *The Treatment of Hypertension* (Kugelmass, I. Newton, Ed., Charles C Thomas, Springfield, Ill., 175 pp., 1961)
163. Platt, R., *Lancet*, **II**, 55 (1959)
164. Platt, R., *Lancet*, **II**, 1092 (1959)
165. Polzer, K., Schuhfried, F., and Heeger, H., *Brit. Heart J.*, **22**, 140–48 (1960)
166. Popovic, V., and Popovic, P., *J. Appl. Physiol.*, **15**, 727–28 (1960)
167. Rapela, C. E., Machowicz, P., and Green, H. D., *Federation Proc.*, **20**, 100 (1961)
168. Rawson, R. O., and Randall, W. C., *Am. J. Physiol.*, **199**, 112–16 (1960)
169. Rayner, R. R., MacLean, L. D., and Grim, E., *Circulation Research*, **8**, 1212–17 (1960)
170. Reeves, J. T., Grover, R. F., Filley, G. F., and Blount, S. G., Jr., *J. Appl. Physiol.*, **16**, 276–78 (1961)
171. Reeves, J. T., Grover, R. F., Filley, G. F., and Blount, S. G., Jr., *J. Appl. Physiol.*, **16**, 279–82 (1961)
172. Reeves, J. T., Grover, R. F., Blount, S. G., Jr., and Filley, G. F., *J. Appl. Physiol.*, **16**, 283–88 (1961)
173. Richardson, D. W., Wasserman, A. J., and Patterson, J. L., Jr., *J. Clin. Invest.*, **40**, 31–43 (1961)
174. Rochester, D. F., Durand, J., Parker, J. O., Fritts, H. W., Jr., and Harvey, R. M., *J. Clin. Invest*, **40**, 643–48 (1961)
175. Rokotova, N. A., and Gorbunova, I. M., *Sechenov Physiol. J., USSR*, **45**, 69–76 (1959)*
176. Roos, A., Thomas, L. J., Jr., Nagel, E. L., and Prommas, D. C., *J. Appl. Physiol.*, **16**, 77–84 (1961)
177. Rosenberg, E., and Forster, R. E., *J. Appl. Physiol.*, **15**, 883–92 (1960)
178. Rosenblueth, A., Alañis, J., Rubio, R., and Pilar, G., *Am. J. Physiol.*, **200**, 243–46 (1961)
179. Rosomoff, H. L., *J. Appl. Physiol.*, **16**, 395–96 (1961)
180. Ross, J., Jr., Frahm, C. J., and Braun-

wald, E., *Circulation Research*, **9**, 75–82 (1961)

181. Ross, J., Jr., Frahm, C. J., and Braunwald, E., *J. Clin. Invest.*, **40**, 563–71 (1961)

182. Rowe, G. G., Castillo, C. A., Maxwell, G. M., and Crumpton, C. W., *Ann. Internal Med.*, **54**, 405–11 (1961)

183. Rushmer, R. F., Franklin, D. L., Van Citters, R. L., *Federation Proc.*, **20**, 97 (1961)

184. Sawyer, C. H., Hilliard, J., and Ban, T., *Am. J. Physiol.*, **200**, 405–12 (1961)

185. Sayen, A., and Boland, C., *Clin. Sci.*, **20**, 217–21 (1961)

186. Selkurt, E. E., and Rothe, C. F., *Am. J. Physiol.*, **199**, 335–40 (1960)

187. Senay, L. C., Jr., Christensen, M., and Hertzman, A. B., *J. Appl. Physiol.*, **15**, 611–18 (1960)

188. Senay, L. C., Prokop, D., Cronall, L., and Hertzman, A. B., *Federation Proc.*, **20**, 110 (1961)

189. Senft, A. W., and Kanwisher, J. K., *Circulation Research*, **8**, 961–64 (1960)

190. Shephard, R. J., *Quart. J. Exptl. Physiol.*, **46**, 175–87 (1961)

191. Shepherd, R. C., and Warren, R., *Clin. Sci.*, **20**, 99–105 (1961)

192. Shoemaker, W. C., *J. Appl. Physiol.*, **15**, 473–78 (1960)

193. Simmons, D. H., Linde, L. M., Miller, J. H., and O'Reilly, R. J., *Circulation Research*, **9**, 465–71 (1961)

194. Singer, J. R., *J. Appl. Phys.*, **31**, 406S–7S (1960)

195. Sloman, G., and Hare, W. S. C., *Med. J. Australia*, **611**–14, Oct. 15 (1960)

196. Steiner, S. H., and Mueller, G. C. E., *Circulation Research*, **9**, 99–102 (1961)

197. Stubbs, J., and Widdas, W. F., *J. Physiol. (London)*, **148**, 403–16 (1959)

198. Stubbs, J., and Widdas, W. F., *Intern.*

Congr., *21st*, *Buenos Aires*, **267** (1959)

199. Takács, E., Tomity, H. T., and Gellén, J., *Acta Physiol. Hung.*, **17**, 75–80 (1960)

200. Terzioğlu, M., Gökhan, N., Emiroğlu, F., and Özer, F., *Arch. intern. physiol. et biochim.*, **69**, 177–93 (1961)

201. Ting, E. Y., Hong, S. K., and Rahn, H., *J. Appl. Physiol.*, **15**, 557–60 (1960)

202. Tóth, T., and Bártfai, J., *Clin. Sci.*, **20**, 307–13 (1961)

203. Trzebski, A., *Bull. acad. polon. sci.*, **8**, 317–21 (1960)

204. Verstraeten, J. M., and Leusen, I., *Arch. intern. physiol. et biochim.*, **48**, 504–6 (1960)

205. Waaler, B. A., *J. Physiol. (London)*, **154**, 57–58P (1960)

206. Wangensteen, S. L., Orahood, R. C., Luke, W., and Healey, W. V., *Federation Proc.*, **20**, 100 (1961)

207. Waugh, W. H., and Shanks, R. G., *Circulation Research*, **8**, 871–88 (1960)

208. Weckman, N., *Experientia*, **16**, 34–36 (1960)

209. West, J. B., and Dollery, C. T., *J. Appl. Physiol.*, **15**, 405–10 (1960)

210. Westersten, A., Herrold, G., and Assali, N. S., *J. Appl. Physiol.*, **15**, 533–35 (1960)

211. Whittenberger, J. L., McGregor, M., Berglund, E., and Borst, H. G., *J. Appl. Physiol.*, **15**, 878–82 (1960)

212. Wisheart, J. D., *Am. Heart J.*, **60**, 116–20 (1960)

213. Wolter, H. H., and Menke, F., *Z. ges. exptl. Med.*, **133**, 152–62 (1960)

214. Wood, J. E., and Bass, D. E., *J. Clin. Invest.*, **39**, 825–33 (1960)

215. Wretlind, A., *Acta Physiol. Scand.*, **46**, 291–97 (1959)

216. Young, M., *Brit. Med. Bull.*, **17**, 154–59 (1961)

* English translation will be announced in *Technical Translations*, issued by the Office of Technical Services, US Department of Commerce, and will be made available by the Photoduplication Service, Library of Congress, and by the SLA Translation Center at the John Crerar Library, Chicago, Illinois.

HEART[1]

By William R. Milnor

*Gerontology Branch, National Heart Institute, Baltimore City Hospitals,
and Department of Medicine, The Johns Hopkins University,
Baltimore, Maryland*

Myocardial Contractility

Starling's "law of the heart"—that the energy released by ventricular contraction is proportional to myocardial fiber length immediately preceding contraction, if all other relevant factors remain constant—has been the target of several investigators who urge its repeal or amendment. The present consensus of those who have earned a vote is that Starling's law is obeyed, but that other factors rarely do remain constant *in vivo*. The relative importance of Starling's law as compared to other regulatory mechanisms under various conditions remains unsettled.

It has become customary to regard the relation between myocardial work and end-diastolic fiber length as virtually synonymous with myocardial contractility: contractility is said to be decreased if the work associated with any given end-diastolic fiber length is decreased. This essentially arbitrary definition will be assumed in the present review, although the relation between work and catecholamine level might equally well have been used to define contractility if the measurement of catecholamines had preceded the measurement of pressure in the historical develpoment of research methods.

Distensibility.—Changes in ventricular distensibility, the relation between fiber length and distending pressure, can influence ventricular work even though contractility remains constant. Distensibility is apparently not influenced by changes in cardiac output or aortic pressure *per se* [Braunwald, Frye & Ross (1)], however, and is not altered by autonomic stimuli [Mitchell, Linden & Sarnoff (2)]. Linden & Mitchell (3) found a curvilinear relation between ventricular end-diastolic pressure and fiber length in the dog, with ventricular compliance decreasing as pressure was raised from 3 to 36 cm water. Stimulation of cardiac sympathetic or vagal efferent pathways did not alter this curve (2). The augmented atrial contraction and increased stroke work at any given filling pressure that can be elicited by sympathetic stimulation in dogs (2, 4) and in man (5) are therefore not caused by changes in distensibility [Sarnoff *et al.* (4); Randall & McNally (5)]. Distensibility is affected by the development of spontaneous myocardial failure under some experimental conditions (1), however, and by other physical factors considered below.

Ventricular distensibility is not constant throughout the heart cycle; and

[1] The literature reviewed in this chapter appeared during the year ending June 30, 1961.

169

this characteristic, which suggests the operation of viscous or inertial factors, is particularly evident in the effects of hypothermia and tachycardia on distensibility (1, 6). Hennacy & Ogden (7) have introduced the term "renitence" to describe the time-dependent element in distensibility, and define it as the ratio of filling pressure to rate of inflow. This term, though unfamiliar, has a respectable origin in the standard dictionary and avoids objections to the not quite analogous term "impedance". Early in diastole, renitence depends in part on residual tension from the previous systole, while later it reflects intrinsic elastic properties of the myocardium (7). Epinephrine increases the rate of ventricular relaxation, although this action may be obscured in some circumstances by its inotropic effects (8). Ventricular contraction and relaxation rates are not exclusively determined by events in the previous beat, for they can change within the course of a single heart cycle in response to a suddenly applied load [Zeig, Buckley & Porter (9)].

End-diastolic fiber length.—Ventricular responses consistent with Starling's law of the heart have been demonstrated in man by Braunwald *et al.* (10), who made use of the spontaneous beat-to-beat variations in end-diastolic fiber length that occur with atrial fibrillation. Under these conditions, in which extramyocardial factors were presumably constant from beat to beat, they found a close correlation between myocardial segment length at the end of diastole and various indices of the stroke energy of the subsequent beat. In further studies on seven normal subjects they showed that the operation of Starling's law may be obscured *in vivo* by compensatory autonomic stimuli; transfusing 1500 ml of blood, which might be expected to increase ventricular filling pressure, gave small and inconsistent effects in their control series; but when trimethaphan (Arfonad) was administered to block autonomic responses, transfusion led to marked increases in cardiac output, stroke volume, and work [Frye & Braunwald (11)].

Several studies emphasize the effect that atrial contraction may have on ventricular filling and end-diastolic fiber length (3, 4, 12). Hawthorne (12), using his method of "electromagnetic plethysmography" in unanesthetized dogs, found that atrial contraction increased left ventricular volume by an amount equivalent to 30 to 40 per cent of end-diastolic volume. He also described in detail the normal sequence of changes in ventricular volume, noting that apex-to-base length shortens at the beginning of systole while cross-sectional area increases, again demonstrating that this period should be called isovolumic rather than isometric (12).

Since the Starling mechanism can be experimentally elicited in animals and in man and since there is every reason to believe that the organism has need of such a response to compensate for slight temporary differences in the right and left ventricular outputs, it is reasonable to conclude that the work-fiber length relation is one of the normal cardiac control mechanisms. On the other hand, this relation is not adequate to explain some of the common cardiovascular adjustments, and other mechanisms must be available.

Ventricular adjustment to an increase in outflow resistance, for example, cannot be accounted for by Starling's law alone, since end-diastolic volume usually returns to control levels while increased stroke work is maintained, at least in so far as external work can be calculated. This kind of adjustment is termed "homeometric autoregulation" by Sarnoff's group (13) and is found to be prominent in situations requiring the ventricle to increase its systolic pressure, but less marked when cardiac output alone is increased. Since their previous work (14), as well as a more recent report by Monroe & French (15), indicates a relation between myocardial oxygen consumption and myocardial tension, they speculate that tension may be the factor that evokes the homeometric response. Earlier investigators have reached similar conclusions, as Sarnoff (13, 133) is prompt to point out, but there is no doubt that his extensive and technically exacting work has enabled him to state them more clearly and firmly than was possible before.

Catecholamines.—Augmentation of myocardial contractile force by epinephrine and norepinephrine has been demonstrated in man with the aid of a Walton-Brodie strain-gage arch attached to the right ventricular wall [Goldberg *et al.* (16)]. Methoxamine, on the other hand, a pressor amine with similar effects on systemic resistance, has little effect on myocardial contractility (16). The net effect of catecholamines on cardiac output in the intact subject depends on their relative effects on contractility and systemic resistance and on reflex changes in heart rate (16).

The study of myocardial storage and release of catecholamines has been advanced by improved methods for catecholamine measurement [Manger (17)], but the wide individual variations in myocardial catecholamine concentrations are a serious problem; the standard deviation in controls can be 30 per cent of the group mean (18, 21). Kako, Chrysohou & Bing (18) found that nicotine increases the myocardial stores of catecholamine in dogs pretreated with iproniazid and DOPA, apparently by stimulating the adrenal medulla and sympathetic nerve endings and elevating blood levels. This contrasts with the nicotine-induced release of catecholamines from isolated atria described by Burn & Rand (19). The importance of nerve endings as a source of catecholamines is emphasized by the observation that adrenalectomy has no effect on myocardial contractility in the rat [Ullrick, Brennan & Whitehorn (20)].

Reserpine and syrosingopine deplete myocardial norepinephrine and enhance the cardiac effects of exogenous norepinephrine [Orlans, Finger & Brodie (21); Leusen & Verbeke (22)]. The cardiac and sedative effects of reserpine and its analogues involve different mechanisms (21). Syrosingopine, for example, has definite cardiac effects but does not alter norepinephrine levels in the brain (21), and the "tranquilizing" action of meprobamate on the central nervous system in man does not influence the cardiovascular response to epinephrine [Gunnells *et al.* (23)]

The reduction of cardiac output by hexamethonium (24) and by trimethidinium (Gallamine) (25) has been attributed to the removal of sympathetic stimuli from the heart [Zimmerman, Brody & Beck (24); Eckstein & Horsley

(25)]. The evidence on this point seems clear cut for hexamethonium, since its reduction of heart rate and stroke volume do not depend on changes in filling pressure or venous tone, but are prevented by sympathectomy (24). In the case of trimethidinium, a synthetic drug with curare-like effects, the possibility of direct myocardial action has not been ruled out (25). Guanethidine lowers ventricular norepinephrine content in dogs [Butterfield & Richardson (26)], and the hypotensive action for which it is employed clinically is attributed to reduction of cardiac output rather than vasodilatation [Richardson *et al.* (27)]. Nayler (28) doubts that catecholamines are concerned in the relation between inotropic effects and the phenomenon of treppe. In strips of toad ventricle the production of treppe is not prevented by pretreatment with reserpine and tyramine to release endogenous catecholamines (28).

Hanna & O'Brien (29) explored the possibility that calcium and potassium may act in part by changing the intracellular distribution of catecholamines. They found that changes in extracellular concentration of these ions influenced the intracellular distribution of mephentermine, increasing the proportion found in the cell aqueous, but did not modify the cardiac effects of the drug (29).

Isoproterenol has a positive inotropic effect on normal as well as failing hearts in man (30) and dilates systemic vessels directly (31) but there is as yet no unequivocal evidence of its endogenous release in man [Dodge, Lord & Sandler (30); Cobbold, Ginsburg & Paton (31)]. Dichloroisoproterenol (DCI) blocked the ventricular response to isoproterenol in unanesthetized dogs and partly blocked the response to epinephrine and norepinephrine, but had no effect on response to exercise or central stimulation [Van Citters, Baker & Rushmer (32)]. Lacroix & Leusen (33) confirmed that the positive inotropic action of norepinephrine on the isolated rat heart is accompanied by increased phosphorylase activity in the myocardium but found that a similar increase was produced by dichloroisoproterenol, which blocks the inotropic effects of norepinephrine (33).

Physical factors.—Since many recent studies emphasize the importance of ventricular distensibility, it is surprising that relatively little attention has been given to the transmural, or distending, pressure of the ventricle, which equals the difference between intraventricular and intrapericardial pressure. Work by Holt *et al.* (34) on this neglected variable throws a new light on previous studies of the relation between ventricular pressure and fiber length, for he finds that increasing the end-diastolic ventricular pressure by acute enlargement of total blood volume leads to simultaneous increases in pericardial pressure. With increments of intraventricular end-diastolic pressure up to 10 mm Hg above atmospheric pressure, net transmural pressure rose less than 3 mm Hg. It follows that intrapleural pressure is not an accurate measure of extramural ventricular pressure when the pericardium is intact, and many reports on ventricular mechanics must be reexamined in this light. If these results are confirmed in other laboratories, and there is no reason to suppose from Holt's technique and data that they will not, it seems probable that re-examination will still confirm the Starling work-fiber-length relationship, but with a diminished pressure scale. Such an assumption is unwarranted, however, until direct evidence is available.

One further point of interest in Holt's results was the finding of a sudden decrease of intrapericardial pressure early in ventricular systole (34). The rapid atrial inflow in early ventricular systole may therefore be caused by decreased pressure around the atria rather than by downward movement of the atrioventricular groove (34).

The notion that passive recoil of the ventricular walls in diastole aids ventricular filling receives further support from the work of O'Brien (35) and of Bauereisen, Peiper & Weigand (36). O'Brien showed in the isolated hypothermic dog heart that negative diastolic pressures were developed in the beats following inflow occlusion (35), while Bauereisen and his associates found that the isolated frog ventricle would fill at pressures down to -6 mm Hg (36). "Diastolic suction" may not be the ideal description of this phenomenon, but the finite volume of the relaxed ventricle at zero transmural pressure argues that something of this kind must occur.

Myocardial edema is another factor that may influence both distensibility and contractility. Salisbury, Cross & Rieben (37) find that excessive stretching of the dog ventricle decreases its distensibility, and suggest that this may be related to edema of the ventricular walls.

An increase in either extracellular or intracellular water could change the physical characteristics of the myocardium, but the site of myocardial edema in congestive heart failure is still uncertain. Davis's group found that increased myocardial water in his animals (dogs with heart failure or ascites produced by lesions of the heart valves or vena cavae) could be attributed to an increase in extracellular water, provided that chloride ions remained outside the cell [Yankopoulos et al. (38)]. There is increasing evidence, however, that the chloride is not confined to the extracellular space under all conditions [Taylor, Huffines & Young (39); Flear & Crampton (40)]. The degree of myocardial edema in right heart failure was found to be more closely correlated with right atrial pressure than with other relevant factors, including plasma aldosterone levels (38). Elevation of coronary arterial pressure above 200 mm Hg can in itself produce myocardial edema in the isolated dog heart, as can perfusion by some commercial oxygenators at normal pressures [Salisbury et al. (41)]. Coronary perfusion pressure also has an influence on ventricular distensibility quite unrelated to myocardial edema, since ventricular distensibility falls with increased coronary pressure and volume [Salisbury, Cross & Rieben (109)].

Failing and nonfailing hearts showed no difference in physicochemical properties of cardiac myosin (42), or in specific nucleotide composition [Davis et al. (42); Buckley & Tsuboi (43)].

Digitalis and other drugs.—The positive inotropic action of digitalis even in the absence of heart failure (44) is firmly established in man, and research on its action is now largely concentrated at the cellular level.

The interaction of digitalis glycosides and calcium is of particular interest

because of the possibility that calcium entry may be a link between depolarization and contraction (45). Sekul & Holland (45) conclude that digitalis
affects calcium exchange during cellular activation only, since they found an
increase in calcium uptake when rabbit atria were driven by electrical
stimulation, but not when they were quiescent. Comparison in the frog heart
of the contractures induced by ouabain and by iodoacetate, and by their responses to EDTA, supports the hypothesis that neither toxic nor inotropic
actions of digitalis glycosides interfere with the energy supply of the cell
[Thomas (46)]. The action of digitalis glycosides on potassium transport has
been confirmed by reports of inhibition of potassium influx by ouabain in the
embryonic chick heart (47), an initially negative myocardial potassium
balance in dogs given acetylstrophanthidin (48), and a direct correlation
between the toxicity of certain glycosides and their effects on potassium
transport in the red cell (49). Other contributions in this field have been
made by Klein & Evans (47), Blackmon et al. (48), and Machová (49). The
metabolism of cardiac glycosides has been concisely reviewed by Wright
(50), including evidence that suggests binding of glycosides to lipoproteins
rather than albumin.

Out of many papers on the inotropic effects of substances other than
digitalis, only a few can be mentioned. The action of monoamine oxidase
inhibitors on the heart is being investigated in a number of laboratories;
iproniazid, for example, protects dogs against ventricular fibrillation secondary to coronary ligation, but the mechanism of this protection is unknown
[Regelson, Hoffmeister & Wilkens (51)]. Mersalyl decreases contractility and
shortens the duration of the action potential in guinea pig atria, effects which
Stein, Magin & Kleinfeld (52) attribute to inhibition of cellular protein
sulfhydryls. Buckley, Tsuboi & Zeig (53) have studied the inotropic effects of
purines and pyrimidines on the isolated dog heart, and find that certain
constituent bases of naturally occurring nucleotides have inotropic effects like
those of the nucleotides themselves. The positive inotropic effects of nucleotides can be correlated to some extent with molecular configuration (53).

Synthetic angiotensin II has been found to be a more potent pressor
agent than norepinephrine [Finnerty et al. (54), Gross, Bock & Turrian (55),
McQueen & Morrison (56), Page & Bumpus (57)]. Its hemodynamic effects
include a slight decrease in heart rate, with marked increase in systemic
vascular resistance and systemic venous pressure (54 to 57). Forte, Potgieter
& Schmitthenner report that synthetic hypertensin II increased left ventricular work in intact dogs, with increased myocardial lactate utilization the
only detectable metabolic effect (58). The constituent responsible for the
positive inotropic action of plasma has not been identified, but Nayler &
McCulloch (59) present evidence that its action on the perfused toad heart is
not related to that of digitalis, as proposed by Hajdu, Weiss & Titus (60).
Intropic effects of plasma were more rapid in onset than those of digitalis
glycosides and were not inhibited by quinidine (59).

The first volume of a review of the literature on chemical agents that act on the cardiovascular system has appeared (61), covering publications from 1951 to 1955. Two additional volumes are planned.

Metabolic factors.—Depression of myocardial contractility by high pCO_2 was confirmed by Monroe, French & Whittenberger (62), who were able to demonstrate this effect with only moderate increases in pCO_2; they found no impairment of contractility in the dog when pCO_2 was lowered to 6 mm Hg. Either increased pCO_2 or metabolic acidosis may influence myocardial contractility in myocardial ischemia (62, 63). Waddell & Hardman (64) have described a method for measurement of intracellular pH in isolated hearts, an essential datum in determining whether the effects of any active agent are ascribable to its ionic or undissociated form.

The role of high-energy phosphates in myocardial activity remains problematic (65), but the experiments of Tsuboi, Buckley & Zeig (66) indicate that neither RNA nor the phosphate moiety of the phospholipids is involved in the energy reactions associated with cardiac work (66). Bíró & Mühlrad (67, 68) could find no evidence that nucleotide bound to myofibrils took part in the transphosphorylation associated with contraction. According to Gertler & Mancini (69), mitochondria from guinea pig heart, as well as from liver and kidney, oxidize citrate, but this reaction is not accompanied by phosphorylation. Feinberg & Sister Mary Alma (70) found a direct correlation between ammonia production and cardiac work in the isolated rabbit heart but cautioned that this relation may be fortuitous.

The place of glycogen in myocardial metabolism is still under investigation (71, 72, 73). In isolated rat trabeculae carneae there is no relation between work and glycogen mobilization, a fact suggesting that substrates other than carbohydrate are employed as an immediate energy source [Hazlewood & Ullrick (71)]. The inhibitory effects of sodium fluoroacetate on cell respiration and cardiac output led Hashimoto (72) to conclude that glycolysis was sufficient to supply the energy needs of the heart in his preparations only at low metabolic levels. The inotropic actions of fluoride and malonate are probably not related to glucose metabolism (72, 73) and it may be that an endogenous substrate such as fatty acid is involved [Rice & Berman (73)].

Hackel (74) has presented further evidence that insulin facilitates transfer of glucose into myocardial cells, although the possibility that increased epinephrine production participates in this phenomenon was not excluded.

Immunologic factors.—The cardiac effects of histamine are similar to those of anaphylactic shock, and release of histamine in the myocardium can be demonstrated by bioassay in guinea pigs during anaphylaxis [Feigen *et al.* (75)]. These effects include decreased coronary flow, decreased membrane resting potential, and frequently the appearance of atrial tachycardia or fibrillation, all of which are consistent with an excessive permeability of the cell membrane to sodium (75). Feigen and his colleagues have also devised quantitative methods to determine the amount of antibody adsorbed by the heart and its relation to the dose of antigen and the amount of histamine released [Feigen *et al.* (76)]. Curiously enough, histamine antagonists apparently do not block the cardiac effects of histamine [Trendelenburg (77)].

No clear examples of naturally occurring myocardial autoimmunity have yet been established, but Kaplan and his associates used fluorescent antibody methods to demonstrate myocardial deposits of bound gamma globulin in cardiac tissue from patients with rheumatic heart disease; these were not associated with Aschoff lesions and were not found in nonrheumatic subjects [Kaplan & Dallenbach (78)]. Efforts to determine whether an antigen-antibody reaction was responsible for these deposits were inconclusive [Kaplan, Meyeserian & Kushner (79)].

Hemodynamics

Cardiac output at rest.—It is axiomatic that the normal resting cardiac output varies with the size of the subject, and the resulting problem of comparing outputs in different individuals has never been solved satisfactorily. The ratio of cardiac output to body surface area (cardiac index) is widely used in spite of its numerous shortcomings, but Reeves and co-workers (80) take the position that the arteriovenous oxygen difference is a better comparative measure of normal blood flow because its variance in any group of normal subjects is smaller than that of the cardiac index. In fifty normal subjects they found that the relatively poor correlation between cardiac output and surface area led to a standard deviation of ± 20 per cent of the group mean for the cardiac index, compared with ± 14.5 per cent for arteriovenous oxygen difference. A more important advantage in their view is the fact that this arteriovenous difference is an index of the relation between blood flow and metabolic demand (80), or more exactly that it depends on the ratio of blood flow to oxygen consumed. The question is whether one wants to know what constitutes normal blood flow for the size of the subject, or for his metabolic rate. If the flow-metabolism relation is of interest, then arteriovenous oxygen difference will be the index of choice. If the relation of flow to body size, or total cell mass, is needed, then either height, weight, or some more accurate measurement such as total intracellular water must be used. Body surface area is admittedly an unsatisfactory compromise.

Adjustments of cardiac output.—Debates on the methods by which cardiac output is adjusted to exercise or other demands have become less heated as the participants realize that no one claims omnipotence for any one mechanism. The differences in cardiac response to exercise in the supine and in the erect position are now well recognized (81 to 88). Cardiac output and stroke volume diminish in normal subjects rising from a supine position and standing quietly, while the arteriovenous oxygen difference rises [Wang, Marshall & Shepherd (82); Reeves *et al.* (83); Chapman, Fisher & Sproule (84)]. Moderate exercise in the erect position (e.g. walking on a treadmill) increases stroke volume to about the resting supine level (82, 84, 86). When the effects of exercise in erect and supine positions are compared at equal levels of oxygen uptake, cardiac output is smaller in the erect position (83). Stroke volume increases gradually with increasing exercise (84, 89). In exercising dogs, increases in heart rate greatly exceed those in stroke volume, but atropinization or infusion of catecholamines during exercise can produce wide variations in the relative increments of rate and stroke volume [Wang, Marshall & Shepherd (90); Keck *et al.* (91)].

The effects of posture do not entirely explain the existing lack of agreement on stroke volume changes with exercise: some maintain that stroke volume changes very little with exercise (81, 90), others that there is an essentially linear relation between stroke volume and the level of exercise (89), and still others that the relation differs in mild and severe exercise (82, 84, 85). The data given by almost all investigators show some increase in stroke volume with exercise, however, the differences being quantitative rather than qualitative. There is some suggestion in the available data that increases in rate play a more prominent part in the dog than in man.

Quiet standing causes a redistribution of blood flow, the flow to the legs being reduced out of proportion to the over-all drop in cardiac output, as reflected by the changes in femoral and over-all arteriovenous oxygen differences (73). A similar phenomenon occurs with supine exercise, with the oxygen needs of mild exercise being met largely by increased oxygen extraction, and those of severe exercise by increased blood flow [Reeves *et al.* (92)] although this distinction is more evident in femoral than in pulmonary arteriovenous differences (83, 92).

Training results in lower heart rates and larger stroke volumes for a given work-load in human subjects (93) as well as dogs (89). Gradual training over a period of months increases the capacity for work in man more effectively than does intensive training over a few days (93), as empiric observations have long indicated. The bradycardia induced by muscular training is caused by vagal action on the sinus node and is not related to myocardial catecholamine levels, according to Herrlich, Raab & Gigee (94), who found that training increased atrial levels of acetylcholine in rats but did not alter ventricular levels of cholinesterase or acetylcholine. The prolongation of the isometric (isovolumic) period that accompanies training is presumably the result of sympathetic inhibition (94). Training also protects rats against myocardial necrosis induced by severe stress [Bajusz & Selye (95)]. An increase in the volume of the coronary bed with repeated exercise has been demonstrated by Tepperman & Pearlman (96) with vinyl acetate casts of the coronary bed in rats and guinea pigs.

The relative inaccessibility of subjects rotating in a human centrifuge has proved no obstacle to Wood and his colleagues (97), who have measured cardiac output under these conditions. After 20 to 40 sec of acceleration at 4 g, with subjects in a sitting position but undergoing headward acceleration, cardiac output fell 22 per cent, with a decrease in stroke volume and increase in heart rate [Lindberg *et al.* (97)]. This is perhaps a less severe response than might be expected, and might be well tolerated, but the effects of prolonged acceleration have not been examined. Acceleration perpendicular to the long body axis in dogs was found by Steiner, Mueller & Taylor (98) to produce only slight changes in cardiac output and other hemodynamic variables. Doubtless an increasing amount of work in this field will appear in future reviews.

Energetics of blood flow.—Some features of the ventricular pressure pulse and the transmission of pressure pulses through the aorta and its branches are still not completely explained, in part because a satisfactory mathematical description of pulsatile flow in distensible tubes has yet to be formulated [Remington (99, 100)]. A recent book by McDonald (101) ably presents the information presently available on these problems, including the outstanding contributions made by Womersley.

Farrow & Stacy (102) interpret their Fourier analyses of a large number of pulses from two sites in the dog aorta under varying circulatory conditions as strongly indicative of the presence of reflected waves. Remington, on the other hand, points out flaws in the hypothesis of reflected waves as well as in a number of others and concludes that none of the theories proposed to date completely explains augmentation of the pressure-pulse in the distal aorta (100). In addition to reviewing some of the unsolved problems in this field in the light of his considerable experience with pressure-pulses, he presents a detailed scale map of the variations in pressure in the major branches of the aorta of the dog (100). Studies on longitudinal stress-strain and displacement relations in the aorta of the intact dog by Patel, Mallos & Fry (103) supplement similar information already available on radial stress and strain.

Myocardial Blood Supply

Two major factors influence resistance to blood flow in the coronary bed: the intrinsic response of the vessels to vasomotor stimuli, and the extravascular compression arising from myocardial contraction (104, 105). Coronary resistance falls with the onset of ventricular fibrillation or arrest (104, 106, 107), while coronary blood volume rises [Salisbury, Cross & Rieben (107)]. Vasodilatation by coronary perfusion of cold blood in normothermic dogs [Hardin, Scott & Haddy (108)] may be a related phenomenon. Lewis, Coffman & Gregg (104) used this resistance drop during asystole to measure the extravascular contribution to coronary resistance and found that epinephrine, norepinephrine, and isoproterenol have little or no effect on the extravascular component, although they do reduce coronary resistance by intrinsic action on the vessels. Tachycardia lowers net coronary resistance, even though it increases the extravascular component (104) and decreases coronary blood volume (107); evidently the intrinsic and extrinsic effects on coronary caliber are exerted in different parts of the vascular bed.

Coronary blood flow is more consistently correlated with perfusion pressure than with any other variable, in contrast to the "autoregulation" of blood flow seen in some other organs [Scott, Hardin & Haddy (106); Grayson & Mendel (110)]. At low to moderate rates of flow the coronary pressure-flow relation is consistent with the expected effects of transmural pressure, but the coronary bed reaches its limit of distention at levels of 75 to 220 ml per min in the dog (106). Coronary perfusion pressure also influences ventricular distensibility by controlling the degree of distention of the coronary bed [Salisbury, Cross & Rieben (109)]. While some investigators take the position that adjustment of myocardial blood flow to demand is accomplished primarily by changes in effective coronary pressure (105), the abundant evidence that autonomic (121, 122, 123) and chemical (114, 115) stimuli act on coronary resistance encourages the view that all of these factors are involved.

The relation between external cardiac work and coronary blood flow is variable. Myocardial blood flow is decreased in patients with mitral stenosis and diminished left ventricular output and work [Rowe et al. (111)], but in the isolated heart major increases in work can be elicited with no change in coronary flow [Rosenblueth et al. (112)]. Lowering the oxygen content of coronary arterial blood increases coronary flow, even when oxygen tension is kept constant by using hemoglobin solutions of varying oxygen capacity [Guz, Kurland & Freedberg (113)]. Myocardial oxygen consumption is closely correlated with cardiac effort, as indicated by heart rate and systemic blood pressure, in the dog in open-chest experiments [Feinberg, Gerola & Katz (114)]. Changes in arterial carbon dioxide do not affect myocardial oxygen consumption in relation to cardiac effort, but coronary blood flow is increased by elevated blood carbon dioxide levels (114). Accumulation of carbon dioxide may be one factor concerned in the reactive myocardial hyperemia that follows temporary interruption of coronary flow [Coffman & Gregg (115)]. The duration of the hyperemia is proportional to the duration of the occlusion, a fact showing that the substances responsible are not immediately washed out, and the magnitude of the hyperemia is such as to "overpay" twofold the flow debt incurred during occlusion (115).

Alimentary lipemia reduces myocardial blood flow and oxygen consumption in man at rest, although there is no significant change in coronary perfusion pressure or ventricular work (116). Control values are restored when the plasma lactescence is cleared by the administration of heparin [Regan et al. (116)]. It is not known whether the decreased flow is caused by coronary constriction or by the effects of lipemia on blood viscosity (116). Similar effects have been shown with exercise [Regan et al. (117)]. Lipid deposition in the coronary vessels and endocardium of hypercholesteremic rats is favored by chronic anemia and by exposure to high altitude with its resulting polycythemia [Fillios, Andrus & Naito (118)]. Since cobalt-induced polycythemia does not have this effect, hypoxia is presumably the common factor in these phenomena (118). Intimal thickening and reduction of the lumen in coronary vessels can be elicited by repeated intra-aortic infusions of 5-hydroxytryptamine (serotonin) over two to four weeks in young dogs [Rossi et al. (119)]. A new variety of lipid involvement in coronary obstruction is revealed by the discovery of a phosphoglyceride belonging to the group of plasmalogens that appears in the infarcted area following coronary ligation in dogs [Hack & Ferrans (120)].

Sympathetic control and parasympathetic control of the coronary bed have been separately demonstrated many times, but few experiments have tried to evaluate the net effect of normal autonomic tone. Brachfeld, Monroe & Gorlin (121) have approached the latter problem by measuring the effects of pericoronary neurectomy in dogs. Using direct dissection around the vessels to accomplish coronary denervation, they found that coronary flow was increased for any level of myocardial oxygen consumption by this procedure and concluded that the net effect of autonomic stimuli to the coronary vessels is some degree of vasoconstriction (121). Coronary constriction and dilatation have been produced by selective stimulation of the branches of the left stellate or inferior cervical ganglia in the dog, in the absence of changes in systemic blood pressure or myocardial oxygen consumption [Juhász-Nagy & Szentiványi (122, 123)]. Numerous reports in the Russian literature concerning participation of visceral reflexes in the regulation of coronary flow have been reviewed by Simonson (124). The experimental observation that intestinal distention can produce abnormalities in the ECG similar to those of myocardial ischemia (124) has many clinical counterparts, but it is impossible to translate T wave abnormalities into estimates of myocardial blood flow or oxygen consumption.

Forte and his associates (125) have summarized an extensive experience with the Kety method of determining myocardial blood flow with nitrous oxide and conclude that it is accurate and reproducible. They find that the net errors of infrared and of manometric analysis of blood nitrous oxide are about equal in their hands. Efforts to measure coronary flow in intact animals by indicator-dilution methods, with sampling from coronary sinus or right heart, have been unsuccessful (126, 127).

The gross anatomy and major variations of the coronary vessels in the dog have been described by Blair (128), and the surprisingly frequent myocardial bridges and coronary loops in man by Poláček (129). In dogs the left coronary almost always predominates, and the left circumflex artery supplies most of the left ventricle and portions of the right (128). Determination of regional blood flow in the heart from the distribution of Rb^{86} 20 sec after intravenous injection in the dog showed that flow to the left ventricular muscle exceeded that to the right by about 50 per cent, while the two atria received almost as much as the right ventricle [Levy & Martins de Oliveira (130)].

The anastomotic potentialities of the coronary bed were illustrated in a case reported by Sabiston, Neill & Taussig (131), who showed by direct measurements in a patient with an anomalous left coronary artery arising from the pulmonary artery that flow was retrograde, i.e., from heart to pulmonary artery. Pressure in the left coronary rose well above pulmonary artery pressure when the anastomosis between them was occluded; and blood drawn from the coronary was fully saturated with oxygen, thus confirming a hypothesis about this specific anomaly that was put forward by Brooks 75 years ago (132).

Neural and Reflex Control

In a paper that summarizes their present views on cardiac regulation, Sarnoff and his associates (133) conclude that the role of the carotid sinus in regulating stroke work is as important as its control of heart rate. Experiments in which pressure in the carotid sinus of the dog can be varied at will demonstrate that reflexes originating in the sinus can control the vigor of ventricular contraction (both directly and by way of influencing the strength of atrial contraction), vary ventricular filling pressure by effects on venous distensibility, and indirectly bring homeometric regulation (13) into play by changes in systemic resistance [Sarnoff et al. (133)]. Rushmer and his colleagues have extended their work on the cardiovascular and respiratory responses to stimulation of a specific area in the diencephalon, which closely resemble the responses to exercise, to show that the carotid sinus baroreceptors function normally under these conditions [Wilson et al. (134)]. Leusen & Lacroix (135), however, do not believe that the carotid sinus is essential for the cardiac response to exercise. In dogs with one carotid sinus denervated and the other kept under constant stretch by a balloon, they found that treadmill exercise was accompanied by the usual increase in cardiac output (135).

The involvement of atrial or other cardiac receptors in the control of blood volume and urine flow has been examined further by a number of investigators (136 to 142). Langrehr (137, 138) recorded impulses from fibers of the left vagus on stimulating specific receptor sites in the atrial walls and found that impulse frequency was proportional to the speed of stretch. In further experiments he varied the total blood volume by various maneuvers and showed that while there was no relation between mean atrial pressure and impulse frequency, there was a direct correlation between "thoracic" blood volume (the volume between right atrium and aortic root determined by the indicator-dilution method) and the total activity recorded from atrial receptors (136). Eliahou, Clarke & Bull (139) propose that the amplitude of the pulsatile expansions of the atria determines the response of the atrial receptors. In dogs they showed that the amplitude of atrial pulsation increased with increasing filling pressure up to 24 cm water, then declined with further increases in pressure (139). This fits neatly with the hypothesis that atrial receptors respond to pulsation amplitude, that their response increases as atrial pressure increases to moderate levels, and that diuresis is thus induced as a step in the regulation of blood volume [Henry & Pearce (140); Anderson, McCally & Farrell (141)]. Overstretching of the atria, with resulting diminution in atrial pulsations, could then explain the failure of diuresis in congestive heart failure (139). While this is an attractive theory, further evidence is needed to lend it support and to reconcile it with some other observations, such as the large atrial pulsations sometimes seen with heart failure. Since amplitude of pulsation and rate of stretch frequently vary in the same direction, it is difficult to separate their effects. The peripheral circulation also responds to stimulation of intracardiac baroreceptors, as Ross, Frahm & Brunwald (142) showed by recording an increase in total vascular volume and decrease in systemic resistance when left heart pressures were increased in dogs with innervated, but hemodynamically isolated, hearts (142). Taquini & Aviado (143) have searched for the afferents concerned in homeometric adjustments of ventricular work (13) and conclude that they run with the cardiac sympathetics since the relevant cardiac adjustments to partial occlusion of the pulmonary artery are prevented by sympathectomy (T1–T4), but not by vagotomy or by transection of the spinal cord (143). The receptors are not yet identified. Kolosova (144) has shown that localized trauma can produce histologic changes in certain structures in the atrial wall that are probably receptors.

So-called "vasovagal" reactions in man may be accompanied by a rise in systemic vascular resistance, according to measurements reported by Greene, Boltax & Ulberg (145). Measurements in two subjects who developed acute hypotension, nausea, and sweating in the course of cardiac catheterization showed a decrease in cardiac output and stroke volume out of proportion to the change in arterial pressure (145). Vagus-mediated bradycardia on submerging under water is a response found in terrestial birds (146) as well as in ducks (146) and seals (147). Murdaugh, Seabury & Mitchell (147) used long leads to record the ECG from seals during voluntary diving; there was pronounced bradycardia and sometimes partial atrioventricular block. Atropine prevented the bradycardia, and one seal so treated drowned (147).

Complete denervation of the heart by meticulous excision of all neural pathways around the base of the heart and great vessels, while preserving the main vagal and sympathetic trunks, was carried out in dogs by Cooper *et al.* (148). In such preparations, ventricular catecholamines were virtually absent three days after operation, in contrast to their incomplete disappearance after sympathetic ganglionectomy. The information presently available on the anatomic organization of the central nervous system in relation to control of the heart and blood vessels has been reviewed by Bard (149).

MEMBRANE POTENTIALS AND ION TRANSFER

The sodium-potassium hypothesis of Hodgkin & Huxley (150) needs certain modifications to adapt it to the events observed in cardiac fibers (151 to 154). Two modifications would suffice: (*a*) that the activation and inactivation processes have two components, one fast and one slow; (*b*) that depolarization decreases rather than increases potassium permeability (membrane chord conductance) [Brady & Woodbury (151); Noble (153)]. The difference in membrane conductance for depolarizing and hyperpolarizing currents (152), as well as the superimposability of the later parts of action potentials whose durations are altered by stimulus rate (151), suggests that conductance changes are voltage-dependent. Membrane conductance is considerably lower for depolarizing than for hyperpolarizing currents in Purkinje tissue (which thus resembles skeletal muscle but differs from nerve), a fact supporting the hypothesis that potassium conductance drops with depolarization [Hutter & Noble (152)]. Noble (153) has formulated equations based on these hypotheses which enable a computer to predict with reasonable accuracy the normal resting and action potentials, the current needed for all-or-none repolarization, and the slight shifts that lead to pacemaker-like diastolic instability (153).

Johnson & Tille (154) have proposed an additional modification of the sodium-potassium theory, derived from measurements in the ventricular wall of the rabbit with double-barreled intracellular electrodes. Their data suggest that increase in sodium permeability with depolarization is very brief, and returns almost to the resting level by the time the action potential reaches its crest (154). This conflicts with Weidmann's estimate that membrane resistance at the crest is about 1 per cent of the resting value in Purkinje fibers (155), but the technique used by Johnson & Tille (154) may be more reliable on this point. Decreased potassium permeability on depolarization (151) would be compatible with this theory of early sodium inactivation if it were assumed that sodium permeability remained higher than potassium permeability long enough for the completion of depolarization (154).

Although chloride conductance is usually regarded as constant throughout activity (151), decreased potassium conductance with depolarization may give a larger role to chloride ions as carriers of charge in comparison to their relatively minor part in resting Purkinje fibers [Carmeliet (156)].

Myocardial potassium and sodium exchange undergo marked changes during embryonic development in the chick (157). Klein (157) reports that intracellular potassium gradually increases to a maximum of 72 to 85 mM at 13 days; sodium exchange rate is relatively low and intracellular sodium extremely high (650 mM) in the early embryonic stages, which may be a phylogenetic remnant from more saline ancestors (157). The possibility that ion-movement studies of this kind with radioisotopes may be distorted by exchange diffusion (exchange of labeled and nonlabeled ions across the cell membrane with no net movement) appears to be ruled out by Humphrey's demonstration that potassium-equilibration curves were essentially unchanged by perfusion of his isolated hearts with potassium-free solutions (158).

Henrotte, Cosmos & Fenn (159) report that calcium exchangeability is higher in turtle ventricle than in frog skeletal muscle by a factor of four, which may have some bearing on the relative sensitivity of heart muscle to decreased extracellular calcium. They found that calcium exchange was not significantly affected by stimulation but was increased by stretch (159). The effect of calcium on myocardial contractility is enhanced by epinephrine, in that less is required for a given response when epinephrine is present, yet calcium inhibits the contractile response to epinephrine [Briggs & Holland (160)]. The positive inotropic effect of epinephrine appears, therefore, to involve at least two mechanisms, one of which is concerned with increased binding of calcium in the membrane (160). It may be that neither epinephrine nor digitalis affects sodium and potassium transport directly, but only by way of effects on calcium [Briggs & Holland (160); Trautwein & Schmidt (161)].

Further work by Bozler (162, 163) on nonelectrolytes and osmotic balance in the stomach and sartorius muscles of the frog has implications that may also apply to cardiac tissues. He finds that urea and glycerol in Ringer's solution cause a loss of potassium and sodium as well as water, that sucrose causes a loss of water but not cations, and that the efflux of sucrose and other sugars is not a simple first-order process. These and other apparently contradictory observations can be reconciled by the hypothesis that most of the fiber water is contained in relatively segregated spaces, hindering diffusion of all but small molecules (162, 163).

ELECTRICAL ACTIVITY

Specialized conducting tissues.—The electrical activity of the atrioventricular node and other specialized conducting tissues of the mammalian heart has now been studied in considerable detail (164, 165, 166, 169, 170, 171). Transmission through the atrioventricular node itself is relatively slow, and activity in the bundle of His appears a little less than halfway through the conventional P–R interval [Hoffman *et al.* (164); Medrano and associates (165)]. Much of the remaining P–R interval represents delay in the bundle and its branches [Hoffman *et al.* (164); Alanís & Pilar (166)]. Transmission time from the Purkinje system through the free walls of the ventricles is approximately the same in right and left ventricles, indicating that the slight normal asynchronism of contraction must originate more proximally [Medrano *et al.* (165)].

Analysis of the irregular ventricular response in clinical atrial fibrillation shows that this response is not random, but suggests a mixture of periodic and nonperiodic events [Braunstein & Franke (167); Horan & Kistler (168)]. Whether the known characteristics of the excitability curve of the atrioventricular conducting system suffice to explain these findings remains to be seen.

DeMello & Hoffman (169) postulate that the membrane permeability of specialized cardiac tissues differs from that of other myocardial fibers and that this accounts for the relative insensitivity of the sinoatrial and atrioventricular nodes to increased extracellular potassium. Action potentials could be evoked in these specialized fibers in the rabbit at extracellular potassium levels that completely inhibit myocardial response, and the amplitude of the action potential showed little change as the resting potential was altered (169). On the other hand, these same tissues are particularly sensitive to ischemia and hypoxia. The entire ventricular conducting system, including the Purkinje fibers, shows this vulnerability, but the atrioventricular node is the most sensitive region (170). Bagdonas and co-workers (170) found in experiments on the canine heart that ischemia produced ventricular fibrillation in some experiments and totally abolished electrical activity in the affected area in others. Since hypoxia did not produce these extreme effects, they conclude that the consequences of ischemia do not come from hypoxia alone (170). Hypothermia prolongs the action potential in Purkinje fibers, as it does in other cardiac cells, but the mechanical contraction of isolated fibers is not proportionately prolonged [Schmidt & Chang (171)].

Excitation.—The origin of rhythmic activity has been studied under controlled conditions in tissue cultures (172, 173, 174). In cultures grown from several isolated contracting cells taken from the hearts of young rats (2 to 42 days), the rhythmic contractions of the individual cells became synchronous as soon as cell multiplication brought them into contact with each other. This synchronism appeared to be effected by physical contact alone. Such cultures eventually formed sheets of cells that had the appearance of a syncytium in stained preparations [Harary & Farley (172)]. Cunningham & Estborn (173) have developed a method of culturing whole embryonic chick hearts; they find that the magnitude and rate of electrical activity in such cultures reaches a steady state by the fourth day and remains constant for at least eight days thereafter (174).

Myocardial excitability to square waves of varying amplitude or duration has been studied thoroughly in the past, but a third parameter—the rate of rise of the leading edge of the electrical stimulus—has been little explored in the heart with modern techniques. Ushiyama & Brooks (175) investigated this aspect of excitation in strips of trabecular muscle from the dog ventricle and found that the rate of rise must exceed a certain minimal gradient in order to excite, just as in nerve. The minimal gradient varied widely in different preparations but was essentially the same for linearly and exponentially rising currents. For all gradients steeper than the minimum, the response occurred when rheobase was reached. Attempts to test this same phenomenon with conditioning currents plus superimposed pulses gave different results, a consideration leading them to conclude that more than one fundamental process is concerned in accommodation (175).

Van Dam & Durrer (176) found that strips of left atrial appendage excised from two patients with dilated fibrillating atria could not be excited under his experimental conditions, although similar strips from two subjects with normal rhythm could. In the latter the recorded potentials did not show a smooth progress of excitation through the strip, and excitation curves suggested that fibers differed widely in excitability. It is impossible to tell whether these results were a consequence of the experimental procedure, but they were not seen in atrial strips taken from cats in the same way, and rheumatic changes in the myocardium may be responsible for the irregular spread of excitation (176).

Ventricular excitation and recovery.—Fetal human hearts have been revived and perfused in order to study the pattern of ventricular excitation [Durrer *et al.* (177)]. The epicardial sequence was similar to that found in the dog. "Unipolar" epicardial leads showed rS complexes over most of the anterior walls of both ventricles. while some portions of the left ventricle gave entirely negative (QS) complexes. The method looks promising, although the relation between this preparation and the adult heart *in situ* remains to be determined. Sodi-Pallares and his colleagues (178) found marked variations in the form of "unipolar" QRS complexes throughout the ventricular free wall, although QS forms predominated. They suggest that this variability has its origin in the irregular distribution of sites at which the Purkinje system excites adjacent muscle fibers (178).

The ventricular activation process in the goat was investigated by Hamlin & Scher (179) because of previously observed electrocardiographic differences between ruminants and other mammals. Their finding that the final 15 msec of the QRS complex represents activation of the basilar one-third of the interventricular septum, as well as other differences in the sequence of activation, explains the orientation of the major QRS vectors toward the base of the heart in this animal.

Some of the inherent difficulties in determining the sequence of repolarization in the ventricle have been circumvented by using strength-interval excitability curves as an index of repolarization [van Dam & Durrer (180)]. In the dog they found a relatively orderly pattern, although recovery was usually more advanced in the midportion of the ventricular walls than in adjacent subepicardial or endocardial layers. They were unable to correlate the polarity of the T wave in "unipolar" epicardial leads with the course of recovery (180). Further evidence that the ST alterations in acute myocardial ischemia are caused by a combination of positive currents during the ST interval and negative currents throughout diastole has been presented by Samson & Scher (181), who studied single-cell transmembrane potentials in the injured area as well as records from multiple extracellular electrodes. Ligation of a coronary artery in dogs rapidly produced true ST elevation in epicardial leads over the affected area, with additional TQ segment depression thereafter. The relation between membrane potentials and epicardial complexes was not entirely consistent, but in general a decrease in resting potential accompanied the TQ depression, which can therefore be regarded as a persistent "current of injury" (181). The action potential of cells in the ischemic area was shortened; thus elevation of the ST segment in the ECG was a manifestation of earlier repolarization in injured cells, rather than failure of such cells to depolarize as some theories imply. The shortened action potential and refractory period gradually lengthened again, and after about four hours the effective refractory period was prolonged beyond control values [Reynolds, Vander Ark & Johnston (182)].

Haas and associates (183) conclude from study of the epicardial spread of excitation in the dog ventricle that the ventricular gradient in the peripheral ECG is related to inhomogeneous spread of depolarization and repolarization.

Electrical field of the heart.—Accurate analysis of the electrical field generated by the heart in a conducting medium is a complex theoretic and experimental task, but several recent reviews have at least made the problems more accessible (184 to 188). Brody, Bradshaw & Evans (184) have summarized the lead tensor theory which is their method of approaching the intrinsic characteristics of individual ECG leads. This tensor theory provides a symbolism that can be manipulated by existing mathematical methods and can be applied to either multipole or electromotive surface models of the heart (184). Burger's theories of heart-vectors and lead-vectors were clearly set forth as part of a symposium in the Einthoven centennial at Leiden [Burger, van Brummelen & van Herpen (185)]. Other papers analyze the mathematical basis for electrocardiographic cancellation studies [Helm (186)], application of boundary potentials [Bayley (187)], and measurement of heart vectors in isolated heart preparations [Nelson (188)].

The electrical resistance of the blood contained in the heart chambers has in itself an effect on the electrical field of the heart, and this property has been used by Horan, Andreae & Yoffee (189) to separate the right and left ventricular contributions to the ECG. Carbon dioxide, which has a higher resistivity than blood, was used to displace blood from one ventricle, reducing the peripheral effect of activation spreading radially to the mass of carbon dioxide, while enhancing the effect of spread in a tangential direction. Filling the right ventricle with carbon dioxide displaced the whole QRS loop of the spatial vectorcardiogram posteriorly, as expected, while filling the left ventricle altered the midportion of the QRS loop predominantly (189). Removal of the free wall of the right ventricle in the perfused heart or intact dog also displaces the early QRS vectors leftward and toward the base and at the same time reveals significant contributions by the right septum to early QRS vectors [Gould, Scher & Hamlin (190)].

It is important to remember that conduction through extracardiac tissues causes so-called "unipolar" epicardial leads (one electrode on the heart and another some distance away) to be affected by events remote from the exploring electrode. Such remote effects can be partly eliminated by insulating the ventricular surfaces from other intrathoracic structures [Sayen, Katcher & Peirce (191].

The direction of mean spatial QRS and T vectors in man is related to the configuration of the thorax, but the correlation is not good enough to be of predictive value in individuals [Simonson, Brožek & Schmitt (192)]. The relation between the ECG and the anatomic position of the heart has been carefully re-explored by Guntheroth, Ovenfors & Ikkos (193) with biplane angiocardiography. They show clearly that there is no consistent relation between the mean electrical axis and the anatomic axis of the heart, nor between the precordial transition zone and the interventricular septum; but it seems futile to hope that this additional evidence will suppress the clinical dogma that "electrocardiographic position of the heart" has some spatial significance.

Vectorcardiography and electrocardiography.—Horan, Burch & Cronvich (194) studied the effects of localized myocardial lesions on the spatial vectorcardiogram (VCG) in the dog, using injections of formaldehyde to damage specific parts of the heart. Although they found it difficult to produce permanent changes in the VCG from anterior wall lesions with this method, posterior lesions produced permanent abnormalities of the QRS loop that were consistent with the loss of electromotive forces from the area of destruction. Damage to the basal part of the anterior papillary muscle alone led to VCG changes similar to those of transmural posterior infarcts (194).

Pipberger has continued his efforts to establish objective criteria for the identification of ECG abnormalities so that such criteria could be applied by a digital computer [Pipberger, Arms & Stallmann (195)]. One of the salutary results of research in this direction is an increasing awareness that we need more carefully controlled investigations of the accuracy of clinical ECG interpretation; it also demonstrates how efficient the human computer is in recognizing subtle differences in contour and in filtering out "noise".

A report by Cropp & Manning (196) emphasizes again the poorly under- stood relation of central nervous system lesions to changes in the ECG. They describe several patients with spontaneous intracranial hemorrhage who developed ECG abnormalities like those of acute myocardial infarction, but proved at autopsy to have no myocardial lesion (196). The origin of the U wave is still obscure, but negative U waves are frequently associated with elevated systemic arterial pressure; the depth of the U wave (197) and the contour of the U loop (198) are correlated with the severity of the hyper- tension [Georgopoulos, Proudfit & Page (197); Sano et al. (198)]. Normal and abnormal complexes from intracavitary leads have been studied by Caceres et al. (199), who find among other things that the atrial complex has an appreciable high-frequency content (>400 cps). The extensive literature on clinical electrocardiography is not covered in this review.

ARRHYTHMIAS

Cellular events.—Holland and his colleagues (200, 201) have obtained further evidence to support their thesis that fibrillation is initiated by in- crease in sodium influx above a critical rate. In perfused rabbit hearts they found that electrically induced ventricular fibrillation was accompanied by an increase in potassium efflux and sodium influx similar to that previously demonstrated in rabbit atria [Briggs & Holland (200)]. These changes were of considerably larger magnitude than those elicited in nonfibrillating atria by stimulation at similar rates [Klein & Holland (201)]. They conclude that fibrillation under these conditions is initiated whenever sodium gain and potassium loss exceed a critical value. In atrial tissue this critical rate can be obtained only with rapid electrical stimulation plus acetylcholine, while in the ventricle it can be established readily by lowering extracellular potassium (200).

The effects of quinidine on sodium and potassium flux are consistent with the hypothesis that it acts primarily by inhibiting sodium entry [Klein, Holland & Tinsley (202)]. Depression of potassium efflux by quinidine is probably secondary to depressed sodium influx; the reversal of this depressed potassium efflux by increased extracellular sodium, the differing time course of quinidine effects on potassium efflux and influx, and the drop in net sodium uptake in the spontaneously beating heart on addition of quinidine all favor this conclusion (202), as does the enhancement of quinidine effect by decreased extracellular sodium [Mannaioni (203)]. Stimulation at rapid rates increases sodium influx (200) but leads to no change in its net uptake (202); since quinidine increases net sodium uptake in hearts undergoing rapid stimulation, it must also inhibit active sodium extrusion (202). Although quinidine inhibition of passive sodium influx appears with relative rapidity and could explain all the electrical and mechanical effects of quinidine on the heart (202), the more slowly developing decreased permeability to potassium and inhibition of active sodium and potassium transport (202) could nevertheless contribute to antiarrhythmic effects.

Changes in membrane potential produced by quinidine show that it alters both depolarization and recovery [West & Amory (204)]. The rise time of the action potential in rabbit atria is slowed by quinidine, as would be expected if the drug inhibits sodium entry, although this effect can be demonstrated only with relatively rapid rates of stimulation (204). Repolarization time is prolonged at all stages of recovery by quinidine, independently of rate (204). Although the prolonged refractory period is a result of these changes in both depolarization and repolarization, West & Amory (204) propose that the antiarrhythmic action of quinidine arises primarily through prolongation of recovery, which not only prolongs the conventional refractory period but also extends through diastole to slow the rise time of the next action potential. If this hypothesis is correct, it rules out the possibility of an "ideal" antiarrhythmic drug that would speed conduction while prolonging refractory period (204).

The antiarrhythmic effects of pyrilamine and tripelennamine (77), as well as other antihistaminic agents [Sharma & Singh (205)], may be related to the properties they share with quinidine and procaine, rather than their antagonism to histamine. The mechanism by which diphenylhydantoin sodium (Dilantin) stops aconitine flutter in dogs is not known (206).

Although the movement of sodium ions and potassium ions appears to be intimately involved in the origin of fibrillation and the action of antiarrhythmic drugs, the factor that precipitates changes in ion flux in clinical and experimental arrhythmias remains to be identified. It will continue to be difficult to distinguish between causes and effects until further investigation clarifies: (a) the at least qualitative similarity of rapid stimulation and sustained fibrillation in their effects on sodium and potassium movement (200), (b) the very rapid shifts in membrane permeability that underlie changes in the contour of action potentials when stimulation rate is altered (207), and (c) the gradual return of ion exchange to normal levels with prolonged fibrillation, which suggests that the arrhythmia is initiated and sustained by different processes (200).

Viewed at a multicellular level, the facilitation of re-entry by shortening of the refractory period seems to be the essential phenomenon in many kinds of arrhythmia (208, 209). Experimental flutter, induced by acetylcholine and rapid stimulation in the rabbit atrium, can be explained by a refractory period short enough to permit fibers just recovered to be restimulated (re-entry) by the electrical field of other excited fibers nearby [West & Cox (208)]. The minimum amount of tissue in which flutter can be induced may thus be related to the magnitude of the electrical field produced by active fibers (208). Dresel, MacCannell & Nickerson (209) concluded that the ventricular tachycardia produced by epinephrine and cyclopropane is not caused by an ectopic focus, since with small doses of epinephrine they could produce ventricular bigeminy, with extrasystoles that maintained a fixed coupling period regardless of atrial rate. Re-entry seems the most probable mechanism for such bigeminy (209), but it is not certain that ventricular tachycardia arises in the same way. Moreover, it is conceivable that activity continuously maintained in a small area of the ventricle by re-entry might in itself act as an ectopic focus (208).

Catecholamines.—The suspicion that endogenous catecholamines play some part in the genesis of arrhythmias is still based on circumstantial evidence. Infarcted areas produced by coronary ligation in dogs lose about 75 per cent of their normal catecholamine content within 24 hours, and the action of the released norepinephrine on other cells could induce ectopic rhythms [Russell, Crafoord & Harris (210)]. In experimental ventricular tachycardia initiated by intramyocardial injection of hypertonic saline or delphinine, intravenous epinephrine has relatively little effect on the ventricular rate and does not induce ventricular fibrillation [Scherf, Taner & Yildiz (211)], possibly because blood catecholamines are already elevated [Nakano *et al.* (212)].

It seems reasonable to suppose that the bradycardic effect of reserpine is related to depletion of myocardial norepinephrine [Orlans (21)]. Reduction of heart rate by phenylephrine, however, is caused solely by arterial hypertension and the sinoaortic reflex [Varma *et al.* (214)]. Reduction of myocardial catecholamines by reserpine and hexamethonium slows the ventricular as well as the atrial rate in dogs with complete heart block, according to Roberts & Modell (213). Although they interpret their evidence to mean that the inherent rhythmicity of the ventricle depends on catecholamine activity, their records do not preclude the possibility that the ventricles are being driven by a pacemaker in the atrioventricular node. The tachycardic effect of triiodothyronine and the increased digitalis requirement for control of ventricular rate in thyrotoxic atrial fibrillation are reduced by reserpine or syrosingopine [Frye & Braunwald (215)].

Conduction abnormalities and cardiac arrest.—No mechanical abnormalities in onset or sequence of ventricular contractions were found in seven of twelve patients with the Wolff-Parkinson-White syndrome studied by March, Selzer & Hultgren (216), and the findings in five others varied widely.

The varieties and significance of atrioventricular dissociation, with and without block, have been reviewed by Jacobs, Donoso & Friedberg (217).

The discovery by Kouwenhoven, Jude & Knickerbocker (218) that rhythmic compression of the unopened thorax is a more than adequate substitute for open-chest cardiac massage is an advance of great practical importance. This method of resuscitation is useful in the treatment of ventricular fibrillation as well as cardiac standstill, since it maintains coronary and cerebral blood flow at a viable level until a defibrillator can be applied (218). Its efficacy has been confirmed by many physicians, and in combination with mouth-to-mouth artificial respiration [Safar *et al.* (219)] it represents the treatment of choice for circulatory arrest. In situations where the intrinsic pacemakers of the heart are inadequate for long periods of time, the use of artificial pacemakers with electrodes such as those devised by Ross & Hoffman (220) for insertion through the intact chest wall may be practical.

TECHNIQUES

The transseptal method of catheterizing left heart chambers in man, introduced by Ross, Braunwald & Morrow (221), is now widely used, and its safety and efficacy have been confirmed [Singleton & Scherlis (222); McGaff *et al.* (223)].

Indicator-dilution methods continue to be widely used for the measurement of cardiac output and will probably retain their popularity until continuous flow meters become readily available and easily used. Satisfactory estimates of cardiac output have been obtained with thermal dilution methods (224, 225), and by precordial scanning of radioactivity (226), although the time components of the resulting dilution curves are not identical with those of simultaneous dye-dilution curves. Precordial scanning is also a useful screening method for the detection of left-to-right shunts (226, 227), as is an uncalibrated hydrogen-platinum electrode system (228). A variety of substances labeled with radioisotopes have been shown to be useful for single-injection (229, 230) and constant infusion (231) dilution methods.

Holt's (232) dilution method (233, 234) and cineangiography (235) have been used to measure ventricular stroke and residual volumes. Cineangiography showed that blood entering from the left atrium did not mix immediately with the ventricular residual volume in dogs (234), but in the absence of quantitative data relating mean diastolic concentrations in the ventricle and in blood sampled from the aortic root, the effect of nonmixing on measurements of ventricular volume cannot be evaluated. Cineangiography has also been used to study regurgitation through the normal mitral valve, which often occurs in dogs when the heart rate is such that diastasis lasts more than 0.39 sec [Carter, Southard & Chungcharoen (236)].

One aspect of the possible predictive value of ballistocardiography has been analyzed by Starr & Wood (237). In a group of normal subjects followed for seventeen years or more after recording their ballistocardiograms, they found that clinical signs of heart disease developed during the follow-up period more often in subjects with relatively low ballistocardiographic deflections for their age than in those with deflections of large amplitude (237).

Cation-selective glass microelectrodes to measure intracellular sodium and potassium activities have been described by Hinke (238). Methods for chronic implantation of electrodes in the heart (239, 240) and of catheters in the coronary sinus (241) have also been reported. Spectral and conventional oscillographic phonocardiography have been compared by Brody and associates (242), who conclude that each method has some advantages not shared by the other. Ultrasonic methods have been devised to study heart motion, the Doppler principle being used to identify reflections from various blood-tissue interfaces; high-frequency beams are said to be affected predominantly by motion of the heart valves [Yoshida and co-workers (243)].

As instrumentation becomes more complex it is increasingly important for the investigator to understand the limitations as well as the capabilities of his equipment; and Stacy's textbook on biologic and medical electronics (244), together with Fry's review on the measurement of pressure and other variables (245), is a helpful guide to this end.

PERSPECTIVE

Finally, the circulatory physiologist interested in the philosophy of science should be directed to an essay by Richards on the development of concepts in cardiovascular physiology (246) and to Gillispie's recent volume on the history of scientific ideas (247). Gillispie gives a key place in the development of the natural sciences to William Harvey and his *De Motu Cordis*. Harvey's far-reaching discovery, he reminds us—and it is a profitable reminder for investigators of any period—was largely a fresh synthesis of facts already known to many of his predecessors.

LITERATURE CITED

1. Braunwald, E., Frye, R. L., and Ross, J., Jr., *Circulation Research*, **8**, 1254–63 (1960)
2. Mitchell, J. H., Linden, R. J., and Sarnoff, S. J., *Circulation Research*, **8**, 1100–7 (1960)
3. Linden, R. J., and Mitchell, J. H., *Circulation Research*, **8**, 1092–99 (1960)
4. Sarnoff, S. J., Brockman, S. K., Gilmore, J. P., Linden, R. J., and Mitchell, J. H., *Circulation Research*, **8**, 1108–22 (1960)
5. Randall, W. C., and McNally, H., *J. Appl. Physiol.*, **15**, 629–31 (1960)
6. Lendrum, B., Feinberg, H., Boyd, E., and Katz, L. N., *Am. J. Physiol.*, **199**, 1115–20 (1960)
7. Hennacy, R. A., and Ogden, E., *Circulation Research*, **8**, 825–30 (1960)
8. Hennacy, R. A., *Circulation Research*, **8**, 831–36 (1960)
9. Zelg, N. J., Buckley, N. M., and Porter, E. P., *Circulation Research*, **9**, 531–40 (1961)
10. Braunwald, E., Frye, R. L., Aygen, M. M., and Gilbert, J. W., Jr., *J. Clin. Invest.*, **39**, 1874–84 (1960)
11. Frye, R. L., and Braunwald, E., *J. Clin. Invest.*, **39**, 1043–50 (1960)
12. Hawthorne, E. W., *Circulation Research*, **9**, 110–19 (1961)
13. Sarnoff, S. J., Mitchell, J. H., Gilmore, J. P., and Remensnyder, J. P., *Circulation Research*, **8**, 1077–91 (1960)
14. Sarnoff, S. J., Braunwald, E., Welch, G. H., Case, R. B., Stainsby. W. N., and Macruz, R., *Am. J. Physiol.*, **192**, 148–56 (1958)
15. Monroe, R. G., and French, G., *Circulation Research*, **9**, 362–74 (1961)
16. Goldberg, L. I., Bloodwell, R. D., Braunwald, E., and Morrow, A. G., *Circulation*, **22**, 1125–32 (1960)
17. Manger, W. M., *Chemical Quantitation of Epinephrine and Norepinephrine in Plasma* (Charles C Thomas, Springfield, Ill., 1959)
18. Kako, K., Chrysohou, A., and Bing, R. J., *Circulation Research*, **9**, 295–99 (1961)
19. Burn, J. H., and Rand, M. J., *Brit. Med. J.*, **I**, 137–39 (1958)
20. Ullrick, W. C., Brennan, B. B., and Whitehorn, W. V., *Am. J. Physiol.*, **200**, 117–21 (1961)
21. Orlans, F. B. H., Finger, K. F., and Brodie, B. B., *J. Pharmacol. Exptl. Therap.*, **128**, 131–39 (1960)
22. Leusen, I., and Verbeke, R., *Arch. intern. pharmacodynamie*, **125**, 246–47 (1960)
23. Gunnells, J. C., Gorten, R., Bogdonoff, M. D., and Warren, J. V., *Am. Heart J.*, **60**, 231–36 (1960)
24. Zimmerman, B. G., Brody, M. J., and Beck, L., *Am. J. Physiol.*, **199**, 319–24 (1960)
25. Eckstein, J. W., and Horsley, A. W., *J. Clin. Invest.*, **40**, 555–62 (1961)
26. Butterfield, J. L., and Richardson, J. A., *Proc. Soc. Exptl. Biol. Med.*, **106**, 259–62 (1961)
27. Richardson, D. W., Wyso, E. M., Magee, J. H., and Cavell, G. C., *Circulation*, **22**, 184–90 (1960)
28. Nayler, W. G., *J. Gen. Physiol.*, **44**, 393–404 (1960)
29. Hanna, C., and O'Brien, J. E., *Arch. intern. pharmacodynamie*, **127**, 361–68 (1960)
30. Dodge, H. T., Lord, J. D., and Sandler, H., *Am. Heart J.*, **60**, 94–105 (1960)
31. Cobbold, A. F., Ginsburg, J., and Paton, A., *J. Physiol. (London)*, **151**, 539–50 (1960)
32. Van Citters, R. L., Baker, D., and Rushmer, R. F., *Am. J. Physiol.*, **200**, 990–94 (1961)
33. Lacroix, E., and Leusen, I., *Arch. intern. pharmacodynamie*, **126**, 482–85 (1960)
34. Holt, J. P., Rhode, E. A., and Kines, H., *Circulation Research*, **8**, 1171–81 (1960)
35. O'Brien, L. J., *Circulation Research*, **8**, 956–60 (1960)
36. Bauereisen, E., Peiper, U., and Weigand, K. H., *Z. Kreislaufforsch.*, **49**, 195–200 (1960)
37. Salisbury, P. F., Cross, C. E., and Rieben, P. A., *Circulation Research*, **8**, 788–93 (1960)
38. Yankopoulos, N. A., Davis, J. O., Cotlove, E., and Trapasso, M., *Am. J. Physiol.*, **199**, 603–8 (1960)
39. Taylor, I. M., Huffines, W. D., and Young, D. T., *J. Appl. Physiol.*, **16**, 95–102 (1961)
40. Flear, C. T. G., and Crampton, R. F., *Clin. Sci.*, **19**, 495–504 (1960)
41. Salisbury, P. F., Cross, C. E., Katsuhara, K., and Rieben, P. A., *Circulation Research*, **9**, 601–6 (1961)
42. Davis, J. O., Carroll, W. R., Trapasso,

M., and Yankopoulos, N. A., *J. Clin. Invest.*, 39, 1463–71 (1960)

43. Buckley, N. M., and Tsuboi, K. K., *Circulation Research*, 9, 618–25 (1961)

44. Braunwald, E., Bloodwell, R. D., Goldberg, L. I., and Morrow, A. G., *J. Clin. Invest.*, 40, 52–59 (1961)

45. Sekul, A. A., and Holland, W. C., *Am. J. Physiol.*, 199, 457–59 (1960)

46. Thomas, L. J., Jr., *Am. J. Physiol.*, 199, 146–50 (1960)

47. Klein, R. L., and Evans, M. L., *Am. J. Physiol.*, 200, 735–40 (1961)

48. Blackmon, J. R., Hellerstein, H. K., Gillespie, L., Jr., and Berne, R. M., *Circulation Research*, 8, 1003–12 (1960)

49. Machová, J., *Experientia*, 16, 553–54 (1960)

50. Wright, S. E., *The Metabolism of Cardiac Glycosides* (Charles C Thomas, Springfield, Ill., 1960)

51. Regelson, W., Hoffmeister, F. S., and Wilkens, H., *Ann. N. Y. Acad. Sci.*, 80, 981–87 (1959)

52. Stein, E., Magin, J., and Kleinfeld, M., *Am. J. Physiol.*, 199, 460–62 (1960)

53. Buckley, N. M., Tsuboi, K. K., and Zeig, N. J., *Circulation Research*, 9, 242–49 (1961)

54. Finnerty, F. A., Jr., Massaro, G. D., Chupkovich, V., and Tuckman, J., *Circulation Research*, 9, 256–63 (1961)

55. Gross, F., Bock, K. D., and Turrian, H., *Helv. Physiol. et Pharmacol. Acta*, 19, 42–57 (1961)

56. McQueen, E. G., and Morrison, R. B. I., *Brit. Heart J.*, 23, 1–6 (1961)

57. Page, I. H., and Bumpus, F. M., *Physiol. Revs.*, 41, 331–90 (1961)

58. Forte, I. E., Potgieter, L., and Schmitthenner, J. E., *Circulation Research*, 8, 1235–41 (1960)

59. Nayler, W. G., and McCulloch, M., *Australian J. Exptl. Biol. Med. Sci.*, 38, 127–34 (1960)

60. Hajdu, S., Weiss, H., and Titus, E., *J. Pharmacol. Exptl. Therap.*, 120, 99–113 (1957)

61. Welt, I. D., Ed., *Index-Handbook of Cardiovascular Agents*, 2 (1951–55) Parts I and II (Natl. Acad. Sci., Washington, D. C., 1568 pp., 1960)

62. Monroe, R. G., French, G., and Whittenberger, J. L., *Am. J. Physiol.*, 199, 1121–24 (1960)

63. Darby, T. D., Aldinger, E. E., Gadsden, R. H., and Thrower, W. B.,

Circulation Research, 8, 1242–53 (1960)

64. Waddell, W. J., and Hardman, H. F., *Am. J. Physiol.*, 199, 1112–14 (1960)

65. Hochrein, H., and Döring, H. J., *Arch. ges. Physiol.*, 271, 548–63 (1960)

66. Tsuboi, K. K., Buckley, N. M., and Zeig, N. J., *Circlation Research*, 8, 703–12 (1960)

67. Bíró, N. A., and Mühlrad, A., *Acta Physiol. Acad. Sci. Hung.*, 18, 85–93 (1960)

68. Bíró, N. A., and Mühlrad, A., *Acta Physiol. Acad. Sci. Hung.*, 18, 95–101 (1960)

69. Gertler, M. M., and Mancini, D., *Am. J. Physiol.*, 200, 355–58 (1961)

70. Feinberg, H., and Sister Mary Alma, *Am. J. Physiol.*, 200, 238–42 (1961)

71. Hazlewood, R. L., and Ullrick, W. C., *Am. J. Physiol.*, 200, 999–1003 (1961)

72. Hashimoto, K., *Japan. J. Physiol.*, 11, 212–21 (1961)

73. Rice, L. I., and Berman, D. A., *Am. J. Physiol.*, 200, 727–31 (1961)

74. Hackel, D. B., *Am. J. Physiol.*, 199, 1135–38 (1960)

75. Feigen, G. A., Vaughan Williams, E. M., Peterson, J. K., and Nielsen, C. B., *Circulation Research*, 8, 713–23 (1960)

76. Feigen, G. A., Vurek, G. G., Irvin, W. S., and Peterson, J. K., *Circulation Research*, 9, 177–83 (1961)

77. Trendelenburg, U., *J. Pharmacol. Exptl. Therap.*, 130, 450–60 (1960)

78. Kaplan, M. H., and Dallenbach, F. D., *J. Exptl. Med.*, 113, 1–16 (1961)

79. Kaplan, M. H., Meyeserian, M., and Kushner, I., *J. Exptl. Med.*, 113, 17–36 (1961)

80. Reeves, J. T., Grover, R. F., Filley, G. F., and Blount, S. G., Jr., *J. Appl. Physiol.*, 16, 276–78 (1961)

81. Rushmer, R. F., and Smith, O. A., Jr., *Physiol. Revs.*, 39, 41–68 (1959)

82. Wang, Y., Marshall, R. J., and Shepherd, J. T., *J. Clin. Invest.*, 39, 1051–61 (1960)

83. Reeves, J. T., Grover, R. F., Blount, S. G., Jr., and Filley, G. F., *J. Appl. Physiol.*, 16, 283–88 (1961)

84. Chapman, C. B., Fisher, J. N., and Sproule, B. J., *J. Clin. Invest.*, 39, 1208–13 (1960)

85. Holmgren, A., Jonsson, B., and Sjöstrand, T., *Acta Physiol. Scand.*, 49, 343–63 (1960)

86. Bevegård, S., Holmgren, A., and

Jonsson, B., *Acta Physiol. Scand.*, **49**, 279–98 (1960)

87. Gullbring, B., Holmgren, A., Sjöstrand, T., and Strandell, T., *Acta Physiol. Scand.*, **50**, 62–71 (1960)

88. Bruce, R. A., Cobb, L. A., Morledge, J. H., and Katsura, S., *Am. Heart J.*, **61**, 476–84 (1961)

89. Bailie, M. D., Robinson, S., Rostorfer, H. H., and Newton, J. L., *J. Appl. Physiol.*, **16**, 107–11 (1961)

90. Wang, Y., Marshall, R. J., and Shepherd, J. T., *Circulation Research*, **8**, 558–63 (1960)

91. Keck, E. W. O., Allwood, M. J., Marshall, R. J., and Shepherd, J. T., *Circulation Research*, **9**, 566–70 (1961)

92. Reeves, J. T., Grover, R. F., Filley, G. F., and Blount, S. G., Jr., *J. Appl. Physiol.*, **16**, 279–82 (1961)

93. Holmgren, A., Mossefeldt, F., Sjöstrand, T., and Ström, G., *Acta Physiol. Scand.*, **50**, 72–83 (1960)

94. Herrlich, H. C., Raab, W., and Gigee, W., *Arch. intern. pharmacodynamie*, **129**, 201–15 (1960)

95. Bajusz, E., and Selye, H., *Am. J. Physiol.*, **199**, 453–56 (1960)

96. Tepperman, J., and Pearlman, D., *Circulation Research*, **9**, 576–84 (1961)

97. Lindberg, E. F., Sutterer, W. F., Marshall, H. W., Headley, R. N., and Wood, E. H., *Aerospace Med.*, **31**, 817–34 (1960)

98. Steiner, S. H., Mueller, G. C. E., and Taylor, J. L., *Aerospace Med.*, **31**, 907–14 (1960)

99. Remington, J. W., *Am. J. Physiol.*, **199**, 328–30 (1960)

100. Remington, J. W., *Am. J. Physiol.*, **199**, 331–34 (1960)

101. McDonald, D. A., *Blood Flow in Arteries* (Williams & Wilkins, Baltimore, Md., 1960)

102. Farrow, R. L., and Stacy, R. W., *Circulation Research*, **9**, 395–401 (1961)

103. Patel, D. J., Mallos, A. J., and Fry, D. L., *J. Appl. Physiol.*, **16**, 293–99 (1961)

104. Lewis, F. B., Coffman, J. D., and Gregg, D. E., *Circulation Research*, **9**, 89–95 (1961)

105. Cross, C. E., Rieben, P. A., and Salisbury, P. F., *Circulation Research*, **9**, 589–600 (1961)

106. Scott, J. B., Hardin, R. A., and Haddy, F. J., *Am. J. Physiol.*, **199**, 765–69 (1960)

107. Salisbury, P. F., Cross, C. E., and Rieben, P. A., *Am. J. Physiol.*, **200**, 633–36 (1961)

108. Hardin, R. A., Scott, J. B., and Haddy, F. J., *Am. J. Physiol.*, **199**, 163–66 (1960)

109. Salisbury, P. F., Cross, C. E., and Rieben, P. A., *Circulation Research*, **8**, 794–800 (1960)

110. Grayson, J., and Mendel, D., *Am. J. Physiol.*, **200**, 968–74 (1961)

111. Rowe, G. G., Maxwell, G. M., Castillo, C. A., Huston, J. H., and Crumpton, C. W., *Circulation*, **22**, 559–62 (1960)

112. Rosenblueth, A., Alanís, J., Rubio, R., and Pilar, G., *Am. J. Physiol.*, **200**, 243–46 (1961)

113. Guz, A., Kurland, G. S., and Freedberg, A. S., *Am. J. Physiol.*, **199**, 179–82 (1960)

114. Feinberg, H., Gerola, A., and Katz, L. N., *Am. J. Physiol.*, **199**, 349–54 (1960)

115. Coffman, J. D., and Gregg, D. E., *Am. J. Physiol.*, **199**, 1143–49 (1960)

116. Regan, T. J., Binak, K., Gordon, S., DeFazio, V., and Hellems, H. K., *Circulation*, **23**, 55–63 (1961)

117. Regan, T. J., Timmis, G., Gray, M., Binak, K., and Hellems, H. K., *J. Clin. Invest.*, **40**, 624–30 (1961)

118. Fillios, L. C., Andrus, S. B., and Naito, C., *J. Appl. Physiol.*, **16**, 103–6 (1961)

119. Rossi, P., Stevenson, M., Khaksar, P., and Bellet, S., *Circulation Research*, **9**, 436–40 (1861)

120. Hack, M. H., and Ferrans, V. J., *Circulation Research*, **8**, 738–41 (1960)

121. Brachfeld, N., Monroe, R. G., and Gorlin, R., *Am. J. Physiol.*, **199**, 174–78 (1960)

122. Juhász-Nagy, A., and Szentiványi, M., *Am. J. Physiol.*, **200**, 125–29 (1961)

123. Juhász-Nagy, A., and Szentiványi, M., *Arch. intern. pharmacodynamie*, **131**, 39–53 (1961)

124. Simonson, E., *Circulation*, **22**, 1179–84 (1960)

125. Forte, I. E., Potgieter, L., Schmitthenner, J. E., Neal, H., and Hafkenschiel, J. H., *Am. Heart J.*, **61**, 81–87 (1961)

126. Forte, I. E., Schmitthenner, J. E., and Neal, H. S., *Circulation Research*, **9**, 547–51 (1961)

127. Marchioro, T., Feldman, A., Owens, J. C., and Swan, H., *Circulation Research*, **9**, 541–56 (1961)

128. Blair, E., *Circulation Research*, **9**, 333–41 (1961)

129. Poláček, P., *Am. Heart J.*, **61**, 44–52 (1961)
130. Levy, M. N., and Martins de Oliveira, J., *Circulation Research*, **9**, 96–98 (1961)
131. Sabiston, D. C., Neill, C. A., and Taussig, H. B., *Circulation*, **22**, 591–97 (1960)
132. Brooks, St. J., *J. Anat. Physiol.*, **20**, 26–29 (1886)
133. Sarnoff, S. J., Gilmore, J. P., Brockman, S. K., Mitchell, J. H., and Linden, R. J., *Circulation Research*, **8**, 1123–36 (1960)
134. Wilson, M. F., Clarke, N. P., Smith, O. A., Jr., and Rushmer, R. F., *Circulation Research*, **9**, 491–96 (1961)
135. Leusen, I., and Lacroix, E., *Arch. intern. pharmacodynamie*, **130**, 470–72 (1961)
136. Langrehr, D., and Kramer, K., *Arch. ges. Physiol.*, **271**, 797–807 (1960)
137. Langrehr, D., *Arch. ges. Physiol.*, **271**, 257–69 (1960)
138. Langrehr, D., *Arch. ges. Physiol.*, **271**, 270–82 (1960)
139. Eliahou, H. E., Clarke, S. D., and Bull, G. M., *Clin. Sci.*, **19**, 377–90 (1960)
140. Henry, J. P., and Pearce, J. W., *J. Physiol. (London)*, **131**, 572–85 (1956)
141. Anderson, C. H., McCally, M., and Farrell, G. L., *Endocrinology*, **64**, 202–7 (1959)
142. Ross, J., Jr., Frahm, C. J., and Braunwald, E., *J. Clin. Invest.*, **40**, 563–72 (1961)
143. Taquini, A. C., and Aviado, D. M., *Am. J. Physiol.*, **200**, 647–50 (1961)
144. Kolosova, A. A., *Doklady Biol. Sci. Sections*, **129**, 1016–19 (1960)*
145. Greene, M. A., Boltax, A. J., and Ulberg, R. J., *Circulation Research*, **9**, 12–17 (1961)
146. Bond, C. F., Douglas, S. D., and Gilbert, P. W., *Am. J. Physiol.*, **200**, 723–26 (1961)
147. Murdaugh, H. V., Jr., Seabury, J. C., and Mitchell, W. L., *Circulation Research*, **9**, 358–61 (1961)
148. Cooper, T., Gilbert, J. W., Jr., Bloodwell, R. D., and Crout, J. R., *Circulation Research*, **9**, 275–81 (1961)
149. Bard, P., *Physiol. Revs.*, **40**, Suppl. 4, 3–26 (1960)
150. Hodgkin, A. L., and Huxley, A. F., *J. Physiol. (London)*, **117**) 500–44, (1952)
151. Brady, A. J., and Woodbury, J. W., *J. Physiol. (London)*, **154**, 385–407 (1960)

152. Hutter, O. F., and Noble, D., *Nature*, **188**, 495 (1960)
153. Noble, D., *Nature*, **188**, 495–97 (1960)
154. Johnson, E. A., and Tille, J., *J. Gen. Physiol.*, **44**, 443–67 (1961)
155. Weidmann, S., *J. Physiol. (London)*, **115**, 227–36 (1951)
156. Carmeliet, E. E., *J. Physiol. (London)*, **156**, 375–88 (1961)
157. Klein, R. L., *Am. J. Physiol.*, **199**, 613–18 (1960)
158. Humphrey, E. W., *Am. J. Physiol.*, **200**, 133–34 (1961)
159. Henrotte, J. G., Cosmos, E., and Fenn, W. O., *Am. J. Physiol.*, **199**, 779–82 (1960)
160. Briggs, A. H., and Holland, W. C., *Am. J. Physiol.*, **199**, 609–12 (1960)
161. Trautwein, W., and Schmidt, R. F., *Arch. ges. Physiol.*, **271**, 715–26 (1960)
162. Bozler, E., *Am. J. Physiol.*, **200**, 651–55 (1961)
163. Bozler, E., *Am. J. Physiol.*, **200**, 656–57 (1961)
164. Hoffman, B. F., Cranefield, P. F., Stuckey, J. H., and Bagdonas, A. A., *Circulation Research*, **8**, 1200–11 (1960)
165. Medrano, G. A., Sodi-Pallares, D., deMicheli, A., Bisteni, A., Plansky, J. B., and Hertault, J., *Am. Heart J.*, **60**, 562–80 (1960)
166. Alanís, J., and Pilar, G., *Am. J. Physiol.*, **199**, 775–78 (1960)
167. Braunstein, J. R., and Franke, E. K., *Circulation Research*, **9**, 300–4 (1961)
168. Horan, L. G., and Kistler, J. C., *Circulation Research*, **9**, 305–11 (1961)
169. de Mello, W. C., and Hoffman, B. F., *Am. J. Physiol.*, **199**, 1125–30 (1960)
170. Bagdonas, A. A., Stuckey, J. H., Piera, J., Amer, N. S., and Hoffman, B. F., *Am. Heart J.*, **61**, 206–18 (1961)
171. Schmidt, R. F., and Chang, J. J., *Arch. ges. Physiol.*, **272**, 393–99 (1961)
172. Harary, I., and Farley, B., *Science*, **132**, 1839–40 (1960)
173. Cunningham, A. W. B., and Estborn, B. D., *Lab. Invest.*, **9**, 656–68 (1960)
174. Estborn, B. D., and Cunningham, A. W. B., *Lab. Invest.*, **10**, 98–110 (1961)
175. Ushiyama, J., and Brooks, C. McC., *Am. J. Physiol.*, **200**, 718–22 (1961)
176. van Dam, R. T., and Durrer, D., *Circulation Research*, **9**, 509–14 (1961)
177. Durrer, D., Büller, J., Graaff, P., Lo,

G. I., and Meyler, F. L., *Circulation Research*, **9**, 29–38 (1961)

178. Sodi-Pallares, D., Medrano, G. A., deMicheli, A., Testelli, M. R., and Bisteni, A., *Circulation*, **23**, 836–46 (1961)

179. Hamlin, R. L., and Scher, A. M., *Am. J. Physiol.*, **200**, 223–28 (1961)

180. van Dam, R. T., and Durrer, D., *Am. Heart J.*, **61**, 537–42 (1961)

181. Samson, W. E., and Scher, A. M., *Circulation Research*, **8**, 780–87 (1960)

182. Reynolds, E. W. Jr., Vander Ark, C. R., and Johnston, F. D., *Circulation Research*, **8**, 730–37 (1960)

183. Haas, H. G., Blömer, A., Ley, M., and Schaefer, H., *Cardiologia*, **37**, 66–84 (1960)

184. Brody, D. A., Bradshaw, J. C., and Evans, J. W., *Bull. Math. Biophys.*, **23**, 31–42 (1961)

185. Burger, H. C., van Brummelen, A. G. W., and van Herpen, G., *Am. Heart J.*, **61**, 317–23 (1961)

186. Helm, R. A., *Am. Heart J.*, **60**, 251–65 (1960)

187. Bayley, R. H., *Am. Heart J.*, **61**, 684–91 (1961)

188. Nelson, C. V., *Science*, **133**, 1831–32 (1961)

189. Horan, L. G., Andreae, R. L., and Yoffee, H. F., *Am. Heart J.*, **61**, 504–14 (1961)

190. Gould, J. P., Scher, A. M., and Hamlin, R. L., *Am. Heart J.*, **61**, 796–801 (1961)

191. Sayen, J. J., Katcher, A. II., and Peirce, G., *Circulation Research*, **9**, 497–508 (1961)

192. Simonson, E., Brožek, J., and Schmitt, O. H., *Cardiologia*, **38**, 258–66 (1961)

193. Guntheroth, W. G., Ovenfors, C.-O., and Ikkos, D., *Circulation*, **23**, 69–76 (1961)

194. Horan, L. G., Burch, G. E., and Cronvich, J. A., *J. Appl. Physiol.*, **15**, 624–28 (1960)

195. Pipberger, H. V., Arms, R. J., and Stallmann, F. W., *Proc. Soc. Exptl. Biol. Med.*, **106**, 130–32 (1961)

196. Cropp, G. J., and Manning, G. W., *Circulation*, **22**, 25–38 (1960)

197. Georgopoulos, A. J., Proudfit, W. L., and Page, I. H., *Circulation*, **23**, 675–80 (1961)

198. Sano, T., Tsuchihashi, H., Takigawa, S., and Shimamoto, T., *Am. Heart J.*, **61**, 802–10 (1961)

199. Caceres, C. A., Kelser, G. A., Jr., and

Calatayud, J., *J. Appl. Physiol.*, **16**, 300–4 (1961)

200. Briggs, A. H., and Holland, W. C., *Am. J. Physiol.*, **200**, 122–24 (1961)

201. Klein, R. L., and Holland, W. C., *Am. J. Physiol.*, **199**, 346–48 (1960)

202. Klein, R. L., Holland, W. H., and Tinsley, B., *Circulation Research*, **8**, 246–52 (1960)

203. Mannaioni, P. T., *Sperimentale*, **110**, 320–36 (1960)

204. West, T. C., and Amory, D. W., *J. Pharmacol. Exptl. Therap.*, **130**, 183–93 (1960)

205. Sharma, V. N., and Singh, K. P., *Arch. intern. pharmacodynamie*, **131**, 24–31 (1961)

206. Scherf, D., Blumenfeld, S., Taner, D., and Yildiz, M., *Am. Heart J.*, **60**, 936–47 (1960)

207. Gibbs, C. L., and Johnson, E. A., *Circulation Research*, **9**, 165–70 (1961)

208. West, T. C., and Cox, A. R., *J. Pharmacol. Exptl. Therap.*, **130**, 303–10 (1960)

209. Dresel, P. E., MacCannell, K. L., and Nickerson, M., *Circulation Research*, **8**, 948–55 (1960)

210. Russell, R. A., Crafoord, J., and Harris, A. S., *Am. J. Physiol.*, **200**, 995–98 (1961)

211. Scherf, D., Taner, D., and Yildiz, M., *Proc. Soc. Exptl. Biol. Med.*, **105**, 30–32 (1960))

212. Nakano, J., Zekert, H., Griege, C. W., Wang, K.-M., Schaefer, H. S., and Wégria, R., *Am. J. Physiol.*, **200**, 413–16 (1961)

213. Roberts, J., and Modell, W., *Circulation Research*, **9**, 171–76 (1961)

214. Varma, S., Johnsen, S. D., Sherman, D. E., and Youmans, W. B., *Circulation Research*, **8**, 1182–86 (1960)

215. Frye, R. L., and Braunwald, E., *Circulation*, **23**, 376–82 (1961)

216. March, H. W., Selzer, A., and Hultgren, H. N., *Circulation*, **23**, 582–92 (1961)

217. Jacobs, D. R., Donoso, E., and Friedberg, C. K., *Medicine*, **40**, 101–18 (1961)

218. Kouwenhoven, W. B., Jude, J. R., and Knickerbocker, G. G., *J. Am. Med. Assoc.*, **173**, 1064–67 (1960)

219. Safar, P., Brown, T. C., Holtcy, W. J., and Wilder, R. J., *J. Am. Med. Assoc.*, **176**, 574–76 (1961)

220. Ross, S. M., and Hoffman, B. F., *J. Appl. Physiol.*, **15**, 974–76 (1960)

221. Ross, J., Jr., Braunwald, E., and Mor-

row, A. G., *Circulation*, 22, 927–34 (1960)

222. Singleton, R. T., and Scherlis, L., *Am. Heart J.*, 60, 879–85 (1960)

223. McGaff, C. J., Roveti, G. C., Glassman, E., and Ross, R. S., *Am. Heart J.*, 61, 161–64 (1961)

224. Evonuk, E., Imig, C. J., Greenfield, W., and Eckstein, J. W., *J. Appl. Physiol.*, 16, 271–75 (1961)

225. Hershgold, E. J., Steiner, S. H., and Sapirstein, L. A., *J. Appl. Physiol.*, 15, 1062–64 (1960)

226. Sharpe, A. R., Jr., and Shapiro, W., *Am. Heart J.*, 61, 650–55 (1961)

227. Cornell, W. P., Braunwald, E., and Morrow, A. G., *Circulation*, 23, 21–29 (1961)

228. Hyman, A. L., Hyman, E. S., Quiroz, A. C., and Gantt, J. R., *Am. Heart J.*, 61, 53–60 (1961)

229. Homer, G. M., Zipf, R. E., Hieber, T. E., and Katchman, B. J., *J. Appl. Physiol.*, 15, 953–57 (1960)

230. Crane, M. G., Holloway, J. E., Selvester, R., and Crawford, R., *Am. J. Physiol.*, 199, 1131–34 (1960)

231. Rochester, D. F., Durand, J., Parker, J. O., Fritts, H. W., Jr., and Harvey, R. M., *J. Clin. Invest.*, 40, 643–48 (1961)

232. Holt, J. P., *Circulation Research*, 4, 187–95 (1956)

233. Freis, E. D., Rivara, G. L., and Gilmore, B. L., *Am. Heart J.*, 60, 898–906 (1960)

234. Swan, H. J. C., and Beck, W., *Circulation Research*, 8, 989–98 (1960)

235. Gribbe, P., Hirvonen, L., and Pel-

tonen, T., *Acta Physiol. Scand.*, 51, 169–74 (1961)

236. Carter, B. L., Southard, M., and Chungcharoen, D., *Proc. Soc. Exptl. Biol. Med.*, 104, 613–15 (1960)

237. Starr, I., and Wood, F. C., *Circulation*, 23, 714–32 (1961)

238. Hinke, J. A. M., *J. Physiol. (London)*, 156, 314–35 (1961)

239. Makevnin, G. Ia., *Physiol. J. USSR*, 45, 107–9 (1959)*

240. Stuckey, J. H., Hoffman, B. F., Bagdonas, A. A., and Venerose, R. S., *Proc. Soc. Exptl. Biol. Med.*, 106, 90–92 (1961)

241. Galla, S. J., Williamson, A. W. R., and Vandam, L. D., *J. Appl. Physiol.*, 16, 209–10 (1961)

242. Brody, D. A., Erb, B. D., Evans, J. W., and Bradshaw, J. C., *Am. Heart J.*, 60, 581–91 (1960)

243. Yoshida, T., Mori, M., Nimura, Y., Y., Hikita, G., Takagishi, S., Nakanishi, K., and Satomura, S., *Am. Heart J.*, 61, 61–75 (1961)

244. Stacy, R. W., *Biological and Medical Electronics* (McGraw-Hill, New York, N. Y., 1960)

245. Fry, D. L., *Physiol. Revs.*, 40, 753–88 (1960)

246. Richards, D. W., *Disease and the Advancement of Basic Science*, 160–76 (Harvard Univ. Press, Cambridge, Mass., 1960)

247. Gillispie, C. C., *The Edge of Objectivity. An Essay in the History of Scientific Ideas* (Princeton Univ. Press, Princeton, N. J., 1960)

* English translation will be announced in *Technical Translations*, issued by the Office of Technical Services, US Department of Commerce, and will be made available by the Photoduplication Service, Library of Congress, and by the SLA Translation Center at the John Crerar Library, Chicago, Illinois.

CUTANEOUS SENSIBILITY[1]

By G. Weddell and S. Miller[2]

Department of Anatomy, Oxford University, Oxford, England

INTRODUCTION

It is impossible, at present, to give a concise account of the mechanism of cutaneous sensibility. This would require detailed information from a number of different experimental fields in which many necessary techniques have still to be developed. As an indication of the magnitude of the problem, a short analysis of the known requirements in some of the fields involved is given before a synopsis of our present knowledge.

Anatomy.—This involves a knowledge of:

(a) The number, size, and morphology of the individual fibres comprising the peripheral sensory nerves and their terminals serving the skin, and the relationship of the terminals to surrounding tissue cells.

(b) The precise pathways as well as the synaptic connections available to the sensory cutaneous nerves from their entry into the spinal cord to their destinations elsewhere in the central nervous system.

Physiology.—This involves a knowledge of:

(a) The biophysical and biochemical mechanisms by which stimuli, having different physical attributes and given energy content, are transduced into propagated disturbances of a given number and frequency along nerve fibres, taking into account the effect upon the system of continued stimulation and the evoked nervous activity.

(b) The degree and significance of interaction among sensory axons in their passage from the skin to the spinal cord.

(c) The conduction velocity of the disturbances evoked.

(d) Analysis of the spatial and temporal patterns of propagated activity reaching the spinal cord and higher centres, evoked by controlled stimuli resembling those occurring in normal life.

(e) The precise pattern as well as the nature (inhibitory or excitatory) of the synaptic activity which is evoked by incoming impulses in the spinal cord and at higher centres, when the subject is under strictly controlled experimental conditions.

(f) Changes in activity throughout the sensory system which may be evoked in the various pathways available, in subjects under a series of widely different, yet measurable, postural and environmental conditions.

Clinical observations.—These consist of records of reports following stimulation of the skin and other parts of the sensory pathways of subjects who have surgical, traumatic, or pathologic lesions involving a part, or

---

[1] The survey of literature pertaining to this review was concluded in October 1961.
[2] Medical Research Council scholar.

parts, of the nervous pathway from the skin to the "highest" levels in the nervous system.

Behavioural experiments.—The results of the anatomical, physiological, and clinical studies outlined above must be correlated and appear ultimately in terms of behaviour, as such studies cannot by themselves account for the mechanism of cutaneous sensibility. Controlled human sensory tests, designed in the light of anatomical, physiological, and clinical data, are therefore required to test the validity of, and to extend, the conclusions drawn from these basic experiments. In man this means a correlation of all the anatomical and physiological findings with statistically significant reports of particular sensations from subjects of different social and educational backgrounds under, as far as possible, natural conditions.

ANATOMY

Nerve Terminations in the Human Integument

Hairy skin.—In man only two groups of nerve terminations have been found consistently: (*a*) those ending in relation to hair follicles and (*b*) arborizations of fine nonmyelinated axons. The former are arranged in two separate layers, running approximately at right angles to one another, and form a basket-like network which may be quite simple or highly complex, depending on the size of the hair follicle and the number and diameter of the myelinated nerve fibres which radiate from it (21). The arborizations are seen by light microscopy to terminate by attenuation in various layers of the skin (140, 151) and appear to be naked before they become too fine to resolve. By contrast, electron micrographs reveal fine prolongations of Schwann cell cytoplasm accompanying the axon as far as it can be traced (107). Although the histological picture may not yet be complete, the most recent observations fail to reveal the presence of terminals in the epidermis, except on rare occasions (15). The arborizations of fine nerve terminations are commonly referred to collectively as "free" nerve endings, to distinguish them from encapsulated or compact forms, neither of which are found in undamaged hairy skin from healthy children in the first decade of life but may appear in increasing numbers with age. "Free" nerve endings are served by myelinated and nonmyelinated stem axons, whose diameter varies inversely as the size of their receptive fields (132). The hairy skin of the human hand and of the leg in both rabbits and cats contains specialized nerve terminals similar in appearance to Merkel discs (16, 32). In the cat, up to five are found per square centimetre and one large myelinated stem axon may serve several of these endings (62).

Nonhairy skin.—This includes palms of the hands, soles of the feet, and parts of the fingers and toes. Here, three types of nerve termination are described.

(*a*) Meissner's corpuscles—elaborate and encapsulated nerve endings attached to the epidermis in the dermal papilli. From the anatomical point of view they have two outstanding features in common with hair follicle nerve terminals: their capsules are in structural continuity with the epidermis and they are foci from which a number of myelinated axons of different diameters radiate (14).

(b) Merkel's discs—arborizations of nonmyelinated axons (serving large myelinated stem axons) ending in expanded terminals on specialized tactile cells. These are attached to the epidermis at the base of intermediate rete ridges which dip into the dermis (16, 151).

(c) "Free" nerve endings—similar in structure and distribution to those in hairy skin but more numerous (140, 151).

Exposed mucous membranes and other specialized areas of body integument.—(a) In the lips, the anal mucous membrane, and the external genital organs there are, in addition to "free" nerve endings [some of the terminals of which undoubtedly pass into the epithelium (129a)], a multitude of compact but unencapsulated nerve endings (served by myelinated axons of different diameters), the organization and size of which are so variable as to defy anatomical classification. These particular zones are among the most profusely innervated parts of the body integument (149).

(b) The cornea contains many "free" nerve endings (some of which pass into the epithelium) served by nonmyelinated axons of different diameters which join myelinated stem fibres at the limbus. It is now certain that the terminal arborizations do not fuse with each other but intertwine and overlap extensively (147, 155). It is interesting that the pattern of innervation of the integument covering the dorsal fin of *Amphioxus*—an animal at the threshold of vertebrate evolution—is very much like that of the cornea (78).

(c) The conjunctiva in young healthy laboratory mammals is served by a wide range of myelinated and nonmyelinated stem axons and usually contains only "free" nerve endings arranged less densely than in the cornea. The same is true in man, although just beneath the epithelium nerve end-bulbs are occasionally seen, which are irregular in size, form, and axonal content. They are seldom found in children although they can be demonstrated in increasing numbers during the second and later decades of life. Occasionally they are found in oxen (104, 110).

Variations.—Although the descriptions given above apply fairly constantly, variations in the standard pattern occur.

(a) Hairy skin: highly complex nerve end-bulbs, similar in appearance to the "sterile" end-bulbs described by Cajal in the proximal stumps of divided nerve bundles, are found in increasing numbers in persons in the middle and later decades of life and in skin which has been injured by trauma or disease (137, 138).

(b) Nonhairy skin: Meissner corpuscles in the finger pads of manual workers and in persons in the later decades of life are morphologically far more complex than those seen in young persons. A continuous loss and replacement of neural substance from within these terminals has been suggested (17).

(c) Conjunctiva: the end-bulbs are similar to the "sterile" end-bulbs in the skin and it is clear that they also represent part of a process of degeneration and repair, for their parent axons show early signs of Wallerian change. Nerve fibres and terminals in the walls of the human carotid sinus, particularly in the age group 50 to 80, show this neural turnover even more clearly (111).

Fitzgerald (30, 31) finds, in the pig's snout, that an orderly series of changes, depending upon the degeneration and regeneration of nerve fibres and their terminals, begins soon after birth and continues during postnatal development. These observations, taken together, suggest that terminal and preterminal axons, as well as the axonal components of the end-corpuscles of the sensory peripheral nervous system, are constantly adapting themselves, by a process of degeneration and regeneration, to the structural changes taking place in surrounding tissues. The increase in the number of end-bulbs with age is probably traceable to the "hardening" of the tissues which provides an obstruction to regenerating axons (111). On the basis of this hypothesis, anything causing a structural alteration of the skin itself might tend to alter the otherwise relatively constant pattern and distribution of the preterminal and terminal nerve fibres. Confirmation of this hypothesis is suggested by some recent observations on the thickened skin of patients with psoriasis, in which the number of the "free" nerve endings was increased and the patterned arrangement of the fibres serving them was far more complex than in control skin from the contralateral normal side (137).

THE DISTRIBUTION OF NERVE FIBRES WITHIN THE SKIN

Numerous small bundles of axons of different diameters converge from all directions towards the cutaneous nerves they serve. Under the microscope the nerves serving the more superficial layers of the dermis are seen to pass through a highly complex meshwork, the cutaneous nerve plexus. It is quite impossible, therefore, to determine the source of the various fine divisions and subdivisions of a single stem axon which leaves the plexus, without simplifying the pattern by experimental nerve section. This has been done in common laboratory mammals, including the rhesus monkey (132), and from clinical observations it is evident that the arrangement in human skin is similar (15, 104, 131, 133, 138).

The most detailed analysis of the myelinated fibres of the plexus has been carried out in the rabbit ear (139, 141, 142). All the dorsal root axons tested supplied either hairs or "free" nerve endings and none could be traced which served both types by different daughter axons. Every hair follicle is innervated by a variable number of daughter axons of different diameters, each of which follows a tortuous course through the cutaneous plexus to join its larger parent stem fibre. Although the number of hair follicles is more than twenty times the number of dorsal root axons serving the ear, no hair follicle is served by less than two dorsal root fibres and some may receive as many as thirty such fibres. The receptive fields of the dorsal root axons vary inversely as the size of the fibre and the follicle, and the pattern of distribution of the hairs is characteristically irregular throughout. This arrangement gives rise to a continuously variable pattern of overlapping receptive fields.

The "free" nerve endings in the ear are supplied almost exclusively by nonmyelinated and the finer myelinated fibres, but it was not possible to estimate their receptive fields or degree of overlap. The determination of the receptive field of a single dorsal root axon serving "free" nerve terminals is impracticable with present neurohistological techniques. Degeneration experiments demand a gap of at least two to three days before an undamaged axon can be traced throughout its course among the mass of degenerating axons. In addition, the undamaged "free" nerve endings develop sprouts which grow some distance into the denervated area before they can be distinguished from the surrounding debris. The receptive field is therefore larger than it was before the lesion was made (154). With the alternative and less laborious evoked potential technique (which requires a single fibre lead), it has been possible to estimate the receptive fields even of nonmyelinated C fibres (61). As many as fifteen C fibres may be carried in one Schwann cell pathway (38), so the actual size of the areas measured must be considered provisional, as histological controls are usually not made of the fibres from which recordings are taken. In comparing the two techniques it is interesting that when bundles of a few myelinated fibres are investigated, the area mapped histologically is always larger (142).

In the skin from the back of the ear in man, many of the hair follicles are as lavishly innervated as in the rabbit, despite the small size of the hairs. Although quantitative investigations of the kind described above cannot be made in man, it is reasonable to assume, on the basis of present histological evidence, that the over-all pattern of innervation is not dissimilar.

The Distribution of Nerve Fibres Within the Cornea

The arborizations of nonmyelinated daughter axons are gathered together at different points around as much as three-quarters of the circumference of the cornea to form eventually a single myelinated ciliary nerve stem axon, of which there are about 500 in the cat. The receptive areas for each stem axon overlap extensively and seldom extend over less than one quadrant (122). The plexiform arrangement of innervation is therefore comparable to that in the skin (81, 135). The histological picture in man is similar, except that more axons are seen to enter at the limbus (155).

Availability of Nerve Endings to Stimulation

Recent studies on the neurohistology of the skin [particularly the photomicrographs in (94)] emphasize that any natural stimulus delivered to human skin can potentially activate a very large number of terminals. Even fine punctate stimuli of, for example, one square millimetre will cover more than a hundred endings. In the extreme case it is highly improbable that the finest quartz needle (121) inserted into the skin could stimulate only one ending. This does not imply that a single ending cannot be stimulated physiologically, if it displays a very much lower threshold than any of its neighbouring terminals.

THE DISTRIBUTION OF SENSORY CUTANEOUS NERVE FIBRES IN NERVE TRUNKS PASSING TOWARDS THE SPINAL CORD

In the rabbit ear, degeneration studies on myelinated fibres have revealed that axons central to the dorsal root ganglion and stem axons at the base of the ear are grouped together in relation to focal receptive fields. Between the division of the primary rami and the entrance of the nerve trunks into the ear, this topographical arrangement is lost and a randomization of the fibres takes place (142). Wall (127) finds in the cat that the myelinated fibres proximal to the ganglion in lumbar dorsal roots are grouped into even finer bundles with respect to neighbouring cutaneous receptive fields. In nonmyelinated nerves there is a comparable, though more complex, regrouping by an exchange of axons between Schwann cell pathways (40). It is not clear at present if this regrouping of fibres within a peripheral nerve reduces interaction to a minimum, preserves the over-all pattern of sensory data from the periphery in the face of partial damage to a nerve trunk, or is merely an "accident" of development.

Variations.—It is of interest that the number of fibres in human peripheral nerve trunks decreases with age (19a). (See also Nerve Terminations in the Human Integument: *Variations.*)

HISTOCHEMICAL OBSERVATIONS

In the embryo, all cutaneous nerve fibres (including myelinated axons) in the skin and the coil of fibres at the base of the developing Meissner corpuscle give a strong positive specific cholinesterase reaction. This reaction is also given quite consistently in the adult by nerves ending in relation to hair follicle nerve terminations and by some of the finer nerve fibres in the cutaneous plexus. Autonomic fibres innervating eccrine sweat glands and cutaneous blood vessels are also cholinesterase positive. A nonspecific cholinesterase reaction seems to be given consistently by the nerves within all specialized nerve end-organs except hair-follicle nerve endings, which are occasionally negative. An alpha-esterase reaction is sometimes given by the nerves within Meissner corpuscles in man (96, 150). It is difficult to be certain whether the enzymes concerned are concentrated in the axons or in adjacent cells. These different relationships do not form any regular pattern or conform to any known physiological process within the skin (16).

Other histochemical techniques have been used to demonstrate nerve fibres and their terminals selectively in animals but few have yet been applied to human skin (96, 150). There is no doubt that the analysis of enzyme reactions may become more useful as time goes on. All that can be said now is that the specific reactions demonstrated in human skin do not form any obvious pattern which can be used in the analysis of receptors into groups having any clear relationship to the mechanism of cutaneous sensibility (16).

Under the electron microscope, "synaptic" vesicles are seen in the cells close to the terminations of "free" nerve endings but not in the endings themselves. There is also a report of similar vesicles in both the nerve filaments and the laminar cells of Meissner corpuscles (17). Although the vesicles are labeled "synaptic" their precise function is unknown.

The Pathways and Synaptic Connections of Afferent Cutaneous Sensory Nerves Within the Central Nervous System

The majority of the most rapidly conducting myelinated axons from the skin travel directly up the dorsal columns of the spinal cord to the gracile and cuneate nuclei. Here secondary neurons decussate and reach the ventrobasal nuclear complex of the thalamus by way of the medial lemnisci (19, 109, 125). Some dorsal column fibres end below the medulla and are relayed to their respective nuclei by internuncial neurons, but it is not known if they serve cutaneous nerve terminals (43). Such a description greatly oversimplifies the anatomical picture as every fibre entering the dorsal column divides immediately into ascending and descending branches, whose collaterals synapse segmentally with cells in the grey matter.

The smaller nerve fibres (myelinated and nonmyelinated) from the skin enter the spinal cord, where most of them divide a few millimetres after their entrance into rostral and caudal branches synapsing at different segmental levels with cells of the dorsal horn. Again it is not clear how many of the various groups of cells are concerned with cutaneous nerve impulses (143) although, in the cat, Wall (127) has characterized one group related to cutaneous A fibres. Many second-order neurons in the dorsal horn cross over to the opposite anterolateral column, where they give rise to ascending and descending collaterals. The smallest ascending fibres probably synapse within the column, medulla, or brainstem (5, 92), and only a few of the larger fibres reach the ventrobasal nuclear complex of the thalamus directly (19, 41, 42, 109, 148). In the cat and monkey other fibres reach the posterior group and intralaminar nuclei (19, 109). It is presumed on clinical grounds and the lack of any anatomical evidence to the contrary that most of the cutaneous nerve fibres entering the anterolateral column—even though they may relay a number of times—project on to the thalamus. Beyond this the connections are obscure, as it is difficult to predict central sensory projections in man from animal experiments (5). Clinical reports, however, suggest that the nuclei in the thalamus related to the anterolateral columns project either directly or indirectly on to the cortex (119).

PHYSIOLOGY

Receptor Specificity

In recent electrophysiological studies on cutaneous receptors, authors have tended to express the concepts of receptor and receptor-specificity in biophysical terms. Receptors are considered as transducers of mechanical or thermal energy into propagated nervous activity. Their specificity is defined (strictly within the framework of the experiment) in terms of the physical attributes of the stimulus which evokes the largest response for the least energy input. In more refined terms specificity is determined by the relationship of stimuli, applied at the receptor membrane, to the amplitude and frequency of the generator potential in the terminal axon. From such data (47a, 87a, 90) it is possible in certain cases to determine the energy barrier which has to be overcome in the conversion of a stimulus into a generator potential. Two such mammalian receptors have been characterized in this way: the muscle spindle (70) and the Pacinian corpuscle (64). In the Pacinian corpuscle the deformation-sensitive area was found to be restricted to the length of nonmyelinated nerve extending proximally from its tip to the point at which the first intracorpuscular sleeve of myelin began (90). The receptor membrane is composed of a mosaic of mechanically excitable areas, the electrical responses of which sum to give the generator potential (87b), which, as has been shown, varies as the strength of the stimulus (47a, 87a). In further experiments (64) the temperature of the preparation was varied, and from the concomitant changes in the rate of rise of the generator potential it was possible to calculate the energy of excitation of the receptor. Within this framework, specificity becomes solely a function of the properties of the receptor membrane. Unfortunately, cutaneous nerve terminals are morphologically so very much more intricate than the Pacinian corpuscle that it is impossible with present techniques to determine the stimulus-sensitive zone or to quantify the stimulus-response relationship as described above.

The accompanying Table I gives a general survey of some of the results of recent experiments. Relatively few animals and cutaneous areas have been investigated, and in all but the experiments upon the Pacinian corpuscle the nature, depth, and arrangement of the receptors are unknown. In these experiments specificity becomes a question of relating the activity in a nerve bundle or single fibre to a specific stimulus applied to the variable number of terminals in the skin, supplied by that bundle or fibre. On the basis of anatomical observations (particularly in man) it should be emphasized that the activity in a single stem fibre, with the exception of those supplying isolated endings, generally represents the summed effect, both spatial and temporal, of the response to stimulation of a population of nerve endings.

Although many authors do not publish the number of nerves or animals they test or give any estimate of the number of fibres responding to the different stimuli applied, it seems clear that there is a spread of stimulus specificity throughout the range of fibre diameters. [See table and papers cited, particularly (57, 127).] Recent studies of C fibres suggest, at least in the animals used, that this fibre group is unlikely to be concerned solely with nociception. Nevertheless, in the few experiments in which the C fibre group has been subdivided, the C_2 division appears to be nociceptive in function, as high thresholds to stimulation are consistently found (24, 152). Witt observes that many C_1 fibres in the cat are also nociceptive as they respond to all forms of stimulation at high threshold, and she concludes that the receptors involved lie superficially in the skin, as they respond with short latency to the application of acid (152). It is becoming evident that a strict classification of cutaneous receptors according to the categorical stimulus modalities of touch, warmth, and cold may be quite arbitrary. There seems to be a spread of sensitivity among these three methods of stimulation.

In view of the size of receptive fields and the complexity of the cutaneous nerve network (61, 127, 142), one wonders if all the receptors of the "free" nerve-ending type served by a single parent axon display a common specificity or if there is a spread of sensitivity among them to different stimuli (68). So far there is no physiological evidence for either theory from mammalian experiments, but recent investigations on the ampulla of Lorenzini of the dogfish may throw light on the problem. Although this organ was thought by some workers (51, 115) to be primarily a thermoreceptor, Loewenstein (88) has shown that the receptor membrane is sensitive only to mechanical stimuli. Nevertheless, the regular discharge pattern to a constant pressure differential is modulated by changes of temperature.

There are several reports of single mammalian fibres activated by both mechanical and thermal stimulation of the skin (see last four columns of Table I), but it is impossible to say at present if temperature exerts a metabolic effect upon the deformation-sensitive receptor membrane or on neighbouring cells capable of influencing its response, or if there are thermosensitive endings attached to the same axon which modify the response of the active deformation-sensitive endings. In the sural nerve of the cat there are A fibres whose frequency of firing is slower and more maintained for thermal than for mechanical stimulation of the skin (57). Although this does not resolve the question of specificity, it does indicate that a population of such fibres would transmit significantly different patterns of response to different types of stimulus.

In final analysis the degree of specificity of a receptor, as Loewenstein (89) points out, depends upon the following factors: "1) the relative energy requirements for excitation for the various stimuli; 2) the accessibility of the receptor and its peripheral axon portions to the stimuli under normal physiological conditions; and 3) the relative requirements of spatial summation for the stimuli." Only when techniques for recording from single cutaneous receptors comparable to those applied to the Pacinian corpuscle have been developed can this problem be properly evaluated.

CONDUCTION VELOCITY OF SKIN SENSORY FIBRES

There is no doubt that the various sensations which can be evoked from the skin are reported at different times after the application of the stimulus. For example, the reaction time is shorter for touch than for heat transfer, and both conduction times (disturbance of EEG alpha rhythm) and reaction times have shorter latencies for stimuli evoking fast pain than for those evoking slow pain (47). Measurements of reaction times to different stimuli led several authors to make indirect estimates of the conduction velocity,

TABLE I
ELECTROPHYSIOLOGICAL STUDIES OF CUTANEOUS RECEPTORS

References	Type of lead	Fibre size	Specific fibres			Nonspecific fibres			
			Cool & cold	Warm & hot	Mech.	Cold & mech.	Hot & mech.	Hot, cold, & mech.	Temp. mods. mech.
CAT									
Tongue									
Hensel & Witt, 1959 (55)	Single	A	+						
Infraorbital nerve									
Boman, 1958 (8)	Single	A	+			+			
Iriuchijima & Zotterman, 1960 (63)	Single	C	+	+	+	+	+	+	
Saphenous and sural nerves									
Iggo, 1959 (60)	Single	A			+				
Witt & Hensel, 1959 (153)	Single	A	+	+		+			
Hunt & McIntyre, 1960 (56)	Single	A			+	+	+	+	
Hunt & McIntyre, 1960 (57)	Single	A			+	+	+	+	+
Wall, 1960 (127)	Single	A			+			+	+
Douglas & Ritchie, 1957 (23)	A-dromic	A			+				
Iggo, 1959 (59)	Single	C	+	+	+	+			
Iggo, 1959 (60)	Single	C	+	+	+	+	+		+
Iggo, 1960 (61)	Single	C	+	+	+			+	
Hensel, Iggo & Witt, 1960 (54)	Single	C	+	+		+			
Iriuchijima & Zotterman, 1960 (63)	Single	C	+	+	+	+	+	+	
Douglas & Ritchie, 1957 (23)	A-dromic	C			+				
Douglas & Ritchie, 1959 (24)	A-dromic	C_1			+	+			
		C_2	+						
Douglas, Ritchie & Straub, 1959 (25)	A-dromic	C	+		+	+			
Witt, 1961 (152)	Single	C_1						+	
		C_2		+					
Pacinian corpuscle									
Ishiko & Loewenstein, 1960 (64)	Single	A			+				+
Loewenstein, 1961 (89)	Single	A			+				+
Cornea									
Lele & Weddell, 1959 (81)	Bundle	A						+	
Weddell, 1960 (122a)	Bundle	A				+	+	+	
DOG									
Infraorbital nerve									
Boman, 1958 (8)	Single	A	+			+			
Iriuchijima & Zotterman, 1960 (63)	Single	C	+	+	+	+	+	+	
Saphenous nerve									
Iriuchijima & Zotterman, 1960 (63)	Single	C	+	+	+	+	+	+	
RAT									
Infraorbital nerve									
Boman, 1958 (8)	Single	A	+			+			
Saphenous nerve									
Iriuchijima & Zotterman, 1960 (63)	Single	C	+	+	+			+	

TABLE I (*continued*)

References	Type of lead	Fibre size	Specific fibres			Nonspecific fibres		
			Cool & Cold	Warm & hot	Mech.	Cold & mech.	Hot & mech.	Hot, cold, & mech.	Temp. mods. mech.

			RABBIT						
Ear									
Weddell, Taylor & Williams, 1955 (142)	Bundle	A			+				

			MAN						
Radial nerve, superficial branch									
Hensel & Boman, 1960 (53)	Single	A	+		+	+			
Hensel, 1961 (52)	Single	A	+		+			+	

Crosses indicate fibres activated by the cutaneous stimuli indicated. On account of wide variations in experimental approach, it is impossible to make any quantitative comparisons. See papers cited against each author for more detailed information.

Type of lead.—Single: single fibre preparation, either teased or isolated by collision technique, or micro-electrode intracellular recording. Bundle: lead from a bundle. A-dromic: antidromic recording technique.

Nerves tested.—A: fibres described by the authors as Group A or myelinated. C (C_1 or C_2): Group C fibres.

Specific fibres.—Cool and cold: warm and hot: fibres activated by stimuli below or above skin temperature respectively. Mech.: fibres activated by any kind of mechanical stimulus.

Nonspecific fibres.—Cold and mech.: cold or cool fibres responding also to mechanical stimuli. Hot and mech.: warm or hot fibres responding also to mechanical stimuli. Hot, cold, and mech.: fibres activated by positive and negative heat transfer and to mechanical stimuli. Temp. mods. mech.: mechanoreceptors, the afferent discharge of which is modulated by a change of temperature.

and so of the diameters, of the fibres serving these sensations (93).

It seemed unlikely (142) that a simple stimulus deforming the skin would activate a single dorsal root axon exclusively; thus the reaction time would depend on the delay of response to a complex pattern thrown on to the nervous system. In support of this it has been shown that the reaction time to touch varies directly with the number of nerve fibres excited, regardless of their conduction velocity, i.e., to the intensity of the stimulation and to the size of the area stimulated (79).

PRIMARY CENTRAL NEURONS IN THE SPINAL CORD

Wall has made a comparison of afferent fibres serving touch receptors in the hairy skin of the cat's leg and the primary central cells with which they synapse (127). The primary central neurons were arranged in a discrete lamina in the dorsal part of the dorsal horn, in which the leg was topographically represented. Each cell in this group responded to light touch in a sharply defined oval area of skin of an average size of 63×32 mm, which differed considerably from the average receptive field of an afferent dorsal root fibre (5×4 mm). In contrast to motor neurons, the receptive field showed no signs of a subliminal fringe and was unaffected by such measures as posttetanic potentiation, strychnine, asphyxia, small doses of a barbiturate, or temperature changes. Fibres of many different diameters conveying all sensory modalities evidently converged on these central cells, since the cells responding to light touch also responded to changes of skin temperature of a few degrees. The pattern of discharge, however, varied with the nature of the stimulus, as has been observed in peripheral nerve fibres (57), in the dorsal column nuclei (40), and in the thalamus (108).

It is possible that the convergence of afferent nerves on the cells described by Wall (127) and Wall & Cronly-Dillon (128) may account in part for the central mechanism of referred pain proposed by Gordon (45) and Weddell (134). Since pain threshold is raised by lightly vibrating skin (142), could referred pain be modified by vibration applied either to the referred area or, where possible, to the primarily affected region?

There is good evidence that some analysis of stimulus modality is made at the periphery and transmitted by separate central transmission pathways. Such a system appears to exist for light touch in Mountcastle's lemniscal system (112) although the response of cells in the gracile nucleus is modified by temperature changes in their receptive fields (40). An alternative to separate transmission of impulses for each modality is the encoding of modality as a particular temporal pattern of impulses in common carrier cells. Unfortunately the connections of the axons of the primary central cells described by Wall (127) are not yet known and the methods used did not allow a complete survey of all the types of cell present in this region. Moreover, he had no information on the primary central neurons serving C fibres, for the two new techniques developed to study them (23, 58) are unsuitable for examing their effect centrally. For these reasons Wall is cautious in relating these cells to any specific functional system. It has been suggested that the axons of cells in this position form part of the antero lateral column system in man (128).

Anterolateral Columns

Studies in animals of evoked potentials after section of various fibre pathways have often given information which has conflicted with what could be inferred from the known anatomy of the system (112). Bohm (6) and Bohm & Petersén (7), for example, found that selective sectioning of the posterior columns abolished responses from the first and second somatic areas to electrical stimulation of a peripheral nerve. From this they concluded that discharges in the anterolateral columns are not relayed to the cortex. In contrast, others have reported that the potentials evoked in the contralateral sensory areas—primary and secondary—by nerve stimulation are relayed through the ipsilateral dorsal and contralateral anterolateral columns (34 to 37, 109). This agreed with the anatomical picture, except that impulses also reached the cortex by the ipsilateral anterolateral column. In experiments on the cat and monkey in which the only ascending pathway was one anterolateral column, cutaneous stimuli over wide receptive fields evoked activity bilaterally, though primarily contralaterally, in the following thalamic nuclei: ventrobasal nuclear complex, posterior nuclear group, and the intralaminar nuclei (108, 109). Fibres from the anterolateral column terminating in the ventrobasal complex are associated with proprioception as well as cutaneous sensibility and, like the components of the lemniscal system, are somatotopically represented. Cells of the posterior nuclear group have large receptive fields from both sides of the body and are excited by a wide range of stimuli, cutaneous as well as auditory and possibly visual and vibratory (109). Diverse influences appear to converge upon these thalamic cells, and on the basis of the preliminary experiments quoted it would seem that these particular thalamic neurons are similar to the common carrier cells described by Wall (127, see also 45a). The intralaminar nuclei appear to respond only to noxious stimuli. The medial lemniscal system and the anterolateral columns are related by way of their thalamic relays with the first and second somatic sensory areas of the cortex, respectively. Although this is their principal projection, fibres from both systems can be traced to each sensory area (109). The significance of the dual projection of the anterolateral columns and medial lemnisci in the ventrobasal nuclear complex of the thalamus is not yet known.

Dorsal Columns

Rose & Mountcastle's systematic studies confirm that the medial lemniscal system mediates primarily discriminative touch and pressure sense from the skin (112). Despite overlapping receptive fields, the topographical relations of the skin are well preserved in their projection through several relays to the first somatic sensory area of the cortex, and studies in which various regions of the cortex were ablated show that projection also extends to the second and third areas. It is not yet certain whether the system projects entirely contralaterally or whether there is a small ipsilateral component. Although the response patterns in the system are influenced considerably by anaesthesia, trains of stimuli on the skin of increasing frequency can be followed in the thalamic neurons beat for beat within a wide range. In contrast (46, 46a), it has been shown in the cat not only that there is a marked degree of functional differentiation in the rostrocaudal axis of the gracile nucleus, but that the cells synapse with many other brainstem areas. For example, fibres projecting centrally from the rostral portion of the nucleus can be excited antidromically from the anterior lobe of the cerebellum. Furthermore, there is a recent report that the response of the cells of the gracile nucleus may be modified by thermal stimuli applied to their cutaneous receptive fields (40).

From the dorsal column nuclei, fibres are relayed to the contralateral ventrobasal nuclear complex of the thalamus. Brodal & Walberg (12) and Brodal & Kaada (11) claim the existence of bulbocortical and spinocortical tracts, the former passing directly from the dorsal column nuclei and the latter from cells in the cord by way of the pyramidal tracts to the cortex. Patton & Amassian (105) and Landau (76), on the other hand, suggest an alternative interpretation. Other ascending systems have also been postulated (13, 39, 90a, 98). In common laboratory mammals the body surface can be mapped topographically in the thalamus to give a distorted image, with densely innervated areas having greater representation (112). Studies with electrodes introduced stereotactically into the ventrobasal nuclear complex confirm a similar arrangement in man (95). From the thalamus of the cat the total pattern recorded in the ventrobasal nuclear complex is projected on to the cortex with further distortions.

RETICULAR FORMATION

From anatomical and physiological studies it is now clear that both the classical ascending pathways interact extensively with the brainstem reticular formation (92). Other parts of the central nervous system, including cerebral and cerebellar cortices, have similar but less definite interrelations (85). From pharmacological studies of the reticular formation (10, 29) it is evident that if central anaesthetics are used in electrophysiological studies they alter its interaction with the ascending sensory systems. Furthermore, there is evidence that each of the major afferent relay stations in the spinal cord, medulla, and thalamus is susceptible to interference by centrifugal inhibitory influences which are normally tonically active in the unanaesthetized animal (48a, 55a, b, 85, 90b).

Central feedback for receptors has been established for several sensory systems (33) and it seems permissible to look for similar systems in cutaneous receptors. Loewenstein (87) has shown in the frog that stimulation of sympathetic nerves supplying the test region modified the sensitivity of tactile organs in the skin and even caused these receptors to fire spontaneously. In man there is good clinical evidence (97) that lesions in the skin can be produced solely by emotional disturbances, and it seems probable that these are mediated by the "nocifensor" system of Lewis (49, 84). Woolf (18) has further shown that chemical changes in the skin affecting local blood flow and the healing of standard burns are influenced by efferent activity over dorsal roots. In the trigeminal nerve in man, King (74, 75) observed impulses passing outwards at different latencies following stimulation of trigeminal cutaneous receptive fields. Wall (126) reports similar reflex activity in the dorsal roots of cats.

The information is too incomplete at present to define specifically the relationships of the classical sensory pathways and the other parts of the nervous system discussed above. Livingston (85) nevertheless concludes that the cortex not only modifies its own pattern of input and output, but through the reticular formation can have an indirect influence back upon the sensory patterns as they are initiated and relayed at all levels from the skin to the thalamus.

CLINICAL OBSERVATIONS

RECEPTORS

From studies on patients with leprosy (138) it is becoming clear that no particular sensory modality, nerve fibre, or type of terminal is preferentially lost in the course of the "dimorphous" (borderline) form of the disease, but that the destruction of nervous tissue and sensory loss occur randomly. Normal sensory tests are often misleading: a pinprick may not be felt, but pinching in the same area may give rise to intense pain. Biopsies from these regions show that there are still some nerve fibres and terminals present, but that they are surrounded by adventitial cells. Where only "free" nerve endings were seen, records showed that appropriate stimuli applied over large areas evoked reports in all the four primary sensory modalities. The high threshold in such cases may be caused by the adventitial cells surrounding the nerves and their terminals, thus "insulating" them from adequate stimulation. This supports Trotter's theory (124) of peripheral nerve insulation and emphasizes the importance of nerve endings to stimulation in the mechanism of cutaneous sensibility.

PERIPHERAL NERVES

A reassessment of the sensory changes which result from peripheral nerve lesions in the light of recent anatomical studies (see Anatomy section) makes it clear that the cutaneous nerve plexus has the same general characteristics in man as in the other mammals investigated (9). Partial division of sensory nerve trunks (proximal to branching) results in decreased sensory acuity throughout the receptive field, but never in focal areas of complete sensory loss, which confirms that the stem axons between the skin and the dorsal roots also undergo topographical randomization in man.

CENTRAL PATHWAYS

Dorsal columns.—In the presence of intact anterolateral columns, the dorsal columns appear to be concerned only with discriminative touch apart from proprioception. If cordotomy has been performed, vigorous stimulation of the dorsal columns may give rise to intolerable pain (144). A reassessment of the effects of crude electrical stimulation of the dorsal columns in conscious patients was made recently (136). The subjects reported that the sensation they experienced could not be described in terms of anything they had felt before, but that it was extremely unpleasant and frightening. The sensation was not painful in the ordinary sense, but had a shocklike tingling quality.

Anterolateral columns.—From studies of patients with Brown-Séquard syndromes it is clear that the anterolateral column conveys poorly localized touch, temperature, and pain sensibility. White & Sweet recently stimulated the anterolateral column with very fine bipolar electrodes and obtained reports of pain (quality unspecified) throughout (145). There was no laminar arrangement of fibres in respect of sensory modalities, and the fibres mediating pain and temperature were intermingled. The distribution of the reports was as follows: 54 per cent pain, 37 per cent warm, 9 per cent cold, and no touch. Twelve per cent of the reports were referred to the ipsilateral side and 6 per cent to both sides of the body. Coarse mechanical or electrical stimulation seldom evokes any sensation. Following anterolateral cordotomy, the extent of the thermal anaesthesia accompanying analgesia varies with the level and completeness of the section. Although it is usually co-extensive when a complete unilateral incision is placed high in the cervical region, a comparable bilateral incision may be required to give complete loss of pain and temperature sense. Tickle (of the kind which can be self induced) similar to that evoked by an insect crawling over the skin is also abolished by cordotomy, although the touch component of the tickle stimulus remains unaltered. It therefore appears possible that cordotomy disturbs the activity of secondary neurons [of the type described by Wall & Cronly-Dillon (128)] which are responsible for the cutaneous spread of excitation to tickle reported by Ebbecke (27).

Higher centres of the nervous system.—Studies of patients with complete hemianaesthesia following vascular lesions of the midbrain have confirmed that the anterolateral columns are closely related in function to the thalamus. It is remarkable that pain sensibility often returns slowly on the affected side until a thalamic pain syndrome develops (22). The precise relationship of the thalamus to the somaesthetic cortex in pain and temperature sensibility is obscure. Crude electrical stimulation of the undamaged primary sensory area usually evokes reports of an indeterminable tingling sensation, but it seldom gives rise to pain, unless the patient is simultaneously experiencing severe pain elsewhere in the body (119). Lesions destroying small parts of the primary sensory area may result in a diminished response to painful and thermal cutaneous stimuli and rarely to analgesia. Later the hypalgesic area may become hyperpathic, and in some cases there is even sensory recovery with hyperpathia (91, 113). Many observers comment, however, that pain sensibility is reduced less by large zonal than small focal lesions (91). Although the cerebral cortex is evidently involved in temperature and pain sensibility, it is impossible at present to define its function in this connection more precisely (129).

DISTURBANCES OF SENSATION FOLLOWING ALTERATIONS OF THE NORMAL PATTERN OF SENSORY INPUT

Dysaesthesia.—When a peripheral nerve trunk is blocked with a local anaesthetic, an area of complete sensory loss usually results distally. The margins of this anaesthetic area contain many unblocked nerve fibres, on account of the overlap of receptive fields in the skin. The thresholds to stimulation within certain of these marginal regions are raised and unusually painful sensations are reported to pinprick. When encouraged to speak, the subjects describe the sensation as something unpleasant, unlike anything experienced in everyday life. If a cutaneous nerve trunk is severed, a zone of anaesthesia results surrounded by a similar kind of partially innervated margin from which comparable sensations can be evoked. Within forty-eight hours the threshold to stimulation starts to fall and, in anaesthetic areas surrounded by densely innervated skin in which overlap is minimal, it is possible to evoke by light brush strokes intolerable pain, accompanied occasionally by autonomic disturbances such as sweating and even syncope. This form of dysaesthesia is correlated temporally with the invasion into the denervated area of a mass of short, active growth cones from surrounding normal nerves. Biopsies taken a few days or weeks later show that although a number of nerves have extended some distance into the denervated zone they are not grouped into bundles, the terminals do not intertwine, and the number of growth cones has decreased. Simultaneously the area of anaesthesia shrinks, the dysaesthesia to brushing has disappeared, and the zone is hypaesthetic, but touch, temperature, and painful stimuli still give rise to unpleasant sensations (86, 136).

Symonds (120) has pointed out that comparable sensations can be evoked

from the skin wherever there is a degree of incompleteness in lesions involving any of the sensory pathways from the skin to the thalamus. In the cases
he quoted, the threshold for all cutaneous stimuli was raised and the accompanying sensations, usually reported as pain, had explosively unpleasant,
indeterminable qualities (cf. subsection *Higher centres of the nervous system*
above). The more peripheral the lesion, the more the reports related to the
stimulus used.

Noordenbos (102) has described four cases of elderly patients with post-
herpetic neuralgia in which intolerable pain of indeterminable quality
could be evoked easily from the skin. In each case he found an increase both
absolute and relative in the number of nonmyelinated and fine myelinated
fibres in the dorsal roots just distal to the ganglion. He suggested that the
sensory disturbances in these cases resulted from the new spatiotemporal
patterns transmitted centrally by the altered fibre array.

Itch.—Arthur & Shelley (2) confirm that itch can be evoked in normal
subjects by a number of different cutaneous stimuli, but never in patients
following successful anterolateral cordotomy. Some spots on the skin are
more sensitive than others for the production of itch by mechanical or
chemical stimuli. In atopic dermatitis, however, every point becomes responsive to pruritic agents; and even vasodilatation, following a rise of
environmental temperature, causes a great increase in the number of itch
spots.

Pain.—In terms of patterns of nervous activity, three contrasted types of
cutaneous pain can be recognized. The first is referred to imminent or actual
tissue damage and is related either to intense activity in a few nerve fibres or
to considerable activity in a large number of nerve fibres (82) [spatial summation (4, 33a, 48)]. The pain stops as soon as the stimulus is withdrawn. The
second is of the more unpleasant type described above and is the result of a
pattern of activity whose origin the brain is presumably unable to localize or
to identify from past experience. The patients tend to report all sensations of
this kind as pain, although close questioning reveals that what they feel is
something indescribable, unpleasant, and frightening. When the sensations
are evoked by stimuli normally giving rise to touch, they are more closely
related to touch than to pain. On the other hand, pinpricks evoke very unpleasant pain. The third type is regionally preferred pain evoked by psychological disturbances (129b).

Pain, as Keele (71) points out, only becomes intolerable in respect of the
amount of attention it claims. At all levels of the nervous system, modification of the pattern of sensory activity, related to and emanating from the
affected region, may alleviate the pain. Rubbing, counterirritation (123),
hypnosis, conditioning (106), and psychiatric treatment are all examples.
It is interesting that the application of cold stimuli to the skin (e.g. ethyl
chloride spray) has been successfully used to relieve pain of muscle spasm
(123, 123a) and of acute coronary thrombosis (122a). If these measures fail,
the pain may become perpetuated and prolonged cycles of intractable pain
may arise spontaneously as the result of a mild cutaneous stimulus, particularly in the affected area, or following an emotional shock. Leriche (83)

and, particularly, Henderson & Smyth (50) stress that the social and environmental background and the personality of the patient may profoundly inhibit or facilitate perpetuation. An example of intractable pain is found in causalgia, a condition—as defined by Barnes (3)—characterized by persistent, usually burning, pain which occurs a few hours to several weeks after a high velocity missile wound in the arm or leg (3, 118). The pain, which is precipitated by autonomic or emotional disturbances, is completely relieved by sympathetic nerve block. In view of this it has been suggested that in causalgia (3) the primary injury is a stretch lesion of one or more peripheral nerve trunks in which autonomic efferent fibres become intimately related to small somatic afferent fibres. Activity in the autonomic fibres is thought to excite the somatic nerves which starts an afferent and efferent cycle of activity. The resulting unpleasant and painful sensations are thought to be related to the abnormal patterns of activity transmitted centrally by the small fibres involved. Neuromata in amputation stumps may also lead to the perpetuation of pain, and Russell (114) has demonstrated that this can almost always be relieved by repeated percussive treatment, which damages the nerve fibres. By degeneration and regeneration, a redistribution of their axons takes place and a new pattern of activity reaches the spinal cord.

In treating perpetuating pain syndromes it is important to break any obvious cyclical process (e.g. muscle spasm) reinforcing the pain at the earliest possible moment and to prevent facilitation by employing various forms of "peripheral counterirritation" and by educating or conditioning the patient to suppress the sensation of pain. Cases of causalgia which respond to sympathetic nerve block should be relieved permanently by sympathectomy. Painful neuromata should not be excised but treated as suggested by Russell (114). Any therapeutic measure which further destroys parts of the nervous system may aggravate the painful condition, by increasing the occurrence of abnormal sensory patterns. Because of this and the high percentage of failures in the relief of pain by relatively unselective interruption of fibre pathways in the central nervous system (103, 146), "tractotomies" at any level should only be considered in cases in which all other nonsurgical measures have completely and consistently failed.

HUMAN SENSORY EXPERIMENTS

PUNCTATE THEORY OF SENSATION

Until recently it was generally believed that there was a mosaic of "spots" in the skin, each of which, however stimulated, gave rise to one, and only one, of the so-called primary modalities of common sensibility—touch, warmth, cold, and pain. For each modality the thresholds were supposed to be lower in respect of the stimuli which were the physical counterparts of the sensation evoked. Cold "spots", for example, responded most readily to cold stimuli, but under certain conditions to warm stimuli; yet the sensation evoked was still cold and was labeled "paradoxical". This theory was based [in error (80)] on Mueller's doctrine of specific nervous energies and was apparently supported by a large number of experiments. Descriptions of procedure essential for their repetition, however, were mostly omitted and the design of the experiments did not permit of any statistical treatment (73, 80).

THE THEORY CHALLENGED

The theory received no serious challenge until it was discovered that morphologically characteristic end-organs could seldom be seen beneath marked sensory spots on the skin (20, 72, 116, 117). Nafe, in particular, questioned the existence of specific warmth and cold nerve endings (99, 100) and brought forward an alternative theory [disputed by Jenkins (65 to 69)] that temperature sensibility depended upon deformation-sensitive endings which are activated by the movement of smooth muscle elements in the integument in response to temperature changes (72, 101). Further reports that temperature "spots" on the skin were not constant in position, again questioned the orthodox view (20, 130). Recently Kibler & Nathan (73) repeated Goldscheider's work (44), insofar as they could without his technical notes. In their carefully controlled experiments they were unable to confirm his findings and were forced to discard the punctate hypothesis. In other experiments very fine quartz needles were inserted into the skin and reports of touch, pain, itch, tickle, or no sensation were evoked (77). Many thousands of experiments have been carried out since then and no reports of warmth or cold have ever been obtained by this method (121). Steel needles, capable of transferring heat to or from the skin, were, however, effective on rare occasions. From a comparison of the size of stimulus objects necessary to evoke reports of warmth and cold, Lele (77) suggested that the endings transducing cold lie close to the skin surface and those for warmth at a deeper level. From all these observations it became clear either that many terminals have to be stimulated to give the necessary discharge pattern for temperature sensation or that, because of their spatial distribution, the terminals cannot be appropriately stimulated by quartz needles.

"FREE" NERVE ENDINGS AND TEMPERATURE SENSIBILITY

Since hairy skin rarely possesses morphologically specialized nerve endings other than those in hair follicles (which are not discharged by warmth or cold) it became evident that "free" nerve endings must have thermoreceptive properties. Their diffuse arrangement and the fact that naturally occurring warm and cold stimuli are seldom punctate suggested that such unbiological stimuli might evoke misleading reports (77). Lele, Weddell & Williams used an external source (black body) to apply thermal stimuli to areas of skin of 3 to 40 sq cm (82). They found that reports were not directly related to the absolute temperature of the skin, for subjects with static skin temperatures ranging from 20 to 35°C reported no sensations from the test areas. Ebbecke has confirmed this more recently (28). For rates of heat transfer of -0.006 to $+0.020$ cal per sq cm per sec, the reports evoked could be divided into eight broad categories: cold, cool, innominate, nothing, innominate, faint warm, warm, and very warm or hot (82). At all rates of heat transfer there was good correlation between the intensity of the stimulus and the report evoked. When the surface temperature of the skin was raised by gradually increasing rates of heat transfer, additional reports were obtained: stinging or burning, tolerable pain, and finally intolerable pain, accompanied by a withdrawal reflex. The particular sensation reported was related to the magnitude and rate of change of the temperature of the surface of a given area of skin. The mean reaction time to low rates of heat transfer was significantly longer than to high rates, when the area stimulated was constant. On the other hand, the mean reaction time to a given range of transfer rates was significantly shorter, the larger the area stimulated.

These observations on spatial summation suggest that both the sensation reported and the reaction time to the stimulus depend upon the pattern and magnitude of the nervous activity evoked: the greater the nervous activity, the stronger the sensation and the shorter the reaction time. At the time of publication, Lele, Weddell & Williams suggested that spatial summation of warm stimuli without tissue damage would lead to pain, and this has now been confirmed (4, 45a). Cold sufficient to evoke pain without tissue damage could only be obtained by immersion of the area tested in ice-cold water (82). Incidentally, it has been shown recently that spatial summation of touch stimuli can also give rise to pain (33a). Further confirmation that the magnitude and gradient of heat transfer are the effective stimuli in temperature sensibility came from studies on paradoxical cold (26) and from reports of subjects in response to small temperature changes of the water in which an immersed limb had previously reached thermal equilibrium (82).

To test the response of "free" nerve endings, the cornea was selected as it is avascular and neither its histological structure nor its mode of innervation differs significantly in man and common laboratory animals (155). In a series of experiments, Lele & Weddell stimulated the cornea in subjects of different ages and different social and educational backgrounds (80). Their results showed that reports in all the four primary sensory modalities could be evoked.

It is evident from the preceding discussion that "free" nerve endings in the human integument are capable of transducing both mechanical and thermal stimuli. From the few experiments on man (52, 53) there seem to exist specific and nonspecific fibres, and comparative studies on animals confirm this fully [see (128) and Physiology section]. It is tempting to speculate that the fibres serving "free" nerve endings in human skin may show a range of specificity to the three types of stimulus, thus each fibre may be specific in that it displays definite thresholds to each kind of stimulus. A cutaneous nerve bundle can therefore be considered multispecific, for it will contain fibres having different conduction velocities and combinations of specificity between and including the modes of touch, warmth, and cold. With improved recording techniques it may be possible to demonstrate a similar range of stimulus specificity among the "free" nerve endings served by one stem axon, and in this sense a stem fibre may prove to be multispecific.

NOTE

As stated above, an understanding of the mechanism of cutaneous sensibility requires detailed information from many diverse fields of research. However objective the authors try to be, their selection and presentation of material are necessarily biased by their own particular interests, and the summary given above is to this extent incomplete. In conclusion they would like to refer to Lord Adrian's introduction to sensory mechanisms in the *Handbook of Physiology* (1) as a pointer to the direction in which progress is likely to be made.

LITERATURE CITED

1. Adrian, E. D., in *Handbook of Physiology*, Sect. I *Neurophysiology*, **1**, Chap XV, 365–67 (J. Field, Ed,. Am. Physiol. Soc., Washington, D.C., 779 pp., 1959)
2. Arthur, R. P., and Shelley, W. B., in *Pain and Itch, Ciba Foundation Study Group*, 84–97 (Wolstenholme, G. E. W. & O'Connor, M., Eds., J. & A. Churchill, London, 120 pp., 1959)
3. Barnes, R., "Causalgia—a review of forty eight cases," in *Peripheral Nerve Injuries, Med. Research Council Spec. Rept. Series, No. 282*, Chap. IV, 156–85 (1954)
4. Benjamin, F. B., *Proc. Soc. Exptl. Biol. Med.*, **101**, 380–82 (1959)
5. Bishop, G. H., in *Advances in Biology of Skin*, **1**, *Cutaneous Innervation*, Chap. VI, 99–111 (Montagna, W., Ed., Pergamon Press, Oxford, 203 pp., 1960)
6. Bohm, E., *Acta Physiol. Scand.*, **29**, Suppl. 106, 106–37 (1953)
7. Bohm, E., and Petersén, I., *Acta Physiol. Scand.*, **29**, Suppl. 106, 138–49 (1952)
8. Boman, K. K. A., *Acta Physiol. Scand.*, **44**, Suppl. 149, 7–79 (1958)
9. Bowden, R., "Factors influencing functional recovery," in *Peripheral Nerve Injuries, Med. Research Council Spec. Rept. Series, No. 282*, Chap. VII, 298–353 (1954)
10. Bradley, P. B., and Key, B. J., *Electroencephal. and Clin. Neurophysiol.*, **10**, 97–110 (1958)
11. Brodal, A., and Kaada, B. R., *J. Neurophysiol.*, **16**, 567–86 (1953)
12. Brodal, A., and Walberg, F., *Arch. Neurol. Psychiat.*, **68**, 755–75 (1952)
13. Catalano, J. V., and Lamarche, G., *Am. J. Physiol.*, **189**, 141–44 (1957)
14. Cauna, N., *Am. J. Anat.*, **99**, 315–50 (1956)
15. Cauna, N., *J. Comp. Neurol.*, **113**, 169–210 (1959)
16. Cauna, N., *Bibl. Anat.*, **2**, 128–38 (1961)
17. Cauna, N., and Ross, L. L., *J. Biophys. Biochem. Cytol.*, **8**, 467–82 (1960)
18. Chapman, L. F., Goodell, H., and Wolff, H. G., in *Advances in Biology of Skin*, **1**, *Cutaneous Innervation*, Chap. VIII, 161–88 (Montagna, W., Ed., Pergamon Press, Oxford, 203 pp., 1960)
19. Clark, W. E. Le Gros, *J. Anat.*, **71**, 7–40 (1936)
19a. Corbin, K. B., and Gardner, E. D., *Anat. Record*, **68**, 63–74 (1937)
20. Dallenbach, K. M., *Am. J. Psychol.*, **39**, 402–27 (1927)
21. Dastur, D. K., *Brain*, **78**, 615–33 (1955)
22. Déjerine, J., and Roussy, G., *Rev. neurol.*, **14**, 521–32 (1906)
23. Douglas, W. W., and Ritchie, J. M. *J. Physiol. (London)*, **139**, 385–99 (1957)
24. Douglas, W. W., and Ritchie, J. M., in *Pain and Itch, Ciba Foundation Study Group*, 26–40 (Wolstenholme, G. E. W. & O'Connor, M., Eds., J. & A. Churchill, London, 120 pp., 1959)
25. Douglas, W. W., Ritchie, J. M., and Straub, R. W., *J. Physiol. (London)*, **146**, 47–48P (1959)
26. Ebbecke, U., *Arch. ges. Physiol.*, **169**, 395–462 (1917)
27. Ebbecke, U., *Arch. ges. Physiol.*, **264**, 1–16 (1957)
28. Ebbecke, U., *Arch. ges. Physiol.*, **268**, 11 (1958)
29. Feldberg, W., *Brit. Med. J.*, **II**, 771–82 (1959)
30. Fitzgerald, M. J. T. (In press, 1961)
31. Fitzgerald, M. J. T. (Personal communication to be submitted for publication shortly)

32. Frankenhaeuser, B., *Acta Physiol. Scand.*, **18**, 68–74 (1949)

33. French, J. D., in *Handbook of Physiology*, Sect. I, *Neurophysiology*, **2**, Chap. 52, 1281–1305 (Field, J. Ed., Am. Physiol. Soc., Washington, D.C., 781–1439 pp., 1960)

33a. Galletti, R., Marra, N., and Vecchiet, L., *Sperimentale*, **110**, 264–85 (1960)

34. Gardner, E., and Haddad, B.. *Am. J. Physiol.* **172**, 475–82 (1953)

35. Gardner, E., and Morin, F., *Am. J. Physiol.*, **174**, 149–54 (1953)

36. Gardner, E., and Morin, F., *Am. J. Physiol.*, **189**, 152–58 (1957)

37. Gardner, E., and Noer, R., *Am. J. Physiol.*, **168**, 437–41 (1952)

38. Gasser, H. S., *J. Gen. Physiol.*, **38**, 709–28 (1955)

39. Gaze, R. M., and Gordon, G., *Quart. J. Exptl. Physiol.*, **40**, 187–94 (1955)

40. Gentry, J. R., Whitlock, D. G., and Perl, E. R., *Federation Proc.*, **20**, 349 (1961)

41. Glees, P., *Acta Neuroveget.*, **7**, 160–74 (1953)

42. Glees, P., and Bailey, R. A., *Monatschr. Psychiat. u. Neurol.*, **122** 129–41 (1952)

43. Glees, P., and Soler, J., *Z. Zellforsch. u. mikroskop. Anat.*, **36**, 381–400 (1952)

44. Goldscheider, A., *Ges. Abhandl.*, **I** (J. A. Barth, Leipzig, 432 pp., 1898)

45. Gordon, G., *Proc. Roy. Soc. Med.*, **50**, 586–88 (1957)

45a. Gordon, G., Landgren, S., and Seed, W. A., *J. Physiol. (London)*, **158**, 544–59 (1961)

46. Gordon, G., and Paine, C. H., *J. Physiol. (London)*, **153**, 331–49 (1960)

46a. Gordon, G., and Seed, W. A., *J. Physiol. (London)*, **155**, 589–601 (1961)

47. Gordon, G., and Whitteridge, D., *Lancet*, **II**, 700–1 (1943)

47a. Gray, J. A. B., and Sato, M., *J. Physiol. (London)*, **122**, 610–36 (1953)

48. Hall, K. R. L., *Nature*, **182**, 307–9 (1958)

48a. Hagbarth, K. E., and Fex, J., *J. Neurophysiol.*, **22**, 321–38 (1959)

49. Harpman, J. A., Part I, and Harpman, J. A., and Whitehead, T. P., Part II, *Brain*, **78**, 634–60 (1955)

50. Henderson, W. R., and Smyth, G. E., *J. Neurol. Psychiat.*, **11**, 88–112 (1948)

51. Hensel, H., *Arch. ges. Physiol.*, **263**, 48–53 (1956)

52. Hensel, H., *J. Physiol. (London)*, **155**, 32P (1961)

53. Hensel, H., and Boman, K. K. A., *J. Neurophysiol.*, **23**, 564–78 (1960)

54. Hensel, H., Iggo, A., and Witt, I. *J. Physiol. (London)*, **153**, 113–26 (1960)

55. Hensel, H., and Witt, I., *J. Physiol. (London)*, **148**, 180–87 (1959)

55a. Holmquist, B., Lundberg, A., and Oscarsson, O., *Arch. ital. biol.*, **98**, 60–80 (1960)

55b. Holmquist, B., Lundberg, A., and Oscarsson, O., *Arch. ital biol.*, **98**, 402–22 (1960)

56. Hunt, C. C., and McIntyre, A. K. *J. Physiol. (London)*, **153**, 88–98 (1960)

57. Hunt, C. C., and McIntyre, A. K., *J. Physiol. (London)*, **153**, 99–112 (1960)

58. Iggo, A. *J. Physiol. (London)*, **142**, 110–26 (1958)

59. Iggo, A., *Quart. J. Exptl. Physiol.*, **44**, 362–70 (1959)

60. Iggo, A., in *Pain and Itch Ciba Foundation Study Group*, 41–59 (Wolstenholme, G. E. W., and O'Connor, M., Eds., J. & A. Churchill, London, 120 pp., 1959)

61. Iggo, A., *J. Physiol. (London)*, **152**, 337–53 (1960)

62. Iggo, A., in *Symposium on Central Mechanisms of Cutaneous Nervous Functions, Intern. Symposium of the Soc. for Neuroveget. Research, Turin, June, 1961* (In press)

63. Iriuchijima, J., and Zotterman, Y., *Acta Physiol. Scand.*, **49**, 267–78 (1960)

64. Ishiko, N., and Loewenstein, W. R., *Science*, **132**, 1841–42 (1960)

65. Jenkins, W. L., *J. Exptl. Psychol.*, **25**, 373–88 (1939)

66. Jenkins, W. L., *J. Exptl. Psychol.*, **25**, 519–27 (1939)

67. Jenkins, W. L., *J. Exptl. Psychol.*, **28**, 517–23 (1941)

68. Jenkins, W. L., *J. Exptl. Psychol.*, **29**, 413–19 (1941)

69. Jenkins, W. L., *J. Exptl. Psychol.*, **29**, 511–16 (1941)

70. Katz, B., *J. Physiol. (London)*, **111**, 261–82 (1950)

71. Keele, K. D., *Anatomies of Pain*, Chap. 7, 175–97 (Blackwell Sci. Publs., Oxford, 206 pp., 1957)

72. Kenshalo, D. R., and Nafe, J. P., in *Symposium on Cutaneous Sensitivity, US Army Med. Research Lab. Rept., No. 424*, 1–25 (US Army Med. Research and Devel. Command, 165 pp., 1960)

73. Kibler, R. F., and Nathan, M. D., *Neurology*, **10**, 874–80 (1960)

74. King, R. B., and Meagher, J. N., *J. Neurosurg.*, **12**, 393–402 (1955)

75. King, R. B., Meagher, J. N., and Barnett, J. C., *J. Neurosurg.*, **13**, 176–83 (1956)

76. Landau, W. M., *Science*, **123**, 895–96 (1956)

77. Lele, P. P., *J. Physiol.* (*London*), **126**, 191–205 (1954)

78. Lele, P. P., Palmer, E., and Weddell, G., *Quart. J. Microscop. Sci.*, **99**, 421–40 (1958)

79. Lele, P. P., Sinclair, D. C., and Weddell, G., *J. Physiol.* (*London*), **123**, 187–203 (1954)

80. Lele, P. P., and Weddell, G., *Brain*, **79**, 119–54 (see p. 150) (1956)

81. Lele, P. P., and Weddell, G., *Exptl. Neurol.*, **1**, 334–59 (1959)

82. Lele, P. P., Weddell, G., and Williams, C. M., *J. Physiol.* (*London*), **126**, 206–34 (1954)

83. Leriche, R., *The Surgery of Pain*, Chap. 19, 476–91 (Young, A., Transl. and Ed., Baillère, Tindall & Cox, London, 512 pp., 1939)

84. Lewis, T., *Clin. Sci.*, **4**, 365–84 (1942)

85. Livingston, R. B., in *Handbook of Physiology*, Sect. I, *Neurophysiology*, **1**, Chap. 31, 741–60 (Field J., Ed., Am. Physiol. Soc., Washington, D.C., 779 pp., 1959)

86. Livingstone, W. K., *J. Neurosurg.*, **4**, 140–45 (1947)

87. Loewenstein, W. R., *J. Physiol.* (*London*), **132**, 40–60 (1956)

87a. Loewenstein, W. R., *J. Gen. Physiol.*, **41**, 825–45 (1958)

87b. Loewenstein, W. R., *Sci. Am.*, **203**, 99–108 (1960)

88. Loewenstein, W. R., *Nature*, **188**, 1034–35 (1960)

89. Loewenstein, W. R., *J. Neurophysiol.*, **24**, 150–58 (1961)

90. Loewenstein, W. R., and Rathkamp, R., *J. Gen. Physiol.*, **41**, 1245–65 (1958)

90a. Lundberg, A., and Oscarsson, O., *Acta Physiol. Scand.*, **51**, 1–16 (1961)

90b. Lundberg, A., and Voorhoeve, P. E., *Experientia*, **17**, 46–47 (1961)

91. Marshall, J., *J. Neurol.*, **14**, 187–204 (1951)

92. Mehler, W. R., Feferman, M. E., and Nauta, W. J. H., *Brain*, **83**, 718–50 (1960)

93. Michon, P., *Le temps de réaction. Techniques, applications cliniques* (Masson & Cie, Paris, 98 pp., 1939)

94. Miller, M. R., Ralston, H. J. III, and Kasahara, M., in *Advances in Biology of Skin*, **1**, *Cutaneous Innervation*, Chap. I, 1–47 (Montagna, W., Ed., Pergamon Press, Oxford, 203 pp., 1960)

95. Monnier, M., *Rev. neurol.*, **93**, 267–77 (1955)

96. Montagna, W., in *Advances in Biology of Skin*, **1**, *Cutaneous Innervation*, Chap. IV, 74–87 (Montagna, W., Ed., Pergamon Press, Oxford, 203 pp., 1960)

97. Moody, R. L., *Lancet*, **II**, 934–35 (1946)

98. Morin, F., *J. Physiol.* (*London*), **183**, 245–52 (1955)

99. Nafe, J. P., *Am. J. Psychol.*, **39**, 367–89 (1927)

100. Nafe, J. P., *J. Gen. Psychol.*, **2**, 199–211 (1929)

101. Nafe, J. P., and Wagoner, K. S., *J. Psychol.*, **2**, 421–77 (1936)

102. Noordenbos, W., *Pain: Problems pertaining to the transmission of nerve impulses which give rise to pain*, Chap. 1, 4–10; Chap. 10, 68–80 (Elsevier Publ. Co., Amsterdam, 177 pp., 1959)

103. Noordenbos, W., *Pain: Problems pertaining to the transmission of nerve impulses which give rise to pain*, Chap. 20, 165–72 (Elsevier Publ. Co., Amsterdam, 177 pp., 1959)

104. Oppenheimer, D. R., Palmer, E., and Weddell, G., *J. Anat.*, **92**, 321–52 (1958)

105. Patton, H. D., and Amassian, V. E., *Am. J. Physiol.*, **183**, 650 (1955)

106. Pavlov, I. P., *Conditioned Reflexes* (Anrep, G. V., Transl. and Ed., Oxford Univ. Press, Oxford, 430 pp., 1927)

107. Pease, D. C., and Pallie, W., *J. Ultrastruct. Research*, **2**, 352–65 (1959)

108. Perl, E. R., and Whitlock, D. G., *Exptl. Neurol.*, **3**, 256–96 (1961)

109. Poggio, G. F., and Mountcastle, V. B., *Bull. Johns Hopkins Hosp.*, **106**, 266–316 (1960)

110. Riisager, P. M. (Personal communication, 1961)

111. Riisager, P. M., and Weddell, G., *J. Anat.* (In press, 1961)

112. Rose, J. E., and Mountcastle, V. B., in *Handbook of Physiology*, Sect. I, *Neurophysiology*, **1**, Chap. 17, 387–429 (Field, J., Ed., Am. Physiol. Soc., Washington, D. C., 779 pp., 1959)

113. Russell, W. R., *Brain*, **68**, 79–97 (1945)

114. Russell, W. R., and Spalding, J. M. K., *Brit. Med. J.*, **2**, 68–73 (1950)

115. Sand, A., *Proc. Roy. Soc.* (*London*), [B] **125**, 524–53 (1938)

116. Schiller, F., *Arch. Neurol. Psychiat.*, **75**, 203–19 (1956)

117. Sinclair, D. C., *Brain*, **78**, 584–614 (1955)
118. Sunderland, S., and Bradley, K. C., *Brain*, **84**, 102–19 (1961)
119. Sweet, W. H., in *Handbook of Physiology*, Sect. I, *Neurophysiology*, 1, Chap. 19, 492–97 (Field, J., Ed., Am. Physiol. Soc., Washington, D. C., 779 pp., 1959)
120. Symonds, C. P., *Lancet*, **II**, 723–26 (1931)
121. Taylor, D. T., and Weddell, G. (Unpublished observations, 1961)
122. Tower, S. S., *J. Neurophysiol.*, **3**, 486–500 (1940)
122a. Travell, J., *Circulation*, **3**, 120–24 (1951)
123. Travell, J., *Arch. Phys. Med.*, **33**, 291–98 (1952)
123a. Travell, J., *J. Prosthetic Dentistry*, **10**, 745–63 (1960)
124. Trotter, W., *Lancet*, **II**, 107–12 (1926)
125. Walker, A. E., *The Primate Thalamus* (Univ. Chicago Press, Chicago, 305 pp., 1938)
126. Wall, P. D., *J. Neurophysiol.*, **22**, 305–20 (1959)
127. Wall, P. D., *J. Neurophysiol.*, **23**, 197–210 (1960)
128. Wall, P. D., and Cronly-Dillon, J. R., *Arch. Neurol. Psychiat.*, **2**, 365–75 (1960)
129. Walshe, F. M. R., *Brain*, **80**, 510–39 (1957)
129a. Walter, P., *Z. Zellforsch. u. mikroskop. Anat.*, **53**, 394–410 (1961)
129b. Walters, A., *Brain*, **84**, 1–18 (1961)
130. Waterston, D., *Brain*, **46**, 200–8 (1923)
131. Weddell, G., *Proc. Roy. Soc. Med.*, **34**, 776–78 (1941)
132. Weddell, G., *J. Anat.*, **75**, 346–67 (1941)
133. Weddell, G., *Brit. Med. Bull.*, **3**, 167–72 (1945)
134. Weddell, G., *Proc. Roy. Soc. Med.*, **50**, 581–86 (1957)
135. Weddell, G., in *Advances in Biology of Skin*, 1, *Cutaneous Innervation*, Chap. VII, 112–59 (Montagna, W., Ed., Pergamon Press, Oxford, 203 pp., 1960)
136. Weddell, G., in *Conf. on Brain and Behavior, 1st, Los Angeles, Feb., 1961* (Brazier, M., Ed., Univ. of Calif.) (In press)
137. Weddell, G., in *Symposium on Central Mechanisms of Cutaneous Nervous Functions. Intern. Symposium Soc. for Neuroveget. Research, 11th, Turin, June, 1961* (In press)
138. Weddell, G., Jamison, D. G., and Palmer, E., in *Leprosy in Theory and Practice*, Chap. VIII, 96–113 (Cochrane, R. G., Ed., John Wright, Bristol, Engl., 407 pp., 1959)
139. Weddell, G., and Pallie, W., *J. Anat.*, **89**, 175–88 (1955)
140. Weddell, G., Pallie, W., and Palmer, E., *Quart. J. Microscop. Sci.*, **95**, 483–501 (1954)
141. Weddell, G., Pallie, W., and Palmer, E., *J. Anat.*, **89**, 162–74 (1955)
142. Weddell, G., Taylor, D. A., and Williams, C. M., *J. Anat.*, **89**, 317–42 (1955)
143. White, J. C., and Sweet, W. H., in *Pain; Its Mechanisms and Neurosurgical Control*, Chap. 2, 36–46 (Charles C Thomas, Springfield, Ill., 736 pp., 1955)
144. White, J. C., and Sweet, W. H., in *Pain; Its Mechanisms and Neurosurgical Control*, Chap. 2, 45 (Charles C Thomas, Springfield, Ill., 736 pp., 1955)
145. White, J. C., and Sweet, W. H., in *Pain; Its Mechanisms and Neurosurgical Control*, Chap. 9, 272–75 (Charles C Thomas, Springfield, Ill., 736 pp., 1955)
146. White, J. C., and Sweet, W. H., in *Pain; Its Mechanisms and Neurosurgical Control*, Chap. 9, 285–86 (Charles C Thomas, Springfield, Ill., 736 pp., 1955)
147. Whitear, M., *J. Anat.*, **94**, 387–409 (1960)
148. Whitlock, D. G., and Perl, E. R., *Exptl. Neurol.*, **3**, 240–55 (1961)
149. Winkelmann, R. K., *Proc. Staff Meetings Mayo Clinic*, **34**, 39–47 (1959)
150. Winkelmann, R. K., in *Advances in Biology of Skin*, 1, *Cutaneous Innervation*, Chap. II, 48–62 (Montagna, W., Ed., Pergamon Press, Oxford, 195 pp., 1960)
151. Winkelmann, R. K., *Nerve Endings in Normal and Pathologic Skin*, (Charles C Thomas, Springfield, Ill., 195 pp., 1960)
152. Witt, I., in *Symposium on Central Mechanisms of Cutaneous Nervous Functions Intern. Symposium Soc. for Neuroveget. Research., 11th Turin, June, 1961* (In press)
153. Witt, I., and Hensel, H., *Arch. ges. Physiol.*, **268**, 582–96 (1959)
154. Zander, E., and Weddell, G., *Brit. J. Ophthalmol.*, **35**, 61–88 (1951)
155. Zander, E., and Weddell, G., *J. Anat.*, **85**, 68–99 (1951)

ADENOHYPOPHYSIS AND ADRENAL CORTEX[1,2,3]

By Claude Fortier

*Laboratoires d'Endocrinologie, Département de Physiologie, Faculté de Médicine,
Université Laval, Québec, Canada*

During the past year the pace of developments in the pituitary-adrenal field precluded complete coverage of the relevant literature within the allotted space. An attempt has been made, instead, to chart out some of the prevalent trends of investigation in this area, limiting discussion to significant advances. Selection was necessarily biased by the reviewer's background and interests, at the cost, no doubt, of regrettable omissions. Not included in this survey are topics pertaining chiefly to methodology, clinical pathology, pharmacology, and therapeutics. The interested reader is referred to lucid reviews by Munson (224) and by Gaunt *et al.* (99) on endocrine pharmacology, to a jointly sponsored conference on the biological activities of steroids in relation to cancer edited by Pincus & Vollmer (241), and to an excellent textbook of clinical endocrinology, including a section on tests and bioassays, edited by Astwood (3). Neuroendocrinology, which is emerging as a discipline in its own right, has prompted a monograph by Endröczi & Lissák (204), two collections of seminars from the Collège de France (14, 33), and reviews by Harris (141), Knigge (178), Bauer (13), Bajusz (7), Martini *et al.* (213), and Fortier (85).

Biochemistry of ACTH

Structure-activity relationships.—A previous report by Li and his associates (199) on the 39-amino-acid sequence of bovine adrenocorticotropin (196) has been confirmed by a microbiological method (200). From esterification studies with this peptide, Li (197) infers that the free carboxyl groups in the molecule are essential for its ACTH activity, which was markedly reduced by the procedure, but are not implicated in its intrinsic melanocyte-stimulating activity which remained unaltered. On the other hand, blockage of the α-amino group of the NH_2-terminal serine and the ϵ-amino groups of the lysine residues by succinylation of the peptide hormone resulted in a marked decrease of both ACTH and melanocyte-stimulating activities (198).

According to Dedman *et al.* (53), oxidation of hog $ACTH-A_1$ with hydrogen peroxide yields a biologically inactive product which can be regenerated

---

[1] The survey of literature pertaining to this review was concluded in June 1961.

[2] The preparation of this chapter was supported in part by grants from the Office of Scientific Research, United States Air Force (AF-AFOSR-61-15), and from the National Institutes of Health, United States Public Health Service (B-2827).

[3] Among the abbreviations used in this review are: DPN (diphosphopyridine nucleotide); DPNH (reduced diphosphopyridine nucleotide); TPN (triphosphopyridine nucleotide); and TPNH (reduced diphosphopyridine nucleotide).

by reduction. From a correlation of biological activity to the extent of oxidation of the methionine contained in the hormone, it is now concluded that the oxidation-reduction center of ACTH is the thioether grouping of methionine (54).

Studies involving partial hydrolysis of the ACTH molecule with dilute acid (see 142) had shown that the N-terminal peptide consisting of the first 24 amino acids in the molecule retained biological activity. This peptide, being the smallest fully active fragment isolated from the natural hormone, was generally considered as the essential core of ACTH activity (195). Recent synthetic studies have shown, however, that the N-terminal tridecapeptide (137), nonadecapeptide (201), and icosapeptide (23) portions of the molecule also possess some biological activity. Moreover, Hofmann et al. (158) report that a synthetic tricosapeptide, the structure of which corresponds to the postulated arrangement of 23 amino acid residues from the amino end of the ACTH sequence, is endowed with the full in vivo ascorbic acid depleting and plasma corticosterone elevating activity of the natural hormone (103 ± 10 IU/mg). This report opens the way to further investigations on the relationships of peptide structure to function.

Adrenal-weight factor.—To assess Young's suggestion (40, 315) that ACTH may be composed of two factors, one causing adrenal ascorbic acid depletion (AA) and one influencing adrenal weight (AW), Lanman & Dinerstein (190) tried to determine the nature of the AW factor in an alkaline extract of beef pituitaries reportedly rich in this factor and poor in AA (41). Two AW factors were respectively identified as luteinizing hormone and growth hormone. There was no evidence that ACTH or a possible precursor was present in sufficient amount to influence either adrenal weight or histology, and it appeared unnecessary to postulate that ACTH was separable into an AA and an AW factor.

Biogenesis of ACTH.—C^{14}-labeled glucose was used by Goodner & Freinkel (115) with slices of anterior and posterior pituitaries from rat and calf to assess the carbohydrate metabolism of these tissues and its responsiveness to insulin. In both portions of the pituitary, insulin significantly increased the formation of $C^{14}O_2$, glycogen, and lipid from glucose. This demonstration of active glycogenesis and oxidative glycolysis within the pituitary suggests the hexomonophosphate pathway as a possible site for metabolic modification of pituitary hormonogenesis.

Using the concentration of ribonucleic acid (RNA) in the rat pituitary as an indicator of protein synthetic activity, Hess et al. (153) observed a correlation between the alterations of pituitary RNA levels consequent to bilateral adrenalectomy and to cortisone administration, and the changes in pituitary ACTH concentration previously described as a result of these procedures (83, 84). These findings are interpreted as further evidence of the regulatory effect of adrenal cortical steroids on ACTH synthesis. The same investigators made the important observation that the administration to intact rats of RNA prepared from beef or rat pituitaries, as distinct from other tissues, induced a twofold increase in pituitary ACTH concentration (152). It could not be ascertained, however, whether the observed effect was related to accelerated synthesis of ACTH, inhibition of release, or both.

ACTH RELEASE AND ITS CONTROL

In a provocative survey of current trends in adrenocortical research, Dwight Ingle (166) recalls receiving from Professor W. B. Cannon the following query in 1937: "If the pituitary regulates the adrenal cortex, what regulates the pituitary?" In the intervening 25 years, an impressive amount of work has been directed to this problem, which still awaits a complete answer. The reason may lie, to some extent, in the unicist approach originally favored by most investigators, according to which a single regulatory mechanism should account for the various modalities of pituitary-adrenocortical adjustment to changing requirements. It now appears that two mechanisms, at least, are involved in this control: one concerned with rapid responses to external environmental changes, the other with slower adjustments to changing blood levels of adrenal cortical hormones, and both probably mediated by the hypothalamus in its complex interplay with impinging systems.

Stimuli.—Extending his interesting observations on the effect of infantile experience on endocrine activity, Levine (194) reports that repeated daily manipulations of the infant rat are reflected, in the adult animal, by peculiarities of the pituitary-adrenocortical response to brief faradic stimulation. Rats handled in infancy showed a significant elevation of the plasma corticosteroids as early as 15 seconds after the stimulus, whereas a latency of five minutes was observed in controls. Moreover, the corticosteroid levels were consistently higher in the conditioned subjects. It is inferred therefrom that one of the major differences between the stimulated and nonstimulated organisms resides in the rapidity and efficiency of the neural mechanisms responsible for ACTH release. The age at which conditioning is applied is apparently critical since, according to Holub *et al.* (162), prior treatment of adult rats with daily saline injections for seven days prior to a scald stress results in a marked reduction of the pituitary ACTH response to the stimulus. Pretreated rats showed ACTH depletions of 18 and 25 per cent of the initial level, one and four hours after stress, as compared to 52 and 66 per cent for uninjected controls. In the light of preliminary data indicating that similar amounts of ACTH are released in controls and pretreated animals, it appears that prior treatment, in the adult animal, may increase the capacity of the pituitary gland to synthesize ACTH rapidly in response to stress.

Hume & Egdahl (164) conclude from their studies on the effects of exposure to cold on adrenocorticotropic activity (ascertained by pituitary ACTH and adrenal venous corticosteroid determinations) in the dog that hypothermia does not, at any time, act as a stimulant to pituitary-adrenocortical secretion in this animal, but that it significantly depresses the pituitary ACTH response to a superimposed stimulus (surgical trauma), the corticoidogenic effect of exogenous ACTH, and the rate of metabolic disposal of corticosteroids. Boulouard (25) reports, on the other hand, that exposure of rats to cold (4.5°C) during a 48-hr fast enhanced the rise of the plasma 17-hydroxycorticosteroid level induced by this stimulus. Furthermore, according to D'Angelo (38), guinea pigs maintained at $7 \pm 2°C$ for seven weeks showed significant increases in adrenal to body weight ratios and in urinary excretion of corticoids. Enhanced adrenal function was clearly referable to augmented ACTH secretion, in the light of assay data showing a ten- to fifteen-fold increase of the pituitary ACTH concentration in refrigerated guinea pigs. The effect of cold on pituitary-adrenocortical activity obviously varies with the intensity and duration of the stimulus and with the efficiency of thermostatic adjustment in different animal species.

Using free corticosterone in plasma as an index of adrenal cortical activity in the rat, Skelton & Hyde (274) found that, whereas mature males and immature animals of both sexes responded equally to stress, the response of mature females was several times greater. Gonadectomy increased the cortical response of mature males and decreased the response of mature females significantly. Adrenocorticotropin induced identical responses in immature and mature males and females despite differences in body size and adrenal weights. It is therefore suggested that sex and age modify the adrenal cortical response through changes in hypophysial reactivity.

ACTH field.—Numerous studies have confirmed the original observation of de Groot & Harris (58) that ACTH release could be induced by electrical stimulation of the floor of the third ventricle and that, conversely, the adrenocorticotropic response to stress was prevented by electrolytic lesions in the same area. There is as yet no general agreement, however, on the exact localization of the ACTH field or center, except that it roughly extends from the rostral aspect of the infundibulum to the mammillary bodies (122, 141), with possible species differences. In view of the scarcity of its cellular components, this funnel-like area may represent, instead of a center in the usual sense, a sort of relay or end-station for the nerve fibers of diverse origins which terminate in the vicinity of the primary portal plexus.

Basal ACTH activity.—Assessment of the pituitary's inherent ability to maintain the morphological and functional integrity of the adrenal cortex necessitates deafferentiation of the gland by transplantation to a distant site, section of its stalk, or localized destruction of the ventral hypothalamus. Since all of these procedures interfere with the portal vascular supply to some extent, it has proved difficult to differentiate the effects of ischemia from the consequences of deprivation of a specific hypothalamic influence. Relevant to this topic are two recent reports by British workers on the effects of section of the pituitary stalk, in the monkey, on pituitary-adrenocortical activity. Holmes *et al.* (161) failed to note any involution of the adrenal cortices as a result of the procedure, whereas Daniel and co-workers (39) did observe, in the immediate postoperative interval, a transient drop of the plasma 17-hydroxycorticosteroids to 25 per cent of the normal level. A return to near-normal values within 50 to 100 days followed. Plates were inserted, in both cases, between the cut ends of the stalk, in an attempt to prevent portal revascularization. In view of the remarkable propensity of portal vessels to regenerate, and to re-establish connections with the pituitary (89), fulfilment of this requirement remains questionable.

The extent to which heterotopic transplants of the anterior pituitary contribute to the maintenance or recovery of adrenal cortical activity in hypophysectomized animals is still debatable. Timmer et al. (292) report complete failure of pituitary autografts beneath the kidney capsule to maintain the weight of the adrenals in the rat. Martinovitch and co-workers (214), on the other hand, found that homotransplants of the adenohypophysis in the anterior chamber of the eye of the hypophysectomized rat are capable, to a considerable degree, of both maintaining and restoring adrenal weight and functional activity. Differences in technique probably account for this discrepancy.

Ganong et al. (97) observed markedly reduced outputs of hydrocortisone, corticosterone, 11-deoxycortisol, and aldosterone in the adrenal venous blood of dogs, six weeks after electrolytic destruction of the median eminence. In view of the ACTH-releasing effect of adrenal vein cannulation in the intact animal, these findings have not been interpreted in terms of basal activity. From a concurrent study of the changes in adenohypophysial ACTH and adrenal corticoidogenesis consequent to destruction of the bulbus of the median eminence in the rat, it was inferred by Fortier & de Groot (86) that suppression of hypothalamic influence, associated in all likelihood with impairment of the adenohypophysial blood supply, results in a significant depression of both synthesis and release of ACTH. A new and relatively stable steady state was established, however, at the lower level (20 to 40 per cent of normal), within two or three weeks of the lesioning procedure.

Steroid feedback.—The facts that adrenocorticotropic activity can be suppressed by a high blood level of corticosteroids and that patients or animals with adrenocortical insufficiency exhibit high levels of circulating ACTH provide strong arguments for the existence of a peripheral humoral mechanism controlling ACTH secretion. Recent studies emphasize certain limitations of this mechanism. Confirming previous observations that a lag of three to five weeks elapses before the occurrence of elevated levels of circulating ACTH, as a result of adrenalectomy in the rat (34), and that further elevation can be induced by stress (156), Hodges & Vernikos (157) report that administration of a single large dose of hydrocortisone to adrenalectomized rats does not affect the high resting level of ACTH in the blood, but completely prevents the stress-induced rise in circulating hormone. On the other hand, the increase in pituitary ACTH concentration observed to result from adrenalectomy (83, 287) can be prevented by daily treatment of adrenalectomized animals with doses of hydrocortisone far too small to influence the release of ACTH in response to stress (157). These findings are in keeping with the view that the chief regulatory effect of steroids is exerted on pituitary

ACTH synthesis rather than release. A similar conclusion had been reached by Fortier & de Groot (88) from a study of the changes in pituitary ACTH concentration and cortical secretory activity associated with regeneration of the enucleated adrenal cortex in the rat.

Additional evidence points to the hypothalamus as the site of the regulatory effect of steroids on ACTH secretion. Moll (217, 218) and DeWied (62) have confirmed older reports that lesions in the median eminence or its immediate vicinity interfere with the compensatory hypertrophy of the remaining gland induced by unilateral adrenalectomy in the rat; and, according to Fortier & de Groot, the increase of the pituitary ACTH concentration consequent to removal of the two glands is likewise blocked by destruction of the median eminence (see 85). No consistent correlation was observed by Curri et al. (36) between the oxygen consumption of the hypothalamus and steroid-induced changes in the synthesis and release of ACTH by the anterior pituitary.

Response to stress.—The ability of heterotopic transplants of the adenohypophysis to release ACTH in response to certain stimuli has been confirmed by Martinovitch and co-workers (214), who observed a significant fall of the adrenal cholesterol concentration as a result of X irradiation in hypophysectomized rats with homotransplants of the pituitary in the anterior chamber of the eye, and by Timmer et al. (292), who noted that pituitary autografts beneath the renal capsule are capable of effecting a marked depletion of adrenal ascorbic acid in response to surgical stress. Of particular interest in this connection are preliminary observations by Brodish (26) on the ACTH-releasing activity of peripheral blood from stressed hypophysectomized rats with or without lesions in the median eminence, which suggest that a neurohumoral agent released by hypothalamic neurons under the influence of stress can reach and stimulate the pituitary via the systemic circulation.

It was shown by the same investigator (26) that rats with small anterior hypothalamic lesions did not liberate ACTH in response to either unilateral adrenalectomy or surgical laparotomy, unless both procedures were combined, the effectiveness of the lesion being apparently related to the intensity of the applied stimulus. Differences in stimulus intensity may likewise partially explain Smelik's reported blockade of the adrenal ascorbic acid response to emotional stress in the rat by mammillary and premammillary lesions which did not affect the responses to unilateral adrenalectomy, epinephrine, histamine, Pitressin, electric shock, and asphyxia, all of which were blocked by tuberal lesions (281), with the exception of the responses to Pitressin and histamine. It is equally possible that the hypothalamic collaterals involved in these responses differed with the nature of the stimuli.

The interpretation of findings based on adrenal ascorbic acid depletion as an indicator of stress-induced release of ACTH should be tempered with caution. Fisher & de Salva (82) report that whereas neurohypophysectomy in the rat prevents the adrenal ascorbic acid response to epinephrine, it does not interfere with the rise in plasma corticosterone induced by this stimulus. A similar dichotomy had been previously noted by Slusher (277) between stress-induced adrenal ascorbic acid depletion and release of corticosterone into the adrenal venous effluent of rats with electrolytic lesions in various parts of the hypothalamus. Among possible explanations for this phenomenon was the existence of threshold differences in these responses to alterations in the circulating level of ACTH. This possibility was satisfactorily excluded by Slusher & Roberts (280), who failed to observe any difference in the sensitivity of the two adrenal responses to varying doses of ACTH in hypophysectomized rats. It is nevertheless possible that the sensitivity of the adrenal ascorbic acid and steroid responses to ACTH be differentially altered by hypothalamic damage resulting in the observed dissociation.

The adrenal ascorbic acid response has been ascertained, in most studies, one hour after the outset of the stress stimulus. It now appears, in the light of Brodish's data (26), that lesions in the anterior, middle, or posterior hypothalamus which may be effective in preventing the one-hour response to unilateral adrenalectomy do not necessarily affect the two- and four-hour responses to the same stimulus.

According to Hume & Jackson (165), the corticoidogenic response to trauma is not immediately suppressed in the dog by lesions in the anterior median eminence or even by removal of the ventral hypothalamus, but may persist for a few days after surgery. Thus particular attention should be paid to choice of criterion, duration of response, time interval after lesion, and nature and intensity of the test stimuli before general conclusions can be drawn regarding the extent of hypothalamic involvement in the mediation of the stress response.

Afferent systems.—The wide variety of the emotional and sensory stimuli which result in adrenocorticotropic activation suggests that many pathways contribute to the afferent input of the hypothalamus. Of these, the limbic and reticular activating systems have received special notice. From erudite anatomical considerations, Nauta (228) concludes that the hypothalamus forms part of two neural circuits, one of which connects with the limbic forebrain structures, the other with a medial zone of the midbrain.

Viewed in this manner, the hypothalamus appears as a nodal point in a vast neural system extending from the medial wall of the cerebral hemisphere caudalward to the lower boundary of the mesencephalon, and it seems logical to assume that the functional state of the hypothalamus is continuously influenced by the prevailing activity patterns in the limbic forebrain-midbrain circuit as a whole.

Additional evidence that two limbic structures are involved in the control of ACTH secretion has been presented. Confirming Mason's observations in the monkey (215) in other species (cat, dog, and rat), Endröczi and his associates (75) showed that electrical stimulation of the amygdaloid nucleus resulted in the activation of the stress mechanism, and that of the hippocampus in its inhibition. Likewise, according to Okinaka *et al.* (232), in the dog, stimulation of the amygdaloid nuclear complex and of the hippo-campal formation respectively induced a moderate rise and a significant de-pletion of circulating ACTH and 17-hydroxycorticosteroids. A sharp and transient rise of these response parameters as a result of stimulation of the posterior orbital cortex (prepyriform area) was reported by the same group (231). Lesions of the hippocampus were shown by Knigge (179) to increase basal plasma corticosterone levels, while amygdalar lesions delayed or de-pressed the adrenocortical response to the stress of immobilization in rats. The marked enhancement of corticoidogenesis in the dog, which was ob-served to result from subcallosal lesions of the septum, paralleled the effect of stimulation of the amygdaloid or pyriform cortex and was ascribed by Endröczi & Lissák (74) to the interruption of important afferent connec-tions of the hippocampus. From Egdahl's finding of markedly elevated rest-ing corticosteroid outputs in bilaterally decorticated dogs (68), it appears that the over-all influence of the cerebral cortex is one of tonic inhibition of the lower central nervous areas involved in the control of ACTH release.

The results of electroencephalographic studies indicating similarities be-tween the hypothalamus and midbrain reticular formation (81) are in keep-ing with recent anatomical and endocrinological findings which underline the relationship between the two structures. Thus reticular projections from the medial region of the caudal midbrain to the posterior, dorsal, and infundibu-lar zones of the hypothalamus have been described by Nauta & Kuypers (229), and increased adrenocortical activity as a result of electrical stimula-tion of the midbrain reticular formation has been reported by Okinaka et al. (232) and by Endröczi & Lissák (74). The existence of an inhibitory com-ponent in this vicinity is suggested by Slusher & Hyde's observation that 30-second stimulation in the ventral midbrain tegmentum of cats prepared as encéphales isolés evoked a specific and rapid decrease in adrenal effluent corticoids (279). Moreover, transection of the midbrain is reportedly com-patible, in dogs, with a high resting level of adrenal corticoids (46, 64), though it allegedly prevents the adrenocorticotropic response to a number of stressing stimuli (46, 109). The latter fact is hardly surprising in view of the indiscriminate interruption by this procedure of ascending pathways to the hypothalamus. Since numerous afferent and efferent systems connect the midbrain with both the peripheral nervous system and more rostral portions of the central nervous system, destruction of specific areas in the midbrain and consequent severance of these pathways would be expected, according to Slusher (278), to modify the interdependency of the hypothalamus and lower brainstem in the control of ACTH release. This expectation is rein-forced by the observation that dorsal tegmental lesions at the rostral pons level were associated in the rat with an augmented corticosteroid release following acute stress, while ventral tegmental lesions inhibited the response (278). The interrelationship between midbrain and diencephalic areas con-cerned with ACTH release is further illustrated by the observed reversal of the effects (increase, decrease, or absence of significant change in corticosteroidogenesis) of electrical stimulation in the posterior diencephalon of the cat *encéphale isolé* preparation by simultaneous stimulation of the ventral midbrain tegmentum (279).

Egdahl has confirmed and extended his surprising observation that isolation of the pituitary through complete removal of the brain (hypothalamus included) down to the level of the inferior colliculus, in the dog, results in high resting corticosteroid outputs and does not interfere in most animals with a further response to acute superimposed stress. Burn trauma (65) and sciatic nerve stimulation (64) were used as test stimuli in the original studies. It now appears that caval constriction is even more effective in this respect, since five out of six dogs with "isolated pituitaries" responded to this stimulus with maximal increases of adrenal venous 17-hydroxycorticosteroids (67). It was inferred therefrom that higher regions of the brain inhibit lower areas, including one in the hindbrain, which produce and release ACTH-stimulating neurohumors.

According to a recent report (66), administration of small amounts of sodium pentobarbital to decorticate animals induced a rapid depression of corticosteroid secretion to normal basal levels, although nerve stimulation still resulted in significantly increased 17-hydroxycorticosteroid outputs. On the other hand, even large doses of barbiturate failed to inhibit the elevated secretion in dogs with isolated pituitaries, and in some animals a significant increase in corticosteroid secretion was observed following drug administration. Boldly speculating on the significance of these findings, Egdahl concludes that the cerebral cortex exerts a tonic inhibition of the reticular formation, which in turn tonically stimulates the hypothalamic center controlling ACTH secretion. Pentobarbital would inhibit the reticular formation, which would then fail to stimulate the hypothalamus. The persistence of a response to nerve stimulation in decorticate dogs anesthetized with pentobarbital is imputed to the relative insensitivity of the hypothalamus to barbiturates, whereas the failure of the barbiturate to depress, when it does not increase, the adrenal venous corticosteroid output, following brain removal, is interpreted as evidence that the reticular formation does not stimulate, but may even depress, the hindbrain center controlling ACTH release.

Granting the elegance and ingenuity of these important experiments, it appears difficult to accept unreservedly, on the basis of present evidence, Egdahl's chief contention regarding the existence of a separate and independently controlled center in the hindbrain, concerned with the elaboration and release of an ACTH-stimulating neurohumor. Teleological considerations aside, the absence of known direct neural or vascular connections between hindbrain and adenohypophysis, and the failure to demonstrate, so far, the postulated Hind-Brain-Factor (HBF) should leave the door open to likelier alternatives, among which the possible role of catecholamines that are released through activation of the sympathetic adrenal system may not have been satisfactorily excluded.

Corticotropin-releasing factor.—Although elaboration by the hindbrain of an ACTH-releasing principle of its own remains largely hypothetical, substantial progress has been made in the identification of the chemotransmitter presumably conveyed, through the portal circulation, from median eminence to pars distalis. Following experimental elimination of known neurohumors as possible candidates for this role [see Guillemin (126)], interest has centered on peptides of neurohypophysial or hypothalamic origin.

Additional evidence has been presented that vasopressin can break through the blockade of the pituitary-adrenocortical response to stress induced in the rat by treatment with pentobarbital and morphine (303), cortisone (28) or hydrocortisone (109) administration, midbrain section, or heterotopic transplantation of the adenohypophysis (109). Only part of this effect, however, should be ascribed to release of ACTH from the anterior pituitary, in view of Hilton's findings, based on arterial perfusion of the adrenal glands of the hypophysectomized dog, that synthetic lysine, arginine, and acetyl-arginine vasopressins stimulate the adrenal cortex directly to secrete hydrocortisone (155). In contrast to ACTH and to 3',5'-adenosine monophosphate which cause continuous stimulation during prolonged perfusion, the effect of vasopressin is relatively short-lived under similar conditions. It is inferred from this fact that vasopressin may act in some manner to activate the adrenal phosphorylase presumably involved in steroidogenesis (145) rather than to stimulate its production.

Kwaan & Bartelstone (189) showed that as little as 2 mU of arginine vasopressin will cause a maximal increase of adrenal cortical activity, when injected directly into the third ventricle of the dog. Since this amount is notably less than the 7 mU needed to stimulate minimal hydrocortisone secretion in Hilton's preparation (155), it would appear that vasopressin acts at both pituitary and adrenal cortical levels. However, some parallelism between antidiuretic activity and ACTH release would be implied by the claim, now generally discarded (see 87, 94, 141, 178), that vasopressin is the mediator of the adrenocorticotropic response to stress. In this connection, numerous studies, those of Shuster (272, 273), Guillemin (130), and Baisset et al. (5) among the latest, have failed to show any correlation between spontaneous or experimentally induced changes in water intake or diuresis and ACTH secretion. DeWied (61, 63) recently noted, on the other hand, that the plasma corticosterone response to "neurogenic", as opposed to "systemic", stimuli in the rat was depressed by neurohypophysectomy and restored to normal by chronic administration of Pitressin, thus suggesting a complementary role of antidiuretic hormone in the actuation of this response.

If distinct from vasopressin, the physiological mediator of ACTH release appears to be closely related to this polypeptide, as judged by the difficulty involved in the separation of their respective activities. Progress in this field, which will be outlined briefly, should be specially credited to Saffran (261, 262, 263), Guillemin (127, 129, 133, 134, 136, 268), and their associates, who independently isolated, from material of neurohypophysial or hypothalamic origin, the first ACTH-releasing principle relatively free of pressor activity. Similar claims have since been made by others (55, 56, 57, 123, 225, 258, 259, 267).

The activity *in vitro* of the corticotropin-releasing factor in Saffran & Schally's pituitary incubation system (262), which served as the basis of its isolation, was shown to be specifically related to enhanced release of ACTH (131, 135), as opposed to alternative modes of action (10, 90). The secretory nature of the process was further intimated by the concurrent increase in the incorporation of radioactive phosphorus into the phospholipid fraction of the incubated pituitary, observed by Hokin *et al.* (159). The corticotropin-releasing factor would appear to be equally active *in vivo*, since it shares with stress the ability to deplete pituitary ACTH in rats (251) and to elicit its release in human subjects (30). Furthermore, according to Guillemin *et al.* (130, 133), a small dose of their original and relatively crude chromatographic Fraction D, inactive in the hypophysectomized animal, could overcome the blockade of the plasma corticosteroid response to stress, induced in the rat by median eminence lesions or pentobarbital-morphine administration, whereas equipotent vasopressor amounts of vasopressin could not.

Elaborate separative steps involving ion exchange chromatography (268, 269), countercurrent distribution, and zone electrophoresis (270) have recently yielded two active polypeptides of neurohypophysial origin, termed α- and β-corticotropin-releasing factors, and respectively related by their physical characteristics and amino acid composisitions to α-melanocyte-stimulating hormone and to vasopressin (129, 136). The α-corticotropin-releasing factor has a relatively low specific activity and shares properties suggesting a possible role as a precursor of β-ACTH with a peptidic fraction isolated by de Garilhe *et al.* (55, 56, 57, 123) and with recently synthesized peptides (170, 202), whereas the β-corticotropin-releasing factor, in view of its high potency, possibly represents the physiological mediator of ACTH release.

Direct evidence of portal chemotransmission was provided in 1956 by Porter & Jones' detection of ACTH-releasing activity in plasma (or extracts thereof) obtained from the portal vessels of stressed-hypophysectomized dogs (242). A recent claim (244) that the active substance can be dialyzed away from the proteins of lyophilized portal plasma suggests that a plasma protein, Cohn's Fraction III_0, according to previous evidence (243), may serve as a carrier for the ACTH releaser in portal blood. Clarification of the relationship between Guillemin & Schally's β-corticotropin-releasing factor and Porter's dialyzable principle might bridge an important gap in our understanding of neuroendocrine processes.

ACTH AND CORTICOIDOGENESIS

Mode of action of ACTH.—Haynes, Sutherland & Rall (146) have reviewed the evidence in favor of their concept that the primary action of ACTH is on the accumulation of adenosine-3′,5′-monophosphate (also known as 3′,5′-AMP or cyclic adenylic acid) within the adrenal cortex. Glucose-6-phosphate, when made available by the activation of phosphorylase via ACTH action upon adenosine-3′,5′-monophosphate, would give rise to reduced triphosphopyridine nucleotide (TPNH) via the dehydrogenase-activated pentose shunt, and thus stimulate corticoidogenesis. Consistent with this thesis are the observations that adenosine-3′,5′-monophosphate (143), as well as ACTH (73, 144), stimulates phosphorylase activity, that ACTH induces the accumulation of this monophosphate in the adrenal cortex (143), and that adenosine-3′,5′-monophosphate duplicates the effect of ACTH on corticoidogenesis (18, 145, 154). It has been conclusively shown, furthermore, that TPNH serves as a source of energy for a number of steps involved in cholesterol side-chain cleavage (139) and in corticosteroid synthesis (117, 286). Recent histochemical studies by Greenberg & Glick showing that ACTH markedly depresses glycogen values (121), while significantly increasing glucose-6-phosphate and 6-phosphogluconate dehydrogenase activity (120) and oxidized pyridine nucleotide concentration (119) in the fascicular zone of the rat adrenal cortex, provide corroborative evidence that TPNH is generated via oxidation of glucose-6-phosphate derived from glycogen. Missing links have been uncovered by Haynes & Riley's finding that adenosine triphosphate and magnesium are required for phosphorylase activation by adenosine-3′,5′-monophosphate (146), and by Koritz & Péron's report of a dramatic stimulation by calcium of steroid production by rat adrenal homogenates in the presence of glucose-6-phosphate and TPNH (182). Birmingham *et al.* (18) observed that the activating effect of adenosine-3′,5′-monophosphate on corticosteroid secretion by incubated rat adrenal glands is markedly enhanced by addition of calcium to the medium. Both calcium and glucose increased the steroidogenic response *in vitro* to prolonged incubation with ACTH, but not to short contact with the hormone. Glucose had little, if any, effect on the response to adenosine-3′,5′-monophosphate. It was inferred from this that some step between contact of the tissue with ACTH and the elaboration of this monophosphate requires the presence of glucose and not necessarily that of calcium, and that a reaction in the sequence between elaboration of the nucleotide and steroid production requires the presence of calcium but not of glucose.

Koritz & Péron's finding that incubated adrenal tissue maximally stimulated with ACTH will respond to TPN and glucose-6-phosphate with a further increase in corticosteroid output and that, conversely, adrenal tissue maximally stimulated with these substances will also respond to ACTH had been interpreted to suggest that TPNH is not the only factor under ACTH control and that ACTH acts also by making additional precursor available (181). More difficult to explain in the light of Haynes' concept is the reported failure of glucose-6-phosphate (18, 181) (unless it be added to the medium with TPN) or of insulin and glucose (18) (which presumably result in increased intracellular glucose-6-phosphate formation) to stimulate corticoidogenesis *in vitro*. It would appear, as suggested by Hechter & Lester (148), that somehow,

G6P derived from glycogen or from glucose in the presence of ACTH, can act with endogenous TPN to generate TPNH available for the steroidogenic sequence, whereas in the absence of ACTH, G6P either entering from the medium or formed from external glucose does not react to generate TPNH at specific sites, involving the enzymes of the steroidogenic sequence.

According to the same authors, the importance of adenosine-3',5'-monophosphate in ACTH action might be its potential of acting as a link between the cell membrane and specific enzymatic sites of the cellular interior (148). This view represents the outcome of Hechter's interesting speculations on fundamental mechanisms of hormone action.

Studies by Hechter and his group had revealed that, *in vivo*, hypophysectomy markedly reduced the distribution of D-xylose, a nonutilizable pentose, in the intracellular water of the rat adrenal, whereas exogenous ACTH specifically increased xylose entry to levels approaching those found in stressed animals with intact pituitaries (69). Similarly, opposite effects of hypophysectomy and ACTH were noted with regard to the accumulation in the adrenal of α-aminoisobutyric acid (AIB), an amino acid analogue (70). These findings had originally been interpreted to suggest that the physiological effects of ACTH could be secondary to its influence on cell permeability and the consequent intracellular availability of substrate. However, further studies on the permeability characteristics of bisected rat adrenals *in vitro* failed to demonstrate any significant influence of ACTH on the rate of penetration or the intracellular distribution of D-xylose, under conditions in which a corticoidogenic response was observed (114). This showed conclusively that ACTH can influence the activity of intracellular enzymatic processes via mechanisms which are not dependent upon a simple increase of substrate entry into the cell. A revised unitary system of hormone action was therefore proposed, which postulates spatial arrangements and compartmentalization of enzyme systems in a metastable pattern of ordered lattices representing a continuum throughout the cell. Adrenocorticotropin, considered as a prototype for other hormones such as insulin, would act on this continuum by opening a "valve" at specific points in the cell membrane where the endoplasmic reticulum is attached, thus permitting certain sugars and amino acids to enter this selective diffusion system which directs substrate to specific compartments. The selectivity of the permeability event would be associated with the "valve" controlling transfer of substrate from membrane to reticulum (147, 148). This ingenious working hypothesis would account for some of the facts left unexplained by Haynes' proposed scheme for ACTH action; its eventual usefulness will depend upon the experimentation it will suggest along new lines.

Extra-adrenal effects of ACTH.—The enhancing effect of ACTH on the release of nonesterified fatty acids from rat adipose tissue *in vitro* was corroborated by several groups. A significant lipolytic effect was observed by Schotz *et al.* (271) with one-fiftieth the minimal effective ACTH concentration previously reported by White & Engel (304), and well within the range of effects on the adrenal cortex *in vitro*. According to Hollenberg and co-workers (160), this effect of ACTH, which is inhibited by glucose and insulin, presumably through promotion of esterification of the fatty acids, is equally manifest *in vivo*, since intravenous administration of the hormone to acutely adrenalectomized rats produced a rapid increase of free fatty acids in adipose tissue and plasma. The reported production of glycerol, as well as fatty acids, as a consequence of ACTH action *in vitro* (193, 210) supports the view that the adipokinetic effect of ACTH results from direct activation of a lipase in adipose tissue. The identity of the enzyme, whose pH optimum differs from that of lipoprotein lipase (160), has not been ascertained. Since epinephrine is also endowed with lipolytic activity (9, 210), its absence possibly accounts for the depression of basal and ACTH-enhanced release of fatty acids from the rat epididymal adipose tissue as a result of prior adrenalectomy of the donors [Schotz *et al.* (271)].

Steelman & Smith (284) report that the adipokinetic activity of various pepsin-degraded and nondegraded ACTH preparations generally parallels their steroidogenic potency, as ascertained by Guillemin (128), and that, in spite of structural similarities with ACTH, α- and β-melanocyte-stimulating hormones are largely devoid of fat-mobilizing activity. Since, on the other hand, periodate-treated ACTH lost 90 per cent of its steroidogenic activity but only 50 per cent of its adipokinetic potency, it appears that the structures necessary for these two types of activity may not be identical. Rudman and his associates (260) have recently isolated from the hog pituitary gland a so-called "Fraction H" which, though devoid of steroidogenic activity, shares with ACTH the ability to mobilize free fatty acids into the blood of the fed rabbit (108).

Studies of the pathway of carbon in rat epididymal adipose tissue with the use of labeled glucose revealed a significant effect of ACTH, as well as of epinephrine and growth hormone, on carbohydrate metabolism. In addition to causing an outpouring of fatty acids and glycerol into the medium, these hormones were found to increase oxygen utilization, glucose uptake, and lactic acid concentration (1, 193, 210). From a comparison of the effects of insulin and of ACTH and epinephrine on patterns of glucose utilization by adipose tissue, it was concluded by Lynn *et al.* (210) that the lipolytic effect of ACTH and of epinephrine is independent of substrate, oxygen, or active glycolysis. However, since incubation in a medium containing high concentrations of free fatty acids has been shown to promote their uptake and esterification (27, 193) and, simultaneously, to stimulate glucose carbon metabolism in a manner similar to that resulting from the presence of epinephrine (9), growth hormone, and ACTH (193) (i.e., by apparently promoting the Embden-Meyerhof pathway at the expense of the phosphogluconate oxidative pathway while increasing oxidation by the citric acid cycle), the inference is drawn by Leboeuf & Cahill (193) that these hormones may influence glucose metabolism as a secondary result of accelerated lipolysis.

The observed ability of ACTH, shared with growth hormone, to decrease urea formation in the adrenalectomized-nephrectomized rat was interpreted by Engel & Frederick (76) as evidence of an extra-adrenal action on some phase of nitrogen metabolism. Since it was possible that this effect of ACTH was due to an initial stimulation of amino acid transport, Kostyo & Engel (185) studied the effects *in vitro* of various ACTH preparations on the transport of α-aminoisobutyric acid -1-C^{14} into diaphragms of hypophysectomized rats. In contrast to purified growth hormone which was very active in this system, purified ACTH had no effect on amino acid transport *in vitro*. The studies *in vivo* of Eichhorn *et al.* (70) showed, however, that purified ACTH, as well as insulin, increases aminoisobutyric acid uptake into the diaphragm of functionally nephrectomized rats. The possibility is therefore not excluded that the nitrogen-sparing action of ACTH in the intact animal is accounted for by facilitation of amino acid transport.

It is becoming evident from recent studies that the mechanism of ACTH action in raising blood steroid levels may not be a simple, uncomplicated stimulation of the adrenal cortex, but may also involve an influence on some factor or factors controlling the rate at which corticosteroids and their metabolites are removed from blood and urine. It has thus been shown by Berliner and co-workers (15) that ACTH, when it is exogenously administered or endogenously produced, causes a retention of hydrocortisone and its metabolites in the blood, kidney, thymus, and liver of adrenalectomized mice. Adrenocorticotropin was likewise observed to slow down the disappearance rate of endogenous and exogenous hydrocortisone in normal and Addisonian subjects (59, 60). Of particular interest, in this connection, are studies *in vitro*, with livers from adrenalectomized and ACTH-treated rats and mice, which demonstrated the inhibition of conjugation of hydrocortisone, corticosterone, and tetrahydro-11-keto-progesterone by ACTH (15). Other sites of action will eventually be uncovered, in all likelihood, to account for the extra-adrenal effect of ACTH on steroid metabolism. Evidence for this effect now appears sufficient to suggest caution in the assessment of adrenal cortical activity on the basis of unsupplemented blood and urinary corticosteroid data.

In apparent contradiction with a previous report according to which release of ACTH from the pituitary gland of the adrenalectomized rat is inhibited by the prolonged administration of exogenous ACTH (177), Holub *et al.* (163) observed normal responses to the SU-4885 test in patients who had undergone prolonged therapy with progressively decreasing doses of ACTH. The postulated extra-adrenal effect of ACTH on pituitary release of the hormone therefore remains in question.

Corticoidogenesis.—From a spectroscopic survey by Spiro & Ball (283) of the respiratory enzymes of the beef adrenal cortex, it appears that, similar to what has been reported for the adrenal medulla (282), the activity of the enzymes responsible for the transfer of electrons from TPNH to oxygen is much lower than that of the enzymes responsible for the production of this reduced enzyme. In comparison with the TPNH-generating activity of approximately 2000 µeq per hr per g of cortex reported by Kelly *et al.* (172) via glucose-6-phosphate dehydrogenase, the adrenal cortex seems capable of handling only about 200 µeq per hr of TPNH via both TPNH-cyto-chrome-*c* reductase and transhydrogenase. Such a relationship confirms the need in the cortex for TPNH in the various reductive reactions involved in corticoidogenesis and the fact that in the adrenal cortex, as in most other tissues, this nucleotide exists mostly in reduced form.

According to Grant & Mongkolkul (118), the relatively feeble stimula-tion by citrate of the 11β-hydroxylation of 11-deoxycorticosterone in beef ad-renal cortex is not caused by failure of citrate to enter the mitochondria or to be oxidized via isocitrate, but may be related to the failure of isocitrate oxidation, which appears to be predominantly DPN-linked in these mito-chondria, to produce adequate amounts of TPNH. In contrast to Greenberg & Glick's report of a marked enhancement of glucose-6-phosphate dehydro-genase activity in the fascicular-reticular border of the rat adrenal cortex, as a result of ACTH administration (120), Cohen (32) failed to note any change in the activity of this enzyme in response to either stress or hypophysectomy in the corresponding zones of the rat adrenal. Utilization by Cohen of a cruder method of quantitation (direct microscopic assessment of the histo-chemical reaction vs. enzyme assay) probably accounts for the discrepancy.

Prompted by reports of a diurnal variation in rat plasma corticosterone concentration (132, 226), Glick and co-workers (112) found that coenzyme-A concentration and succinic dehydrogenase activity in rodent adrenals are both circadian periodic functions, since they can be synchronized with a 24-hr regimen of alternating light and darkness. However, whereas circadian changes in succinic dehydrogenase activity were roughly in phase with changes in corticosterone concentration, the circadian rhythm of adrenal coenzyme A showed a significant phase difference with these two variants.

Extending their observation that vitamin-A deficiency in the rat causes a decrease in the incorporation of cholesterol-4-C^{14} into corticosterone by adrenal homogenates (297), Van Dyke *et al.* (298) report that addition of vitamin-A alcohol or acid to homogenates from deficient animals at least partially restores synthesis of corticosterone *in vitro*. The inference is drawn that some form of vitamin A may act as a cofactor for one of the enzymes in-volved in the transformation of cholesterol to corticosterone. From ultra-centrifugation studies aimed at localizing the system responsible for the stimulation by freezing or by the calcium ion of corticosteroid production by rat adrenal homogenates in the presence of TPN and glucose-6-phosphate (182), Péron & Koritz (238) conclude that the stimulated system is present in the large particles of the rat adrenal and that, in the sequence of reactions leading to the synthesis of corticosteroids from endogenous precursors, the stimulated step(s) appears to be concerned with the transformation of choles-terol to pregnenolone. According to Koritz (180), DPN, in the presence of TPN and glucose-6-phosphate, inhibits the production of corticosteroids from endogenous precursors in frozen rat adrenal homogenates prepared from preincubated adrenal sections. Since the DPN inhibition is reversed by ascorbate, as well as by pyruvate and oxalacetate, but not by lactate or malate, it appears that the inhibitor is DPNH rather than DPN and that the inhibition is not due to a transhydrogenase-mediated decrease in TPNH concentration. The observation that ascorbate and pyruvate not only reverse the inhibition, but also increase the conversion of pregnenolone to corticoids in the presence of DPN suggests, furthermore, that the inhibition occurs at the oxidation of pregnenolone to progesterone.

Addition of dinitrophenol, with and without ACTH, to the perfused calf adrenal reportedly resulted in a striking suppression of corticoid production without a commensurate metabolic depression and induced an 80 to100 per cent depletion in the ability of exposed glands to perform 11β-, 17α-, and 21-hydroxylation without affecting their transformation of the $\Delta 5$-3β-OH group to $\Delta 4$-3-ketone. According to Rosenfeld (254), these effects would be consistent with inhibition of TPNH formation, which would also result in suppression of corticoidogenesis and of the specific hydroxylation reactions involved; as a consequence of dinitrophenol-induced uncoupling of oxidative phosphorylation and adenosine triphosphatase activation, the amounts of adenosine triphosphate would be drastically reduced and, in turn, probably those of glucose-6-phosphate and TPNH, since regeneration of TPN from DPN conceivably depends upon adenosine triphosphate for maximal activity of the phosphorylase system.

The previously reported ACTH-like effect of 5-hydroxytryptamine (serotonin) in inducing the release from the quartered rabbit adrenal of a blue-tetrazolium–reducing material (255) has been confirmed by further studies of Rosenkrantz & Laferte (256), in which the specificity of serotonin for this effect was established. In spite of preliminary findings on chromatographic mobility and sodium-retaining activity which suggest a possible relationship of the blue-tetrazolium–reducing material to aldosterone, its identity remains unknown. Equally unknown is the nature of the blue-tetrazolium–reducing, nonultraviolet-absorbing compound(s) allegedly released by the incubated rat adrenal gland under the influence of acetylcholine (211). Progress has been made, however, in the isolation and identification of the corticosteroids normally released by incubated rat adrenal tissue. Of four distinct ultraviolet-absorbing zones isolated by Péron (236) from chromatography of lipid extracts of pooled preincubation media of rat adrenal sections, or of incubated rat adrenal homogenates, two were identified by infrared spectroscopy and other criteria as free corticosterone and the 21-monoacetate of aldosterone. The remaining two compounds, originally unidentified, were designated as X_1 and X_2. It now appears from a thorough study of its physical characteristics by the same investigator (237) that X_1 corresponds to 18-hydroxycorticosterone. Compelling evidence is presented, on the other hand, by Birmingham & Ward (19, 300) for the identification of an ultraviolet-absorbing, lipid-soluble Porter-Silber chromogen released by the incubated adrenal, and apparently corresponding to Péron's X_2, as the $20 \rightarrow 18$-hemiketal of 18-hydroxy-11-deoxycorticosterone.

From a comparative study of the changes in adrenal ascorbic acid and in adrenal and plasma corticosterone concentration induced, by unilateral adrenalectomy in the rat, adrenal ascorbic acid depletion appears to be more closely related in time to release than to synthesis of corticosterone, since maximal depletion did not correspond to maximal corticosterone concentration in the gland (30 min postoperatively), but was achieved at the same time (60 to 120 min postoperatively) as its peak concentration in plasma, when the rate of release of the hormone presumably reached equilibrium with its rate of removal or inactivation (246). The observed temporal relationship may be purely coincidental, however, and fails to provide a clue as to the role, if any, of adrenal ascorbic acid in steroidogenesis. Of interest in this connection is Hechter's suggestion, based on his cellular permeability theory, that ACTH-induced adrenal ascorbic acid depletion may be the consequence of an anion exchange reaction, whereby ascorbic acid would be replaced in the cells by phosphogluconate or other acids formed during glucose metabolism (148). It appears from recent findings of Harding et al. (140) that adrenal permeability to ascorbic acid may be restricted to its oxidized form. According to these authors, adrenal ascorbic acid in the rat is oxidized, in the early period after ACTH stimulation, into dehydroascorbic acid which is rapidly lost by the adrenal. Dehydroascorbic acid, when recovered, under these conditions, in the adrenal venous blood, could not be detected in the gland either before or after ACTH stimulation. Since ACTH-induced adrenal ascorbic acid depletion is limited to the rat and a few other species, it is tempting to speculate that failure of other species to respond to ACTH in this respect may be related either to the lack of a factor necessary for, or to the presence of a factor interfering with, oxidation of ascorbic acid into dehydroascorbic acid. Possibly consistent, albeit indirectly, with the latter alternative is Perek & Eilat's intriguing finding that removal of the *Bursa Fabricii* (a structure peculiar to immature Aves) in the normally unresponsive chick allows adrenal ascorbic acid depletion in response to ACTH (235).

According to DeWied and co-workers (296), corticoid production *in vitro* by the incubated rat adrenal gland accurately reflects changes *in vivo* in free corticosterone levels in plasma induced by environmental stress (rise) or hypophysectomy (marked and rapid decline). However, ACTH added *in vitro* to the incubating medium of adrenals from rats exposed to a strange environment only moderately increased corticoid production, whereas the same amount of hormone markedly stimulated the steroid formation of adrenals from nonstressed and hypophysectomized rats (8). Thus prior endogenous stimulation apparently interferes with the response *in vitro* of the incubated glands. Prompted by the observation that the adrenal response to ACTH after preincubation was more pronounced than that of nonpreincubated glands, Bakker & DeWied (8) found, in addition, that the preincubation medium contains a thermolabile ACTH-inactivating material, which they believe to be an enzyme leaking into the medium from the cut surface of the glands. Conversely, inactivation of oxycellulose-purified ACTH by treatment with potassium persulfate allegedly results in a derivative which potentiates the biological activity of the untreated hormone *in vitro*. The potentiating effect of the inactive ACTH analogue is ascribed by Cohen & Frieden (31), on the basis of evidence derived from the incubation of various tissue homogenates with ACTH in the presence and absence of this derivative, to inhibition by the latter of an ACTH-inactivating system through competition with the untreated hormone.

Recent studies indicate that thyroid hormones may play a significant role in the control of corticoidogenesis. According to Roche and his group, steroid production *in vitro* by rat adrenal glands incubated in the presence or absence of ACTH was markedly depressed by prior thyroidectomy of the donors (250) and enhanced, on the contrary, by addition of 3,5,3'-triiodothyroacetic acid to the medium (249). In agreement with these observations, Kruskemper reports that treatment with thyroxine or triiodothyronine prevented cortisone or hydrocortisone-induced adrenal atrophy in intact rats (187) and increased the relative weight of the adrenal and the size of the nuclei in the cells of the fascicular zone of hypophysectomized animals (188). Enhancement, by the simultaneous administration of thyroid-stimulating hormone, of ACTH-induced adrenal hypertrophy in hypophysectomized rats (188) was also taken to indicate a direct influence of thyroid hormones on the adrenal cortex.

Female rats reportedly demonstrated markedly higher and more consistently increased plasma levels of corticosterone after stress than did male animals (176, 274). The possible implication of progesterone in this sex difference is suggested by Telegdy & Endröczi's report that adrenal cortical secretion, as well as the hydrocortisone to corticosterone ratio in the dog, is significantly increased by administration of this hormone for seven to twelve days (289). However, the mechanism of the response to progesterone has not been fully elucidated by these Hungarian workers and is as compatible with an effect on trophic hormone secretion as it is with an effect on adrenal corticoidogenesis. The same remark could apply to Saffran & Vogt's observation that methylandrostenediol, in contrast to estradiol which is allegedly ineffective in this respect (107), helps to maintain adrenal size in rats treated with large doses of corticosteroids but has an adverse effect on the secretory capacity of the gland (264).

Although compelling evidence indicates that the inhibitory effect of corticosteroids on adrenal cortical activity is chiefly mediated through interference with ACTH secretion, the possibility of a direct inhibitory effect of cortical hormones on the adrenal cortex remains in question. Against it are the observations of Martini *et al.* (213) and of Sakiz (265) on the failure of these hormones to accelerate or enhance the adrenal atrophy consequent to hypophysectomy in the rat. In favor of such a direct effect, on the other hand, is a report by Péron *et al.* (239) according to which the corticoidogenic effect of ACTH was decreased by pretreatment of hypophysectomized rats with corticosterone. Studies *in vitro* do not provide a clear-cut answer to this question, since the same investigators (239) failed to corroborate the alleged inhibition by corticosterone and hydrocortisone of the corticoidogenic response to ACTH of incubated rat adrenal glands (17).

CATABOLISM OF CORTICOSTEROIDS

Protein binding.—The interaction of steroids and plasma proteins has been the subject of recent comprehensive reviews (41, 266). From a survey of their findings, Daughaday & Mariz (43) come to the conclusion that three proteins in human plasma contribute to steroid binding. The first is albumin, which binds all steroid hormones but has the greatest affinity for estrogens, less for progesterone, and least for corticosteroids. The second, an α-glycoglobulin known as "Corticosteroid-Binding Globulin" (43) or as "transcortin" (276), is more active at 4° than at 37°C and seems to be relatively specific for corticosteroids, though its concentration in plasma is so small that it can bind only about 20 µg of hydrocortisone per 100 ml. The third, which can be detected in plasma during pregnancy and as a result of estrogen administration, resembles corticosteroid-binding globulin in its electrophoretic behavior but can be differentiated from it on the basis of its lesser affinity for hydrocortisone at 4°C and of its lesser dependence on temperature. According to Daughaday *et al.* (42), who compared the binding characteristics of sera from pregnant or estrogen-treated subjects to those of controls in a system of double equilibrium dialysis similar to the one devised by Warren & Salhanick (301), increased binding of hydrocortisone-C^{14} can be demonstrated by "estrogen" plasma under conditions of minimal hydrocortisone loading only at 37°, and not at 4°C. The total concentration of hydrocortisone-binding protein induced by estrogens at 37°C was found to be two or three times greater than that of corticosteroid-binding globulin. This difference in binding behavior is considered as evidence that the binding sites induced by estrogens are qualitatively different from those on corticosteroid-binding globulin.

Hepatic inactivation.—The major metabolic changes responsible for inactivation of corticosteroids by the liver appear to be Δ4-3-ketone and C-20 reduction. Previously noted sex differences in the two processes have been confirmed by three reports, according to which side-chain reduction is more rapid in the male, and ring-A reduction in the female (110, 138, 176). As could be expected, castration of the male depressed side-chain reduction and increased the rate of ring-A metabolism, whereas testosterone administration immediately after surgery prevented these changes. Conversely, giving estradiol to males and testosterone to females depressed the side-chain and ring-A reduction respectively (138). The half-time for the disappearance of corticosterone from plasma is reportedly much shorter in female than in male rats (110, 149). According to Glenister & Yates (110), this sex difference in inactivation rates, though largely accounted for by a difference in Δ4-steroid hydrogenase activity, may also be related to supposedly greater availability of TPNH in the female liver, in view of larger amounts therein of the glucose-6-phosphate and 6-phosphogluconate dehydrogenases which catalyze TPNH-generating reactions.

In studies involving different noxious stimuli in the rat, Herbst *et al.* (149) found that all stimuli which diminished food intake also decreased the capacity of the liver to inactivate adrenal cortical hormones by ring-A reduction, whereas the others had no such effect, and that in every case the loss of hepatic capacity for inactivation of corticosterone following exposure to effective stimuli could be duplicated by pair-feeding control animals. Furthermore, hepatic Δ4-steroid hydrogenase activity was found to be a nearly linear function of food intake in the day preceding the assay. In view of a recent report by Dailey *et al.* (37) that ring-A reduction was diminished in liver homogenates from sodium deficient rats, it would be of interest to know the effect of salt deprivation on food consumption. Since the supply of TPNH from the hexose monophosphate shunt is also dependent on food intake (113, 291) and since, on the other hand, the Δ4-steroid hydrogenase activity of liver homogenates is reportedly not affected by reductions in the food intake of donors as long as the exogenous supply of TPNH in the incubating medium is abundant (149), it seems logical to assume with Herbst and co-workers that the influence of food intake on Δ4-steroid hydrogenase activity is mediated through nonspecific alterations in the amount of liver TPNH. A similar conclusion had been reached by McGuire & Tomkins (227) regarding the mediation by TPNH of the increased Δ4-steroid hydrogenase activity of liver homogenates from thyroxine-pretreated rats. The observed thyroxine-induced rise in Δ4-3-ketosteroid hydrogenase in the microsomal fraction of the liver paralleled an increase in available TPNH, related, in all likelihood, to enhanced glucose-6-phosphate dehydrogenase activity (227). Melby *et al.* (216) suggest that the markedly increased hydrocortisone output that follows the administration of thyroxine analogue in the dog may be the consequence of accelerated release of ACTH through the operation of the negative feedback called into play by accelerated enzymatic reduction of circulating cortical hormones. On the other hand, as seen in a previous section, ACTH in its turn reportedly slows down the disappearance rate of corticosteroids, thus tending to counterbalance the over-all increase in corticosteroid turnover initiated by thyroid hormones.

Bohus & Endröczi report from studies of the metabolism *in vitro* of cortisone (22) and hydrocortisone (21) with liver slices or homogenates from the dog, cat, guinea pig, and rat of both sexes that, in addition to its main role in inactivating corticosteroids through ring-A reduction and production of tetrahydro compounds, the liver is also capable of transforming these hormones, chiefly through 17α- and 11β-dehydroxylation, into less polar and still biologically active derivatives with the Δ4-3-keto structure unchanged, such as corticosterone, 11-dehydrocorticosterone, and 17-hydroxy-11-deoxycorticosterone.

Peripheral inactivation.—The blood was shown by Axelrod & Werthessen (4) to be an important site for the inactivation of corticosteroids. Of the metabolites recovered following incubation of hydrocortisone with blood of guinea pig, baboon, or man, most had been reduced in the α-β unsaturated 3-ketone position. It is apparent, on the other hand, from Sweat & Bryson's studies that hydrocortisone can be degraded in muscle tissue via at least five different pathways, namely, cleavage of the C-17 side-chain, oxidation at C-11, deoxygenation at C-17, and reduction at C-4, C-5, and C-20. The reaction hydrocortisone→ cortisone was found to be TPN-specific and inhibited by DPN. Reduction at C-4, C-5, and C-20 appeared to be TPNH-dependent (285).

Urinary metabolites.—Studies by Fukushima *et al.* (92), who used reverse isotope dilution and paper chromatography, of the metabolic transformation of hydrocortisone-4-C^{14} in normal men revealed that eleven known metabolites accounted for approximately 90 per cent of the radioactivity in the neutral steroid fraction obtained after hydrolysis of conjugates with β-glucuronidase. The major transformation products as a group were the tetrahydro derivatives, which comprised 45 to 50 per cent of the radioactivity. The glycerol side-chain derivatives, cortols and cortolones, accounted for 18 to 33 per cent of the neutral steroid, with the 11-keto derivatives present in much larger amount. Cleavage of the side-chain of hydrocortisone occurred to a limited extent, as evidenced by the isolation of 2 to 12 per cent of the neutral steroid metabolites as 3α, 11β-dihydroxyetiocholane-17-one and 3α-hydroxyetiocholane-11,17-dione. Very low radioactivity was found in their 5α-H epimers.

The finding by Ulstrom *et al.* (295) of significant amounts of highly polar corticosteroids, such as 6β-hydroxycortisol, in the urine of normal newborn infants lends support to a number of earlier studies suggesting that the steroid metabolic pathways in the newborn differ in important quantitative respects from those in adults and indicates, furthermore, that the high percentages of free urinary steroids previously reported in the neonate may not be the result of a limited ability to conjugate steroids but may reflect, instead, a deviation in metabolism at a point preceding reduction of ring A.

METABOLIC EFFECTS OF CORTICOSTEROIDS

So varied are the effects of glucocorticoids on glucose uptake and utilization, glycogen synthesis, protein catabolism, amino acid metabolism and transport, and the oxidation of fat, among others, that it has proved difficult, so far, to determine their sequence from a primary site of action. The classical studies of Long and his group (206) were originally interpreted to suggest that acceleration of tissue protein catabolism initiated the sequence by providing a new and important source of carbohydrate. The same investigators have recently reviewed evidence showing that, depending on the conditions under which they are studied, the effects of corticosteroids on protein and carbohydrate metabolism are not always associated with each other. In fasted animals, a satisfactory quantitative relationship is observed between increased protein breakdown and extra carbohydrate deposited as liver or muscle glycogen, or accumulating as glucose in body fluids. In fed animals, however, a marked alteration in the pattern of carbohydrate metabolism can be found without any significant changes in protein catabolism (207).

Carbohydrate metabolism.—Increased blood glucose and lactate levels were observed by Glenn and co-workers (111), as a result of hydrocortisone administration to fasted adrenalectomized rats, in the absence of any alterations of amino acids, nonesterified fatty acids, and protein levels. Moreover, of administered amino acids, fat, protein, lactate, and glucose, only the latter two substrates significantly influenced the glycogenic response to hydrocortisone. It is inferred from this that hydrocortisone is primarily concerned with the disposition and metabolism of glucose or one of its immediate metabolites and that the rapid rise in blood glucose levels, which reportedly precedes by an appreciable interval increased liver glycogen formation (205, 223), is due to the inhibitory effects of the hormone on glucose metabolism in peripheral tissues, as opposed to a primary effect on gluconeogenesis or conversion of noncarbohydrate precursors to glucose. Consistent with this viewpoint is Munck's finding of a decreased rate of glucose uptake by isolated adipose tissue from rats injected with glucocorticoids (221, 222, 223). Conflicting results have been yielded, however, by experiments on glucose uptake by the isolated rat muscle. In contrast to the hydrocortisone-induced inhibition of glucose uptake by the incubated rat diaphragm, reported by Herman & Ramey (150), Munck & Koritz (223) observed that glucocorticoids slightly enhance incorporation of glucose by the isolated rat gastrocnemius. Clarification of this discrepancy must await repetition of the experiments with the two muscle types.

Using C^{14}-bicarbonate as substrate, Ashmore *et al.* (2) found that hydrocortisone increased incorporation of the label into the liver glycogen of fasted rats, without any significant rise in the activity of either blood glucose or liver dicarboxylic acid. Studies with labeled glucose revealed increased deposition of glycogen from this substrate, and little recycling of C^{14} from glucose via the Cori cycle. Since, on the other hand, hydrocortisone failed to stimulate hepatic glucose production, it is suggested that blood glucose is the most probable source of the glycogen laid down under initial stimulation with this hormone.

In view of the profound inhibition of glycogen storage observed in the adrenalectomized rat, when challenged by a carbohydrate load, Winternitz & Forrest (308) believe that excess utilization of carbohydrate in the adrenalectomized state may be secondary to failure of glycogenesis and may occur over all available pathways.

Protein metabolism.—A growing body of evidence suggests that adrenal steroids lead to increased protein synthesis by the liver (183, 184, 306) despite induction of negative nitrogen balance in the body as a whole (16, 35, 125, 167, 169 203). Studies with aminoisobutyric acid clearly indicate that glucocorticoids enhance the trapping of amino acids by the liver (29, 169). This effect no doubt contributes to steroid-induced facilitation of protein synthesis, a process whose complexity is illustrated by Korner's elegant experiments on the incorporation of radioactive amino acids into protein by rat liver microsomes (184). He found that adrenalectomy, although its immediate outcome is to increase the ability of microsomes to incorporate amino acid into protein, ultimately has the opposite effect. The high rate of incorporation initially induced by adrenalectomy was depressed by hydrocortisone. Normal rats, on the other hand, responded to administered corticosteroids with increased incorporation of amino acid by their liver microsomes. It would thus appear that the full potential of liver microsomes to incorporate amino acids into protein is held in check by corticosteroid-induced gluconeogenesis and that this check is removed by adrenalectomy. When corticosteroids are given to normal rats, however, the effect of flooding the liver with amino acids derived from extrahepatic tissue overshadows their inhibitory effect on protein synthesis, whereas the reverse is true in the case of acutely adrenalectomized rats, where incorporation already occurs at a near-maximal rate (184).

Wool (309) has summarized the evidence that three separate processes contribute to the catabolic effect of corticosteroids on muscle, namely: increase in protein breakdown, decrease in protein synthesis, and decrease in rate of amino acid penetration into the cell. His conclusion that corticosteroids alter protein biosynthesis in the isolated rat diaphragm by a mechanism independent of amino acid entry rests on the observation that adrenalectomy enhances, and corticosteroids depress, the incorporation into protein not only of C^{14}-amino acids added to the medium (212, 310, 312), but also of amino acids formed within the cell from C^{14}-labeled glucose, dicarboxylic acid, or bicarbonate (311). Evidence of actual dissociation of the two processes is derived from the reported failure of adrenalectomy to alter the rate of entry of amino acids into the intact or cut isolated diaphragm of the rat despite its enhancing effect on protein synthesis from available amino acid precursors. Cortisone administration, on the other hand, depressed both processes (309). Among related observations, corticosteroids were found to decrease amino acid incorporation into the proteins of mouse kidney homogenates (91), and of rat skin, small intestine (290), and epididymal tissue (151).

Lipid metabolism.—According to Jeanrenaud & Renold (168), administration of cortisone to fasting adrenalectomized rats resulted in a significant decrease in lipogenesis from 2-C^{14}-pyruvate by subsequently isolated epididymal adipose tissue. When added *in vitro*, however, corticosterone and hydrocortisone failed to alter lipogenesis by adipose tissue, but significantly stimulated the release of nonesterified fatty acids into the medium, an observation extended by Reshef & Shapiro's finding that adrenalectomy and corticosteroid administration respectively depressed and enhanced the release of free fatty acids from the mesenteric adipose tissue of starved rats (248).

In apparent contradiction to an earlier report by Perry & Bowen (240), Willmer & Foster (307) observed that adrenalectomy increased the ability of rat liver slices to synthesize cholesterol from C^{14}-acetate. Use of older rats by the first group is offered as a possible explanation for the different results.

Corticosteroids and enzymes.—Further attempts have been made to correlate corticosteroid-induced alterations of enzymatic activity with the observed metabolic effects of these hormones. Consistent with increased gluconeogenesis is the enhancement, confirmed in recent studies (71, 173, 245), of liver transaminase activity by cortisone or hydrocortisone. In conformity with the postulated relationship of gluconeogenesis to the level of liver glutamic pyruvic transaminase, Eisenstein (71) noted that depletion of vitamin B_6, a cofactor of the enzyme, depressed the enhancing effect of hydrocortisone on both liver glutamic pyruvic transaminase activity and liver glycogen deposition in the rat.

According to Willmer (305), the activity of liver phosphorylase, phosphoglucomutase, and phosphoglucoseisomerase in rats is reduced by adrenalectomy and restored to normal by corticosteroid administration. Kerppola (174) reports, on the other hand, an inhibitory effect of cortisone on oxidative phosphorylation and oxygen uptake by rat liver mitochondria which, through consequent reduction of adenosine triphosphate production, could presumably result in impairment of hexokinase function, of oxidation of fatty acids in the Krebs cycle, and of protein synthesis and thus account for many of the symptoms of hypersecretion or excess dosage of corticosteroids. Further studies by Kerppola & Pitkanen (175) indicate that the inhibitory effect of cortisone is located at the cytochrome oxidase level, since only minor or no changes were found in the succinic dehydrogenase and DPN–cytochrome-*c* reductase activities.

Engel & Scott (77) recently reported a 10 to 15 per cent stimulation of glutamic dehydrogenase activity in the presence of low concentrations of corticosterone or hydrocortisone. An increase in the dehydrogenation of glutamic to α-ketoglutaric acid would admittedly make available more Krebs cycle intermediates for glycogen production and thus possibly represent a primary site of corticoid action. The significance of this observation is obscured, however, by the failure of Yielding *et al.* (314) to observe consistent stimulation of glutamic dehydrogenase activity under analogous conditions.

REGULATION OF ALDOSTERONE SECRETION

Aldosterone and hypertension.—The finding by Genest and his group (100, 101, 104, 105, 106) of a mean increase in urinary aldosterone excretion in hypertensive patients has been corroborated by several reports (98, 299, 252, 302). However, whereas a two- to fourfold increase in urinary aldosterone was observed by Genest *et al.* in patients with essential, renal, and malignant hypertension, Laragh and co-workers (192), while confirming the excessive aldosterone secretion rates of patients with severe or malignant hypertension, reported normal values in less severe cases. The apparent discrepancy between secretion rates and urinary excretion of aldosterone in patients with primary benign hypertension has been tentatively ascribed by Genest (100) to a difference in the metabolism of the hormone. Since, in confirmation of this view, the excretions of pregnanetriol and of aldosterone were found to

vary in opposite directions in patients with hypertension (230), the pregnanetriol to aldosterone ratio was adopted by the Montreal group as a more
sensitive index of hypertensive cardiovascular disease. This ratio was reportedly below the lower limits of the normal range in 92 per cent of all patients so tested with essential, renal, or malignant hypertension (100). Although the possibility has not been excluded that hyperaldosteronism may
be concomitant with or secondary to hypertension, it appears more likely, in
the light of present evidence, that aldosterone is causally involved in the
pathogenesis of the disease or, at any rate, of some of its prevalent forms.
This practical implication may add to the interest of the many studies devoted to the elucidation of the regulatory mechanisms of aldosterone secretion.

Peripheral factors.—Under physiological conditions, various peripheral
and central factors no doubt participate in the regulation of aldosterone
secretion. From an exhaustive survey of the former, Gross (124) concludes
that, in spite of a strict inverse relationship between sodium and aldosterone
output, plasma sodium concentration is not an essential factor in the control
of this secretion. Sodium deficiency has nevertheless been reported to result
in increased aldosterone output by incubated rat adrenal glands (72) and,
more recently, by the autotransplanted adrenal of the conscious sheep (247).
Sodium sensitivity detectors somewhere within the vascular system therefore remain a possibility, but, thus far, none have been described. Most available evidence, on the other hand, supports the view that hemodynamic
factors are chiefly responsible for controlling the secretion of aldosterone,
which decreases when the circulating blood volume is diminished and vice
versa (11). On the basis of acute experiments with caval and carotid constriction and release in the dog, Bartter and his associates conclude that
aldosterone output is influenced by local changes in intracarotid and right
atrial volumes, regardless of total intravascular volume, through a dual
mechanism in which increases and decreases in secretion are respectively
mediated by afferents from receptors located at the thyrocarotid arterial
junction (11, 12) and by the vagus nerves activated by stretch detectors in
the right atrium (93). The latter's existence had already been inferred from
the finding by Baisset *et al.* (6) of a 75 per cent decrease in aldosterone secretion as a result of right atrium distention in the dog.

Anterior pituitary.—It is generally admitted that the pituitary gland is
not an essential link in aldosterone regulation. That it does, however, play an
ancillary role in this process is indicated by the fall in basal aldosterone output (52, 220), and reduction of the aldosterone responses to acute hemorrhage (220) and to caval constriction (49, 52) observed as a result of hypophysectomy in the dog, and by the allegedly significant aldosterone-stimulating effect of ACTH in human subjects (116), as well as in hypophysectomized (220) and hypophysectomized-nephrectomized dogs (219). According
to Mulrow & Ganong (220), the metabolic state of the adrenal may alter the
pattern of response to ACTH, since it appears from their studies that, when

glucocorticoids are being maximally produced, administration of ACTH to the intact or hypophysectomized dog stimulates mainly aldosterone secretion, whereas ACTH stimulates both glucocorticoids and aldosterone when glucocorticoid synthesis is not at maximal rate. From a correlation of these findings with Koritz & Péron's proposed scheme for ACTH action (181), the view is advanced that if, under conditions of maximal glucocorticoid secretion, the rate-limiting factor is available TPNH, steroid precursors could be synthesized to aldosterone through a corticosterone-bypassing, less TPNH-dependent, pathway (220). The opposite interpretation was drawn by Lucis *et al.* (208) from studies *in vitro* which revealed that the maximum effect of purified ACTH on the biosynthesis of aldosterone by incubated rat adrenal glands occurred at the origin of the log dose-response curve for corticosterone. It was accordingly postulated that the limiting factor in the response to ACTH may be a saturation of the enzyme systems involved in the biosynthesis of aldosterone, and a shift to pathways leading to increased formation of corticosterone. Both interpretations may be correct, granted the possibility of different limiting factors, for aldosterone synthesis according to the relative availability of enzymes, cofactors, and substrates under conditions *in vivo* and *in vitro*.

The ability of ACTH peptides to stimulate aldosterone *in vitro* was reportedly found to reside in a labile factor which could easily be destroyed without affecting their capacity to stimulate corticosterone secretion (208).

Studies by Lucis & Venning (209) showed that porcine, monkey, and human growth hormone preparations have no effect on the secretion of aldosterone by the rat adrenal gland *in vitro*. When, however, monkey growth hormone was injected into hypophysectomized rats, the adrenals of these animals secreted, *in vitro*, increased amounts of aldosterone, with no change in the secretion of corticosterone. The observed aldosterone-stimulating effect of plasma from hypophysectomized rats treated with growth hormone was interpreted to suggest the presence of some trophic factor for aldosterone synthesis and release.

Adrenoglomerulotropin.—The role of the pineal body in the control of aldosterone secretion, suggested by Farrell's isolation from this structure of a lipid-soluble, aldosterone-stimulating principle termed "adrenoglomerulotropin", has been challenged by the alleged failure of destruction of the pineal gland and associated structures to affect urinary aldosterone and sodium excretion or the aldosterone response to thoracic caval constriction in the dog (44), and by the reported lack of effect of pinealectomy or of an acetone-insoluble pineal extract on the relative size of the zona glomerulosa, the urinary potassium excretion, and the elective saline intake in the rat (313). Pineal powders and extracts used by Lucis *et al.* (208) likewise proved without effect on aldosterone secretion by the incubated rat adrenal gland, whereas an acetone-soluble fraction prepared by Kovács and co-workers (186) was reportedly effective under similar conditions. According to Romani *et al.*, various pineal preparations induced marked sodium retention in intact, as opposed to adrenalectomized, rats (253) and duplicated the effects of sodium deprivation on the aliesterase activity of the zona glomerulosa (171). This may be related to the isolation by two groups (233, 257) of a sodium-retaining factor from the urine of adrenalectomized rats deprived of sodium.

Recent studies by Farrell and his associates may help to dispel some of the confusion apparent from the foregoing. The initial inhibition of aldosterone secretion induced by pinealectomy in the dog was found to be short lived, and rapidly gave way to normal or even enhanced secretory activity (78). On the other hand, preliminary observations by Taylor (288) on the effect of destruction of the subcommissural organ in the cat suggest that this structure may be the source of stimulatory influences on aldosterone secretion. The stimulatory effect of glomerulotropin, a lipid factor obtained from pineal extracts, was confirmed (80); but a second factor, also from the pineal body, was found to inhibit the output of aldosterone, as well as hydrocortisone (78, 79). It is therefore tentatively suggested that the control of aldosterone secretion may be operated by an excitatory-inhibitory system involving the interplay of pituitary ACTH, pineal, or subcommissural adrenoglomerulotropin, and an anticorticotropin of pineal origin (78, 79). Available data are obviously inadequate to support this interesting working hypothesis.

Angiotensin and the renal pressor system.—Suggestive evidence of a correlation between the renal juxtaglomerular cells, the adrenal zona glomerulosa, and sodium regulation has been outlined in recent reviews (234, 293, 294). Of particular interest in this connection is the observation by Genest and his associates that infusions of synthetic angiotensin II, a vasoactive octapeptide analogous to the natural principle resulting from the action of renin on a plasma substrate, specifically stimulated urinary aldosterone excretion in both normal and hypertensive subjects (20, 100, 102, 103). Prompted by this finding, shortly corroborated by Laragh *et al.* (191) in terms of aldosterone secretion rates, Davis and co-workers and Ganong & Mulrow reported that nephrectomy depressed basal aldosterone secretion (45, 48, 50, 51) as well as the aldosterone responses to acute hemorrhage (50, 51, 95) or to caval constriction (48) in the hypophysectomized dog, whereas administration of renal extracts (48, 50, 51, 95), renin (47, 275), or angiotensin (47, 96, 275) markedly enhanced aldosterone secretion in the hypophysectomized-nephrectomized animal. If, in the light of these observations, a correlation between the renal pressor mechanism and aldosterone secretion appears well established, the relationship of this integrated system to the pathogenesis of essential hypertension remains elusive. Factors such as deoxycorticosterone acetate administration, high sodium intake, or high renal artery pressure, which result in experimental hypertension, reportedly depress the granularity of the renal juxtaglomerular cells, the renin content of the kidney, and the width of the zona glomerulosa, which have been found to vary in a parallel manner, whereas opposite changes have converse effects on these parameters [see reviews by Tobian (293, 294) and by Genest (100)]. Why, then, isn't the feedback mechanism suggested by these observations likewise operative in essential hypertension? A possible clue may be found in Genest's finding of a basic difference in response to angiotensin between normal and hypertensive subjects. Whereas the increased aldosterone excretion induced by angiotensin was accompanied in normal subjects by a fall in glomerular filtration rate, marked sodium retention, and lowering of the urinary sodium to potassium ratio, the glomerular filtration, urinary sodium, and sodium to potassium ratio increased in patients with benign essential hypertension (20, 100). It is tempting to speculate that this paradoxical hemodynamic and electrolytic response to angiotensin may deprive the hypertensive patient of a normal regulatory check on renin production by the kidney, and thereby tend to perpetuate the process. A comparative study of blood angiotensin levels in normal and hypertensive patients, made possible by a recently improved bioassay (24), should contribute to the elucidation of this problem.

LITERATURE CITED

1. Ashmore, J., Cahill, G. F., and Hastings, A. B., *Recent Progr. in Hormone Research*, **16**, 547–73 (1960)
2. Ashmore, J., Stricker, F., Love, W. C., and Kilsheimer, G., *Endocrinology*, **68**, 599–606 (1961)
3. Astwood, E. B., Ed., *Clinical Endocrinology*, *I* (Grune & Stratton, New York, 724 pp., 1960)
4. Axelrod, L. R., and Werthessen, N. T., *Endocrinology*, **68**, 180–84 (1961)
5. Baisset, A., Bessou, P., Cotonat, J., and Montastruc, P., *Compt. rend. soc. biol.*, **153**, 848–52 (1959)
6. Baisset, A., Douste-Blazy, L., and Montastruc, P., *J. physiol. (Paris)*, **51**, 393–94 (1959)
7. Bajusz, E., *Progr. in Neurol. and Psychiat.*, **15**, 233–51 (1960)
8. Bakker, R. F. M., and DeWied, D., *Can. J. Biochem. and Physiol.*, **39**, 23–30 (1961)
9. Bally, P. R., Cahill, G. F., Leboeuf, B., and Renold, A. E., *J. Biol. Chem.*, **235**, 333–36 (1960)
10. Barrett, A. M., and Sayers, G., *Endocrinology*, **62**, 637–45 (1958)
11. Bartter, F. C., and Gann, D. S., *Circulation*, **21**, 1016–23 (1960)
12. Bartter, F. C., Mills, I. H., and Gann, D. S., *J. Clin. Invest.*, **39**, 1330–36 (1960)
13. Bauer, H. G., *J. Nervous Mental Disease*, **128**, 323–38 (1959)
14. Benoit, J., Ed., *Histophysiologie du complexe hypothalamo-hypophysaire* (Séminaire Coll. de France, Chaire d'Histophysiol., Paris, 350 pp., 1961)
15. Berliner, D. L., Keller, N., and

Dougherty, T. F., *Endocrinology*, **68**, 621–32 (1961)
16. Berry, L. J., and Smyth, D. S., *Am. J. Physiol.*, **199**, 407–12 (1960)
17. Birmingham, M. K., and Kurlents, E., *Endocrinology*, **62**, 47–60 (1958)
18. Birmingham, M. K., Kurlents, E., Lane, R., Muhlstock, B., and Traikoy, H., *Can. J. Biochem. and Physiol.*, **38**, 1077–85 (1960)
19. Birmingham, M. K., and Ward, P. J., *J. Biol. Chem.*, **236**, 1661–67 (1961)
20. Biron, P., Chrétien, M., Koiw, E., Nowaczynski, W., and Genest, J., *Proc. Can. Fed. Biol. Soc.*, **4**, 12 (1961)
21. Bohus, B., and Endröczi, E., *Acta Physiol. Acad. Sci. Hung.*, **18**, 179–84 (1960)
22. Bohus, B., and Endröczi, E., *Acta Physiol. Acad. Sci. Hung.*, **18**, 185–89 (1960)
23. Boissonnas, R. A., Guttmann, S., Waller, J. P., and Jaquenoud, P. A., *Experientia*, **12**, 446–48 (1956)
24. Boucher, R., Biron, P., and Genest, J., *Can. J. Biochem. and Physiol.*, **39**, 581–90 (1961)
25. Boulouard, R., *J. physiol. (Paris)*, **52**, 249–50 (1960)
26. Brodish, A., *Acta Endocrinol.*, **35**, Suppl. 51, 35 (1960)
27. Cahill, G. F., Leboeuf, B., and Flinn, R. B., *J. Biol. Chem.*, **235**, 1246–50 (1960)
28. Chauvet, J., and Acher, R., *Ann. endocrinol. (Paris)*, **20**, 111–15 (1959)
29. Christensen, H. N., in *Metabolic Effects of Adrenal Hormones*, 56–68

(Wolstenholme, G. E. W., and O'Connor, M., Eds., J. & A. Churchill, London, 109 pp., 1960)

30. Clayton, G. W., Bell, W. R., and Guillemin, R., *Proc. Soc. Exptl. Med.*, **96**, 777–79 (1957)

31. Cohen, A. I., and Frieden, E. H., *J. Biol. Chem.*, **236**, 765–69 (1961)

32. Cohen, R. B., *Endocrinology*, **68**, 710–15 (1961)

33. Courrier, R., and Guillemin, R., Eds., *Études d'endocrinologie*, **2**, 222–350 (Hermann, Paris, 350 pp., 1961)

34. Cox, G. S., Hodges, J. R., and Vernikos, J., *J. Endocrinol.*, **17**, 177–82 (1958)

35. Coye, R. D., and Donkle, J., *Endocrinology*, **68**, 950–56 (1961)

36. Curri, G., Pellegrini, G., and Zanoboni, A., *Acta Endocrinol.*, **35**, Suppl. 51, 67 (1960)

37. Dailey, R. E., Karickhoff, E. R., Swell, L., Field, H., and Treadwell, C. R., *Proc. Soc. Exptl. Biol. Med.*, **105**, 326–28 (1960)

38. D'Angelo, S. A., *Federation Proc.*, **19**, 51–56 (1960)

39. Daniel, P. M., Pratt, O. E., and Treip, C. S., *J. Physiol. (London)*, **153**, 44–45 (1960)

40. Dasgupta, P. R., and Young, F. G., *Nature*, **182**, 32–33 (1958)

41. Daughaday, W. H., *Physiol. Revs.*, **39**, 885–902 (1959)

42. Daughaday, W. H., Holloszy, J., and Mariz, I. K., *J. Clin. Endocrinol. and Metabolism*, **21**, 53–61 (1961)

43. Daughaday, W. H., and Mariz, I. K., in *Biological Activities of Steroids in Relation to Cancer*, 61–73 (Pincus, G., and Vollmer, E. P., Eds., Academic Press, New York, 530 pp., 1960)

44. Davis, J. O., *Am. J. Med.*, **29**, 486–507 (1960)

45. Davis, J. O., *Recent Progr. in Hormone Research*, **17**, 293–331 (1961)

46. Davis, J. O., Anderson, E., Carpenter, C. C. J., Ayers, C. R., Haymaker, W., and Spence, W. T., *Am. J. Physiol.*, **200**, 437–43 (1961)

47. Davis, J. O., and Ayers, C. R., *Federation Proc.*, **20**, 178 (1961)

48. Davis, J. O., and Carpenter, C. C. J., *Federation Proc.*, **20**, 178 (1961)

49. Davis, J. O., Carpenter, C. C. J., Ayers, C. R., and Bahn, R. C., *Am. J. Physiol.*, **199**, 212–17 (1960)

50. Davis, J. O., Carpenter, C. C. J., Ayers, C. R., Holman, J. E., and Bahn, R. C., *Federation Proc.*, **20**, 178 (1961)

51. Davis, J. O., Carpenter, C. C. J., Ayers, C. R., Holman, J. E., and Bahn, R. C., *J. Clin. Invest.*, **40**, 684–96 (1961)

52. Davis, J. O., Yankopoulos, N. A., Lieberman, F., Holman, J., and Bahn, R. C., *J. Clin. Invest.*, **39**, 765–75 (1960)

53. Dedman, M. L., Farmer, T. H., and Morris, C. J. O. R., *Biochem. J.*, **66**, 166–77 (1957)

54. Dedman, M. L., Farmer, T. H., and Morris, C. J. O. R., *Biochem. J.*, **78**, 348–52 (1961)

55. de Garilhe, M. P., in *Études d'endocrinologie*, **2**, 317–43 (Courrier, R., and Guillemin, R., Eds., Hermann, Paris, 350 pp., 1961)

56. de Garilhe, M. P., Gros, C., Chauvet, J., Fromageot, C., Mialhe-Voloss, C., and Benoit, J., *Biochim. et Biophys. Acta*, **29**, 603–11 (1958)

57. de Garilhe, M. P., Gros, C., Porath, J., and Lindner, E. B., *Experientia*, **16**, 414–15 (1960)

58. de Groot, J., and Harris, G. W., *J. Physiol. (London)*, **111**, 335–46 (1950)

59. de Moor, P., Hendrikx, A., and Hinnekens, M., *J. Clin. Endocrinol. and Metabolism*, **21**, 106–9 (1961)

60. de Moor, P., and Hinnekens, M., *Acta Endocrinol.*, **37**, 1–13 (1961)

61. DeWied, D., *Acta Endocrinol.*, **35**, Suppl. 51, 119 (1960)

62. DeWied, D., *Acta Endocrinol.*, **37**, 279–88 (1961)

63. DeWied, D., *Endocrinology*, **68**, 956–70 (1961)

64. Egdahl, R. H., *Acta Endocrinol.*, **35**, Suppl. 51, 49 (1960)

65. Egdahl, R. H., *Endocrinology*, **66**, 200–16 (1960)

66. Egdahl, R. H., *Abstr. Endocrine Soc., 43rd Meeting*, 1 (New York, 1961)

67. Egdahl, R. H., *Endocrinology*, **68**, 226–31 (1961)

68. Egdahl, R. H., *Endocrinology*, **68**, 574–81 (1961)

69. Eichhorn, J., Halkerston, I. D. K., Feinstein, M., and Hechter, O., *Proc. Soc. Exptl. Biol. Med.*, **103**, 515–17 (1960)

70. Eichhorn, J., Scully, E., Halkerston, I. D. K., and Hechter, O., *Proc. Soc. Exptl. Biol. Med.*, **106**, 153–57 (1961)

71. Eisenstein, A. B., *Endocrinology*, **67**, 97–101 (1960)

72. Eisenstein, A. B., and Hartcroft, P. M., *Endocrinology*, **60**, 634–41 (1957)

73. Emberland, R., *Acta Endocrinol.*, **34**, 69–76 (1960)
74. Endröczi, E., and Lissák, K., *Acta Physiol. Acad. Sci. Hung.*, **17**, 39–51 (1960)
75. Endröczi, E., Lissák, K., Bohus, B., and Kovács, S., *Acta Physiol. Acad. Sci. Hung.*, **16**, 17–22 (1959)
76. Engel, F. L., and Fredericks, J., *Endocrinology*, **64**, 409–14 (1959)
77. Engel, L. L., and Scott, J. F., *Recent Progr. in Hormone Research*, **16**, 79–92 (1960)
78. Farrell, G., *Circulation*, **21**, 1009–15 (1960)
79. Farrell, G., *Acta Endocrinol.*, **34**, Suppl. 50, 57–61 (1960)
80. Farrell, G., *Abstr. Endocrine Soc.*, *43rd Meeting*, 15 (New York, 1961)
81. Feldman, S., van der Heide, C. S., and Porter, R. W., *Am. J. Physiol.*, **196**, 1163–67 (1959)
82. Fisher, J. D., and de Salva, S. J., *Am. J. Physiol.*, **197**, 1263–64 (1959)
83. Fortier, C., *Proc. Soc. Exptl. Biol. Med.*, **100**, 13–16 (1959)
84. Fortier, C., *Proc. Soc. Exptl. Biol. Med.*, **100**, 16–19 (1959)
85. Fortier, C., in *Comparative Endocrinology* (von Euler, U. S., and Heller, H., Eds., Academic Press, New York, In press)
86. Fortier, C., and de Groot, J., *Abstr. 21st Intern. Congr. Physiol. Sci.*, 96 (Buenos Aires, 1959)
87. Fortier, C., and de Groot J., *Progr. in Neurol. and Psychiat.*, **14**, 256–69 (1959)
88. Fortier, C., and de Groot, J., *Am. J. Physiol.*, **196**, 589–92 (1959)
89. Fortier, C., Harris, G. W., and McDonald, I. R., *J. Physiol. (London)*, **136**, 344–64 (1957)
90. Fortier, C., and Ward, D. N., *Can. J. Biochem. and Physiol.*, **36**, 111–18 (1958)
91. Frieden, E. H., Cohen, E. H., and Harper, A. A., *Endocrinology*, **68**, 862–66 (1961)
92. Fukushima, D. K., Bradlow, H. L., Hellman, L., Zumoff, B., and Gallagher, T. F., *J. Biol. Chem.*, **235**, 2246–52 (1960)
93. Gann, D. S., Mills, I. H., Cruz, J. F., Gasper, A. G., and Bartter, F. C., *Proc. Soc. Exptl. Biol. Med.*, **105**, 158–61 (1960)
94. Ganong, W. F., and Forsham, P. H., *Ann. Rev. Physiol.*, **22**, 579–614 (1960)
95. Ganong, W. F., and Mulrow, P. J., *Federation Proc.*, **20**, 177 (1961)
96. Ganong, W. F., Mulrow, P. J., and Cera, G., *Abstr. Endocrine Soc.*, *43rd Meeting*, 14 (New York, 1961)
97. Ganong, W. F., Nolan, A. M., Dowdy, A., and Luetscher, J. A., *Endocrinology*, **68**, 169–71 (1961)
98. Garst, J. B., Shumway, N. P., Schwartz, H., and Farrell, G. L., *J. Clin. Endocrinol. and Metabolism*, **20**, 1351–59 (1960)
99. Gaunt, R., Chart, J. J., and Renzi, A. A., *Science*, **133**, 613–21 (1961)
100. Genest, J., *Can. Med. Assoc. J.*, **84**, 403–19 (1961)
101. Genest, J., Koiw, E., Nowaczynski, W., and Leboeuf, G., *Proc. Soc. Exptl. Biol. Med.*, **97**, 676–79 (1958)
102. Genest, J., Koiw, E., Nowaczynski, W., and Sandor, T., *Circulation*, **20**, 700 (1959)
103. Genest, J., Koiw, E., Nowaczynski, W., and Sandor, T., *Acta Endocrinol.*, **35**, Suppl. 51, 173 (1960)
104. Genest, J., Koiw, E., Nowaczynski, W., and Sandor, T., *Acta Endocrinol.*, **35**, 413–25 (1960)
105. Genest, J., Lemieux, G., Davignon, A., Koiw, E., Nowaczynski, W., and Steyermark, P., *Science*, **123**, 503–4 (1956)
106. Genest, J., Nowaczynski, W., Koiw, E., Sandor, T., and Biron, P., in *Essential Hypertension*, 126–46 (Bock, K. D., and Cottier, P. T., Eds., Springer-Verlag, Berlin, 392 pp., 1960)
107. Girod, C., *Compt. rend. soc. biol.*, **154**, 969–73 (1960)
108. Girolamo, M. D., Rudman, D., Reid, M. B., and Seidman, F., *Endocrinology*, **68**, 457–65 (1961)
109. Giuliani, G., Martini, L., and Pecile, A., *Acta Endocrinol.*, **35**, Suppl. 51, 37 (1960)
110. Glenister, D. W., and Yates, F. E., *Endocrinology*, **68**, 747–58 (1961)
111. Glenn, E. M., Bowman, B. J., Bayer, R. B., and Meyer, C. E., *Endocrinology*, **68**, 386–410 (1961)
112. Glick, D., Ferguson, R. B., Greenberg, L. J., and Halberg, F., *Am. J. Physiol.*, **200**, 811–14 (1961)
113. Glock, G. E., and McLean, P., *Biochem. J.*, **61**, 390–97 (1955)
114. Golden, M., Scully, E., Eichhorn, J., and Hechter, O., *Proc. Soc. Exptl. Biol. Med.*, **106**, 354–56 (1961)
115. Goodner, C. J., and Freinkel, N., *Clin. Research*, **8**, 25 (1960)
116. Grabbe, J., Reddy, J., Ross, E. J., and

Thorn, G. W., *J. Clin. Endocrinol. and Metabolism,* **19,** 1185–91 (1959)

117. Grant, J. K., and Brownie, A. C., *Biochim. et Biophys. Acta,* **18,** 433–34 (1955)

118. Grant, J. K., and Mongkolkul, K., *Biochem. J.,* **71,** 34–38 (1959)

119. Greenberg, L. J., and Glick, D., *J. Biol. Chem.,* **235,** 2744–48 (1960)

120. Greenberg, L. J., and Glick, D., *J. Biol. Chem.,* **235,** 3028–31 (1960)

121. Greenberg, L. J., and Glick, D., *Federation Proc.,* **20,** 178 (1961)

122. Greer, M. A., *Recent Progr. in Hormone Research,* **13,** 67–98 (1957)

123. Gros, C., and de Garilhe, M. P., *Compt. rend. acad. sci.,* **249,** 2234–36 (1959)

124. Gross, F., *Schweiz. med. Wochschr.,* **89,** 1–7 (1959)

125. Grossman, J., Yalow, A. A., and Weston, R. E., *Metabolism, Clin. and Exptl.,* **9,** 528–50 (1960)

126. Guillemin, R., *Endocrinology,* **56,** 248–55 (1955)

127. Guillemin, R., *Diabetes,* **8,** 352–57 (1959)

128. Guillemin, R., *Endocrinology,* **66,** 819–23 (1960)

129. Guillemin, R., *Schweiz. med. Wochschr.,* **90,** 1328–29 (1960)

130. Guillemin, R., in *Études d'endocrinologie,* **2,** 285–308 (Courrier, R., and Guillemin, R., Eds., Hermann, Paris, 350 pp., 1961)

131. Guillemin, R., in *Études d'endocrinologie,* **2,** 309–16 (Courrier, R., and Guillemin, R., Eds., Hermann, Paris, 350 pp. 1961)

132. Guillemin, R., Dear, W. E., and Liebelt, R. A., *Proc. Soc. Exptl. Biol. Med.,* **101,** 394–95 (1959)

133. Guillemin, R., Dear, W. E., Nichols, B., and Lipscomb, H. S., *Proc. Soc. Exptl. Biol. Med.,* **101,** 107–11 (1959)

134. Guillemin, R., Hearn, W. R., Cheek, W. R., and Householder, D. E., *Endocrinology,* **60,** 488–506 (1957)

135. Guillemin, R., and Schally, A. V., *Endocrinology,* **65,** 555–62 (1959)

136. Guillemin, R., Schally, A., Andersen, R., Lipscomb, H., and Long, J., *Compt. rend. acad. sci.,* **250,** 4462–64 (1960)

137. Guttmann, S., and Boissonnas, R. A., *Helv. Chim. Acta,* **42,** 1257–64 (1959)

138. Hagen, A. A., and Troop, R. C., *Endocrinology,* **67,** 194–203 (1960)

139. Halberstron, I. D. K., Eichhorn, J.,

and Hechter, O., *Arch. Biochem. Biophys.,* **85,** 287–89 (1959)

140. Harding, B. W., Rutherford, E. R., and Nelson, D. H., *Abstr. Endocrine Soc., 43rd Meeting,* 45 (New York, 1961)

141. Harris, G. W., in *Handbook of Physiology, Section 1, Neurophysiology II,* 1007–39 (Field, J., Magoun, H. W., and Hall, V. E., Eds., Am. Physiol. Soc., Washington, D. C., 1439 pp., 1960)

142. Harris, I., *Brit. Med. Bull.,* **16,** 189–95 (1960)

143. Haynes, R. C., *J. Biol. Chem.,* **233,** 1220–22 (1958)

144. Haynes, R. C., and Berthet, L., *J. Biol. Chem.,* **225,** 115–24 (1957)

145. Haynes, R. C., Koritz, S. B., and Péron, F. G., *J. Biol. Chem.,* **234,** 1421–23 (1959)

146. Haynes, R. C., Sutherland, E. W., and Rall, T. W., *Recent Progr. in Hormone Research,* **16,** 121–39 (1960)

147. Hechter, O., *Acta Endocrinol.,* **34,** Suppl. 50, 167–70 (1960)

148. Hechter, O., and Lester, G., *Recent Progr. in Hormone Research,* **16,** 139–87 (1960)

149. Herbst, A. L., Yates, F. E., Glenister, D. W., and Urquhart, J., *Endocrinology,* **67,** 222–38 (1960)

150. Herman, M. S., and Ramey, E. R., *Endocrinology,* **67,** 650–57 (1960)

151. Herrera, M. G., and Renold, A. E., *Biochim. et Biophys. Acta,* **44,** 165–67 (1960)

152. Hess, M., Corrigan, J. J., and Hodak, J. A., *Endocrinology,* **68,** 548–52 (1961)

153. Hess, M., Corrigan, J. J., and Hodak, J. A., *Proc. Soc. Exptl. Biol. Med.,* **106,** 420–22 (1961)

154. Hilton, J. G., Kruesi, O. R., Nedeljkovic, R. I., and Scian, L. F., *Endocrinology,* **68,** 908–13 (1961)

155. Hilton, J. G., Scian, L. F., Westermann, C. D., Nakano, J., and Kruesi, O. R., *Endocrinology,* **67,** 298–311 (1960)

156. Hodges, J. R., and Vernikos, J., *Acta Endocrinol.,* **30,** 188–96 (1959)

157. Hodges, J. R., and Vernikos, J., *J. Physiol. (London),* **150,** 683–93 (1960)

158. Hofmann, K., Yajima, H., Yanaihara, N., Liu, T., and Lande, S., *J. Am. Chem. Soc.,* **83,** 487–89 (1961)

159. Hokin, M. R., Hokin, L. E., Saffran, M., Schally, A. V., and Zimmerman, B. U., *J. Biol. Chem.,* **233,** 811–14 (1958)

160. Hollenberg, C. H., Raben, M. S., and Astwood, E. B., *Endocrinology*, **68**, 589–98 (1961)

161. Holmes, R. L., Hughes, E. B., and Zuckerman, S., *J. Endocrinol.*, **18**, 305–16 (1959)

162. Holub, D. A., Kitay, J. I., and Jailer, J. W., *Endocrinology*, **65**, 968–71 (1959)

163. Holub, D. A., Wallace, E. Z., and Jailer, J. W., *J. Clin. Endocrinol. and Metabolism*, **20**, 1294–96 (1960)

164. Hume, D. M., and Egdahl, R. H., *Ann. N.Y. Acad. Sci.*, **80**, 435–44 (1959)

165. Hume, D. M., and Jackson, B. T., *Federation Proc.*, **18**, 481 (1959)

166. Ingle, D., *Am. Scientist*, **47**, 413–26 (1959)

167. Izzo, J. L., and Glasser, S. R., *Endocrinology*, **68**, 189–98 (1961)

168. Jeanrenaud, B., and Renold, A. E., *J. Biol. Chem.*, **235**, 2217–23 (1960)

169. Kaplan, S. A., and Nagareda, C. S., *Am. J.Physiol.*, **200**, 1035–38 (1961)

170. Kappeler, H., and Schwyzer, R., *Experientia*, **16**, 415–17 (1960)

171. Keller, A., Piotti, L. E., and Romani, J. D., *Ann. endocrinol. (Paris)*, **22**, 82–86 (1961)

172. Kelly, T. L., Nielson, E. D., Johnson, R. B., and Vestling, C. S., *J. Biol. Chem.*, **212**, 545–54 (1955)

173. Kenney, F. T., *Biochem. Biophys. Research Communs.*, **2**, 333–35 (1960)

174. Kerppola, W., *Endocrinology*, **67**, 252–63 (1960)

175. Kerppola, W., and Pitkanen, E., *Endocrinology*, **67**, 162–65 (1960)

176. Kitay, J. I., *Endocrinology*, **68**, 818–24 (1961)

177. Kitay, J. I., Holub, D. A., and Jailer, J. W., *Endocrinology*, **64**, 475–82 (1959)

178. Knigge, K. M., *Federation Proc.*, **19**, 45–51 (1960)

179. Knigge, K. M., *Federation Proc.*, **20**, 185 (1961)

180. Koritz, S. B., *Federation Proc.*, **20**, 179 (1961)

181. Koritz, S. B., and Péron, F. G., *J. Biol. Chem.*, **230**, 343–52 (1958)

182. Koritz, S. B., and Péron, F. G., *J. Biol. Chem.*, **234**, 3122–28 (1959)

183. Korner, A., in *Metabolic Effects of Adrenal Hormones*, 38–56 (Wolstenholme, G. E. W., and O'Connor, M., Eds., Ciba Foundation Study Group No. 6, J. & A. Churchill, London, 109 pp., 1960)

184. Korner, A., *J. Endocrinol.*, **21**, 177–89 (1960)

185. Kostyo, J. L., and Engel, F. L., *Endocrinology*, **67**, 708–17 (1960)

186. Kovács, K., David, M. A., and Weisz, P., *Med. Exptl.*, **3**, 113–16 (1960)

187. Kruskemper, H. L., *Acta Endocrinol.*, **28**, 373–83 (1958)

188. Kruskemper, H. L., *Acta Endocrinol.*, **36**, 327–34 (1961)

189. Kwaan, H. C., and Bartelstone, H. J., *Endocrinology*, **65**, 982–85 (1959)

190. Lanman, J. T., and Dinerstein, J., *Endocrinology*, **67**, 1–9 (1960)

191. Laragh, J. H., Angers, M., Kelly, W. G., and Lieberman, S., *J. Am. Med. Assoc.*, **174**, 234–40 (1960)

192. Laragh, J. H., Ulick, S., Januszewicz, V., Deming, Q. B., Kelly, W. G., and Lieberman, S., *J. Clin. Invest.*, **39**, 1091–1106 (1960)

193. Leboeuf, B., and Cahill, G. F., *J. Biol. Chem.*, **236**, 41–46 (1961)

194. Levine, S., *Acta Endocrinol.*, **35**, Suppl. 51, 41 (1960)

195. Li, C. H., *Lab. Invest.*, **8**, 574–87 (1959)

196. Li, C. H., *Science*, **129**, 969–70 (1959)

197. Li, C. H., *J. Biol. Chem.*, **235**, 1383–85 (1960)

198. Li, C. H., and Bertsch, L., *J. Biol. Chem.*, **235**, 2638–41 (1960)

199. Li, C. H., Dixon, J. S., and Chung, D., *J. Am. Chem. Soc.*, **80**, 2587–88 (1958)

200. Li, C. H., Dixon, J. S., and Chung, D., *Biochim. et Biophys. Acta*, **46**, 324–34 (1961)

201. Li, C. H., Meienhofer, E., Schnabel, E., Chung, D., Lo, T., and Ramachandran, J., *J. Am. Chem. Soc.*, **82**, 5760–62 (1960)

202. Li, C. H., Schnabel, E., Chung, D., and Lo, T., *Nature*, **189**, 143 (1961)

203. Liddle, G. W., *J. Clin. Endocrinol. and Metabolism*, **20**, 1539–60 (1960)

204. Lissák, K., and Endröczi, E., *Die Neuroendokrine Steuerung der Adaptationstätigkeit* (Ungarischen Akad. Wissenschaften, Budapest, 172 pp., 1960)

205. Long, C. N. H., Fry, E. G., and Bonnycastle, M., *Acta Endocrinol.*, **35**, Suppl. 51, 819–20 (1960)

206. Long, C. N. H., Katzin, B., and Fry, E. G., *Endocrinology*, **26**, 309–44 (1940)

207. Long, C. N. H., Smith, O. K., and Fry, E. G., in *Metabolic Effects of Adrenal Hormones*, 4–19 (Wolstenholme, G. E. W. and O'Connor, M., Eds., Ciba Foundation Study Group No. 6, J. & A. Churchill, London, 109 pp., 1960)

208. Lucis, O. J., Dyrenfurth, I., and

Venning, E. H., *Can. J. Biochem. and Physiol.*, **39**, 901–13 (1961)

209. Lucis, O. J., and Venning, E. H., *Can. J. Biochem. and Physiol.*, **38**, 1069–76 (1960)

210. Lynn, W. S., MacLeod, R. M., and Brown, R. H., *J. Biol. Chem.*, **235**, 1904–11 (1960)

211. Macchi, I. A., and Scotch, D. S., *Proc. Soc. Exptl. Biol. Med.*, **106**, 324–27 (1961)

212. Manchester, K. L., Randle, P. J., and Young, F. G., *J. Endocrinol.*, **18**, 395–408 (1959)

213. Martini, L., Pecile, A., and Giuliani, G., *Mem. Soc. Endocrinol. No. 9*, 34–52 (1960)

214. Martinovitch, P. N., Bacq, Z. M., Pavitch, D., and Simitch-Sladitch, D., *Arch. intern. physiol. et biochim.*, **69**, 9–18 (1961)

215. Mason, J. W., in *Reticular Formation of the Brain*, 645–62 (Jasper, H. H., et. al., Eds., Little, Brown & Co., Boston, Mass., 766 pp., 1958)

216. Melby, J. C., Egdahl, R. H., Story, J. L., and Spink, W. W., *Endocrinology*, **67**, 389–93 (1960)

217. Moll, J., *Z. Zellforsch.*, **49**, 515–24 (1959)

218. Moll, J., *Acta Endocrinol.*, **34**, 19–26 (1960)

219. Mulrow, P. J., and Ganong, W. F., *Yale J. Biol. and Med.*, **33**, 386–95 (1961)

220. Mulrow, P. J., and Ganong, W. F., *J. Clin. Invest.*, **40**, 579–85 (1961)

221. Munck, A., *Biochim. et Biophys. Acta*, **48**, 618–20 (1961)

222. Munck, A., *Endocrinology*, **68**, 178–80 (1961)

223. Munck, A., and Koritz, S. B., *Acta Endocrinol.*, **35**, 821–22 (1960)

224. Munson, P. L., *Ann. Rev. Pharmacol.*, **1**, 315–51 (1961)

225. McCann, S. M., and Haberland, P., *Proc. Soc. Exptl. Biol. Med.*, **102**, 319–25 (1959)

226. McCarthy, J. L., Corley, R. C., and Zarrow, M. X., *Proc. Soc. Exptl. Biol. Med.*, **104**, 787–89 (1960)

227. McGuire, J. S., Jr., and Tomkins, G. M., *J. Biol. Chem.*, **234**, 791–94 (1959)

228. Nauta, W. J. H., *Physiol. Revs.*, **40**, 102–4 (1960)

229. Nauta, W. J. H., and Kuypers, H. G. J. M., in *Reticular Formation of the Brain*, 3–30 (Jasper, H. H., et al., Eds., Little, Brown & Co., Boston, Mass., 766 pp., 1958)

230. Nowaczynski, W., Koiw, E., and Genest, J., *J. Endocrinol. and Metabolism*, **20**, 1503–14 (1960)

231. Okinaka, S., Ibayashi, H., Motohashi, K., Fujita, T., Yoshida, S., and Ohsawa, N., *Endocrinology*, **67**, 319–25 (1960)

232. Okinaka, S., Ibayashi, H., Motohashi, K., Fujita, T., Yoshida, S., Ohsawa, N., and Murakawa, S., *Acta Endocrinol.*, **35**, Suppl. 51, 43 (1960)

233. Orti, E., and Ralli, E. P., *Am. J. Physiol.*, **199**, 43–48 (1960)

234. Page, I. H., and Bumpus, F. M., *Physiol. Revs.*, **41**, 331–90 (1961)

235. Perek, M., and Eilat, A., *J. Endocrinol.*, **20**, 251–55 (1960)

236. Péron, F. G., *Endocrinology*, **66**, 458–69 (1960)

237. Péron, F. G., *Abstr. Endocrine Soc.*, *43rd Meeting*, 44–45 (New York, 1961)

238. Péron, F. G., and Koritz, S. B., *J. Biol. Chem.*, **235**, 1625–28 (1960)

239. Péron, F. G., Moncloa, F., and Dorfman, R. I., *Endocrinology*, **67**, 379–89 (1960)

240. Perry, W. F., and Bowen, H. F., *Am. J. Physiol.*, **184**, 59–62 (1956)

241. Pincus, G., and Vollmer, E. P., Eds., *Biological Activities of Steroids in Relation to Cancer* (Academic Press, New York, 530 pp., 1960)

242. Porter, J. C., and Jones, J. C., *Endocrinology*, **58**, 62–67 (1956)

243. Porter, J. C., and Rumsfeld, H. W., *Endocrinology*, **58**, 359–64 (1956)

244. Porter, J. C., and Rumsfeld, H. W., *Endocrinology*, **64**, 948–54 (1959)

245. Rasina, L. G., *Problems Med. Chem. (USSR)*, **6**, 136–45 (1960)*

246. Reck, D. C., and Fortier, C., *Proc. Soc. Exptl. Biol. Med.*, **104**, 610–13 (1960)

247. Reich, M., and McDonald, I. R., *J. Endocrinol.*, **21**, 387–400 (1961)

248. Reshef, L., and Shapiro, B., *Metabolism, Clin. and Exptl.*, **9**, 551–55 (1960)

249. Roche, J., Michel, R., and Jouan, P., *Compt. rend. soc. biol.*, **153**, 255–58 (1959)

250. Roche, J., Michel, R., and Jouan, P., *Compt. rend. soc. biol.*, **153**, 1147–51 (1959)

251. Rochefort, G. J., Rosenberger, J., and Saffran, M., *J. Physiol. (London)*, **146**, 105–16 (1959)

252. Romanelli, R., Biancalana, D., and Materazzi, F., *Acta Endocrinol.*, **35**, Suppl. 51, 171 (1960)

253. Romani, J. D., Keller, A., and Piotti,

L. E., *Ann. endocrinol. (Paris)*, **21**, 612–16 (1960)

254. Rosenfeld, G., *Am. J. Physiol.*, **200**, 477–82 (1961)

255. Rosenkrantz, H., *Endocrinology*, **64**, 355–63 (1959)

256. Rosenkrantz, H., and Laferte, R. O., *Endocrinology*, **66**, 832–41 (1960)

257. Ross, E. J., and McLean, E. K., *Acta Endocrinol.*, **35**, Suppl. 51, 69 (1960)

258. Royce, P. C., and Sayers, G., *Proc. Soc. Exptl. Biol. Med.*, **98**, 677–80 (1958)

259. Royce, P. C., and Sayers, G., *Proc. Soc. Exptl. Biol. Med.*, **103**, 447–50 (1960)

260. Rudman, D., Seidman, F., and Reid, M. B., *Proc. Soc. Exptl. Biol. Med.*, **103**, 315–20 (1960)

261. Saffran, M., *Can. J. Biochem. and Physiol.*, **37**, 319–31 (1959)

262. Saffran, M., and Schally, A. V., *Can. J. Biochem. and Physiol.*, **33**, 408–15 (1955)

263. Saffran, M., Schally, A. V., and Benfey, B. G., *Endocrinology*, **57**, 439–45 (1955)

264. Saffran, M., and Vogt, M., *J. Physiol. (London)*, **151**, 123–30 (1960)

265. Sakiz, E., *Compt. rend. soc. biol.*, **153**, 267–69 (1959)

266. Sandberg, A. A., Slaunwhite, W. R., and Antoniades, H. N., *Recent Progr. in Hormone Research*, **13**, 209–60 (1957)

267. Sayers, G., *Acta Endocrinol.*, **34**, Suppl. 50, 25–31 (1960)

268. Schally, A. V., and Guillemin, R., *Proc. Soc. Exptl. Biol. Med.*, **100**, 138–39 (1959)

269. Schally, A. V., and Guillemin, R., *Texas Repts. Biol. and Med.*, **18**, 133–46 (1960)

270. Schally, A. V., and Guillemin, R., *Acta Endocrinol.*, **35**, Suppl. 51, 63 (1960)

271. Schotz, M. C., Masson, G. M. C., and Page, I. H., *Proc. Soc. Exptl. Biol. Med.*, **101**, 159–61 (1959)

272. Shuster, S., *J. Endocrinol.*, **21**, 171–76 (1960)

273. Shuster, S., *Acta Endocrinol.*, **35**, Suppl. 51, 61 (1960)

274. Skelton, F. R., and Hyde, P. M., *Federation Proc.*, **20**, 181 (1961)

275. Slater, J. D. H., Casper, A. G. T., Dolan, C. S., and Bartter, F. C., *Clin. Research*, **9**, 209 (1961)

276. Slaunwhite, W. R., and Sandberg, A. A., *J. Clin. Invest.*, **38**, 384–91 (1959)

277. Slusher, M. A., *Endocrinology*, **63**, 412–19 (1958)

278. Slusher, M. A., *Endocrinology*, **67**, 347–53 (1960)

279. Slusher, M. A., and Hyde, J. E., *Endocrinology*, **68**, 773–82 (1961)

280. Slusher, M. A., and Roberts, S., *Endocrinology*, **67**, 873–75 (1961)

281. Smelik, P. G., *Autonomic Nervous Involvement in Stress-Induced ACTH Secretion* (N. V. Drukkerij V./H., H. Born, Assen, Netherlands, 80 pp., 1959)

282. Spiro, M. J., and Ball, E. G., *J. Biol. Chem.*, **236**, 225–30 (1961)

283. Spiro, M. J., and Ball, E. G., *J. Biol. Chem.*, **236**, 231–35 (1961)

284. Steelman, S. L., and Smith, W. W., *Acta Endocrinol.*, **33**, 67–72 (1960)

285. Sweat, M. L., and Bryson, M. J., *Biochim. et Biophys. Acta*, **44**, 217–23 (1960)

286. Sweat, M. L., and Lipscomb, M. D., *J. Am. Chem. Soc.*, **77**, 5185–87 (1955)

287. Sydnor, K. L., and Sayers, G., *Endocrinology*, **55**, 621–36 (1954)

288. Taylor, A. N., *Acta Endocrinol.*, **35**, Suppl. 51, 73 (1960)

289. Telegdy, G., and Endröczi, E., *Acta Physiol. Acad. Sci. Hung.*, **16**, 23–25 (1959)

290. Telford, J. M., and West, G. B., *Brit. J. Pharmacol.*, **15**, 532–39 (1960)

291. Tepperman, J., and Tepperman, H. M., *Am. J. Physiol.*, **193**, 55–64 (1958)

292. Timmer, R. F., Sanders, A. E., and Rennels, E. G., *Texas Repts. Biol. and Med.*, **17**, 632–38 (1959)

293. Tobian, L., *Physiol. Revs.*, **40**, 280–312 (1960)

294. Tobian, L., *Ann. Internal Med.*, **52**, 395–410 (1960)

295. Ulstrom, R. A., Colle, E., Burley, J., and Gunville, R., *J. Clin. Endocrinol. and Metabolism*, **20**, 1080–94 (1960)

296. Van der Vies, J., Bakker, R. F. M., and DeWied, D., *Acta Endocrinol.*, **34**, 513–23 (1960)

297. Van Dyke, R. A., Johnson, B. C., and Wolf, G., *Federation Proc.*, **19**, 412 (1960)

298. Van Dyke, R. A., Wolf, G., and Johnson, B., *Biochem. Biophys. Research Communs.*, **3**, 123–26 (1960)

299. Venning, E. H., Dyrenfurth, I., Dossitor, J. B., and Beck, J. C., *Circulation*, **23**, 168–76 (1961)

300. Ward, P. J., and Birmingham, M. K., *Biochem. J.*, **76**, 269–79 (1960)

301. Warren, J. C., and Salhanick, H. A., *Proc. Soc. Exptl. Biol. Med.*, **105**, 624–28 (1960)

302. Warter, J., Schwartz, J., and Bloch, R., *Presse méd.*, **68**, 5–6 (1960)

303. Weber, E. J., and Hearn, W. R., *Federation Proc.*, **20**, 186 (1961)

304. White, J. E., and Engel, F. L., *J. Clin. Invest.*, **37**, 1556–63 (1958)

305. Willmer, J. S., *Can. J. Biochem. and Physiol.*, **38**, 1095–1104 (1960)

306. Willmer, J. S., and Foster, T. S., *Can. J. Biochem. and Physiol.*, **38**, 1387–92 (1960)

307. Willmer, J. S., and Foster, T. S., *Can. J. Biochem. and Physiol.*, **38**, 1393–97 (1960)

308. Winternitz, W. W., and Forrest, W. G., *Am. J. Physiol.*, **199**, 1059–63 (1960)

309. Wool, I. G., *Am. J. Physiol.*, **199**, 715–19 (1960)

310. Wool, I. G., and Weinshelbaum, E. I., *Am. J. Physiol.*, **197**, 1089–92 (1959)

311. Wool, I. G., and Weinshelbaum, E. I., *Am. J. Physiol.*, **198**, 360–62 (1960)

312. Wool, I. G., and Weinshelbaum, E. I., *Am. J. Physiol.*, **198**, 1111–15 (1960)

313. Wurtman, R. J., Altschule, M. D., Greep, R. O., Falk, J. L., and Grave, G., *Am. J. Physiol.*, **199**, 1109–11 (1960)

314. Yielding, K. L., Tomkins, G. M., Munday, J. S., and Curran, J. F., *Biochem. Biophys. Research Communs.*, **2**, 303–6 (1960)

315. Young, F. G., in *Adrenal Cortex*, 97–162 (Ralli, E. P., Ed., Trans. Fifth Conf. Josiah Macy, Jr., Foundation, New York, 187 pp., 1954)

* English translation will be announced in *Technical Translations*, issued by the Office of Technical Services, US Department of Commerce, and will be made available by the Photoduplication Service, Library of Congress, and by the SLA Translation Center at the John Crerar Library, Chicago, Illinois.

HIGHER NERVOUS FUNCTION: THE PHYSIOLOGICAL BASES OF MEMORY[1]

By J. A. Deutsch

Departments of Psychology and Psychiatry, Stanford University, Stanford, California

This review will be devoted to some physiological aspects of the problems of memory. The storing of information is one of the most remarkable achievements of the nervous system, and recent work in the laboratory has given us fresh material for speculation about this capacity. However, it is true here that old clinical observations present some of the most interesting problems, as they often do. Accordingly, we shall begin with the manifestations of retrograde amnesia, which pose the problem of consolidation of the memory trace in a most dramatic manner. We shall then consider this problem as it has been studied in the laboratory and the methods which apparently increase or decrease the rate of this consolidation. The relevance of clinical material is once again introduced when we turn to the role of epileptiform phenomena and disorders of consolidation of the memory trace. We then ask what is known about the physical change which underlies memory. A further section of the review is devoted to the split-brain preparation in its relation to memory storage. In the last two sections, electrical manipulations and manifestations of the central nervous system are briefly considered as they could be said to assume the functions of signal or memory trace in the nervous system.

Retrograde Amnesia and Consolidation of the Memory Trace

That some kind of consolidation of memory occurs is suggested by retrograde amnesia in man. In such an amnesia, of which the Korsakoff syndrome is an example, recent memories are lost, while old memories are preserved. The loss of memory may gradually extend backwards to obliterate the memory of progressively more distant episodes, until perhaps only childhood scenes are preserved. Retrograde amnesia may occur as a result of head injury, electroshock therapy, cerebral anoxia, and such mishaps as carbon monoxide poisoning. An extensive review by Russell & Nathan (76) showed conclusively that it was memories of recent events which were lost, even if the memories of recent events were important. Several years of recent memories may be entirely lost, while events further back, however trivial, may be unimpaired and easily remembered. Similarly, recovery occurs not in order of importance, but in order of time. The less recent memories return first. It would therefore seem that the more recent a memory the more vulnerable it is. This suggests that the physical change initiated at the time of registration or learning "consolidates" and continues to do so. The simplest assumption to account for this consolidation is that the physical change which has been initiated continues to grow in magnitude.

[1] The survey of literature pertaining to this review was concluded in October 1961.

The loss of more recent memory would then be accounted for by two different hypotheses. The first is that the physical change initiated by the act of registration or learning dissipates with time, being progressively dissipated or reversed by some biochemical or other change. It does not seem that an explanation can be so simple. If amnesia were in all cases due to a reversal of the physical change in memory, it would be difficult to account for the recovery of memory. If memory can return, then it seems that some physical change underlying memory must have been preserved, and one sufficient to allow a reconstruction of the normal change. It is simpler to suppose that the normal change has itself remained. It could be said that the normal change has remained but has diminished until it is below the threshold necessary for access, that it has become too faint. Nevertheless, it could further be argued that during recovery this change could increase again in magnitude and raise itself above the threshold for recall. This argument is not regarded as plausible because it would imply a very large range of magnitudes below threshold. It is difficult to believe that if a memory change relating to five years ago is below threshold of accessibility, a memory change relating to a month ago has not disappeared altogether in a retrograde amnesia. A second hypothesis to account for the evidence would be as follows. There are degrees of magnitude of memory change which vary with time of storage. That is, some process set in motion by the act of registration does increase with time as the first hypothesis supposed. But an amnesic episode does not diminish the accumulated memory change. Instead it is supposed that some biochemical abnormality prevents the memory change from carrying out its usual function, canceling out, as it were, the effect of the memory change but leaving the physical memory change intact. If the accumulated memory change is large, a greater abnormality is necessary to counteract its normal function. In such a way, we may understand why some amnesias are retrograde and why recovery of memory is often possible. Whatever hypothesis we may finally wish to adopt, the conclusion that a memory change consolidates seems inescapable. To the discussion of such consolidation in a more experimental setting we shall now turn.

The Consolidation Hypothesis

It has been suggested by Muller & Pilzecker (60) and Hebb (30) that the physiological change leading to permanent learning becomes gradually consolidated as a result of the perseveration of neural activity after a learning trial. Hebb (30), for instance, supposes that reverberation of firing in neural chains leads to a permanent modification of the excitability of one neuron by another. This reverberating activity in a system continues for some time and gives rise to a permanent growth change. It would, on this theory, be expected that, if the temporary reverberation were cut short the permanent change would not take place, or would take place to a lesser extent. Consequently, permanent learning should show a decrement if the process of consolidation is prevented.

Whether the notion of reverberating neural chains is correct or not, it may still be the case that it takes some time for a "learning" change to become permanently established. To determine whether this is true, we should be able to impair or improve learning by subjecting the nervous system to different types of treatment at various times after a learning trial is concluded. And agents which will produce such changes in learning ability have indeed been discovered. It has been found that the administration of electroconvulsive shock after a learning trial does impair learning [Duncan (19); Thompson & Dean (93); Thomson et al. (92)]. Similarity to the effects of electroconvulsive shock has been claimed for the effects of hypoxia [Thompson & Pryer (94)] and the administration of depressant drugs [Leukel (41); Pearlman et al. (69)]. Narcosis induced by heat in goldfish at various intervals after learning also produces learning losses which are the more severe, the closer the narcosis to the preceding learning [Cerf & Otis (9)].

It has been possible to demonstrate, by use of electroconvulsive shock, that the closer a seizure is to the end of a preceding learning trial, the more severe the learning loss. It has also been shown that the effect cannot be attributed to possible punishing effects of electroconvulsive shock, because the same shock applied across the hindlegs of rats under the same conditions produces no such decrement of learning [Duncan (19)] except at the shortest interval used (20 sec). Thomson et al. (92) have demonstrated different effects of electroconvulsive shock on learning in descendants of the Tryon maze-bright strain and those of the maze-dull strain of rats. In the maze-dull strain, electroconvulsive shock produces a learning decrement after a much longer interval than that observed in the maze-bright strain. This evidence indicates to Thomson et al. that the process of consolidation takes a longer time in the Tryon maze-dull strain. Such results are of particular interest because it has been shown in McGaugh's laboratory (46) that the maze-dull strain is only inferior to the maze-bright in learning mazes if the trials are massed. If the trials are spaced, the difference in learning rate between the two strains disappears. It is, of course, possible that such results are only coincidental. It could be argued that the maze-dull strain is in some way more sensitive to a given level of electric shock. Against this argument there is the finding of Woolley et al. (97) that the maze-bright animals have lower thresholds in terms of current for seizures than the maze-dull rats, but such an argument is not conclusive because the threshold being measured is for seizure and not for effects on memory processes.

It seems from the results on shock administered after learning trials that such administration has no effect if the delay exceeds one hour. Animals receiving shock after such a delay do not perform more poorly than un-shocked controls. So it would seem from this evidence that the process of fixing or consolidation of the change occurring in learning tapers off at around one hour.

Further evidence on the process of consolidation comes from the injection of anesthetic drugs administered to rats at various times after a learning trial. Leukel (41) found some impairment in learning in a water maze when thiopental was injected intraperitoneally one minute after each daily trial. However, if the injection was made thirty minutes after the end of each trial, no such effect was noted. Pearlman *et al.* (69) have studied the effects of pentobarbital and ether administered after different intervals at the end of the learning trial. They trained rats to press a lever for a reward of water. After each animal had reached a certain criterion it received an electric shock through the lever. Administration of the drugs occurred after this single learning experience. An attempt to produce equal amounts of anesthesia in all groups was made. Retention tests were made twenty-four hours after learning. There was little or no effect if ether was aministered at an interval of 10 minutes after the learning trial. If the ether was administered after ten seconds, the animals would press the lever at 30 per cent of their initial rate. After five minutes, the rate would fall to 17 per cent. Pentobarbital had a more profound and long lasting effect. After a 10-second interval, the rate of lever pressing was 76 per cent of the previous rate, which means that memory of the shock was almost obliterated. When treatment with the pentobarbital was postponed for ten minutes, the rate of lever pressing was only 23 per cent of the previous level. After an interval of twenty minutes, memory for the shock was intact, as the rate of bar pressing was only 1 per cent of the previous level.

On the basis of their experimental findings, Coons & Miller (17) have recently put forward an ingenious argument about the effects of electroconvulsive shock on the retention of a habit. They point out that the work demonstrating "loss of memory" for a given habit after electroconvulsive shock is vitiated by the fact that, if the shock were felt, it would produce avoidance of a response which could be mistaken for amnesia in regard to that response. Accordingly, these workers used a somewhat complex design in which electroconvulsive shock, if felt, would facilitate learning. The results of their study support their contention. However, more recent results [Abt *et al.* (1) using ether, McGaugh (46) using electroconvulsive shock, and Pearlman *et al.* (69) using anesthetic drugs to produce amnesia] do not support Coons and Miller's findings. Creating a simpler situation, Abt *et al.* (1) and McGaugh (46) place a rat on a small restrictive platform raised slightly above a much larger platform. Very shortly the rat steps off the small platform, and it obtains an electric shock from the large platform. Under these conditions, when these animals are placed on the small platform a second time, they stay there even when no amnesic agent has been applied. If an amnesic agent is applied quickly after the animal steps off the small platform and obtains a shock, the animal steps off the platform again when placed on it a second time. The effect of the amnesic agent diminishes, as it did in the studies already quoted, when application is postponed until after the crucial response. In this situation, effects of shock to the feet and of clectroconvulsive shock should summate if the animal is avoiding the electroshock. The same argument could be applied to the more complex situation devised by Pearlman *et al.* (69) when an animal "forgot" that it had been punished after pressing a lever. In all these cases the amnesic agent, instead of increasing fear or avoidance, produced what is most plausibly interpreted as an amnesia.

Not only is it possible to impair learning by various procedures after a training trial, but it seems that it is also possible to improve learning as we might expect if the consolidation hypothesis is correct. McGaugh and co-workers have demonstrated in an impressive series of studies that administration of various stimulant drugs, such as strychnine and picrotoxin, both before and after a training trial, increases the rate at which learning proceeds.

It is the evidence that learning can be improved with injections of stimulants after a training trial which is of the greater interest here. Any effect of improved learning that is associated with injections which take place before the trial could be attributed to an increase of motivation, alertness, or some other such factor, not necessarily connected with the process of storage *per se*. On the other hand, injection of a stimulant after the completion of a trial makes it much more likely that any observed improvement of learning is caused by the drug. Of course, it could still be the case that the drug's action persisted until the next batch of trials. However, McGaugh (46) has shown that the closer the injection to the previous trial, the greater the improvement in performance on the succeeding trial. If the drug affected some process occurring during a learning trial and not one occurring immediately thereafter, then we should expect the opposite result. The further the injection from the previous day's trial, the greater the likely influence of the drugs on the succeeding day's test. So, if we obtain less effect with an injection closer to the succeeding day's test than with one which is nearer the previous day's trials, we may conclude that the effect of the drug was on some process occurring and diminishing after a day's trial.

McGaugh and co-workers (47) have also found, in their two strains of rats, striking differences in the facilitative effects of drugs on learning which can be compared with those differences they have already found in reactions to electroconvulsive shock (see above p. 261). They used a newly synthesized compound (1757 1.S.) similar in effect, but not in structure, to strychnine. This was injected ten minutes before daily massed trials in a complex alley maze. They found that the descendants of the Tryon maze-dull animals which were injected with the drug showed a significant improvement over controls of the same strain which were not injected with this drug. On the other hand, no facilitation of learning was found in the descendants of the maze-bright animals. The number of errors these animals made was not lower than that of controls of the same strain which had not been injected with 1757 1.S. It is interesting that without the drug there was a large difference between maze-dull and maze-bright strains in the mean number of errors: for the maze-bright strain it was 12.86 (S.D., 4.64), whereas for the maze-dull it was 33.15 (S.D., 18.12). When we compare the two strains under the influence of the drug, we find that the mean number of errors for the maze-bright animals is 15.71 (S.D., 8.94) and that of the maze-dull, 17.33 (S.D., 10.30). In other words, when the drug is used, the difference between the strains under massed conditions of learning tends to disappear. As noted above, the maze-dull strain is only inferior in learning to the maze-bright when the trials are massed.

If injections of a stimulant abolish the difference between the maze-bright and -dull rats under massed conditions by leading to an improvement of the maze-dull, we might naturally expect that the maze-dull strain would actually surpass the maze-bright after stimulant treatment under special conditions of learning. This is what has been found [Breen & McGaugh (5)]. In this study, the rats were given an injection of the stimulant picrotoxin

TABLE I

Effect of Picrotoxin on Maze Learning

(M, Mean Number of Errors Made on Trials 2 to 7; S.D., Standard Deviation of Mean; N, Number of Animals)

Strain	Control group 0.9% saline			Low-dose 0.75 mg/kg			Medium-dose 1.0 mg/kg			High-dose 1.25 mg/kg		
	N	M	S.D.	N	M	S.D.	N	M	S.D.	N	M	S.D.
Maze-bright	10	26.5	4.48	10	25.6	8.67	10	25.9	5.94	12	20.2	5.35
Maze-dull	10	22.2	2.99	10	16.6	9.41	11	14.5	7.28	11	13.8	4.57

after each day's trial (only one trial was given each day). Three different levels of dosage were used. As can be seen from Table I, the maze-dull rats under the drug's influence were superior to the maze-bright animals.

It is tempting to suppose with McGaugh that the observed differences in the effects of electroconvulsive shock, stimulants, and distribution of practice on the maze-dull and maze-bright animals are caused by a difference in the rate of consolidation of the neural trace. However, there are difficulties in this view which further research may resolve. For instance, it is difficult to see why the maze-dull animals should actually surpass the maze-bright animals in rate of learning under a stimulant when spaced trials are used. We could explain why the maze-dull animals became as efficient as the maze-bright under massed conditions when a stimulant is administered by supposing that the stimulant increased the speed of consolidation of a trace after each trial. We would further have to suppose that, if a new process of consolidation was started before the previous one finished, less of a "trace" would be laid down than if both processes of consolidation had gone on to completion. However, this would not explain why the drug-treated maze-dull animals make fewer errors than the treated or untreated maze-bright animals when the trials are spaced a day apart. It seems that here the postulated process of consolidation would reach an asymptote within twenty-four hours even when the animals are untreated. (At least this is used as an argument concerning the consolidation hypothesis to account for the lack of a difference between the maze-bright and maze-dull animals when the trials are widely spaced. It is argued that in these conditions the processes of consolidation do not overlap.) A speeding up of the processes of consolidation should therefore have no effect if the trials are widely spaced. If the factor of the overlap of consolidation is already minimal, a further speeding up of the consolidation process by drugs can hardly have an effect.

There are other difficulties in attempting to explain the speeding up of learning by drugs on the basis of a simple consolidation hypothesis: this speeding up rests on some increase in consolidation after each learning trial. The assumption is made that degree of consolidation of a memory trace is reflected in the goodness of performance. However, there is little justification for this assumption since there is no evidence that performance improves with time after a learning trial as the process of consolidation, as shown by vulnerability to electroconvulsive shock, proceeds. Animals benefit from the experience of an immediately preceding trial when the consolidation of the trace of this trial must be almost nil, if the process of consolidation begins when a trial is over. So it seems that goodness of performance of a learned task cannot be regarded as an index of consolidation of its memory trace, as measured by its vulnerability to electroconvulsive shock. However, the premises of the consolidation theory which would account for these experimental results have not been explicitly stated. It would be of interest to see how complex the assumptions of such a theory would have to be to explain the data.

There may be no single explanation of the above experiments. Many factors unconnected with learning *per se* such as a tendency to alternation or other biases, enter into the performance of a task, especially in a complex T-maze. They obscure the expression of learning as it is manifested in performance. The tendency toward spontaneous alternation decreases with time between trials, and so a greater tendency to alternate on the part of the maze-dull rats could make their performance worse when trials are closely spaced. Wide spacing of the trials reduces this tendency greatly and we should consequently find, as is the case, that the difference in errors between the maze-bright and the maze-dull rats should diminish greatly. The maze-dull and maze-bright rats differ in many ways, many of them apparently unconnected with the qualities for which they were originally selected. For instance, it has been found in the writer's laboratory that there exist not only large differences in the amounts of saline and water drunk but also divergencies in the very manner of drinking. Thus, it is entirely possible that accidental correlations of drug sensitivity are confounding the results and that further genetic selection may be necessary to dissolve the perplexities in the results which have been expressed above.

Nevertheless, whatever the difficulties are in the interpretation of the data that have been expressed, it cannot be doubted that certain drugs have an effect on some process which persists after a learning trial is over and which affects the performance of the learnt habit on future occasions. It is clear that such a discovery is potentially of great importance in unravelling the neurophysiological basis of learning.

McGaugh's work, reviewed above, sprang from an interest in the biochemical correlates of behavior which was kindled by Krech and Rosenzweig. These workers have initiated a program, a model of its kind, for the investigation of correlations between various aspects of behavior and the quantities of acetylcholine and cholinesterase in the central nervous system. As these do not bear directly on the properties of the memory trace, the reader is referred to a recent excellent review (74) by these workers. Of considerable general interest is their recent finding (40a) that, in rats reared in different environments from the time of weaning, "the more complex the environment, the lower the cortical-subcortical ratio of cholinesterase activity". Such results were found to obtain in six different strains of rats, and could not be attributed to activity *per se*, handling, or nutritional differences.

Retrograde amnesia has been noted in patients with destruction of the medial temporal region [Milner and Penfield (49); Scoville & Milner (79)]. Chow & Survis (16) and Orbach & Fantz (68) have shown that temporal neocortical ablations affect the retention of visual habits with less severity when these habits have been overlearnt than when they have not. While there is probably no strict comparability between the practice of a habit and the age of a memory, these experiments do suggest that the greater resistance of a memory to destructive influences might be caused by its dissemination throughout the central nervous system as practice or time proceeds. Such an explanation is put forward by Chow & Survis (16): "As the habit becomes well ingrained, the neural changes must involve or spread to more and more additional regions." However, an alternative explanation would not need to postulate such a spread, or an inequality of destruction of the physical counterpart of the visual memory. One need only suppose that, during prolonged training, irrelevant tendencies which obscure learning are ironed out so that, if an equal amount of destruction of the memory trace for the visual memory is assumed, the overtrained habit would be less affected because there would be fewer irrelevant tendencies to compete with it than in the case of the habit which was not so greatly practiced. In support of this alternative interpretation there is the finding of Chow & Survis (16) that six out of eight of the monkeys in this study retained a color discrimination taught as a pre-training problem, which had not been overlearnt and which was lost following ablation of the same cortical regions under identical conditions in monkeys to whom no subsequent visual training was given before operation [Chow (11)]. As the color problems were not overlearnt in this study, a spread because of practice cannot be postulated. On the other hand, irrelevant tendencies, which would interfere with the habit, could have been diminished by training in other habits, as they have been during the acquisition of "learning set" [Harlow (29)].

Compared with that from animals, the evidence from retrograde amnesia in man suggests an entirely different time scale, that of years or a lifetime, for the process of consolidation. The animal studies discussed above dealt in minutes or hours at the most. There may be two different processes or a species difference here. Whatever the answer, such observations make it difficult to interpret the results of the animal studies.

It has, however, been shown in one study [Pearlman *et al.* (69)] that retrograde amnesia measured in days can be produced in rats, so that the argument for a species difference is rendered less plausible. In this study (described above, page 262), seizures, produced by means of pentelenetetrazol (Metrazol), were induced in a group of rats. One such convulsion, given four days after the single learning trial, produced almost as much amnesia as pentobarbital anesthesia induced ten seconds after the trial. (The response level of the metrazol-treated group was 70 per cent of their previous level, that of untreated controls 1 per cent.) So it seems that a metrazol-induced seizure was able to produce amnesia for an event which occurred four days before. It is possible that Metrazol may have been acting on a different process from that affected by pentobarbital and ether. A more plausible view is that Metrazol is simply a much more effective agent. When administered ten seconds after the learning trial, it produces complete amnesia. (Response is 100 per cent, whereas it is 76 per cent when pentobarbital is administered ten seconds after the trial.) Alternatively, it would be necessary to postulate that Metrazol severely affects both a short-term and a long-term process of consolidation.

With reference to the last alternative, it seems likely that there are two processes with different time scales present in memory: a short term and a long term, which may be distinguished on other grounds. For instance, it has long been known that, if different lists of items are learnt correctly, to the same level of proficiency, by a subject on successive days, the number of items correctly recalled on each following day from the previous day's list decreases. This lessened efficiency of recall has been ascribed to an interference with the processes of recall of a list by the previous lists learnt, and called "proactive inhibition". However, it becomes apparent [Deutsch & Mamakos (18)] that the number of trials needed to reach a certain standard of recall decreases on each successive day, and that to this can be attributed the corresponding decrease in success of recall on the following day. It appears that recall immediately after a list has been seen can rapidly improve with practice. Such practice does not improve recall of the same list twenty-four hours later. Such recall remains a function of the number of trials during which a list has been presented. If subjects are not trained to a given standard on the different successive lists on each day but the number of trials on each day is kept constant, recall on each successive day shows no decrement.

Another recent line of evidence is presented by Weiskrantz (96). Monkeys with functionally disrupted frontal lobes were inferior to normal controls in easy discrimination tasks, requiring only a few trials to solve the given problem. There was no lag in learning difficult tasks for which training stretched over many days. Further evidence is furnished for the interpretation that the frontal deficit is here one of immediate memory, whereas long-term memory is unimpaired. A paradoxical state is thereby revealed: events are laid down in the long-term memory store and are accessible there. Whereas they do not enter the short-term memory store or else are inaccessible there [for older evidence on this dichotomy, see Broadbent (6)].

EPILEPTIFORM PHENOMENA AND LEARNING

We saw above that electrically and chemically induced convulsions produced memory disorders. Memory defects have also been observed in epileptic patients. Here such defects may be caused either by the seizures themselves, as in the case of the electrically induced seizure, or by the activity of the epileptogenic focus of abnormal activity which, when it spreads to the surrounding neural tissue, produces a seizure. Such a focus can be demonstrated in the electroencephalogram as a steady discharging focus of abnormal activity. This is sharply localized and only spreads to the surrounding tissue to produce a seizure at times which may be months apart. Morrell (50, 51), in a series of interesting studies, has been able to shed light on the relation of these foci of abnormal activity to learning by using the technique of the alpha block conditional response. When a visual stimulus is presented to a subject (for instance, a bright flash of light to a subject with his eyes shut) the 8 to 13 cycles per sec alpha rhythm is replaced by low-amplitude, high-frequency activity. The alpha rhythm is not affected when a sound or touch of sufficiently low intensity impinges on the subject. However, if such a sound or touch is paired with the light stimulus, a normal subject will show blocking of his alpha rhythm in response to the sound or touch alone. The number of paired presentations of sound or touch required in a normal subject varies from one to twenty trials. Morrell (50) investigated the ability to form such an alpha-block conditioned response in patients with sharply localized temporal lobe spike foci. In such cases it is expected that the auditory system would be expecially involved.

To obtain a measure of the selective impairment of auditory function, Morrell (50) used not only auditory but also tactile stimuli. It was found that the capacity to form an alpha-block conditioned response to a tone was extremely impaired whereas learning to a tactile stimulus remained essentially normal. However, Morrell found no difference in these patients in the motor reaction time to touch and to tone stimuli. This finding may be related to that by Chow & Obrist (15), for instance, in which production of an epileptogenic focus does not interfere with habits previously acquired.

In a similar study with monkeys, Morrell (51) was again able to show that epileptic foci impair selectively the formation of an alpha-block conditioned response. Epileptic foci were experimentally created by the placement of aluminum hydroxide cream in selected locations in the central nervous system. This substance gives rise to chronically discharging seizure foci, resembling those of epileptic foci when electrographically recorded. Morrell was able to show that extreme impairment of learning occurred. Animals with foci in the auditory cortex showed a deficit in conditioning to tone but not to touch. Those with foci in the postcentral leg area showed a deficit to touch but not to tone. Morrell (51) was also able to show that, if the paired stimuli were presented when a small and well-circumscribed focus was quiescent, conditioned alpha block to touch would appear. However, though such learning was well established, blocking to the conditioned stimulus (touch) would suddenly and completely disappear when a pairing of the stimuli occurred during a spike discharge. The unconditioned alpha block to light was, on the other hand, unaffected. As soon as the spike discharge subsided, on the next trial less than a minute later, the touch stimulus produced alpha block, showing that learning had remained intact. Excisions of the discharging focus, where this was unilateral, led to a marked improvement in forming an alpha-block conditional response. It seems, therefore, that the abnormal discharge of a focus causes a greater deficit than the simple absence of the discharging tissue, if excision is unilateral. The contralateral tissue can then presumably function without interference.

Other investigators [Kraft (40); Stamm and Pribram (89)] have confirmed Morrell's observation that learning of a particular type is affected, depending on the site of the discharging focus. Kraft, for instance, found that monkeys with occipital implants of aluminum hydroxide cream showed impairment in learning visual discrimination tasks. However, no deficit was evident in their learning of an alternation task. Such a learning deficit has also been demonstrated for an alternation task when aluminum hydroxide cream is placed bilaterally on the frontal cortex [Stamm & Pribram (89)]. Though the learning deficit was very large, no detectable deficit was found in the retention of the same habit acquired preoperatively. These data should be contrasted with the findings of Chow (13), who found in monkeys an inability to learn and retain visual habits when a bilateral electrographic discharge was induced in their temporal cortices. However, retention was not disturbed with bilateral hippocampal or occipital discharge.

The Nature of the Physiological Change in Learning

At present, the physiological change underlying learning is unknown. There have, however, been changes discovered recently which are of suggestive significance. One of the most interesting which has been reported is by Morrell (57). This has arisen from his studies of "mirror" focus epileptiform discharge. It has often been observed clinically that a discharging focus in one hemisphere will set off a similar discharge in a corresponding area of the other hemisphere. Two stages of such a secondary or reflected discharge have been demonstrated. In the dependent stage such a spike discharge will only occur when the original focus discharges. Also, ablation of the original focus will abolish the discharge in the secondary region. In the independent stage the secondary region will discharge without such activity in the primary region and will continue to discharge even when the primary focus has been surgically removed. Morrell produced primary foci by applying ethyl chloride to a small area of the cortex. It was observed that the independent stage of the secondary contralateral epileptiform focus takes about twenty-four hours to several days to develop in the rabbit, four weeks to three months in the cat, and about eight weeks in the monkey. This stage appears to be permanent. Having been altered in its properties, the cortical region concerned retains this alteration. For instance, it was possible to isolate neuronally the region of the secondary discharge. Epileptiform discharge from this focus was abolished, as shown by EEG recording for several months. After this period the cortex was again exposed and it was possible to demonstrate that the isolated focus had retained its abnormal properties. Morrell states:

We believe this to be a crucial observation because it demonstrates that the mirror focus is a region which has not only "learned" to behave in terms of paroxysmal discharge, but which "remembers" this behavior even after months of inactivity. The isolation experiment has excluded reverberating impulses as the basis of the changed electrical behavior and makes it necessary to search for structural alterations.

Such a search for structural alterations was in fact undertaken. A chemical alteration at the site of the focus was found. It appears that changes indicative of abnormally high concentrations of ribonucleic acid, or of its intracellular state, occur in the cells at the site of the abnormally discharging focus. It appears from the report that the cases which were used for analysis of chemical changes had not been subjected to the neuronal isolation spoken of above. It is in such cases that we would see changes which could be interpreted as being due to long-term storage rather than abnormal activity. However, Morrell states (56) that some such neuronally isolated cases have been examined and that they appear to have similar alterations to those already reported.

Hyden & Pigon (34) have also observed changes in amounts of ribonucleic acid in situations involving neural activity and simultaneous learning in which it is difficult to separate these factors. These authors report that ribonucleic acid concentrations rise in neurons during activity and, perhaps, learning, and that after such activity a decreased amount is to be found in the neurons, but an increased amount in the glial cells surrounding the neurons. Such glial cells are very numerous in the nervous system, being in the cortex at least twice as numerous as neurons. Galambos (23) has presented a theory concerning their role. He conceives the glia "as genetically charged to organise and program neuron activity so that the best interests of the organism will be served; the essential product of glia action is visualized to be what we call innate and acquired behavioral responses".

The work above quoted on ribonucleic acid does not necessarily lend support to speculations [such as those of Katz & Halstead (38); and Hyden (34)] which attempt to link the molecular basis of heredity with the mechanism of memory. Information storage in memory would, in this mechanism, consist of patterning of special large protein molecules, such as occurs in the mechanism of hereditary transmission; ribonucleic acid is related to this process. However, the difficulty with a molecular storage hypothesis is that no plausible mechanism altering the molecule or retrieval when it has been altered can be envisaged. It is difficult to see how information stored or to be stored in a molecule could function with sufficient speed in the nervous system, as complex temporal coding would be necessitated to take advantage of the storage capacity of the molecule; but this coding would be lengthy in the slow biological system.

It has been reported that there is a lowering of cytoplasmic ribonucleic acid concentrations in the cells of the receptor and bipolar layers of the retina in animals which have been reared in the dark [Riesen (72); Rasch *et al.* (70)]. Riesen (72) says that "these changes in protein content are related to an effect of stimulation on the rate of protein turnover in cells engaged in the transmission of impulses".

This evidence emphasizes that the case for supposing ribonucleic acid to be involved in the physical change underlying learning rests more on *a priori* grounds than on empirical evidence, for all the phenomena so far described could be attributed to differences in rate of stimulation. What has made the identification of ribonucleic acid plausible is the argument that a change in the excitability of a cell could not be permanent unless there was some change in the genetic information in the cell. All other cell constituents have a high rate of turnover, and there must be something which keeps them different after learning. However, it seems that there are other possibilities which should not be lost sight of. There are phenomena such as the influx of melanin into the neurons of the nucleus niger in horses (37a), which suggests that the contents of a cell may be stably modified without any presumptive change in its genetic apparatus. It is also within the bounds of possibility to suppose that such a change of intracellular content might modify excitability characteristics of the cell. If such suppositions are accepted, we need only postulate a sudden increase of permeability to a specific substance on the reception of a given signal to provide for an equally plausible learning substrate. It is easy to conceive that such a process would have the characteristics of high vulnerability at the outset, before permeation was complete, and that permeation could continue slowly in the long term to give the characteristics of long-term consolidation.

Besides the observations of Morrell (57) on "mirror" foci described above, other phenomena which may be related have been described which show moderately long-term effects of stimulation on the subsequent behavior of neural tissue. It has been found that, after a prolonged burst of high-frequency excitation at a synaptic region, there is a larger postsynaptic potential than before such stimulation took place. This phenomenon is called posttetanic potentiation, or PTP. Such an enhancement of responsiveness in motoneurons can be measured, sometimes up to a period of hours, when disuse has been produced at the synapse by sectioning the afferent fibers distal to their ganglia about thirteen days previously. (Such a procedure led to depressed synaptic efficacy. Eccles (21) points out that inactivation of a synapse by this means complicates the interpretation of the findings. The parent cell of the afferent nerve fiber is left attached to the part of the fiber leading to the synapse. Consequently, there is probably regenerative outgrowth to replace the severed part of the fiber, distal to the parent cell body. Such growth may impair the functional efficiency of the synaptic junction, rather than the lack of neural impulses. A reduction of the rate of afferent neural bombardment by other, admittedly not so effective, means produces no such depression of efficiency in the synapse.) In a normal fiber, a conditioning tetanus of 6000 volleys at 400 a second produces an enhancement of synaptic efficiency which disappears completely after about two minutes [Eccles & McIntyre (22)]. These workers also report that normal excessive use of a synapse by overloading a muscle, so that its stretch receptors discharge at an abnormally high rate, also results in a heightened synaptic efficiency.

It appears unlikely that these phenomena form the change in learning. The changes described occur when one unit in the nervous system has excited another such unit, making excitation of the latter unit more likely. This would lead to a type of learning in which the organism would simply repeat what it had done previously.

Enhancement of single-unit firing in the central nervous system is reported by Olds & Olds (67). These workers implanted electrodes on sites producing high frequencies of response as a result of electrical brain self-stimulation, namely, in the region of the medial forebrain bundle. Microelectrodes were then inserted into the brain. When slow repetitive discharges were picked up from single cells with the microelectrode, a pulse was inserted into the electrode in the medial forebrain bundle region at a fixed time after a discharge had occurred. It is reported that some cells, mainly in the subcortical regions, augmented their rate of firing in response to such stimulation. This suggests an analogy to learning by reward, an activity of a cell being rewarded instead of an act of the whole animal. It is unknown at present how such findings are related to the supernormal period in the structures studied. Chow (10) suggests that during such a procedure peripheral responses are being rewarded and that what is observed with the microelectrodes are cerebral counterparts (causes or effects) of such peripheral responses. These of course are not criticisms, but simply interpretations of this important work. [For a general interpretation of electrical brain stimulation, see Deutsch (18a).] It is hoped that fuller accounts, especially on the statistical side of these studies, will be forthcoming.

Other possibilities which have been canvassed as explanations for the physical change in learning have little basis in demonstrated alterations of neural function. Holt (32) suggested that there was a growth change, leading to new connections in the nervous system during learning. Such growth does take place during embryonic development but there is no evidence that it takes place during learning. Hebb (30) makes a similar suggestion. He supposes that the connections (end-boutons) of one cell to another increase in number during excitation of one cell by the other, but there seems to be no good evidence for this.

Till very recently, the supposition that growth could occur as a regular feature of the central nervous system whether in learning or regeneration did not seem very plausible. It had been observed that some central axons and dendrites could sprout, but such cases were rare and no generality could be attached to the findings. However, recently, Rose and associates (73) have produced interesting evidence with regard to the growth of nerve fibers in the cortex. These workers have been able selectively to destroy very narrow layers (about 100 to 200 μ) in the cortex, below its surface by bombardment with heavy subatomic particles. Such lesions are usually three to four millimeters wide. In such a lesion there is a destruction of nerve cells and fibers. However, a regrowth of nerve fibers from outside the lesion is seen (after seven weeks with moderate dosage) though nerve cells show no reappearance in the affected area. There is no evidence that no such growth is connected with learning. Geiger's (24, 25) studies *in vitro*, in which neurons show a surprising amount of mobility, are also of interest with regard to plasticity in the nervous system.

One of the problems of investigating the physiological basis of learning has been our inability to pinpoint the locus of learning charge. Horridge (33a) has now discovered the learning of leg posture by the ventral cord ganglia in the absence of a brain in cockroaches, locusts, and similar large insects. Careful controls have been undertaken to exclude other possible factors other than associative learning. The relevant ganglion which learns contains only about 3000 cells.

INTEROCULAR TRANSFER AND STORAGE OF THE MEMORY TRACE

The bilateral symmetry of the nervous system offers interesting opportunities for its investigation. We may ask whether information which the animal has obtained through learning is stored in both hemispheres, whether it can be made available to the other hemisphere even if at the time of learning this hemisphere received no direct sensory input, and so on. Most of the experiments on this subject involve the sectioning of the corpus callosum, a massive structure of nerve fibers which joins the two halves of the cortex. Studies of learning employing this technique were initiated by Bykoff (8). This worker taught a dog to expect food after a mechanical stimulus to the skin on one side. This causes the animal to salivate when the mechanical stimulus is applied. In the intact animal, salivation is produced without further training when the contralateral point on the skin is stimulated. However, in the animal with callosal section no such transfer was observed.

Beritoff & Chichinadze (3, 4) studied the problem of interhemispheric transfer in pigeons. They found that habits learned with one eye were not transferred when testing was done with the other eye. However, later studies by Levine (42, 43, 44) and Siegel (82) have shown that such transfer can occur. As there is complete crossover of visual fibers from one eye to the opposite hemisphere in the pigeon, it seems that such transfer must be mediated at a fairly high neural level. The contradiction with the earlier Russian work has been explained as being caused by the use of different retinal loci. In the pigeon, transfer depends on the part of the visual field stimulated during training.

For monkey and man, each hemisphere receives input from both retinas in such a way that each hemisphere has projected on it about half the visual field; therefore, training the animal in only one eye means that both hemispheres are receiving messages from that eye. However, if the optic chiasma is cut in the sagittal plane, the animal becomes hemianopic when either eye is shut, but has a complete visual field with both eyes open, except for nasal interference. The two hemispheres can be trained separately by restricting vision to one eye only. Myers (61) found that cats with such a section of the chiasma could transfer from one eye what they had learned with the other eye. Also Myers (62) and Sperry *et al.* (84) found that if the corpus callosum was sectioned in addition to the optic chiasma, no transfer of learning from one eye to the other occurred. It seems, therefore, that the transfer found in the first study of Myers was carried by fibers in the corpus callosum from one hemisphere to the other. It has further been found that such interhemispheric transfer is contingent upon the intactness of a posterior portion of the corpus callosum. It appears from Myers' (64) data that there is a considerable degree of functional equivalence between the various parts of the posterior corpus callosum. The intactness of any posterior part of the structure leads to interocular transfer after section of the chiasma. It seems that, in different cats, entirely different parts of the posterior corpus callosum sufficed for transfer of the same visual discrimination problem. However, around two to three million callosal fibers were needed for successful transfer (though not all of these were visual fibers).

Such findings lead logically to other experiments. The lack of communication between the hemispheres that is caused by callosal section prevents the utilization by the left hemisphere of information laid down in the right. We may ask whether this is because during normal learning information is laid down in both hemispheres at the time of training, or whether one hemisphere draws on information stored in the other during the time of testing. Work by Myers (63) and Myers & Sperry (84, 85) would indicate that, for some types of discrimination, storage appears to be bilateral, whereas it is unilateral for other more difficult visual discriminations. Sectioning of the corpus callosum or removal of the cortex to which visual information passed during learning, before testing with the contralateral hemisphere has taken place, results in almost perfect retention in tests with the contralateral eye.

However, this has only been found true where the patterns to be discriminated are vertical and horizontal striations. For instance, where the patterns are small filled circles against larger unfilled wide ones, such transfer does not occur. The obvious conclusion which has been drawn is that there is carryover of information from one hemisphere to the other during learning when the discrimination is simple, but no such carryover when the discrimination is more complex. Whether this conclusion is correct will be decided by further investigation.

It has also been found that the animal with sectioned chiasma and callosum can learn diametrically opposed habits with no interference between the two habits [Myers (62); Sperry (85)]. Similar results have been obtained with the monkey and the cat [Sperry (85); Trevarthen (95)]. Work has also been undertaken on the transfer of somesthetic habits in animals with a section of the corpus callosum. As has been mentioned above, Bykoff (8) found an absence of the usual transfer of a touch stimulus to the contralateral side. Stamm & Sperry (90) found no transfer when cats with sectioned callosum had been trained to discriminate between two levers on the basis of touch. When the front paw on one side had been trained, there was no transfer to the other paw. Similar results have been obtained by Glickstein & Sperry (26) and Ebner & Myers (20) in the case of tactile object discrimination in monkeys, and by Myers & Henson (65) in chimpanzees. This is somewhat surprising as there is a bilateral representation of somesthetic function. If a point on the body surface is stimulated, evoked potentials can be observed bilaterally although the great majority of fibers cross. However, Glickstein & Sperry (26) noted that such a bilateral connection was utilized by the nervous system if one somesthetic area was injured or ablated. In such a case, transfer of a somesthetic discrimination learned with the use of one paw transfers to the other paw in an animal with a section of corpus callosum. It is presumed that the intact hemisphere mediates learning for both paws. This finding is very interesting because it is a clear-cut case of one part of the cortex taking over the functions of another only if the other part is incapacitated. It suggests that one side must in some way inform some other part of the nervous system of its intactness, or nonintactness, in such a way that appropriate inaction or action occurs on the contralateral side. The experiment also demonstrates that such a message is not sent from one side to the other via the corpus callosum, but suggests some subcortical mechanism. Sperry (86) has found a remarkable autonomy of function of the somesthetic cortex in cats. The removal of most of the cortex on the same side and callosal section did not affect the retention of learned somesthetic discriminations by the somesthetic cortical remnant, nor the speed of new learning. A similar autonomy has not been found for the visual cortex [Sperry et al. (88)].

A variant of the technique of callosal sectioning in the study of memory has been introduced by Bureš & Burešová (7), using Leão's spreading depression. If a high concentration of a chemical agent such as potassium chloride is used, a series of waves of depression is generated with no recovery between them. Electroencephalographic activity in such a case may remain depressed for several hours. The production of such a depression in both hemispheres does not anesthetize an animal; the animal moves around much as usual. However, during the depression it does not manifest signs of previous learning.

If produced in one hemisphere, such depression does not spread to the other and this is what makes it a convenient tool in the study of interhemispheric transfer. Using this technique Bureš & Burešová trained rats in a simple avoidance habit. When the same hemisphere was depressed on the two successive days of learning, there was considerable saving in the retention of the habit on the second day. However, if one hemisphere was depressed on the first day and the second on the second day of learning, there was no saving on the second day. The memory trace had apparently remained localized in the hemisphere which had been involved in learning on the first day. On the second day this first hemisphere was inactivated so that the trace of the learning on the first day was unavailable to the animal. It therefore seems that there is no transfer of a memory trace between the two hemispheres during the twenty-four hours or so during which they both function normally. Russell & Ochs (77) report that such transfer occurs very quickly if the unilaterally learnt habit is practised while both hemispheres are functioning. Whether a hemisphere can draw on traces stored in the other remains an open question on the basis of these experiments. To decide this question we should have to arrange an experiment in which the first hemisphere was inactivated while learning proceeded with the second. In the test situation neither of the hemispheres should be inactivated, but input should be restricted to the first hemisphere. As a control, to make sure that the memory trace had not transferred from one hemisphere to the other in the interval between the two experimental sessions in this case, we should have to inactivate the second hemisphere in the test also. Only if there were no transfer in this situation would we be justified in saying that the memory trace once formed can be transmitted only to those parts of the brain that are active during the training procedure.

Myers & Sperry (63, 66), on the basis of their experiments on callosal section after input to one hemisphere only, suggested that, for some visual-discrimination learning, the storage of the memory trace was bilateral even though input was unilateral. It looks from the experiment of Bureš & Burešová (7) as though such storage must occur during the process of learning, and not as a result of transfer from one hemisphere to the other after the experiment. However, it seems too early to draw any definite conclusions.

It has been shown earlier in work on callosal sectioning that it is possible to train the two hemispheres separately in relation to conflicting habits without any signs of interference. Bureš & Burešová (7) were also able to show the coexistence of traces of conflicting habits in the two hemispheres, even when the callosum was intact. Animals were trained to escape by going to the left when one hemisphere was inactivated and to the right when the other was inactivated. On the second day they would choose to go either left or right depending on which hemisphere it was which was not inactivated. It was also observed that on recovery from spreading depression, memory traces of habits learned before the depression were left intact.

Studies of interocular transfer in relation to memory have also been carried out in fish [Sperry & Clark (87); Schulte (78); McCleary (45)]. The study is of some interest because there is a complete crossover from a retina to the contralateral portion of the nervous system. This means that each eye is represented separately and unilaterally. Further, as there is no neocortex, there is also no corpus callosum; there are, however, commisural fibers. Sperry & Clark (87) and Schulte (78) covered one eye in fish which were then required to swim towards the correct one of two stimuli for food. Transfer was found when the original eye used in the training was covered and the 'naive' eye uncovered. McCleary (45) found interocular transfer in a simple type of avoidance situation using conditioned heart rate as an index. When a skeletal motor response of a simple nature is learned with one eye while the other eye is covered, no transfer occurs. However, when the naive eye is left uncovered during training though it cannot see the training stimuli, transfer does occur. Covering an eye, however, does not prevent transfer if conditioned heart rate is used as an index. Failure of transfer occurred with blinders when a simple swimming escape response was required, even if both eyes were covered with translucent blinders during training and also in the transfer tests. The stimulus was a thin beam of white light, which was focused on one blinder during training and on the other blinder during transfer tests. The explanation of these findings is obscure.

STEADY POTENTIAL SHIFTS AND LEARNING-LIKE PHENOMENA

Morrell (56), following the work of Rusinov (75), has been able to demonstrate phenomena resembling learning which follow the application of low (2 to 10 μa) anodal constant current to a part of the motor cortex. Such a current does not produce limb movement by itself. However, it seems that a flash or sound or touch will produce the limb movement which one would expect to occur as a result of the adequate stimulation of the motor area to which the constant current was applied. Even after the current has been switched off, such a movement can be produced by various stimuli for a period up to half an hour. It is possible, however, to conduct the experiment another way. A group of stimuli is selected and all members of this group are repeated individually until habituation (as judged by the EEG record) to them occurs. Then one of these stimuli is chosen to be presented repeatedly while the constant anodal current is applied to the motor area of the cortex; it then elicits a limb movement and continues to do so even when the current is switched off. The other members of the group to which habituation has occurred and which have not been paired with the constant current do not elicit such a movement. However, other stimuli (to which habituation has not taken place and which are outside the previously selected group) will elicit the limb movement for some time after the constant current has been switched off.

It looks as if the steady current applied to the motor area renders it hyperexcitable and liable to be triggered by any disturbances. However, the process of habituation of a stimulus appears to attenuate the functional connection between the receiving area for this stimulus and the motor regions. The pairing of a habituated stimulus with the constant current application, however, results in a loss of this habituation, so that this stimulus becomes effective in eliciting the appropriate limb movement.

Another interesting phenomenon obtained in the same study concerns the application of the constant anodal current to the visual receiving area. Recordings were obtained from single units which respond to a single flash by a high-frequency burst of spikes. These units responded by a similar burst after each flash when such flashes were delivered at the rate of 3 per sec. The effect of the constant current seemed to be that such a single unit would respond to a single flash delivered up to twenty minutes after the end of the 3-per-sec flicker, by a series of bursts of spikes spaced at 3 per sec. Morrell reports that no trace of such rhythmic activity was apparent in the record during this interval. Similar observations have been made by Shelanski (81) in *Amblystoma tigrinum*. These findings are evidence against the notion that reverberating circuits are necessary as short-term storage of information in the central nervous system.

Such grouping of single cell discharge has been observed by Jasper *et al*. (35) in the monkey during low-frequency flicker and by Strumwasser & Rosenthal (91) in the frog during intermittent direct-current stimulation of single neurons. However, no storage of the pattern of stimulation when such stimulation is absent has been reported by these authors. It may well be that the steady potential shifts induce, mimic, or produce some physiological changes to be found in the normal functioning of the central nervous system. Goldring & O'Leary (27, 28) have reported negative DC shifts of cortex when the midline thalamic reticular system is stimulated. Findings of a similar nature are also reported by Arduini (2). Morrell (55), coupling an auditory signal with stimulation of the midline thalamic reticular nuclei (which produce a negative DC shift), found that this shift would occur after thirty paired trials to the tone alone. Morrell used low-frequency (4 to 5 per sec) unilateral stimulation of the centromedian nucleus in the rabbit. Such stimulation produced a negative DC shift in the central cortex on the same side as the stimulated area.

ELECTRICAL ACTIVITY OF THE BRAIN AND ITS RELATION TO THE MEMORY TRACE

We shall now turn to a brief review of EEG phenomena in an effort to assess the possibility that the electrical events recorded are used by the central nervous system as a signal in transmission or storage. Any criticism therefore is not of EEG studies, which give exceedingly useful information about the behavior of the nervous system, but only of certain interpretations of these studies.

When a novel stimulus is presented to an animal, a desynchronization of its EEG rhythm occurs. Large slow waves, repeating at more or less regular intervals, are replaced by low-voltage, fast electrical activity.

What does this measure of brain activity tell us about other behavior of the nervous system? Kogan (39) measured thresholds of neural excitability during desynchronization. He found that the threshold for such excitability decreased in the primary sensory area to which the alerting sensory stimulus was relayed, but that it increased in other areas, though all showed EEG desynchronization. It has been shown by Ricci et al. (71) that activity of individual units can be increased, decreased, or unaffected by desynchronization.

When a novel stimulus is repeatedly presented alone, a gradual decrease in the period of desynchronization occurs until it fails to develop altogether. Such a process is termed "habituation" and is selective and specific. A stimulus differing only slightly from that previously presented repeatedly will cause desynchronization [Hernández-Peón et al. (31); Sokolov (83); Sharpless & Jasper (80)].

Changes in evoked potential during the process of habituation have also been described. What such a change means in functional terms is still, however, obscure. It would be tempting to suppose that such a diminution is caused by a lessening of the impact of the incoming signal. However, Horn (33), in an interesting study, makes it possible to argue that the reverse is true, at least in some cases. When a cat is attending to a mouse in a flickering field, the cortical response to flicker is smaller than when it is ignoring the mouse. The over-all size of a neural response is the sum of a very large number of positive and negative voltages occurring at any one time. It is evident that differences in timing or in composition of the population of cells firing at any one time could affect the sum of voltages in many different ways, so that functional interpretation is rendered tenuous.

When habituation to a signal is complete, training is begun. The stimulus to which habituation has occurred is paired with some other stimulus, which has either rewarding or punishing properties; arousal to the previously habituated stimulus tends to occur under such circumstances. Many papers [e.g. John & Killam (36); Morrell (54)] describe the distribution of responses to a flickering light during conditioning. There is apparently an enhancement of the response to the flicker in the reticular formation and the hippocampus. Later in training such an enhancement occurs in the nucleus ventralis anterior and structures of the visual system. However, it seems that when reward rather than punishment is introduced, the sequence of changes during learning is altered. These experiments raise the question whether we are observing in the EEG some signal which is identifiable with a short-term or long-term memory trace, or some part of the process connected with learning.

Observations have been made of EEG waves during learning, but there are so many other factors in play, such as changes in motivation and attention, during the observational period that we cannot be precisely sure how the EEG changes observed are connected to learning. It seems very likely from the studies of Harlow (29) on "learning set" that learning occurs in one trial, once various built-in biases (which can be considered as error tendencies) have been eradicated through a process of training. Even if the measurements being taken were considered to be good indices of underlying processes, it is unlikely that in them we are observing the set of changes in the nervous system which underlies learning. The electrical changes observed show a gradual shift, in the same way as behavioral changes do, and it is therefore likely that they are as contaminated by other irrelevant factors. [For a similar point of view, see Miller (48).]

The unlikelihood of identifying EEG rhythms as signals used by the central nervous system either in transmission or storage is increased by an excellent experiment by Chow (12). This worker implanted electrodes in the inferior temporal cortex of the monkey and then required the animal to learn a discrimination which it is less able to perform without this part of the cortex. The animal was presented with visual patterns, the significance of which changed according to the frequency of the flicker in which they were displayed. No signs of this discontinuous stimulation appeared on the EEG record in the temporal area, even though it was an ingredient which had to be distinguished. The EEG changed in the temporal area only during the middle trials, being the same at the beginning and the end of learning. This is most plausibly interpreted by Chow as being caused by attentional factors. "The experiment of Chow serves to demonstate that the material basis of the engram or durable memory trace is not likely to be revealed by the techniques of electrophysiology" [Morrell (58)].

Various other EEG phenomena have been noted during conditioning. Slow waves appear when an animal is required to wait or to suppress a response. John, Leiman & Sachs (37) claim that "inhibition of conditioned response is consistently accompanied by slow waves". However, they also report that such slow waves also occur in relation to excitation as well as to inhibition, and there appear to be no differences between the waves under these two circumstances.

It has also been noted by numerous workers [e.g. Morrell (53)] that slow waves can be elicited by a steady tone, if this tone has been coupled with a flickering light. The experimental procedure used to show this was as follows. A pure tone of low intensity was presented to an animal repeatedly until it produced no alteration in the electroencephalographic record. At this point a low-frequency visual flicker was introduced at a fixed time after the beginning of the tone. The frequency of flicker was 3 to 12 per sec and it produced "photic driving" of the EEG rhythm. By this we mean that an EEG rhythm of the same frequency as the light flicker could be observed from the visual cortex. After the few trials in which the tone and flicker were presented together, the tone alone began to produce a desynchronized EEG record in the same way that it did before habituation to the tone had taken place. This has been called stage I and it may last from fifteen to sixty trials depending on the animal. In stage II, when the tone was sounded and before presentation of the visual flicker, an EEG rhythm appeared, similar in frequency to that evoked by the flicker itself. This stage is brief (two to ten trials) and is soon replaced by stage III, which was a desynchronization localized to the visual cortex and which persisted, so that it may be regarded as the final stage. However, it is the frequency of the discharge in stage II after the tone is sounded and before the light appears that is of main interest here. It has been regarded by some workers as a neural memory trace of the flicker which the nervous system produces in order to compare an incoming frequency of flicker with those flicker frequencies which have already been presented. However, Morrell, Barlow & Brazier (59) report two points of interest in relation to such a hypothesis. These workers found, contrary to general impression, that

the shift in frequency was not directly or linearly related to the shift in flash rate. For example, one animal when first conditioned with a 3 per second flash, developed a conditioned response at 6 per second. A second experiment, using a 4 per second flash resulted in a conditioned response at 3 per second. A third experiment using a 6 per second flash rate resulted in a response that was at or very close to 6 per second.

These authors also examined the records from stage III with the help of a computer in order to see whether anything resembling the frequency of the flash appeared in the desynchronized record. When a large number of successive records were superimposed and the fluctuations for each moment of the record were averaged, random components, which may accidentally bias the record in a positive or negative direction, tended to be ironed out. The average record then emerged, and this should reveal any regularly repeating changes which are masked by random fluctuations on the individual records. Using this technique then, to see whether the fluctuations of stage II persisted in stage III, Morrell *et al.* found evidence, which they consider unequivocal, that the rhythm of stage II disappears.

   In view of these results, these workers raise the possibility that the slow rhythms described in stage II represent the hippocampal arousal pattern which consists of slow waves and which occurs at a certain stage in the conditioning procedure described. It has been suggested by some that the occurrence of slow rhythms during stage II is a part of a memory storage mechanism. For instance, John *et al.* (37) write:

A mechanism of this sort would appear to provide means for storage of a representation of a temporal sequence of events, lasting beyond the duration of the events themselves. Such a mechanism for internal representation of a past event seems, on logical basis, to be essential to enable an animal to perform two differentiated responses to two similar stimuli, either of which may be presented in a given experimental situation.

This view is reminiscent of ancient theories of hearing in which it was considered that in order to recognize a sound it had to be compared with a similar sound stored in the ear. It is clear that such a mechanism is not essential on logical bases. It is merely a possible, though somewhat clumsy, mechanism. We can equally well suppose that there are arrangements of cells which are differentially set into activity by different incoming frequencies, in a manner analogous to resonators. We do not, then, need to suppose that the occurrence of a frequency is stored by having a copy of it played by the nervous system. We only need to suppose that a record is kept of which "resonator" system has been activated by an incoming set of signals. Similar criticisms can be made of Sokolov's (83) suggestions.

Whatever the theoretical possibilities are, the notion that the rhythms detected by the electroencephalograph carry information which is used by the nervous system has received experimental attention. Chow, Dement & John (14) used an avoidance task, in which a cat had to jump from one compartment to another in order to avoid shock. The imminence of the shock was signalled by a flickering light. The light also produced an EEG wave at the frequency of the flicker, or photic driving, as it is called, which is usual in such a situation. In time the cat would jump from one compartment to another simply when the flicker occurred. After this phase of the experiment, a tone was sounded before the flickering stimulus, outside the avoidance situation. When animals had reached stage II in this procedure, that is, when the tone alone produced a low-frequency EEG rhythm similar to the photic driving, they were placed once again in the avoidance situation. The tone was sounded and it produced the same EEG as the flicker. However, it did not produce any behavioral response. It does not therefore seem that the signal generated by flicker and picked up by the EEG electrodes is used by the nervous system itself as a signal.

Another study [John, Leiman & Sachs (37)] attempted to inject or mimic the EEG rhythm evoked by flicker by direct electrical stimulation to see if such stimulation would function to reinforce or negate the flicker which appeared simultaneously. Two cats were trained to make an avoidance response, one to 4 cps flicker and the other to 10 cps flicker. After such training, electrical stimulation was applied to mimic the EEG activity picked by the electrode. Three types of stimulus wave-form were used. The first was a burst of 100 cps square waves, lasting for one-twentieth of a second and recurring every tenth of a second. The second type of stimulus was the same, except that it recurred every quarter of a second, while the third consisted of bursts of the 100 cps square wave recurring also at every quarter of a second, but with each burst of 125 msec in length. Thus, photic 4 cps stimulation could be simulated centrally by employing electrical bursts which were equated to those simulating 10 cps photic stimulation either in length of each individual burst or in total length of application of square-wave stimulation. The results of applying such stimulation while flicker is also used fail to support the notion either that the central activity as displayed by the EEG is being mimicked or, if it is being mimicked, that EEG activity at a certain frequency carries information utilized by the nervous system. For instance, it was found

at a very high significance level, that a 4 cps electrical stimulation of the visual cortex is much more effective than a 10 cps input in achieving inhibition of the CAR [avoidance response] to a simultaneously presented CS [warning signal] in *both* cat 10 and cat 4, although the meaning of a 4 cps flicker is the opposite for these two animals.

In view of the technical difficulties in testing the signal-carrying hypothesis of evoked EEG rhythm by introducing a similar signal into the central nervous system, it would seem to be less equivocal to attempt to abolish or alter the EEG rhythm by means of drugs in order to test such a hypothesis. A correct performance sustained in spite of an absence of the signal would provide more crucial evidence.

Concluding Remarks

At the risk of stating the obvious it should perhaps be pointed out that the physical memory trace stands in a position relative to the physiological problem of memory similar to that of the photosensitive pigments relative to the physiology of visual perception. The knowledge that, in a particular computer, electromagnetic changes form the "memory trace" does not tell us, for instance, how the stored information is retrieved. The speed with which man recognizes familiar items is remarkable; and this is caused not by the physical nature of the physiological change used in the storage mechanism, but by the way such physiological changes are arranged in the brain system as a whole, to make stored information swiftly accessible. It is our present lack of theoretical understanding of how the cerebral storage system might operate that hampers us in the search for its physical bases, as we do not have any clear idea of what type of phenomena to look for. It is dubious whether genetics would have enjoyed its recent biochemical triumphs had it not been for a clearly elaborated theory resting on, and explaining the phenomena of, heredity. It is felt that there is a similar need in the study of memory, and that a closer look at the phenomena of memory would guide our search and give us criteria for deciding when it has been successful. At present, however, even though it cannot be stated with any confidence that we have found something about the physical basis of memory, the search has proved extremely fruitful from the standpoint of physiological discovery.

Acknowledgments

My thanks are due to many friends—Drs. Chow, Glickstein, Howarth, McGaugh, Morrell, and Weiskrantz, whose help and interest have contributed whatever may be of value in the present review—and, last but not least, to my wife.

This work was wholly supported by a grant from the National Institute of Mental Health (USPHS M-4563).

LITERATURE CITED

1. Abt, J. P., Essman, W. B., and Jarvik, M. E., *Science*, **133**, 1478–78 (1961)
2. Arduini, A., in *Reticular Formation of the Brain* (Jasper, H. H., *et al.*, Eds., Little, Brown & Co., Boston, 1958)
3. Beritoff, J., and Chichinadze, N., *Bull. Exptl. Biol. Med. (USSR)*, **2**, 105–7 (1936)
4. Beritoff, J., and Chichinadze, N., *Trans. Beritov Inst. Tiflis*, **3**, 361–76 (1937)
5. Breen, R. A., and McGaugh, J. L., *J. Comp. and Physiol. Psychol.* (In press)
6. Broadbent, D. E., *Perception and Communication* (Pergamon Press, London, 1959)
7. Bureš, J., and Burešová, O., *J. Comp. and Physiol. Psychol.*, **53**, 558–65 (1960)
8. Bykoff, K. M., *Russ. Fisiol. Zhurn.*, **7**, 294–95 (1924)
9. Cerf, J. A., and Otis, L. S., *Federation Proc.*, **16**, 20 (1957)
10. Chow, K. L. (Personal communication)
11. Chow, K. L., *J. Comp. and Physiol. Psychol.*, **45**, 430–37 (1952)
12. Chow, K. L., in *Recent Advances in Biol. Psychiat.*, 149 (Wortis, J., Ed., Grune & Stratton, New York, 1960)
13. Chow, K. L., *J. Neurophysiol.*, **24**, 391–400 (1961)
14. Chow, K. L., Dement, W. C., and John, E. R., *J. Neurophysiol.*, **20**, 482–93 (1957)
15. Chow, K. L., and Obrist, W. D., *Arch. Neurol. Psychiat.*, **72**, 80–87 (1954)
16. Chow, K. L., and Survis, J., *Arch. Neurol. Psychiat.*, **79**, 640–46 (1958)
17. Coons, E. E., and Miller, N. E., *J. Comp. and Physiol. Psychol.*, **53**, 524–31 (1960)
18. Deutsch, J. A., and Mamakos, S. (Presented at Exptl. Psychol. Soc., Cambridge, Mass., 1959)
18a. Deutsch, J. A., *The Structural Basis of Behavior* (Chicago Univ. Press, 1960)
19. Duncan, C. P., *J. Comp. and Physiol. Psychol.*, **42**, 32–34 (1949)
20. Ebner, F. F., and Myers, R. E., *Federation Proc.*, **19**, 292 (1960)
21. Eccles, J. C., in *Brain Mechanisms and Learning* (Delafresnaye, J. F., Ed., Blackwell, Oxford, 1961)
22. Eccles, J. C., and McIntyre, A. K., *J. Physiol. (London)*, **121**, 492–516 (1953)
23. Galambos, R., *Proc. Natl. Acad. Sci. US*, **47**, 129–36 (1961)
24. Geiger, R. S., *Exptl. Cell Research*, **14**, 541–66 (1958)
25. Geiger, R. S., *J. Neuropsychiat.*, **1**, 185–99 (1960)
26. Glickstein, M., and Sperry, R. W., *J. Comp. and Physiol. Psychol.*, **53**, 322–27 (1960)
27. Goldring, S., and O'Leary, J. L., *Electroencephal. & Clin. Neurophysiol.*, **9**, 381 (1957)
28. Goldring, S., and O'Leary, J. L., *Electroencephal. & Clin. Neurophysiol.*, **9**, 577–84 (1957)
29. Harlow, H. F., in *Psychology: A Study of a Science*, **2**, 706 (Koch, S., Ed., McGraw Hill, New York, 1959)
30. Hebb, D. O., *The Organization of Behavior* (Wiley, New York, 1949)
31. Hernández-Peón, R., Guzmán-Flores, C., Alcarez, M., and Fernandez-Guardiola, A., *Acta Neurol. Latinoam.*, **4**, 121–29 (1958)
32. Holt, E. B., *Animal Drive and The Learning Process*, 26 (Holt, New York, 1931)
33. Horn, G., *Brain*, **83**, 57–76 (1960)
33a. Horridge, G. A., *Nature* (In press, 1962)
34. Hyden, H., and Pigon, A., *J. Neurochem.*, **6**, 57–72 (1960)
35. Jasper, H. H., Ricci, G., and Doane, B., in *Moscow Colloq. Electroencephal. of Higher Nervous Activity* (*Electroencephal. & Clin. Neurophysiol. Suppl.* **13**, 1960)
36. John, E. R., and Killam, K. F., in *Recent Advances in Biol. Psychiat.*, Chap. 10, 138–48 (Wortis, J., Ed., Grune and Stratton, New York, 417 pp., 1960)
37. John, E. R., Leiman, A. C., and Sachs, E., *Ann. N. Y. Acad. Sci.*, **92**, 1160–82 (1961)
37a. Jung, R., and Hassler, R., in *Handbook of Physiol.*, I, *Neurophysiol.*, **2** (Am. Physiol. Soc., Washington, D. C., 1960)
38. Katz, J. J., and Halstead, W. C., *Comp. Psychol. Monographs*, **20**, 1–38 (1950)
39. Kogan, A. B., in *Moscow Colloq. Electroencephal. of Higher Nervous Activity* (*Electroencephal. & Clin. Neurophysiol. Suppl.* **13**, 1960)
40. Kraft, M. S., Obrist, W. D., and Pribram, K. H., *J. Comp. and Physiol. Psychol.*, **53**, 509–19 (1960)
40a. Krech, D., Rosenzweig, M. R., and

Bennett E. L. *J. Comp. and Physiol. Psychol.*, **53**, 509–19 (1960)

41. Leukel, F. A., *J. Comp. and Physiol. Psychol.*, **50**, 300–6 (1957)
42. Levine, J., *J. Genet. Psychol.*, **67**, 131–42 (1945)
43. Levine, J., *J. Genet. Psychol.*, **67**, 131–42 (1945)
44. Levine, J., *J. Genet. Psychol.*, **82**, 19–27 (1952)
45. McCleary, R. A., *J. Comp. and Physiol. Psychol.*, **53**, 549–52 (1960)
46. McGaugh, J. C. (Personal communication, 1961)
47. McGaugh, J. L., Westbrook, W. H., and Burt, G., *J. Comp. and Physiol. Psychol.* (In press)
48. Miller, N. E., *Ann. N. Y. Acad. Sci.*, **92**, 830–39 (1961)
49. Milner, B., and Penfield, W., *Trans. Am. Neurol. Assoc.*, **80**, 42–48 (1955)
50. Morrell, F., *Neurology*, **6**, 327–33 (1956)
51. Morrell, F., *Univ. Minn. Med. Bull.*, **29**, 82–102 (1957)
52. Morrell, F., in *Conditionnement et reactivité en electroencephal. (Electroencephal. and Clin. Neurophysiol., Suppl. 6*, 1957)
53. Morrell, F., *Proc. Intern. Congr. Neurol. Sci., 1st* (Brussels, 1957)
54. Morrell, F., in *Moscow Colloq. Electroencephal. of Higher Nervous Activity (Electroencephal. and Clin. Neurophysiol. Suppl. 13*, 1960)
55. Morrell, F., *Ann. N. Y. Acad. Sci.*, **92**, 860–76 (1961)
56. Morrell, F. in *Molecular Specificity and Biological Memory: MIT Seminar-Lecture Ser.*, Spring 1961 (Schmitt, F. O., Ed., Mass. Inst. Technol. Press, Cambridge, Mass., 1961)
57. Morrell, F., in *Brain Mechanisms and Learning*, 375–92 (Delafresnaye, J. F., Ed., Blackwell, Oxford, 1961)
58. Morrell, F., *Physiol. Revs.*, **41**, 443–94 (1961)
59. Morrell, F., Barlow, J., and Brazier, M. A. B., in *Recent Advances in Biol. Psychiat.*, Chap. 9, 123–37 (Wortis, J., Ed., Grune & Stratton, New York, 1960)
60. Muller, G. E., and Pilzecker, A., *Z. Psychol. Physiol. Sinnesorg.*, **I**, 1–300 (1900)
61. Myers, R. E., *J. Comp. and Physiol. Psychol.*, **48**, 470–73 (1955)
62. Myers, R. E., *Brain*, **79**, 358–63 (1956)
63. Myers, R. E., *Federation Proc.*, **16**, 92 (1957)
64. Myers, R. E., *Arch. Neurol.*, **1**, 74–77 (1959)
65. Myers, R. E., and Henson, C. O., *Arch. Neurol.*, **3**, 404–9 (1960)
66. Myers, R. E., and Sperry, R. W., *Arch. Neurol. Psychiat.*, **80**, 298–303 (1958)
67. Olds, J., and Olds, M. E., in *Brain Mechanisms and Learning*, 153–88 (Delafresnaye, J. F., Ed., Blackwell, Oxford, 1961)
68. Orbach, J., and Fantz, R. L., *J. Comp. and Physiol. Psychol.*, **51**, 126–29 (1958)
69. Pearlman, C. A., Sharpless, S. K., and Jarvik, M. E., *J. Comp. and Physiol. Psychol.*, **54**, 109–12 (1961)
70. Rasch, E., Riesen, A. H., and Chow, K. L., *J. Histochem. and Cytochem.*, **7**, 321–22 (1959)
71. Ricci, G., Doane, B., and Jasper, H. H., *Excerpta Med.*, **4**, 401–15 (1957)
72. Riesen, A. H., *Am. J. Orthopsychiat.*, **30**, 23–36 (1960)
73. Rose, J. E., Malis, L. I., Kruger, L., and Baker, C. P., *J. Comp. Neurol.*, **115**, 243–55 (1960)
74. Rosenzweig, M. R., Krech, D., and Bennett, E. L., *Psychol. Bull.*, **57**, 476–92 (1960)
75. Rusinov, V. S., *Communs. Intern. Physiol. Congr. Montreal, 19th* (1953)
76. Russell, W. R., and Nathan, P. W., *Brain*, **69**, 280–300 (1946)
77. Russell, I. S., and Ochs, S., *Science*, **133**, 1077–78 (1961)
78. Schulte, A., *Z. vergleich. Physiol.*, **39**, 432–76 (1957)
79. Scoville, W. B., and Milner, B., *J. Neurol., Neurosurg., Psychiat.*, **20**, 11–21 (1957)
80. Sharpless, S., and Jasper, H. H., *Brain*, **79**, 655 (1956)
81. Shelanski, M. (Personal communication)
82. Siegel, A. I., *J. Comp. and Physiol. Psychol.*, **46**, 249–52 (1953)
83. Sokolov, E. N., in *Central Nervous System and Behavior*, 187–239 (Brazier, M. A. B., Ed., Josiah Macy, Jr. Foundation, New York, 1960)
84. Sperry, R. W., Stamm, J. S., and Miner, N., *J. Comp. and Physiol. Psychol.*, **49**, 529–33 (1956)
85. Sperry, R. W., *Anat. Record*, **131**, 297 (1958)
86. Sperry, R. W., *J. Neurophysiol.*, **22**, 78–87 (1959)
87. Sperry, R. W., and Clark, E., *Physiol. Zoöl.*, **22**, 372–78 (1949)
88. Sperry, R. W., Myers, R. E., and Schrier, A. M., *Quart. J. Exptl. Psychol.*, **12**, 65–71 (1960)

89. Stamm, J. S., and Pribram, K. H., *J. Neurophysiol.*, **23**, 552–63 (1960)

90. Stamm, J. S., and Sperry, R. W., *J. Comp. and Physiol. Psychol.*, **50**, 138–143 (1957)

91. Strumwasser, F., and Rosenthal, S., *Am. J. Physiol.*, **198**, 405–13 (1960)

92. Thomson, C. W., McGaugh, J. C., Smith, C. E., Hudspeth, W. J., and Westbrook, W. H., *Can. J. Psychol.*, **15**, 67–74 (1961)

92a. Weiskrantz, Z., Mihailovic, Lj., and Gross, C. G., *Brain* (In press, 1962)

93. Thompson, R., and Dean, W. A., *J. Comp. and Physiol. Psychol.*, **48**, 488–91 (1955)

94. Thompson, R., and Pryer, R. S., *J. Comp. and Physiol. Psychol.*, **49**, 297–300 (1956)

95. Trevarthen, C. B., *Am. Psychologist*, **15**, 485 (1960)

96. Weiskrantz, L. (Personal communication)

97. Woolley, D. E., Rosenzweig, M. R., Krech, D., Bennett, E. L., and Timiras, P. S., *Physiologist*, **3**, 182 (1960)

SOMATIC FUNCTIONS OF THE NERVOUS SYSTEM[1]

By Alberto Zanchetti

Istituto di Patologia Medica, Università di Siena, Siena, Italy[2]

The broad title of this review requires some qualification. The reader must be cautioned that it refers primarily to the reading done by the reviewer. Indeed, since more than nine hundred papers have appeared since the previous review, a summary of one year's activity in "somatic" neurophysiology cannot cover all the published material, but has to rely on a much more selective approach in order to present a coherent, intelligible body of data and of physiological thinking.

This is not an easy task, but does not appear beyond possibility, if the information resulting from current research is organized according to trends, problems, and ideas. A proper selection of problems is suggested by the experimentation itself, which from time to time brings some topics to the fore. While undue importance may thus be conceded to the fashion, it must humbly be recognized that this will necessarily influence the short-sighted work of a reviewer.

With these concepts in mind, the organization of the sensory systems is here considered only under the two aspects of their "specific" or "unspecific" functions and of their subjection to centrifugal control. As to the former problem, evidence is mostly derived from the somatic sensory system, and data referring to other sensory inputs will be used only when deemed necessary to the organization of our material. Neo- and archicortical electrical events are discussed in terms of their intrinsic significance. Finally, among the more integrated phenomena, that of wakefulness and sleep regulation is given prominent consideration. Unfortunately, space limitation has not permitted a discussion of motor mechanisms even though several important articles have been published in this field during the year.

While the reviewer feels himself excused for having neglected hundreds of recent publications in order to present a less dispersed picture of current research, he requires the greater benevolence from his readers, the shorter he has come of his purpose of integration and the more he has failed to give a faithful and coherent account of some current trends of research.

SPECIFIC AND UNSPECIFIC SENSORY MECHANISMS
Evidence from the Somatic Sensory System

Specificity of skin receptors and afferent fibers.—A discussion of the specificity of the sensory systems must obviously start at the receptor level, par-

---

[1] This review is based upon publications which were available to the author for the period extending through June 1961.

[2] The neurophysiological program of this laboratory is sponsored by Wright Air Development Division of the Office of Aerospace Research, United States Air Force, through its European Office, under Contract No. AF 61 (052)–253, and by Consiglio Nazionale delle Ricerche.

ticularly since in recent times the classical doctrine of specific energy of the senses, as formulated by Müller and von Frey, has been subjected to extensive criticism and re-evaluation. Some aspects of this problem have recently been touched upon by Davis (89). The evidence adduced against the specific-energy doctrine is twofold, histological and physiological. Weddell and his colleagues (211, 327, 328) have just summarized their arguments which are mainly founded on morphological observations. According to the Oxford group, only hair follicle endings, which are generally served by myelinated axons, may be specifically excited by light mechanical stimuli. All other receptors in the skin are represented by free nerve endings, without histological differentiation, most of which are connected to smaller fibers, and would serve all cutaneous sensory modalities (touch, pressure, heat, cold, pain). Discriminative information would be conveyed to the centers on a time-code basis, because different stimuli are supposed to bring forth a different pattern of firing in the same type of fiber. These arguments have been supported by two sets of recent physiological findings, viz. (a) that certain myelinated nerve fibers are excited by stimuli of different modality, mainly touch and cold (149, 168, 169, 211, 324, 325, 338), and (b) that small myelinated C fibers from skin, which were long thought to mediate pain only, are also excited by touch and thermal stimuli, showing what has been called a dual specificity (99, 101). As far as the first argument is concerned, caution has to be used before accepting evidence for receptors sensitive to both mechanical and thermal energies. Indeed a change in temperature can alter the charge transfer through the mechanically excited receptor membrane causing variations in the impulse frequency, although temperature *per se* may not excite the receptor membrane [Ishiko & Loewenstein (178, 179)]. A good example is furnished by the Lorenzinian ampulla of selachians, a pressure receptor whose activity is influenced by temperature only when pressure in the ampulla is maintained within physiological levels [Loewenstein (220)]. Moreover, temperature has been shown to influence receptors with organization as specific as that of the muscle spindles (107, 215). Effects of temperature on the receptor potential of the Pacinian corpuscles have been studied by Inman & Peruzzi (174). Hensel, Iggo & Witt (150), as well as Loewenstein (221), have pointed out that receptors can be described as serving a sensory modality only after a quantitative examination has been made of the relative energy requirement for excitation from the various stimuli. Receptors in human and cat's skin (149, 338) which show high mechanical sensitivity and very low dynamic sensitivity to cooling have to be considered as mechanoreceptors which may be involved in the phenomenon of Weber's illusion, the sensory impression that weights feel heavier when cold.

The observation that C fibers, which presumably ramify in free endings only, are also activated by tactile and thermal stimuli certainly fits well in the scheme of the Oxford group, the plea of these authors being further supported by the multifiber preparations of Douglas & Ritchie, which suggest a dual specificity of most C fibers (99, 101). However, the past year has brought forth evidence that highly specific unmyelinated fibers exist. Iriuchijima & Zotterman (175) and Iggo (171) have recorded from C afferent fibers supplying cutaneous mechanoreceptors. These fibers can have a very high mechanical sensitivity (threshold loads down to 25 mg) and quite limited receptive fields, thus favorably comparing with A pressure fibers, though being lower in sensitivity than most A touch and hair receptors (171); their thermal sensitivity is low and only transient (171, 175). Also C fibers selectively excited by either warming or cooling of the skin have been described (150, 175). Changes in skin temperature as low as 0.1 to 0.2°C are sufficient to excite the most sensitive of C fibers (150); their threshold for mechanical stimulation is very high (150, 175). It might be interesting to compare the dynamic sensitivity of thermo- and mechanoreceptors, both supplied by C afferent fibers, to thermal stimuli. That of the former is 30 impulses per sec per degree C, while that of the latter can be calculated as one impulse per sec per degree C (150, 171). More disappointing has been the search for specific C fibers subserving pain. It is reasonable that some of the fibers responding only to extreme temperatures or to heavy mechanical stimuli may represent pain receptors (171, 175, 176); however, the search for more specific tests to identify nociceptors has not been successful. The close-arterial injection of several substances known to produce local pain in man has been shown to produce unspecific activation of both myelinated and unmyelinated fibers (123). There is some discrepancy between different reports as far as potency and constancy of the chemical stimuli are concerned (99, 100, 123). It might well be, as suggested by Fjällbrant & Iggo (123), that a general test for selectively stimulating all the nociceptors cannot be found: even among nociceptors, modality specificity might exist, some of the receptors being sensitive to extreme heat, some to extreme warmth, others to heavy mechanical stimuli, and so on. It must be remarked that unmyelinated afferent fibers from mammalian skeletal muscle have been recently described by Iggo (172) to be excited by the classical deep pain stimulant, a hypertonic salt solution. Group III fibers from muscle have also been found responsive to this stimulus [Paintal (269)]. The conclusion that both sets of fibers are connected with muscle pain receptors awaits decision on the specific nature of this stimulus, a question on which opinions presently disagree (172, 269). Also, the function of some of Group III fibers from muscle which are activated by strong pressure only may be related to pain [Bessou & Laporte (36)]. This is further suggested by the effect of Group III fibers on arterial pressure (209; see also 304), an argument which has been used to characterize so-called "post-delta" fibers from cutaneous nerves as nociceptive (199).

Summing up the evidence, it appears that several aspects of the doctrine of specific energies have resisted the tide of recent criticism. Nobody doubts that there are some receptors served by myelinated fibers which are specifically sensitive to touch, pressure, or vibration, a category to which we can now add the Pacinian corpuscles responsive to vibration just described in the tibial periosteum (165, 167, 305). On the specificity of Pacinian corpuscles one can consult the careful paper by Loewenstein (221). Furthermore, specific responsiveness to either touch or temperature has been ascertained for a large set of unmyelinated C afferents. This might be taken to mean that free nerve endings in skin are actually specialized, though the differences are too subtle to be revealed by available histological methods. As long as single fiber recordings present a biased sample of the nerve population, it cannot be ruled out, however, that some at least of the small unmyelinated fibers may be excited by two or more different energies, thus substantiating Head's classical hypothesis of a protopathic type of sensation. This issue will be taken up again in a subsequent paragraph. On the contrary, another of the corollaries of the specific energy doctrine has come to be reappraised as a result of current research. The thesis that each of the different cutaneous sensory modalities is conveyed by fibers of one particular range of velocity is now hardly tenable. The careful analysis of Hunt & McIntyre (169) demonstrates that such a hypothesis does not hold even within the category of myelinated cutaneous afferents. Although it is undecided as yet whether C fiber mechanoreceptors actually mediate touch or rather tickling, as suggested by Iriuchijima & Zotterman (175), there is little doubt, to use Bishop's words, that a number of cutaneous sensations are represented twice in the sensory fiber spectrum and tactile sense is possibly represented three times (38).

Organization of the somatic sensory pathways.—The classical assumption that somatic sensory information is conveyed along two distinct pathways—the medial lemniscal system endowed with highly discriminative capacities and mediating touch and kinesthesis, the spinothalamic system transmitting thermal and painful signals—is undergoing considerable reassessment. On a phylogenetic basis, Bishop (39) proposes to distinguish at least five afferent paths dealing with somatic sensations, although it remains to be demonstrated to what extent each of these paths can really be correlated with afferent and central fibers of different caliber and myelinization.

Recent research will now be grouped into two main divisions, referring (a) to the medial lemniscal system, including the main sensory trigeminal nuclei, and (b) to all the remaining systems characterized by the interposition of a spinal relay, including the trigeminal paths arising in the spinal nucleus of the fifth nerve. Previous information not quoted here is admirably summarized by Rose & Mountcastle (288). It will be seen from the following references that some degree of unspecificity can be found also in the lemniscal system, while some at least of the other paths can serve rather discriminative functions.

Some of the characteristics expected of a highly specific system have been observed by Darian-Smith (87) in the main sensory trigeminal nucleus of the cat. Powerful synaptic excitatory effects and limited synaptic convergence have been found in one monosynaptically activated group of neurons. A second group of cells appear to be excited polysynaptically, to be subjected to wider synaptic convergence, and to have larger receptive fields. The latter neurons are supposed to be activated through recurrent collaterals from axons of monosynaptically excited cells. Other studies [Darian-Smith & Mayday (88)] have shown a dorsoventral somatotopic organization within the main sensory nucleus and the rostral part of the spinal trigeminal nucleus; also the latter aggregation is believed to contribute to the medial lemniscal projection (88, 203). A rather varied organization, in terms of receptive field and synaptic convergence, has been described in the gracilis nucleus by Gordon & Paine (136). A marked functional differentiation exists in the rostrocaudal axis, cells with very small receptive fields being clustered in the middle section while the largest peripheral fields are represented in the rostral pole of the nucleus. Mutual inhibition is common in the middle part only; thus neurons of this region seem well qualified to pass on information related to spatial discrimination. While relations of receptive field size to cell position along the rostrocaudal axis of the nucleus have been confirmed by Gentry, Whitlock & Perl (128), these authors, as well as Kruger et al. (203), place more emphasis on relations of receptive field size to receptor location (128, 203) and type (128). Like neurons in the ventroposterior complex and in the somatosensory cortex, cells in the dorsal column nuclei have larger receptive areas when these are located on proximal parts of the limbs and on the trunk (128, 203). Smaller fields have been observed for "hair" or "tap" units than for cells responding to touch (128). The whole contralateral body is represented at all levels, more medial units being connected with more caudal receptive areas; but no spatial segregation of neurons responding to different modalities has been found (203). Most of the tactile gracilis units can also be activated by thermal stimuli (128). Large synaptic convergence on gracilis neurons is confirmed also by the important spatial facilitation shown by several neurons (136); this suggests that true internuncial cells might be present within the nucleus. It seems interesting that, while almost all cells in the middle part of the nucleus are activated antidromically from the contralateral medial lemniscal region (and thus may be thought to project to the thalamus), only 60 per cent of the units in the rostral and caudal portions could thus be fired [Gordon & Seed (137)].

Relative to the sensory pathways relaying at the spinal level, recent data have accumulated on the activation of spinal interneurons by afferent somatic impulses. Unfortunately, the projection of their axons is in most cases unknown, and it is difficult to decide whether we are dealing with true sensory pathways or with afferent branches of a motor reflex. In this context, paths identified as directed to the cerebellum [dorsal (106b, 224) and ventral (106a, 265) spinocerebellar tracts] will not be discussed here, as their destination and the heavy contribution they receive from Group I and II muscle afferents indicate that they are presumably engaged in motor regulation only. Spinal interneurons have been shown to possess different degrees of specific

responsiveness. Neurons selectively excited by cutaneous rather than pro-
prioceptive stimuli have been isolated. They have a strong synaptic linkage
as demonstrated by input-output curves (243) and by absence of a subliminal
fringe (324). At least some of them are monosynaptically activated (31, 166,
243); they are also characterized by repetitive firing (166, 243). There is common agreement that their receptive fields are rather wide (166, 200, 243, 324),
generally larger than for primary afferent neurons, and in some cases have
widely separated areas (200). However, neurons responding only to stimulation of a discrete and small region of the skin have also been recorded (166,
200, 243). While a number of cells react to one sensory modality only, such
as touch, hair-bending, or noxious stimuli (200), others respond to two of
these modalities (200); and a population of neurons in the dorsal part of the
dorsal horn is excited by touch, damage, and skin temperature changes (324,
325). Inhibition from one sensory field associated with excitation from a
different area, as is the case for several lemniscal neurons, has been described
by some authors (166, 200, 243) and denied at least for tactile stimuli by
others (324, 325). On the other hand, a highly discriminative tract ascending
in the ventrolateral funiculus and forwarding a modality-specific message
has been described by Eccles, Eccles & Lundberg (106) and by Lundberg &
Oscarsson (225). Its units respond to light touch applied to quite small areas
of the foot and hindlimb (225). The pathway is located in the most dorsolateral part of the lateral funiculus, in almost complete separation from the
adjacent dorsal spinocerebellar tract; it is further distinguished from this
tract by being activated on stimulation below the caudal end of Clarke's
column but not antidromically from the cerebellum. It is believed to relay in
the lateral cervical nucleus (225), whose ascending connections to the cerebellum and to the somatic sensory areas are known. It is interesting that a
small lesion of this pathway, leaving intact the rest of the lateral funiculus as
well as the dorsal columns, selectively abolishes tactile placing reactions
(223), a highly discriminative phenomenon which requires the participation
of both cortical and cerebellar structures.

The caudal part of the trigeminal spinal nucleus, which is considered the
trigeminal equivalent of the spinothalamic neurons, shows some differentiated
organization. According to Gordon, Landgren & Seed (135), the majority of
cells respond to light, well-localized mechanical stimuli to hair or skin with
a short-latency, short-lived discharge and can be fired antidromically from
the contralateral medial lemniscus region. Units with similar specific characteristics have been described by Kruger *et al.* (203). A second group of
cells respond to tactile as well as noxious and intense thermal stimuli, have
quite large receptive fields, and yield longer-latency prolonged discharges.
No antidromic firing from the lemniscus could be observed (135). Wide receptive areas and lack of somatotopic arrangement are also characteristic of
medullary reticular units responsive to physiological trigeminal stimulation
(207). It is therefore apparent that both in the anterolateral funiculus of the

spinal cord and in the spinal trigeminal nucleus, neurons can be found exhibiting discriminative characteristics comparable to those of most units of the lemniscal system, as well as neurons receiving information from wider receptive areas and from more than one sensory modality. The "common carrier" function of these cells will be further elaborated below.

Preliminary to the discussion of somatosensory thalamic mechanisms, anatomical data from a recent comprehensive research on the projection of fibers ascending through the anterolateral funiculus will be recalled. As shown by Mehler, Feferman & Nauta (244) in silver-stained preparations, most of these fibers distribute to various cell groups in the brainstem reticular formation (spinoreticular path). The relatively small remaining group of spinal fibers terminates separately either in the magnocellular part of the medial geniculate body, or in certain intralaminar thalamic nuclei (mainly in the nucleus centralis lateralis; remarkably not in the centrum medianum proper), or in nucleus ventralis posterolateralis. It has been pointed out by the same authors that medial lemniscus fibers ascend without evidence of any termination caudal to the thalamus and terminate profusely throughout the nucleus ventralis posterolateralis, in sharp contrast with the parcellated distribution of the spinothalamic fibers. Contrasting features of the thalamic organization of the lemniscal system and of a region anatomically related to the spinothalamic system have been described by Poggio & Mountcastle (275). The lemniscal transfer region is characterized by restricted, modality-specific, unchanging receptive fields in the contralateral side of the body, by high probability of synaptic transmission and strong temporal facilitation, and therefore by a strict dependence on the excitability of the peripheral receptors themselves. On the other hand, neurons in the posterior group of nuclei, including the magnocellular part of the medial geniculate, the suprageniculate nucleus, and surrounding structures, often respond to noxious stimuli only; when activated by gentle cutaneous stimuli, this response occurs from very large, often bilateral, and widely separate receptive fields (see also 202); no response is modality-specific, the polysensory nature of these neurons being further demonstrated by their frequent activation from auditory impulses as well. Poggio & Mountcastle's suggestion (275) that the posterior group neurons could be excited through some component of the spinothalamic tract has been substantiated by Whitlock & Perl (272, 334, 335), who have shown posterior group neurons of both cats and monkeys to be fired by large, scattered, bilateral receptive fields after cord transections sparing only one anterolateral funiculus. Further important information is derived from this work (272, 335), insofar as a few neurons in the nucleus ventralis posterolateralis respond to spinothalamic impulses, an observation confirming the previously reported anatomical findings (244). This is a highly specific projection, these units being excited by modality-specific (hair, touch, or noxious) stimuli from very restricted contralateral fields (272). On the other hand, functional nonspecific projections from the anterolateral funiculus of the cord are not limited to the posterior group, but extend also to the intralaminar thalamic nuclei and to the region defined by most physiologists as the centrum medianum. The latter region includes a much larger area than that accepted as the centrum medianum proper by such anatomists as Mehler, Feferman & Nauta (244). Activity in these nuclei is excited from bilaterally located regions of the skin without any somatotopic arrangement (202, 272). Also, neurons in the thalamic nuclei lateralis posterior and ventralis anterior receive tactile information from wide areas of the skin (233). Responses evoked in the centrum medianum have been studied in particular detail by Albe-Fessard's group: these neurons have been found to respond to somatic (8, 231, 232) as well as visual and auditory stimuli (10, 11, 246) and to be subjected to excitatory and inhibitory influences from the cerebral cortex (9, 240, 241, 333). Convergence of cortical and peripheral afferents on the same unit of the centrum medianum has been shown in un-anesthetized cats and cats anesthetized with chloralose (9). It is interesting that, although an important afferent contribution to the centrum medianum from the anterolateral funiculus of the cord by direct spinothalamic, or indirect spinoreticulothalamic connections is well demonstrated (202, 245, 272, 335), this nucleus has been claimed to receive also some lemniscal input, as responses have been recorded from it following electrical stimulation of an isolated dorsal column (202).

Another important target of fibers from the anterolateral funiculus is the brainstem reticular formation, from whence neurons are known to project to intralaminar thalamic nuclei and the centrum medianum. Activation of reticular neurons in the medulla or ventral midbrain by C fibers [Collins & Randt (75)] should not be taken to mean that they represent a central path for pain, as C fibers are now known to serve other sensory modalities also (see above). Unspecificity in terms of multiplicity, extent, and overlapping of receptive fields is a characteristic common to both the reticular formation and intralaminar thalamic nuclei. This does not mean, however, that altogether undifferentiated activity is aroused in reticular neurons upon excitation from different inputs. Indeed, the spontaneous discharge of different reticular neurons, and their responses to diverse forms of afferent stimulation, are known to be nonuniform in term of spatiotemporal patterns, an observation which has been substantiated by simultaneous recording from closely spaced reticular units [Amassian, Macy & Waller (16)]. Specific functions of reticular neurons have been speculated upon by Anokhin (23). Whether reticular neurons might be held to receive a large set of multifarious presynaptic fibers or to be activated through common carrier cells, like those observed at the spinal level, cannot yet be decided. An important difficulty in evaluating the function of reticular and intralaminar neurons in the frame of sensory organization is their participation in motor mechanisms as well. Discharge of one of these neurons in response to peripheral stimulation can hardly be labeled *prima facie* as a sensory phenomenon; indeed the multiple input to these cells is also suggestive of afferent convergence upon a final common motor path. This might be the significance of the activation of reticular units by motor structures such as the pallidum (2), or of the multimodal afferent input to the caudatum (13, 14) through the centrum medianum and nucleus centralis medialis (13). According to an extensive study by Massion (239), a sensory convergence indistinguishable from that displayed by reticular units is observed also in the parvi- and magnocellular parts of the red nucleus, the latter structure obviously belonging to motor mechanisms because of its known connections from the cerebellum (239, 276) and to the spinal cord. The sensory functions of reticular neurons might be more properly assessed after identification of their ascending projection by antidromic firing; the antidromic test has recently been used to identify descending reticulospinal neurons (339).

Further evidence on evoked responses of presumably sensory neurons as compared to afferent responses of identified motor cells is furnished by some recent papers on the sensorimotor cortex of the cat. As reported by Brooks, Rudomin & Slayman (59, 60), neurons in the anterior and posterior sigmoid gyri have either fixed or labile receptive fields for somatic stimulation. Fixed fields can be either local or wide, the former showing all the properties of the medial lemniscal system, while the latter have shapes rather similar to those described for thalamic posterior group neurons [see also (255) for a comparable finding in the monkey]. Interestingly enough, both cells antidromically activated from the medullary pyramids (PT cells) and those not excited by this route (non-PT cells) may show any of the observed fields, except for non-PT cells in the posterior sigmoid gyrus which had only fixed, often local fields. Therefore these cells appear to experience less sensory convergence than do PT cells. A tentative subdivision of the cat's sensorimotor cortex into one anterior division where multimodal activation, visual and auditory as well as somatic, of corticifugal cells prevails, and a posterior area predominantly somatic sensory (but partially motor) in nature, is suggested by Buser and co-workers (65, 66). The region of the posterior sigmoid gyrus immediately posterior to the cruciate sulcus would also belong to the multimodal division (65); indeed, Towe & Kennedy (319) have shown that units in this region can be fired by stimulation of a variety of sites, at least in the animal under the influence of chloralose. It is interesting that barbiturates seem to attenuate the receptive fields of all these cells, but particularly of PT neurons (319). As for the pathways leading to the multifarious excitation of the corticifugal neurons of the anterior sigmoid gyrus, there is indication that it is mediated, not through direct corticocortical paths (66), but by way of medial thalamic nuclei such as the centrum medianum and surrounding structures (65; see also 94); but afferent impulses from the specific sensory areas, for example the visual area, can also converge upon these thalamic relays (61). Here, again, it is hard to assess how far the pyramidal responses can be taken to signify a true unspecific sensory phenomenon, or rather the integrated activity of motor neurons in a final common path.

Finally, there has been some recent discussion on the afferent pathways feeding into the second somatic area. Carreras & Levitt (70) have found that many cells in the region are both mode and place specific, properties which have been defined as lemniscal, though the results of Perl & Whitlock (272) indicate that these properties are also characteristic of ventroposterior neurons activated through the anterolateral funiculi. However, Carreras & Andersson (69) have found cells in the anterior ectosylvian gyrus which were activated by noxious stimuli from wide bilateral peripheral fields, and by visual and auditory stimuli as well. Anatomical projections to SII from discrete portions of the ventroposterior complex and from more caudal structures probably corresponding to the posterior group [Macchi, Angeleri & Guazzi (226)] might serve both the specific and the unspecific representations in the second somatic cortical area.

Summing up, at each level along the somatic sensory pathways several different degrees of specific organization are found. Although two main sets of systems, one relaying through the dorsal columns and the other relaying through the anterolateral funiculi, are respectively considered as examples of high and low discrimination, this is true only with several qualifications. Wide receptive fields and multimodal inputs have been observed also for neurons in the gracilis nucleus and primary somatosensory cortex, while highly discriminative units have been recorded from the anterolateral spinal cord, the spinal trigeminal nucleus, the ventroposterior nucleus of the thalamus (also when activated through spinothalamic paths), and from the second somatic area. Also, gradation in unspecificity is observed, varying from unimodal wide receptive fields to bimodal or multimodal responsiveness within the somatic sphere, to truly polysensory reactions to cutaneous visual and auditory stimuli. Whether some of these systems act as common carriers discriminating on a temporal code basis is undecided, although it seems probable at least for the more unspecific of them, such as the reticular formation. Whether there is some reason to revive some of Head's conceptions on "epicritic" and "protopathic" sensations will be decided only by future investigations.

EVIDENCE FROM OTHER SENSORY SYSTEMS

Some recent papers are relevant in showing that different degrees of specific organization are also present in the auditory and visual systems. Galambos, Myers & Sheatz (127) have made the interesting observation that both early and late evoked activity in the auditory cortex is unmodified, except for a 1 to 2 msec delay in onset, by chronic bilateral section of the classical auditory pathways at the level of the brachium of the inferior colliculus. This extralemniscal activation of the auditory cortex is not prevented by chloralose, but is abolished by administration of pentobarbital. This response might be defined as unspecific only insofar as it is obtained when the so-called specific pathways are interrupted. However, as long as more information is accumulated on the brainstem mechanisms (cerebellar, reticular, etc.) mediating this activity and on the significance of the cortical evoked response itself, judgment will be better reserved as to whether the response might depend on some accessory private auditory pathway, or on activity of the multimodal reticular formation.

The visual system has usually been taken as a classical example of highly specific organization. Additional evidence to this effect is given by recent contributions of Jung (191), Hubel & Wiesel (159, 160), Li *et al.* (212), Vastola (320, 321), and Arden & Liu (25, 26), who have emphasized the wealth of inhibitory effects which can be observed at all levels along the visual pathway. These effects are believed to accomplish differentiation of information by contrast and localized sharpening of the receptive fields. However, convergence of several sense modalities has also been described for most neurons of the visual cortex [Jung (191); Grüsser & Grüsser-Cornehls (144); Lømo & Mollica (222)]. Lømo & Mollica point out that painful stimuli may be effective also in the darkness, an observation which rules out indirect activation of visual neurons through pupillary dilatation. Hubel & Wiesel (159, 160) call attention to the great complexity and variety of receptive fields in the striate cortex, where no types of field have the concentric, circular symmetrical pattern found at lower levels. Moreover, according to evidence presented by Doty (98), cortical responses to photic stimuli and to electrical stimulation of the retina suggest both a topographically organized process and a slower, more diffuse process which activates major portions of the visual cortex following localized excitation.

With reference to the organization of the visual system, besides an exhaustive monograph by Brindley (53), some recent important investigation should not be forgotten. Using an admirably novel approach, Maturana *et al.* (242) have shown that the retina in the frog appears not to transmit information about the point-to-point pattern of distribution of light and dark in the image formed on it. On the contrary, its function is mainly to analyze this image at every point in terms of four qualitative contexts and of a measure of illumination and to send this information to the colliculi, where these functions are separated into the four congruent layers of terminals. Of course, this is a highly specific organization, although of a character not previously considered. Activity of cortical neurons in response to patterned visual stimuli has been studied also by Grafstein, Burns & Heron (138).

Finally, the recent body of evidence presented by Arduini's group should be mentioned. Quantitative measurement of the integrated activity of the optic chiasma has shown that this is definitely higher during dark adaptation than during continuous illumination (30). This finding clearly substantiates the hypothesis that suppression of a heavy dark discharge (see also 108) is likely to be responsible for EEG synchronization (29) and for enhancement of evoked visual responses (27, 28) induced by sustained light or a high rate of flickering light. The depressing effect of the dark discharge on the visual responses might be due either to true inhibition or to an occlusion effect (27).

However, experiments recently reported by Söderberg & Arden (306), showing an increase of the spontaneous discharge of lateral geniculate neurons
during visual deafferentation, would seem to support the inhibitory hypothesis. Just what the dark discharge contributes to the organization of the
visual system cannot be said so far; a rather specific bearing is suggested by
the observation that only visual, not auditory, responses are checked by the
dark discharge (27), while a more widespread unspecific influence is favored
by the generalized effect on the EEG. Both types of influences might well
coexist.

CENTRIFUGAL CONTROL OF THE SENSORY INFLOW

There is continued interest in this exciting problem. Much of the evidence
collected so far on this topic is now widely used for current theories of learning, as testified by the proceedings of a recent symposium (120), by the extensive article of Galambos & Morgan (126) in the *Handbook of Physiology*
(121), and by the reviews by Hernández-Peón (151) and Jouvet (185). Although these aspects of the question are within the scope of another review
in this volume and will not be discussed here, there are other sides which
have an important bearing on sensory physiology and have duly been emphasized by recent authors. It is my opinion, moreover, that settlement of some
of these points should precede generalization of physiological findings to
psychological or psychophysiological concepts.

The role of specific control systems for each sensory input is now being
extensively investigated and compared, or even contrasted, to the unspecific
reticular mechanisms which had previously been emphasized. For the
somesthetic system, detailed evidence has been furnished by Kuypers (204,
205; see also 46, 57) that fibers incorporated in the pyramidal tract and
originating from precentral, postcentral, and posterior parietal cortices are
distributed to the region of the nuclei cuneatus and gracilis, as well as the
nucleus proprius of the spinal cord, thus providing the anatomical basis for a
specific sensory feedback mechanism. Fibers of subcortical origin also terminate within the cuneate and gracilis nuclei, but these seem to originate from
lateral rather than medial portions of the reticular formation (206). After the
observations of Magni *et al.* (229), showing occlusive interference between
direct pyramidal and sensory influences on the dorsal column nuclei, a
number of authors have resorted to unitary recording from these structures.
Siminoff (303) and Waller (326) have found no effect of sensorimotor cortex
stimulation on dorsal column units, unless a cortical convulsive afterdis-
charge ensued (326). However, Jabbur & Towe (181, 318a), Chambers *et al.*
(72), and Guzmán, Buendia & Lindsley (146) have found units driven by and
others inhibited by sensorimotor cortex stimulation. In the anesthetized cats
of Jabbur & Towe (181, 318a), one-third of cuneate units could be driven and
two-thirds inhibited from the pericruciate cortex, while the reverse was true
for the gracile units. Only the sensorimotor cortex appeared to be effective.

Preparations with either complete transection of the brainstem except for the pyramidal tracts, or with section of the pyramidal tracts only, gave evidence that the excitatory pathway is exclusively represented by the pyramidal system, while the inhibitory pathway involves both the pyramidal and an extrapyramidal system (181). It is interesting that, according to Guzmán *et al.* (146), while inhibition of dorsal column nuclei is easily produced by stimulation of the midbrain reticular formation, this changes to facilitation when the sensorimotor cortex is ablated. The inhibitory control exerted by the sensorimotor area would extend also to its specific thalamic relay, according to evidence provided by Ogden (261).

Specific corticothalamic interrelationships have also been described in the visual system by Widén & Ajmone-Marsan (337). Unitary activity evoked in the lateral geniculate nucleus by optic tract or photic stimulation could often be inhibited, and sometimes facilitated, by conditioning stimuli applied to the nonprimary visual area II. These appear to be extrareticular orthodromic effects. The existence of extrareticular centrifugal fibers projecting to auditory relays is re-emphasized by Desmedt (95): some of these fibers would directly inhibit the cochlear nucleus, while others would activate the olivocochlear bundle, thus acting on the primary neurons. These physiological findings are consistent with Rasmussen's (283) detailed anatomical description. It is rather interesting that these centrifugal relays are very close to the classical ascending acoustic system, yet not actually included in it. Also, the starting point of the auditory centrifugal system is to be found not in the primary projection cortex, but in a more ventrally located "associative" area in the temporoinsular cortex, auditory area IV (95). The functions of the olivocochlear bundle [also called efferent cochlear bundle, as proposed by the anatomical investigations of Boord (45)] are now described as more extensive than previously supposed, since stimulation of the tract can inhibit evoked responses in the auditory cortex, medial geniculate, and inferior colliculus at lower intensity than the cochlear response [Ruben & Sekula (291)]. The effect, at least at the cochlear level, appears to be truly inhibitory, as it is suppressed by strychnine [Desmedt & Monaco (96)].

Additional reports of a reticular inhibitory control of sensory potentials have been published [Reinoso-Suárez (285)]. However, although confirming a reduction of evoked potentials in the dorsal cochlear nucleus as a result of reticular stimulation, Hugelin, Dumont & Paillas (163) maintain in a very critical article that this effect is only due to contraction of the middle ear muscles, mainly the stapedius (164). This is not the only instance of sensory evoked potentials peripherally influenced through extraneural apparatuses; according to Naquet *et al.* (257), responses in the optic chiasma and lateral geniculate body depend more on the pupil size than on the state of cortical activation. This is not the case for evoked cortical responses, which seem to be relatively independent of pupil diameter (257) or stapedius contraction

(163) and to be strongly influenced by cortical EEG arousal (163, 257). How far these considerations apply to the reduction of evoked potentials in the lower sensory relays during attention and habituation has been widely discussed. Hugelin *et al.* (163) suggest that the effects of attention on cochlear nucleus potentials are probably independent of middle ear muscle contraction. In the somatic system, where peripheral regulatory apparatuses are not present, responses in the nucleus ventralis posterolateralis are unaffected during attention, while potentials in the centrum medianum and in the associative cortex are greatly depressed [Albe-Fessard *et al.* (12)]. Habituation of chiasma and lateral geniculate responses appears to be prevented by atropine blockade of pupil reactions, while persisting at the cortical level [Fernández-Guardiola *et al.* (119)]. Further, auditory habituation has been observed to persist in the cortex in the absence of middle ear muscles [Moushegian *et al.* (256)], but it has variously been reported to persist [Altman (15)] or to disappear [Guzmán *et al.* (145)] in the specific relay nuclei after removal of the tympanic muscles. Affanni, Mancia & Marchiafava (5) duly point out that distinction of true habituation from fatigue hinges upon the existence of true dishabituation. In their experiments on *cerveau isolé* cats, when the pupil size was rigorously controlled by interruption of the pupillary constrictor pathway and by darkened contact lenses having in the middle a sagittal fissure that simulated a fissurated myosis, thus avoiding both the use of atropine and the glare produced by excessive illumination, "habituation" of optic tract and geniculate photic responses was moderate and late in onset, and no "dishabituation" could be induced by reticular stimulation. Using similar techniques to control the pupil in the intact unanesthetized cat, Palestini, Armengol & Gallardo (269a) have been unable to observe clear-cut habituation of visual evoked potentials even at the cortical level. The problem of habituation is further complicated by a recent detailed study of Marsh *et al.* (238) which shows that during this process a decrease of the evoked potential at the cochlear nucleus and auditory cortex may be associated with an increase at the inferior colliculus and medial geniculate body. Apparently, the mechanisms of sensory habituation still need extensive basic investigation.

Be this as it may, the possible role of the reticular formation in checking sensory information appears to be further challenged by other investigations which, reversing some previous opinions, have shown that reticular stimulation actually facilitates cortically evoked responses. Most of this work has been done on the visual system. Either electrical stimulation of the optic chiasma [Dumont & Dell (103)] or of the lateral geniculate nucleus [Bremer, Stoupel & van Reeth (52)], or repetitive 5 to 20 per sec flashes [Steriade & Demetrescu (313)] have to be used as "sensory" stimuli in order to unveil the reticular facilitation. Less synchronous activity, like that evoked by natural stimuli such as single flashes or clicks, is likely to be masked at the cortical level by the neuronal activation induced by arousal (49, 52). However, in these conditions latent facilitation is shown by an accelerated succession of the positive-negative components of the cortically evoked potential (52). Reticular facilitation is exerted at the thalamic stage (103, 313), but it acts at the cortical level (52, 103) as well. Indeed, under the proper conditions the direct cortical response can also be augmented by reticular stimulation [Loeb, Massazza & Stacchini (218, 219); Akimoto *et al.* (6)]. Akimoto *et al.* (6) report that reticular facilitation of thalamically evoked responses in several sensory areas of the cortex is associated with increased single neuron firing. Further evidence on reticular facilitation of sensory responses concerns units in the posterior suprasylvian cortex which respond more easily following reticular arousal (173), and secondary responses to sciatic stimulation which are potentiated by reticular stimulation (84). Finally, Palestini & Lifschitz (270) report that photic cortical potentials are augmented in size, and less easily habituated, in the cat transected at the midpontine pretrigeminal level, which, it has been suggested, displays a high degree of reticular activity. However, no difference in the size of primary visual potentials has been observed by Meulders, Massion & Colle (247) in midpontine and *cerveau isolé* cats, while responses in associative areas are reported as increased in amplitude after intercollicular section. Interesting speculations on the significance of reticular facilitation of sensory responses are presented by Bremer *et al.* (49, 51, 52) and by Dumont & Dell (103). The latter authors emphasize that this facilitation corresponds in time to Pavlov's orienting reaction and is without relation to later-occurring phenomena such as attention or habituation. Some apparently divergent results obtained by Evart's group should, however, be recalled. In their experience, cortical responses to lateral geniculate shocks show decreased amplitude and more prolonged subnormality during wakefulness than during sleep (114, 115). Although unit discharge in the visual cortex, either spontaneous or evoked by lateral geniculate stimulation, is decreased during waking, it is interesting that the ratio of the evoked to spontaneous discharge is increased, a fact which might indicate heightened sensitivity during the alert state (112, 113). In this connection, a recent report by Fuster (124) should also be mentioned. In the intact free-moving rabbit several units in the visual area are either facilitated or inhibited by brief reticular stimulation. Identification of these units by photic stimuli shows that units activated by diffuse light tend to be accelerated by reticular excitation, whereas units inhibited by diffuse light tend to be inhibited by the reticular stimulus. Evaluation of these interesting findings should take into account Hubel's (158) suggestion that most units in the striate cortex responding to diffuse light are afferent fibers from the lateral geniculate nucleus.

Finally, before closing this section, a word of caution should be spoken on the interpretation of changes in the so-called sensory potentials. Some of these changes are prevalent in the later components of the potential (238), whose significance is unknown. How much attention is deserved by this point is emphasized also by the recent observation of Kiang, Neame & Clark (197) that the pattern of evoked electrical activity, at least in the cerebral cortex, is quite different in awake animals from the classical evoked potentials obtained in anesthetized animals. Furthermore, especially when dealing with the somatic inflow (see e.g. 152), care should be used in distinguishing afferent responses engaged in local motor reflexes, as is the case described in (162), or in more complex motor reactions, as is probably the case for activity in Flechsig's fasciculus (147), from truly sensory responses. Indeed it is known that several of these afferent connections are under a tonic supraspinal control (155, 156, 161, 162, 225, 229a).

SIGNIFICANCE OF ELECTRICAL CORTICAL ACTIVITY

An increasing number of investigations are being devoted to clarification of the origin and nature of the cortical spontaneous or evoked electrical potentials, and the properties of the active elements, in an attempt to decode at the cortical level the messages conveyed through the diverse sensory or, broadly speaking, afferent pathways or to understand the neurophysiological meaning of several electrical correlates of animal behavior. Unfortunately, this difficult matter has been further obscured by excessive theorizing and generalization, going well beyond experimental evidence. More than an objective review, this is an attempt at a cautious assessment of current opinions in the field based on recent factual findings. Thoughtful articles published during the past year by Bremer (50) and by Eccles (105) can also be consulted.

Most of the analysis of cortical potentials is still based on the volume conductor theory, so that surface-positive deflections are interpreted as a sign of deep activity, and surface-negative components as indicating superficial activity. It is no longer felt to be true that brain waves represent envelopes of unitary spikes. Some useful information, however, comes from simultaneous recording of slow waves and unitary activity from the various cortical layers. Spencer & Brookhart (308) report that the surface-positive component of the primary response and of the augmenting wave is coincident in time with a short-latency sink developed in layers III, IV, and V of the sensorimotor cortex, and with tightly clustered bursts of action potentials in the same layers. On the other hand, typical recruiting potentials which were characterized by surface-negativity only, resulting from a relatively small superficial sink, were accompanied by dispersed and irregular unitary spikes in layers III to V of the cortex (308). Loose relationships between recruiting waves and unit behavior have also been observed by Morillo (251), several units being recorded rather deeply, even from the exposed white matter. It is no surprise, however, that recruiting waves may also be accompanied by synchronous efferent discharges in the pyramidal tracts, as recently shown by Purpura & Housepian (282) and by Schlag et al. (296), since "augmenting-like" components can sometimes be superposed to the basic recruiting pattern (308). It must be remarked, however, that corticospinal discharge has also been described as associated with recruiting waves lacking any initial surface-positivity (282) and that previous reports of the absence of efferent discharge during recruitment have been ascribed to bipolar recording from an amazingly uniform potential field (296). Studying the transcallosal response, Latimer & Kennedy (210) have found that three-fourths of the units discharge initially during the surface-positive component, but these units are located in all layers of the cortex, with the possible exception of layer I. No definite correlation between sensory evoked potential and reflex discharge of PT and non-PT cells has been found by Kennedy, Towe & Patton (196) in the sensorimotor cortex under the influence of chloralose; most units respond to an ipsilateral stimulus, while the ipsilateral evoked wave is negligible. On their part, Widén & Ajmone-Marsan (336) report that a positive correlation exists between the amplitude of the fourth and fifth components of the cortical photic response and the probability of discharge of postsynaptic cortical units. It is, however, remarkable that no units discharging during the middle and late parts of the large surface-negative fifth wave could be recorded.

In recent times there has been an increasing tendency in the neurophysiological literature to interpret any surface-negative cortical potential, either spontaneous or evoked by direct or afferent stimulation, as signaling dendritic depolarization; and consequently several properties of dendritic activation have been described. Such generalization should, however, take into account the fact that a surface-negative wave which is similar to the direct neocortical response, the phenomenon most commonly labeled as dendritic, is recorded from the hippocampal ventricular surface upon its direct stimulation (194, 315). Kandel, Spencer & Brinley (194) duly emphasize that this occurs in spite of the reverse arrangement of the hippocampal surface, where somata are superficial and apical dendrites point downwards. This hippocampal component may result from activity of the basal dendrites (22a). Also, hippocampal potentials evoked through afferent stimulation may have surface configuration not dissimilar to neocortical evoked responses (17, 18, 19, 79). Further caution is called for by the findings of Spencer & Brookhart (308) that recruiting and augmenting waves are generated by entirely different intracortical mechanisms, as revealed by a profile of potential change in depth and time. The same differences characterize two basic patterns of spontaneous spindle waves, one resembling the augmenting, the other the recruiting potentials (309). Equivalence of augmenting and recruiting potentials has, however, been claimed by Bishop, Clare & Landau (40) on the basis of depth recording and mutual occlusion studies. It is remarkable that these authors describe augmenting potentials in the visual cortex as predominantly negative waves, apparently without the increasing positivity classically observed in the sensorimotor area. Moreover, mutual occlusion of the negative deflections of recruiting and augmenting, and sometimes of the specific visual responses (40, 208), although important in indicating some degree of interdependency between these cortical phenomena, cannot be taken as a definite proof of a common substrate. Also, the common cortical origin of the direct cortical response and of the recruiting potentials might appear challenged by the different effects of pharmacologic agents on the two responses; but this difference has been reasonably ascribed to differences in the route by which the responses are evoked (129).

Bishop and his co-workers (40, 74, 208) reiterate a scheme of cortical behavior whereby the direct cortical response and augmenting and recruiting potentials would represent synaptically generated activity in apical dendrites, while the negative deflection of the specific sensory and transcallosal responses would indicate antidromic invasion of the apical dendrite from the previously activated soma. The possibility of antidromic invasion of apical dendrites was discussed in a thoughtful paper by Jabbur & Towe (182), who have studied the antidromic cortical response to stimulation of the medullary pyramids. When the stimulated pyramidal tract is dissected free from the adjacent tissue, and current spread to lemniscal fibers is avoided, only a sur-face-positive spike and a following positive wave are recorded at the peri-cruciate cortex. Therefore, if apical dendrites are antidromically invaded from the soma, they make no significant contribution to cortical surface-negativity. Phillips (274) does not find any evidence of apical dendritic activation in his intracellular records of Betz cells antidromically stimulated. Likewise, Euler & Green (110) report that, in extracellular records from hippocampal pyramids, soma spikes are usually not followed by excitation of the dendritic membrane unless repetitive stimulation is employed. Jabbur & Towe have used their data to deny the existence of recurrent collateral activity of pyramidal cells as measurable at the cortical surface. On the other hand, evidence favoring inhibitory and excitatory effects of recurrent collaterals of pyramidal axons, when antidromically excited, is furnished by the intracellular recordings of Phillips (274), although it remains to be proved whether they are actually mediated through the Golgi recurrent collaterals. The participation of retrograde axonal collaterals in producing the callosal antidromic response (preparations in which dromic callosal fibers had been allowed to degenerate) is suggested by Clare, Landau & Bishop (74). Finally, before holding to the interpretation of the negative component of the primary response as apical dendritic activity antidromically excited, consideration should be paid to a hypothesis recently advanced by Jankowska & Albe-Fessard (183) that it may be the reflection of a horizontal dipole, whose positive pole would lie in the closely adjacent somatic associative area.

An ingenious attempt to get more crucial evidence on the role played by dendrites and other neural elements in cortical electrogenesis has been made by Purpura, Carmichael & Housepian (280), and by Do Carmo (97), by comparing the patterns of the direct cortical response and of recruiting waves with morphological features of cortical neurons at various developmental stages. Substantially concordant physiologic data have been obtained by the two groups: direct cortical responses have a surprisingly long duration and a prolonged unresponsive period, coming to approximately the adult characteristics only at the third postnatal week (97, 280). Also, recruiting waves, though present at birth, do not reach the adult configuration for 15 days (97). Unfortunately there is not so much agreement on the morphological features. Purpura *et al.* (280) describe densely packed apical dendrites of pyramidal neurons and dendrites of Cajal-Retzius cells in neonatal kittens, with gradual decrease in dendritic density during development, and ascribe the physiological changes to dendritic maturation. On the other hand, Eayrs & Goodhead (104) and Schadé & Baxter (295), the latter authors using quantitative methods, report that dendrites are hardly countable in rats and rabbits at birth, but progressively increase in volume and surface during the first neonatal weeks. It is the cell body density and volume which would decrease in postnatal period (295).

More crucial evidence on the basis of cortical electrogenesis continues to be sought in the hippocampus, the anatomical architecture of which lends itself more suitably to identification of the elements responsible for the various potential deflections, and to application of the volume conductor theory. In this respect, the archicortex has some advantages over the neocortex, i.e., rather definite segregation of basal dendrites, cell bodies and apical dendrites in successive layers, and different synaptic organization of afferents from diverse sources. In the neocortex the so-called specific and unspecific afferents cannot be translated, as is too often conceded, to mean axosomatic and axodendritic connections, respectively, and no evidence has yet been provided for a different origin of the two sets of fibers. By contrast, in the hippocampus convincing anatomical data indicate the existence of axosomatic connections from the septum, and axodendritic synapses with the perforating pathway. Other anatomical findings suggest that interhippocampal fibers mostly relay at the apical dendrites in the CA 1 field, and at the basal dendrites in the CA 3 field (17, 109, 111). In agreement with these morphological data, von Euler (109) finds that, following septal stimulation, depth recordings from area CA 1 of the dorsal hippocampus show a negative wave in the layers of basal dendrites and pyramidal cell bodies, inverting to a positive deflection at the level of apical dendrites. When the hippocampal portion of the perforating pathway is stimulated, the sink is found at the depth occupied by apical dendrites, while a positive wave is recorded from the more superficial layers (109). Unitary recordings suggest that the two afferent systems make synaptic contacts mainly with different neurons (111). Further, according to Andersen, Bruland & Kaada (22), septal stimulation evokes a negative wave surmounted by a negative spike in the pyramidal cell layer. Activation of the dentate area by septal stimulation has also been investigated (21). In a series of careful studies on interhippocampal connections (17 to 20), Andersen reports that field CA 1 stimulation evokes on the contralateral homotopic field a response which is recorded as negative in the layer of the apical dendrite shaft and is followed by a propagated spike, while the CA 3 commissural response is characterized by negativity in the basal dendritic layer, thus confirming the aforementioned anatomical arrangement of commissural connections.

The origin of the hippocampal theta rhythm has been studied in depth and with unit recordings. Von Euler & Green (111) suggest that it may arise because of synchronously occurring "inactivation processes" in many pyramidal neurons. Indeed, deep depolarization leading to initial excitation followed by inactivation of spike generation has been found to be a commonly operating mechanism in the hippocampal pyramids. That the theta rhythm is generated within the hippocampus might be questioned as a result of researches by Petsche & Stumpf (273) which suggest that the generator might be in the ventricle. However, subsequent experiments by Green *et al.* (142), using a penetrating microelectrode, have shown a phase reversal of the theta rhythm just below the cell layer, immediately preceded by disappearance of activity in a very narrow null zone. The suggestion is advanced (141, 142) that the theta wave is apparently a nonpropagated disturbance which is generated by the hippocampal pyramids between the cell bodies and the proximal two-thirds of the apical dendrites. For the majority of neurons there is a strong tendency to fire at a particular phase angle of the wave. Distribution and phase relationships of hippocampal and entorhinal slow waves have been examined with auto- and cross-correlation techniques by Adey *et al.* (3, 154) during approach learning.

There has been some recent discussion on the nature of activity in dendrites. Chang (73) maintains that it is not a local electrotonic potential, but a decrementally conducted phenomenon. Interaction studies on the direct cortical response suggested to Ochs & Booker (259) that apical dendrites may be capable of all-or-none responses. Concerning the possibility of spike responses of dendrites, von Euler's data on the hippocampal response to the perforating pathway (109) support the hypothesis that dendrites exert only electrotonic effects on the cell body [see similar evidence for the spinal motoneuron monosynaptically excited from a dorsal root in the pentobarbital-treated animal in (116)]. On the other hand, Andersen (18) has recorded a spike conducted in both directions in the apical dendritic layer of field CA 1, and he postulates that the CA 1 apical dendritic membrane is composed of two parts, the first responsible for electrotonic postsynaptic potentials, the other for the initiation and propagation of spikes. The part of the dendritic membrane capable of generating spikes would change in size according to the excitability level (22). Eccles (105), on reviewing previous evidence and on theoretical grounds, concludes that no characteristic difference between soma and dendrites has been shown so far and that dendrites can also be supposed to generate spikes. One can find in this article (105), as well as in other recent reports (17, 73, 252), extensive criticism of the concept that dendrites are electrically inexcitable. Crucial evidence on the mechanisms of activation of cortical neurons is derived from intracellular recordings. Not only the neocortical Betz cells have successfully been explored and shown to be played upon by excitatory and inhibitory synaptic actions (274); the hippocampal pyramidal neurons have now been impaled, and a series of brilliant studies (193, 195, 310, 311) gives a full account of their action potential configuration, synaptic organization (both excitatory and inhibitory), after-potentials, firing level, and time constant. Of particular interest is the observation of small fast prepotentials which are supposed to arise in the main apical dendritic bifurcation and which would serve as a trigger zone for the axon hillock (311). Spencer & Kandel (311) emphasize that the fast prepotential does not conduct regeneratively, since it is of small amplitude and is not blocked by hyperpolarizing currents. According to their interpretation, dendrites would not be capable of generating true spikes.

The finding that neocortical and archicortical cells may display both excitatory and inhibitory postsynaptic potentials, obviously of opposing polarity, heavily supports the claim, also recently re-emphasized by Grundfest (143), that indiscriminate application of the volume conductor theory to the interpretation of cortical waves is not without dangers. However, the use of pharmacological substances, such as γ-aminobutyric acid (GABA), to distinguish between the two types of postsynaptic potentials has been questioned. The just-published proceedings of a recent symposium (287) can profitably be consulted for information on this subject and on the broad field of GABA action. Grundfest (143) and Purpura (279) reiterate the concept that inversion of the surface-negative direct cortical response by GABA represents the unmasking of dendritic hyperpolarizing inhibitory postsynaptic potentials. Unselective block of responsiveness in the superficial layers is discarded on account of differences between the effects of KCl, pentobarbital, and GABA (281). Differences in the effects of KCl and GABA on the secondary response have also been described [Iwama & Yamamoto (180)]. Several experimental findings pointing at different interpretations have, however, been reported. According to Mahnke & Ward (230), GABA affects evoked potentials in a nonpredictable way, with simultaneously excitatory and inhibitory components. This reaction has been mentioned also by Crepax & Infantellina (81) in studies on the isolated cortical slab. O'Leary and his group (132, 286), by showing that the initial cortical deflection to direct stimulation of both cerebral and cerebellar cortices is inverted by GABA, question the interpretation of cortical potential polarity in terms of de- and hyperpolarizations, as well as the inference that the cerebellar cortex lacks inhibitory synapses. Jasper (184) reviews personal contributions to this problem. When tested on the direct cortical response, GABA inverts only the local potential and is without effect on the conducted response; the indirect cortical response is also inverted, simultaneously with the development of a deep negative wave; finally, the presumed blocking action of strychnine upon the surface-positive response of the GABA-treated cortex also occurs on the normal surface-negative deflection, an observation which can hardly be explained by a selective blockade on inhibitory synapses. That most GABA effects can be explained by its low capacity for diffusion is supported by calculations of Kandel, Spencer & Brinley (194). Although the observation that higher concentrations of GABA also invert the deep negative potentials has been taken to mean that additional factors besides volume conduction may be involved (284), Curtis & Watkins (86) duly emphasize the difficulty of interpreting positive extracellular potentials when GABA is applied to a group of cells. These authors have shown that a motoneuron excitatory synaptic potential, extracellularly recorded, may be inverted to a positive deflection by GABA, while the intracellularly recorded membrane potential is unchanged and both excitatory and inhibitory postsynaptic potentials are depressed. It has been suggested that the effect of GABA on neurons consists of an increase in membrane conductance, because of increased permeability to chloride ions (86). Its action appears not to involve change in membrane permeability to potassium (54).

It is the reviewer's opinion that, in such a confused matter as the interpretation of electrical cortical activity, great caution should be used in the assessment of experimental data, and that desires for generalization, however clever and fashionable, should be continuously mortified. Attributing such complex phenomena as spreading depression to dendrites (260) seems premature. The same consideration applies to the tentative hypothesis that glia might be involved in this phenomenon (125), though the large release of ions occurring during spreading depression (55, 64, 201) and the surprisingly large part of extraneuronal volume occupied by glia might loosely suggest this relationship. The current interpretation of epileptic potentials as resulting from apical dendritic activity is not supported by the observation that self-sustained convulsive activity in the hippocampus may occur when the excitation wave has already left the apical dendrite layer (131a). Transcortical steady potential gradients (264), as well as the so-called ultra-slow potentials (7), still await convincing explanation. Terms like "excitatory" and "inhibitory postsynaptic potentials" should be reserved to the appropriate phenomena intracellularly recorded. Free recourse to pharmacological testing to infer physiological conclusions, in itself a justifiable procedure, may accumulate a so-called body of evidence which is rapidly falsified by subsequent research (see e.g. 34). As long as more crucial evidence is lacking, cortical electrical activity should provisionally be defined in terms of its polarity in surface and depth, and of other directly measurable characteristics, and correlated with extra- and intracellularly recorded unitary activity. Further, a statistical approach like that elaborated by Goldstein (134) might prove valuable.

THE RETICULAR FORMATION

Some studies on the brainstem reticular formation have been reviewed in previous chapters because of the functions of this structure as an "unspecific" sensory system and of its postulated participation in sensory control. Emphasis will be placed on reticular participation in sleep and wakefulness regulation, one of the most fully substantiated among the functions ascribed to the reticular formation. The proceedings of an important symposium on the nature of sleep should be consulted (340), as well as the exhaustive chapter written by Lindsley (214) for the third volume of the *Handbook of Physiology* (121). As there is increasing evidence that the reticular influences on sleep and wakefulness are complex and that different effects are likely to depend on separate structures within the brainstem, we have tentatively organized the surveyed material as referring to three different reticular mechanism or effects.

Activating or arousal system.[3]—Antonelli & Rüdiger (24) have provided the demonstration, which was surprisingly lacking, that EEG arousal can be evoked by direct stimulation of reticular neurons, independently of co-stimulation of extralemniscal sensory paths ascending through the central brainstem. Generalized EEG activation has been produced by cortical stimulation: only selective regions are effective [Kaada & Johannessen (192)], and they correspond to those from which a behavioral attention response is elicited in the unrestrained cat [Fangel & Kaada (117)]. Sensorimotor area stimulation blocks recruiting potentials in both the cortex and thalamus by excitation of the reticular activating system, as the effect is abolished following precollicular midbrain transection [Narikashvili *et al.* (258)]. Activating structures, probably driven reflexly by the retinal dark discharge, are still at work in the *cerveau isolé* cat with a postcollicular transection, since the EEG synchronization of the isolated cerebrum increases following bilateral suppression of the retinal dark discharge [Bizzi & Spencer (41a)].

The problem of the chemical mediation of reticular activating neurons is still considerably debated. The cholinergic nature of them, suggested to some authors by atropine blockade of sensory and reticular arousal, is definitely not supported by recent observations of Loeb, Magni & Rossi (217). Indeed, atropine has no influence on reticular responses to single sensory or reticular stimuli, nor does it affect the blockade of recruiting potentials by reticular stimulation. Reticular excitability is therefore not depressed by the drug (217). However, high doses of atropine are not devoid of behavioral effects, especially when tested in man with the use of suitable criteria (266).

The hypothesis of an adrenergic reticular transmission has also been questioned recently. Lack of EEG effects from intracarotid epinephrine and norepinephrine as contrasted to their effectiveness when given intravenously [Mantegazzini *et al.* (236); Capon (67)], association of cortical with systemic pressor effects (67), and lack of mutual facilitation between subthreshold reticular stimulation and subliminal doses of epinephrine [Bradley (47)] have all been taken to signify that epinephrine has only an indirect action on electrocortical activity. Furthermore, no epinephrine-like substance is liberated following strong prolonged reticular stimulation [Marley (237)];

---

[3] Terms such as "activation", "synchronization", and "desynchronization", as well as their derivatives, are used operationally to denote EEG patterns, without commitment as to the nature of the intracortical changes.

the pressor substance released from the brain during reticular stimulation is likely to be vasopressin [Rothballer & Sharpless (290, 302)]. Tonkikh (317) suggests that the cortical effects of systemic epinephrine might also be mediated through vasopressin release, giving some evidence that they would be abolished by hypophysectomy. On the other hand, Dell (90) makes a clever defense of his viewpoint by indicating several experimental conditions unduly favoring negative results and by showing that the metabolic potentiator of epinephrine, pyrogallol, greatly intensifies and prolongs arousal produced by intravenous epinephrine, the cortical effect persisting well beyond the end of the pressor changes (102). Goldstein & Muñoz (133) suggest that pressor and cortical effects of epinephrine are independent. Such an independence has been observed by Savoldi *et al.* (292, 293) in the anesthetized, though not in the unanesthetized, rabbit. An interesting approach has been followed by Mantegazzini & Glässer (235), who have injected dihydroxyphenylalanine (DOPA) intravenously or into a carotid, thus augmenting the intracerebral content of dopamine and norepinephrine. This treatment results in clear-cut cortical activation, unaccompanied by arterial pressure or cerebral blood flow changes. In (130), one can read an analogous work on the EEG effects of 5-hydroxytryptamine and of its amino acid precursor; but for slightly different results see (78). Be this as it may, before it can be taken for granted that catecholamines are mediators or reinforcing agents at reticular synapses (90) other objections have to be ruled out. Insignificant or very slow uptake of circulating norepinephrine occurs in the brain (329) [but DOPA easily penetrates into the brain from the blood (68)]. Vogt (323) has emphasized that in several conditions animal behavior is independent of considerable changes in brain catecholamines. Finally, Curtis & Koizumi (85) demonstrate the important fact that neither norepinephrine nor acetylcholine, electrophoretically applied through micropipettes to reticular neurons, influences their discharge as extracellularly recorded. Intracellular recording from reticular units, which has just become possible [Limanski (213)], should further help to clarify definitively this interesting problem.

Synchronizing effects.—Two aspects, although not necessarily correlated to the same mechanism, will be discussed here: (*a*) the relation between cortical synchronization and low-frequency activity in deep structures; (*b*) the synchronizing functions of the lower brainstem.

As to the first topic, Jouvet (187, 188) has emphasized that spindles and slow waves which are recorded from the thalamus and reticular formation, simultaneously with similar activity in the neocortex during the first stages of sleep, require the presence of the neocortex, since they are altogether absent in the decorticate animal or behind a section of the brainstem. This has been confirmed even in *cerveau isolé* (301) animals or animals under the influence of barbiturates (300, 301). Flattening of the EEG with disappearance of barbiturate spindles in the reticular formation has also been observed during the functional cortical inactivation accompanying spreading depression (331). As recruiting potentials are often identified with spindle waves, it is remarkable that thalamic stimulation can easily evoke these responses in the reticular formation following decortication also [Schlag & Faidherbe (298)]. However, in the experience of these authors, even when the cortex was intact, spontaneous reticular spindles were much smaller than recruiting potentials.

As to the second topic Moruzzi (253) has amply reviewed the evidence brought forward by his group for tonic synchronizing influences in the lower brainstem and has elaborated on the possibility that these influences may be engaged in Pavlovian sleep. Activity in these synchronizing structures would be responsible for predominance of synchronized patterns in the *encéphale isolé* cat [Ho *et al.* (153)]. Dell, Bonvallet & Hugelin (91) present evidence that the same mechanisms may be phasically excited from the activating system to curtail the duration of any arousal reaction. Prebulbar sections would interrupt this inhibitory feedback loop, as indicated by the longer persistence of arousal patterns in the neocortex (43) and in the mesencephalic reticular formation (42). Some important work has been performed in the attempt to evoke cortical synchronization by brainstem stimulation. This approach has been successful, and Magnes, Moruzzi & Pompeiano (227, 228) and Rossi's group (118) agree that bursts of low-frequency waves can be induced in the EEG from the lower brainstem only following 4 to 12 cps stimulation with a suitable EEG background, neither too fully activated nor too fully synchronized; the slow cortical waves, whose frequency is rather independent of the rate of stimulation, may occasionally outlast the end of the stimulus for some time. Favale *et al.* (118), who have used unrestrained cats with implanted electrodes, have also shown that EEG changes are accompanied by a behavior suggestive of sleep. This would correspond to the "telencephalic" stage of sleep of Jouvet (187, 188), although the term "telencephalic" might convey the idea, inconsistent with the above mentioned results, that this stage starts in the forebrain. Some discrepancy arises between Moruzzi's and Rossi's groups as far as the location of the brainstem region yielding the synchronization effect. Favale *et al.* (118) have implanted electrodes in various reticular regions and found that all sites were capable of eliciting either synchronization or desynchronization depending upon the pattern of the stimulus and the background activity. Magnes *et al.* (227, 228), who have confined themselves to stimulation of the structures around the solitary tract nucleus in the *encéphale isolé* cat, have found closely adjacent areas either capable or incapable of the synchronizing effect. They emphasize that the anatomical aspect of the question is important. In their experience synchronization could be induced from the nucleus of the solitary tract and the nucleus reticularis ventralis. Localization and dissociation of effects obtained by stimulating the reticular formation may indeed be very difficult, or altogether impossible, because of its intricate anatomical organization, as further shown by Mannen's Golgi studies of (234). As for the mechanisms by which stimulation of the lower brainstem brings forth synchronization, both Moruzzi's and Rossi's groups (118, 227) suggest that connection with the midline nuclei of the thalamus might explain the response during stimulation (phasic effect), while synchronization outlasting the stimulus (tonic effect) might well depend on a sort of reciprocal inhibition of the activating structures. The latter mechanism is particularly emphasized by Dell *et al.* (91). The existence of two distinct systems at the medial thalamic level also, the recruiting one and the activating one, has again been emphasized by Monnier *et al.* (249, 250), who support their hypothesis with experiments involving drug administration, brain section, and cortical unit recording. The recent finding of Schlag *et al.* (297, 299) that the desynchronizing, though not the recruiting, effects of medial thalamic stimulation are impaired by coagulation around the posterior commissure does not necessarily support Monnier's contention, as reticular recruiting potentials are also abolished by a similar lesion (298).

The problem of the afferents contributing to the synchronizing system has been taken up by Pompeiano & Swett (277, 278), who report that in unrestrained cats low-frequency low-voltage stimulation of cutaneous (although not muscular) Group II fibers is followed by cortical synchronization, provided of course that a suitable excitability background be utilized. Higher-rate stimulation of the same fibers, as well as stimulation of cutaneous and muscle Group III fibers at any frequency, yields EEG and behavioral arousal. Neither kind of stimulus gives behavioral signs of pain.

As pressoceptive carotid sinus afferents are commonly held to have synchronizing influences, probably relaying in the bulbar mechanisms just described [see the mentioned EEG effects of solitary tract nucleus stimulation (227, 228)], some recent studies on ascending neural effects of carotid sinus stimulation or inactivation may be relevant at this point, although bearing no obvious connection with synchronization phenomena. Bartorelli *et al.* (32; see also 341, 342) have shown that the diencephalic centers responsible for the sham rage behavior of the decorticate cat are under a tonic inhibitory influence from the carotid sinus, and probably aortic, pressoceptors. They have suggested that this effect might be mediated either through a direct deactivation of the activating reticular system or through excitation of lower brainstem mechanisms, which might well correspond to those exerting the synchronizing influence. It can also be mentioned that sham rage outbursts can be called forth in the decorticate animal by chemoceptive sinoaortic stimuli [Bizzi *et al.* (41)], which are known to be capable of exciting both ascending and descending reticular mechanisms [Dell, Hugelin & Bonvallet (44, 92); Baumgartner, Creutzfeldt & Jung (33)].

Finally, synchronizing effects obtained from extrareticular structures should briefly be recalled. Low-frequency stimulation of basal forebrain areas results in cortical synchronization and behavioral sleep [Sterman & Clemente (314)]; synchronized patterns associated with myosis and lowering of the arterial pressure are obtained by high-rate stimulation of the cerebellar pyramis and uvula and are followed by rebound in the opposite direction [Sawyer *et al.* (294)]. The relationship of these effects to the reticular synchronizing mechanisms is unknown. On rather scanty evidence, the caudate nucleus, which evokes cortical and subcortical spindling on low-frequency stimulation, has been considered as a part of an inhibitory feedback circuit acting antagonistically to the reticular activating system [Buchwald *et al.* (62, 62b, 62c, 152a)].

"Activated" sleep.—In the last few years a considerable body of evidence has grown showing that electrocortical patterns of activation, indistinguishable from those of arousal, can be present during sleep and, indeed, during deeper stages of sleep than those characterized by slow waves and spindles (35, 148, 157). Jouvet, who has himself greatly contributed to our knowledge in this field, summarizes his relevant results (186, 187, 188). Activated sleep (or "paradoxical phase" of sleep in Jouvet's terminology) is characterized by repeated cycles of fast cortical, diencephalic, and mesencephalic activity, with slow waves in the pontine reticular formation. It is associated with sudden loss of neck muscle tone and with rapid jerks of eyeballs, vibrissae, and tail. According to Mikiten *et al.* (248) these jerks would be simultaneous to biphasic eight-per-second spikes in the lateral geniculate nucleus (possibly on-off responses caused by ocular movements). Electroencephalographic and behavioral components of the activated sleep complex can be dissociated by suitable brainstem sections, with survival of the only component whose anatomical substrate remains connected to the rostral pons. Localized lesions of the nucleus pontis caudalis and of the posterior part of the nucleus pontis oralis abolish activated sleep. It appears therefore that this sleep phase depends upon a rhombencephalic pacemaker. A rhinencephalic role was suggested by persistence of activated sleep following a midbrain transection sparing only the basal structures which are on the passage of the so-called limbic-midbrain circuit. Conversely, lesions localized to the superior central nucleus of Bechterew, to the interpeduncular nucleus, or to the septum completely abolish the cortical, though not the behavioral, manifestations of the activated sleep (190). As the effective lesions include the superior central nucleus of Bechterew, which is a raphe nucleus, the reader can usefully consult the recent description by Brodal's group of the connections of the raphe nuclei as compared to the reticular ones (56, 58, 316). That this phase of sleep is an active phenomenon is supported by the possibility of precipitating long-lasting periods of activated sleep upon brief stimulation of the pontine tegmentum (187). These findings have been confirmed by Rossi *et al.* (289), who were able, however, to trigger activated sleep from every part of the reticular formation whenever the stimulus was made to occur in a late period of the slow phase of sleep. The effective stimuli were high-rate pulses, which could arouse the same animal if applied to the same reticular site during lighter sleep. Rossi *et al.* (289) have contributed other experiments which suggest that activated sleep is characterized by functional depression of synchronizing systems (no spontaneous slow bursts nor recruiting potentials being apparent) and that this depression is likely to be caused by active inhibition (since both types of slow waves reappear after small doses of thio-

pental, this reappearance being interpreted as a release phenomenon). A similar interpretation is advanced by Moruzzi (254). The hypothesis that active mechanisms are at work during sleep is supported also by recent observations of Huttenlocher (170) that there is an increased discharge of many brainstem neurons during this stage of sleep. Of course, it would be important to identify these neurons and to know whether they are different from those belonging to the activating system.

Finally, studies on activated sleep in humans should be mentioned. There is no question that it occurs also in man (122, 189, 198), but it is not clear whether it represents a light or deep stage. Unfortunately the tests valuable for cats do not hold for men, as human posture during sleep is different (122, 189). It has been confirmed that activated sleep in man seems associated with dreaming (189, 198), and dream deprivation by repetitive arousals at the beginning of such phases has been said to produce some emotional disturbance (93).

Intracortical activity in wakefulness and sleep.—Further important researches have been carried out on this problem. Almost all of them refer to "synchronized" sleep. Evoked cortical responses during arousal and sleep have already been reviewed in a previous chapter. As far as the spontaneous neural activity is concerned, Evarts (112, 113) has found considerable variability between units in the visual cortex: the firing of some neurons, generally those with higher discharge, was decreased, while that of others, generally those with lower discharge, was increased during natural sleep. In the motor cortex, Creutzfeldt & Jung (83), often using multiple microelectrodes, have observed initial diminution followed by later increase in firing upon sensory arousal, the length of the inhibitory phase being shorter and the importance of the later activation greater in faster discharging units. Sleep is characterized by periodic grouped discharges better seen in fast neurons. Burst activity of a single unit, and synchronized discharge between neighboring neurons, are increased by mild barbiturate anesthesia (82). Verzeano & Negishi (322), by recording with close multiple microelectrodes from the cortex or thalamus, have shown that during sleep or anesthesia there are an increased firing of individual neurons, a larger number of neurons engaged, and various changes in the propagated activity between neighboring neurons. The experience of Monnier *et al.* (250) is quite different from that of the other authors, 90 per cent of units recorded from the motor and the visual cortices being found increased by an arousing reticular stimulation. A suppressor action of the reticular formation on the cerebral cortex might be suggested by the finding that morphine generalizes low-frequency convulsive waves in constant association with increase in arousal threshold [Crepax & Fadiga (80)]. Finally, the slow cortical potential changes described by Caspers (71) in free-moving animals should be recalled. Although their significance is hard to assess, steady negativity during arousal might tentatively be taken as a sign of superficial depolarization, i.e. of cortical excitation.

Hippocampo-reticular relationships.—Some interest has been aroused by the hypothesis elaborated by Lissák and Grastyán (140, 216) that the hippo-campus exerts an inhibitory influence upon the reticular formation thus in-hibiting the orienting response; the slow theta rhythm recorded from the hippocampus during this reaction should be interpreted as a sign of func-tional depression of this structure. This interpretation has been questioned by Beteleva & Novikova (37) who have observed the 4 to 7 cps rhythm both in the hippocampus and in the reticular formation during the orienting reac-tion. Bureš, Burešová & Fifková (63) have found no changes in reticular formation activity following functional inactivation of the hippocampus by local spreading depression. Hippocampal spreading depression appears not to influence neocortical activity (332). Beteleva & Novikova (37), as well as other authors (76, 273, 330), have noticed a theta rhythm synchronous with the hippocampal one in neocortical areas also. Corazza & Parmeggiani (76) give some evidence, to be added to that of Green et al. (142) already cited, that the neocortical theta rhythm is a sign of local activity neurally elicited, rather than physically propagated, through the septal region (77). As for the behavioral significance of the hippocampal theta activity, Adey et al. (1, 3, 154) in a series of studies using auto- and cross-correlation techniques (see 4, 48) in training animals maintain that it is correlated with motor perform-ance. Torii & Sugi (318) claim that in rabbits hippocampal electrical activity is more easily correlated with behavior manifestations than neocortical ac-tivity. Finally, Parmeggiani (271) describes some effects of hippocampal stimulation on sleep behavior.

Behavioral aspects of reticular formation activity.—Several topics will briefly be touched upon here. A number of papers have appeared indicating that complex behavior can be produced in man during electroencephalo-graphically deep sleep. While Fischgold & Schwartz (122) report that a motor response to a sensory stimulus is lost during Loomis's stage C, Granda & Hammack (139) claim that operant behavior is still present even during Dement & Kleitman's stage 4. Likewise, Oswald et al. (267, 268) have ob-served behavioral and EEG reactions to an important (personal or pre-selected) name, as discriminated from insignificant names, in Loomis's stages C, D, and E. This has been taken to support the view that the cortex may continue to function during sleep.

Isaac (177) reports that reticular stimulation reduces the latency of discrete motor response in cats. On the contrary, low-frequency caudate stimulation simultaneously induces cortical and subcortical spindles and im-pairs the performance of a visual discrimination task [Buchwald et al. (62a)]. Spehlmann, Creutzfeldt & Jung (307) have shown predominant inhibition of units in the motor cortex during caudate stimulation. Glickman (131) has studied the reinforcing properties of arousal evoked by self-stimulation of the midbrain tegmentum; they appear to vary considerably from one rat to the next. Olds & Peretz (262) have found three anatomically separated regions in the midbrain which yield at low threshold arousal, or escape, or self-stimulation. With higher voltage, arousal is evoked from the self-stimulating region also. Relationship of the diencephalic self-stimulation system to the parasympathetic areas of Hess, and of the escape regions to the sympathetic areas, has been suggested by comparing maps of effective points [Olds, Travis & Schwing (263)], but recording of visceral phenomena is necessary before these generalizations can be accepted.

Finally, a careful study by Sprague, Chambers & Stellar (312) should be mentioned. These authors report that lesions of the specific sensory pathways in the midbrain of the cat, leaving intact most of the reticular formation, are followed by complex and important disturbances, consisting of restless, stereotyped, unemotional behavior. Surprisingly, extensive lesions of the reticular core, sparing the sensory pathways, produced animals which, after due recovery, could display a general behavior much like that of a normal cat.

To sum up, the functional picture of the reticular formation has greatly increased in complexity as a result of recent research. In the field of sleep and wakefulness regulation, the simplified scheme of an activating system cyclically aroused or inactive, which seemed so useful only a few years ago, is now definitely outdated. The term "reticular formation", unless it is a mere anatomical reference, itself needs to be qualified in order to convey a functional meaning. Indeed we have to reckon not only with the idea of an actively evoked sleep, but probably with two different types of sleep with separate triggers, both located somewhere within the reticular formation and intermingled with the classical activating system. How far these three circuits are separate in the anatomical space, how far they utilize private neuronal chains, how they are reciprocally related and how the mutual relationships can be disrupted, how electrical and chemical phenomena contribute to the stereotyped sleep-wakefulness rhythm—these are the problems which are likely to be actively investigated in the next years.

LITERATURE CITED

1. Adey, W. R., in *Brain Mechanisms and Learning*, 577–88 (Blackwell, Oxford, 1961)
2. Adey, W. R., Buchwald, N. A., and Lindsley, D. F., *Electroencephal. and Clin. Neurophysiol.*, 12, 21–40 (1960)
3. Adey, W. R., Dunlop, C. W., and Hendrix, C. E., *Arch. Neurol.*, 3, 74–90 (1960)
4. Adey, W. R., Walter, D. O., and Hendrix, C. E., *Exptl. Neurol.*, 3, 501–24 (1961)
5. Affanni, J. M., Mancia, M., and Marchiafava, P. L., *Arch. ital. biol.* (In press)
6. Akimoto, H., Saito, Y., Nakamura, Y., Maekawa, K., and Kuroiwa, S., *Proc. Ann. Meeting Japan. EEG Soc., 11th,* 67–71 (1960)
7. Alavzhalova, N. A., and Koshtoiants, O. K., *Sechenov Physiol. J. USSR (Engl. Transl.)*, 46, 1–10 (1960)
8. Albe-Fessard, D., *Compt. rend. acad. sci.*, 250, 2618–20 (1960)
9. Albe-Fessard, D., and Gillet, E., *Electroencephal. and Clin. Neurophysiol.*, 13, 257–69 (1961)
10. Albe-Fessard, D., and Mallart, A., *Compt. rend. acad. sci.*, 251, 1040–42 (1960)
11. Albe-Fessard, D., and Mallart, A., *Compt. rend. acad. sci.*, 251, 1191–93 (1960)
12. Albe-Fessard, D., Mallart, A., and Aleonard, P., *J. physiol. (Paris)*, 53, 244–45 (1961)
13. Albe-Fessard, D., Oswaldo-Cruz, E., and Rocha-Miranda, C., *Electroencephal. and Clin. Neurophysiol.*, 12, 405–20 (1960)
14. Albe-Fessard, D., Oswaldo-Cruz, E., and Rocha-Miranda, C., *Electroencephal. and Clin. Neurophysiol.*, 12, 649–61 (1960)
15. Altman, I. A., *Sechenov Physiol. J. USSR (Engl. Transl.)*, 46, 617–29 (1960)
16. Amassian, V. E., Macy, J., Jr., and Waller, H. J., *Ann. N. Y. Acad. Sci.*, 89, 883–95 (1961)
17. Andersen, P., *Acta Physiol. Scand.*, 47, 63–90 (1959)
18. Andersen, P., *Acta Physiol. Scand.*, 48, 178–208 (1960)
19. Andersen, P., *Acta Physiol. Scand.*, 48, 209–30 (1960)
20. Andersen, P., *Acta Physiol. Scand.*, 48, 329–51 (1960)
21. Andersen, P., Bruland, H., and Kaada, B. R., *Acta Physiol. Scand.*, 51, 17–28 (1961)
22. Andersen, P., Bruland, H., and Kaada, B. R., *Acta Physiol. Scand.*, 51, 29–40 (1961)
22a. Andersen, P., and Jansen, J., Jr., *Arch. ital. biol.*, 99, 349–68 (1961)
23. Anokhin, P., *Electroencephal. and Clin. Neurophysiol.*, Suppl. 13, 257–67 (1960)
24. Antonelli, A. R., and Rüdiger, W., *Arch. ital. biol.*, 98, 423–29 (1960)
25. Arden, G., and Liu, Y. M., *Acta Physiol. Scand.*, 48, 36–48 (1960)
26. Arden, G., and Liu, Y. M., *Acta Physiol. Scand.*, 48, 49–62 (1960)
27. Arduini, A., and Goldstein, M. H., Jr., *Arch. ital. biol.*, 99, 397–412 (1961)
28. Arduini, A., and Hirao, T., *Arch. ital. biol.*, 98, 182–205 (1960)
29. Arduini, A., and Hirao, T., *Arch. ital. biol.*, 98, 275–92 (1960)
30. Arduini, A., and Pinneo, L., *Boll. soc. ital. biol. sper.*, 37, 430–32 (1961)
31. Armett, C. J., Gray, J. A. B., and Palmer, J. F., *J. Physiol. (London)*, 156, 611-22 (1961)
32. Bartorelli, C., Bizzi, E., Libretti, A., and Zanchetti, A., *Arch. ital. biol.*, 98, 308–26 (1960)
33. Baumgartner, G., Creutzfeldt, O., and Jung, R., in *Cerebral Anoxia and the Electroencephalogram*, 5–34 (C. C Thomas, Springfield, Ill., 1961)
34. Baxter, C. F., and Roberts, E., *Proc. Soc. Exptl. Biol. Med.*, 104, 426–27 (1960)
35. Benoit, O., and Bloch, V., *J. physiol. (Paris)*, 52, 17–18 (1960)
36. Bessou, P., and Laporte, Y., *Arch. ital. biol.*, 99, 293–321 (1961)
37. Beteleva, T. G., and Novikova, L. A., *Sechenov Physiol. J. USSR (Engl. Transl.)*, 46, 48–59 (1960)
38. Bishop, G. H., in *Advances in Biology of Skin*, 1, *Cutaneous Innervation*, 88–98 (Pergamon Press, Oxford, 1960)
39. Bishop, G. H., in *Advances in Biology of Skin*, 1, *Cutaneous Innervation*, 99-111 (Pergamon Press, Oxford, 1960)
40. Bishop, G. H., Clare, M. H., and Landau, W. M., *Electroencephal. and Clin. Neurophysiol.*, 13, 34–42 (1961)
41. Bizzi, E., Libretti, A., Malliani, A., and Zanchetti, A., *Am. J. Physiol.*, 200, 923–26 (1961)

41a. Bizzi, E., and Spencer, W. A. (Personal communication)

42. Bloch, V., and Bonvallet, M., *J. physiol. (Paris)*, **53**, 280–81 (1961)

43. Bonvallet, M., and Bloch, V., *Science*, **133**, 1133–34 (1961)

44. Bonvallet, M., and Hugelin, A., *Electroencephal. and Clin. Neurophysiol.*, **13**, 270–84 (1961)

45. Boord, R. L., *Exptl. Neurol.*, **3**, 225–39 (1961)

46. Borri, P., and Macchi, G., *Riv. neurobiol.*, **6**, 234–51 (1960)

47. Bradley, P. B., in *Adrenergic Mechanisms*, 410–20 (J. & A. Churchill, Ltd., London, 1960)

48. Brazier, M., *Exptl. Neurol.*, **2**, 123–43 (1960)

49. Bremer, F., *Electroencephal. and Clin. Neurophysiol.*, Suppl. 13, 125–34 (1960)

50. Bremer, F., in *Structure and Function of the Cerebral Cortex*, 173–91 (Elsevier Publ. Co., Amsterdam, 1960)

51. Bremer, F., in *CIBA Foundation Symposium: The Nature of Sleep*, 30–50 (1961)

52. Bremer, F., Stoupel, N., and van Reeth, P. C., *Arch. ital. biol.*, **98**, 229–47 (1960)

53. Brindley, G. S., *Physiology of the Retina and Visual Pathway* (E. Arnold, Ltd., London, 1960)

54. Brinley, F. J., Jr., Kandel, E. R., and Marshall, W. H., *J. Neurophysiol.*, **23**, 237–45 (1960)

55. Brinley, F. J., Jr., Kandel, E. R., and Marshall, W. H., *J. Neurophysiol.*, **23**, 246–56 (1960)

56. Brodal, A., Taber, E., and Walberg, F., *J. Comp. Neurol.*, **114**, 239–59 (1960)

57. Brodal, A., and Walberg, F., in *Structure and Function of the Cerebral Cortex*, 116–23 (Elsevier Publ. Co., Amsterdam, 1960)

58. Brodal, A., Walberg, F., and Taber, E., *J. Comp. Neurol.*, **114**, 261–81 (1960)

59. Brooks, V. B., Rudomin, P., and Slayman, C. L., *J. Neurophysiol.*, **24**, 286–301 (1961)

60. Brooks, V. B., Rudomin, P., and Slayman, C. L., *J. Neurophysiol.*, **24**, 302–25 (1961)

61. Bruner, J., Buser, P., and Sindberg, R., *J. physiol. (Paris)*, **53**, 284–85 (1961)

62. Buchwald, N. A., Heuser, G., Wyers, E. J., and Lauprecht, C. W., *Electroencephal. and Clin. Neurophysiol.*, **13**, 525–30 (1961)

62a. Buchwald, N. A., Wyers, E. J., Carlin, J., and Farley, R. E., *Exptl. Neurol.*, **4**, 23–36 (1961)

62b. Buchwald, N. A., Wyers, E. J., Lauprecht, C. W., and Heuser, G., *Electroencephal. and Clin. Neurophysiol.*, **13**, 531–32 (1961)

62c. Buchwald, N. A., Wyers, E. J., Okuma, T., and Heuser, G., *Electroencephal. and Clin. Neurophysiol.*, **13**, 509–18 (1961)

63. Bureš, J., Burešová, O., and Fifková, E., *Arch. ital. biol.*, **99**, 23–32 (1961)

64. Bureš, J., and Křivánek, J., *Physiol. Bohemosloven.*, **9**, 488–93 (1960)

65. Buser, P., *Schweiz. Arch. Neurol. Psychiat.* (In press)

66. Buser, P., and Ascher, P., *Arch. ital. biol.*, **98**, 123–64 (1960)

67. Capon, A., *Arch. intern. pharmacodynamie*, **127**, 141–62 (1960)

68. Carlsson, A., Lindqvist, M., and Magnusson, T., in *Adrenergic Mechanisms*, 432–39 (J. & A. Churchill, Ltd., London, 1960)

69. Carreras, M., and Andersson, S. A. A. (Personal communication)

70. Carreras, M., and Levitt, M., *Federation Proc.*, **18**, 24–24 (1959)

71. Caspers, H., in *CIBA Foundation Symposium: The Nature of Sleep* 237–53 (1961)

72. Chambers, W. W., Levitt, M., Carreras, M., and Liu, C. N., *Science*, **132**, 1489–89 (1960)

73. Chang, H.-T., *Studii Cercetari Neurol.*, **5**, 133–43 (1960)

74. Clare, M. H., Landau, W. M., and Bishop, G. H., *Electroencephal. and Clin. Neurophysiol.*, **13**, 21–33 (1961)

75. Collins, W. F., and Randt, C. T., *J. Neurophysiol.*, **23**, 47–53 (1960)

76. Corazza, R., and Parmeggiani, P. L., *Arch. sci. biol.*, **44**, 435–63 (1960)

77. Corazza, R., and Parmeggiani, P. L., *Boll. soc. ital. biol. sper.*, **37**, 377–78 (1961)

78. Costa, E., Pscheidt, G. R., van Meter, W. G., and Himwich, H. E., *J. Pharmacol. Exptl. Therap.*, **130**, 81–88 (1960)

79. Cragg, B. G., *Exptl. Neurol.*, **2**, 547–72 (1960)

80. Crepax, P., and Fadiga, E., *Arch. sci. biol.*, **44**, 385–409 (1960)

81. Crepax, P., and Infantellina, F., *Arch. sci. biol.*, **44**, 279–99 (1960)

82. Creutzfeldt, O., Bark, J., and Fromm, G. H., in *Cerebral Anoxia and*

the Electroencephalogram, 35–45 (Charles C Thomas, Springfield, Ill., 1961)

83. Creutzfeldt, O., and Jung, R., in *CIBA Foundation Symposium: The Nature of Sleep,* 131–70 (1961)

84. Crighel, E., Kreindler, A., and Neştianu, V., *Exptl. Neurol.,* **3,** 411–18 (1961)

85. Curtis, D. R., and Koizumi, K., *J. Neurophysiol.,* **24,** 80–99 (1961)

86. Curtis, D. R., and Watkins, J. C., in *Inhibition in the Nervous System and γ-Aminobutyric Acid,* 425–44 (Pergamon Press, Oxford, 1960)

87. Darian-Smith, I., *J. Physiol. (London),* **153,** 52–73 (1960)

88. Darian-Smith, I., and Mayday, G., *Exptl. Neurol.,* **2,** 290–309 (1960)

89. Davis, H., *Physiol. Revs.,* **41,** 391–416 (1961)

90. Dell, P., in *Adrenergic Mechanisms,* 393–409 (J. & A. Churchill, Ltd., London, 1960)

91. Dell, P., Bonvallet, M., and Hugelin, A., in *CIBA Foundation Symposium: The Nature of Sleep,* 86–102 (1961)

92. Dell, P., Hugelin, A., and Bonvallet, M., in *Cerebral Anoxia and the Electroencephalogram,* 46–58 (Charles C Thomas, Springfield, Ill., 1961)

93. Dement, W., *Science,* **131,** 1705–7 (1960)

94. Dennery, J. M., and Combs, C. M., *Exptl. Neurol.,* **3,** 127–40 (1961)

95. Desmedt, J. E., in *Neural Mechanisms of the Auditory and Vestibular Systems,* 152–64 (Charles C Thomas, Springfield, Ill., 1960)

96. Desmedt, J. E., and Monaco, P., *Arch. intern. pharmacodynamie,* **129,** 244–48 (1960)

97. Do Carmo, R. J., *J. Neurophysiol.,* **23,** 496–504 (1960)

98. Doty, R. W., in *Symposium on the Physiology on the Visual System (Freiburg i.B., Germany)* (In press)

99. Douglas, W. W., and Ritchie, J. M., in *Pain and Itch. Nervous Mechanisms,* 26–39 (J. & A. Churchill, Ltd., London, 1959)

100. Douglas, W. W., and Ritchie, J. M., *J. Physiol. (London),* **150,** 501–14 (1960)

101. Douglas, W. W., Ritchie, J. M., and Straub, R. W., *J. Physiol. (London),* **150,** 266–83 (1960)

102. Dresse, A., Dumont, S., and Dell, P., *Compt. rend. soc. biol.,* **154,** 849–51 (1960)

103. Dumont, S., and Dell, P., *Electroencephal. and Clin. Neurophysiol.,* **12,** 769–96 (1960)

104. Eayrs, J. T., and Goodhead, B., *J. Anat.,* **93,** 385–402 (1959)

105. Eccles, J. C., in *Structure and Function of the Cerebral Cortex,* 192–203 (Elsevier Publ. Co., Amsterdam, 1960)

106. Eccles, J. C., Eccles, R. M., and Lundberg, A., *J. Physiol. (London),* **154,** 80–114 (1960)

106a. Eccles, J. C., Hubbard, J. L., and Oscarsson, O., *J. Physiol. (London),* **158,** 486–516 (1961)

106b. Eccles, J. C., Oscarsson, O., and Willis, W. D., *J. Physiol. (London),* **158,** 517–43 (1961)

107. Eldred, E., Lindsley, D. F., and Buchwald, J. S., *Exptl. Neurol.,* **2,** 144–57 (1960)

108. Erulkar, S. D., and Fillenz, M., *J. Physiol. (London),* **154,** 206–18 (1960)

109. Euler, C. von, in *Structure and Function of the Cerebral Cortex,* 372–77 (Elsevier Publ. Co., Amsterdam, 1960)

110. Euler, C. von, and Green, J. D., *Acta Physiol. Scand.,* **48,** 95–109 (1960)

111. Euler, C. von, and Green, J. D., *Acta Physiol. Scand.,* **48,** 110–25 (1960)

112. Evarts, E. V., *Federation Proc.,* **19,** 828–37 (1960)

113. Evarts, E. V., in *CIBA Foundation Symposium: The Nature of Sleep,* 171–82 (1961)

114. Evarts, E. V., Fleming, T. C., Etienne, M., and Posternak, J. M., *Helv. Physiol. et Pharmacol. Acta,* **19,** 70–83 (1961)

115. Evarts, E. V., Fleming, T. C., and Huttenlocher, P. R., *Am. J. Physiol.,* **199,** 373–76 (1960)

116. Fadiga, E., and Brookhart, J. M., *Am. J. Physiol.,* **198,** 693–703 (1960)

117. Fangel, C., and Kaada, B. R., *Electroencephal. and Clin. Neurophysiol.,* **12,** 575–88 (1960)

118. Favale, E., Loeb, C., Rossi, G. F., and Sacco, G., *Arch. ital. biol.,* **99,** 1–22 (1961)

119. Fernández-Guardiola, A., Roldán, E., Fanjul, M. L., and Castells, C., *Electroencephal. and Clin. Neurophysiol.,* **13,** 564–76 (1961)

120. Fessard, A., Gerard, R. W., and Konorski, J., Eds., *Brain Mechanisms and Learning* (Blackwell, Oxford, 1961)

121. Field, J., Magoun, H. W., and Hall,

V. E., Eds., *Handbook of Physiology, Sect. I: Neurophysiology*, III (Am. Physiol. Soc., Washington, D. C., Williams & Wilkins Co., Baltimore, Md., 1960)

122. Fischgold, H., and Schwartz, B. A., in *CIBA Foundation Symposium: The Nature of Sleep*, 209–31 (1961)

123. Fjällbrant, N., and Iggo, A., *J. Physiol.* (*London*), **156**, 578–90 (1961)

124. Fuster, J. M., *Science*, **133**, 2011–12 (1961)

125. Galambos, R., *Proc. Natl. Acad. Sci. US*, **47**, 129–36 (1961)

126. Galambos, R., and Morgan, C. T., in *Handbook of Physiology, Neurophysiology*, III, 1471–99 (Am. Physiol. Soc., Washington, D. C., 1960)

127. Galambos, R., Myers, R. E., and Sheatz, G. C., *Am. J. Physiol.*, **200**, 23–28 (1961)

128. Gentry, J. R., Whitlock, D. G., and Perl, E. R., *Federation Proc.*, **20**, 349–49 (1961)

129. Gerber, C. J., *Electroencephal. and Clin. Neurophysiol.*, **13**, 354–64 (1961)

130. Glässer, A., and Mantegazzini, P., *Arch. ital. biol.*, **98**, 351–66 (1960)

131. Glickman, S., *J. Comp. and Physiol. Psychol.*, **53**, 68–71 (1960)

132. Goldring, S., and O'Leary, J. L., *Federation Proc.*, **19**, 612–18 (1960)

133. Goldstein, L., and Muñoz, C., *J. Pharmacol. Exptl. Therap.*, **132**, 345–53 (1961)

134. Goldstein, M., Jr., *Information and Control*, **3**, 1–17 (1960)

135. Gordon, G., Landgren, S., and Seed, W. A., *J. Physiol.* (*London*), **158**, 566–59 (1961)

136. Gordon, G., and Paine, C. H., *J. Physiol.* (*London*), **153**, 331–49 (1960)

137. Gordon, G., and Seed, W. A., *J. Physiol.* (*London*), **155**, 589–601 (1961)

138. Grafstein, B., Burns, B. D., and Heron, W., in *Structure and Function of the Cerebral Cortex*, 234–38 (Elsevier Publ. Co., Amsterdam, 1960)

139. Granda, A. M., and Hammack, J. T., *Science*, **133**, 1485–86 (1961)

140. Grastyán, E., in *Brain Mechanisms and Learning*, 243–51 (Blackwell, Oxford, 1961)

141. Green, J. D., in *Structure and Function of the Cerebral Cortex*, 266–71 (Elsevier Publ. Co., Amsterdam, 1960)

142. Green, J. D., Maxwell, D. S., Schind-ler, W. J., and Stumpf, C., *J. Neurophysiol.*, **23**, 403–20 (1960)

143. Grundfest, H., in *Inhibition in the Nervous System and γ-Aminobutyric Acid*, 47–65 (Pergamon Press, Oxford, 1960)

144. Grüsser, O.-J., and Grüsser-Cornehls, U., *Arch. ges. Physiol.*, **270**, 227–38 (1960)

145. Guzmán, C. F., Alcarez, M., and Harmony, T., *Bol. inst. estud. méd. y biol.* (*Mex.*), **18**, 135–40 (1960)

146. Guzmán, C. F., Buendia, N., and Lindsley, D. B., *Federation Proc.*, **20**, 330–30 (1961)

147. Hagbarth, K.-E., and Fex, J., *J. Neurophysiol.*, **22**, 321–38 (1959)

148. Hara, T., Favale, E., Rossi, G. F., and Sacco, G., *Riv. neurol.*, **30**, 448–60 (1960)

149. Hensel, H., and Boman, K. K. A., *J. Neurophysiol.*, **23**, 564–78 (1960)

150. Hensel, H., Iggo, A., and Witt, I., *J. Physiol.* (*London*), **153**, 113–26 (1960)

151. Hernández-Peón, R., *Electroencephal. and Clin. Neurophysiol.*, Suppl. 13, 101–14 (1960)

152. Hernández-Peón, R., and Brust-Carmona, H., in *Brain Mechanisms and Learning*, 393–408 (Blackwell, Oxford, 1961)

152a. Heuser, G., Buchwald, N. A., and Wyers, E. J., *Electroencephal. and Clin. Neurophysiol.*, **13**, 519–24 (1961)

153. Ho, T., Wang, Y. R., Lin, T. A. N., and Cheng, Y. F., *Physiol. Bohemosloven.*, **9**, 85–92 (1960)

154. Holmes, J. E., and Adey, W. R., *Am. J. Physiol.*, **199**, 741–44 (1960)

155. Holmqvist, B., *Acta Physiol. Scand.*, **52**, Suppl. 181 (1961)

156. Holmqvist, B., Lundberg, A., and Oscarsson, O., *Arch. ital. biol.*, **98**, 60–80 (1960)

157. Hubel, D. H., *Arch. ital. biol.*, **98**, 171–81 (1960)

158. Hubel, D. H., *J. Physiol.* (*London*), **150**, 91–104 (1960)

159. Hubel, D. H., and Wiesel, T. N., *J. Physiol.* (*London*), **154**, 572–80 (1960)

160. Hubel, D. H., and Wiesel, T. N., *J. Physiol.* (*London*), **155**, 385–98 (1961)

161. Hugelin, A., *Arch. ital. biol.*, **99**, 244–69 (1961)

162. Hugelin, A., and Dumont, S., *Arch. ital. biol.*, **99**, 219–43 (1961)

163. Hugelin, A., Dumont, S., and Paillas, N., *Electroencephal. and Clin. Neurophysiol.*, **12**, 797–818 (1960)

164. Hugelin, A., Paillas, N., and Dumont, S., *Compt. rend. soc. biol.*, **154**, 30–34 (1960)

165. Hunt, C. C., *J. Physiol. (London)*, **155**, 175–86 (1961)

166. Hunt, C. C., and Kuno, M., *J. Physiol. (London)*, **147**, 364–84 (1959)

167. Hunt, C. C., and McIntyre, A. K., *J. Physiol. (London)*, **153**, 74–87 (1960)

168. Hunt, C. C., and McIntyre, A. K., *J. Physiol. (London)*, **153**, 88–98 (1960)

169. Hunt, C. C., and McIntyre, A. K., *J. Physiol. (London)*, **153**, 99–112 (1960)

170. Huttenlocher, P. R., *J. Neurophysiol.*, **24**, 451–68 (1961)

171. Iggo, A., *J. Physiol. (London)*, **152**, 337–53 (1960)

172. Iggo, A., *J. Physiol. (London)*, **155**, 52P–53P (1961)

173. Imbert, M., *J. physiol. (Paris)*, **52**, 126–27 (1960)

174. Inman, D. R., and Peruzzi, P., *J. Physiol. (London)*, **155**, 280–301 (1961)

175. Iriuchijima, J., and Zotterman, Y., *Acta Physiol. Scand.*, **49**, 267–78 (1960)

176. Iriuchijima, J., and Zotterman, Y., *Acta Physiol. Scand.*, **51**, 283–89 (1961)

177. Isaac, W., *J. Comp. and Physiol. Psychol.*, **53**, 234–36 (1960)

178. Ishiko, M., and Loewenstein, W. R., *Science*, **132**, 1841–42 (1960)

179. Ishiko, M., and Loewenstein, W. R., *J. Gen. Physiol.*, **45**, 105–24 (1961)

180. Iwama, K., and Yamamoto, C., *Electroencephal. and Clin. Neurophysiol.*, **13**, 2–8 (1961)

181. Jabbur, S. J., and Towe, A. L., *J. Neurophysiol.*, **24**, 499–509 (1961)

182. Jabbur, S. J., and Towe, A. L., *J. Physiol. (London)*, **155**, 148–60 (1961)

183. Jankowska, E., and Albe-Fessard, D., *J. physiol. (Paris)*, **53**, 374–75 (1961)

184. Jasper, H., in *Inhibition in the Nervous System and γ-Aminobutyric Acid*, 544–53 (Pergamon Press, Oxford, 1960)

185. Jouvet, M., *Biol. méd. (Paris)*, **49**, 282–360 (1960)

186. Jouvet, M. in *Brain Mechanisms and Learning*, 445–75 (Blackwell, Oxford, 1961)

187. Jouvet, M., in *CIBA Foundation Symposium: The Nature of Sleep*, 188–206 (1961)

188. Jouvet, M., Dechaume, J., and Michel, F., *Lyon méd.*, **204**, 479–521 (1960)

189. Jouvet, M., Michel, F., and Mounier, D., *Rev. neurol.*, **103**, 189–205 (1960)

190. Jouvet, M., and Mounier, D., *J. physiol. (Paris)*, **53**, 379–80 (1961)

191. Jung, R., in *Structure and Function of the Cerebral Cortex*, 204–33 (Elsevier Publ. Co., Amsterdam, 1960)

192. Kaada, B. R., and Johannessen, N. B., *Electroencephal. and Clin. Neurophysiol.*, **12**, 567–73 (1960)

193. Kandel, E. R., and Spencer, W. A., *J. Neurophysiol.*, **24**, 243–59 (1961)

194. Kandel, E. R., Spencer, W. A., and Brinley, F. J., Jr., *Am. J. Physiol.*, **198**, 687–92 (1960)

195. Kandel, E. R., Spencer, W. A., and Brinley, F. J., Jr., *J. Neurophysiol.*, **24**, 225–42 (1961)

196. Kennedy, T. T., Towe, A. L., and Patton, H. D., *Physiologist*, **3** (3), 93–93 (1960)

197. Kiang, N. Y.-S., Neame, J. H., and Clarke, L. F., *Science*, **133**, 1027–28 (1961)

198. Kleitman, N., in *CIBA Foundation Symposium: The Nature of Sleep*, 349–64 (1961)

199. Koll, W., Haase, J., Schütz, R.-M., and Mühlberg, B., *Arch. ges. Physiol.*, **272**, 270–89 (1960)

200. Kolmodin, G. M., and Skoglund, C. R., *Acta Physiol. Scand.*, **50**, 337–55 (1960)

201. Křivánek, J., and Bureš, J., *Physiol. Bohemosloven.*, **9**, 494–503 (1960)

202. Kruger, L., and Albe-Fessard, D., *Exptl. Neurol.*, **2**, 442–67 (1961)

203. Kruger, L., Siminoff, R., and Witkovsky, P., *J. Neurophysiol.*, **24**, 333–49 (1961)

204. Kuypers, H. G. J. M., in *Structure and Function of the Cerebral Cortex*, 138–43 (Elsevier Publ. Co., Amsterdam, 1960)

205. Kuypers, H. G. J. M., *Brain*, **83**, 161–84 (1960)

206. Kuypers, H. G. J. M., Fleming, W. R., and Farinholt, J. W., *Science*, **132**, 38–40 (1960)

207. Lamarche, G., Langlois, J. M., and Héon, M., *Can. J. Biochem. and Physiol.*, **38**, 1163–66 (1960)

208. Landau, W. M., Bishop, G. H., and Clare, M. H., *Electroencephal. and Clin. Neurophysiol.*, **13**, 43–53 (1961)

209. Laporte, Y., Bessou, P., and Bouisset, S., *Arch. ital. biol.*, **98**, 206–21 (1960)

210. Latimer, C. N., and Kennedy, T. T., *J. Neurophysiol.*, **24**, 66–79 (1961)

211. Lele, P. P., and Weddell, G., *Exptl. Neurol.*, **1**, 334–59 (1959)

212. Li, C.-L., Ortiz-Galvin, A., Chou, S. N., and Howard, S. Y., *J. Neurophysiol.*, **23**, 592–601 (1960)

213. Limanski, Y. P., *Sechenov Physiol. J. USSR (Russian ed.)*, **47**, 671–77 (1961)*

214. Lindsley, D. B., in *Handbook of Physiology, Neurophysiology*, **III**, 1553–93 (Am. Physiol. Soc., Washington, D. C., 1960)

215. Lippold, O. C. J., Nicholls, J. G., and Redfearn, J. W. T., *J. Physiol. (London)*, **153**, 218–31 (1960)

216. Lissák, K., and Grastyán, E., *Electroencephal. and Clin. Neurophysiol.*, Suppl. 13, 271–77 (1960)

217. Loeb, C., Magni, F., and Rossi, G. F., *Arch. ital. biol.*, **98**, 293–307 (1960)

218. Loeb, C., Massazza, G., and Stacchini, G., *Boll. soc. ital. biol. sper.*, **36**, 399–401 (1960)

219. Loeb, C., Massazza, G., and Stacchini, G., *Boll. soc. ital. biol. sper.*, **36**, 401–2 (1960)

220. Loewenstein, W. R., *Nature*, **188**, 1034–35 (1960)

221. Loewenstein, W. R., *J. Neurophysiol.*, **24**, 150–58 (1961)

222. Lømo, T., and Mollica, A., *Arch. ital. biol.* (In press)

223. Lundberg, A., and Norsell, U., *Experientia*, **16**, 123–23 (1960)

224. Lundberg, A., and Oscarsson, O., *Acta Physiol. Scand.*, **50**, 356–74 (1960)

225. Lundberg, A., and Oscarsson, O., *Acta Physiol. Scand.*, **51**, 1–16 (1961)

226. Macchi, G., Angeleri, F., and Guazzi, G., *J. Comp. Neurol.*, **111**, 387–405 (1959)

227. Magnes, J., Moruzzi, G., and Pompeiano, O., *Arch. ital. biol.*, **99**, 33–67 (1961)

228. Magnes, J., Moruzzi, G., and Pompeiano, O., in *CIBA Foundation Symposium: The Nature of Sleep*, 57–78 (1961)

229. Magni, F., Melzak, R., Moruzzi, G., and Smith, C. J., *Arch. ital. biol.*, **97**, 357–77 (1959)

229a. Magni, F., and Oscarsson, O., *Arch. ital. biol.*, **99**, 369–96 (1961)

230. Mahnke, J. H., and Ward, A. A., *Exptl. Neurol.*, **2**, 311–23 (1960)

231. Mallart, A., *J. physiol. (Paris)*, **52**, 159–60 (1960)

232. Mallart A., *J. physiol. (Paris)*, **53**, 422–23 (1961)

233. Mallart, A., Martinoya, C., and Albe-Fessard, D., *J. physiol. (Paris)*, **53**, 421–23 (1961)

234. Mannen, H., *Arch. ital. biol.*, **98**, 333–50 (1960)

235. Mantegazzini, P., and Glässer, A., *Arch. ital. biol.*, **98**, 367–74 (1960)

236. Mantegazzini, P., Poeck, K., and Santibañez, G., *Arch. ital. biol.*, **97**, 222–42 (1959)

237. Marley, E., in *Adrenergic Mechanisms*, 424–27 (J. & A. Churchill, Ltd., London, 1960)

238. Marsh, J. T., McCarty, D. A., Sheatz, G., and Galambos, R., *Electroencephal. and Clin. Neurophysiol.*, **13**, 224–34 (1961)

239. Massion, J., *Contribution à l'étude de la régulation cérébelleuse du système extrapyramidal* (Thèse d'Aggregation, Univ. Catholique de Louvain, Editions Arscia, Bruxelles, 1961)

240. Massion, J., and Meulders, M., *J. physiol. (Paris)*, **52**, 172–73 (1960)

241. Massion, J., and Meulders, M., *Arch. intern. physiol.*, **69**, 26–29 (1961)

242. Maturana, H. R., Lettvin, J. Y., McCulloch, W. S., and Pitts, W. H., *J. Gen. Physiol.*, **43**, 129–75 (1960)

243. McIntyre, A. K., and Mark, R. F., *J. Physiol. (London)*, **153**, 306–30 (1960)

244. Mehler, W. R., Feferman, M. E., and Nauta, W. J. H., *Brain*, **83**, 718–50 (1960)

245. Meulders, M., and Massion, J., *Arch. intern. physiol.*, **68**, 865–66 (1960)

246. Meulders, M., and Massion, J., *Arch. intern. physiol.*, **69**, 407–9 (1961)

247. Meulders, M., Massion, J., and Colle, J., *J. physiol. (Paris)*, **53**, 427–28 (1961)

248. Mikiten, T. M., Niebyl, P. H., and Hendley, C. D., *Federation Proc.*, **20**, 327–29 (1961)

249. Monnier, M., *Schweiz. med. Wochschr.*, **90**, 1406–16 (1960)

250. Monnier, M., Kalberer, M., and Krupp, P., *Exptl. Neurol.*, **2**, 271–89 (1960)

251. Morillo, A., *Electroencephal. and Clin. Neurophysiol.*, **13**, 9–20 (1961)

252. Morlock, N., and Ward, A. A., *Electroencephal. and Clin. Neurophysiol.*, **13**, 60–67 (1961)

253. Moruzzi, G., *Electroencephal. and Clin. Neurophysiol.*, Suppl. 13, 231–53 (1960)

254. Moruzzi, G., *Progr. med.*, **16**, 781–86 (1960)

255. Mountcastle, V. B., and Powell, T. P. S., *Bull. Johns Hopkins Hosp.*, **105**, 201–32 (1959)

256. Moushegian, G., Rupert, A., Marsh, J. T., and Galambos, R., *Science*, **133**, 582–83 (1961)

257. Naquet, R., Regis, H., Fischer-Williams, M., and Fernandez-Guardiola, A., *Brain*, **83**, 52–56 (1960)
258. Narikashvili, S. P., Butkhuzi, S. M., and Moniava, E. S., *Sechenov Physiol. J. USSR (Engl. Transl.)*, **44**, 765–78 (1960)
259. Ochs, S., and Booker, H., *Exptl. Neurol.*, **4**, 70–82 (1961)
260. Ochs, S., and Hunt, K., *J. Neurophysiol.*, **23**, 432–44 (1960)
261. Ogden, T. E., *Electroencephal. and Clin. Neurophysiol.*, **12**, 621–34 (1960)
262. Olds, J., and Peretz, B., *Electroencephal. and Clin. Neurophysiol.*, **12**, 445–54 (1960)
263. Olds, J., Travis, R. P., and Schwing, R. C., *J. Comp. and Physiol. Psychol.*, **53**, 23–32 (1960)
264. O'Leary, J. L., and Goldring, S., *Epilepsia*, **1**, 561–83 (1960)
265. Oscarsson, O., *Acta Physiol. Scand.*, **49**, 171–83 (1960)
266. Ostfeld, A. M., Machne, X., and Unna, K. R., *J. Pharmacol. Exptl. Therap.*, **128**, 265–72 (1960)
267. Oswald, I., Taylor, A. M., and Treisman, M., *Brain*, **83**, 440–53 (1960)
268. Oswald, I., Taylor, A. M., and Treisman, M., in *CIBA Foundation Symposium: The Nature of Sleep*, 343–48 (1961)
269. Paintal, A. S., *J. Physiol. (London)*, **152**, 250–70 (1960)
269a. Palestini, M., Armengol, V., and Gallardo, R. (Personal communication)
270. Palestini, M., and Lifschitz, W., in *Brain Mechanisms and Learning*, 413–29 (Blackwell, Oxford, 1961)
271. Parmeggiani, P. L., *Helv. Physiol. et Pharmacol. Acta*, **18**, 523–36 (1960)
272. Perl, E. R., and Whitlock, D. G., *Exptl. Neurol.*, **3**, 256–96 (1961)
273. Petsche, H., and Stumpf, C., *Electroencephal. and Clin. Neurophysiol.*, **12**, 589–600 (1960)
274. Phillips, C. G., in *CIBA Foundation Symposium: The Nature of Sleep*, 4–24 (1961)
275. Poggio, G. F., and Mountcastle, V. B., *Bull. Johns Hopkins Hosp.*, **106**, 266–316 (1960)
276. Pompeiano, O., *Arch. sci. biol.*, **44**, 473–96 (1960)
277. Pompeiano, O., and Swett, J. E., *Boll. soc. ital. biol. sper.*, **37**, 432–35 (1961)
278. Pompeiano, O., and Swett, J. E., *Boll. soc. ital. biol. sper.*, **37**, 913–15 (1961)
279. Purpura, D. P., in *Inhibition in the Nervous System and γ-Aminobutyric Acid*, 495–514 (Pergamon Press, Oxford, 1960)
280. Purpura, D. P., Carmichael, M. W., and Housepian, E. M., *Exptl. Neurol.*, **2**, 324–47 (1960)
281. Purpura, D. P., Girado, M., and Grundfest, H., *Electroencephal. and Clin. Neurophysiol.*, **12**, 95–110 (1960)
282. Purpura, D. P., and Housepian, E. M., *Electroencephal. and Clin. Neurophysiol.*, **13**, 365–81 (1961)
283. Rasmussen, G. L., in *Neural Mechanisms of the Auditory and Vestibular Systems*, 105–15 (Charles C Thomas, Springfield, Ill., 1960)
284. Rech, R. H., and Domino, E. F., *J. Pharmacol. Exptl. Therap.*, **130**, 59–67 (1960)
285. Reinoso-Suárez, F., *J. Comp. Neurol.*, **114**, 209–15 (1960)
286. Rhoton, A., Goldring, S., and O'Leary, J. L., *Am. J. Physiol.*, **199**, 677–82 (1960)
287. Roberts, E., Ed., *Inhibition in the Nervous System and γ-Aminobutyric Acid* (Pergamon Press, Oxford, 1960)
288. Rose, J. E., and Mountcastle, V. B., in *Handbook of Physiology, Neurophysiology*, **I**, 387–429 (Am. Physiol. Soc., Washington, D. C., 1959)
289. Rossi, G. F., Favale, E., Hara, T., Giussani, A., and Sacco, G., *Arch. ital. biol.*, **99**, 270–92 (1961)
290. Rothballer, A. B., and Sharpless, S. K., *Am. J. Physiol.*, **200**, 901–8 (1961)
291. Ruben, R. J., and Sekula, J., *Science*, **131**, 163–63 (1960)
292. Savoldi, F., Maggi, G. C., and Noli, S., *Boll. soc. ital. biol. sper.*, **36**, 542–44 (1960)
293. Savoldi, F., Maggi, G. C., and Noli, S., *Boll. soc. ital. biol. sper.*, **36**, 545–47 (1960)
294. Sawyer, C. H., Hilliard, J., and Ban, T., *Am. J. Physiol.*, **200**, 405–12 (1961)
295. Schadé, J. P., and Baxter, C. F., *Exptl. Neurol.*, **2**, 158–78 (1960)
296. Schlag, J., Chaillet, F., and Faidherbe, J., *Arch. intern. physiol.*, **68**, 793–802 (1960)
297. Schlag, J., Chaillet, F., and Herzet, J. P., *J. physiol. (Paris)*, **53**, 471–71 (1961)
298. Schlag, J., and Faidherbe, J., *Arch. ital. biol.*, **99**, 135–62 (1961)
299. Schlag, J., Herzet, J. P., and Chaillet, F., *J. physiol. (Paris)*, **53**, 470–70 (1961)

300. Sergio, C., and Longo, V. G., *Arch. intern. pharmacodynamie*, **125**, 65–82 (1960)
301. Sekov, F. N., Makul'kin, R. F., and Russev, V. V., *Sechenov Physiol. J. USSR (Engl. Transl.)*, **46**, 482–93 (1960)
302. Sharpless, S. K., and Rothballer, A. B., *Am. J. Physiol.*, **200**, 909–15 (1961)
303. Siminoff, R., *Federation Proc.*, **19**, 300–0 (1960)
304. Skoglund, C. R., *Acta Physiol. Scand.*, **50**, 311–27 (1960)
305. Skoglund, C. R., *Acta Physiol. Scand.*, **50**, 385–86 (1960)
306. Söderberg, U., and Arden, G., in *Symposium on the Physiology of the Visual System (Freiburg i.B., Germany)* (In press)
307. Spehlmann, R., Creutzfeldt, O. D., and Jung, R., *Arch. Psychiat. u. Z. ges. Neurol.*, **201**, 332–54 (1960)
308. Spencer, W. A., and Brookhart, J. M., *J. Neurophysiol.*, **24**, 26–49 (1961)
309. Spencer, W. A., and Brookhart, J. M., *J. Neurophysiol.*, **24**, 50–65 (1961)
310. Spencer, W. A., and Kandel, E. R., *J. Neurophysiol.*, **24**, 260–71 (1961)
311. Spencer, W. A., and Kandel, E. R., *J. Neurophysiol.*, **24**, 272–85 (1961)
312. Sprague, J. M., Chambers, W. W., and Stellar, E., *Science*, **133**, 165–73 (1961)
313. Steriade, M., and Demetrescu, M., *J. Neurophysiol.*, **23**, 602–17 (1960)
314. Sterman, M. B., and Clemente, C. D., *Federation Proc.*, **20**, 334–34 (1961)
315. Suzuki, H., *Tôhoku J. Exptl. Physiol.*, **71**, 331–45 (1960)
316. Taber, E., Brodal, A., and Walberg, F., *J. Comp. Neurol.*, **114**, 161–87 (1960)
317. Tonkikh, A. V., *Pavlov J. Higher Nervous Activity (Russian ed.)*, **10**, 285–90 (1960)*
318. Torii, S., and Sugi, S., *Folia Psychiat. et Neurol. Japon.*, **14**, 95–103 (1960)
318a. Towe, A. L., and Jabbur, S. J., *J. Neurophysiol.*, **24**, 488–98 (1961)
319. Towe, A. L., and Kennedy, T., *Exptl. Neurol.*, **3**, 570–87 (1961)
320. Vastola, E. F., *Electroencephal. and Clin. Neurophysiol.*, **12**, 399–403 (1960)
321. Vastola, E. F., *Exptl. Neurol.*, **2**, 221–31 (1960)
322. Verzeano, M., and Negishi, K., in *CIBA Foundation Symposium: The Nature of Sleep*, 108–26 (1961)
323. Vogt, M., in *Adrenergic Mechanisms*, 382–85 (J. & A. Churchill, Ltd., London, 1960)
324. Wall, P., *J. Neurophysiol.*, **23**, 197–210 (1960)
325. Wall, P., and Cronly-Dillon, J. R., *Arch. Neurol.*, **2**, 365–75 (1960)
326. Waller, H. G., *Federation Proc.*, **19**, 302–2 (1960)
327. Weddell, G., in *Progress in the Biological Science in Relation to Dermatology*, 55–63 (Cambridge Univ. Press, London, 1960)
328. Weddell, G., Palmer, E., and Taylor, D., in *Pain and Itch. Nervous Mechanisms*, 3–10 (J. & A. Churchill, Ltd., London, 1959)
329. Weil-Malherbe, H., in *Adrenergic Mechanisms*, 421–23 (J. & A. Churchill, Ltd., London, 1960)
330. Weiss, T., *Physiol. Bohemosloven.*, **10**, 21–26 (1961)
331. Weiss, T., *Physiol. Bohemosloven*, **10**, 109–16 (1961)
332. Weiss, T., and Fifková, E., *Electroencephal. and Clin. Neurophysiol.*, **12**, 841–50 (1960)
333. Weiss, T., and Fifková, E., *Arch. intern. physiol.*, **69**, 69–78 (1961)
334. Whitlock, D. G., and Perl, E. R., *J. Neurophysiol.*, **22**, 133–48 (1959)
335. Whitlock, D. G., and Perl, E. R., *Exptl. Neurol.*, **3**, 240–45 (1961)
336. Widén, L., and Ajmone-Marsan, C., *Arch. ital. biol.*, **98**, 248–74 (1960)
337. Widén, L., and Ajmone-Marsan, C., *Exptl. Neurol.*, **2**, 468–502 (1960)
338. Witt, I., and Hensel, H., *Arch. ges. Physiol.*, **268**, 582–96 (1959)
339. Wolstencroft, J. H., *J. Physiol. (London)*, **157**, 26 P–26 P (1961)
340. Wolstenholme, G. H. W., and O'Connor, M., Eds., *CIBA Foundation Symposium: The Nature of Sleep* (1961)
341. Zanchetti, A., in *Cerebral Anoxia and the Electroencephalogram*, 529–32 (Charles C Thomas, Springfield, Ill., 1961)
342. Zanchetti, A., in *Proc. Joint World Health Organization & Czechoslovak Cardiol. Soc. Symposium on Pathogenesis of Essential Hypertension*, 191–98 (State Med. Publ. House, Prague, 1961)

* English translation will be announced in *Technical Translations*, issued by the Office of Technical Services, US Department of Commerce, and will be made available by the Photoduplication Service, Library of Congress, and by the SLA Translation Center at the John Crerar Library, Chicago, Illinois.

EXCITATION AND SYNAPTIC TRANSMISSION[1,2]

By C. A. Terzuolo and C. Edwards

*Department of Physiology, University of Minnesota Medical School,
Minneapolis, Minnesota*

The emphasis placed on the topics covered in this review reflects our bias and interests. We apologize to the authors whose work has been overlooked.

The Membrane

The main properties of nerve and muscle cells to be considered in this section are the differences in potential and in ion contents between the interior of the cell and its normal environment, and excitability. The most widely accepted model used to explain these properties is that of a membrane of limited permeability separating the internal and external phases, in which the potential, ion gradients, and excitability are ascribed to the properties of the membrane. An alternative model in which the potential and ion gradients are ascribed to the properties of the protoplasm (195, 196, 201) will not be considered here.

Among the membrane hypotheses, that of Hodgkin & Huxley (157), originally proposed for the squid giant axon, has been frequently used to account for findings in other excitable tissues. In this hypothesis Na^+, K^+, and Cl^- currents are considered to be independent both at rest and during activity, and the membrane is considered to behave as though the individual ionic elements were connected in parallel (127, 212, 221, 309). If appropriate values be given to the several parameters included in Hodgkin & Huxley's empirical formulation, it is possible to picture and to account for striking differences in behavior among excitable tissues. Some recent examples are the accounts of potential changes in cardiac muscle (28, 229), in the lobster giant axon (70), and in crustacean muscle (see below).

However, data have been obtained in the last few years which, according to the investigators, cannot be fitted to the above hypothesis. The problem has been discussed here in preceding reviews (124, 268), and some new findings will be mentioned below. Prominent in the interpretations of many of these findings is the suggestion that fixed charges are present within the membrane, as in the model analyzed by Teorell (284).

Active transport.—A comprehensive review of the current status of the problem of active transport of ions across nerve and muscle membranes was given by Edelman (98). Investigations of the mechanisms involved have been somewhat limited in the past by the difficulty of obtaining cell membrane material. A method has now been described for isolating this material which offers hope of circumventing this difficulty (213).

---

[1] This survey was limited to the literature available up to June 1, 1961.

[2] Among the abbreviations used in this chapter are: ACh (acetylcholine); ATP (adenosine triphosphate); EPSP (excitatory postsynaptic potential); IPSP (inhibitory postsynaptic potential); RNA (ribonucleic acid).

A model, originally proposed to account for active transport of Na^+ in the salt gland of the albatross [Hokin & Hokin, 159)], has been extended to include Na^+ secretion from cholinoceptive neurons following activation by acetylcholine (ACh) (160). Incubation of slices of salt gland tissue with $10^{-5}M$ per liter ACh and $10^{-4}M$ per liter physostigmine leads to a 13-fold increase in the rate of incorporation of P^{32} into phosphatidic acid, and a 3-fold increase in the incorporation of P^{32} and inositol-2-H^3 into phosphoinositide. The rate of oxygen consumption is increased at the same time (159). Similar effects of ACh on P^{32} incorporation were shown in the cat's sympathetic ganglia and in tissue slices from certain regions of the cat's central nervous system (160). The incorporated phosphate is found largely in the microsomal fraction, which is said to include fragments of the endoplasmic reticulum. The enzymes responsible for the turnover of phosphatidic acid are also concentrated in this fraction. The following scheme of active Na^+ transport is suggested from this study: Na^+ combines with phosphatidate on the inner surface of the membrane, the compound diffuses across and is hydrolyzed at the outer surface into diglyceride and Na^+ phosphate; the Na^+ leaves the cell, and the diglyceride remains in the membrane and reacts with adenosine triphosphate (ATP) to reconstitute the phosphatidate (159).

Several points have to be considered in applying this scheme to the active Na^+ transport in cholinoceptive neurons. First, there is no evidence that the mechanism of Na^+ transport following ACh activation differs from that at rest; and while Na^+ transport does not seem to be localized along the membrane, sensitivity to ACh in cholinoceptive neurons may be localized. Second, even if it is assumed that the cholinergically activated secretion of a hyperosmotic solution [containing up to 0.85 meq NaCl per liter (110)] by the salt gland of the albatross does imply primary active Na^+ transport, the active Na^+ movement in excitable tissues is different, at least to the extent that there is apparently no osmotic gradient. Further, Hokin & Hokin point out that there is not yet conclusive evidence for the existence of cholinergic synapses in some of the neuronal structures which show the phospholipid effect in the presence of ACh (160).

Another model which attempts to account for the active, linked transport of K^+ and Na^+ across the nerve membrane has been proposed by Skou (261, 262). It is based on an adenosine triphosphatase prepared from crab nerve; a close relation between this enzyme and the ion pump in the red blood cell membrane has also been suggested (93, 237). The crab nerve enzyme is active in the presence of Na^+, Mg^{++}, and ATP; the addition of K^+ considerably increases activity of the enzyme but high concentrations of K^+ inhibit it, apparently by competitive displacement of Na^+. It is suggested that the reaction proceeds by way of an enzyme-Mg-ATP-Na-K complex. G-strophanthin, which inhibits active transport in red blood cells and frog skin, also inhibits the increase in activity of the adenosine triphosphatase produced by the addition of Na^+, or Na^+ and K^+; presumably it interferes with the binding of these ions to the complex. The enzyme is contained in the submicroscopic particle fraction; and Skou quotes evidence suggesting that these particles consist, in part at least, of fragments of membrane. He visualizes

. . . an arrangement of the system in the membrane according to which the site of the Na^+ affinity faces the intracellular water phase, while the site of the K^+ affinity is in contact with the extracellular water phase. At the site with highest Na^+ affinity the saturation of the enzyme with Na^+ depends on both the Na^+ and the K^+ concentration, and it appears . . . that the Na^+ saturation is about 40% when the Na^+ and K^+ concentrations are 40 and 350 mM/l respectively, i.e. identical with the intracellular concentrations of these ions in crab nerve. Since the activity varies with the Na^+ saturation, a change in Na^+ concentration above and below that corresponding to the intracellular level must consequently lead to a change in the enzyme activity. Moreover, due to the competition between Na^+ and K^+ a decrease in the K^+ concentration will increase the activity of the enzyme, while an increase in the concentration of K^+ will decrease the activity.

At the site with highest K^+ affinity the saturation with K^+ is equal to 80–90% when the K^+ concentration is around 12 mM/l, i.e. identical with the extracellular K^+ concentration in the crab (262).

In the intact squid giant axon the role of energy-rich phosphate compounds in active Na^+ transport has been further elucidated. In the presence of dinitrophenol or cyanide (CN), the ATP and arginine phosphate levels decrease. These inhibitors are known to reduce the Na^+ efflux. However, ouabain, which also inhibits the Na^+ efflux, does not significantly alter the levels of ATP or arginine phosphate (42). When the Na^+ efflux is blocked by CN, it can be restored by injecting ATP or other energy-rich phosphate compounds; these are without effect if applied externally. The increment of Na^+ extruded is roughly proportional to the amount of phosphate ester injected; with injections of large amounts of arginine phosphate, the efflux rate approaches the control level. Therefore, Caldwell and co-workers (43) conclude that energy-rich phosphate compounds are required for active Na^+ transport, and while CN and dinitrophenol appear to interfere with this transport by acting on the formation of energy-rich phosphate compounds, ouabain may act more directly on the transport mechanism (42).

The Na^+ efflux from CN-poisoned axons following injection of arginine phosphate or phosphoenolpyruvate resembles the normal efflux in being reduced by removal of external K^+. However, the Na^+ efflux set up by injection of ATP, ADP, or guanosine triphosphate is not sensitive to the external K^+ concentration. On the other hand, the K^+ influx of CN-poisoned axons is increased by injecting arginine phosphate, but not by ATP (43). The distinction between the roles of ATP and arginine phosphate is shown in axons poisoned by a concentration of dinitrophenol which reduces the latter but not the former. In this case the Na^+ efflux is unaffected by the removal of K^+. The sensitivity to K^+ is restored, however, by the injection of arginine phosphate (44). From the above data Caldwell et al. conclude that the normal coupling between K^+ influx and Na^+ efflux is dependent on the presence of arginine phosphate (43, 44).

Ion movements across resting nerve membranes.—The simplest model to explain ion exchanges is that of homogeneous internal and external compartments separated by a thin membrane. In *Sepia* axons the exchange seems to follow an exponential time course as predicted by this model (180). However, the K^+ exchange in the squid axon is more complex, and the deviation from the above model has been attributed by Shanes & Berman (258) to the presence of an intermediate compartment. The K^+ movement has now been analyzed in more detail by measuring the activity of the extruded axoplasm so as to divide the active material between the intra- and extracellular compartments, and by injecting the radioactive K^+ directly into the axon. The intermediate compartment is said to be extracellular and is tentatively identified with the Schwann cell layer and the connective tissue (45). It might be interpolated here that study of the slit axon, which consists largely of Schwann cells, reveals a system which has a metabolic rate higher than that of the axon and which concentrates K^+ above the level in sea water (51).

The rate of appearance in the external solution of ions injected into the squid giant axon varies for different substances. The sodium ion is lost at a faster rate than K^+ (43, 278), Cl^- is lost at a slower rate than K^+ (45, 278), and sulfate at a still slower rate (278). In the absence of both Ca^{++} and Mg^{++}, injected tracer Na^+ leaves the resting axon more rapidly. The time constant of the rate of appearance of phosphate in the bath solution is long, and that for Ca^{++} is short; the time constants of both increase with time, suggesting that some binding occurs (278). The finding that the time constant for Cl^- is about an order of magnitude larger than those for monovalent cations is interpreted as suggesting " . . . that the nerve membrane has properties of a 'charged membrane' in which negatively charged radicals are more-or-less immobile" (278). It may be noted, however, that in the data of Caldwell & Keynes (45) the rate constant for Cl^- efflux is close to that for K^+.

In an attempt to localize the site of binding of Ca^{++} in nerve cells, the effects of ribonuclease on cell homogenates were examined with the result that no large amount of Ca^{++}, Na^+, or K^+ was found to be firmly bound to ribonucleic acid (254).

Ion movements across the resting muscle membranes.—One of the problems faced in studies *in vitro* is that the ionic contents of the tissue change with time; Na^+ content in particular is likely to increase (cf. 60). It has previously been found that the Na^+ content of frog muscle is better maintained in plasma (46); the same effect has now been found for rat diaphragm muscle bathed in serum (60). In the latter case, the agent responsible for the effect is in the crude globulin fraction. The addition of insulin and lactate facilitates Na^+ extrusion from Na^+-rich frog muscles under conditions (see below) in which there would be no extrusion in their absence (179). Insulin also increases the K^+ content of rat muscle (60, 314) by reducing the efflux more than the influx (315). The effects of hormonal factors on Na^+ and K^+ distributions have been reviewed (50).

Muscles with elevated Na^+ levels, resulting from storage in solutions containing 120 mM per liter Na^+ and 0 mM per liter K^+, are said to extrude Na^+ in the presence of 10 mM per liter K^+ only if the Na^+ level of the solution is reduced (47). On the basis of measurements of membrane potential and measurements of Na^+ secretion at different levels of external Na^+ and K^+, Conway, Kernan & Zadunaisky (56) conclude that there is a critical energy barrier for Na^+ movement. The barrier is due to both the Na^+ gradient and the membrane potential. Factors reducing the barrier lead to a net Na^+ efflux, which is accompanied by an increased oxygen uptake.

The time course of K^+ uptake in frog muscle is known not to follow a single exponential as would be expected from the simplest model of ion exchange (cf. 152). To explain this deviation, Harris & Sjodin (152) proposed that exchange involves two processes,

... the first is an exchange with ions adsorbed near the cell surface (which may include the reticulum), and the second is diffusion inwards from the source provided by the adsorbed ions at the same time as an equal outward diffusion of the internal ions. The model is essentially a "three compartment" one, with the intermediate compartment having ion-exchange properties and within which movement is slow, so that it is the analogue of the resistive membrane.

The time course of the K^+ uptake agrees with the predictions of this model.

An absorption membrane model has also been proposed by Sjodin to explain the interactions between K^+, Rb^+, and Cs^+ observed in measurements of their rate of entry into frog muscle (260). These rates are consistent with the above model in which the inward movement is determined by the number of occupied sites.

The similarity of the kinetics of Mg^{++} and Ca^{++} exchange in frog muscle has been pointed out by Gilbert (137). The nonexchangeable fraction of Mg^{++} is higher than that of Ca^{++}; they both have several fractions which exchange with different time constants.

Muscle membrane potential.—The permeability of the resting membrane can vary in different tissues. In tonic muscle fibers of the frog, the resting potential is only slightly sensitive to changes of external K^+, but does vary with alterations in the external Na^+ level (181). This is in contrast with the properties of twitch fibers. In different cardiac tissues, the reduction of the membrane potential on increasing the external K^+ is not equal, suggesting differences in permeability (81).

Frog sartorius muscles soaked in hypertonic sucrose solution for periods long enough to remove 80 per cent of the K^+ are reported by Koketsu & Kimura to have practically normal resting and action potentials when replaced in Ringer solution. The cells gain potassium following prolonged soaking in this solution but the resting potential is unchanged (185). Moreover, the membrane potential is said to be independent of temperature when the muscle is in normal Ringer, but to be temperature dependent in Ca^{++}-poor or K^+-rich solutions. These results are said to indicate that the Nernst equation does not apply to the resting potential and that this potential is regulated by the concentration of Ca^{++} bound to the membrane (5; cf. also 186). The following points, however, should be considered. First, there are reports that the membrane potential does follow the Nernst equation for temperatures between 5 and 20°C (cf. 88). Second, while the potentials of only a small percentage of the total fibers are measured, and these are likely to be the surface fibers, the K^+ content measured is that of the whole muscle. Because of the size of the muscle used, the K^+ uptake after replacement of K^+ cannot be assumed to be uniform within the muscle (59, 184). For a single isolated muscle fiber the membrane potential closely follows changes in the external K^+ level; however, the potential varies more quickly when the K^+ is increased than when it is decreased (156).

In the absence of Ca^{++} the resting membrane potential of frog muscle is reduced [Koketsu & Noda (187); for nerve see (257)]. The loss of resting potential is associated with a transient increase in the efflux of tracer Ca^{++}; if cocaine, Mg^{++}, strontium, or cobalt be added to the Ca^{++}-free solution, there is neither depolarization nor the transient increase of Ca^{++} efflux. Since the Ca^{++} content of muscles soaked in Ca^{++}-free solution is only slightly reduced (186), it might be argued that the Ca^{++} involved in the maintenance of membrane potential is only a small part of that in the cell. The effluxes of Ca^{++} from frog muscle and tendon under different experimental conditions have also been studied (21, 22).

The active nerve membrane.—In the giant axon of the squid, Na^+ and K^+ currents have been measured by an improved voltage clamp technique in which the potential is clamped at only one point (53). From a theoretical analysis, Cole (52) concludes that the membrane potential can be well controlled at this point and that " . . . reasonably accurate current measurements can be made within a few tenths of a mm. of the control point." If the clamping is adequate, the current trace does not show notches or oscillations; these, when present, are presumably due to failure of the space clamp caused by high resistance of the current electrode (53, 283). The patterns of the Na^+ and K^+ currents found with the improved technique (53, 54) are essentially in agreement with those previously reported by Hodgkin & Huxley [summarized in (157)]. However, the currents for both ions are larger (53) and the analytical expression for the K^+ current has been drastically modified (54).

The constant field equation for the Na^+ current in the squid giant axon has been modified by Frankenhaeuser (127) to include a layer of fixed charges. The new empirical equation, which better fits previously known behavior, includes fixed charges at one membrane boundary while the movement of ions across the remaining portion of membrane is described by the constant field equation.

The electrochemical activities of Na^+ and K^+ in the axoplasm of the squid giant axon were studied with microelectrodes constructed of glass selectively permeable to either Na^+ or K^+. The difference between the inside and outside Na^+ electrode potentials exceeds the total height of the action potential, as in the Hodgkin-Huxley model. The Na^+ gain and K^+ loss on stimulation, measured with these electrodes, are consistent with previous results. Comparison of electrode measurements and analyses of axoplasm show that if K^+ is 100 per cent "free", an estimated 24 per cent of the Na^+ is "bound". If some K^+ is bound, then more Na^+ must be bound [Hinke (154)].

At the node of Ranvier of a toad nerve the Na^+ permeability under voltage clamp conditions can be described by equations similar to those appropriate to the squid giant axon (126).

Excitability of nerve under abnormal conditions.—A number of cases are known in which an active response may occur in the absence of Na^+ (268). The presence of this response depends on the properties of the membrane and of the electrolyte substituting for Na^+. For instance, if the node of Ranvier of a frog nerve is depolarized in isotonic KCl and repolarized by anodal current, active responses are produced. The height of this potential change has now been found to be a logarithmic function of the K^+ level and to be accompanied by a decrease in membrane resistance, suggesting a transient phase of increased permeability to K^+ ions. The increase in permeability decays spontaneously, but with a slower time course than that for Na^+ in normal bathing solution [Lüttgau (210)].

In other tissues, the active responses produced in the absence of Na^+ are also usually prolonged in duration. Similar prolongations are also found to follow various chemical and physical treatments (183, 267, 270). During the prolonged responses, an anodal pulse will induce an active repolarization which has a threshold and is all-or-none. A recent example of such behavior is found in the neuron of the crayfish stretch receptor, in which the action potential can be prolonged by strychnine; repolarization can also be initiated in this cell either by increasing Ca^{++} or by an inhibitory postsynaptic potential (305).

To interpret these transitions, Tasaki (276, 277) suggested that two stable states exist in excitable tissues and that abolition of the action potential is the reverse of the process by which it is initiated. This topic was discussed in last year's review (124). To study the transitions between these states, Spyropoulos (267) developed methods to produce brief variations in temperature and in the chemical composition of the medium bathing the node of a toad nerve. The nodal response is initiated in an all-or-none manner by sudden cooling, or by a sudden rise in local K^+ level. Responses prolonged by Ni^{++} or hypertonic Ringer (membrane maintained in the upper state) are abruptly terminated by a sudden temperature rise or an increase in Ca^{++} level. The prolonged response is further lengthened by K^+ increase, Ca^{++} depletion (addition of ethylenediamine tetra-acetic acid), or sudden cooling. The results are interpreted in terms of a membrane with negative fixed charges, in which the species of ion preferentially sorbed in the membrane determines in which of the two stable states the membrane is.

Transitions between different states of K^+ dependence have been found in neurons of the pulmonate mollusc *Onchidium verruculatum* (148). Hyperpolarizing currents of sufficient intensity applied to the cell soaked in high K^+ solutions sometimes give an active hyperpolarization; but, to judge from the records, this does not seem to be all-or-none. In addition, there is an active response at the termination of the hyperpolarizing pulse (232, 313). The conductance is increased during this response; the equilibrium level of the response is similar to that of the hyperpolarizing afterpotential which follows the normal spike and to that of the delayed rectification of the membrane. The potential level of these three processes depends on the external K^+ level; the resting membrane potential, however, is dependent on both the K^+ and Cl^- levels (148).

After-potentials.—The mechanisms responsible for hyper- and depolarizing after-potentials may vary in different cells. In the giant axon of the cockroach the depolarizing after-potential seems to be caused by the presence of accumulated K^+ in the vicinity of the nerve membrane (226). Administration of DDT increases and prolongs the depolarizing after-potential; in the absence of K^+, a plateau develops (225, 227). The barium ion prolongs both the rising and the falling phase of the action potential, and increases the depolarizing after-potential (223).

In the node of the frog nerve, where no extra-axonal barrier to diffusion of ions seems to exist (216), the brief depolarizing after-potential following a single spike has been attributed to a phase of increased Na^+ and K^+ permeability (215) and the hyperpolarizing after-potential following repetitive stimulation to a phase of increased K^+ permeability (216).

The active muscle membrane.—In the muscle fibers of the grasshopper *Romalea microptera* and of *Crustacea*, the normal electrical response is graded rather than all-or-none (49, 114). Partial substitution of external Na^+ with Ba^{++}, Sr^{++}, or tetraethylammonium (TEA) ions changes this graded response into a full-sized, all-or-none spike (309, 310) as previously reported for crayfish muscle (114). Following such substitution, the resting membrane resistance and time constant increase. Werman & Grundfest (309) attribute the absence of an all-or-none spike to a very high K^+ permeability. This conductance is reduced by Ba^{++} or other cations, as shown by the decreased sensitivity of the membrane potential to changes of the external K^+. Since Ba^{++} augments the amplitude of the action potential in the presence of low Na^+ concentrations, Werman & Grundfest propose that although Na^+ movement normally causes active depolarization, Ba^{++}, Sr^{++}, or tetraethylammonium can also carry charges (309, 310). Furthermore, the presence of Ca^{++} is not necessary for excitability; in the absence of Ca^{++} in the bathing solution, lobster (309) and frog muscle fibers (187) become depolarized and inexcitable, but excitability is restored by anodal polarization.

Frog muscle in low Ca^{++} solution becomes rhythmically active. A pacemaker type of generator potential is set up, the slope of which is influenced by stretch (190) and by small changes in membrane potential (189) as well as by changes in temperature (259). Denervation increases the frequency of the rhythmic activity, and the slope of the prepotentials is correspondingly increased (190; cf. also 199).

Role of anions in active membrane processes.—Substitution of large impermeable anions for Cl⁻ reveals that this ion plays no role in the fast phase of the action potential in frog muscle at 20°C (108, 163) but that it does participate in the rapid repolarization at lower temperatures (163). Following such substitution the depolarizing after-potential is increased and prolonged and the membrane may remain depolarized for as long as one or two minutes; oscillations are found in some fibers (108, 163). If the external K^+ level be increased, the plateau is shortened; if decreased, it is prolonged. Under these conditions, the oscillations may last indefinitely. In the complete absence of K^+ and Cl^- the membrane potential takes either of two values which correspond to two stable states (109).

In the Purkinje fibers of sheep hearts, substitution of large impermeable anions for Cl^- prolongs the action potential. This and other results are taken by Carmeliet to suggest that while Cl^- conductance is low, Cl^- becomes important for carrying charges when the membrane is depolarized (48). Impulse activity in the squid giant axon has only a small effect on the Cl^- fluxes (45, 278).

Effects of acetylcholine and other agents on the active membrane.—Acetylcholine, previously shown to excite sensory nerve endings [cf. (10) for bibliography], has recently been said to have a stimulant effect on the preganglionic nerve terminals of the superior cervical ganglion of the cat (248). This view has now been questioned; in the rabbit the activity initiated by ACh in the preganglionic trunk is attributed to the presence in this trunk of postganglionic fibers (87).

Acetylcholine has been shown to affect nerve conduction in C fibers, causing depolarization, reduction of conduction velocity, and enhancement of the after-potential (10). The effect is inhibited not only by *d*-tubocurarine and related compounds, but also by the anticholinesterases physostigmine, prostigmine, and diisopropylfluorophosphonate (DFP) (11). The authors conclude: "There seems no reason to infer from the present experimental findings that it (ACh) plays a role in conduction along the nerve membrane similar to its well established role in neuromuscular and synaptic transmission" (11).

Findings relevant to a possible role of ACh in the conduction of nerve impulses (222) were obtained from the effects of compounds known to react with the ACh system (83, 240; cf. also 303, 312). Data on the action of ACh on the membrane of muscle and electroplaques were also reported (155, 251, 252). A protein has been isolated from electric organs which binds curare, ACh, and related compounds. From the parallelism between the binding strength and the efficacy of the compounds at the electroplaque junction, it has been suggested that this isolated protein may be the receptor for ACh (101). However, the relation between physiological effect and binding remains to be determined.

In studies of anesthetic action, the time course of diminution of the frog nerve action potential after application of procaine or xylocaine was found to be largely explicable in terms of free diffusion of the base of these compounds into the nerve trunk (253). Urethane increases the threshold to stimulation and decreases the height of the nodal action current in frog nerve (166, 295).

Treatment of a single node of a frog nerve with a thiamine-complexing agent reversibly decreases the spike height (235). Substitution of hydrazine ion for Na^+ permits an action potential to develop in nerve and muscle, while phosphorylation is reduced by as much as 80 per cent (1). Dinitrophenol at low concentration also markedly inhibits phosphorylation without altering excitability. Higher levels of this agent, however, produce inexcitability and depolarization, but excitability is restored by anodal polarization (2). Dinitrophenol and cyanide are reported to block conduction in rat nerve (256).

New studies on the effect of temperature on the action potentials of the giant axon of the earthworm show that conduction can occur at $-5°C$, although the action potential is altered (298, 299; cf. 211). When an improved amplifier was used (169), in frog nerve the impedance change during activity was shown to lag behind the action potential at low temperature; this delay decreases with temperature increase (39).

Tetrodotoxin, a toxic substance from the globefish, blocks the action potential of frog muscle; this effect is attributed to inactivation of the Na^+ regenerative mechanisms (224).

TRANSMISSION AT SYNAPTIC JUNCTIONS

The concept advocated by Grundfest (142, 143, 144) that subsynaptic membranes are "electrically inexcitable" was discussed in last year's review (124). Since then the absence of impulse activity in portions of the postjunctional membrane at the endplate has been demonstrated by Werman (308). The results suggest the coexistence within small regions of membrane of "electrically inexcitable" and "electrically excitable" patches of such dimensions as to permit recording of different patterns of current flow with an external microelectrode. Moreover, the properties attributed to "electrically inexcitable" membranes were demonstrated directly by studies of the electric organs of marine electric fishes (18, 19, 20). The amplitude of the postsynaptic potential has been shown to be a linear function of membrane polarization and, therefore, of the electrochemical gradient of the ions involved. Hyper- and depolarization of the membrane of these electroplaques do not elicit a response; the potential change is linearly related to the applied current. Delayed rectification is absent here, but not in all otherwise "electrically inexcitable" membranes (20). If this fact is neglected, or the absence of impulse activity alone is taken to characterize "electrical in-excitability", there seems to be little objection to Grundfest's concept. Equating "electrical inexcitability" to "chemical excitability" may, on the contrary, be somewhat questionable. On the one hand, there may be regions of membrane in excitable tissues in which both "electrical" and "chemical" excitability are absent; on the other hand, subsynaptic membranes might not be the only portion of membrane sensitive to transmitter substances. Furthermore, models of synaptic transmission can be conceived which would include selective ion fluxes without the participation of specific transmitter substances. No consideration will, however, be given to these alternative models since there is no supporting evidence for them and since the available data at all junctions so far examined, with the exception only of the giant motor synapse of the crayfish (133), seem to be consistent with the model of chemical transmission.

Neuromuscular junction.—Evidence has recently been presented that in vertebrates some specific characteristics of the muscle fiber depend on the presence of motor innervation. The process of muscle differentiation from the neonatal state into fast and slow muscles [bibliography in (33)], which occurs in mammals during the first few weeks after birth, has been reinvestigated by Buller, Eccles & Eccles (33). Differentiation of slow muscles in the cat hindlimb is found not to occur when the lumbosacral cord is deprived of inputs by transection of the cord at the thoracic level and sectioning of the dorsal roots. Moreover, if, in otherwise intact animals, motor nerve fibers from phasic motoneurons are made to innervate slow muscles and tonic motoneurons are made to innervate fast muscles, fast muscles are converted into slow muscles and slow into fast (34). These changes do not occur if the lumbosacral segments are surgically isolated as described above. The authors suggest that a neuronal influence is exerted upon the muscle fiber via the release of a chemical agent. This influence is said not to result from the nerve impulse as such but to be specific for tonic and phasic motoneurons and to depend on an intact afferent input to the involved motoneurons. Since cross-innervation appears to be as effective in adult animals as in kittens, a principle of continuous differentiation is advocated (34).

The presence of motor innervation also regulates the extent of the muscle membrane which is sensitive to ACh and to other chemicals [Thesleff (291)]. Normally this area is limited to the neuromuscular junction and to the closely surrounding region [see discussion in Katz & Miledi (177)], as carefully established by iontophoretic application of ACh in muscles of the rat (218), cat (14), and frog (217). In the frog sartorius, for instance, the sensitivity to ACh decreases to 1/10,000 at a 1.1 mm distance from the center of the endplate. Following denervation, the extent of the chemo-sensitive region increases progressively, both in cat (14) and frog (217) muscles, moving from the endplate region towards the tendons. The reverse process, a progressive decrease of the chemosensitive region from the tendons towards the endplate, occurs during reinnervation (219) and during the first few weeks after birth in the muscle fibers of the rat diaphragm (86). The whole membrane of these fibers is, in fact, sensitive to ACh in the fetal and newborn rat (86).[3]

The mechanisms which regulate the extent of the chemosensitive region are still not clearly defined, although it is agreed that the presence of activity is not involved (172, 217). Since the chemosensitive area increases after treatment with botulinum toxin (292), which is said to block selectively the release of ACh (292), Thesleff concludes that the lack of transmitter release, rather than degeneration of the motor fibers, is the responsible factor. A different view is suggested by Miledi on the basis of experiments involving partial denervation (217) and regeneration (219). Since the area of membrane sensitive to ACh increases after partial denervation and returns to normal size before neuromuscular transmission is restored, he suggests that the factor controlling its extent is liberated independently of impulse activity in motor fibers and that it is not the transmitter.

Thesleff & Miledi agree that the sensitivity of the chemosensitive membrane to ACh is not increased following denervation, in contrast to previous beliefs. In a discussion of the factors responsible for supersensitivity following denervation, Thesleff (291) points out that while the increase in membrane resistance following denervation (217, 228) would increase the amplitude of the endplate potential (178), this change alone is inadequate to explain supersensitivity. The increase in the size of the area sensitive to ACh seems to be the major factor. Unlike that of ACh, the affinity constant for curare has been found to increase after denervation (170).

Morphological and physiological changes at the endplate have been studied during degeneration (24) and regeneration (219) of the motor nerve. The disappearance of spontaneous miniature endplate potentials following denervation was confirmed. However, after several weeks the miniature endplate potentials reappear and persist in the absence of motor nerve fibers, although their frequency is much lower than in normal muscle (24). The amplitude distribution of these miniature endplate potentials is highly irregular; their dispersion is much wider than in innervated endplates, and the lower amplitude potentials predominate. Since these miniature endplate potentials seem to be due to liberation of the transmitter from a source outside the muscle fiber, it has been proposed that the Schwann cells, which fill the space previously occupied by the nerve terminals, acquire the ability to release the transmitter intermittently. It is also stated that the presence of miniature endplate potentials after nerve degeneration does not preclude the hypothesis according to which the vesicular bags inside the nerve terminals are responsible for the quantal nature of transmission at the

---

[3] Similar findings by A. G. Ginetsinskii *et al.* (cited by A. K. Voskresenskaya in *Problems of Evolution of Physiological Functions*, 46–59, Engl. transl. by the Natl. Sci. Foundation and Dept. of Health, Education and Welfare, Washington, D.C., 162 pp., 1960) have recently come to the attention of the authors.

normal neuromuscular junction, since vesicles are present in the Schwann cells. It seems unlikely that glial tissue participates in transmission in normal junctions since elevated K^+ (275) and other factors which affect the discharge rate of the miniature endplate potentials in the normally innervated endplate do not alter the frequency in the denervated endplate (24). The fact that at the normal endplate the motor nerve terminals and the muscle membrane are in juxtaposition, without glia being interposed, also favors this conclusion.

The amount of ACh liberated in the isolated rat diaphragm by a nerve impulse has been measured by bioassay (191, 269). The estimated mean release from a single nerve ending (10^{-17} moles) is of the same order of magnitude as the smallest amount effective when applied iontophoretically (191). The measured spontaneous release was found to be compatible with the hypothesis that the miniature endplate potentials are caused by spontaneous release of ACh (cf. 77). The kinetics of ACh-receptor function have also been examined (116).

The conductance change at the endplate caused by the transmitter action has been studied in recent years by the voltage clamp method (231, 271 to 274). The measured time course agrees with the one previously calculated by Fatt & Katz (115). The equilibrium potential of the current flowing during the transmitter action was unaltered when the Cl^- ions in the perfusion fluid were replaced by larger and presumably impermeable ions. This suggests that the permeability to Cl^- is not changed by the transmitter [Takeuchi & Takeuchi (273)]. Therefore, the original hypothesis of a short circuit, i.e., a nonspecific permeability increase to all ions (77, 115), has to be modified to exclude an increase in Cl^- conductance.

The action potential at the endplate following nerve stimulation has been recorded in a nerve-muscle preparation containing a single muscle fiber (230). The records are similar to those described originally by Fatt & Katz (115) and therefore support the interpretation proposed by these authors.

Synaptic transmission from autonomic nerves to smooth muscle fibers of the vas deferens was studied by Burnstock & Holman (41). Spontaneous miniature potentials are present at this junction. The time course of these potentials and of those evoked by nerve stimulation is much longer than that of the endplate potentials of twitch muscle fibers. Facilitation is a marked feature at this junction, and summation is necessary to reach threshold depolarization for impulse initiation. Treatment with botulinum toxin is followed by failure of transmission (244). This is taken as further evidence for a cholinergic process in sympathetic transmission [Burn & Rand (40)], although results by Rand, quoted in (41), suggest that the transmitter is norepinephrine.

The quantal nature of transmission at the neuromuscular junction of *Crustacea* has been established by Dudel & Kuffler (89). There is a spontaneous release of the transmitter (92, 247), the frequency of which is influenced by moderate depolarization, by excess K+, and by an increase of the osmotic pressure, as at the neuromuscular junction of vertebrates. The pronounced facilitation present at the crustacean neuromuscular junction during low-frequency stimulation of the motor axon is attributed to an increase in the number of quanta released (90).

Junctions between neurons.—The experimental evidence indicating that postsynaptic excitation is caused by the transient membrane depolarization known as the excitatory postsynaptic potential (EPSP) was summarized by Frank & Fuortes in last year's review (124). The ionic flow causing this potential change, i.e. the synaptic current, is ascribed to an increase of membrane conductance initiated by transmitter action. The time course of the conductance change has been measured by the voltage clamp method at invertebrate junctions (149, 150). For cat spinal motoneurons, calculations of the synaptic current from the EPSP (94) are uncertain because the geometry of the cell seems to preclude direct measurement of the membrane time constant (242). On the basis of a motoneuron model with a large dendrite-to-soma conductance ratio, Rall (243) concludes that the decay of the EPSP is determined mostly by the dendritic time constant, as previously suggested by Fatt (112). Therefore, the presence of a significant residual synaptic current lasting well into the falling phase of the EPSP (61) is doubtful (243). In voltage clamp experiments, the synaptic current was found to subside in about 2 msec (Araki & Terzuolo, unpublished results).

In neurons of *Aplysia* (279) and at the electroplaque of marine electric fishes (20), a much longer-lasting conductance change should be present, however, since the membrane time constant is too short to account for the slow decay of the EPSP. The data on the electroplaque exclude a self-supporting permeability increase, leaving open the question of whether a prolonged transmitter release or a slow return of the conductance to its original level following a brief transmitter action may cause the long-lasting synaptic current.

The magnitude of the synaptic current is related to the electrochemical potential gradient of the ions whose permeability is increased by the excitatory transmitter (cf. 94). Since the potential at which the EPSP reverses is near to the liquid junction potential between the axoplasm and the extracellular fluid, as in the case of the endplate potential, it is currently thought that the short-circuit hypothesis originally proposed for the endplate potential also applies to the EPSP (cf. 94). However, the finding that Cl⁻ permeability does not appear to be increased at the endplate (273) may be relevant to other synapses.

Turning to inhibitory postsynaptic events, Frank & Fuortes (124) presented arguments to invalidate the claim of Lloyd & Wilson (204) that the potential change known as the inhibitory postsynaptic potential (IPSP) "may differ from the actual (the so-called 'direct' or 'Ia') inhibition in latency and time course." Data which have been presented against this claim by Araki, Eccles & Ito (6) include: (a) evidence that the central latency is the same for "direct" inhibition and the IPSP; and (b) evidence that the time course of the "direct" inhibition is the same as that of the IPSP recorded either intracellularly, or from small ventral root filaments where it spreads electrotonically. A relation between potential changes recorded electrotonically in the ventral root and suppression of motoneuron activity had also been reported following supraspinal stimulation (289).

Eccles and colleagues (6) emphasize that both the increased ionic conductance, caused by the inhibitory transmitter, and the longer-lasting membrane potential change, or IPSP, contribute to the postsynaptic inhibitory action. The second of these factors has sometimes been overlooked in favor of the first. However, since an inhibitory action contributes to integrative processes only when acting concomitantly with excitatory actions, either spontaneous (pacemaker potential) or induced (generator potential or postsynaptic potential), it will necessarily produce a membrane potential change because the level of membrane polarization will be displaced by the excitatory actions from the equilibrium potential of the ions involved in the inhibitory process. Since the resulting IPSP is longer lasting than the conductance increase, and because the excitability of the cell is strictly dependent on the level of the membrane potential, the IPSP undoubtedly plays an important role in integrative processes. It is relevant in this context that the long-lasting changes in excitability of the cat's spinal motoneurons resulting from supraspinal inhibitory and excitatory actions are closely related to the changes in membrane potential that they produce (285).

The problem of the ionic conductance changes causing the IPSP has been most recently reviewed by Eccles (95; cf. 113, 193). To extend the original study of Coombs, Eccles & Fatt (58), additional ions were injected iontophoretically into the cat's spinal motoneurons (7). The changes in the IPSP following injection of ions with hydrated size close to that of Cl^- are similar to those observed when the intracellular concentration of the Cl^- ion is increased. Larger ions, on the contrary, do not affect the IPSP. The results, therefore, agree with the original proposal by Coombs, Eccles & Fatt (58) that the permeability increase causing postsynaptic inhibition is highly selective with respect to hydrated ion size and that Cl^- movement is involved in the production of the IPSP. A role for K^+ ions in the inhibitory process in cat spinal motoneurons is deduced indirectly (95). In the crayfish stretch receptor, K^+ ions were known to be involved in the inhibitory process (100), and recently it has been demonstrated that Cl^- ions also participate (147). The synaptic inhibitory current has been measured by the voltage clamp method in the crustacean stretch receptor (147), in *Onchidium verruculatum* (146), and in cat spinal motoneurons (9, cf. 95).

The presence of an inhibitory interneuron in the central pathway for "direct" or "Ia" inhibition in the cat spinal cord has been reaffirmed (6). In agreement with previous investigations [(6, 95) for bibliography], it was found that the IPSP evoked by stimulation of group Ia fibers invariably begins to develop later than the EPSP evoked by the same volley. Furthermore, the interneurons of the intermediate nucleus respond to a volley in group Ia fibers as would be expected for a neuron interposed in the pathway for direct inhibition [bibliography in (6)]. Also, the IPSP evoked in spinal motoneurons of the monkey by impulses traveling in the pyramidal tract has a longer latency than the EPSP produced by the same stimulation. These differences in latency are said to be compatible with the interposition of an interneuron between the pyramidal tract fibers and the spinal motoneurons (95, 238, 239).

The presence of an inhibitory interneuron, when considered in conjunction with the principle that a single transmitter is liberated at all endings of a neuron,[4] provides a simple scheme for central integrative processes, for it allows the conversion of an excitatory action into an inhibitory one. In fact, since different types of permeability changes produce the EPSP and the IPSP, different transmitters are generally thought to produce excitation and inhibition. This in turn would imply two different neurons synapsing on the postsynaptic cell.

Generalization from this scheme might not be safe, however, since there are findings which suggest other schemes. For instance, the activity of a single axon may produce opposite effects upon two different postsynaptic neurons. Stimulation of the extrinsic inhibitory axon of the cardiac ganglion of the lobster causes depolarizing postsynaptic potentials, which lead to an increase of excitability in one of the nine neurons of the ganglion, and produces hyperpolarizing postsynaptic potentials in another cell of this ganglion (288). No interneuron is interposed. Similarly, activity in the collaterals of the axon of the eccentric cell of the *Limulus* eye suppresses activity in the axon of the eccentric cell of adjacent ommatidia (131, 245, 294), while centrally the axon is likely to induce excitatory actions. No interneurons were demonstrated in this preparation either (220). Although in *Limulus* the mechanisms of inhibition have not yet been detailed, the former example alone, if considered in the light of the Dale principle, indicates that the same agent may cause either excitation or inhibition in different neurons. Even if the applicability of the Dale principle here is questioned, the above conclusion is supported by findings of the action of ACh. Acetylcholine induces depolarizing potential changes at the vertebrate endplate and at the electroplaque (20) and induces firing of Renshaw cells (66); however, it causes inhibition in the heart [but not in that of cyclostomes where there are no inhibitory synapses and in which ACh is excitatory (13)] and produces potential changes similar to those caused by synaptic inhibition in some invertebrate neurons (146). Furthermore, ACh produces inhibitory and excitatory effects in different neurons belonging to the same visceral ganglia in both the snail (282) and *Aplysia* (281). In the latter, iontopho-

---

[4] This principle is referred to by Eccles (94) as the Dale principle.

retic application of ACh produces hyperpolarization and suppression of activity in some neurons, while other neurons are depolarized. In both types of cells the action of ACh is enhanced by physostigmine but only the hyperpolarizing responses induced both by ACh or nerve stimulation are blocked by d-tubocurarine. The response to ACh and other compounds tested is the same in both the axon, where the synapses are located, and the soma, where there are no synapses; but the sensitivity of the axon is greater.

From the above data one may conclude that the type of postsynaptic response elicited may depend on the characteristics of the postsynaptic membrane rather than the transmitter itself. If so, according to the chemical model of synaptic transmission, the specificity might reside in the receptor or in steps beyond the receptor. The second alternative seems to us to provide the simpler interpretation. It might also be interpolated here that more than one type of receptor site may initiate the same permeability changes since compounds with different chemical structures may produce similar effects. For instance, the potential changes induced in *Onchidium verruculatum* by ACh and in the stretch receptor of *Crustacea* by γ-aminobutyric acid are similar, and γ-aminobutyryl choline produces the same effect in both preparations (146).

In the above interpretation, specificity might depend on the presence and properties of channels for different ions within the postsynaptic membrane. This thesis neither supports nor denies the existence of receptors, and one might choose to debate the general applicability of the concept of receptor sites and to argue that an unspecific pharmacological action is responsible for transmission at some junctions. These arguments will not be developed further; they have been presented only to indicate how insecure some of the concepts relating to chemical transmission between neurons are. As a consequence one should not be too concerned about intellectual impasses in matters concerning transmitter substances. One example is the over-rigid formulation of requirements of a substance for it to be considered a transmitter (118). The minimal requirements can actually be reduced to the following: its liberation by activity in the presynaptic fibers and its ability, when applied in physiological concentrations, to reproduce the conductance changes which occur during synaptic transmission. Evidence bearing on these points is available only for ACh at the neuromuscular junction and in the heart.

A second impasse is the argument that, although a compound reproduces the permeability changes caused by the transmitter, it is doubtful that it is the actual transmitter at this synapse because it also acts similarly on other neurons which do not possess synapses (99). This reasoning may have to be abandoned in view of the findings that ACh is active upon membranes which do not possess synapses and that the whole muscle fiber membrane is sensitive to ACh in the absence of innervation.

Another difficulty is a reluctance to admit that more than one transmitter may produce similar postsynaptic effects on one cell. However, the

Renshaw cell which is excited by the axon collaterals of motoneurons and is therefore cholinoceptive may probably also be excited monosynaptically by dorsal root fibers which are not cholinergic (121; see also 68). A second example is provided by heterogenic reinnervation of the superior cervical ganglion in the cat. De Castro has shown that vagal afferent fibers can establish functional synaptic connections with the neurons of this ganglion (74), but the application of eserine does not increase or prolong the response of the postsynaptic neurons to this presynaptic input. Finally, gland cells respond in a similar manner to both cholinomimetic and adrenomimetic substances (209).

Some of the above points and others are mentioned in the literature and were summarized by Florey in a discussion of difficulties inherent in investigations of transmitter substances (120).

Effects of amino acids (67, 68, 69) and other agents (64, 65) on brainstem (63) and spinal neurons were examined by Curtis and colleagues. There is a correlation between the chemical structure of the amino acids and the effects produced. Excitatory actions (depolarization) are associated with the presence of two acidic groups and one basic group, while a depressant action is associated with one acidic and one basic group. This structure-activity relationship suggests that activity is dependent upon interaction of the compounds " . . . with membrane structures of definite shape, size, and charge distribution" (68). Since the compounds are equally effective upon the cholinoceptive Renshaw cell (see, however, above) and the non-cholinoceptive inter- and motoneurons, their action is considered unspecific. Discrepancies between the results mentioned above and the properties attributed to axon-dendritic synapses of the cerebral cortex (241), as inferred from the effects of topical applications of amino acids on surface cortical potentials, are discussed.

The search for the transmitter at the noncholinergic junctions of *Crustacea* [bibliography in (297)] led to the isolation from crustacean tissue extracts of a Factor S which differs from previously recognized excitatory substances (297).

The current status of ideas concerning γ-aminobutyric acid and inhibitory processes is presented in a book (see beginning of bibliography) and elsewhere (31, 71, 103, 129, 153, 161, 194). In brief, there seems to be little or no evidence that γ-aminobutyric acid is the inhibitory transmitter in the central nervous system of mammals. The presumed relationship between depletion of γ-aminobutyric acid and convulsive activity following hydrazine injection (182) has been questioned (290); convulsions can be observed in the presence of an elevated γ-aminobutyric acid content if hydroxylamine is simultaneously injected (17). In the crustacean stretch receptor, γ-aminobutyric acid produces permeability changes similar to those initiated by synaptic inhibition (99, 100, 147), but Florey denies that it is the inhibitory transmitter in *Crustacea* since he finds that " . . . only traces of GABA are present in the peripheral and central nervous system of *Crustacea*" (118). A different factor, called Substance I, was isolated from crustacean extracts (118); this agent, also liberated during inhibition of the heart, causes inhibition of the crustacean heart, stretch receptor, and hind gut (119) and is effective at much lower concentrations than γ-aminobutyric acid.

PROCESSES OF EXCITATION IN RECEPTORS

Since specific characteristics of different receptor organs are reviewed in another chapter, only some general aspects of the processes which occur in the transducer membrane of receptor organs and lead to the generator potential will be considered here (36, 73, 138, 144). The behavior of the generator potential as studied in the Pacinian corpuscle and crustacean stretch receptor appears to be similar to that of postsynaptic potentials. The amplitude is graded (138, 139, 205) and is a function of the electrochemical gradient of the ions involved for a stimulus of constant intensity (84, 206). Moreover, the generator potential acts as an adequate electrical stimulus upon the portion of membrane in which depolarization generates an action potential, and the impulse does not seem to invade the transducer membrane (85, 205).

The processes leading to the generator potential and those responsible for the action potential differ substantially in their temperature sensitivity. The rate of rise and the amplitude of the generator potential in the Pacinian corpuscle change markedly with temperature changes which do not affect the action potential; on cooling, the action potential is abolished, while the generator potential persists (167, 168). In the crayfish stretch receptor the amplitude of the generator potential also changed with temperature increase (38). Results similar to those in the Pacinian corpuscle have been obtained for the excitatory postsynaptic potential of spinal motoneurons in the isolated frog spinal cord (McMullen and Washizu, unpublished results).

IMPULSE ACTIVITY IN NERVE CELLS

The available data indicate that in most neurons impulse activity originates in the axon, though the depolarization leading to impulse initiation (either generator potential or postsynaptic potential) is usually set up in the soma-dendrite complex. The extent of the subsequent invasion of this complex by the action potential varies, however, in different cells. This problem was discussed here last year (124). New data by Araki & Terzuolo, not yet presented *in extenso* (286), support the hypothesis that in the cat's spinal motoneuron the action potential invades the soma region and propagates along at least some portion of the dendrites (57, 132). Antidromic invasion of the portion of membrane responsible for the SD (or B) spike [i.e., the second of the two components of the intracellularly recorded action potential (57, 132)] is prevented if the potential of the soma membrane is clamped at the resting level. Moreover, intracellular recordings made simultaneously from two regions of the same motoneruon suggest the active invasion of some portion of the dendrites.

The change in membrane resistance of spinal motoneurons during excitation, as measured under voltage clamp conditions (286), is smaller than the change found in other neurons (145), but greater than that previously reported (125).

Responses of spinal motoneurons to direct currents have been studied in the cat (29, 123) and rat (29). Accommodation is minimal and is almost complete within 40 to 80 msec (29). The rate of repetitive activity is less in spinal motoneurons of the rat than in those of the cat. This is attributed to the greater duration of the hyperpolarizing after-potential in the former (29). Accommodation is more prominent in toad spinal motoneurons, particularly in the axon, but even here it is much less than in peripheral nerves (233). The difference in accommodation between axon and soma may lead to impulse initiation in the latter (8). Mechanisms of repetitive firing were discussed by Frank & Fuortes (124) and by MacIntyre & Mark (214).

To the model of nerve cell behavior, as based on the properties of spinal motoneurons (94), other features may have to be added in specific cases (e.g. 37). In hippocampal neurons of the cat, a large depolarizing after-potential accounts, according to Kandel & Spencer (175), for the characteristic short-lasting high-frequency bursts which they describe in these neurons following appropriate synaptic activation or direct stimulation. Since the bursts are self-limiting, these neurons are said to be able to transform a sustained input into a discontinuous output.

As more neurons are adequately studied, other differences in behavior from that of the general model are likely to be found, some of which may be unique for particular neurons. These differences will relate ultimately to the role of these cells in integrative actions. One may now argue, in view of the findings of Kandel & Spencer (105), that the burst pattern of hippocampal neurons is the basis of the tendency to synchronization of hippocampal electrical activity and of the characteristic EEG pattern recorded from this structure under certain conditions (3, 104, 141).

PARAMETERS OF INTEGRATIVE PROCESSES

In addition to structural organization, a number of properties are known which are involved in and account for integrative processes (35, 36, 130). The most important advance in this field was the demonstration of graded responses (the EPSP and IPSP) at synaptic junctions; these potential changes interact to regulate the excitability of the postsynaptic neuron (94). It should be emphasized that EPSP's and IPSP's have been demonstrated in neurons throughout the central nervous system [(94); recent contributions are (174, 176, 200, 255)].

The efficacy of synaptic inputs will vary with the location of the presynaptic terminations on the postsynaptic membrane (124). The EPSP initiated in frog spinal motoneurons by dorsal root stimulation shows a slower rate of rise and decay than the EPSP initiated by stimulation of the lateral column (32, 111). Correspondingly, the extracellular potential changes are maximal in the latter case in the region of the cord where the somas of motoneurons are localized, while in the former case the largest potential changes are found in the region of the cord where the dendrites are most concentrated (32). According to present views, membrane potential changes resulting from integration of synaptic activity caused by inputs synapsing in distal dendrites may be largely responsible for the smoothly graded and sustained changes of excitability of the cell (36, 124, 285). These potential changes would not be abolished by the action potential if it did not propagate to the distal dendrites. Synapses located close to the site of impulse origin, on the other hand, " . . . would have a commanding effect over immediate impulse initiation, but their effect would last only until the next impulse" (124).

A somewhat different scheme of the role of dendrites in integrative processes and of their effect on impulse initiation in hippocampal neurons was suggested by Spencer & Kandel (264). Some of these neurons show a fast prepotential of small but constant amplitude which precedes the action potential evoked by orthodromic activation. This potential is interpreted as being caused by localized firing of a restricted portion of the dendrites, possibly located in the region of the bifurcation of the main apical dendrite, as previously suggested by Eccles (94). If so, a " . . . booster zone for otherwise ineffectual distal dendritic synapses might be present."

If this interpretation is correct and since the time of decay of this prepotential is faster than that expected from electrotonic spread (265), the above observation recalls the suggestion by Lorente de Nó that decremental conduction (i.e., active responses) " . . . of variable magnitude capable of propagating through variable, but limited lengths" (208) plays a role in integrative processes (cf. 124, 207).

Factors which are capable of influencing the postsynaptic efficacy of a given input may change in the course of activity. These include mechanisms involved in release of the transmitter and alterations of the sensitivity of the subsynaptic membrane. Combinations of these factors lead to changes in postsynaptic efficacy following single, or during and after repetitive stimulation (162). Recent contributions are those by Bishop and co-workers (25, 26, 27), who examined pre- and postsynaptic changes in the lateral geniculate nucleus of the cat; and by Eccles & associates, who recorded potential changes in primary afferent fibers and spinal motoneurons (62, 96, 97). Following a single presynaptic volley, or during brief repetitive stimulation at frequencies below 40 per sec, the EPSP of spinal motoneurons undergoes a potentiation which is superimposed on a phase of depression. The latter can be overcome at higher frequencies of stimulation (62). In electroplaques (20), neuromuscular junctions (41, 90), and in several neurons of invertebrates (176, 197, 279, 288), the amplitude of the postjunctional potentials markedly increases during low-frequency stimulation; the evidence suggests that the mechanisms responsible for this increase differ at the different junctions. At the neuromuscular junction (291) and in electroplaques (20), transmission may also be affected by desensitization of the cholinoceptive membrane following exposure to ACh. Finally, there is evidence for Wedensky inhibition in the isolated toad spinal cord (8), at the neuromuscular junction of frog (188, 234), and in the cortex of mammals (30).

Other characteristics of the postsynaptic neuron besides desensitization might alter the input-output relationship during activity. Among these are block of activity by excessive depolarization (104, 192); a possible nonlinear relationship between sustained depolarization and frequency of impulse activity (285); changes in threshold because of accommodation; and the characteristics of the output pattern (175).

A process recently shown to be important in determining the synaptic efficacy of a given input is presynaptic inhibition. The occurrence in the cat spinal cord of an inhibitory process which is not associated with recordable changes of membrane potential of motoneurons was previously demonstrated by Frank & Fourtes (122). A reduction of the EPSP is the only sign of this inhibition, the excitability of the cell being unaltered. Eccles, Eccles & Magni (95) now have evidence that this depression of the EPSP arises from a diminution in the size and number of the afferent impulses which produce the EPSP. This presynaptic inhibition would be caused by an alteration of the membrane potential of group Ia fibers, the mechanism of which remains to be determined. At the crayfish neuromuscular junction presynaptic inhibition also occurs, and the mechanism here appears to be chemical (91). The importance of presynaptic inhibition as a possible parameter in integrative processes is given by its ability to suppress inputs without altering the excitability of the postsynaptic neuron, as for postsynaptic inhibition.

Voltages are present throughout the nervous system which are adequate to alter the excitability of nerve cells and thereby may effect ongoing activities (106, 287, 311). Electrical interactions between neurons of *Aplysia* have been reported (280). It is conceivable that currents flowing as a result of activity in the postsynaptic neuron might affect the presynaptic nerve terminals. While this hypothesis might be extended to apply to modifications of synaptic efficacy usually denoted by the term "temporary connections" (171), there is no supporting evidence at present.

A subtle structural factor in integrative processes was demonstrated recently in the lobster cardiac ganglion. The existence of low-resistance protoplasmic bridges between some neurons of this ganglion was previously inferred from the presence of electrical connections between these cells (150, 306). The rhythm of pacemaker neurons has now been shown to be influenced by subthreshold potential changes which presumably spread electrotonically along such bridges (307). Similar electrical connections have also been shown between supramedullary neurons in the puffer fish (307) and between crustacean muscle fibers (246). The finding that some motoneurons of the toad can be activated antidromically via two ventral roots may also be taken to indicate the existence of bridges, but in this instance there are alternative possibilities (304).

A possible participation of glial tissue in the function of the nervous system has been suggested (134).

MORPHOLOGICAL, PHYSICAL, AND BIOCHEMICAL STUDIES

Electron microscopic examination has revealed the striking similarity of macromolecular arrangements in the lipoprotein matrix of cell membranes. Data on biological lamellar systems can be found in (117) and (250). Reports on the appearance of myelin sheath ultrastructure (55), infolding of nerve membranes in molluscs (16), presence of neurofilaments in unmyelinated fibers of the cat (102), and X-ray diffraction of myelin have appeared (158). This list of morphological studies is by no means complete.

Electron microscope studies of the Schwann cells surrounding the giant axon of the tropical squid *Doryteuthis plei* have revealed narrow channels (301), which are said to constitute a compartment resembling the space suggested by Frankenhaeuser & Hodgkin (128) to account for the slow potentials following activity in *Loligo* axons (302). While the channels restrict the movement of water and ions, the major barrier to movement between the axoplasm and the outside is said to be the axolemma. The discrimination shown by this membrane between small molecules and water leads to an estimate of membrane pore size of 4.25 A (300).

The pH of the cytoplasm of the squid giant axon bathed in sea water was found to be 7.35 and the buffering capacity of the extruded axoplasm to be very high (266). The acid-base balance of the dialyzable portion of the axoplasm was determined, and several new neutral substances identified (75, 76).

A voltage gradient applied to the squid giant axon moves axoplasm water cathodally and axoplasm anodally. Proteases, previously shown to affect the structure of the membrane without altering excitability, have now been found to penetrate into the axoplasm. Their action may lower slightly the membrane resistance while the capacitance is unchanged. Phospholipases block activity and markedly reduce the electrical constants of the membrane. Thus, while phospholipid integrity is essential for excitability, a certain amount of membrane proteolysis is tolerable (293).

Observation of a squid axon impaled by a quartz microneedle reveals the axoplasm to be thixotropic and rheopectic. In many cases the amount of light emerging from an axon impaled by an illuminated needle is reduced during activity (263).

The changes in the ultraviolet absorption of the *Sepia* giant axon during activity are initially reversible, but become less so with time. At wavelengths in the 275 to 280 mμ range, the absorption increases by as much as 30 per cent during activity; absorption appears to be maximal in the immediate vicinity of the membrane (173). The same wavelengths are maximally effective in changing the action current of nerve (203). Since absorption of these wavelengths is likely to be caused by proteins, the results are said to recall the findings of Ungar and co-workers (296) on the changes in structure of nerve proteins with activity. The sorption of neutral red dye by frog spinal ganglia is altered by activity (198).

Data on the effects of irradiation on nerve (15) and muscle (72, 236) have been reported. Damage to frog muscle following irradiation is markedly reduced by posttreatment storage at 3°C (72). High doses of X ray are said to increase the K^+ permeability of frog muscle (236).

The effects of light on nerve cells of *Aplysia* have been further investigated by Arvanitaki & Chalazonitis. The light-absorbing pigments are localized in organelles of 1 to 2 μ diameter. Differences in response between cells are observed: hyperpolarization leads to suppression of activity and depolarization leads to excitation; and the effects of monochromatic light of different wavelengths, which are specifically absorbed by the different pigments, are described (12). The action potential of a squid axon stained with eosin is little changed in the dark but its duration is increased on illumination (202).

New studies have been made of the fine structure of the neuromuscular junction in the frog (23, 249) and in the rat (4), in which tridimensional reconstructions have been made from serial sections. Synaptic junctions have been examined by electron microscopy in the brain (80, 151) and ciliary ganglion (78), and in the crayfish spinal cord (79). In conjunction with some of these results, de Lorenzo questioned the identification of synaptic vesicles with loci containing the transmitter. Intact nerve endings and isolated synaptic vesicles were obtained from different fractions of homogenates of nerve tissue (82, 140). Granules which release norepinephrine were isolated by high-speed centrifugation of homogenates of the bovine splenic nerve (107).

With reference to metabolic processes in nerve tissue, we shall mention only the main lines of work in areas close to the subject of this review. These are: studies of RNA and protein turnover under a variety of conditions (164) and the possible implications of these findings for nerve cell function (171); localization and quantitative analysis of enzymes in nerve tissue and single nerve cells and in junctional regions (135, 136); and the recent studies on the functional relationships between glial and nerve tissues (165). The RNA content of the oligodendrocytes of Deiter's nucleus is much lower than in the nerve cells, while cytochrome oxidase and succinoxidase activities are twice as high in the oligodendroglia as in nerve cells. After protracted vestibular stimulation, the RNA and the respiratory enzyme activity decrease in the glia, while the RNA and proteins increase in the nerve cell (165).

LITERATURE CITED

BOOKS

Some books of interest published during the period covered by this review are:

The Cell (Brachet, J., and Mirsky, A. E., Eds., Academic Press, New York, **IV**, 215 pp., 1960)

Regulation of the Inorganic Ion Content of Cells, Ciba Foundation Study Group No. 5 (Wolstenholme, G. E. W., and O'Connor, C. M., Eds., Little, Brown & Co., Boston, 100 pp., 1960)

Electrical Activity of Single Cells (Katsuki, Y., Ed., Igaku Shoin Ltd., Tokyo, 312 pp., 1960)

The Regional Chemistry, Physiology and Pharmacology of the Nervous System (Kety, S. S., and Elkes, J., Eds., Pergamon Press, New York, 540 pp., 1961)

Inhibition in the Nervous System and γ-Aminobutyric Acid (Roberts, E., Ed., Pergamon Press, New York, 591 pp., 1960)

Adrenergic Mechanisms, Ciba Foundation Symposium (Vane, J. R., Wolstenholme, G. E. W., and O'Connor, M., Eds., Little, Brown & Co., Boston, 632 pp., 1960)

The Utrecht Symposium on the Innervation of Muscle (Bouman, H. D., and Woolf, A. L., Eds., Williams & Wilkins Co., Baltimore, 223 pp., 1960)

Structure and Function of the Cerebral Cortex (Tower, D. B., and Schadé, J. P., Eds., Elsevier Publ. Co., Amsterdam, 448 pp., 1960)

International Review of Neurobiology (Pfeiffer, C. C., and Smythies, J. R., Eds., Academic Press, New York, 410 pp., 1960)

The Structure and Function of Muscle (Bourne, G. H., Ed., Academic Press, New York, **I**, 472 pp.; **II**, 593 pp., 1960)

REFERENCES

1. Abood, L. G., Koketsu, K., Barbato, L., and Dobbs, B., *Am. J. Physiol.*, **200**, 425–30 (1961)

2. Abood, L. G., Koketsu, K., and Noda, K., *Am. J. Physiol.*, **200**, 431–36 (1961)

3. Adey, W. R., Dunlop, C. W., and Hendrix, C. E., *Arch. Neurol.*, **3**, 74–90 (1960)

4. Andersson-Cedergen, E., *J. Ultrastruct. Research*, **3**, Suppl. 1, 1–191 (1959)

5. Apter, J. T., and Koketsu, K., *J. Cellular Comp. Physiol.*, **56**, 123–28 (1960)

6. Araki, T., Eccles, J. C., and Ito, M., *J. Physiol. (London)*, **154**, 354–77 (1960)

7. Araki, T., Ito, M., and Oscarsson, O., *Nature*, **189**, 65 (1961)

8. Araki, T., and Otani, T., *Japan. J. Physiol.*, **9**, 69–83 (1959)

9. Araki, T., and Terzuolo, C. A., *Inhibition in the Nervous System and γ-Aminobutyric Acid*, 115–17 (Roberts, E., Ed., Pergamon Press, New York, 591 pp., 1960)

10. Armett, C. J., and Ritchie, J. M., *J. Physiol. (London)*, **152**, 141–58 (1960)

11. Armett, C. J., and Ritchie, J. M., *J. Physiol. (London)*, **155**, 372–84 (1961)

12. Arvanitaki, A., and Chalazonitis, N., *Bull. inst. océanog.*, No. 1164, 1–83 (1960)

13. Augustinsson, K. B., Fänge, R., Johnels, A., and Östlund, E., *J. Physiol. (London)*, **131**, 257–76 (1956)

14. Axelsson, J., and Thesleff, S., *J. Physiol. (London)*, **147**, 178–93 (1959)

15. Bachofer, C. S., and Gautereaux, M. E., *Am. J. Physiol.*, **198**, 715–17 (1960)

16. Batham, E. J., *J. Biophys. Biochem. Cytol.*, **9**, 490–92 (1961)

17. Baxter, C. F., and Roberts, E., *Proc. Soc. Exptl. Biol. Med.*, **104**, 426–27 (1960)

18. Bennett, M. V. L., and Grundfest, H., *J. Gen. Physiol.*, **44**, 805–18 (1961)

19. Bennett, M. V. L., and Grundfest, H., *J. Gen. Physiol.*, **44**, 819–43 (1961)

20. Bennett, M. V. L., Wurzel, M., and Grundfest, H., *J. Gen. Physiol.*, **44**, 757–804 (1961)

21. Bianchi, C. P., *J. Gen. Physiol.*, **44**, 845–58 (1961)

22. Bianchi, C. P., and Shanes, A. M., *J. Cellular Comp. Physiol.*, **56**, 67–76 (1960)

23. Birks, R., Huxley, H. E., and Katz, B., *J. Physiol. (London)*, **150**, 134–44 (1960)

24. Birks, R., Katz, B., and Miledi, R., *J. Physiol. (London)*, **150**, 145–68 (1960)

25. Bishop, P. O., Burke, W., and Hayhow, W. R., *Exptl. Neurol.*, **1**, 534–55 (1959)

26. Bishop, P. O., and Davis, R., *J. Physiol. (London)*, **150**, 214–38 (1960)

27. Bishop, P. O., and Davis, R., *J. Physiol. (London)*, **154**, 514–46 (1960)

28. Brady, A. J., and Woodbury, J. W., *J. Physiol. (London)*, **154**, 385–407 (1960)

29. Bradley, K., and Somjen, G. G., *J. Physiol. (London)*, **156**, 75–92 (1961)

30. Bremer, F., and Stoupel, N., *J. physiol. (Paris)*, **52**, 34–35 (1960)

31. Brindley, F. J., Kandel, E. R., and Marshall, W. H., *J. Neurophysiol.*, **23**, 237–45 (1960)

32. Brookhart, J. M., and Fatiga, E., *J. Physiol. (London)*, **150**, 633–55 (1960)

33. Buller, A. J., Eccles, J. C., and Eccles, R., *J. Physiol. (London)*, **150**, 399–416 (1960)

34. Buller, A. J., Eccles, J. C., and Eccles, R., *J. Physiol. (London)*, **150**, 417–39 (1960)

35. Bullock, T. H., *Exptl. Cell Research*, Suppl. 5, 323–37 (1958)

36. Bullock, T. H., *Revs. Mod. Phys.*, **31**, 504–14 (1959)

37. Bullock, T. H., and Terzuolo, C. A., *J. Physiol. (London)*, **138**, 341–64 (1957)

38. Burkhardt, D. v., *Z. Biol.*, **78**, 22–62 (1959)

39. Burlakova, Ye. V., Veprintsev, B. N., and Rass, I. T., *Biophysics*, **4**, No. 5, 127–31 (1959) (Engl. Transl.)

40. Burn, J. H., and Rand, M. J., *Brit. J. Pharmacol.*, **15**, 56–66 (1960)

41. Burnstock, G., and Holman, M. E., *J. Physiol. (London)*, **155**, 115–33 (1961)

42. Caldwell, P. C., *J. Physiol. (London)*, **152**, 545–60 (1960)

43. Caldwell, P. C., Hodgkin, A. L., Keynes, R. D., and Shaw, T. I., *J. Physiol. (London)*, **152**, 561–90 (1960)

44. Caldwell, P. C., Hodgkin, A. L., Keynes, R. D., and Shaw, T. I., *J. Physiol. (London)*, **152**, 591–600 (1960)

45. Caldwell, P. C., and Keynes, R. D., *J. Physiol. (London)*, **154**, 177–89 (1960)

46. Carey, M. J., and Conway, E. J., *J. Physiol. (London)*, **125**, 232–50 (1954)

47. Carey, M. J., Conway, E. J., and Kernan, R. P., *J. Physiol. (London)*, **148**, 51–82 (1957)

48. Carmeliet, E. E., *J. Physiol. (London)*, **156**, 375–88 (1961)

49. Cerf, J. A., Grundfest, H., Hoyle, G., and McCann, F. V., *J. Gen. Physiol.*, **43**, 377–95 (1959)

50. Cier, J. F., *J. physiol. (Paris)*, **53**, 3–74 (1961)

51. Coelho, R. R., Goodman, J. W., and Bowers, M. B., *Exptl. Cell Research*, **20**, 1–11 (1960)

52. Cole, K. S., *Biophys. J.*, **1**, 401–18 (1961)

53. Cole, K. S., and Moore, J. W., *J. Gen. Physiol.*, **44**, 123–67 (1960)

54. Cole, K. S., and Moore, J. W., *Biophys. J.*, **1**, 1–14 (1960)

55. Condie, R. M., Howell, A. E., Jr., and Good, R. A., *J. Biophys. Biochem. Cytol.*, **9**, 429–44 (1961)

56. Conway, E. J., Kernan, R. P., and Zadunaisky, J. A., *J. Physiol. (London)*, **155**, 263–79 (1961)

57. Coombs, J. S., Curtis, D. R., and Eccles, J. C., *J. Physiol. (London)*, **139**, 198–231 (1957)

58. Coombs, J. S., Eccles, J. C., and Fatt, P., *J. Physiol. (London)*, **130**, 326–73 (1955)

59. Creese, R., *J. Physiol. (London)*, **154**, 133–44 (1960)

60. Creese, R., and Northover, J., *J. Physiol. (London)*, **155**, 343–57 (1961)

61. Curtis, D. R., and Eccles, J. C., *J. Physiol. (London)*, **145**, 529–46 (1959)

62. Curtis, D. R., and Eccles, J. C., *J. Physiol. (London)*, **150**, 374–98 (1960)

63. Curtis, D. R., and Koizumi, K., *J. Neurophysiol.*, **24**, 80–90 (1961)

64. Curtis, D. R., Perrin, D. D., and Watkins, J. C. *J. Neurochem.*, **6**, 1–20 (1960)

65. Curtis, D. R., and Phillis, J. W., *J. Physiol. (London)*, **153**, 17–34 (1960)

66. Curtis, D. R., Phillis, J. W., and Wat-

kins, J. C., *J. Physiol. (London)*, **146**, 185–203 (1959)

67. Curtis, D. R., Phillis, J. W., and Watkins, J. C., *J. Physiol. (London)*, **150**, 656–82 (1960)

68. Curtis, D. R., and Watkins, J. C., *J. Neurochem.*, **6**, 117–41 (1960)

69. Curtis, D. R., and Watkins, J. C., *Inhibition in the Nervous System and γ-Aminobutyric Acid*, 424–44 (Roberts, E., Ed., Pergamon Press, New York, 591 pp., 1960)

70. Dalton, J. C., and FitzHugh, R., *Science*, **131**, 1533–34 (1960)

71. Damjanovich, S., Fehér, O., Halasz, P., and Melcher, F., *Acta Physiol. Acad. Sci. Hung.*, **18**, 57–63 (1960)

72. Darden, E. B., Jr., *Am. J. Physiol.*, **198**, 709–14 (1960)

73. Davis, H., *Physiol. Revs.*, **41**, 391–416 (1961)

74. De Castro, F., *Arch. intern. physiol.*, **59**, 479–513 (1951)

75. Deffner, G. G. J., and Hafter, R. E., *Biochim. et Biophys. Acta*, **42**, 189–99 (1960)

76. Deffner, G. G. J., and Hafter, R. E., *Biochim. et Biophys. Acta*, **42**, 200–5 (1960)

77. Del Castillo, J., and Katz, B., *Progr. in Biophys. and Biophys. Chem.*, **6**, 121–70 (1956)

78. de Lorenzo, A. J., *J. Biophys. Biochem. Cytol.*, **7**, 31–36 (1960)

79. de Lorenzo, A. J., *Biol. Bull.*, **119**, 325 (1960)

80. de Lorenzo, A. J., *Bull. Johns Hopkins Hosp.*, **108**, 258–67 (1961)

81. de Mello, W. C., and Hoffman, B. F., *Am. J. Physiol.*, **199**, 1125–30 (1960)

82. De Robertis, E., Pellegrino De Iraldi, A., Rodriguez, G., and Gomez, C. J., *J. Biophys. Biochem. Cytol.*, **9**, 229–35 (1961)

83. Dettbarn, W. D., *Biochim. et Biophys. Acta*, **41**, 377–86 (1960)

84. Diamond, J., Gray, J. A. B., and Inman. D. R., *J. Physiol. (London)*, **142**, 382–94 (1958)

85. Diamond, J., Gray, J. A. B., and Sato, M., *J. Physiol. (London)*, **133**, 54–67 (1956)

86. Diamond, J., and Miledi, R., *J. Physiol. (London)*, **149**, 50P (1959)

87. Douglas, W. W., Lywood. D. W., and Straub, R. W., *J. Physiol. (London)*, **153**, 250–64 (1960)

88. Draper, M. H., and Karzel, K., *J. Physiol. (London)*, **156**, 30P–31P (1961)

89. Dudel, J., and Kuffler, S. W., *J. Physiol. (London)*, **155**, 514–29 (1961)

90. Dudel, J., and Kuffler, S. W., *J. Physiol. (London)*, **155**, 530–42 (1961)

91. Dudel, J., and Kuffler, S. W., *J. Physiol. (London)*, **155**, 543–62 (1961)

92. Dudel, J., and Orkand, R. K., *Nature*, **186**, 476–77 (1960)

93. Dunham, E. T., and Glynn, I. M., *J. Physiol. (London)*, **156**, 274–93 (1961)

94. Eccles, J. C., *The Physiology of Nerve Cells* (Johns Hopkins Press, Baltimore, Md., 270 pp., 1957)

95. Eccles, J. C., *Proc. Roy. Soc. (London)*, B, **153**, 445–76 (1961)

96. Eccles, J. C., and Krnjević, K., *J. Physiol. (London)*, **149**, 250–73 (1959)

97. Eccles, J. C., and Krnjević, K., *J. Physiol. (London)*, **149**, 274–87 (1959)

98. Edelman, I. S., *Ann. Rev. Physiol.*, **23**, 37–70 (1961)

99. Edwards, C., *Inhibition in the Nervous System and γ-Aminobutyric Acid*, 386–408 (Roberts, E., Ed., Pergamon Press, New York, 591 pp., 1960)

100. Edwards, C., and Hagiwara, S., *J. Gen. Physiol.*, **43**, 315–21 (1959)

101. Ehrenpreis, S., *Biochim. et Biophys. Acta*, **44**, 561–77 (1960)

102. Elfvin, L. G., *J. Ultrastruct. Research*, **5**, 51–64 (1961)

103. Elliott, K. A. C., and van Gelder, N. M., *J. Physiol. (London)*, **153**, 423–32 (1960)

104. Euler, C. v., *Structure and Function of the Cerebral Cortex*, 272–77 (Tower, D. B., and Schadé, J. P., Eds., Elsevier Publ. Co., Amsterdam, 448 pp., 1960)

105. Euler, C. von, and Green, J. D., *Acta Physiol. Scand.*, **48**, 95–109 (1960)

106. Euler, C. von, Green, J. D., and Ricci, G., *Acta Physiol. Scand.*, **42**, 87–111 (1958)

107. Euler, U. S. von, and Lishajko, F., *Acta Physiol. Scand.*, **51**, 193–203 (1961)

108. Falk, G., and Landa, J. F., *Am. J. Physiol.*, **198**, 289–99 (1960)

109. Falk, G., and Landa, J. F., *Am. J. Physiol.*, **198**, 1225–31 (1960)

110. Fänge, R., Schmidt-Nielsen, K., and Robinson, M., *Am. J. Physiol.*, **195**, 321–26 (1958)

111. Fatiga, E., and Brookhart, J. M., *Am. J. Physiol.*, **198**, 693–703 (1960)

112. Fatt, P., *J. Neurophysiol.*, **20**, 61–80 (1957)
113. Fatt, P., *Inhibition in the Nervous System and γ-Aminobutyric Acid*, 104–14 (Roberts, E., Ed., Pergamon Press, New York, 591 pp., 1960)
114. Fatt, P., and Ginsborg, B. L., *J. Physiol.* (*London*), **142**, 516–43 (1958)
115. Fatt, P., and Katz, B., *J. Physiol.* (*London*), **115**, 320–70 (1951)
116. Fehér, O., and Bokri, E., *Arch. ges. Physiol.*, **272**, 553–61 (1961)
117. Fernández-Morán, H., *Revs. Mod. Phys.*, **31**, 319–30 (1959)
118. Florey, E., *Inhibition in the Nervous System and γ-Aminobutyric Acid*, 72–84 (Roberts, E., Ed., Pergamon Press, New York, 591 pp., 1960)
119. Florey, E., *J. Physiol.* (*London*), **156**, 1–7 (1961)
120. Florey, E., *Ann. Rev. Physiol.*, **23**, 501–28 (1961)
121. Frank, K., and Fuortes, M. G. F., *J. Physiol.* (*London*), **131**, 424–35 (1956)
122. Frank, K., and Fuortes, M. G. F., *Federation Proc.*, **16**, 39–40 (1957)
123. Frank, K., and Fuortes, M. G. F., *Arch. ital. biol.*, **28**, 165–70 (1960)
124. Frank, K., and Fuortes, M. G. F., *Ann. Rev. Physiol.*, **23**, 357–86 (1961)
125. Frank, K., Fuortes, M. G. F., and Nelson, P. G., *Science*, **130**, 38–39 (1959)
126. Frankenhaeuser, B., *J. Physiol.* (*London*), **151**, 491–501 (1960)
127. Frankenhaeuser, B., *J. Physiol.* (*London*), **152**, 159–66 (1960)
128. Frankenhaeuser, B., and Hodgkin, A. L., *J. Physiol* (*London*), **131**, 341–76 (1956)
129. Fukuya, M., *Japan. J. Physiol.*, **11**, 126–46 (1961)
130. Fuortes, M. G. F., *Am. Naturalist*, **93**, 213–24 (1959)
131. Fuortes, M. G. F., *Inhibition in the Nervous System and γ-Aminobutyric Acid*, 418–23 (Roberts, E., Ed., Pergamon Press, New York, 591 pp., 1960)
132. Fuortes, M. G. F., Frank, K., and Becker, M. C., *J. Gen. Physiol.*, **40**, 735–52 (1957)
133. Furshpan, E. J., and Potter, D. D., *J. Physiol.* (*London*), **145**, 289–325 (1959)
134. Galambos, R., *Proc. Natl. Acad. Sci. US*, **47**, 129–36 (1961)

135. Gerebtzoff, M. A., *Cholinesterases* (Pergamon Press, New York, 195 pp., 1959)
136. Giacobini, E., *Acta Physiol. Scand.*, **45**, Suppl. 156, 1–45 (1959)
137. Gilbert, D. L., *J. Gen Physiol.*, **43**, 1103–18 (1960)
138. Gray, J. A. B., *Progr. in Biophys. and Biophys. Chem.*, **9**, 285–324 (1959)
139. Gray, J. A. B., and Sato, M., *J. Physiol.* (*London*), **122**, 610–36 (1953)
140. Gray, E. G., and Whittaker, V. P., *J. Physiol.* (*London*), **153**, 35P–36P (1960)
141. Green, J. D., Maxwell, D. S., Schindler, W. J., and Stumpf, C., *J. Neurophysiol.*, **23**, 403–20 (1960)
142. Grundfest, H., *Physiol. Revs.*, **37**, 337–61 (1957)
143. Grundfest, H., *Handbook of Physiology-Neurophysiology*, **I**, 147–97 (Am. Physiol. Soc., Washington, D. C., 779 pp., 1959)
144. Grundfest, H., *Evolution of Nervous Control from Primitive Organisms to Man*, 43–86 (Bass, A.D., Ed., Am. Assoc. Advance. Sci., Washington, D. C., 231 pp., 1959)
145. Hagiwara, S., *Electrical Activity of Single Cells*, 145–57 (Katsuki, Y., Ed., Igaku Shoin Ltd., Tokyo, 312 pp., 1960)
146. Hagiwara, S., and Kusano, K., *J. Neurophysiol.*, **24**, 167–75 (1961)
147. Hagiwara, S., Kusano, K., and Saito, N., *J. Neurophysiol.*, **23**, 505–15 (1960)
148. Hagiwara, S., Kusano, K., and Saito, N., *J. Physiol.* (*London*) **155**, 470–89 (1961)
149. Hagiwara, S., and Tasaki, I., *J. Physiol.* (*London*), **143**, 114–37 (1958)
150. Hagiwara, S., Watanabe, A., and Saito, N., *J. Neurophysiol.*, **22**, 554–72 (1959)
151. Hamlyn, L. H., *Nature*, **190**, 645–46 (1960)
152. Harris, E. J., and Sjodin, R. A., *J. Physiol.* (*London*), **155**, 221–45 (1961)
153. Hichar, J. K., *J. Cellular Comp. Physiol.*, **55**, 195–206 (1960)
154. Hinke, J. A. M., *J. Physiol.* (*London*), **156**, 314–35 (1961)
155. Hinterbuchner, L. P., and Nachmansohn, D., *Biochim. et Biophys. Acta*, **44**, 554–60 (1960)
156. Hodgkin, A. L., and Horowicz, P., *J. Physiol.* (*London*), **153**, 370–85 (1960)

157. Hodgkin, A. L., and Huxley, A. F., J. Physiol. (London), 117, 500–44 (1952)
158. Höglund, G., and Ringertz, H., Acta Physiol. Scand., 51, 290–95 (1961)
159. Hokin, L. E., and Hokin, M. R., J. Gen. Physiol., 44, 61–85 (1960)
160. Hokin, M. R., Hokin, L. E., and Shelp, W. D., J. Gen. Physiol., 44, 217–26 (1960)
161. Honour, A. J., and McLennon, H., J. Physiol. (London), 150, 306–18 (1960)
162. Hughes, J. R., Physiol. Revs., 58, 91–113 (1958)
163. Hutter, O. F., and Noble, D., J. Physiol. (London), 151, 89–102 (1960)
164. Hydén, H., The Cell, IV (Brachet, J., and Mirsky, A., Eds., Academic Press, New York, 215 pp., 1960)
165. Hydén, H., and Pigon, A., J. Neurochem., 6, 57–72 (1960)
166. Ichioka, M., Uehara, Y., and Kitamura, S., Japan. J. Physiol., 10, 235–45 (1960)
167. Inman, D. R., and Peruzzi, P., J. Physiol. (London), 155, 280–301 (1961)
168. Ishiko, N., and Loewenstein, W. R., Science, 132, 1841–42 (1960)
169. Iur'ev, S. A., Biophysics (Engl. Transl.), 4, No. 5, 109–16 (1959)
170. Jenkinson, D. H., J. Physiol. (London), 152, 309–24 (1960)
171. John, E. R., Ann. Rev. Physiol., 23, 451–84 (1961)
172. Johns, T. R., and Thesleff, S., Acta Physiol. Scand., 51, 136–42 (1961)
173. Kaiushin, L. P., Liudkovskaia, R. G., and Shmelev, I. P. Biophysics (Engl. Transl.), 5, No. 3, 323–28 (1960)
174. Kandel, E. R., and Spencer, W. A., J. Neurophysiol., 24, 225–42 (1961)
175. Kandel, E. R., and Spencer, W. A., J. Neurophysiol., 24, 243–59 (1961)
176. Kao, C. Y., J. Neurophysiol., 23, 618–35 (1960)
177. Katz, B., and Miledi, R., J. Physiol. (London), 155, 399–415 (1961)
178. Katz, B., and Thesleff, S., J. Physiol. (London), 137, 268–78 (1957)
179. Kernan, R. P., Nature, 190, 347 (1961)
180. Keynes, R. D., J. Physiol. (London), 114, 119–50 (1951)
181. Kiessling, A., Arch. ges. Physiol., 271, 124–38 (1960)
182. Killam, K. F., Dasgupta, S. R., and Killam, E. K., Inhibition in the Nervous System and γ-Amino-

butyric Acid, 302–16 (Roberts, E., Ed. Pergamon Press, New York, 591 pp., 1960)
183. Kitamura, S., Japan. J. Physiol., 10, 51–63 (1960)
184. Klaus, W., Lüllmann, H., and Muscholl, E., Arch. ges. Physiol., 271, 776–81 (1960)
185. Koketsu, K., and Kimura, Y., J. Cellular Comp. Physiol., 55, 239–44 (1960)
186. Koketsu, K., and Miyamoto, S., Nature, 189, 403–4 (1961)
187. Koketsu, K., and Noda, K., Nature, 187, 243–44 (1960)
188. Kostiuk, P. G., Biophysics (Engl. Transl.), 4, No. 2, 6–16 (1959)
189. Kostiuk, P. G., and Shapovalov, A. I., Biophysics (Engl. Transl.), 5, No. 5, 664–73 (1960)
190. Kostiuk, P. G., Sorokina, Z. A., and Shapovalov, A. I., Biophysics (Engl. Transl.), 4, No. 3, 59–70 (1959)
191. Krnjević, K., and Mitchell, J. F., J. Physiol. (London), 155, 246–62 (1961)
192. Kuffler, S. W., Exptl. Cell Research, Suppl. 5, 493–519 (1958)
193. Kuffler, S. W., The Harvey Lectures, 1958–59, 176–218 (Academic Press, New York, 1960)
194. Kuno, M., Proc. Japan. Acad., 36, 513–15 (1960)
195. Kurella, G. A., Biophysics (Engl. Transl.), 4, No. 3, 48–59 (1959)
196. Kurella, G. A., Biophysics (Engl. Transl.), 5, No. 3, 303–13 (1960)
197. Kusano, K., and Hagiwara, S., Japan. J. Physiol., 11, 96–101 (1961)
198. Lev, A. A., Biophysics (Engl. Transl.), 4, No. 2, 17–26 (1959)
199. Li, C. L., Science, 132, 1889–90 (1960)
200. Li, C. L., Ortiz-Galvin, A., Chou, S. N., and Howard, S. Y., J. Neurophysiol., 23, 592–601 (1960)
201. Ling, G., J. Gen Physiol., 43, No. 5, Suppl., 149–74 (1960)
202. Liudkovskaia, R. G., and Kaiushin, L. P., Biophysics (Engl. Transl.), 4, No. 4, 23–32 (1959)
203. Liudkovskaia, R. G., and Kaiushin, L. P., Biophysics (Engl. Transl), 5, No. 1, 38–44 (1960)
204. Lloyd, D. P. C., and Wilson, V. J., J. Gen. Physiol., 43, 335–45 (1959)
205. Loewenstein, W. R., Ann. N. Y. Acad. Sci., 81, 367–87 (1959)
206. Loewenstein, W. R., and Ishiko, N., J. Gen. Physiol., 43, 981–98 (1960)
207. Lorente de Nó, R., Structure and Func-

tion of the Cerebral Cortex, 278–81 (Tower, D. B., and Schadé, J. P., Eds., Elsevier Publishing Co., Amsterdam, 448 pp., 1960)

208. Lorente de Nó, R., and Condouris, G. A., *Proc. Natl. Acad. Sci. US*, **45**, 592–617 (1959)

209. Lundberg, A., *Physiol. Revs.*, **38**, 21–40 (1958)

210. Lüttgau, H. C., *Arch. ges. Physiol.*, **271**, 613–33 (1960)

211. L'vov, K. M., Kaiushin, L. P., and Liudkovskaia, R. G., *Biophysics (Engl. Transl.)*, **5**, No. 3, 437–40 (1960)

212. Mauro, A., *Biophys. J.*, **1**, 353–72 (1961)

213. McCollester, D. L., *Biochim. et Biophys. Acta*, **41**, 160–61 (1960)

214. McIntyre, A. K., and Mark, R. F., *J. Physiol. (London)*, **153**, 306–30 (1960)

215. Meves, H., *Arch. ges. Physiol.*, **271**, 655–79 (1960)

216. Meves, H., *Arch. ges. Physiol.*, **272**, 336–59 (1961)

217. Miledi, R., *J. Physiol. (London)*, **151**, 1–23 (1960)

218. Miledi, R., *J. Physiol. (London)*, **151**, 24–30 (1960)

219. Miledi, R., *J. Physiol. (London)*, **154**, 190–205 (1960)

220. Miller, W. H., *J. Biophys. Biochem. Cytol.*, **3**, 421–28 (1958)

221. Mullins, L. J., *J. Gen. Physiol.*, **43**, No. 5, Suppl., 105–17 (1960)

222. Nachmansohn, D., *Chemical and Molecular Basis of Nerve Activity* (Academic Press, New York, 235 pp., 1959)

223. Narahashi, T., *J. Physiol. (London)*, **156**, 389–414 (1961)

224. Narahashi, T., Deguchi, T., Urakawa, N., and Ohkubo, Y., *Am. J. Physiol.*, **198**, 934–38 (1960)

225. Narahashi, T., and Yamasaki, T., *J. Cellular Comp. Physiol.*, **55**, 131–42 (1960)

226. Narahashi, T., and Yamasaki, T., *J. Physiol. (London)*, **151**, 75–88 (1960)

227. Narahashi, T., and Yamasaki, T., *J. Physiol. (London)*, **152**, 122–40 (1960)

228. Nicholls, J. G., *J. Physiol. (London)*, **131**, 1–12 (1956)

229. Noble, D., *Nature*, **188**, 495–97 (1960)

230. Ogata, M., and Wright, E. B., *J. Neurophysiol.*, **23**, 646–58 (1960)

231. Oomura, Y., and Tomita, T. *Electrical Activity of Single Cells*, 181–205 (Katsuki, Y., Ed., Igaku Shoin Ltd., Tokyo, 312 pp., 1960)

232. Ooyama, H., and Wright, E. B., *Am. J. Physiol.*, **200**, 209–18 (1961)

233. Otani, T., *Electrical Activity of Single Cells*, 133–44 (Katsuki, Y., Ed., Igaku Shoin Ltd., Tokyo, 312 pp., 1960)

234. Otsuka, M., and Endo, M., *Nature*, **188**, 501–2 (1960)

235. Petropulos, S. F., *J. Cellular Comp. Physiol.*, **56**, 7–13 (1960)

236. Portela, A., Hines, M., Perez, J. C., Brandes, D., Bourne, G. H., Stewart, P., and Groth, D., *Exptl. Cell Research*, **21**, 468–81 (1960)

237. Post, R. L. *Federation Proc.*, **18**, 121, (1959)

238. Preston, J. B., and Whitlock, D. G., *J. Neurophysiol.*, **23**, 154–70 (1960)

239. Preston, J. B., and Whitlock, D. G., *J. Neurophysiol.*, **24**, 91–100 (1961)

240. Prudnikova, I. F., *Biophysics (Engl. Transl.)*, **4**, No. 6, 23–32 (1959)

241. Purpura, D. P., Girado, M., Smith, T. G., Callan, D. A., and Grundfest, H., *J. Neurochem.* **3**, 238–68 (1959)

242. Rall, W., *Exptl. Neurol.*, **1**, 491–527 (1959)

243. Rall, W., *Exptl. Neurol.*, **2**, 503–32 (1960)

244. Rand, M. J., and Chang, V., *Nature*, **188**, 858–59 (1960)

245. Ratliff, F., Miller, W. H., and Hartline, H. K., *Ann. N. Y. Acad. Sci.*, **74**, 210–22 (1958)

246. Reuben, J. P., *Biol. Bull.*, **119**, 334 (1960)

247. Reuben, J. P., and Grundfest, H., *Biol. Bull.*, **119**, 335–36 (1960)

248. Riker, W. K., and Szreniawski, Z., *J. Pharmacol. Exptl. Therap.*, **126**, 233–38 (1959)

249. Robertson, J. D., *Am. J. Phys. Med.*, **39**, 1–43 (1960)

250. Robertson, J. D., *Fourth International Conference on Electron Microscopy*, **2**, 159–71 (Springer-Verlag, Berlin, 1960)

251. Rosenberg, P., and Higman, H., *Biochim. et Biophys. Acta*, **45**, 348–54 (1960)

252. Rosenberg, P., Higman, H., and Nachmansohn, D., *Biochim. et Biophys. Acta*, **44**, 151–60 (1960)

253. Rud, J., *Acta Physiol. Scand.*, **51**, Suppl. 178, 1–171 (1961)

254. Rudenberg, F. H., and Tobias, J. M., *J. Cellular Comp. Physiol.*, **55**, 149–57 (1960)

255. Salmoiraghi, G. C., and Baumgarten, R. v., *J. Neurophysiol.*, **24**, 203–18 (1961)

256. Sant'Ambrogio, G., Frazier, D. T., and Boyarsky, L. L., *Science*, **133**, 876–77 (1961)

257. Schmidt, H., *Arch. ges. Physiol.*, **271**, 634–54 (1960)

258. Shanes, A. M., and Berman, M. D., *J. Gen Physiol.*, **39**, 279–300 (1955)

259. Shapovalov, A. I., *Biophysics (Engl. Transl.)*, **5**, No. 3, 314–23 (1960)

260. Sjodin, R. A., *J. Gen. Physiol.*, **44**, 929–62 (1961)

261. Skou, J. C., *Biochim. et Biophys. Acta*, **23**, 394–401 (1957)

262. Skou, J. C., *Biochim. et Biophys. Acta*, **42**, 6–23 (1960)

263. Solomon, S., and Tobias, J. M., *J. Cellular Comp. Physiol.*, **55**, 159–66 (1960)

264. Spencer, W. A., and Kandel, E. R., *J. Neurophysiol.*, **24**, 260–71 (1961)

265. Spencer, W. A., and Kandel, E. R., *J. Neurophysiol.*, **24**, 272–85 (1961)

266. Spyropoulos, C. S., *J. Neurochem.*, **5**, 185–94 (1960)

267. Spyropoulos, C. S., *Am. J. Physiol.*, **200**, 203–8 (1961)

268. Spyropoulos, C. S., and Tasaki, I., *Ann. Rev. Physiol.*, **22**, 407–32 (1960)

269. Straughan, D. W., *Brit. J. Pharmacol.*, **15**, 417–24 (1960)

270. Takahashi, H., Murai, T., and Sasaki, T., *Japan. J. Physiol.*, **10**, 280–91 (1960)

271. Takeuchi, A., and Takeuchi, N., *J. Neurophysiol.*, **22**, 395–411 (1959)

272. Takeuchi, A., and Takeuchi, N., *J. Neurophysiol.*, **23**, 397–402 (1960)

273. Takeuchi, A., and Takeuchi, N., *J. Physiol. (London)*, **154**, 52–67 (1960)

274. Takeuchi, A., and Takeuchi, N., *Electrical Activity of Single Cells*, 207–216 (Katsuki, K., Ed., Igaku Shoin Ltd., Tokyo, 312 pp., 1960)

275. Takeuchi, A., and Takeuchi, N., *J. Physiol. (London)*, **155**, 46–58 (1961)

276. Tasaki, I., *J. Gen. Physiol.*, **39**, 377–95 (1956)

277. Tasaki, I., *J. Physiol. (London)*, **148**, 306–31 (1959)

278. Tasaki, I., Teorell, T., and Spyropoulos, C. S., *Am. J. Physiol.*, **200**, 11–22 (1961)

279. Tauc, L., *Arch. ital. biol.*, **96**, 78–110 (1958)

280. Tauc, L., *Compt. rend. acad. sci.*, **248**, 1857–59 (1959)

281. Tauc, L., and Gershenfeld, H., *Compt. rend. acad. sci.*, **251**, 3076–78 (1960)

282. Tauc, L., and Gerschenfeld, H., *J. physiol. (Paris)*, **52**, 236 (1960)

283. Taylor, R. E., Moore, J. W., and Cole, K. S., *Biophys. J.*, **1**, 161–202 (1960)

284. Teorell, T., *Progr. in Biophys. and Biophys. Chem.*, **3**, 305–69 (1953)

285. Terzuolo, C. A., *Arch. ital. biol.*, **97**, 316–39 (1959)

286. Terzuolo, C. A., *Univ. Minn. Med. Bull.*, **32**, 180–85 (1961)

287. Terzuolo, C. A., and Bullock, T. H., *Proc. Natl. Acad. Sci. US*, **42**, 687–94 (1956)

288. Terzuolo, C. A., and Bullock, T. H., *Arch. ital. biol.*, **96**, 117–34 (1958)

289. Terzuolo, C. A., and Gernandt, B. E., *Am. J. Physiol.*, **186**, 263–70 (1956)

290. Terzuolo, C. A., Sigg, B., and Killam, K. F., *Inhibition in the Nervous System and γ-Aminobutyric Acid*, 336–37 (Roberts, E., Ed., Pergamon Press, New York, 591 pp., 1960)

291. Thesleff, S., *Physiol. Revs.*, **40**, 734–52 (1960)

292. Thesleff, S., *J. Physiol. (London)*, **151**, 598–607 (1960)

293. Tobias, J. M., *J. Gen. Physiol.*, **43**, No. 5, Suppl., 57–71 (1960)

294. Tomita, T., Kikuchi, R., and Tanaka, I., *Electrical Activity of Single Cells* 11–23 (Katsuki, K., Ed., Igaku Shoin Ltd., Tokyo, 312 pp., 1960)

295. Uehara, Y., *Japan. J. Physiol.*, **10**, 267–74 (1960)

296. Ungar, G., Aschheim, E., Psychoyos, S., and Romano, D. V., *J. Gen. Physiol.*, **40**, 635–52 (1957)

297. Van der Kloot, W. G., *J. Neurochem.*, **5**, 245-52 (1960)

298. Verprintsev, B. N., *Biophysics (Engl. Transl.)*, **4**, No. 4, 19–22 (1959)

299. Verprintsev, B. N., and Antonov, V. F., *Biophysics (Engl. Transl.)*, **4**, No. 5, 34–41 (1959)

300. Villegas, R., and Barnola, F. V., *J. Gen. Physiol.*, **44**, 963–78 (1961)

301. Villegas, G. M., and Villegas, R., *J. Ultrastruct. Research*, **3**, 362–73 (1960)

302. Villegas, R., and Villegas, G. M., *J. Gen. Physiol.*, **43**, No. 5, Suppl., 73–103 (1960)

303. Walsh, R. R., and Nielsen, T. W., *Biochim et Biophys. Acta*, **44**, 280–83 (1960)

304. Washizu, Y., *Japan. J. Physiol.*, 10, 121–31 (1960)

305. Washizu, Y., Bonewell, G. W., and Terzuolo, C. A., *Science*, 133, 333–34 (1961)

306. Watanabe, A., *Japan. J. Physiol.*, 8, 305–18 (1958)

307. Watanabe, A., and Bullock, T. H., *J. Gen. Physiol.*, 43, 1031–45 (1960)

308. Werman, R., *Nature*, 188, 149–50 (1960)

309. Werman, R., and Grundfest, H., *J. Gen. Physiol.*, 44, 997–1027 (1961)

310. Werman, R., McCann, F. V., and Grundfest, H., *J. Gen. Physiol.*, 44, 979–95 (1961)

311. Werner, G., *J. Neurophysiol.*, 24, 401–13 (1961)

312. Whitcomb, E. R., and Friess, S. L., *Arch. Biochem. Biophys.*, 90, 260–70 (1960)

313. Wright, E. B., and Ooyama, H., *Am. J. Physiol.*, 200, 219–22 (1961)

314. Zierler, K. L., *Am. J. Physiol.*, 197, 515–23 (1959)

315. Zierler, K. L., *Am. J. Physiol.*, 198, 1066–70 (1960)

KIDNEY, WATER AND ELECTROLYTE METABOLISM[1,2]

By Gerhard Giebisch[3]

Department of Physiology, Cornell University Medical College, New York, N. Y.

INTRODUCTION

The numerous recent reviews dealing with renal physiology permit the author some selectivity in choice of topics and extent of coverage of the many subdivisions in this field. Some important topics have been almost entirely excluded from this discussion: newer developments in the field of renal morphology, a number of surveys and key references on which are available (33 to 36, 100, 115, 162, 180, 232, 249, 277, 278, 304, 309, 326, 327, 390); and many aspects of renal metabolism and renal histochemistry, both fields of obvious and paramount importance, but which the author does not feel competent to assess critically.

Several pertinent reviews dealing with the newer concepts in renal physiology deserve special attention. Kruhøffer (229) has made a comprehensive, up-to-date, and lucidly written evaluation of the present status of renal electrolyte metabolism. Ussing's important chapter in the same volume (410) covers authoritatively the characteristic distribution of electrolytes between living cells and their surroundings, and their net transport across various epithelial membranes. Cier (70) has also discussed the factors governing the distribution of sodium and potassium across cell membranes. The *Handbuch der experimentellen Pharmakologie* further contains chapters on various extrarenal aspects of fluid and electrolyte distribution by Thaysen, Kruhøffer, and Thorn (463). Another comprehensive work, with contributions from several authors, is a treatise on *Mineral Metabolism* (466), two volumes of which have appeared. The first treats general aspects of mineral metabolism, including thermodynamics, chelation, compartmental analysis, and ion transport. Succeeding chapters deal with processes and organ systems concerned with mineral intake and output. Of particular interest here is one on renal excretory mechanisms by Walser & Mudge (425). The second volume covers hormonal effects primarily. The reader is also referred to three more specialized monographs: those of Pitts (480); Lotspeich (465); and Forster (462). The ninth *Henry Ford Hospital Symposium* (467), devoted to the biology of pyelonephritis, contains some papers primarily concerned with basic aspects of normal renal structure and function. In the first of the new *Annual Reviews of Pharmacology* is a chapter on *Renal Pharmacology* by Orloff & Ber-

---

[1] The survey of the literature was concluded in July 1961.

[2] Abbreviations used in this chapter include: ACTH (adrenocorticotropic hormone), ADH (antidiuretic hormone); DOCA (deoxycorticosterone acetate), GFR (glomerular filtration rate); PAH (*p*-aminohippurate), RBF (renal blood flow).

[3] Established Investigator of the American Heart Association.

liner (310). Renal transport mechanisms for electrolytes and the action upon them by several groups of diuretics (chlorothiazide, mercurials, cardiotonic steroids, antagonists of aldosterone) are emphasized and given a thorough up-to-date coverage. Also devoted to newer diuretics is a volume of the *Annals of the New York Academy of Sciences* (474) and one of *Chemotherapia* (461). The *University of Michigan Medical Bulletin* devoted one issue to a symposium on the kidney (464). The *Göttingen Nierensymposion* (476) deals with renal tubular ion transport, localization of nephron function, renal medullary blood flow, and the medullary countercurrent system. Two issues of *Progress in Cardiovascular Diseases* devoted to heart, kidney, and electrolytes have recently appeared (471). These contain papers dealing with basic aspects of renal tubular transport functions: a review of present knowledge of the countercurrent system in the mammalian kidney (408), a critical evaluation of the stop-flow method by the originator of this technique (267), a survey of the relationship between renal blood flow and diuresis (307), and an article concerned with electrical phenomena observed on single nephrons (132). This series also contains more clinically oriented contributions. Other relevant publications include the Proceedings of the First International Congress on Nephrology (472), of the Eleventh Annual Conference on the Nephrotic Syndrome (473), and of a symposium on water and salt metabolism held in Amsterdam (485); and a highly instructive volume on *Regulation of the Inorganic Ion Content of Cells* (482). Other monographs deal with the effect of adrenal cortical hormones on water and electrolyte metabolism (479) and with the influence of the central nervous system on renal functions (475). Finally, a number of monographs and texts of more clinical orientation have appeared (459, 469, 470, 471, 478, 481, 483, 484, 486).

RENAL CIRCULATION AND GLOMERULAR FUNCTION

Two aspects of renal circulatory physiology have attracted much attention. First, considerable controversy has evolved over the mechanism underlying the phenomenon of autoregulation of the renal circulation. Second, the importance of the renal medullary circulation has become evident in relation to the urinary concentrating mechanism and to other aspects of renal function. Renal papillary gas tension, metabolism, and electrolyte transfer may be influenced in a unique manner by the blood flow in the renal medulla.

Autoregulation of renal blood flow.—Blood flow through the kidney is generally little affected by a rise in arterial pressure. This behavior constitutes an intrinsic property of the kidney, as it is not brought about by external nervous or hormonal control: it implies increasing renal vascular resistance with increasing arterial pressure. The consistent failure of one laboratory to confirm such autoregulation of renal blood flow should be noted. Langston *et al.* (236) maintain that changes in perfusion pressure always result in proportional changes in renal blood flow when care is taken to avoid interruption of that blood flow. They suggest that only when ischemia is present or the perirenal tissues are damaged can autoregulation be demonstrated in the dog. They conclude that the unique relationship between perfusion pressure and renal blood flow characterizing autoregulation is an artifact. Applying appropriate precautions, however, Hardin *et al.* (160) challenge this conclusion since they invariably observed autoregulation of blood flow as described for semi-isolated or isolated kidneys. They suggest that the inability of Langston *et al.* to demonstrate autoregulation might be explained by the diversion of some of the perfusing blood into aortic branches other than the renal arteries, particularly the lumbar arteries. Unless precautions are taken to prevent such a by-pass, some of the perfusing blood might never traverse the kidney. Distention of these branches with rising perfusion pressure could result in the diversion of increasing volumes of blood from the kidney, since such vessels lack the peculiar renal vascular response. Autoregulation, particularly over the upper pressure range, would thus be obscured if such extrarenal blood flow were included in the calculation of renal vascular resistance. Hardin *et al.* also point out that the anterior abdominal approach, used by Langston *et al.*, leads to uncommonly high initial renal vascular resistance, making autoregulation more difficult to demonstrate. Such high resistance values are avoided by the flank approach which is apparently less traumatic. These objections to the work of Langston *et al.* seem valid. To answer these criticisms, Langston and his co-workers have used spinal anethesia to permit more normal initial blood flow rates. Also, they have presented evidence that none of the perfusing blood by-passes the kidney. Despite these precautions, they report in a brief communication that they are still unable to demonstrate typical autoregulation, and they conclude that this phenomenon is of no importance in the intact kidney (237).

Nevertheless, many investigators report pressure-flow relations typical for renal autoregulation. Evidence favoring the myogenic constriction theory has been reported by Waugh & Shanks (427) using isolated dog kidneys perfused with whole blood or cell-free colloidal solutions. Autoregulation deteriorated when oxygenated polyvinyl-pyrrolidone–Locke solution was used for perfusion, but could be restored by addition of plasma to the colloidal perfusate. It was demonstrated at relatively low levels of intrarenal venous pressure and tissue pressure. From this the authors conclude that the site of increased resistance is upstream from the intrarenal venous system. They sharply distinguish this type of "genuine renal circulatory autoregulation" from a passive, "factitious" type of regulatory response, which is not observed in the intact kidney but occurs only at temperatures of 3 to 10°C, or after chloral hydrate treatment. This particular circulatory adjustment is thought to be the consequence of an abnormally high intrarenal tissue pressure. Only under these conditions was the decreased flow associated with a significant rise in venous resistance. Waugh & Shanks also report that autoregulation was not impaired by procaine in doses not depressing vascular smooth muscle activity. Severe hemorrhage in the dog prior to excision of the kidney led to renal vasoconstriction intense enough to mask autoregulation. These authors concur with a number of other investigators (305, 306, 362,

395, 396, 398) that myogenic vasoconstriction in the preglomerular renal arteriolar tree is the fundamental cause of genuine circulatory autoregulation. The stimulus to this response is thought to be the transmural vascular pressure gradient. The possibility is considered that the myocytes of the juxtaglomerular apparatus are involved in the autoregulatory response. Rosenfeld & Sellers (348) also observed autoregulation of renal blood flow in the heart-lung perfused rabbit kidney, the functional status of which was evaluated in terms of renal plasma flow, creatinine clearance, PAH-extraction, and urine-to-plasma concentration ratios of creatinine and glucose. It was found that cervical spinal cord transection of the unanesthetized rabbit is essential for the subsequent maintenance of strikingly normal renal function during perfusion periods. Under such conditions autoregulation was present, but apparently not related to the level of the creatinine clearance, as one might have expected on the basis of previous work (396).

Hinshaw et al. (176) earlier proposed that the increased resistance underlying autoregulation is caused by compression of vascular channels because of altered interstitial pressure. The relative role of pre- and postglomerular vascular resistance changes was evaluated on isolated dog kidneys perfused during ureteral occlusion. It was assumed that ureteral pressure approximates the pressure in Bowman's capsule, an assumption which would hold only in the absence of glomerular filtration. It is known, however, that glomerular filtration and tubular reabsorption continue even when the ureter is completely occluded (1, 267, 388). As renal arterial pressure was increased, the calculated postglomerular resistance contributed increasingly to the total arteriovenous pressure gradient. Ureteral and renal interstitial pressure ("needle pressure") also increased significantly. It should be noted, however, that the so-calculated peritubular capillary pressures are very high and greatly exceed those measured directly by Wirz (447), Gottschalk & Mylle (150), and Thurau et al. (398) in peritubular capillaries. Also, in the reviewer's opinion, deductions made concerning the magnitude of the renal interstitial pressures based on needle tissue pressures are open to considerable uncertainty. Nevertheless, Hinshaw et al. believe that their data exclude a myogenic reflex of the arteriolar tree as a causative factor in autoregulation. Instead, it is thought to be accounted for by increased intratubular and interstitial pressures, both of which rise as a consequence of increased filtration of fluid at increased pressure levels and curtail postglomerular blood flow. Limited distensibility of the extravascular compartment seems essential for such a proposed mechanism.

Similar conclusions have also been drawn by Samelius & Aström (352) who studied pressure-flow relationships in isolated cat kidney. Most preparations showed autoregulation when the renal arterial pressure was increased from 90 to 220 mm Hg and when red cell–free dextran solutions were used for perfusion. Intrarenal pressure was found to increase markedly in the range of autoregulation. From this observation and the limited distensibility of the renal extravascular compartment, it was concluded that increased renal tissue pressure plays a key role in autoregulation by reducing the distending pressure across the renal vascular tree. This thesis is also supported by observations of Bounous *et al.* (41, 42) who were able to abolish the phenomenon of renal autoregulation by renal decapsulation. On the other hand, no impairment of the renal vascular tree's capacity to increase its resistance to flow was observed after sympathectomy, splanchnicectomy, or bilateral vagotomy. After massive blood transfusion, interstitial renal pressure rose uniformly in the normal dog kidney along with the increase in systemic arterial pressure. The absence of such interstitial pressure increase in the decapsulated kidney always led to loss of autoregulation, emphasizing the importance of the rigid capsular envelope for the development of blood flow restriction at high perfusion pressures. Scher *et al.* (355) also present evidence favoring increased filtration and compression of low-pressure vessels within the kidney occurring with increased perfusion pressure. In particular, the finding that tonicity of the perfusion fluid affects the absolute pressure level at which autoregulation obtains is taken as evidence supporting the filtration theory and stressing its possible participation in the over-all autoregulatory response. As the kidney was perfused with fluid of increased tonicity, flow rates were found to be higher at comparable perfusion pressures than with fluids of normal or low tonicity. Harvey (163) also reported on renal vascular resistance changes produced by hyperosmotic perfusion media. Cold solutions of hyperosmotic mannitol and glucose caused a consistent increase in perfusion flow rates while urea was ineffective. The site of such osmotically induced resistance changes is believed to be postglomerular.

It is quite obvious that some question remains as to site and mechanism of renal autoregulation; indeed, one wonders whether the same phenomenon is studied by all investigators. Also, there is uncertainty concerning the validity of needle pressure measurements as an accurate assessment of interstitial renal pressure, yet this very measurement is of considerable relevance in the interpretation of many results. This problem has received a fresh approach in recent months by Thurau *et al.* (398) who have made direct pressure measurements in proximal tubules and peritubular capillaries of rats *in vivo*. Over an arterial pressure range of about 80 to 190 mm Hg, capillary and tubular pressures remained constant, and only after injection of papaverine was there a linear increase of peritubular capillary pressure with increasing arterial pressure. These experiments strongly indicate that an increase in interstitial pressure plays no important role *in vivo* during augmentation of arterial perfusion pressure. The absence of an increase in directly measured peritubular capillary pressure during elevated levels of arterial pressures also points strongly to a preglomerular site of renal autoregulation and is presently best explained by the thesis that, *in vivo*, this phenomenon depends upon a change in active vascular tone of the arteriolar tree which is regulated by the transmural pressure difference.

Renal medullary circulation.—Although few recent papers deal with the renal medullary circulation, there is growing evidence for the importance of this specialized vascular area (225, 226, 392, 394, 408). The blood supply to the renal medulla is derived from the juxtamedullary arterioles emerging from the glomeruli of this area. These split into vasa recta which are arranged in bundles comprising arterial and returning venous branches in close proximity, exhibiting typical hairpin structure at different levels of the renal papilla.

The renal medullary blood flow cannot be measured directly. However, it can be calculated from the ratio of vascular volume to mean circulation time (226). This method, recently improved by direct measurements of the hematocrit and the hemoglobin concentration of papillary blood (409), yields values for the inner medulla of 0.9 per cent, and for the outer medulla, 11 per cent of the total renal blood flow (408). Although the studies by Lilienfield *et al.* (260) have re-emphasized some difficulties in the estimation of renal medullary blood flow from the distribution of I^{131}-labeled albumin, these authors have obtained quite similar results. Recent observations by Thurau *et al.* (397) of a considerable increase in albumin concentration in vasa recta blood in the tip of the papilla are taken as evidence for a predominantly intravascular location of the exchangeable albumin (260). Lilienfield *et al.* (260) observed an accumulation rate of 25 ml per 100 g per min of I^{131}-labeled albumin in the renal papilla of dogs, and arrived at a value of 22 ml per 100 g per min for medullary blood flow, taking into account the effect of filtration, and the typically low hematocrit of renal medullary blood. The renal medullary circulation does not participate in autoregulation (394), but the medullary vasculature is quite sensitive to antidiuretic hormone and epinephrine, both of which lead to vasoconstriction (394). On the other hand, water diuresis and osmotic diuresis increase renal medullary blood flow (394).

The arrangement of the medullary blood vessels has several functional consequences. Where a gradient for any diffusible material exists between its two ends, a countercurrent exchanger acts as an effective barrier to the net transport along its long axis (241). This holds whether material is added over the whole surface of the countercurrent system along its entire length or is added via the arterial blood which enters the afferent limb of the vascular medullary system. Accordingly, substances added over the whole extent of the countercurrent system will be conserved within the papilla; those added with the arterial blood will be excluded from the papilla in direct proportion to their diffusibility. A quantitative analysis of countercurrent exchange diffusion in the steady state has been attempted by Ullrich *et al.* (408). Lassen & Longley (241) have also investigated the countercurrent exchange in the vessels of the renal medulla. A behavior consistent with the previously presented thesis was demonstrated by comparing the efficiency of papillary exclusion of various test substances having different diffusibility when added to the blood stream. Substances which traverse the vasa recta readily (Kr^{85}, tritiated water) were shunted more effectively at the level of the outer medulla and excluded to a higher degree from the inner medulla than was colloidal material. This situation also has consequences for the kinetics of distribution of various materials in the renal papilla: significant delay of equilibration points to countercurrent distribution in the renal medulla if substances are added by the arterial route. Indeed, Kramer *et al.* (225) observed that the time it takes for equilibration to reach a new level of oxygen saturation after substitution of pure oxygen in the respiratory gas mixture is about 12 times longer in the inner medulla than in the cortex.

The kinetics of exchange of water and sodium along the corticomedullary axis of the kidney have also been comprehensively treated by Morel *et al.* (285, 286), who observed that replacement of labeled medullary water proceeds at a much slower rate than that of medullary sodium. This indicates that water, as a more diffusible compound, is more efficiently short-circuited at the base of the renal papilla than is sodium.

Countercurrent diffusion probably also contributes to the low oxygen tension of renal papillary tissue under steady-state conditions, although the low hematocrit of medullary capillary blood must also be important (343, 397, 409). A low oxygen tension in the renal medulla has been demonstrated by direct polarographic methods by Aukland & Krog (6) and photoelectrically by Kramer *et al.* (225). This may also hold for the low oxygen tension of pelvic urine (182, 343). The high rate of anaerobic glycolysis observed in renal papillary tissue *in vitro* (62, 227), as well as its higher lactic acid content (63, 227) as compared with cortical tissue, may well be an adaptive response to the chronic oxygen lack. As pointed out by Ullrich *et al.* (408), the enzymatic structure of the medullary tissue and the storage of glycogen in the cells of the collecting ducts are also in accord with the observed functional resistance to anoxia. It is interesting that Cohen (72) found the highest respiratory quotient values (significantly in excess of 1.0) under those experimental conditions which favor high sodium chloride reabsorption in the outer renal medulla. It is tempting to speculate, but by no means certain, that there is a direct relationship between increased sodium reabsorption and accelerated anaerobic glycolysis. A number of studies concerned with the renal utilization of glucose (273), lactic acid and pyruvate (371), the distribution of acid-soluble phosphate compounds (130) and of oxidative and hydrolytic enzymes (175) have appeared. Such studies, if correlated specifically with renal tubular Na transport, may clarify some of these problems.

The dependence of carbon dioxide tension in urine on countercurrent diffusion is not clear. On the basis of the previous discussion of medullary trapping, one might expect carbon dioxide tension to increase in tissue and urine from the base to the apex of the papilla (408). However, the pCO_2 of urine is not consistently above that of renal venous blood. It has been pointed out that the medullary carbon dioxide tension could be influenced by processes related to acidification and not only by countercurrent diffusion (408). Also, direct measurements of renal medullary pCO_2 are not at hand.

Another fact to consider is that the smallness of the renal medullary blood flow limits the amount of substrate for secretion by the collecting duct system, as in the case of potassium and ammonia secretion across the collecting ducts (310). Furthermore, changes of renal medullary blood flow, by altering the renal papillary concentration of sodium and chloride, conceivably could influence the concentration gradient against which these ions move from the ascending limb of Henle's loop and the collecting ducts into the renal papillary electrolyte pool. Hulet & Smith (186) have presented indirect evidence that, under certain experimental conditions, a limiting gradient against which sodium can be reabsorbed exists across the ascending limb of Henle's loop. The renal medullary circulation has clearly evolved as an important new area of interest in renal physiology having considerable functional implication beyond the realm of renal hemodynamics.

Renal blood flow and oxygen consumption.—A number of studies relate renal oxygen consumption and blood flow. Levy & Imperial (255, 256) investigated the effects of variations of blood flow on renal oxygen extraction, with particular emphasis on oxygen shunting in cortical and medullary capillaries. The shunting of oxygen from arterial to venous segments of the renal capillary bed was demonstrated by the observation that it traverses the renal vascular bed more rapidly than do erythrocytes. In these studies, the passage of red cells was signaled by an injection of either methemoglobinemic erythrocytes, or high-hematocrit blood. Increased renal venous oxygen saturation was taken as the index for oxygen appearance, the injected blood having been equilibrated at high pO_2. The outer region of the renal cortex could be functionally separated from the medulla and the inner cortex by means of regional hypothermia. Somewhat unexpectedly, no consistent enhancement or attenuation of oxygen shunting was observed by cooling either the superficial or deeper zones. Since the peritubular capillary plexus in the renal cortex also appears to possess some element of hairpin-configuration (405), it was concluded that shunting of oxygen occurs in both the cortex and medulla.

Kramer & Deetjen (224) and Lassen *et al.* (242) have re-evaluated the interrelationship among renal oxygen consumption, renal blood flow, and glomerular filtration rate. In the studies of Kramer & Deetjen, renal blood flow was varied by clamping the aorta, and a linear relationship between renal blood flow and oxygen consumption was observed over a range of perfusion rates from 200 to 800 ml per 100 g kidney weight. Arteriovenous oxygen difference was constant within the linear range of blood flow and oxygen consumption. Importantly, oxygen uptake was also directly related to glomerular filtration rate and to the rate of sodium reabsorption (93, 224, 242, 389). Data in accord with the concept that total oxygen consumption is related to glomerular activity have also been presented by Crosley *et al.* (82). Kramer & Deetjen (224) suggest that renal oxygen consumption is largely determined by tubular sodium reabsorption, the latter being a function of filtration rate. This is an important thesis. It is in agreement with the behavior of a number of other epithelial membranes in which oxygen consumption has likewise been found to vary with active sodium transport (410). Similar conclusions have also been reached by Lassen *et al.* (242) and by Thurau (393). Lassen *et al.* varied arterial pressure by bleeding, and divided renal oxygen uptake into a small and constant "basal" fraction which was observed under conditions of hypotension, cessation of filtration, and hence also of tubular sodium reabsorption. The "suprabasal" oxygen consumption, defined as total renal oxygen uptake less the basal, was found, in full agreement with Kramer & Deetjen, to correlate closely with the quantity of sodium reabsorbed. Thurau studied renal oxygen consumption under conditions of hypoxia and after chlorothiazide administration, both of which depress sodium reabsorption and oxygen consumption in linear fashion (393). A similar correlation has been reported for kidney slices between active net extrusion of sodium (not unidirectional transport) and oxygen uptake (243). Since sodium is absorbed in the renal tubule in large part, if not completely, by an active, energy-consuming process (105, 106, 446), such a relationship offers a very satisfactory explanation for the interdependence between oxygen consumption and tubular sodium transfer.

Various effects on the renal circulation.—Wise & Ganong undertook a systematic study on the effects of brainstem stimulation on renal function (450). Experiments were performed on anesthetized dogs with chronically implanted electrodes, and the responses in some were compared after renal denervation. Upon stimulation of hypothalamic, tectal, pontine, and medullary areas of the brainstem, a considerable variety of vascular responses could be elicited: renal vasoconstriction, vasodilation, and alterations in glomerular filtration rate. Some of these were not correlated with general pressor and depressor effects and suggested selective renal vascular innervation originating from the medullary brainstem. In some instances, sodium excretion could be affected by localized stimulation independent of changes in glomerular filtration rate. Confirming Wise & Ganong, Takeuchi *et al.* (385) found no evidence for nervous impulses originating from the diencephalon which affected the renal circulation selectively, since no changes in renal blood flow could be produced during stimulation at constant arterial pressure. The proceedings of a symposium (475) devoted to the role of the central nervous system in renal function include extensive treatment of neural regulation of the renal circulation. A number of authors stress the key role of the central nervous system in the response of the renal circulation to such stimuli as hypoxia, shock, exercise, psychogenic trauma, and conditioned reflexes. Pappenheimer (318) also reviewed some aspects of the central control of the renal circulation.

Ginn *et al.* (138) studied the denervated kidney after successful transplantation in identical twins. Structure and volume of the extracellular fluid compartment were maintained within normal limits, and acute changes in plasma composition were adequately corrected. No deficiencies were observed in acidification or concentration of the urine or in diurnal variations of water and sodium excretion. It was concluded that the homologous transplanted kidney (ischemic for 47 min), presumably free of all neural control, may maintain its normal circulatory status and role in fluid homeostasis adequately. However, the problem of regeneration of autonomic nerves into a transplanted kidney merits some investigation.

According to Gömöri and associates (145, 146), arterial hypoxia in dogs under chloralose anesthesia reduced renal blood flow (PAH clearance) and the renal fraction of the cardiac output concomitantly with an increase in renal vascular resistance. Arterial hypoxia restricted exclusively to the cephalic circulation by means of isolated head-perfusion produced a similar, sometimes reversible, increase in renal vascular resistance. This observation is taken as evidence for a key role of the brainstem in the hypoxia-induced renal vasoconstriction. Renal denervation or dibenamine treatment suppressed the effects of hypoxia. Hypotension and hypercapnia in the head, isolated from the trunk by a separate circulation, led also to vasoconstrictor effects in the kidney.

Bálint et al. (13) showed that the depth of anesthesia is an important factor for determining recovery after two hours of complete renal ischemia. Dogs in deep chloralose anesthesia, or after spinal transection, survived such an ischemic period, whereas lightly anesthetized animals (morphine, ether) succumbed in uremia. In other papers, Bálint and his associates point out that values of renal blood flow may be erroneously low when the PAH clearance is used to measure renal blood flow in oligemic conditions (9). p-Aminohippurate clearance and directly determined renal venous outflow were compared in hemorrhagic shock (12, 14), hypoxia (11, 145), and severe dehydration after pyloric ligation (10). Under these conditions, the PAH clearance was consistently lower than the directly measured renal blood flow.

The effects of a number of drugs and hormones on the renal circulation have received attention. Passow et al. (320) tested the effects of 5-hydroxytryptamine (serotonin) on the blood flow in the isolated rat kidney preparation perfused with isotonic dextran solution. Reversible renal vasoconstriction was observed over a concentration range of 0.034 to 10 μg per ml in the perfusion fluid. At the higher doses, tachyphylaxis was observed. Lysergic acid diethylamide (LSD) fully reversed or suppressed the serotonin effect. Intrarenal redistribution of blood with cortical glomerular ischemia after serotonin was found in rats by Dolcini et al. (99). The authors assessed the circulatory status in their studies by the benzidine-staining technique and injection of India ink. After an early and transient vasodilator effect, blood seemed to be shunted away from the cortex while the circulation of the juxtaglomerular areas remained unchanged. No cortical necrosis was seen at the highest doses of 10 mg per kg. The effects of various sympathicomimetic drugs on renal hemodynamics in normotensive and hypotensive dogs were investigated by Mills et al. (283). Of six substances tested, a comparable rise in arterial pressure was found to be coexistent with widely varying effects on renal vascular resistance, indicating considerable selectivity of the renal vascular bed to some of the drugs. Heidenreich *et al.* (165, 166) found that the effect of synthetic oxytocin on renal blood flow in normal dogs was small, but in totally hypophysectomized dogs doses of 15 mU per kg uniformly increased glomerular filtration rate and renal blood flow. Mertz (276) describes a study on the acute effects of synthetic oxytocin on renal hemodynamics in man; and a comparison of the renal circulatory effects of angiotensin, vasopressin, and epinephrine in the cat was undertaken by Barer (17). No new concepts as to the possible physiological role of these vasoactive substances in relation to the renal circulation have evolved.

Elevation of the environmental temperature reduces renal blood flow and glomerular filtration rate (196, 200). Increase of body temperature by a pyrogen, on the other hand, leads to renal vasodilation (75), a response independent of the renal nerve supply and believed to be caused by an unknown humoral agent. Renal hypothermia reduces RBF and GFR (25) and is recommended by Kerr *et al.* (206) during surgical interventions necessitating transitory renal artery occlusion. It significantly increases the tolerance of the kidney to ischemia. Kanter (197) reports that hyperventilation in dogs leaves GFR and RPF unchanged.

Heimburg & Ochwadt (167) have studied transvascular fluid shifts in the isolated perfused dog kidney and *in situ* after epinephrine administration or after lowering the arterial perfusion pressure. Both of these induced a drop in kidney weight and a transitory fall in renal venous hemoglobin and albumin concentration. It is argued convincingly that, as capillary pressure falls, either because of diminished perfusion pressure or because of the epinephrine-induced precapillary vasoconstriction, there is a shift of protein-containing fluid into the renal vascular compartment. As origin of this fluid, the interstitial fluid pool and the tubular contents are discussed. It is concluded that this extravascular fluid compartment is equal in size to the intrarenal blood volume and that renal weight changes, as a function of arterial pressure changes, are not only a consequence of alterations in the degree of vascular filling but are also caused by shrinkage or expansion of this extravascular fluid pool.

Blake (28) presents evidence that complete occlusion of a renal artery branch has distinct effects on the ipsilateral kidney (increased GFR per tubule) in addition to eliciting decreased water reabsorption per tubule in the contralateral kidney. This latter effect disappears upon denervation of the experimental kidney.

A number of papers with physiological orientation have dealt primarily with alterations of renal blood flow in some clinical disorders; Bello *et al.* (20) on renal hemodynamic responses to stress in normotensive and hypertensive subjects: Saltzman (351) on renal circulation in pulmonary emphysema; Reubi (344) on general aspects of renal blood flow measurements; and Cottier (78) on renal hemodynamics in hypertension. Swann (384) has summarized his studies on the functional distention of the kidney, including hemodynamic considerations and possible consequences in hypertension and uremia.

TUBULAR FUNCTIONS

TRANSPORT AND EXCRETION OF STRONG ELECTROLYTES

The details of the active process by which sodium is moved from lumen to interstitial fluid remains one of the major unsolved problems of renal tubular electrolyte transport. Nevertheless, definite advances have contributed to a better understanding of the magnitude and site of various ion transport functions, of the general permeability properties of the different nephron segments, and of the driving forces involved in some reabsorptive and secretory processes. Thus, the renewed and wider interest in a more direct approach to the study of renal tubular function by means of micropuncture and various related techniques has led to clarification of certain aspects of water and electrolyte transfer. A number of papers on general aspects of tubular electrolyte transfer have appeared (187, 250, 310, 346, 378), and Edelman's review of *Transport through Biological Membranes* (104) gives up-to-date background dealing with the basic problems of ion movement and distribution.

Transport of sodium and chloride.—Gottschalk (148, 244) has summarized in a Bowditch Lecture the results of micropuncture studies carried out by himself and his associates, which have, in general, been in accord with previous views on the magnitude of water and solute reabsorption in various parts of the mammalian nephron. About 65 per cent of the filtered water is reabsorbed by the end of the convoluted part of the proximal tubule, and the tubular fluid remains isotonic under all experimental conditions studied. Sodium concentration was found to be identical to that of plasma but some acidification of proximal tubular fluid has occurred, indicating preferential bicarbonate reabsorption. This explains the finding that the chloride concentration in tubular fluid exceeds that of plasma (39, 40, 134, 148, 417), particularly under conditions of enhanced hydrogen ion movement into the tubular lumen.

Net water and net Na movement across proximal tubular epithelium in the rat were studied by Windhager & Giebisch (445) during strong osmotic diuresis induced by infusion of hypertonic mannitol solution. Net water movement out of the proximal tubule was less than under nondiuretic conditions. Also, the concentration of Na in proximal tubular fluid was significantly below that of plasma, a finding in agreement with observations by Gottschalk *et al.* (148). Since the tubule lumen is electrically negative with respect to the peritubular fluid pool (372), this net movement of Na must have occurred against an electrochemical gradient. This provides direct evidence for active transport of Na ions across the proximal tubular wall. The relationship between filtered load and extent of proximal tubular Na reabsorption, when load is augmented by an increase in either plasma concentration or filtration rate, has not yet been defined by the direct approach of micropuncture; nor are direct observations available which deal with the problem of saturation of proximal or distal tubular reabsorptive capacity for Na ions.

Recently, the relative contribution of active versus passive proximal tubular Na reabsorption has received renewed attention because the colloid-osmotic pressure gradient and the active proximal reabsorption of glucose constitute a potential driving force for reabsorptive fluid movement. A portion of the Na reabsorbed in this segment could thus be the simple consequence of bulk fluid movement. This thesis, more recently discussed by Bayliss (18) and by Malvin (267), has also been proposed by Bresler (47). In clearance experiments in the dog, the latter studied the renal tubular reabsorptive response to an elevated NaCl load (47), and also reported on the effect of hypotonic glucose loading (48). An increase in tubular Na reabsorption was observed under both of these experimental conditions and is interpreted to mean that passive reabsorption of proximal tubular fluid contributes significantly to the process of Na transfer. Direct evidence that is opposed to this view has recently become available: in experiments on perfused tubules in *Necturus* (105, 106) and in the rat (446) it is clearly indicated that the larger part, probably all, of proximal tubular net Na transfer in these species is active, because net Na movement and short-circuit current [i.e., the net charge transferred actively in unit time (198, 410)] are in good quantitative agreement.

Steeper concentration gradients for Na and Cl ions are found across the distal tubular epithelium (445), a finding in good agreement with previous results of osmotic pressure measurements in early distal tubular fluid samples (148). During urea and mannitol diuresis, the distal tubular Na concentration is less than under nondiuretic conditions, indicating the importance of nonreabsorbable solutes in determining the transtubular Na gradient also in this tubular segment (148). Ureteral urine samples were found to be virtually Na-free in rats on a low-Na diet even though the Na gradient across the distal tubular epithelium was as steep as that found in animals on a normal diet. This observation points to the collecting duct as a site which contributes importantly to the establishment of the final concentration gradient under conditions of maximal Na conservation (445). It should be noted that Vander *et al.* (413), by stop-flow analysis in adrenalectomized dogs, before and after administration of aldosterone, were able to demonstrate a site of hormone action in a distal nephron segment. Normally, the Na concentration in samples emerging first after ureteral release is low. The steepness of this distal Na gradient, diminished by adrenalectomy or by administration of a steroid-antagonist (SC-8109), could be restored by pretreatment with aldosterone. No proximal site of aldosterone action was observed in these experiments, but conclusions concerning proximal tubular functions from stop-flow analysis cannot be accepted without some reserve (229, 267, 310). Other investigators have claimed a proximal tubular site of mineralocorticoid action (443). No direct observations by micropuncture are as yet available on tubular Na movement under the influence of adrenal steroids.

The mode of renal tubular Cl transfer has recently been studied more directly by measuring the electrochemical potential gradient against which this ion moves at various tubular sites. As previously mentioned, the Cl concentration in proximal tubular fluid is normally equal to, or somewhat higher than, that of plasma (39, 40, 134, 148, 417). Both in the rat and in *Necturus* the proximal tubular lumen has been found to be electrically negative (105, 106, 131, 372, 440), and such an electrical potential gradient provides a driving force for reabsorptive Cl movement. In the perfused proximal tubule of *Necturus*, a wholly passive nature of proximal tubular Cl movement has been demonstrated since the transtubular flux ratio of Cl ions can be fully accounted for by the observed degree of electrical asymmetry (133). However, for the mammalian nephron, no data are available permitting decision as to whether the transtubular electrical gradient is adequate to account for proximal Cl reabsorption; such an explanation is, however, generally assumed. Recently, Clapp & Rector (71) have reported briefly on a study in the rat in which the transtubular electrical gradient was measured and correlated with the concentration gradient for Cl ions across the identical distal tubular nephron segment. Normally the electrical potential gradient appeared to be adequate to account for a passive mode of Cl movement. However, administration of sodium sulfate to Na-depleted animals resulted in such steep transtubular ionic concentration gradients that it was felt necessary to invoke a process of active Cl transport. Under the experimental conditions of Clapp & Rector, the distal tubular lumen was found to be electrically negative by as much as 115 mv with respect to the kidney surface. An electrical gradient of such magnitude constitutes a considerable force acting, unspecifically, to establish ionic concentration gradients, promoting reabsorptive movement of anions and secretory movement of cations (132). Similar studies are not yet available concerning other nephron segments. Consequently, nothing is known as to the mode of Cl movement in the ascending limb of Henle's loop and the collecting duct, both segments in which the presence of active Na transport is strongly indicated.

The origin of the electrical potential differences across the renal tubular epithelium has been studied by observing the behavior of the electrical profile across the renal tubule following various ionic substitutions in the perfused amphibian kidney preparation (131) or in single perfused tubules (440). In *Necturus*, the single tubule cell is large enough to permit impalement with a recording microelectrode and to permit the separate measurements of potential differences across the luminal and peritubular cell membrane. From the marked change in the electrical transmembrane potential difference after variations in the extracellular K concentration, it is apparent that proximal tubule cells are characterized, like many other cells, by a high permeability to K ions. Also, the behavior of the luminal cell membrane indicates a higher Na permeability than the peritubular cell membrane (131). This difference in relative Na permeability, coexistent with an active Na extrusion mechanism located at the peritubular cell membrane, provides the framework for a cell model which is compatible with the observation that the renal tubule cell is asymmetrically negative with respect to the tubular lumen and the peritubular fluid (131, 439). This situation resembles the proposed cell model of the frog skin epithelium by Koefoed-Johnsen & Ussing (223), with the exception that the K permeability of the luminal cell membrane of the proximal tubule cell (corresponding to the outer epithelial cell membrane of the frog skin) exceeds that for Na. In the frog skin, ionic selectivity for these ion species is apparently complete. Whittembury *et al.* (439) have evaluated the permeability coefficients in *Necturus* for a number of electrolytes *in vitro* by studies of the uptake of radioactive isotopes and the rate of swelling of kidney slices in various anisotonic solutions. The relative permeabilities for Na and K, so derived, agree well with the differences expected on the basis of the proposed cell schema. The passive fluxes of Na and K, as measured across single proximal tubules in *Necturus*, are also in quantitative agreement with the calculated permeability ratios (308).

A high permeability for K and Cl was also demonstrated in experiments by Kleinzeller (219) who studied the factors affecting the swelling of mammalian kidney cortex slices at 0°C. Evidence is presented that active Na transport is arrested at this temperature since a number of metabolic inhibitors failed to influence the rate and extent of swelling. Increasing concentrations of K in isotonic saline resulted in an increase of tissue water, K, and Cl, and a fall in Na. Also, a linear relationship was shown to exist between the apparent membrane potential calculated from the Donnan ratio of K, and the logarithm of external K concentrations. These results support the thesis that a Donnan system governs the distribution of K, Cl, and water in renal tissue, similar to that for muscle as described by Boyle & Conway (43). They are also in agreement with observations by Giebisch (131) and Whittembury *et al.* (439) that the electrical potential difference across single renal tubule cells is a linear function of the logarithm of external K concentration under conditions favoring constant intracellular K concentration.

There is general agreement as to the key position of active Na transport in such renal tubular functions as fluid reabsorption, generation of the electrical potential difference, and various ion exchange processes; yet little is known about the intimate nature of this ion transfer. Suggestive evidence is available that the active extrusion of Na from the cell interior is linked with K uptake into the cell. Such a coupled pump mechanism has been given credence in studies of the effect of cardiac glycosides on renal electrolyte excretion. Orloff & Burg (311) utilized the renal-portal circulation of the chicken to study tubular effects of strophanthidin. A marked increase in Na excretion and in alkalinization coincident with a reduction of K excretion was found. The data are interpreted to indicate that strophanthidin primarily inhibits some fraction of the Na for K exchange at the peritubular cell membrane, and thereby leads to an increased intracellular Na concentration, this increase depressing the rate of exchange at the luminal cell border, where intracellular K and H are presumed to compete for intraluminal Na at a common carrier site. Such action implies a distal tubular site of action of strophanthidin, but the extent of diuresis (up to 35% of the filtered Na being excreted) suggests that Na reabsorption is partially suppressed throughout the whole nephron. Cade *et al.* (56) investigated the effects of strophanthidin in the dog by infusing this drug directly into the renal artery. Saline-loaded dogs responded with a fall in GFR and an increase in NaCl excretion. Changing the extracellular K concentration led to dramatic results: the diuretic effect of strophanthidin or ouabain was depressed by the administration of K (see also 311) and markedly enhanced by K depletion. Thus the thesis that these drugs act on the Na-K linked pump mechanism is further supported. Cade *et al.* (56) also tested the thesis that strophanthidin acts as an antialdosterone agent by experiments performed in adrenalectomized dogs. Failure to observe any change of the strophanthidin effect indicated that an antialdosterone effect was not of importance in this species. Further studies in bicarbonate-, phosphate-, or sulfate-loaded animals demonstrated that the ability of the renal tubular cells to exchange H ions for Na was unaffected by the cardiac glycosides in the absence of a transtubular H-ion gradient. However, this capacity was markedly impaired under conditions which otherwise lead to maximal acidification. Kupfer & Kosovsky (230) also studied alterations in renal hemodynamics and tubular functions after intra-arterial injection of digitalis glycosides. They confirmed the diuretic effects regarding Na, Cl and water and, in addition, observed an increase in Ca and Mg excretion.

The described effects of cardiac glycosides on K, H, and Na excretion suggest that these compounds act at a distal tubular site. Such a conclusion is also supported by results of stop-flow experiments by Wilde & Howard (442) who injected ouabain directly into the renal artery. Sodium concentration failed to drop to its normally low value at the minimal inflection of the Na stop-flow curve, indicating some impairment of distal tubular Na reabsorption. Strickler & Kessler (380) reported on a comparison of nine digitalis steroids with respect to their diuretic properties. Those compounds which alter cardiac activity and cation movement in a number of preparations *in vitro* also increased Na and water excretion by the kidney when infused via the renal artery; those devoid of an effect on heart muscle and ion movement were nondiuretic. Activity on heart, kidney, and ion fluxes (*in vitro*) is greatest in those compounds having a 5- or 6-membered lactone ring attached in beta-orientation to C-17 of the steroid nucleus, the latter being unsaturated between the alpha and beta carbons. As to the mechanism of action of cardiac glycosides, it is of interest that renal tissue contains an adenosine triphosphatase (214), the activity of which is similar to an enzyme which has been shown to be involved in coupled Na-K transport in red cells (329) and red-cell ghosts (101, 177). This adenosine triphosphatase system is inhibited by strophanthidin and may play a role in the proposed Na-K exchange in the renal tubule (310).

A few other papers are primarily concerned with the details of the process by which Na is actively transported across the renal tubule. Studies on mammalian kidney cortex slices indicate that the maintenance of high K and low Na concentration in the intracellular fluid depends on respiration since cooling, anoxia, and cyanide all lead to K loss and Na gain. The correlation between Na transport and oxygen consumption in isolated renal tissue supports this view. Quantitative studies indicate that the major fraction of oxygen consumed by the kidneys is utilized for the processes underlying active Na reabsorption (224, 242, 243). Whittam (437) noted interesting species differences concerning the oxygen requirement of kidney cortex slices of newborn rabbits, rats, and guinea pigs. He concluded that the high resistance of this tissue from rabbits and rats to anoxia is possible because of the availability of adequate glycolytic pathways for cation transport. On the other hand, the predominantly respiratory pathway in the same tissue from newborn guinea pigs accounts for its oxygen requirement for extrusion of Na and uptake of K. This interpretation of the observed metabolic species differences is also supported by the effects of various metabolic inhibitors on intracellular cations and rate of tissue swelling. The Na, K, and water concentration in kidney cortex slices from newborn rats and rabbits was unaffected by cyanide, while iodoacetate was similarly ineffective in renal tissue from the newborn guinea pigs. Also, in the latter species, the rate of anaerobic liberation of carbon dioxide from a bicarbonate medium and the rate of production of lactic acid were small as contrasted with the behavior of rabbit and rat tissue. The high resistance to anoxia is absent in mature tissues. Čapek & Kleinzeller (62), in a brief communication, have also stressed the importance of anaerobic transport of Na in kidney slices from one-day-old puppies and piglets. Glycolysis appears to provide the energy for this type of renal tubular Na extrusion.

Berndt & LeSher (24) have investigated the effect of various substrates on K accumulation and Na extrusion in rabbit kidney slices. Reaccumulation of K by slices which had been depleted of this ion by a previous leaching procedure was best supported when either glutamate, glutamine, or α-ketoglutarate was added to the incubating medium. Magnesium ions had an additive effect on K reaccumulation. The kinetics of K uptake and Na extrusion was such as to exclude a simple interdependence between these two ionic movements.

A number of brief reports indicate promising approaches to the problem of the nature of renal tubular Na transport. Strickler et al. (381) have studied the direct renal action of a number of metabolic inhibitors, injecting such compounds directly into the renal artery. Antimycin A, a potent and highly specific inhibitor of aerobic glycolysis by virtue of blocking electron transport (330), produces a marked increase in Na and water excretion pointing to the importance of the electron transport system for renal tubular Na transport.

The effects of ethylene-diamine tetra-acetate (EDTA), an agent binding polyvalent metal ions and thereby inhibiting the chelated ion, were studied by Pullman *et al.* (331) who injected this compound into the renal artery. Again, significant unilateral natriuresis and chloruresis ensued, possibly because of the chelation of some ion species critical to the operation of the Na transport system. This is an interesting clue in view of recent evidence for some competitive binding of Ca and Na for a constituent of the renal tubular cell membrane (421), and in view of the abrupt increase in the excretion rate of Na which has been described to follow the intravenous infusion of Ca salts (419). Furthermore, there is some evidence for competition between Na and Ca in other tissues (104, 421). However, it also appears possible that EDTA increases the permeability of the renal tubule to passive inward flux of Na ions into the tubule lumen, thereby causing natriuresis. This mode of action is suggested by the effects of this substance on the frog skin, a preparation in which Curran *et al.* (83) noted increased Na and anion permeability following the addition of the Ca-complexing EDTA to the bathing solution.

Kleinzeller & Cort (220) studied the effect of Ca on the distribution and fluxes of ions in kidney cortex slices. Elevated Ca levels in the medium resulted in a decrease of the passive fluxes of Na^{24}, K^{42}, and urea-C^{14}, and were associated with steeper transcellular concentration gradients for K and Cl. It is concluded that Ca ions decrease renal tubular cell permeability and also result in an increased intracellular electrical polarization.

Cort (77) has also suggested that metabolic acidosis and Hg administration are both associated with an increase in the electrochemical potential gradient (calculated from ionic concentration gradients, and the transcellular Cl distribution) against which Na must be pumped out of tubular cells. Direct verification of this thesis by measurements of respective electrical potential differences is not yet available.

Transport of potassium.—Berliner (23) has reviewed the present knowledge concerning the renal handling of this ion species. From his survey and that of Orloff & Berliner (310) the specific contributions of various tubular segments to the over-all process of renal K excretion are not quite clear. This uncertainty arises because urinary K excretion is the result of simultaneously occurring reabsorptive and secretory processes. Also, so far, no extensive micropuncture study has appeared which would permit assessment of the contribution of various tubular segments to different excretion patterns. However, the methods for ultramicroanalysis of K ions by special flame photometry are available (38, 292).

It is generally agreed that in the mammal a large part of the filtered K moiety is reabsorbed during passage of tubular fluid along the proximal tubule. This is based on the observation that the K concentration in proximal tubular fluid in the rat is equal to, or slightly below, that of plasma water (39, 40). Since there is concomitant fluid reabsorption, this implies proportional K transfer. The orientation of the electrical potential gradient (lumen negative) indicates the operation of an active proximal tubular transport mechanism, although the contribution of solvent drag (410) to proximal tubular K movement has not been excluded. Nothing is known as to the concentration of K in the ascending thick limb of Henle's loop, a site where the presence of active Na transport is strongly indicated (148, 445, 448). As for evidence obtained by micropuncture, little is known as to the behavior of the distal tubular convolution other than a statement by Bott & Litchfield (39) that a drop in concentration of K is observed in this segment. Hierholzer (173) has shown by catheterization of single collecting ducts in the K-loaded golden hamster that some K excretion can occur in this tubular segment.

Several papers have described attempts to localize the site of K secretion and reabsorption by stop-flow analysis. There is general agreement that K secretion can occur in a distal tubular portion of the nephron (as defined by this method); however, there is disagreement as to the site of maximal K reabsorption. Berliner (23), and Jaenicke & Berliner (191) point out that during mannitol diuresis low K concentrations in specimens of "distal" tubular fluid do not indicate a coextensive site of maximal reabsorption. They suggest that the low K concentration noted during mannitol diuresis is caused by the absence of Na ions in such specimens, and that it is the absence of this exchangeable cation which precludes significant K secretion into those specimens as they subsequently pass the K secretory site. Such a thesis presumes that K secretion occurs as a cation exchange process, an assumption supported by considerable evidence (23). The authors conclude that K reabsorption under these stop-flow conditions may be completed proximal to the site of secretion, but it may also occur anywhere between that point and that part of the proximal tubule which is inaccessible to micropuncture.

This view of Berliner (23), Jaenicke & Berliner (191), and Orloff & Berliner (310) has recently received strong support from a study by Walker et al. (418). The mechanism of the distal K-secreting mechanism was investigated by a modified stop-flow technique: only 3 ml of fluid were collected after the first occlusion and the ureter was again occluded. This maneuver permitted urine of maximum K content to escape, and fluid low in Na to advance to the previously demonstrated distal tubular site of K secretion. Samples collected following the second occlusion failed to show a distal secretory K peak. This observation stresses the importance of intratubular Na for the distal Na-K exchange mechanism. The possibility that depression of K secretion is caused by the rapidly repeated ureteral occlusions was excluded: if 8 ml of fluid were collected between occlusions, fluid containing Na and K minima was allowed to escape, and the Na concentration once again was raised at the K secretory site. Such a procedure consistently led to the reappearance of the secretory K peak. However, the importance of intratubular Na is minimized by Sullivan (383), Malvin (267), and Aukland & Kiil (5), who believe their stop-flow experiments indicate that the presence of an increased Na concentration in the distal parts of the nephron had little effect on the minimum K concentration achieved in the stop-flow pattern.

Herrin & Corlett (171) studied the effects of controlled hypotension and simultaneous NaCl infusion on the K excretion pattern. From the observation that K excretion rate was markedly reduced in the presence of still-significant Na excretion, it was felt that increased Na reabsorption, typical for conditions of reduced filtration rate, was not the only factor curtailing K secretion under these experimental conditions. On the other hand, the authors concur with Davidson *et al.* (88) that an elevation of the rate of Na excretion reduces the effect of hypotension on K clearance. No explanation is offered as to what other factors might influence K secretion.

Permeability characteristics of the nephron.—A number of papers concerned with permeability properties of various tubular segments are of interest since such passive permeability characteristics, and not only active transport functions, affect the distribution of urinary constituents at various tubular sites. Evidence is available that the proximal tubular epithelium permits rapid equilibration of water. Such high permeability is essential for about three-quarters of the filtered water to be conserved as a consequence of solute movement. Water and Na exchange in renal tubular fluid has been studied by White and his associates (435, 436). In the first of these studies, tritium-labeled water and Na^{22} were infused at various time intervals after urine flow had been stopped, and specific activity was measured in tissue and urine after reinstatement of free-flow conditions. Evidence was obtained for a slow rate of labeling of renal medullary, as compared with cortical, tissue. From the failure of collecting duct water and Na to come into isotopic equilibrium with medullary water and Na, it was concluded that the collecting duct wall is a tubular site of increased resistance to the diffusion of tritiated water and Na^{22}. On the other hand, proximal transtubular Na exchange was rapid and could be augmented by administration of a mercurial diuretic (435). This latter finding is interpreted as explaining diminished proximal net Na reabsorption after administration of mercurial diuretics. Also, data obtained by stop-flow analysis indicate that nonelectrolyte solutes equilibrate faster across the proximal tubular epithelium than across more distal regions of the nephron (322). Amiel *et al.* (1) have also studied the kinetics of ionic exchanges between interstitial and intratubular fluid. They injected isotopes of Na, K, and Cl, together with glomerular indicators, intravenously during stopped urine flow. From their relative appearance rate in postocclusion urine samples, it was concluded that there are distinctive tubular regions of the nephron with typical permeability characteristics for each ion species. Thus it was shown that the distal reabsorptive area for Na has a high permeability for K, a low permeability for Cl, and virtually none for Na. An area more proximal to this is characterized by a high permeability for Na and Cl and is tentatively identified with Henle's loop. It is stressed by Amiel *et al.* that filtration continues slowly during the stop-flow period but that this process does not affect the "distal" urine samples.

Little is known about the permeability characteristics of the descending limb of Henle's loop, but it is likely that in antidiuresis it shares the properties of the proximal tubule (148, 310). The urinary dilution occurring in the ascending limb of Henle's loop is generally believed to be determined by active Na extrusion and low water permeability.

Considerable evidence has led to the conclusion that antidiuretic hormone enhances water permeability across the distal tubule and the collecting ducts (189, 190). Localization of I^{131}-labeled Pitressin in rat kidneys by autoradiography has supported the view of a site of action at the distal convoluted tubule and the collecting ducts (86). Recent studies on the distribution of urea, thiourea, and sucrose in the dog kidney during antidiuresis indicate that the collecting duct epithelium is permeable to these substances, all of which accumulate by passive diffusion and countercurrent exchange trapping in the renal medulla (46, 213). Further, it has been proved that antidiuretic hormone is also important in determining permeability to urea in the terminal part of the nephron (46, 189). Thus this hormone participates in the urea-mediated enhancement of water reabsorption in the renal tubule (189, 356). Vasopressin has recently been shown to increase the equivalent pore radius of kidney slices from *Necturus*, thus again indicating its direct action on the renal tubule to increase water permeability (438). This action is counteracted by Ca. A study of renal transtubular movement of some divalent ions by Bronner & Thompson (50) has shown that both Ca and Sr reach the urine partly by transtubular influx; this is true only to a much smaller extent for Mg and phosphate.

Two important new developments, both concerned with the mode of action of vasopressin, should be noted. Orloff & Handler (312) have presented evidence, obtained in experiments on the isolated toad bladder, that vasopressin exerts its effect on water permeability by stimulating the production and accumulation of cyclic adenosine-3',5'-phosphate. This compound mimics the effects of vasopressin in the toad-bladder preparation. The second contribution is a series of papers by Schwartz *et al.* (359), Rasmussen *et al.* (335), and Fong *et al.* (119). Again, use was made of the isolated toad bladder, and it was shown that the formation of a covalent bond is an essential step in the interaction of vasopressin and a tissue receptor. Fixation of vasopressin in the tissue and the subsequent specific hormonal effect of increased water permeability depend on the presence of an accessible SH-group in the bladder tissue and the formation of a hormone-receptor disulfide bond. Extension of these studies to the kidney is expected.

ADRENAL STEROIDS AND TUBULAR FUNCTION

A most important recent development is the recognition that the kidney itself is a site of origin for an aldosterone-stimulating material. Also, the renin-angiotensin system and the juxtaglomerular cell apparatus and their possible role in regulating the secretion of aldosterone have received renewed attention. Substantial evidence had previously indicated that the immediate stimulus to aldosterone production is humoral. Although the role of ACTH in promoting aldosterone secretion is recognized, it has become evident that there exists an aldosterone-stimulating agent whose origin is outside of the pituitary. Indirect evidence for such a material was recently presented by Orti & Ralli (313) who recovered a substance from the urine of hypophysectomized-adrenalectomized rats which induced Na retention in normal, but not in adrenalectomized animals. This problem has been investigated more directly by Mulrow & Ganong (293, 125) and by Davis *et al.* (90). Both groups used acute hemorrhage as stimulus for the release of aldosterone. Mulrow & Ganong show that in the normal dog, acute hemorrhage causes the release of ACTH which stimulates both glucocorticoid and aldosterone secretion. In hypophysectomized dogs, however, a mechanism independent of the pituitary stimulates the appearance of aldosterone in the adrenal vein. Concerning the site of origin of a humoral agent promoting aldosterone release, Davis *et al.* (90) investigated several possibilities; they concur with Mulrow & Ganong as to its extrapituitary origin. Decapitated, bled dogs showed an increase in aldosterone secretion almost as great as in normal dogs, a finding which points to an extracranial site. Failure of hepatectomy to interfere with the appearance of aldosterone, on the one hand, and failure of nephrectomized dogs to respond to acute hemorrhage by an increase in aldosterone production, on the other, were taken as evidence for a renal site of origin. This was supported by the striking increase in aldosterone production observed after the infusion of a saline extract of kidney tissues into hypophysectomized-nephrectomized dogs. The role of the kidney in the release of an aldosterone-stimulating agent was also stressed by Mulrow & Ganong (293) who reported the failure of nephrectomized animals to promote aldosterone release subsequent to bleeding. Although it is not established that angiotensin II is the renal aldosterone-stimulating agent, both Mulrow & Ganong (294) as well as Davis *et al.* (90) present corroborative evidence. Angiotensin I is a decapeptide, formed *in vivo* by the action of the renal enzyme renin on the α_2-globulin fraction of blood. It is under the action of a converting enzyme that angiotensin I is transformed into the potent pressor octapeptide angiotensin II. Mulrow & Ganong (294) report that infusion of angiotensin II produces not only a pressor response but also an increase in aldosterone secretion. Since this observation also holds in the hypophysectomized, nephrectomized dog, the possibility that angiotensin II acts via the pituitary is clearly excluded.

Several papers have dealt with the effects of renin and angiotensin on renal electrolyte transport and, in general, confirm their possible role as aldosterone-stimulating agents. Biron *et al.* (27) injected angiotensin II into normal men and describe subsequent Na retention, a marked decrease in urine volume, and a fall in the urinary Na-to-K ratio. Simultaneously with the pressor effect there occurred an augmentation of aldosterone release as indicated by its increase in urinary excretion rate. The Na retention may also have been caused by some fall in GFR, but a direct renal tubular action of angiotensin II is unlikely in view of the recent observation by Leyssac *et al.* (259) that angiotensin produces a powerful reduction of active Na transport in kidney slices. Laragh (238) also observed that angiotensin II uniformly increased the rate of aldosterone secretion. These data support the thesis that a renal-adrenal system is involved in regulation of the aldosterone output. In another study, Schröder *et al.* (357) compared the effects of angiotensin, renin, and vasopressin on electrolyte and water excretion in rats. All of them were effective in reversing a water diuresis, but promoted natriuresis when salt was given. The mechanism of this phenomenon is not clear, but a precise assessment of intrarenal hemodynamics under the various experimental conditions may be rewarding. In the experiments of Schröder *et al.* (357), renin and angiotensin showed no effects on electrolyte transport in the absence of pressor effects. This remains fundamental to the evaluation of these agents as possible physiological mediators, since many stimuli which increase aldosterone secretion are not associated with pressor effects (294).

Tobian (399) has discussed the possibility that a decreased volume or pressure in the afferent arterioles might be the stimulus for release of renin by the juxtaglomerular cell apparatus. Such a mechanism could be effective during hemorrhage. An extensive and detailed survey by Page & Bumpus (316) presents current views of the properties of angiotensin, and a number of papers have appeared on the role of angiotensin, aldosterone and other humoral factors in the pathogenesis of hypertension (52, 129, 239, 240, 291).

Some important papers on the factors controlling the release of aldosterone are as follows. Bartter and his associates (123, 124) have reviewed some of the hemodynamic parameters promoting aldosterone secretion and stressed particularly the effectiveness of a decreased pulse pressure. Farrell (116) has discussed the somewhat controversial role of the epiphysis cerebri in the control of steroid secretion, and Davis (89) has written a clear and comprehensive account of the role of aldosterone in the mechanism of salt and water retention in congestive heart failure. General reviews of the physiological and pathophysiological role of aldosterone are those of Gross (152) and Laragh (238).

The mechanism of the renal action of adrenal steroids has received attention. Doubt is expressed by Berlin *et al.* (22) as to whether aldosterone normally plays an important part in the acute, minute-to-minute regulation of Na excretion. These investigators studied the renal response to a changeover from saline to water loading and compared the behavior of normal and adrenalectomized dogs. Normally a marked increase in water and decrease in Na excretion follows. This response was the same before and after adrenalectomy, provided that replacement therapy with cortisone acetate and deoxycorticosterone acetate was adequate. Hydrocortisone alone restored the water excretion pattern to normal but not the Na response, and the con-

stant infusion of aldosterone alone was also ineffective in restoring the Na
excretion pattern to normal although this steroid lowered the initial excretion
rate. It was concluded that the role of the adrenal steroids, under the experimental conditions chosen, was permissive in that an adequate steroid level
conditioned the renal tubule to the adaptive response, but that acute changes
in the renal handling of Na and water were not mediated by a sudden increase in adrenal cortical secretion. The long latency of an aldosterone-effect
on the kidney argues for this interpretation. On the other hand, Bojesen &
Degn (32) indicate that the mechanism by which aldosterone secretion is
regulated operates with the latency of a few minutes, at least in relation to
changes in the circulating blood volume. Levels of circulating aldosterone
were measured in peripheral blood after a decrease in blood volume, and a
prompt increase in circulating hormone was observed. Thus, the long delay
of the aldosterone effect may occur at the renal level.

There is good evidence that aldosterone and other mineralocorticoids
stimulate a tubular exchange process involving Na and K. This view has
been reconfirmed by Cade & Shalhoub (55) who studied the relationship between Na load and K excretion during the infusion of sodium sulfate. It was
observed that in dogs and human subjects with intact adrenal function, K
excretion was directly proportional to Na load, a finding in agreement with
the proposed Na-K exchange (23). No such relationship was found in untreated adrenal insufficiency, which was characterized by direct proportion-
ality between K excretion and filtered K load. Only under such conditions
does excreted K seem to be derived from filtered load and incomplete reabsorption. Since the proposed Na-K exchange mechanism is located at a distal
tubular site, it seems certain that some mineralocorticoid effects are also
mediated at this tubular segment. Further evidence of a distal effect of
mineralocorticoids on Na reabsorption is found in the studies of Vander *et al.*
(413) and of Williamson *et al.* (443), both of which utilized the stop-flow
approach. Vander *et al.* (412) also attempted to use their stop-flow data for
a Michaelis-Menten analysis, and argue that aldosterone increases the number of distal tubular carrier sites.

The acute effects of adrenal steroids in adrenalectomized dogs were investigated by Slater *et al.* (368). Intravenous infusion of cortisol, prednisolone,
and adrenal cortical extract usually increased GFR. In the case of cortisol and
prednisolone, urinary Na output increased, but this action was clearly dependent upon augmentation of filtration rate. Aldosterone, adrenal cortical
extract, and cortisol led to Na retention, and all steroids increased K excretion. The differential effects of intravenously administered aldosterone and
hydrocortisone on renal electrolyte excretion were also studied by Mills *et al.*
(281), who worked on recumbent human subjects in whom the urine is commonly alkaline. The authors demonstrated conclusively that cortisol stimulates mainly the Na-K exchange mechanism, whereas aldosterone stimulates
not only Na reabsorption in association with Cl, but also augments Na reab-

sorption in exchange for K and H. No effects of aldosterone on GFR were observed. Similar observations indicating that the effects of aldosterone on Na-K exchange may be dissociated from the major action of the hormone, which is NaCl retention, were made by Sonnenblick *et al.* (373) in humans receiving aldosterone intravenously.

A number of other papers have appeared which also suggest that the effects of aldosterone extend beyond selective stimulation of Na-K exchange. Thus, Cheek & Holt (69) compared the effects of aldosterone in young and adult mice. They observed a loss of Na, Cl, and K in young saline-loaded animals, while older animals (150 days) showed a tendency to retain Na and water. It is suggested that in young animals, at least, aldosterone does not augment Na-K exchange; an independent effect on the movement of these ions is postulated. Also, the possibility that a changing steroid pattern with age is responsible for the apparently opposite effects of aldosterone in young and adult animals is considered. A somewhat related phenomenon may be the clinical observation of unresponsiveness, in early infancy, to salt-retaining hormones such as aldosterone and deoxycorticosterone (DOCA) in cases of apparent transient adrenal insufficiency (252).

Uete & Venning (406) also present evidence for an antagonistic effect of cortisone, hydrocortisone, and 9α-fluoro-16α-OH-hydrocortisone on the action of DOCA and aldosterone with respect to Na retention. All of the steroids, however, facilitated the excretion of K in the adrenalectomized mouse. Since GFR was not measured in either of these studies, the role of the tubular Na load at a distal exchange site cannot be evaluated properly. Uete & Venning correctly point out that the antagonistic effect of some steroids may be the consequence of an augmented filtration rate, the latter offsetting the tendency for increased Na reabsorption.

In studies on the isolated perfused cat kidney, Davey & Lockett (87) have concluded that the renal effects of aldosterone in stimulating Na reabsorption and K secretion are not mediated in a simple manner. In the isolated perfused cat kidney, aldosterone caused an increase in renal blood flow, concomitant with retention of Na, K, and Cl, or even an increase in NaCl and K excretion. The latter effect was observed when the head was included in the circulation during the bleeding and operative preparation, and is thought to have been caused by the interaction of oxytocin with aldosterone. This study indicates that there is still considerable uncertainty as to what factors affect the renal tubular activity of aldosterone. The marked hemodynamic effects of aldosterone in this study, quite uncommon *in vivo*, make an evaluation of this observation difficult.

The effects of adrenalectomy and aldosterone on electrolyte metabolism of rat renal cortex slices were studied by Crabbé & Nichols (80). Neither adrenalectomy nor the presence of aldosterone, added to the incubating medium or given *in vivo*, had any effect on tissue composition with regard to Na, K, or water. These findings suggest that changes in the rate of Na transport across tubular cells, induced by adrenal steroids, need not be reflected in a change of tissue electrolyte composition. On the other hand, adrenalectomy decreased ammonia production and oxygen consumption. While this effect upon ammonia production could be reversed by aldosterone, this was not so in the case of the depression of oxygen uptake.

Antagonists of aldosterone.—The most important of the antagonists of aldosterone is a group of compounds structurally related to aldosterone and characterized by a spirolactone configuration at position 17 of the steroid molecule. The generic term "spirolactones" is usually applied to the entire group. The mode of action of these substances has been reviewed recently by Kagawa (194), who first described these steroid derivatives, and by Streeten (379), Krück & Hild (228), Gantt (126), and Coppage & Liddle (74). A monograph on the clinical use of aldosterone antagonists has also appeared (460). Coppage & Liddle summarized the generally accepted view that the spirolactones affect renal electrolyte metabolism purely by antagonizing the renal tubular action of aldosterone or similar mineralocorticoids. This conclusion is based on the following observations. Spirolactones have no effect on urinary electrolytes in the absence of mineralocorticoids, as demonstrated in experiments on adrenalectomized animals or patients with Addison's disease. Thus, administration of spirolactones interferes with the effects of DOCA or aldosterone, as was recently confirmed by Bailey (7) in the adrenalectomized, water-loaded rat. Furthermore, the electrolyte excretion pattern produced by spirolactones is quite similar to that resulting from aldosterone withdrawal: increased Na and Cl excretion and decreased renal excretion of K are observed. Finally, the spirolactones do not directly affect GFR nor do they interfere with adrenal steroid synthesis.

The effect of Aldactone, an aldosterone antagonist, on the renal response to Na restriction was the topic of a study in man by Ross & Winternitz (349). The time period until Na excretion fell to 50 per cent of control levels after the withdrawal of dietary Na was markedly prolonged when the aldosterone antagonist was administered. Thus, the kidney retained some ability to conserve Na independent of aldosterone. Although not measured, one first considers the possibility of a fall in filtration rate as the most likely mechanism of such residual renal adaptation to dietary Na restriction.

Recently, Mills *et al.* (282) briefly reported the interesting observation that Aldactone blocked the Na retention, commonly observed after cortisol administration, but left the enhanced K excretion rate unchanged. Since cortisol, as previously pointed out, predominantly stimulates Na-K exchange, this experimental dissociation of the hormone effect upon Na and K transfer is of considerable interest.

Heparin has also been shown by Majoor *et al.* (264) to have an aldosterone-inhibiting action. An increased output of Na, Cl, and water and a diminution of aldosterone secretion were found in patients during heparin therapy. The exact site of action of the drug is not known.

DIURESIS

Factors affecting the diuretic response to water.—Previous observations that water diuresis is blunted in the absence of an intact adrenal cortex have been confirmed. Kennedy (201) studied the effect of adrenal steroids upon the excretion of a hypotonic urine in the hypophysectomized-adrenalectomized rat. It was concluded that both the failure of distal tubular reabsorption of Na and a fall in GFR contributed to the reduction of the formation of osmotically free water. While cortisone alone only caused a small and transient increase in the urinary output of these doubly-operated rats, full polyuria was restored only by treatment with cortisone and DOCA. Aldosterone was ineffective.

However, Sonnenblick *et al.* (373) have recently presented evidence that in man aldosterone plays a role in urinary dilution. Intravenous administration of this steroid in water-loaded individuals led, after the typical delay period of 20 to 60 minutes, to Na retention and increased K excretion, and to an enhancement of free water clearance as the urine became more dilute, suggesting that this hormone action takes place in the tubule at a site distal to that of isosmotic fluid reabsorption. Again, it was noted that the hormone effect on NaCl reabsorption is dissociated from the effect on K excretion. The latter had frequently ceased before Na retention had reached its peak. This may mean that tubular Na reabsorption is augmented by aldosterone at a site proximal to that of Na-K exchange. Such increased Na reabsorption would limit its availability at the more distally located tubular exchange site.

Anisosmotic reabsorption of solutes was evaluated by Schück *et al.* (358), under conditions of submaximal water diuresis. Expressions are derived which divide distal tubular Na reabsorption into a fraction of Na transfer associated with Cl, and into an exchange fraction with other cations, i.e. H and K.

Kleeman and his associates (217) have continued their studies on the mechanism of impaired water excretion in adrenal and pituitary insufficiency. They conclude that this functional lesion is not caused by altered renal hemodynamics, changed solute excretion, or abnormal release of antidiuretic hormone. It is submitted that glucocorticoids directly affect the diluting nephron segment. This thesis is based on the failure of unspecific factors which increase RBF, GFR, or solute excretion to equal the efficacy with which glucocorticoids enhance the excretory response to ingested water. Another study by this group (218) indicates that in normal individuals acute and chronic administration of glucocorticoids does not alter the release, inactivation, or mode of action of antidiuretic hormone (ADH). The specific effect of glucocorticoids in promoting diminished back-diffusion of water in the distal nephron (in the absence of ADH) is not clear. Redistribution of solute load between proximal and distal tubular segments or diminished water permeability has been suggested. In view of recent recognition of the renal medullary circulation as important in determining urinary osmolality, the possibility of a redistribution of blood flow within the kidney under the influence of various adrenocortical hormones should be considered.

Lindeman et al. (261) agree with Kleeman et al. (217) that in man cortisol increases free water clearance out of all proportion to its effect on total solute excretion. After administration of progesterone, estrogen, aldosterone, or an aldosterone antagonist, or after maintenance on a low-Na diet, the maximal rate of free water clearance was always directly related to variations in solute excretion. Only cortisol changed this relationship, leading to the formation of a disproportionately dilute urine. The decrease in free water clearance observed after infusion of a submaximal dose of vasopressin was unchanged by any of the compounds mentioned. This provides evidence against a direct antagonism between adrenal steroids and vasopressin.

Burg et al. (53) have carefully re-investigated some of the factors affecting the diuretic response to ingested water. Water diuresis in normal adults was induced and examined during changes in posture, during infusion of hypotonic Na salts, and during mannitol and urea diuresis. This experimental design permitted a dissociation of Na excretion from total solute excretion. It was observed that the free water clearance was more closely related to Na excretion than to that of other solutes. It was concluded that changes in free water clearance are principally conditioned by changes in distal reabsorption of Na salts concurrent with the release of osmotically free water. Papper et al. (319) point out that the decrease in water diuresis which occurs after sedative drugs or analgesics are given (such as meperidine or secobarbital) may also be caused by diminished delivery of solute to the distal site of free water formation. A reduction of filtration rate and of distal tubular Na load is the most likely explanation for such curtailment of free water clearance.

Jaenicke & Waterhouse (193) have undertaken a study of the unresponsiveness of the kidney to exogenous vasopressin during sustained overhydration, achieved by high water intake and vasopressin administration. The renal concentrating ability was significantly impaired, and the lack of correlation between solute excretion and urinary osmolality suggests that changes in distal tubular solute load were not the cause for diminished urinary concentrating ability. No data are presently available which permit a decision as to whether reduced water permeability of the distal renal tubular segment or diminished medullary tonicity is the underlying mechanism for this vasopressin insensitivity.

However, a recent study by Hays & Leaf (164), carried out on the toad bladder in vitro, strongly suggests that dilution per se may inhibit the effectiveness of vasopressin. Dilution of the bathing solutions, while maintaining identical osmotic gradients across the toad bladder, significantly reduced the effect of added vasopressin. Augmentation of water movement under identical osmotic driving forces was smaller when total osmolarity was lowered. This may play an important role during the state of insensitivity to vasopressin whenever the extracellular fluids are abnormally dilute. It is interesting that urinary acidity also affects the sensitivity of the renal tubular apparatus to vasopressin: Czaczkes *et al.* (85) report on a diminished antidiuretic response in diabetes insipidus during infusion of sodium bicarbonate, an effect not related to variations in solute load.

Some factors depressing tubular sodium chloride transfer.—A number of conditions have recently been recognized to interfere with the accumulation of Na salts in the renal medulla. This functional lesion is caused by diminished active Na transport in the ascending limb of Henle's loop and in the collecting duct. Frequently, a urinary concentrating defect develops. However, alterations in tubular water permeability and changes in renal medullary blood flow may also contribute to the observed relative medullary and urinary hypotonicity.

One condition which is characterized by a urinary concentrating defect is that of K deficiency. Discussions on the possible mechanisms underlying this functional disturbance are those of Leaf & Santos (251), Lambie (234), Kerpel-Fronius (205), and Holliday (179, 181); and some of the morphological alterations have been studied by Spargo *et al.* (376). The recent observation by Manitius *et al.* (269), in K-depleted rats, of a marked impairment of renal papillary hypertonicity was confirmed by Eigler *et al.* (107). Woods *et al.* (452) have made the important observation that the susceptibility to experimental pyelonephritis is increased in K deficiency. These authors suggest that tubular obstruction or "internal hydronephrosis", morphological changes frequently found, predisposes to infection. Blythe *et al.* (31) also showed that the urinary concentrating defect in K depletion is not caused by excessive water intake since the inability to concentrate the urine maximally was equally exhibited by two groups of animals, one of which had its water intake restricted.

Although, as pointed out, the inability of the kidneys to excrete a maximally concentrated urine may be partly caused by diminished water permeability of the distal tubule and collecting ducts, the important role of impaired active medullary Na transport is well recognized and is consistent with the observation that reduction of extracellular K also depresses Na extrusion from muscle, nerve, and erythrocytes (410). Also, net Na transport is diminished in the frog skin (223, 410) and toad bladder (164) whenever the K concentration in the bathing solution is reduced. A coupled Na-K pump (410) and a limiting energy barrier caused by increased steepness of the electrical gradient (73, 482) by lowering K_0 are possible mechanisms both of which may be affected by low extracellular K in such a way as to diminish active Na transport.

The importance of renal medullary Na transport in the elaboration of a hypertonic urine is also demonstrated by the observation of Baker *et al.* (8) that experimental Na depletion by peritoneal dialysis with Na-free solutions in the rat leads to severe, but reversible impairment of maximum urinary concentrating ability. Sodium restriction by feeding a low-Na diet was not effective. The mechanism of this functional lesion is not entirely clear. The role of an undoubtedly reduced GFR, and the subsequent curtailment of distal Na load, must be prominent. Thus, it seems probable that the interstitial fluid of the renal medulla and papilla of these hyponatremic rats is less highly concentrated. Alterations in renal medullary blood flow and diminished Na transport are likely causes of the reduced concentration of Na in renal papillary tissue. Goldsmith *et al.* (143) have reported on a similar study in the dog. While maximum urinary concentrating ability was only moderately impaired in dogs kept on a low-Na diet, GFR was uniformly lower and free-water clearance depressed. At moderate urine flow rates, hypotonic urine was formed. These authors feel that in their type of Na depletion, the defect in urinary concentration is caused by the failure of distal tubular fluid to equilibrate to isotonicity before reaching the collecting duct. Kerpel-Fronius *et al.* (205) also concluded that Na depletion reduces GFR and concentrating ability. They also observed refractoriness in both Na and K deficiency to exogenous vasopressin.

The effects of prolonged hypercalcemia in man were studied by Gill & Bartter (135) who confirmed previous observations of reduced solute-free water abstraction in hydropenia. It is known that this lesion is also associated with decreased medullary Na and solute content (270). Within this context, the observation should be recalled that Ca excess antagonizes the effect of vasopressin in augmenting the estimated equivalent pore size of renal tubular epithelium in *Necturus* (438). Zeffren & Heinemann (458) also studied the effects of hypercalcemia on the renal concentrating mechanism in man, and concur that insensitivity to vasopressin, as well as changes in intramedullary osmolality, is important. The concentrating defect seems to be independent of alterations in GFR.

Wijdeveld & Jansen (441) have reported a temporary impairment of renal concentrating capacity in hyperthyroidism combined with hypercalcemia. The defect seemed not to be caused by decreased filtration rate, changed osmotic load, or diminished vasopressin output. It was felt that hypercalcemia was not a causative factor. These authors suggest that the increase in cardiac output in hyperthyroidism may increase the blood flow in the vasa recta and thus limit the efficiency of the countercurrent diffusion mechanism. On the other hand, the disturbed utilization of oxygen in hyperthyroidism may also limit the Na transport mechanism which is responsible for the countercurrent multiplication function of Henle's loop.

The change in the distal tubular system which leads to the excretion of a relatively dilute urine after transitory ureteral obstruction has not been fully elucidated although some derangement in the Na transport system seems likely. The problem was investigated by Kessler (207) and Jaenicke & Bray (192); and a clinical case, closely resembling the experimental conditions, was reported by Mees (274). Acute temporary ureteral obstruction leads to the production of less concentrated urine on the experimental side, and to reduction of the Na, Cl, and urea concentration in the papillary tissue. Kessler (207) found that administration of vasopressin to saline-loaded dogs prevented or corrected the reduction of medullary Cl concentration which otherwise developed during ureteral obstruction. While the concentrating ability after ureteral clamping in untreated animals may be impaired over a time period of several hours, injection of vasopressin led to complete recovery in concentrating ability concomitant with reestablishment of renal medullary hypertonicity. On the basis of available data it is not possible to decide whether this action of vasopressin is ascribable to a diminished medullary blood flow leading to increased solute trapping, or to a direct effect of vasopressin on renal medullary Na transport.

   Mercurial diuretics.—The recent review by Orloff & Berliner (310) gives an up-to-date coverage of the mechanism of action of these diuretic compounds, as does the survey by Pitts (324, 480). Kessler (208) deals with the clinical pharmacology of organomercurial diuretics. Two aspects of the mode of action of mercurial diuretics have received noteworthy attention: first, the mechanism of renal tubular binding; and second, the tubular site of action.

   Farah & Kruse (114) have proposed that mercurial diuretics act by attaching to two adjacent molecular binding sites. While the nature of one of these is unknown, strong evidence is presented which indicates that the other tubular receptor site is a protein-bound sulfhydryl group. The observation that nondiuretic mercurials will block protein-bound sulfhydryl groups as diuretic compounds do is taken as evidence that a second point of attachment must also be required for a mercurial compound to produce diuresis. The thesis is advanced that only if a sulfhydryl radical is available for attachment by the mercurial diuretic compound can binding to the proposed second group take place. It is of considerable interest that Miller & Farah (279), in a short communication, have reported blocking of the diuretic effect of a mercurial diuretic by the previous administration of *p*-chloromercuribenzoate, a potent inhibitor of sulfhydryl-dependent enzymes *in vitro*. Chlorothiazide or NaCl diuresis was unaffected by the inhibitor. This finding supports the original thesis by Farah & Kruse (114) that blocking of the SH-groups by a nondiuretic sulfhydryl inhibitor prevents the association of an effective mercurial with an adjacent receptor site. It is this latter site which is believed to be related to tubular ion reabsorption. Protein-bound sulfhydryl inhibition induced by mercurial diuretics is further reported by Farah & Kruse to be increased by acidosis and decreased by alkalosis, a finding interpreted as compatible with the thesis by Levy, Weiner & Mudge (257, 290) that mercuric ions are the active form of mercurial diuretics.

   Campbell (58, 59 ,60) observed in the chicken that bromocresol green and probenecid both suppress excess Hg excretion and solute diuresis which normally follow administration of many mercurial diuretics. It is argued that these compounds prevent the uptake of Hg from the blood by a process of competitive inhibition at a binding site which belongs to the hippurate transport system. The situation in the chicken is thus apparently different from that in the dog in which the secretory mechanisms for PAH and organomercurials are both located in the proximal tubule, but are not the same (209).

Several recent papers deal with attempts to localize the tubular site of action of mercurial diuretics. This topic, in the absence of direct studies by tubular puncture, is still controversial (see also 310). Although there is evidence of some proximal suppression of tubular Na reabsorption, the degree of participation of a distal tubular action of organic mercurial diuretics is not clear. Lambie & Robson (235) and Au & Raisz (3) have studied the effect of mercurial diuretics on the renal tubular reabsorption of solute-free water (T^cH_2O, negative free water clearance) in hydropenic man. Both concluded that at comparable flow rates the urine during mercurial diuresis was less concentrated than during osmotic diuresis. This reduction of T^cH_2O is attributed to inhibition of Na transport in the loop of Henle.

In a similar study in hydropenic man, Porush et al. (328) observed that after administration of mercurial diuretics T^cH_2O remained constant at the very level which obtained prior to development of the saluresis. They point out that the appearance of a renal concentrating defect depends upon the initial rate of solute excretion: persistence of a low T^cH_2O under conditions of low solute excretion may reflect an apparent defect in the renal concentrating ability. Constancy of T^cH_2O under conditions of high solute excretion, on the other hand, explains the absence of an apparent concentrating defect in many reported experiments. A further observation was that during mercurial diuresis T^cH_2O could be increased significantly when solute excretion was initially relatively low and an osmotic diuretic was administered. This observation led the authors to argue against a reabsorption block at the level of the loop of Henle since, as increasing quantities of NaCl are presented during osmotic diuresis, more salt is still reabsorbed and solute-free water reabsorption is effectively augmented. Evidence that mercurials do not act at Henle's loop is also found in the fact that, at high rates of solute excretion, T^cH_2O does not fall when a mercurial diuretic is given. Since a proximal tubular effect is also unlikely in the absence of any significant increase in T^cH_2O, it is suggested that the major effect of organomercurials occurs distal to the loop of Henle.

Goldstein et al. (144) in a study of effects of meralluride have also found that, in hydrated man, nonspecific solute diuresis induced by mannitol, sulfate, urea, or aminophylline consistently led to an increase in free water clearance as the osmolar clearance rose. Intravenous administration of meralluride caused a two-phase response. A first phase was characterized by a prompt increase in C_{H_2O} and C_{osm}, an effect which was largely dissipated after 60 min. Thereafter, identical increments of urine volume and C_{osm} occurred, thus resulting in virtually identical values of free water clearance when compared to those calculated during preinjection control values. However, a nonspecific solute diuresis, induced at this time, was still effective in augmenting the excretion of solute-free water, indicating the ability of distal portions of the nephron to reabsorb increased amounts of electrolyte from the larger load of isosmotic fluid presented to them. The first phase of the meralluride response is thought to be caused by the theophylline component and by increased delivery of proximal fluid to the distal tubule. This is an important observation. It might explain previous discrepancies in interpretation in those instances where theophylline-containing mixtures of mercurial diuretics were given. Two alternate hypotheses are presented to explain the delayed phase of meralluride diuresis. The first proposes a reduction in both proximal and distal solute reabsorption, the latter just sufficient to neutralize the increment in free water clearance produced by isosmotic proximal solute diuresis. The second, favored by the authors, suggests a major meralluride action in a segment distal to that where formation of solute-free water occurs, assuming that salt and water absorption is suppressed there in relatively isosmotic proportions. It should be realized that such a process envisages the abstraction of an isosmotic fluid from distal tubular fluid of variable hypotonicity.

Miller & Riggs (280) have studied mercurial diuresis in dogs with diabetes insipidus undergoing a maintained maximal water diuresis. Mercaptomerin increased urine flow but produced little or no change in free water excretion. This observation is thus in agreement with that of Goldstein *et al.* (144), but Miller & Riggs assign a more important role to proximal tubular inhibition of solute reabsorption in the developing mercurial diuresis. They also observed a consistent fall in urinary pH during mercurial diuresis, an effect possibly related to a distal tubular action. A more acid urine would be formed if the mercurial diuretic were to block K secretion without directly affecting the transport system for which H and K normally compete.

Chlorothiazide.—The renal effects of chlorothiazide, particularly its tubular site of action, have been the topic of a similar approach. Earley *et al.* (103) have studied the effects of this heterocyclic sulfonamide on urinary dilution and concentration in the dog. They also have briefly reported on the antidiuretic action of this compound in diabetes insipidus (102). During water diuresis, chlorothiazide elicits an immediate fall in free water clearance, a finding consistent with the premise that it increases electrolyte excretion by interference with NaCl reabsorption in those distal tubular segments where urinary dilution takes place. In the hydropenic dog, chlorothiazide does not lower solute-free water reabsorption, but uniformly increases values for T^cH_2O at rates of osmolal clearance at which, in the absence of this drug, T^cH_2O usually decreases. This effect is thought to result from diminished dilution of the tubular fluid in the distal tubule, thus allowing passive osmotic equilibration to occur more readily. Absence of a reduction of T^cH_2O suggests that this compound acts in the distal convolution rather than in the ascending limb of Henle's loop. It should be noted that this interpretation differs from that arrived at previously by stop-flow analysis. Kessler *et al.* (210), Vander *et al.* (411) and, more recently, Spencer (377) have argued that in view of an increase in the concentration of NaCl in proximal stop-flow samples, the primary effect of chlorothiazide on Na reabsorption is in the proximal tubule.

Earley & Orloff (102) suggest that the antidiuretic action of hydrochlorothiazide in diabetes insipidus, first demonstrated by Crawford & Kennedy (81), is brought about also by distal tubular interference with NaCl reabsorption. It is submitted that the ensuing Na deficit limits the volume of filtrate reaching the distal nephron, thus resulting in the formation of a lower urine volume with increased osmolality. It is of particular interest that once a Na deficit had been produced, increased urine osmolality was maintained without further administration of the drug. The problem of a possible interaction between chlorothiazide and adrenal steroids is discussed by Kennedy (202) and by Kennedy & Crawford (203).

Some actions of chlorothiazide, such as renal K loss, are enhanced by increased secretion of aldosterone. Thus, Gannt & Synek (127) have recently reported that K excretion after hydrochlorothiazide in adrenalectomized rats was uniformly augmented by small amounts of DOCA. The K loss is believed to result from inhibition of Na reabsorption by hydrochlorothiazide at some site proximal to that of K secretion. Thus, an increased Na load is delivered to the distal Na-K exchange site where aldosterone or DOCA stimulates the cationic exchange process. The increase in K excretion with larger doses by hydrochlorothiazide is in all likelihood related to carbonic anhydrase inhibition.

Some Factors Regulating Renal Electrolyte Transport

Space permits only brief comment on studies dealing with the role of various parts of the central nervous system in salt and water excretion. Wise & Ganong (449) studied the effects of ablation of the area postrema on electrolyte excretion, and present evidence that this medullary brainstem area is part of a reflex mechanism which, when stimulated by hypertonic saline injection, leads to increase in Na excretion. Zaretskii *et al.* (456) have investigated renal function after injury to the thalamohypothalamic region of the brain and observed a number of reversible alterations in GFR, RBF, and urea excretion. Földi and his associates (118) described a reflex increase of Na excretion, elicited by posterior pituitary extract in dogs with crossed circulation allowing the hormone to gain access only to the head of the experimental animal and not to the trunk. They also have summarized their work on the role of a central Na-sensitive receptor (117). An increase in Na concentration, limited to the intracranial circulation (crossed circulation, nervous connection to trunk of experimental animal only), caused an increase in renal Na excretion which could occur in the absence of changes in GFR. Alterations in the secretion rate of aldosterone are thought to be involved, but no direct measurements of the hormone level were performed. A number of papers have appeared dealing with the afferent and efferent impulse traffic of renal nerves (96, 457). Interesting observations relating renal water and electrolyte excretion to central nervous function were recently discussed in a symposium published in book form (475), and in a number of other papers (97, 111, 168, 457).

Horster *et al.* (183) report on the effects of venous congestion in the head region of rats on electrolyte excretion, and Herken *et al.* (170) present evidence that release of vasopressin by electrical stimulation of the paraventricular area in the rat leads to different effects depending on whether isotonic saline or distilled water is administered by stomach tube. Significant augmentation of Na excretion was observed when saline-loaded animals were stimulated, and the possible role of such differential effects is discussed. The reversal of effects of vasopressin, depending on whether a water or NaCl diuresis is present, has been frequently observed (see 434) but is still poorly understood. Goldberg & Handler (142) and Carter *et al.* (68) have reported a number of patients in whom cerebral disease was associated with either salt wasting or inappropriate release of vasopressin. A number of papers on the diurnal rhythm of water and electrolyte excretion in man have appeared. They deal with the role of light in this phenomenon (366), as studied during arctic summer or during artificial shifts in the daily illumination period (365), and with the excretory rhythm in man at high altitudes (262). Lennon *et al.* (253) report on a case of reversal of diurnal rhythm in the excretion of salt and water in primary hyperaldosteronism, and Falk (113) described the phenomenon that marked polydipsia can be produced by an intermittent food schedule in rats trained to press a bar for food pellets on a one-minute variable interval schedule.

The effects of variations in the breathing pattern on the renal excretion of water and electrolytes were carefully studied by Ullmann (407) and Currie & Ullmann (84). Anoxia in healthy human adults was induced by breathing for one hour, a respiratory gas mixture containing approximately 10 per cent O_2. Excretion rates of water, Na, K, bicarbonate, and Cl increased if anoxia was accompanied by hypocapnia. When the development of the latter was prevented, no significant changes in urinary solute output were observed. Evidence was also presented that in acute anoxia the basal rate of ADH secretion is diminished. During other experimental modifications of breathing, such as voluntary hyperventilation, breathing through external nonelastic airways, and CO_2-inhalation or negative pressure breathing, a rise in urine flow was uniformly observed. Currie & Ullmann (84) suggest that a factor common to all these procedures was the augmentation of respiratory fluctuations in intrathoracic pressure; they further postulate that secretion of ADH may be diminished by a reflex which is triggered by intrathoracic deformation receptors under all conditions in which the respiratory intrathoracic pressure variations are increased.

Extensive discussions by Borst *et al.* (37) and deVries *et al.* (95) have dealt with the renal responses controlling volume and osmoregulation. Emphasis is placed upon the spectrum of renal regulatory responses to Na excess and Na lack in the presence of alterations in the circulating blood volume. Possible pathways by which variations in the filling of the arterial system govern the renal excretion rates of water and Na are discussed.

Ion association, and renal excretion of sulfate, bromide, and fluoride.—A significant contribution in this field is a series of papers by Walser and his associates suggesting the importance of the physicochemical status of some ion species in regard to their mode of renal excretion. These authors studied the effects of sulfate infusions on the renal excretion of calcium (420) and, more recently, on strontium (426). The renal excretion rates of both ions are greatly augmented by parenterally administered sodium sulfate. It is suggested that both Sr and Ca form an electrostatic complex with sulfate ions and that these divalent anions, when electrostatically paired with sulfate, are not reabsorbed by the renal tubules. Thus it was demonstrated that after administration of a carrier-free isotope of Sr, the rate of urinary radiostrontium excretion increased up to forty-fold, in direct proportion to sulfate excretion. During the course of sulfate diuresis, the fraction of filtered Sr excreted reached values as high as 80 per cent as compared with a normal value of less than 10 per cent. In about one-half of the experiments, the amount of isotope excreted exceeded the estimated extracellular amount, indicating actual mobilization of radiostrontium from skeletal and other tissues. In another study, Walser (422) reported that the renal clearances of Mg, Ca, and radiostrontium are highly correlated and that these ions are possibly reabsorbed via a common mechanism. Salt depletion reduced the clearances while saline infusion or mercurials increased the excretion rates. Walser (423, 424) also has undertaken a much needed evaluation of the physicochemical state of Ca, Mg, phosphate, and citrate in normal human plasma. By ultafiltration and measurement of total concentration of free cations and that of the respective plasma anions, the extent of complex formations can be calculated from the known dissociation constants. The study gives values for protein binding and the degree of complexing of Ca, Mg, phosphate, and citrate. This information is of considerable importance. First, it provides a background against which the physicochemical status of these ions can be assessed in pathological conditions. And second, it quantitates that fraction of each ion species upon which specific physiological functions depend, amongst them also the degree of glomerular filtration and tubular reabsorption.

Becker *et al.* (19) have investigated the renal mode of excretion of inorganic sulfate in man. Although the results varied considerably, it was established that tubular reabsorption of inorganic sulfate is limited by a maximal transfer rate. Berglund (21) surveyed the present knowledge of inorganic sulfate transport by the renal tubules. This review, based on his own previous work, includes comparative physiological aspects and a characterization of the tubular mechanism for sulfate reabsorption in terms of various competitive interactions with a number of anions, glucose, phlorizin, and amino acids.

Globus *et al.* (141) have investigated renal tubular transport of inorganic sulfate in the dog and chicken, placing emphasis upon the kinetics of transtubular sulfate movement. The extent of unidirectional sulfate flux across the tubular epithelium was assessed either by a modification of Chinard's technique, or by using the renal portal circulation of the chicken kidney. In the latter, urinary appearance of sulfate relative to inulin is measured when both are injected simultaneously into a leg vein. With Chinard's approach, sulfate and a glomerular reference substance are rapidly injected into a renal artery of a dog. Under such conditions, radio-sulfate appeared in the urine before creatinine or inulin, indicating that a portion of the excreted ion enters the tubular fluid by transtubular influx. However, this precession of sulfate relative to a glomerular marker disappeared at high plasma levels, or after glucose infusion which is known to inhibit sulfate reabsorption. This disappearance is probably related to the fact that the fractional transtubular influx becomes a smaller part of urinary sulfate at high plasma levels, or under conditions of suppressed sulfate re-absorption. Stop-flow experiments by Hierholzer et al. (174) have indicated that sulfate reabsorption occurs at a proximal tubular site, a view supported by the observation of Globus et al. since K^{42}, known to be secreted distally, precedes both sulfate and creatinine in its urinary appearance. Precession of sulfate, relative to inulin, was also observed in the chicken when radio-sulfate and inulin were injected as a sudden pulse into a leg vein. Deyrup & Davies (98) studied the uptake of radiosulfate by rat renal tissue *in vitro* and observed that kidney cortex slices accumulate radiosulfate from the incubating medium at 0°C. This process is, however, different from radio-sulfate uptake at 38°. The latter process is energy dependent and requires the presence of K, Rb, or Cs. It is suppressed by metabolic inhibitors and Na. Radiosulfate uptake at low temperatures is similar to that of renal mitochondria, implying that radiosulfate accumulation is related to mito-chondrial activity.

A number of papers on the renal excretion of radiofluoride (64) and radiobromide (374) and on the effect of some diuretics on Br and Cl excretion (195) have appeared. No new information concerning the mechanism of transfer of these anions has evolved.

Bicarbonate, urinary acidification, and ammonia excretion.—A number of reviews dealing with general aspects of renal acid-base regulation have appeared (108, 122, 140). Relman & Levinsky (340), in a survey, discuss acquired renal tubular disorders with special reference to disturbances of acid-base regulation; Kennedy (204) has discussed the effects of carbon dioxide on the kidney in a symposium (468) devoted to the biological role of carbon dioxide.

A recent micropuncture study (134, 444) has confirmed previous observations (148, 149) that the pH may drop significantly within the proximal tubular convolution. The increase in hydrogen-ion concentration of proximal fluid samples collected during respiratory acidosis, sulfate and mannitol diuresis, and hypokalemic alkalosis proves that this tubular segment has a more significant regulatory role in hydrogen-ion excretion than had previously been assumed. Sodium-depleted rats, loaded with sodium sulfate, showed a greater capacity for proximal tubular acidification than rats on a normal diet, providing evidence for Na-H exchange at this tubular site.

This study has also confirmed earlier work by Gottschalk *et al.* (149), who found that the distal tubular convolutions in the rat play only a minor role in the establishment of the plasma-urine hydrogen-ion gradient.

In an effort to define some of the factors determining net transfer of hydrogen ion into the tubular fluid, Bank & Schwartz (16) have investigated the influence of the anion-penetrating ability of a tubular electrolyte load on urinary acidification and the excretion rate of titratable acid. The latter both increase during administration of poorly reabsorbable anions (sulfate, ferrocyanate) in phosphate-loaded dogs after dietary NaCl restriction. Infusion of more easily reabsorbable anions (Cl, thiocyanate) was uniformly associated with an elevation of urinary pH and suppression of titratable acid excretion. The explanation was offered that various anions affect urinary hydrogen-ion transfer through their influence on the transtubular electrical potential gradient. The magnitude of this electrical gradient is determined both by the electromotive force of the Na pump and the penetrating (shunting) ability of tubular anions. Poorly reabsorbable anions establish a steep electrical gradient, thereby providing a greater driving force for passive H^+ transfer into the tubule lumen. On the other hand, those anions which penetrate the tubular epithelium more readily have a greater tendency to dissipate the electrical potential difference, and thereby diminish passive tubular entry of hydrogen ions. The same mechanism could also affect K excretion which is indeed greatly enhanced under those conditions which augment hydrogen-ion excretion. The previously mentioned studies in Na-depleted rats by Clapp & Rector (71), reporting an increase in distal tubular potential gradients during sulfate diuresis, corroborate this thesis of Bank & Schwartz (16).

A number of studies have dealt with the processes governing the renal tubular reabsorption of bicarbonate. In bicarbonate-loaded dogs, according to Rector *et al.* (336), inhibition of carbonic anhydrase depressed the maximal reabsorptive transfer rate of bicarbonate by a constant amount at all CO_2-tensions between 30 and 350 mm Hg. Accordingly, it was concluded that the effect of pCO_2 in augmenting bicarbonate reabsorption is solely mediated through the uncatalyzed hydration of CO_2. From these findings and the kinetics of bicarbonate excretion at submaximal reabsorption rates, accomplished by carbonic anhydrase inhibition at different levels of pCO_2, it was suggested that reabsorption of bicarbonate is normally accomplished by two distinct processes. The first is dependent upon plasma CO_2 tension, independent of carbonic anhydrase, and characterized by a transport system sensitive to the pH of the tubular fluid. Recycling of carbonic acid, either by diffusion through the lipid fraction of the cell membrane or by solvent drag, is an essential feature of this proposed mechanism of bicarbonate reabsorption. The second process has a fixed Tm, is thought to be independent of pCO_2, and can operate efficiently despite sharp hydrogen-ion gradients. Importantly, it is dependent upon carbonic anhydrase. The authors have tentatively localized the latter process exclusively in the distal tubule.

Relman *et al.* (341) have carefully compared in dogs the diuretic response seen after administration of either acetazolamide or CL 8490, its N^2-methyl analogue which has virtually no carbonic anhydrase–inhibiting activity *in vitro*. Massive doses of either drug given intravenously (500 mg per kg) depressed tubular reabsorption of bicarbonate by as much as 80 per cent. Simultaneously, a profound chloruresis was observed. A substantial part of this effect cannot be explained by inhibition of carbonic anhydrase since both drugs had similar effects. Nor can the excessive diuresis be accounted for by the osmotic load of the drugs or by their extracellular alkalinizing effect. The observed suppression of reabsorption of a large fraction of the glomerular filtrate may be caused by transient intracellular alkalosis which could result from cellular accumulation of the monobasic form of the drugs.

Gordon *et al.* (147) reinvestigated the quantitative aspects of bicarbonate reabsorption under the influence of carbonic anhydrase inhibition by acetazolamide, correcting for the bicarbonate excretion caused by administration of this strongly basic compound. They point out that although about 40 per cent of bicarbonate reabsorption was inhibited (dose range, 67 to 120 mg per kg), there also occurred a suppression of inorganic phosphate reabsorption. They suggest that some fraction of over-all bicarbonate reabsorption may share a pathway with phosphate reabsorption, a thesis previously advanced by Malvin & Lotspeich (268). Also concerned with the renal mechanism for bicarbonate reabsorption are a number of reports by Toussaint & Vereerstraeten (401 to 404) and an extensive paper by Toussaint (400). Bicarbonate reabsorption was invariably depressed after acute NaCl loading. The extent of this suppression appeared to be primarily determined by the initial level of bicarbonate reabsorption, since the intensity of the Cl influence on bicarbonate reabsorption was greatest in respiratory acidosis, less in normal animals, and least in acetazolamide-treated dogs. Respiratory acidosis *per se* did not affect Cl reabsorption in acute experiments. In K-depleted rats, however, it should be noted that Levitin & Epstein (254) observed an increased urinary excretion rate of Cl ions after 24 hours exposure to 8 per cent CO_2, an increase caused by direct inhibition of tubular Cl reabsorption. Toussaint & Vereerstraeten (401) also confirmed previous observations that K depletion increases, and K excess diminishes, tubular bicarbonate reabsorption. They submit the thesis that some part of the tubular transport of Cl and bicarbonate is governed by a passive process, since they are interchangeable in the anionic reabsorption. This passive part of anion reabsorption may be determined by the net movement of Na and the relative proportion of anions in the glomerular filtrate. Such a concept is quite similar to that previously developed by Pitts (323) for the proximal tubular transfer of bicarbonate and Cl.

Buttram *et al.* (54) also investigated the effects of K loading on renal bicarbonate reabsorption. They point out that K suppresses bicarbonate reabsorption only by inhibition of the previously discussed pCO_2-dependent system of hydrogen-ion secretion. The carbonic anhydrase-dependent secretory system was entirely unaffected since administration of acetazolamide depressed bicarbonate reabsorption to the same extent in both control and K-treated dogs. On the other hand, Maren et al. (272) did observe that the renal effects of acetazolamide in suppressing bicarbonate reabsorption were less than normal in the extracellular alkalosis of K depletion, a metabolic situation generally thought to elicit intracellular acidosis. It was pointed out that at a decreased intracellular pH, the role of carbonic anhydrase in renal tubular hydrogen-ion transport, and accordingly in bicarbonate reabsorption, is relatively reduced. As the hydrogen-ion gradient from cell interior to tubular lumen is steepened in K depletion, carbonic anhydrase is of lesser importance, as a proportionately larger fraction of hydrogen ions bypasses the catalyzed reaction and is formed by the uncatalyzed hydration of carbon dioxide. Consequently, the relative efficacy of carbonic anhydrase inhibition of bicarbonate reabsorption is diminished in intracellular acidosis.

The maximum rate of excretion of titratable acid was studied in the dog by Handler et al. (158); and the possiblity of tubular secretion of acid phosphate ions, which occurs when there is a rapid increase in plasma phosphate, was raised. It is considered possible that under conditions of severe phosphate loading such secretion, as well as the transfer of hydrogen ions into the tubular fluid, may contribute to the total output of titratable acid. Renal tubular phosphate secretion in the dog is also considered by Brodsky & Carrasquer (49) on the basis of loading experiments with various phosphate salts. Another study on the maximum rate of tubular hydrogen-ion transport is that of Giovannetti and his associates (139). Metabolic acidosis and phosphate loading were followed by a plateau in the rate of excretion of hydrogen ions. From the magnitude of acid excretion. significant proximal tubular acidification was postulated, but the problem of phosphate secretion in metabolic acidosis remains unsolved.

Nutbourne & de Wardener (303), in a careful study, demonstrated a fall in the excretion rate of hydrogen ions during water diuresis whenever urine osmolality fell below 150 mosm per kg. Ammonia excretion remained unchanged. This fall in hydrogen-ion excretion was not related to dilution of phosphate buffers, although such apparent changes in titratable acid are possible and have been analyzed in detail by Nutbourne (302). He demonstrated that changes in titratable acid can be ascribed entirely to the effect of increasing total ionic concentration which causes a shift in the equilibrium $H_2PO_4^- \rightleftharpoons H^+ + HPO_4^=$, so increasing the concentration of the acidic phosphate anion. These considerations, and similar ones previously made by Schwartz et al. (360), are of interest since marked changes in osmolality occur during passage of tubular fluid along the distal tubule and collecting ducts. The estimated rate of excretion of titratable acid will be higher than the true rate of tubular excretion of hydrogen ions in concentrated urines, and lower when the total ionic concentration is less than 250 mosm per kg. Furthermore, the higher the absolute rate of phosphate excretion, the greater this difference will be. Nutbourne points out that discrepancies between measured titratable acid excretion and true renal hydrogen-ion excretion of up to 100 per cent may occur. Methods and correction tables are presented to minimize this source of error in the estimation of the true rate of the renal excretion of hydrogen ions, but they are somewhat problematic in view of the fact that the intrarenal site of acidification and urinary concentration may vary under different conditions.

Pak Poy & Wrong (317) have investigated the urinary pCO_2 in a variety of renal disorders and consistently observed it to be lower than in normal individuals. Differences in urine flow and phosphate excretion rates were not found to be associated with an abnormally low pCO_2, but urinary concentrating ability was often found to be reduced. The authors tentatively invoke a derangement of the renal medullary countercurrent system as being responsible for preventing diffusional exchange between adjacent medullary structures. Such diffusional interference, possibly caused by anatomical distortions and tissue scarring, is envisaged as leading to reduced medullary CO_2-trapping and consequently to a lower urinary pCO_2. Since maximal urinary alkalinity is limited to a pH of approximately 8.0, these low values of pCO_2 curtail the maximal rate of excretion of bicarbonate and may explain the intolerance for alkali shown by some patients with renal disease.

Cade *et al.* (57) present additional evidence in favor of a passive mode of ammonia excretion. Ammonia transfer was studied as a function of intracellular pH which was changed by inducing respiratory acidosis or alkalosis, or by experimental K depletion. It was shown that, at any given urinary pH, elevation of pCO_2 depresses, while a fall in pCO_2 increases ammonium excretion. When animals were depleted of K, ammonium excretion was further reduced. These findings are interpreted within the context of the passive diffusion theory of tubular ammonia transport. As intracellular pCO_2 rises, intracellular hydrogen-ion concentration rises simultaneously and promotes conversion of NH_3 into NH_4^+. Thus the diffusion gradient of the permeant NH_3 is depressed and the rate of ammonia excretion falls. During hyperventilation the reverse sequence of events takes place, favoring formation of NH_3, thereby promoting enhanced excretion rates. As it is virtually certain that intracellular bicarbonate concentration falls in K depletion (2), the proportionately greater fall in intracellular pH during CO_2-breathing should lead to enhancement of the depressant effect of CO_2 on NH_3 excretion. This prediction is fulfilled.

The effect of buffer loading on ammonia excretion in the dog was studied by Bank (15) who demonstrated that under conditions of relatively constant urine pH, progressive increments in titratable acid excretion can take place without having any significant effect upon the concurrent rate of ammonia excretion. This observation holds in the presence of normal acid-base balance, and also in chronic metabolic acidosis, when ammonia excretion is augmented. Availability of hydrogen ions does not appear to constitute a limiting factor in the accumulation of NH_4^+ in the urine, and the mechanism regulating NH_4^+ excretion in the dog may thus be dissociated from that of hydrogen-ion excretion. This dissociation of ammonia excretion from that of titratable acid is consistent with the view of passive trapping of NH_3 by intratubular conversion to NH_4^+, since this process depends primarily upon the hydrogen-ion gradient. Thus, it would be expected to be independent of changes in composition of the tubular fluid except for pH.

A number of studies on the release of ammonia into the renal vein have appeared (314, 315), and evidence is now available that renal ammonia production is decreased during hyperammonemia (314). An interesting recent approach to the problem of urinary and renal ammonia precursors is the attempt by Shalhoub et al. (364) to correlate urinary ammonia excretion with the extraction rate of various possible nitrogenous compounds as studied by column chromatography. In confirmation of Van Slyke and his associates, glutamine is an important source of urinary ammonia; but other compounds, not yet clearly defined, may also play an important role.

Functional disturbances in renal tubular acidosis were investigated by Elkinton and his associates (109, 188, 430), and by Gill et al. (136) and River et al. (347). Brief reports have appeared by Morrin et al. (287, 288) on the acidifying capacity and on renal tubular bicarbonate reabsorption in experimental chronic renal disease.

Excretion of phosphate and calcium and the effects of parathyroid hormone.— Important advances in the purification of the parathyroid hormone (334) have led to a renewed interest in its site and mode of action. Recent reviews on the renal effects of the parathyroid hormone are those of Rasmussen (333), Wesson (434), and Munson (295); and the proceedings of a symposium devoted to parathyroid function have been published in book form (477).

In the absence of direct information on the concentration gradient of phosphate ions along the mammalian nephron, the questions of the possible secretion of phosphate into the tubular lumen and the extent to which such secretion may occur under various conditions remains unsettled. An analysis of the mode of phosphate excretion is presented in recent papers by Carrasquer & Brodsky (67) and by Carrasquer (66). These authors studied the transient renal response to a single instantaneous injection of either NaH_2PO_4 or KH_2PO_4 and creatinine into the renal artery under conditions of normal and high serum phosphate levels. In the latter situation, the increment of phosphate excretion per unit injected per one circulation exceeded that of creatinine. Such an observation suggests the possible existence of a transitory tubular secretory mechanism for phosphate. The authors analyze some of the objections to this interpretation and thus call attention to some of the limitations of their own approach. Other studies on renal transtubular phosphate movement [Heller & Hillman (169), Taugner et al. (387), and Bronner & Thompson (50)] have not uniformly supported the notion of renal tubular secretion of phosphate. The recent observation by Walser (423) according to which only 53 per cent of plasma phosphates are present as "free ions", the rest being either protein-bound or complexed, may have an important bearing on future studies concerned with the mode of renal phosphate excretion.

Tubular reabsorption of phosphate in K-deficient dogs was found to be unchanged from that in normal animals (289), and Reiss et al. (338) report that phosphate Tm per unit of glomerular filtrate remained constant in dogs in which unilateral renal disease (aminonucleoside-induced nephritis, chronic pyelonephritis, or serum glomerulonephritis) was induced. These results indicate that the capacity of the residual nephrons in the dog to transfer phosphate out of the tubule lumen remains unchanged in these experimentally induced renal disorders. Lewis & Ford (258), however, observed that in patients with progressive renal disease a disproportionate fall in phosphate reabsorption occurred as GFR was reduced.

The effects of a highly purified parathyroid extract were studied by Pullman et al. (332) and convincing evidence obtained for a direct action of the hormone at the renal tubular level. Purified parathyroid extract (having an activity of 2500 to 3000 units per mg) was injected into one renal artery at rates of 5 to 20 μg per hr; and a predominantly unilateral phosphaturia was observed, which occurred in the absence of changes in renal hemodynamics or plasma phosphate concentration. Depression of the net tubular reabsorption of phosphate is thus unequivocally one of the actions of parathyroid hormone. In no instance did the rate of urinary excretion of phosphate exceed the filtered load and, accordingly, the question of diminished reabsorption versus stimulation of secretion under the influence of parathyroid hormone remains unsettled. The same problem was also approached by Samiy et al. (353, 354). Phosphaturia without increased filtered phosphate load was produced by single intravenous injection of 200 to 400 units of a purified parathyroid extract. No evidence for net secretion was obtained either under free-flow or under stop-flow conditions. Stop-flow analysis indicated that parathyroid extract increases phosphate excretion by diminished reabsorption in both proximal and distal tubular segments. Injection of P^{32} with inulin during the period of ureteral clamping failed to reveal a significant change in transtubular flux of P^{32}, and the authors conclude that the observed phosphaturic effects are caused by inhibition of renal tubular reabsorption of phosphate.

A rise in bicarbonate excretion and urinary pH was reported after administration of commercial parathyroid extract by Nordin (300), but the nature of this effect is not clear.

Walser (421) has undertaken a study on the excretion of Ca, giving special attention to its interrelation with tubular reabsorption of Na. The important observation was made that in the dog, Na excretion rate is the major determinant of Ca excretion. This holds during diuresis induced either by water, sodium chloride, sodium bicarbonate, mannitol, glucose, or sucrose. Furthermore, these studies have indicated that approximately half of plasma Ca exists as free ion and that Ca clearance equals the Na clearance. From these results, it is considered possible that competitive binding of Ca and Na at a receptor site of the tubular cell membrane might occur. Considerable evidence of competitive binding of these ions is available in other tissues and strengthens Walser's thesis that Na and Ca reabsorption may be functionally interrelated.

A paper by Kleeman et al. (216) deals briefly with the renal effects of parathyroidectomy and administration of partially purified parathyroid extract on Ca excretion. It confirms previous conclusions that parathyroid hormone decreases the renal clearance of diffusible Ca. Laake (233) investigated the complex effects of long-term treatment with various corticosteroids on Ca excretion. Haenze (156) reports briefly that Mg and Ca excretion are augmented by treatment with mersalyl (Salyrgan), chlorothiazide, or hydrochlorothiazide. Kodicek et al. (222) studied the site of deposition of C^{14}-labeled vitamin D_2 by autoradiography of isolated, microdissected nephrons. Vitamin D_2 was found to be localized in the upper two-thirds of the proximal convoluted tubule, a site where phosphate reabsorption and Ca deposition are known to occur.

Copp et al. (76) and Hovig & Laake (184) claim that a limitation of renal tubular Ca reabsorption obtains at increased plasma levels. Previous investigators have not succeeded in defining a Tm mechanism for this ion species (391). One therefore wishes that the study by Copp et al., in which excretion rates were calculated from the slope of the cumulative excretion curves over relatively long periods of time, had been extended by the use of conventional steady-state clearance methods. The effects of hypercalcemia on renal function were reviewed by Epstein (110).

A number of papers on the syndrome of Mg deficiency in man (159) and rats (199), the renal lesions occuring in this deficiency state (199), and magnesium metabolism in man and animals (263) have appeared.

EXCRETION OF ORGANIC COMPOUNDS

Excretion of uric acid.—Additional evidence for a secretory mode of excretion of uric acid in the mongrel dog has become available during the last year. Yü et al. (454) observed urate-to-inulin clearance ratios greater than 1.10 in both Dalmatian and non-Dalmatian dogs. Net tubular secretion of urate was thus demonstrated during mannitol diuresis and urate loading. In the mongrel as well as in the Dalmatian, stop-flow experiments supported the thesis of urate secretion. The stop-flow pattern in the Dalmatian was characterized by secretory peaks in both the proximal and distal tubular segments, both of which were abolished by probenecid and large amounts of PAH. The mongrel showed tubular reabsorption in the proximal region and net tubular secretion only in the distal tubular region. Normally, in the non-Dalmatian dog, filtered urate is largely reabsorbed. Since this reabsorptive mechanism has considerably greater capacity than that in the Dalmatian, the excreted urate exceeds filtered loads only under the special conditions of large urate administration and osmotic diuresis. Renal tubular secretion of uric acid in the mongrel was also demonstrated by Lathem *et al.* (248) under conditions of urate and mannitol loading. They attribute the high excretion rate of urate to diminished reabsorption because of mannitol diuresis and because secretion of urate is stimulated by the elevated plasma urate levels. No evidence was obtained from studies of the effect of urinary pH changes to indicate that uric acid excretion is mediated by a nonionic diffusion mechanism.

Platts & Mudge (325) have studied the accumulation of uric acid by surviving slices of renal cortex in an attempt to define the transport system responsible for urate secretion. Considerable species differences were observed. Uptake of uric acid from the medium was most marked in the chicken, rabbit, and guinea pig, while active accumulation could not be demonstrated for man, mongrel dog, or rat. On the basis of substrate and inhibitor effects, the dependence upon aerobic metabolism, and the competitive effects of PAH, the accumulation of uric acid by the rabbit kidney was shown to have many similarities to PAH transport. The authors point out that some of the agents known to induce uric acid retention in man and mongrel dog, an effect attributed to inhibition of tubular secretion (455), did not affect uric acid accumulation. This observation suggests that some aspects of the secretory mechanism in man and mongrel dog may be qualitatively different from those in the rabbit and chicken.

The elimination of uric acid was studied in man by Sørensen (375) using C^{14}-labeled uric acid. Data on turnover rates and the exchangeable pool of urate are derived in healthy and gouty men, and attention is drawn to a large route of intestinal excretion. Previous results by Nugent & Tyler (301) of an impairment of uric acid excretion in gout have been confirmed in a brief report by Lathem & Rodnan (247). The effects of lactic acid infusions in promoting reduced net excretion of urate have also been re-evaluated by Handler (157) and Smythe & Chrisanthis (370). Handler presents good evidence that it is the increased level of lactic acid which causes augmented net reabsorption of filtered urate and thus is partly responsible for the low level of uric acid clearance in toxemia.

Two reviews dealing with metabolic and renal aspects of uric acid excretion are those of Richet (345) and Talbott & Terplan (386). The latter emphasizes the functional and morphological changes of the kidney in gout.

Excretion of amino acids and proteins.—Recent studies on the excretion of amino acids are mainly concerned with the localization and characterization of the renal tubular transport processes. Thus, Brown *et al.* (51), using stop-flow methods in dogs, have confirmed previous indirect evidence that the site of reabsorption of amino acids is situated in the proximal segments of the renal tubules. A series of amino acids, including glycine, L-alanine, D,L-alanine, L-glutamic acid, L-lysine, and L-arginine, are actively reabsorbed within that portion of the nephron where secretion of PAH is greatest.

From loading experiments in which mutual interference in reabsorption was observed, it was concluded that the basic amino acids arginine, lysine, and ornithine are reabsorbed by a single common transport mechanism. No evidence for secretion of amino acids was obtained. Another study on interactions of amino acids in renal tubular transport is that of Webber *et al.* (429). Amino acid concentrations in both urine and plasma were measured by column chromatography, and conventional clearance methods were used to study the effects of intravenous infusions of L-lysine, L-arginine, L-histidine, L-ornithine, and L-cysteine on plasma level and excretion rates of other naturally occurring amino acids. Each of the basic amino acids depressed the reabsorption of others of the basic group, but also, somewhat less markedly, depressed that of other amino acids. This observation argues against complete specificity of the different transport mechanisms for amino acids. Identity of the reabsorptive pathway for lysine, arginine, ornithine, and cysteine was confirmed. Evidence for a renal tubular amino acid transport system common to glycine, L-proline, and oxy-L-proline was briefly presented by Scriver *et al.* (361); a study on the renal tubular transport system of glycocoll and alanine in the cat was published by Gillissen & Taugner (137).

The mode and site of renal tubular reabsorption of proteins have received attention from several groups. Lathem & Davis (245) used stop-flow analysis and observed that egg-albumin and β-lactoglobulin gave similar distribution patterns, an observation strongly indicating a reabsorptive site in a proximal part of the nephron overlying the site of PAH secretion. Similar conclusions are reached by Brauman and his associates (44). Another stop-flow analysis of renal protein excretion in the dog is that by Aukland (4), who shows that a marked distal discharge of protein frequently occurs in nonproteinuric dogs during the period of ureteral clamping. However, the available data permit no decision as to whether such distal protein discharge (Aukland believes that the site of appearance involves the collecting ducts) occurs continually or whether it is typical only for stop-flow conditions. The latter is more likely. Aukland found no evidence for a proximal tubular reabsorptive site for egg-albumen; but during pathological proteinuria (aminonucleoside nephrosis) or during infusion of human plasma, proximal tubular reabsorption of filtered serum proteins could be shown. Lathem *et al.* (246) also demonstrated by stop-flow analysis that reabsorption of free, unbound hemoglobin occurred in a proximal nephron segment, coexistent with the PAH secretory peak. The absence of secretion was noted. Malmendier *et al.* (266), in a similar study, also assigned hemoglobin reabsorption to the proximal tubule; they observed, in addition, a second, more distal reabsorptive area which coincided with the site of maximal Na reabsorptions. They point out that continued filtration (replacement reabsorption) during the time of ureteral occlusion contributes to the stop-flow pattern of hemoglobin.

Renal tubular reabsorption of protein in rats with experimental proteinuria, produced by means of a nephrotoxic serum, was studied by Mendel (275). He observed that some 70 per cent of the filtered proteins can be re-absorbed by the tubules. Respective reabsorption rates for albumin, α- and β-globulin amounted to 58, 70, and 83 per cent respectively. These reabsorption rates are greater than in the normal rat, and calculations by Mendel indicate that about one-third of the total circulating protein could be re-absorbed by the tubules daily. Malmendier et al. (265) present evidence that an increase in glomerular permeability occurs in proteinuric patients as a consequence of an expansion of the plasma volume by infusion of dextran. This increase in glomerular permeability, possibly caused by stretching of the glomerular membrane, could explain the steeper slope relating urinary albumin output to plasma levels when the plasma volume has been acutely expanded.

A number of other papers, dealing with factors affecting protein excretion rate, deserve mention. Renal function studies carried out by Coye & Donkle (79) in adrenalectomized dogs treated with DOCA, cortisone, and NaCl indicate that adrenal steroids induce only minor alterations in tubular protein transport. Gardner (128), studying the effects of changes in acid-base balance in the male rat, found proteinuria was more marked during acidosis, but was promptly reversed by increasing systemic and thus urinary pH. Suggestive, but indirect evidence is presented that the degree of proteinuria is related to changes in filtration rather than to tubular reabsorption of protein. In another study, Carone & Spector (65) demonstrated that experimental proteinuria in the rat could be suppressed by compounds such as quinine or difluorophosphate, both known to diminish capillary permeability. Such studies indicate that proteinurias produced by anti-rat kidney serum, uranium nitrate, or nucleoside are largely the result of increased permeability of the glomerular capillaries. Such appears to be the case also in postural proteinuria as studied by Slater et al. (369). The time elapsed before the urinary appearance of injected labeled albumin during an induced episode of orthostatic proteinuria, and the similarity of the specific activity of plasma and urine, were taken to suggest an increased glomerular passage of protein. Although this observation is quite consistent with a glomerular orgin of the injected proteins, such a study would gain significance if a glomerular indicator such as inulin had been administered to permit a direct comparison of the time of urinary appearance.

A number of other papers have covered experimental proteinurias, renal hemoglobin transfer, and associated morphological changes (277, 278, 299, 337, 367).

Transport and excretion of organic acids and bases.—The most important recent development in the field of renal handling of organic acids and bases is the realization that both active transport and passive nonionic diffusion contribute to the mechanism of excretion of both groups of compounds. This is particularly well demonstrated by the work of Weiner et al. (431) and of Gutman et al. (155). Weiner et al. (431) studied the mode of renal excretion of four organic acids (salicylate, p-OH-benzoate, chlorphenol red, and salicylurate), and observed net secretion at low plasma levels while net reabsorption was regularly observed at high plasma levels of these compounds. Thus an apparent "self-depression" of a secretory Tm was a regular finding. Previously, a similar phenomenon had been seen when a group of analogues of probenecid (26), some substituted benzoates (221), and nitrofurantoid (321) were studied.

On the basis of earlier work on the behavior of salicylate, probenecid and, more recently, several other organic acids, Weiner *et al.* (431) developed the concept of a tubular two-directional transport system. Evidence is presented that this type of bidirectional, continuous transfer consists of an active, secretory component, having a definite maximal value (Tm), and a passive reabsorptive component which is not Tm-limited. It is this reabsorptive process which has been shown to proceed by nonionic passive back-diffusion. Nonionic diffusion is characterized, filtration rate and urine flow rate being constant, by a dependency of the transfer rate of a particular organic compound on its pK and the pH of the urine. The phenomenon is best explained by the fact that cell membranes are generally relatively more permeable to the lipid-soluble nonionic species than to the ionic one. Thus, penetration of the tubular wall is virtually limited to exclusive diffusion by the nonionic member of a weakly dissociated organic compound. In the experiments by Weiner *et al.* (431), the contribution of reabsorption by this type of nonionic diffusion was taken into account: for the acidic compounds tested it was consistently smaller in more alkaline urines. Titration experiments carried out by increasing the plasma concentrations to assure steady-state conditions led to the previously mentioned reversal of transtubular movement because, at low plasma concentration and small filtered load, the tubular secretory component determines the amount excreted. As the plasma level is increased, it is the filtered amount, from which a constant fraction is lost by reabsorption, which determines the urinary excretion rate. Since secretion is constant, its contribution will diminish as load is augmented. Weiner *et al.* also carefully assessed other variables and factors which influence the apparent Tm under this complex situation.

A similar behavior of active (proximal) secretion and variable passive (distal) nonionic, pH-dependent reabsorption has also been demonstrated for probenecid (433), salicylate (432), p-aminosalicylate (185), and a number of substituted phenylbutazone analogues (155). Newer evidence also indicates the importance of nonionic back-diffusion in the renal excretion of nitrofurantoid (451), a compound which is filtered at the glomerular level and reabsorbed in both proximal and distal tubular segments at a higher rate when the urine is relatively acid. Indolylacetate was shown by Milne *et al.* (284) to be excreted by a similar mechanism in man and rat, its clearance increasing at rising plasma pH. Milne *et al.* point out that indolylacetic acid is the first naturally occurring organic acid in the urine known to be excreted by such a pH-dependent diffusion mechanism.

Gutman and his associates (155) published an extensive study on the nature of excretion of a number of phenylbutazone analogues, a group of acidic compounds closely related structurally, but with pKa values ranging from 2.0 to 5.5. Two distinct effects were closely related to the pK values. First, the rate of renal excretion varied inversely with pKa, a finding which is partly attributable to nonionic back-diffusion. Thus, the more acidic compounds are more rapidly excreted under conditions of a physiologically acid urine than the less acidic analogues. Second, net secretion could be demonstrated, and evidence is presented that phenylbutazone analogues of lower pKa are secreted more rapidly than are compounds with a higher pKa. Thus, the inverse relationship between pKa and rate of renal excretion of those compounds constitutes the sum of two distinct and different effects of the pKa, one directly relating it to nonionic back-diffusion and the other relating it to the rate of tubular secretion. Stop-flow experiments indicate that the proximal part of the nephron is the site of secretion while a distal tubular site emerges as that of back-diffusion. In discussing the general aspects of the renal excretory mechanisms for organic acids, the thesis is advanced that detoxication of organic acids may be expedited by conjugation to form compounds of lower pKa. These, by virtue of a more acidic character, would be more rapidly excreted by the mechanisms outlined above.

A number of studies on the renal transfer of iodopyracet (Diodrast) have appeared. Kinter *et al.* (215) investigated this problem in *Necturus* by a combination of clearance and newly devised autoradiographic techniques. The results support previous views that iodopyracet has a simultaneous bidirectional movement across proximal tubular cells in this species. At low plasma concentrations, both net secretion and net reabsorption were uniformly associated with an accumulation of iodopyracet in proximal tubule cells. Block and co-workers (29, 30) report on a problem arising when I^{131}-labeled iodopyracet is used in kidney function tests. In the first paper, the renal clearance was reported to be relatively depressed at low concentrations. Extraction ratios as low as 0.54 were observed. Since the administration of stable carrier-iodopyracet restores the renal clearance of I^{131}-labeled iodopyracet to normal, it is suggested that plasma protein binding is responsible for suppressed excretion rates at low plasma levels. Dialysis experiments in which binding is prevented by administration of carrier-iodopyracet support this interpretation. Administration of unlabeled iodopyracet also eliminates hepatic uptake and by this mechanism increases subsequent renal excretion of the I^{131}-labeled compound. Because of increased background activity, hepatic uptake and retention can cause a sizable error if an assessment of renal function is attempted by external monitoring of radioactivity. Block *et al.* (30) observed that the renal excretion rate of isotopically marked iodopyracet is doubled by prior administration of one gram of carrier-iodopyracet.

Studies concerned with the mode of renal excretion of PAH indicate that in some species, such as the guinea pig, mouse, cow, pig, and sheep, acetylation of the para-amino group occurs in the kidney (363). If this is not taken into account, errors as large as 20 per cent may occur in the measurment of renal blood flow. Because of this conjugation, truer values of RBF can be obtained by measuring the sum of the clearances of free and conjugated PAH. Kiil (211) undertook a study of the kinetics of the proximal tubular secretory system for PAH. He confirmed the previous observations by Harth *et al.* (161) that extraction of PAH is reduced when renal blood flow is increased at unchanged arterial hematocrit. Kiil's analysis, taking into account the change of substrate concentration (PAH) during renal capillary passage and Michealis-Menten kinetics, suggests that the maximal transport rate may depend on the concentration of enzyme for a rate-limiting reaction. Such a hypothesis explains that extraction of PAH may be reduced without marked reduction of Tm, and it is shown that renal titration curves may yield information on the kinetics of the proposed enzymatic reactions. The urinary secretion of hippuric acid in man has been given an extensive mathematical analysis by Wu & Elliot (453).

A number of studies consider the excretion pattern of citric and other organic acids (61, 91, 92, 151). A paper by Forbes & Magee (120) indicates significant renal extraction of serum nonesterified fatty acids, a phenomenon partly related to renal synthesis of triglycerides. Hohenleitner & Spitzer (178) also studied changes in plasma free fatty acid concentrations on passage through the kidneys. Free fatty acid removal was found to be significant, and proportional to the arterial concentration. It is pointed out that such extraction could be an important factor in the oxidative metabolism of the kidneys. A paper by Cohen (72) also discusses the role of free fatty acid utilization in renal metabolism.

Additional experimental work on the inhibition of the PAH transport system has been undertaken. Essig & Taggart (112) studied the competitive inhibition of the renal transport of PAH by a large number of mono-substituted hippurates in slices of rat kidney cortex. Significant differences in inhibitory potency were found depending on whether substitution (with methyl, fluoro, chloro, bromo, iodo, or nitro groups) was done at the meta, para, or ortho position. The molecular size of the inhibitor was also found to be of importance. Despopoulos (94) examined the inhibition of the active accumulation of PAH by surviving kidney cortex by various oxypyrimidines related to barbituric acid. Inhibition occurred in the absence of respiratory depression. The displacement of PAH from a postulated receptor site apparently does not involve competition for transport since barbiturates are not secreted. From a comparison of the chemical structure with inhibitor potency, it was concluded that inhibition by oxypyrimidines requires participation of three oxygen atoms, one of which can be replaced by sulfur. This latter substitution enhances inhibitor potency. Braun (45) studied the nature of mutual inhibition of phenol red and PAH and found it to be competitive whereas the inhibition of phenol red and PAH by probenecid is noncompetitive.

Some aspects of the renal tubular transport of organic bases have also been investigated. Volle *et al.* (414, 415) have extended their previous studies on the mutual transfer interference of a number of organic bases to the avian kidney. The transport relationships between N'-methylnicotinamide (NMN) and mecamylamine, quinine, quinidine, and quinacrine indicate that the latter compounds inhibit tubular secretion of NMN in the chicken. It is not, however, clear whether these competitors are secreted and subsequently reabsorbed or whether they are bound firmly by the tubule cells, but not subject to transfer across the tubular epithelium. A basic cyanine dye (No. 863) and some bisquarternary compounds also inhibit NMN excretion in the chicken (415). Both of these inhibitors accumulate in the kidney in high concentrations but appear only in small amounts in the urine. Some information as to the intrarenal site of transport of organic bases has become available. Rennick & Moe (342) undertook a stop-flow analysis of the renal tubular excretion of tetraethylammonium and observed the appearance of this compound at about the same proximal tubular level as PAH.

RENAL ASPECTS OF ERYTHROPOIESIS

Recent experimental evidence strongly implicates the kidney as an important site of origin of an erythropoietic hormone. There is uniform agreement as to the key role of the kidney as the organ producing an erythropoietic factor, but some evidence suggests that the kidney is not the sole source.

Suki & Grollman (382) observed a marked reduction in erythropoiesis and hemoglobin production in bilaterally nephrectomized dogs. The rate of disappearance of injected radioiron and the rate of incorporation of Fe^{59} into red cells were used to assess the erythropoietic status of control and bilaterally nephrectomized animals. In the latter group, an aregenerative anemia developed even when the development of azotemia was prevented by peritoneal lavage. Additional evidence that the retention of nitrogenous and other renal excretory products is not the cause of reduced erythropoiesis was presented. Dogs with ureterovenous anastomosis showed normal regeneration of erythrocytes as measured by radioiron uptake. Thus, the regulatory role of the kidney in erythropoiesis is independent of its excretory function. Suki & Grollman also provided direct evidence for a humoral nature of renal erythropoiesis by demonstrating that renal extracts stimulate the incorporation of Fe^{59} into red cells and increase the reticulocyte count.

Essentially similar results were reported in a series of papers by Naets (297) who continued work on the role of the kidney in the production of an erythropoietic factor. Naets observed that bilateral nephrectomy abolishes the capacity of bled or hypoxic dogs to produce erythropoietin, as measured by the incorporation of Fe^{59} into erythrocytes of starved rats. It was reaffirmed that ureteral ligation did not prevent the appearance of erythro-

poietic activity. Mixing plasma from anemic dogs with that from nephrectomized animals does not lead to inhibition of erythropoiesis. This observation makes it unlikely that the presence of an inhibitor in the nephrectomized animal is the cause of the lower erythropoietic titer. Naets (296) has
also reported the important finding that the administration of erythropoietic factor to a bilaterally nephrectomized dog led to maintenance of a
normal erythroblastic marrow picture. In a study of erythropoiesis in acute
and chronic renal insufficiency, Naets et al. (298) showed that Fe^{59}-uptake
was drastically reduced in about one-half of the patients. In some, as indicated by life-span measurements of erythrocytes, exaggerated hemolysis was
also present.

Reissman et al. (339) also emphasized the importance of functioning
renal tissue for the normal erythropoietic response to hypoxia, acute hemorrhage, phenylhydrazine anemia, or cobalt administration. Normally, the
appearance of erythropoietin can be demonstrated under these conditions.
Again, increased urea concentration was eliminated as a factor responsible
for the suppression of erythropoietin production in the bilaterally nephrectomized or mercury bichloride-poisoned rats. Since the renal lesion of the
latter intoxication is mainly tubular, Reissman et al. suggest the renal
tubular apparatus as site of erythropoietin production. Mantz et al. (271)
agree on the importance of the kidney in maintaining normal levels of
plasma erythropoietin.

Gallagher et al. (121) have studied erythropoietin production in uremic
rabbits and did observe some increase of erythropoietin in response to
hypoxia or anemia in nephrectomized animals. This suggests that the kidney
is not the sole source of erythropoietin. In these studies, hypoxia or anemia
was used to stimulate erythropoietin production, and plasma extracts were
bioassayed for erythropoietin content by measuring Fe^{59}-incorporation into
erythrocytes in assay rats made sensitive to exogenous erythropoietin by
transfusion-induced polycythemia. Although the degree of Fe^{59} incorporation was significantly less when polycythemic rats were injected with plasma
from hypoxic nephrectomized rabbits than when they were injected with
hypoxic plasma from control animals, it was still more than when the test
animals were injected with normal plasma extracts. Similar conclusions that
the kidney is not the only source of erythropoietin production were reached
by Rosse & Waldmann (350). They reported experiments in parabiotic
rats, placed in divided chambers. One partner of the pair was nephrectomized, ureter-ligated, or normal, and exposed to anoxia, while the other
breathed room air. Erythropoiesis, as measured by Fe^{59} incorporation into
circulating erythrocytes, was still enhanced when the nephrectomized
partner was exposed to a low pO_2.

The role of the kidney in the formation of an erythropoietic principle is
also stressed by the occasional occurrence of increased erythropoiesis in
cases of renal tumors or cysts (153, 154, 172) although, in general, polycythemia in histologically proven renal disease is rare (428). An interesting

clue to a possible involvement of vascular endothelium as a site of erythropoietin production is given by an observation of Waldmann & Levin (416) who found a high titer of erythropoietin in fluid aspirated from a cystic cerebellar hemangioblastoma. This may suggest that erythropoietin is produced by vascular epithelium. Gurney (153) and Kurotowska (231) have discussed the thesis that the renal vascular system may participate to a large, but not exclusive degree in erythropoietic production. It is possible that the normally low oxygen tension in parts of the renal medulla explains the key role of the kidney in producing the erythropoietic principle.

ACKNOWLEDGMENTS

I would like to acknowledge the assistance of Martha B. MacLeod and Ruth Klose in preparing the bibliography and the manuscript. I am also indebted to Drs. M. F. Levitt, P. J. Mulrow, K. Thurau, and E. E. Windhager for helpful discussion of some aspects of this review.

LITERATURE CITED

1. Amiel, C., Guinnebault, M., Boudiak, C., and Morel, F., *Rev. franç. études clin. biol.*, **6**, 125–37 (1961)
2. Anderson, H. M., and Mudge, G. H., *J. Clin. Invest.*, **34**, 1691–97 (1955)
3. Au, W. Y. W., and Raisz, L. G., *J. Clin. Invest.*, **39**, 1302–11 (1960)
4. Aukland, K., *Scand. J. Clin. & Lab. Invest.*, **12**, 300–10 (1960)
5. Aukland, K., and Kiil, F., *Scand. J. Clin. & Lab Invest.*, **13**, 87–99 (1961)
6. Aukland, K., and Krog, J., *Nature*, **188**, 671 (1960)
7. Bailey, R. E., *Endocrinology*, **67**, 807–14 (1960)
8. Baker, G. P., Levitin, H., and Epstein, F. H., *J. Clin. Invest.*, **40**, 867–73 (1961)
9. Bálint, P. *Nierenfunktion und Nervensystem*, 117–30 (Veb Verlag Volk und Gesundheit, Berlin, 1959)
10. Bálint, P., and Fekete, A., *Acta Physiol. Acad. Sci. Hung.*, **17**, 277–86 (1960)
11. Bálint, P., Fekete, A., Gömöri, P., and Nagy, Z., *Arch. ges. Physiol.*, **271**, 705–14 (1960)
12. Bálint, P., Fekete, A., and Sturcz, J., *Acta Physiol. Acad. Sci. Hung.*, **17**, 287–94 (1960)
13. Bálint, P., Fekete, A., Szalay, E., and Taraba, I., *Arch. exptl. Pathol. Pharmakol.*, **239**, 497–506 (1960)
14. Bálint, P., Kiss, E., and Sturcz, J., *Arch. ges. Physiol.*, **272**, 307–15 (1961)
15. Bank, N., *J. Clin. Invest.*, **40**, 573–78 (1961)
16. Bank, N., and Schwartz, W. B., *J. Clin. Invest.*, **39**, 1516–25 (1960)
17. Barer, G. R., *J. Physiol. (London)*, **156**, 49–66 (1961)
18. Bayliss, L. E., *Modern Views on the Secretion of Urine*, 107 (Little, Brown & Co., Boston, 1956)
19. Becker, E. L., Heinemann, H. O., Igarashi, K., Hodler, J. E., and Gershberg, H., *J. Clin. Invest.*, **39**, 1909–13 (1960)
20. Bello, C. T., Sevy, R. W., Ohler, E. A., Papacostas, C. A., and Bucher, R. M., *Circulation*, **22**, 573–82 (1960)
21. Berglund, F., *Acta Physiol. Scand.*, **49**, Suppl. 172, 1–37 (1960)
22. Berlin, R. D., Barger, A. C., Muldowney, F. P., and Barnett, G. O., *Am. J. Physiol.*, **199**, 275–80 (1960)
23. Berliner, R. W., *Renal Mechanism for Potassium Excretion, Harvey Lectures, Ser. 55* (1961)
24. Berndt, W. O., and LeSher, D. A., *Am. J. Physiol.*, **200**, 1111–15 (1961)
25. Bettge, S., Voss, R., Rothauge, C. F., and L'Allemand, H., *Klin. Wochschr.*, **38**, 1182–87 (1960)
26. Beyer, K. H., *Arch. intern. pharmacodynamie*, **98**, 97–117 (1954)
27. Biron, P., Koiw, E., Nowaczynski, W., Brouillet, J., and Genest, J., *J. Clin. Invest.*, **40**, 338–47 (1961)

28. Blake, W. D., *Am. J. Physiol.*, **199**, 503–8 (1960)

29. Block, J. B., and Burrows, B. A., *J. Lab. Clin. Med.*, **56**, 463–72 (1960)

30. Block, J. B., Hine, G. J., and Burrows, B. A., *J. Lab. Clin. Med.*, **56**, 110–19 (1960)

31. Blythe, W. B., Newton, M., Lazcano, F., and Welt, L. G., *Am. J. Physiol.*, **199**, 912–14 (1960)

32. Bojesen, E., and Degn, H., *Nature*, **190**, 352–53 (1961)

33. Bonting, S. L., deBruin, H., and Pollak, V. E., *J. Clin. Invest.*, **40**, 177–80 (1961)

34. Bonting, S. L., Pollak, V. E., Muehrcke, R. C., and Kark, R. M., *J. Clin. Invest.*, **39**, 1373–79 (1960)

35. Bonting, S. L., Pollak, V. E., Muehrcke, R. C., and Kark, R. M., *J. Clin. Invest.*, **39**, 1381–85 (1960)

36. Bonting, S. L., Tsoudle, A. D., deBruin, H., and Mayron, B. R., *Arch. Biochem. Biophys.*, **91**, 130–37 (1960)

37. Borst, J. G. G., deVries, L. A., and Van Leevwen, A. M., *Clin. Chim. Acta*, **5**, 887–914 (1960)

38. Bott, P. A., *Anal. Biochem.*, **1**, 17–22 (1960)

39. Bott, P. A., and Litchfield, J. B., *Am. J. Med. Sci.*, **237**, 791 (1959)

40. Bott, P. A., and Litchfield, J. B., *Federation Proc.*, **20**, 416 (1961)

41. Bounous, G., Onnis, M., and Shumacker, H. B., Jr., *Surg. Gynecol. Obstet.*, **111**, 682–90 (1960)

42. Bounous, G., Onnis, M., Shumacker, H. B., Jr., and Nash, F., *Surg., Gynecol. Obstet.*, **111**, 540–44 (1960)

43. Boyle, P. J., and Conway, E. J., *J. Physiol. (London)*, **100**, 1–63 (1941)

44. Brauman, H., Vander Veiken, F., Dekoster, J. P., de Myttenaere, M., Gregoire, F., and Lambert, P. P., *Rev. franç. études clin. biol.*, **6**, 232–38 (1961)

45. Braun, W., *Arch. exptl. Pathol. Pharmakol.*, **240**, 25–26 (1960)

46. Bray, G. A., *Am. J. Physiol.*, **199**, 1211–14 (1960)

47. Bresler, E. H., *Am. J. Physiol.*, **199**, 517–21 (1960)

48. Bresler, E. H., and Gilmartin, J. N., *J. Clin. Invest.*, **39**, 974 (1960)

49. Brodsky, W. A., and Carrasquer, G., *Am. J. Physiol.*, **199**, 1232–38 (1960)

50. Bronner, F., and Thompson, D. D., *J. Physiol. (London)*, **157**, 232–50 (1961)

51. Brown, J. L., Samiy, A. H., and Pitts, R. F., *Am. J. Physiol.*, **200**, 370–72 (1961)

52. Bumpus, F. M., Smeby, R. R., and Page, I. H., *Circulation Research*, **9**, 762–66 (1961)

53. Burg, M. B., Papper, S., and Rosenbaum, J. D., *J. Lab. Clin. Med.*, **57**, 533–45 (1961)

54. Buttram, H. M., Rector, F. C., Jr., and Seldin, D. W., *Clin. Research*, **9**, 56 (1961)

55. Cade, R., and Shalhoub, R. J., *J. Clin. Invest.*, **40**, 1028 (1961)

56. Cade, R., Shalhoub, R. J., Canessa-Fischer, M., and Pitts, R. F., *Am. J. Physiol.*, **200**, 373–79 (1961)

57. Cade, R., Shalhoub, R. J., and Hierholzer, K., *Am. J. Physiol.*, **200**, 881–84 (1961)

58. Campbell, D. E. S., *Acta Pharmacol. Toxicol.*, **17**, 213–32 (1960)

59. Campbell, D. E. S., *Acta Pharmacol. Toxicol.*, **17**, 137–50 (1960)

60. Campbell, D. E. S., *Acta Soc. Med. Upsaliensis*, **65**, 361–73 (1960)

61. Canary, J. J., Lynch, H. J., Kyle, L. H., Mintz, D., and Hess, W. C., *J. Lab. Clin. Med.*, **57**, 230–39 (1961)

62. Čapek, K., and Kleinzeller, A., *Excerpta Med.*, **29**, 34 (1960)

63. Capraro, V., Valzelli, G., and DeAgostini, C., *Nature*, **190**, 178–79 (1961)

64. Carlson, C. H., Armstrong, W. D., and Singer, L., *Proc. Soc. Exptl. Biol. Med.*, **104**, 235–39 (1960)

65. Carone, F. A., and Spector, W. G., *J. Pathol. Bacteriol.*, **80**, 55–62 (1960)

66. Carrasquer, G., *J. Clin. Invest.*, **40**, 1028 (1961)

67. Carrasquer, G., and Brodsky, W. A., *Am. J. Physiol.*, **199**, 1239–44 (1960)

68. Carter, N. W., Rector, F. C., Jr., and Seldin, D. W., *New Engl. J. Med.*, **264**, 67–71 (1961)

69. Cheek, D. B., and Holt, A. B., *Clin. Sci.*, **20**, 233–42 (1961)

70. Cier, J. F., *J. physiol. (Paris)*, **53**, 3–74 (1961)

71. Clapp, J. R., and Rector, F. C., *Clin. Research*, **9**, 56 (1961)

72. Cohen, J. J., *Am. J. Physiol.*, **199**, 560–68 (1960)

73. Conway, E. J., Kernan, R. P., and Zadunaisky, J. A., *J. Physiol. (London)*, **155**, 263–79 (1961)

74. Coppage, W. S., Jr., and Liddle, G. W., *Ann. N. Y. Acad. Sci.*, **88**, 815–21 (1960)

75. Cooper, K. E., Cranston, W. I., Demp-ster, W. J., and Mottram, R. F., *J. Physiol. (London)*, **155**, 21 (1961)

76. Copp, D. H., McPherson, G. D., and McIntosh, H. W., *Metabolism, Clin. and Exptl.*, **9**, 680–85 (1960)

77. Cort, J. H., *Excerpta Med.*, **29**, 34 (1960)

78. Cottier, P., *Helv. Med. Acta*, **27**, Suppl. 39, 170 pp. (1960)

79. Coye, R. D., and Donkle, J., *Endocrinology*, **68**, 950–55 (1961)

80. Crabbé, J., and Nichols, G., Jr., *Am. J. Physiol.*, **199**, 871–75 (1960)

81. Crawford, J. D., and Kennedy, G. C., *Nature*, **183**, 891–92 (1959)

82. Crosley, A. P., Jr., Castillo, C., and Rowe, G. G., *J. Clin. Invest.*, **40**, 836–42 (1961)

83. Curran, P. F., Zadunaisky, J., and Gill, J. R., Jr., *Fifth Ann. Meeting Biophys. Soc.*, SA 4 (1961)

84. Currie, J. C. M., and Ullmann, E., *J. Physiol. (London)*, **155**, 438–55 (1961)

85. Czaczkes, J. W., Eliakim, M., and Ullmann, T. D., *J. Lab. Clin. Med.*, **57**, 938–45 (1961)

86. Darmady, E. M., Durant, J., Matthews, E. R., and Stranack, F., *Clin. Sci.*, **19**, 229–42 (1960)

87. Davey, M. J., and Lockett, M. F., *J. Physiol. (London)*, **152**, 206–19 (1960)

88. Davidson, D. G., Levinsky, N. G., and Berliner, R. W., *J. Clin. Invest.*, **37**, 548–55 (1958)

89. Davis, J. O., *Am. J. Med.*, **29**, 486–507 (1960)

90. Davis, J. O., Carpenter, C. J., Ayers, C. R., Holman, J. E., and Bahn, R. C., *J. Clin. Invest.*, **40**, 684–96 (1961)

91. Dedmon, R. E., Dent, C. E., Scriver, C. R. and Westall, R. G., *Clin. Chim. Acta*, **6**, 291–94 (1961)

92. Dedmon, R. E., and Wrong, O., *J. Lab. Clin. Med.*, **56**, 802 (1960)

93. Deetjen, P., and Kramer, K., *Klin. Wochschr.*, **38**, 680–81 (1960)

94. Despopoulos, A., *Am. J. Physiol.*, **200**, 163–66 (1961)

95. deVries, L. A., tenHolt, S. P., Van Daatselaar, J. J., Mulder, A., and Borst, J. G. G., *Clin. Chim. Acta*, **5**, 915–37 (1960)

96. Dieter, E., *Arch. ges. Physiol.*, **273**, 29–38 (1961)

97. Dieter, E., *Arch. ges. Physiol.*, **273**, 39–44 (1961)

98. Deyrup, I. J., and Davies, D. E., *J. Gen. Physiol.*, **44**, 555–70 (1961)

99. Dolcini, H. A., Zaidman, I., Lichtenberg, F., and Gray, S. J., *Am. J. Physiol.*, **199**, 1153–56 (1960)

100. Dubach, U. C., and Recant, L., *J. Clin. Invest.*, **39**, 1364–71 (1960)

101. Dunham, E. T., and Glynn, I. M., *J. Physiol. (London)*, **156**, 274–93 (1961)

102. Earley, L. E., and Orloff, J., *Clin. Research*, **8**, 382 (1960)

103. Earley, L. E., Kahn, M., and Orloff, J., *J. Clin. Invest.*, **40**, 857–66 (1961)

104. Edelman, I. S., *Ann. Rev. Physiol.*, **23**, 37–70 (1961)

105. Eigler, F. W., *Arch. ges. Physiol.*, **272**, 41 (1960)

106. Eigler, F. W., *Am. J. Physiol.*, **201**, 157–63 (1961)

107. Eigler, J. O. C., Salassa, R. M., Bahn, R. C., and Owen, C. A., Jr., *J. Lab. Clin. Med.*, **56**, 807 (1960)

108. Elkinton, J. R., *Mod. Problems in Pediat.*, **6**, 99–123 (1960)

109. Elkinton, J. R., Huth, E. J., Webster, G. D., Jr., and McCance, R. A., *Am. J. Med.*, **29**, 554–75 (1960)

110. Epstein, F. H., *Univ. Mich. Med. Bull.*, **26**, 266–70 (1960)

111. Eremenko, L. F., *Sechenov Physiol. J. USSR (Engl. Transl.)*, **46**, 678–85 (1960)

112. Essig, A., and Taggart, J. V., *Am. J. Physiol.*, **199**, 509–12 (1960)

113. Falk, J. L., *Science*, **133**, 195–96 (1961)

114. Farah, A., and Kruse, R., *J. Pharmacol. Exptl. Therap.*, **130**, 13–19 (1960)

115. Farquhar, M. G., Wissig, S. L., and Palade, G. E., *J. Exptl. Med.*, **113**, 47–66 (1961)

116. Farrell, P., *Federation Proc.*, **19**, 601 (1960)

117. Földi, M., and Kovách, A. G. B., *Nierenfunktion und Nervensystem*, 71–75 (Dutz, H., Ed., Veb Verlag Volk und Gesundheit, Berlin, 1959)

118. Földi, M., Kovách, A. G. B., Papp, N., Koltay, E., and Somlyai, L., *Acta Physiol. (Hung.)*, **17**, 407–28 (1960)

119. Fong, C. T. O., Silver, L., Christman, D. R., and Schwartz, I. L. *Proc. Natl. Acad. Sci. US*, **46**, 1273–77 (1960)

120. Forbes, A. L., and Magee, J. H., *Circulation*, **23**, 750 (1960)

121. Gallagher, N. I., McCarthy, J. M., and Lange, R. D., *J. Lab. Clin. Med.*, **57**, 281–89 (1961)

122. Gamble, J. L., Jr., *Bull. Johns Hopkins Hosp.*, **107**, 247–54 (1960)

123. Gann, D. S., Mills, I. H., and Bartter, F. C., *Federation Proc.*, **19**, 605–10 (1960)

124. Gann, D. S., Mills, I. H., Cruz, J. F., Casper, A. G. T., and Bartter, F. C., *Proc. Soc. Exptl. Biol. Med.*, **105**, 158–61 (1960)

125. Ganong, W. F., and Mulrow, P. J., *Nature*, **190**, 1115–16 (1961)

126. Gantt, C. L., *N. Y. State J. Med.*, **61**, 756–77 (1961)

127. Gantt, C. L., and Synek, J. H., *Proc. Soc. Exptl. Biol. Med.*, **106**, 27–28 (1961)

128. Gardner, K. D., Jr., *J. Clin. Invest.*, **40**, 525–35 (1961)

129. Genest, J., Biron, P., Koiw, E., Nowaczynski, W., Chrétien, M., and Boucher, R., *Circulation Research*, **9**, 775–88 (1961)

130. Gerlach, E., Bader, W., and Schwoerer, W., *Arch. ges. Physiol.*, **272**, 407–33 (1961)

131. Giebisch, G., *J. Gen. Physiol.*, **44**, 659–78 (1961)

132. Giebisch, G., *Progr. in Cardiovascular Diseases*, **3**, 463–82 (1961)

133. Giebisch, G., and Windhager, E. E., *Federation Proc.*, **18**, 52 (1959)

134. Giebisch, G., Windhager, E. E., and Pitts, R. F., *Biology of Pyelonephritis*, 277–87 (Quinn, E. L., and Kass, E. H., Eds., Little, Brown & Co., Boston, 1960)

135. Gill, J. R., Jr., and Bartter, F. C., *J. Clin. Invest.*, **40**, 716–22 (1961)

136. Gill, J. R., Bell, N. H., and Bartter, F. C., *Clin. Research*, **9**, 36 (1961)

137. Gillissen, J., and Taugner, R., *Z. ges. exptl. Med.*, **134**, 179–86 (1961)

138. Ginn, H. E., Jr., Unger, A. M., Hume, D. M., and Schilling, J. A., *J. Lab. Clin. Med.*, **56**, 1–13 (1960)

139. Giovannetti, S., Bigalli, A., Della Santa, M., and Zampieri, A., *Minerva nefrol.*, **7**, 73–77 (1960)

140. Giovannetti, S., Bigalli, A., Della Santa, M., and Zanpieri, A., *Arch. ital. biol.*, **98**, 375–90 (1960)

141. Globus, D. L., Becker, E. L., and Thompson, D. D., *Am. J. Physiol.*, **200**, 1105–10 (1961)

142. Goldberg, M., and Handler, J. S., *New Engl. J. Med.*, **263**, 1037–43 (1960)

143. Goldsmith, C., Beasly, H. K., Whalley, P. J., Rector, F. C., Jr., and Seldin, D. W., *J. Clin. Invest.*, **40**, 2043–52 (1961)

144. Goldstein, M. H., Levitt, M. F., Hauser, A. D., and Poliveros, D., *J. Clin. Invest.*, **40**, 731–42 (1961)

145. Gömöri, P., Kovách, A. G. B., Takács, L., Földi, M., Szabó, G. Y., Nagy, Z., and Wiltner, W., *Acta Med. Acad. Sci. Hung.*, **16**, 37–42 (1960)

146. Gömöri, P., Kovách, A. G. B., Takács, L., Földi, M., Szabó, G. Y., Nagy, Z., and Wiltner, W., *Acta Med. Acad. Sci. Hung.*, **16**, 43–60 (1960)

147. Gordon, G. B., Eichenholz, A., MacDonald, F. M., and Semba, T. T., *J. Lab. Clin. Med.*, **56**, 294–302 (1960)

148. Gottschalk, C. W., *The Physiologist*, **4**, 35–55 (1961)

149. Gottschalk, C. W., Lassiter, W. E., and Mylle, M., *Am. J. Physiol.*, **198**, 581–94 (1960)

150. Gottschalk, C. W., and Mylle, M., *Am. J. Physiol.*, **185**, 430–39 (1956)

151. Grollman, A. P., Harrison, H. C., and Harrison, H. E., *J. Clin. Invest.*, **40**, 1290–96 (1961)

152. Gross, F., *Experientia*, **17**, 57–63 (1961)

153. Gurney, C. W., *J. Am. Med. Assoc.*, **173**, 1828–29 (1960)

154. Gurney, C. W., and Jacobson, L. O., *Univ. Mich. Med. Bull.*, **26**, 271–77 (1960)

155. Gutman, A. B., Dayton, P. G., Yü, T. F., Berger, L., Chen, W., Sicam, L. E., and Burns, J. J., *Am. J. Med.*, **29**, 1017–33 (1960)

156. Haenze, S., *Klin. Wochschr.*, **38**, 1168 (1960)

157. Handler, J. S., *J. Clin. Invest.*, **39**, 1526–32 (1960)

158. Handler, J. S., Wojtczak, A., and Goldberg, M., *J. Clin. Invest.*, **39**, 994 (1960)

159. Hanna, S., Harrison, M., MacIntyre, I., and Fraser, R., *Lancet*, **II**, 172–76 (1960)

160. Hardin, R. A., Scott, J. B., and Haddy, F., *Am. J. Physiol.*, **199**, 1192–94 (1960)

161. Harth, O., Kreienberg, W., and Lutz, J., *Arch. ges. Physiol.*, **270**, 174–83 (1959)

162. Hartroft, P. M., and Newmark, L. N., *Anat. Record*, **139**, 185–200 (1961)

163. Harvey, R. B., *Am. J. Physiol.*, **199**, 31–34 (1960)

164. Hays, R. M., and Leaf, A., *Ann. Internal Med.*, **54**, 700–9 (1961)

165. Heidenreich, O., Kook, Y., Ling, V., and Menzel, H., *Arch. exptl.*

Pathol. Pharmakol., **239**, 328–35 (1960)

166. Heidenreich, O., Kook, Y., Ling, V., and Menzel, H., *Arch. exptl. Pathol. Pharmakol.*, **239**, 336–44 (1960)

167. Heimburg, P., and Ochwadt, B., *Arch. ges. Physiol.*, **273**, 62–70 (1961)

168. Heller, J., *Physiol. Bohemosloven.*, **9**, 13–19 (1960)

169. Heller, S., and Hillmann, G., *Klin. Wochschr.*, **39**, 257–59 (1961)

170. Herken, H., Senft, G., and Natzschka, J., *Arch. exptl. Pathol. Pharmakol.*, **240**, 483–94 (1961)

171. Herrin, R. C., and Corlett, C. M., *Proc. Soc. Exptl. Biol. Med.*, **104**, 744–48 (1960)

172. Hewlett, J. S., Hoffman, G. C., Senhauser, D. A., and Battle, J. D., Jr., *New Engl. J. Med.*, **262**, 1058–61 (1960)

173. Hierholzer, K., *Am. J. Physiol.*, **201**, 318–24 (1961)

174. Hierholzer, K., Cade, R., Gurd, R., Kessler, R., and Pitts, R. F., *Am. J. Physiol.*, **198**, 833–37 (1960)

175. Himmelhoch, S. R., and Karnovsky, M. J., *J. Biophys. Biochem. Cytol.*, **9**, 893–908 (1961)

176. Hinshaw, L. B., Flaig, R. D., Carlson, C. H., and Thong, N. K., *Am. J. Physiol.*, **199**, 923–26 (1960)

177. Hoffman, J. F., *Federation Proc.*, **19**, 127 (1960)

178. Hohenleitner, F. J., and Spitzer, J. J., *Am. J. Physiol.*, **200**, 1095–98 (1961)

179. Holliday, M. A., *J. Pediat.*, **57**, 23–35 (1960)

180. Holliday, M. A., Bright, N. H., Schulz, D., and Oliver, J., *J. Exptl. Med.*, **113**, 971–80 (1961)

181. Holliday, M. A., Segar, W. E., Bright, N. H., and Egan, T., *Pediatrics*, **26**, 950–59 (1960)

182. Hong, S. K., Boylan, J. W., and Tannenberg, A. M., *J. Appl. Physiol.*, **15**, 115–20 (1960)

183. Horster, F. A., Kuschinsky, G., Peters, G., and Brunner, H., *Arch. exptl. Pathol. Pharmacol.*, **239**, 345–58 (1960)

184. Hovig, T., and Laake, H., *Acta Med. Scand.*, **169**, 221–26 (1961)

185. Huang, K. C., Moore, K. B., and Campbell, P. C., Jr., *Am. J. Physiol.*, **199**, 5–8 (1960)

186. Hulet, W. H., and Smith, H. W., *Am. J. Med.*, **30**, 8–25 (1961)

187. Hungerland, H., *Bibliotheca Paediat.*, **6**, 124–36 (1960)

188. Huth, E. J., Webster, G. D., Jr., and Elkinton, J. R., *Am. J. Med.*, **29**, 586–98 (1960)

189. Jaenicke, J. R., *Am. J. Physiol.*, **199**, 1205–10 (1960)

190. Jaenicke, J. R., *J. Clin. Invest.*, **40**, 144–51 (1961)

191. Jaenicke, J. R., and Berliner, R. W., *J. Clin. Invest.*, **39**, 481–90 (1960)

192. Jaenicke, J. R., and Bray, G. A., *Am. J. Physiol.*, **199**, 1219–22 (1960)

193. Jaenicke, J. R., and Waterhouse, C., *J. Clin. Endocrinol. and Metabolism*, **21**, 231–42 (1961)

194. Kagawa, C. M., *Univ. Mich. Med. Bull.*, **26**, 251–61 (1960)

195. Kagawa, C. M., and Van Arman, C. G., *J. Pharmacol. Exptl. Therap.*, **129**, 343–49 (1960)

196. Kanter, G. S., *Am. J. Physiol.*, **200**, 878–80 (1961)

197. Kanter, G. S., *USAF School Aviation Med.*, **60–76**, 1–11 (1960)

198. Karger, W., Eigler, F. W., and Hampel, A., *Arch. ges. Physiol.*, **272**, 187–90 (1960)

199. Kashiwa, H. K., *Endocrinology*, **68**, 80–91 (1961)

200. Kaufmann, W., Nieth, H., and Schlitter, J. G., *Arch. ges. Physiol.*, **272**, 31–32 (1960)

201. Kennedy, G. C., *J. Endocrinol.*, **20**, 365–74 (1960)

202. Kennedy, G. C., *Proc. Roy. Soc. Med.*, **53**, 589–91 (1960)

203. Kennedy, G. C., and Crawford, J. D., *J. Endocrinol.*, **22**, 77–86 (1961)

204. Kennedy, T. J., *Anaesthesiology*, **21**, 704–16 (1960)

205. Kerpel-Fronius, E., Rumhanyi, G., Gati, B., and Dobak, E., *Pediatrics*, **26**, 939–49 (1960)

206. Kerr, W. K., Kyle, V. N., Keresteci, A. H., and Smythe, C. A., *J. Urol.*, **84**, 236–42 (1960)

207. Kessler, R. H., *Am. J. Physiol.*, **199**, 1215–18 (1960)

208. Kessler, R. H., *Clin. Pharmacol. Therap.*, **1**, 723–34 (1960)

209. Kessler, R. H., Hierholzer, K., Gurd, R. S., and Pitts, R. F., *Am. J. Physiol.*, **194**, 540–46 (1958)

210. Kessler, R. H., Hierholzer, K., Gurd, R. S., and Pitts, R. F., *Am. J. Physiol.*, **196**, 1346–51 (1959)

211. Kiil, F., *Nature*, **189**, 927–28 (1961)

212. Kiil, F., and Aukland, K., *Scand. J. Clin. Lab. Invest.*, **12**, 277–89 (1960)

213. Kiil, F., and Aukland, K., *Scand. J. Clin. Lab. Invest.*, **12**, 290–99 (1960)

214. Kinsolving, C. R., and Post, R. L., *The Physiologist*, **3**, 94 (1960)

215. Kinter, W. B., Leape, L. L., and Cohen, J. J., *Am. J. Physiol.*, **199**, 931–41 (1960)

216. Kleeman, C. R., Bernstein, D., Dowling, J. T., and Maxwell, M. H., *Acta Endocrinol.*, **35**, Suppl. 51, 493 (1960)

217. Kleeman, C. R., Koplowitz, J., Cutler, R. E., Maxwell, M. H., and Dowling, J. T., *Acta Endocrinol.*, **35**, Suppl. 51, 177 (1960)

218. Kleeman, C. R., Kaplowitz, J., Maxwell, M. H., Cutler, R., and Dowling, J. T., *J. Clin. Invest.*, **39**, 1472–80 (1960)

219. Kleinzeller, A., *Biochim. et Biophys. Acta*, **43**, 41–50 (1960)

220. Kleinzeller, A., and Cort, J. H., *Physiol. Bohemosloven.*, **9**, 106–15 (1960)

221. Knoeffel, P, K., and Huang, K. C., *J. Pharmacol. Exptl. Therap.*, **126**, 296–303 (1959)

222. Kodicek, E., Darmady, E. M., and Stranack, F., *Clin. Sci.*, **20**, 185–95 (1961)

223. Koefoed-Johnsen, V., and Ussing, H. H., *Acta Physiol. Scand.*, **42**, 298–308 (1958)

224. Kramer, K., and Deetjen, P., *Arch. ges. Physiol.*, **271**, 782 (1960)

225. Kramer, K., Deetjen, P., and Brechtelsbauer, H., *Arch. ges. Physiol.* (In press)

226. Kramer, K., Thurau, K., and Deetjen, P., *Arch. ges. Physiol.*, **270**, 251–69 (1960)

227. Kraus, H., and Ullrich, K. J., *Arch. ges. Physiol.* (In press)

228. Krück, F., and Hild, R., *Klin. Wochschr.*, **38**, 962–65 (1960)

229. Kruhøffer, P., *Handbuch der Experimentellen Pharmakologie*, 233–423 (Eichler, O., and Farah, A., Eds., Springer-Verlag, Berlin, Göttingen, Heidelberg, 1960)

230. Kupfer, S., and Kosovsky, J. D., *Clin. Research*, **8**, 186 (1960)

231. Kurotowska, Z., Lewortowski, B., and Michalak, E., *Bull. acad. polon. sci.*, **8**, 77 (1960)

232. Kurtz, S. M., and McManus, J. F. A., *J. Ultrastruct. Research*, **4**, 81–87 (1960)

233. Laake, H., *Acta Endocrinol.*, **34**, 60–64 (1960)

234. Lambie, A. T., *Water and Electrolyte Metabolism*, 131–42 (Stewart, C. P., and Strengers, T., Eds., Elsevier Publ. Co., Amsterdam, 1961)

235. Lambie, A. T., and Robson, J. S., *Clin. Sci.*, **20**, 123–30 (1961)

236. Langston, J. B., Guyton, A. C., and Gillespie, W. J., Jr., *Am. J. Physiol.*, **199**, 495–98 (1960)

237. Langston, J. B., Guyton, A. C., and Hall, C. G., *Federation Proc.*, **20**, 108 (1961)

238. Laragh, J. H., *J. Am. Med. Assoc.*, **174**, 293–95 (1960)

239. Laragh, J. H., *Circulation Research*, **9**, 792–802 (1961)

240. Laragh, J. H., Angers, M., Kelly, W. G., and Lieberman, S., *J. Am. Med. Assoc.*, **174**, 234–40 (1960)

241. Lassen, N. A., and Longley, J. B., *Proc. Soc. Exptl. Biol. Med.*, **106**, 743–48 (1961)

242. Lassen, N. A., Munck, O., and Thaysen, J. H., *Acta Physiol. Scand.*, **51**, 371–84 (1961)

243. Lassen, U. V., and Thaysen, J. H., *Biochim. et Biophys. Acta*, **47**, 616–17 (1961)

244. Lassiter, W. E., Gottschalk, C. W., and Mylle, M., *Am. J. Physiol.*, **200**, 1139–47 (1961)

245. Lathem, W., and Davis, B. B., *Am. J. Physiol.*, **199**, 644–47 (1960)

246. Lathem, W., Davis, B. B., Zweig, P. H., and Dew, R., *J. Clin. Invest.*, **39**, 840–45 (1960)

247. Lathem, W., and Rodnan, G. P., *J. Clin. Invest.*, **40**, 1056 (1961)

248. Lathem, W., Davis, B. B., and Rodnan, G. P., *Am. J. Physiol.*, **199**, 9–12 (1960)

249. Latta, H., Maunsbach, A. B., and Madden, S. C., *J. Ultrastruct. Research*, **4**, 455–72 (1960)

250. Leaf, A., *Univ. Mich. Med. Bull.*, **26**, 239–44 (1960)

251. Leaf, A., and Santos, R. F., *New Engl. J. Med.*, **264**, 335–41 (1961)

252. Leboeuf, G., Steiker, D. D., Bongiovanni, A. M., and Eberlein, W. R., *Program, 43rd Meeting of the Endocrine Soc.*, 18 (June 22–24, 1961)

253. Lennon, E. J., Ruetz, P. P., and Engstrom, W. W., *Am. J. Med.*, **30**, 475–85 (1961)

254. Levitin, H., and Epstein, F. H., *Am. J. Physiol.*, **200**, 1148–50 (1961)

255. Levy, M. N., *Am. J. Physiol.*, **199**, 13–18 (1960)

256. Levy, M. N., and Imperial, E. S., *Am. J. Physiol.*, **200**, 159–62 (1961)

257. Levy, R. I., Weiner, I. M., and Mudge, G. H., *J. Clin. Invest.*, **37**, 1016–23 (1958)

258. Lewis, J., and Ford, R. V., *J. Lab. Clin. Med.*, **57**, 546–52 (1961)

259. Leyssac, P. P., Lassen, U. V., and

Thaysen, J. H., *Biochem. et Biophys. Acta*, 48, 602–3 (1961)

260. Lilienfield, L. S., Maganzini, H. C., and Bauer, M. H., *Circulation Research*, 9, 614–17 (1961)

261. Lindeman, R. D., Van Buren, H. C., and Raisz, L. G., *J. Clin. Invest.*, 40, 152–58 (1961)

262. Lobban, M. C., and Simpson, H. W., *J. Physiol. (London)*, 155, 64 (1961)

263. Mac Intyre, I., *Proc. Roy. Soc. Med.*, 53, 1057–59 (1960)

264. Majoor, C. L. H., Schlatmann, R. J. A. F. M., Jansen, A. P., and Prenen, H., *Water and Electrolyte Metabolism*, 156–71 (Stewart, C. P., and Strengers, T., Eds., Elsevier Publ. Co., Amsterdam, 1961)

265. Malmendier, C. L., Dekoster, J. P., and Lampert, P. P., *Clin. Sci.*, 19, 605–18 (1960)

266. Malmendier, C. L., Dekoster, J. P., Vander Veiken, F., Brauman, H., de Myttenaere, M., and Lambert, P. P., *Am. J. Physiol.*, 199, 292–94 (1960)

267. Malvin, R. L., *Progr. in Cardiovascular Diseases*, 3, 432–48 (1961)

268. Malvin, R. L., and Lotspeich, W. D., *Am. J. Physiol.*, 187, 51–56 (1956)

269. Manitius, A., Levitin, H., Beck, D., and Epstein, F. H., *J. Clin. Invest.*, 39, 684–92 (1960)

270. Manitius, A., Levitin, H., Beck, D., and Epstein, F. H., *J. Clin. Invest.*, 39, 693–97 (1960)

271. Mantz, J. M., Cholevas, M., and Warter, J., *Compt. rend. soc. biol.*, 154, 1068–71 (1960)

272. Maren, T. H., Sorsdahl, O. A., and Dickhaus, A. J., *Am. J. Physiol.*, 200, 170–74 (1961)

273. McCann, W. P., Gulanti, O. D., and Stanton, H. C., *Bull. Johns Hopkins Hosp.*, 108, 36–47 (1961)

274. Mees, E. J. D., *Acta Med. Scand.*, 168, 193–96 (1960)

275. Mendel, D., *J. Physiol. (London)*, 156, 544–54 (1961)

276. Mertz, D. P., *Arch. exptl. Pathol. Pharmakol.*, 239, 410 (1960)

277. Miller, F., *J. Biophys. Biochem. Cytol.*, 8, 689–718 (1960)

278. Miller, F., *J. Biophys. Biochem. Cytol.*, 9, 157–70 (1961)

279. Miller, T. B., and Farah, A. E., *Federation Proc.*, 19, 363 (1960)

280. Miller, T. B., and Riggs, D. S., *J. Pharmacol. Exptl. Therap.*, 132, 329–38 (1961)

281. Mills, J. N., Thomas, S., and Williamson, K. S., *J. Physiol. (London)*, 156, 415–23 (1961)

282. Mills, J. N., Thomas, S., and Williamson, K. S., *J. Physiol. (London)*, 155, 18P (1961)

283. Mills, L. C., Moyer, J. H., and Handley, C. A., *Am. J. Physiol.*, 198, 1279–83 (1960)

284. Milne, M. D., Crawford, M. A., Girão, C. B., and Loughridge, L., *Clin. Sci.*, 19, 165–79 (1960)

285. Morel, F., and Guinnebault, M., *J. physiol. (Paris)*, 53, 75–130 (1961)

286. Morel, F. F., Guinnebault, M., and Amiel, C., *Helv. Physiol. et Pharmacol. Acta*, 18, 183–92 (1960)

287. Morrin, P. A. F., Bricker, N. S., and Kime, S. W., Jr., *J. Clin. Invest.*, 39, 1013 (1960)

288. Morrin, P. A., Bricker, N. S., Kime, S. W., Jr., Newmark, L. N., and Gedney, W. B., *J. Lab. Clin. Med.*, 56, 931 (1960)

289. Morrison, A. B., Buckalew, V. M., Jr., Miller, R., and Lewis, J. D., *J. Clin. Invest.*, 39, 1014 (1960)

290. Mudge, G. H., and Weiner, I. M., *Ann. N. Y. Acad. Sci.*, 71, 344–54 (1958)

291. Muirhead, E. E., Jones, F., and Stirman, J. A., *J. Lab. Clin. Med.*, 56, 167–80 (1960)

292. Müller, P., *Exptl. Cell Research*, Suppl. 5, 118–52 (1958)

293. Mulrow, P. J., and Ganong, W. F., *J. Clin. Invest.*, 40, 579–85 (1961)

294. Mulrow, P. J., and Ganong, W. F., *Yale J. Biol. and Med.*, 33, 386–95 (1961)

295. Munson, P. L., *Ann. Rev. Pharmacol.*, 1, 315 (1961)

296. Naets, J. P., *J. Clin. Invest.*, 39, 102–10 (1960)

297. Naets, J. P., *Blood*, 16, 1770–76 (1960)

298. Naets, J. P., Brauman, H., and Kraytman, M., *Acta Haematol.*, 24, 169–85 (1960)

299. Niemi, M., and Pearse, A. G. E., *J. Biophys. Biochem. Cytol.*, 8, 279–82 (1960)

300. Nordin, B. E. C., *Clin. Sci.*, 19, 311–20 (1960)

301. Nugent, C. A., and Tyler, F. H., *J. Clin. Invest.*, 38, 1890–98 (1959)

302. Nutbourne, D. M., *Clin. Sci.*, 20, 263–78 (1961)

303. Nutbourne, D. M., and de Wardener, H. E., *Clin. Sci.*, 20, 63–74 (1961)

304. Oberling, C., and Hatt, P. Y., *Ann. anat. pathol.*, 5, 441–75 (1960)

305. Ochwadt, B., *Arch. ges. Physiol.*, **262**, 207–18 (1956)
306. Ochwadt, B., *Arch. ges. Physiol.*, **265**, 112–16 (1957)
307. Ochwadt, B., *Progr. in Cardiovascular Diseases*, **3**, 501–10 (1961)
308. Oken, D. (Personal communication)
309. Oliver, J., *Bull. N. Y. Acad. Med.*, **37**, 81–128 (1961)
310. Orloff, J., and Berliner, R. W., *Ann. Rev. Pharmacol.*, **1**, 287–314 (1961)
311. Orloff, J., and Burg, M., *Am. J. Physiol.*, **199**, 49–54 (1960)
312. Orloff, J., and Handler, J. S., *Biochem. Biophys. Research Communs.*, **5**, 63–66 (1961)
313. Orti, E., and Ralli, E. P., *Am. J. Physiol.*, **199**, 43–48 (1960)
314. Owen, E. E., Johnson, J. A., and Tyor, M. P., *J. Clin. Invest.*, **40**, 215–21 (1961)
315. Owen, E. E., and Tyor, M. P., *Clin. Research*, **9**, 58 (1961)
316. Page, I. H., and Bumpus, F. M., *Physiol. Revs.*, **41**, 331–90 (1961)
317. Pak Poy, R. K., and Wrong, O., *Clin. Sci.*, **19**, 631–40 (1960)
318. Pappenheimer, J. R., *Physiol. Revs.*, **40**, Suppl. 4, 35–37 (1960)
319. Papper, S., Belsky, J. L., Bleifer, K. H., Saxon, L., and Smith, W. P., *J. Lab. Clin. Med.*, **56**, 727–33 (1960)
320. Passow, H., Schwiewind, H., and Weiss, C., *Arch. exptl. Pathol. Pharmakol.*, **240**, 179–86 (1960)
321. Paul, M. F., Bender, R. C., and Nohle, E. G., *Am. J. Physiol.*, **197**, 580–84 (1959)
322. Peña, J. C., and Malvin, R. L., *Federation Proc.*, **19**, 368 (1960)
323. Pitts, R. F., *Am. J. Med.*, **24**, 745–63 (1958)
324. Pitts, R. F., *Progr. in Cardiovascular Diseases*, **3**, 537–62 (1961)
325. Platts, M. M., and Mudge, G. H., *Am. J. Physiol.*, **200**, 387–92 (1961)
326. Pollak, V. E., Bonting, S. L., Muehrcke, R. C., and Kark, R. M., *J. Clin. Invest.*, **39**, 1386–93 (1960)
327. Pollak, V. E., Bonting, S. L., Muehrcke, R. C., and Kark, R. M., *J. Clin. Invest.*, **39**, 1394–1400 (1960)
328. Porush, J. G., Goldstein, M. H., Eisner, G. M., and Levitt, M. F., *J. Clin. Invest.*, **40**, 1475–85 (1961)
329. Post, R. L., Merritt, C. R., Kinsolving, C. R., and Albright, C. D., *J. Biol. Chem.*, **235**, 1796–1802 (1960)
330. Potter, V. R., and Reif, A. E., *J. Biol. Chem.*, **194**, 287–97 (1952)
331. Pullman, T. N., Lavender, A. R., and Aho, I., *J. Clin. Invest.*, **40**, 1073 (1961)
332. Pullman, T. N., Lavender, A. R., Aho, I., and Rasmussen, H., *Endocrinology*, **67**, 570–82 (1960)
333. Rasmussen, H., *Am. J. Med.*, **30**, 112–28 (1961)
334. Rasmussen, H., and Craig, L. C., *J. Biol. Chem.*, **236**, 759–64 (1961)
335. Rasmussen, H., Schwartz, I. L., Schoessler, M. A., and Hochster, G., *Proc. Natl. Acad. Sci. US*, **46**, 1278–87 (1960)
336. Rector, F. C., Jr., Seldin, D. W., Roberts, A. D., Jr., and Smith, J. S., *J. Clin. Invest.*, **39**, 1706–21 (1960)
337. Reger, J. F., Hutt, M. P., and Neustein, H. B., *J. Ultrastruct. Research*, **5**, 28–43 (1961)
338. Reiss, E., Bricker N. S., Kim, S. W., Jr., and Morrin, P. A. F., *J. Clin. Invest.*, **40**, 165–70 (1961)
339. Reissman, K. R., Nomura, T., Gunn, R. W., and Brosius, F., *Blood*, **16**, 1411–23 (1960)
340. Relman, A. S., and Levinsky, N. G., *Ann. Rev. Med.*, **12**, 93–110 (1961)
341. Relman, A. S., Porter, R., Tobias, J. F., and Schwartz, W. B., *J. Clin. Invest.*, **39**, 1551–59 (1960)
342. Rennick, B. R., and Moe, G. K., *Am. J. Physiol.*, **198**, 1267–70 (1960)
343. Rennie, D. W., Reeves, R. B., and Pappenheimer, J. R., *Am. J. Physiol.*, **195**, 120–32 (1958)
344. Reubi, F., *Mod. Problems in Paediat.*, **6**, 3–21 (1960)
345. Richet, G., *Rev. franç. études clin. et biol.*, **6**, (4)(1961)
346. Richterich, R., *Progr. in Cardiovascular Diseases*, **3**, 449–62 (1961)
347. River, G. L., Kushner, D. S., Armstrong, H., Jr., Dubin, A., Slodki, S. J., and Cutting, H. O., *Metabolism, Clin. and Exptl.*, **9**, 1118–33 (1960)
348. Rosenfeld, S., and Sellers, A. L., *Am. J. Physiol.*, **199**, 499–502 (1960)
349. Ross, E. J., and Winternitz, W. W., *Clin. Sci.*, **20**, 143–48 (1961)
350. Rosse, W. F., and Waldmann, T. A., *J. Clin. Invest.*, **40**, 1077 (1961)
351. Saltzman, H. A., Manfredi, F., and Sieker, H. O., *J. Lab. Clin. Med.*, **57**, 694–702 (1961)
352. Samelius, U., and Åström, A., *Acta Physiol. Scand.*, **50**, 139 (1960)
353. Samiy, A. H., Hirsch, P. F., and

Ramsay, A. G., *J. Clin. Invest.*, **40**, 1078 (1961)

354. Samiy, A. H., Hirsch, P. F., Ramsay, A. G., Giordano, C., and Merrill, J. P., *Endocrinology*, **67**, 266–69 (1960)

355. Scher, A. M., MacDonald, P., and Koch, A. R., *Federation Proc.*, **20**, 108 (1961)

356. Schmidt-Nielsen, B., O'Dell, R., and Osaki, H., *Am. J. Physiol.*, **200**, 1125–32 (1961)

357. Schröder, R., Meyer-Burgdorff, C., Rott, D., and Brahms, O., *Arch. exptl. Pathol. Pharmakol.*, **240**, 285–312 (1961)

358. Schück, O., Smahelová, R., Stríbrná, J., and Chyltilová, D., *Physiol. Bohemsloven.*, **10**, 60–65 (1961)

359. Schwartz, I. L., Rasmussen, H., Schoessler, M. A., Silver, L., and Fong, C. T. O., *Proc. Natl. Acad. Sci. US*, **46**, 1288–97 (1960)

360. Schwartz, W. B., Bank, N., and Cutler, R. W. P., *J. Clin. Invest.*, **38**, 347–56 (1959)

361. Scriver, C. R., Schafer, I. A., and Efron, M. L., *J. Clin. Invest.*, **40**, 1080 (1961)

362. Semple, S. J. G., and deWardener, H. E., *Circulation Research*, **7**, 643–48 (1959)

363. Setchell, B. P., and Blanch, E., *Nature*, **189**, 230–31 (1961)

364. Shalhoub, R. J., Canessa-Fischer, M., Webber, W. A., Glabman, S., and Pitts, R. F., *Federation Proc.*, **20**, 415 (1961)

365. Sharp, G. W. G., *J. Endocrinol.*, **21**, 97–106 (1960)

366. Sharp, G. W. G., *J. Endocrinol.*, **21**, 219–24 (1960)

367. Shuster, S., and Callaghan, P., *Brit. J. Exptl. Pathol.*, **42**, 1–6 (1961)

368. Slater, J. D. H., Mestitz, P., Walker, G., and Nabarro, J. D. N., *Acta Endocrinol.*, **37**, 263–78 (1961)

369. Slater, R. J., O'Doherty, N. J., and deWolfe, M. S., *Pediatrics*, **26**, 190–99 (1960)

370. Smythe, C. M., and Chrisanthis, A., *Clin. Research*, **9**, 37 (1961)

371. Soeling, H. D., and Schmidt, L., *Arch. exptl. Pathol. Pharmakol.*, **240**, 140–56 (1960)

372. Solomon, S., *J. Cellular Comp. Physiol.*, **49**, 351–65 (1957)

373. Sonnenblick, E. H., Cannon, P. J., and Laragh, J. H., *J. Clin. Invest.*, **40**, 903–13 (1961)

374. Söremark, R., *Acta Physiol. Scand.*, **50**, 306–10 (1960)

375. Sørensen, L. B., *Scand. J. Clin. Lab. Invest.*, **12**, Suppl. 54 (1960)

376. Spargo, B., Straus, F., and Fitch, F., *Arch. Pathol.*, **70**, 599–613 (1960)

377. Spencer, A. G., *Proc. Roy. Soc. Med.*, **53**, 587–89 (1960)

378. Stalder, G., *Mod. Problems in Pediat.*, **6**, 22–56 (1960)

379. Streeten, D. H. P., *Clin. Pharmacol. Therap.*, **2**, 359–73 (1961)

380. Strickler, J. C., and Kessler, R. H., *J. Clin. Invest.*, **40**, 311–16, (1961)

381. Strickler, J. C., Kessler, R. H., and Pitts, R. F., *The Physiologist*, **3**, 155 (1960)

382. Suki, W., and Grollman, A., *Am. J. Physiol.*, **199**, 629–32 (1960)

383. Sullivan, L. P., *The Physiologist*, **3**, 157 (1960)

384. Swann, H. G., *Texas Repts. Biol. Med.*, **18**, 566–95 (1960)

385. Takeuchi, J., Jagi, S., Nakayama, S., Ikeda, T., Uchida, E., Inoue, G., Shintani, F., and Ueda, H., *Japan. Heart J.*, **1**, 288–99 (1960)

386. Talbott, J. H., and Terplan, K. L., *Medicine*, **39**, 405–68 (1960)

387. Taugner, R., Egidy, H. V., Iravani, J., and Taugner, G., *Arch. exptl. Pathol. Pharmakol.*, **238**, 419–26 (1960)

388. Taylor, M. G., and Ullmann, E., *J. Physiol. (London)*, **157**, 38–63 (1961)

389. Thaysen, J. H., Lassen, N. A., and Munck, O., *Nature*, **190**, 919–21 (1961)

390. Thoenes, W., *Klin. Wochschr.*, **29**, 504–17 (1961)

391. Thompson, D. D., *Arch. Internal Med.*, **103**, 832–38 (1959)

392. Thurau, K., *Nierensymposion* (Göttingen, 1959, Georg Thieme, Stuttgart, 1960)

393. Thurau, K., *Proc. Soc. Exptl. Biol. Med.*, **106**, 714–17 (1961)

394. Thurau, K., Deetjen, P., and Kramer, K., *Arch. ges. Physiol.*, **270**, 270–85 (1960)

395. Thurau, K., and Kramer, K., *Arch. ges. Physiol.*, **268**, 188–203 (1959)

396. Thurau, K., and Kramer, K., *Arch. ges. Physiol.*, **269**, 77–93 (1959)

397. Thurau, K., Sugiura, T., and Lilienfield, L. S., *Clin. Research*, **8**, 383 (1960)

398. Thurau, K., Wirz, H., and Wober, E., *Arch. ges. Physiol.*, **274**, 64 (1961)

399. Tobian, L., *Ann. Internal Med.*, **52**, 395–410 (1960)

400. Toussaint, C., *Rev. belg. pathol. et méd. exptl.*, **28**, 5–140 (1961)

401. Toussaint, C., and Vereerstraeten, P., *J. urol. méd. et chir.*, **6**, 611–19 (1960)

402. Toussaint, C., and Vereerstraeten, P., *Experientia*, **16**, 309–10 (1960)

403. Toussaint, C., and Vereerstraeten, P., *Experientia*, **17**, 80–81 (1961)

404. Toussaint, C., and Vereerstraeten, P., *Experientia*, **17**, 81–83 (1961)

405. Trueta, J., Barclay, A. E., Daniel, P. M., Franklin, K. J., and Prichard, M. M. L., *Studies of the Renal Circulation*, 161 (Charles C Thomas, Springfield, Ill., 1947)

406. Uete, T., and Venning, E. H., *Endocrinology*, **67**, 62–69 (1960)

407. Ullmann, E., *J. Physiol. (London)*, **155**, 417–37 (1961)

408. Ullrich, K. J., Kramer, K., and Boylan, J. W., *Progr. in Cardiovascular Diseases*, **3**, 395–431 (1961)

409. Ullrich, K. J., Pehling, G., Ruiz-Giunazu, A., and Espinar-Lafuente, M., *Arch. ges. Physiol.*, **274**, 64 (1961)

410. Ussing, H. H., *Handbuch der Experimentellen Pharmakologie*, 1–195 (Eichler, O., and Farah, A., Eds., Springer-Verlag, Berlin, Göttingen, Heidelberg, 1960)

411. Vander, A. J., Malvin, R. L., Wilde, W. S., and Sullivan, L. P., *J. Pharmacol. Exptl. Therap.*, **125**, 19–22 (1959)

412. Vander, A. J., Wilde, W. S., and Malvin, R. L., *J. Theoret. Biol.*, **I**, 236–43 (1961)

413. Vander, A. J., Wilde, W. S., and Malvin, R. L., *Proc. Soc. Exptl. Biol. Med.*, **103**, 525–27 (1960)

414. Volle, R. L., Green, R. E., and Peters, L., *J. Pharmacol. Exptl. Therap.*, **129**, 388–93 (1960)

415. Volle, R. L., Peters, L., and Green, R. E., *J. Pharmacol. Exptl. Therap.*, **129**, 377–87 (1960)

416. Waldmann, T. A., and Levin, E. H., *Clin. Research*, **8**, 19 (1960)

417. Walker, A., Bott, P. A., Oliver, J., and McDowell, M., *Am. J. Physiol.*, **134**, 580–95 (1941)

418. Walker, W. G., Cooke, C. R., Payne, J. W., Baker, C. R. F., and Andrew, D. J., *Am. J. Physiol.*, **200**, 1133–38 (1961)

419. Wallach, S., and Carter, A. C., *Am. J. Physiol.*, **200**, 359–66 (1961)

420. Walser, M., and Browder, A. A., *J. Clin. Invest.*, **38**, 1404–11 (1959)

421. Walser, M., *Am. J. Physiol.*, **200**, 1099–1104 (1961)

422. Walser, M., *J. Clin. Invest.*, **40**, 1087 (1961)

423. Walser, M., *J. Clin. Invest.*, **40**, 723–30 (1961)

424. Walser, M., *J. Phys. Chem.*, **65**, 159–60 (1961)

425. Walser, M., and Mudge, G. H., *Mineral Metabolism*, 288–337 (Comar, C. L. and Bronner, F., Eds., Academic Press, New York, 1960)

426. Walser, M., Payne, J. W., and Browder, A. A., *J. Clin. Invest.*, **40**, 234–42 (1961)

427. Waugh, W. H., and Shanks, R. G., *Circulation Research*, **8**, 871–88 (1960)

428. Ways, P., Huff, J. W., Kasmaler, C. H., and Young, L. E., *Arch. Internal Med.*, **107**, 154–62 (1961)

429. Webber, W. A., Brown, J. L., and Pitts, R. F., *Am. J. Physiol.*, **200**, 380–86 (1961)

430. Webster, G. D., Jr., Huth, E. J., Elkinton, J. R., and McCance, R. A., *Am. J. Med.*, **29**, 576–85 (1960)

431. Weiner, I. M., Garlid, K. D., Romeo, J. A., and Mudge, G. H., *Am. J. Physiol.*, **200**, 393–99 (1961)

432. Weiner, I. M., Washington, J. A. II, and Mudge, G. H., *Bull. Johns Hopkins Hosp.*, **105**, 284–97 (1959)

433. Weiner, I. M., Washington, J. A. II, and Mudge, G. H., *Bull. Johns Hopkins Hosp.*, **106**, 333–46 (1960)

434. Wesson, L. G., Jr., *Ann. Rev. Med.*, **12**, 77–92 (1961)

435. White, H. L., Rolf, D., Bisno, A. L., Kasser, I. S., and Tosteson, D. C., *Am. J. Physiol.*, **200**, 885–89 (1961)

436. White, H. L., Rolf, D., and Tosteson, D. C., *Am. J. Physiol.*, **200**, 591–600 (1961)

437. Whittam, R., *J. Physiol. (London)*, **153**, 358–69 (1960)

438. Whittembury, G., Sugino, N., and Solomon, A. K., *Nature*, **187**, 699–701 (1960)

439. Whittembury, G., Sugino, N., and Solomon, A. K., *J. Gen. Physiol.*, **44**, 687–712 (1961)

440. Whittembury, G., and Windhager, E. E., *J. Gen. Physiol.*, **44**, 679–88 (1961)

441. Wijdeveld, P. G., and Jansen, A. P., *Clin. Chim. Acta*, **5**, 618–31 (1960)

442. Wilde, W. S., and Howard, P. J., *J. Pharmacol. Exptl. Therap.*, **130**, 232–38 (1960)

443. Williamson, H. E., Skulan, T. W., and Shideman, F. E., *J. Pharmacol. Exptl. Therap.*, **131**, 49–55 (1961)
444. Windhager, E. E., and Giebisch, G., *Federation Proc.*, **19**, 233 (1960)
445. Windhager, E. E., and Giebisch, G., *Am. J. Physiol.*, **200**, 581–590 (1961)
446. Windhager, E. E., and Giebisch, G., *Federation Proc.*, **20**, 413 (1961)
447. Wirz, H., *Helv. Physiol. et Pharmacol. Acta*, **13**, 42–49 (1955)
448. Wirz, H., *Helv. Physiol. et Pharmacol. Acta*, **14**, 353–62 (1956)
449. Wise, B. L., and Ganong, W. F., *Acta Neuroveg et. (Vienna)*, **22**, 14–32 (1960)
450. Wise, B. L., and Ganong, W. F., *Am. J. Physiol.*, **198**, 1291–95 (1960)
451. Woodruff, M. W., Malvin, R. L., and Thompson, I. M., *J. Am. Med. Assoc.*, **175**, 1132–35 (1961)
452. Woods, J. W., Welt, L. G., and Hollander, W., Jr., *J. Clin. Invest.*, **40**, 599–602 (1961)
453. Wu, H., and Elliot, H. C., Jr., *J. Appl. Physiol.*, **16**, 553–56 (1961)
454. Yü, T. F., Berger, L., Kupfer, S., and Gutman, A. B., *Am. J. Physiol.*, **199**, 1199–1204 (1960)
455. Yü, T. F., and Gutman, A. B., *Proc. Soc. Exptl. Biol. Med.*, **90**, 542–47 (1955)
456. Zaretskii, I. I., Mikhailova, I. A., and Rozanova, N. S., *Byull. Eksptl. Biol. Med.*, **49**, 569–72 (1960)*
457. Zaretskii, I. I., Mikhailova, I. A., and Rozanova, N. S., *Sechenov Physiol. J. USSR (Engl. Transl.)*, **46**, 694–703 (1960)
458. Zeffren, J. L., and Heinemann, N. D., *J. Clin. Invest.*, **39**, 1042 (1960)

BOOKS AND MONOGRAPHS

459. Brooks, S. M., *Basic Facts of Body Water and Ions* (Springer, 160 pp., 1960)
460. Bartter, F. C., *The Clinical Use of Aldosterone Antagonists* (Charles C Thomas, Springfield, Ill., 1960)
461. *Diuretics (Chemotherapia*, **1**, 1960)
462. Forster, R. P., *Kidney Cells*, 89–162 (*The Cell*, **5**, Brachet, J., and Mirsky, A., Eds., Academic Press, New York and London, 1961)
463. *Handbuch der experimentellen Pharmakologie* (Eichler, O., and Farah, A., Eds., Springer-Verlag, Berlin, Göttingen, Heidelberg, 1960)
464. *The Kidney and Its Disorders (Univ. Mich. Med. Bull.*, **26**, August 1960)
465. Lotspeich, W. D., *Metabolic Aspects of Renal Function* (Charles C Thomas, Springfield, Ill., 1959)
466. *Mineral Metabolism*, **I**, Part A and B (Comar, C. L., and Bronner, F., Eds., Academic Press, Inc., New York, 1960)
467. *Biology of Pyelonephritis* (Quinn, E. L., and Kass, E. H., Eds., Little, Brown & Co., Boston, 1960)
468. *Carbon Dioxide and Man, A Symposium; Anesthesiology*, **21**, 585–766 (1960)
469. *Edema, Mechanism and Management*, A Hahnemann Symposium on Salt and Water Retention (Moyer, J. H., and Fuchs, M., Eds., 833 pp., W. B. Saunders Co., Philadelphia, 1960)
470. Grace, W. J., *Practical Clinical Management of Electrolyte Disorders* (Appleton-Century-Crofts, 126 pp., New York, 1960)
471. *Heart, Kidney and Electrolytes (Progr. in Cardiovascular Diseases*, **3**, No. 5 and 6)
472. *Nephrology, First Intern. Congr. (Excerpta Med.*, Intern. Congr. Ser., No. 29, 1960)
473. *Nephrotic Syndrome, Eleventh Conf. on* (Metcoff, J., Ed., Natl. Kidney Disease Foundation, New York, 1960)
474. *New Diuretics and Antihypertensive Agents* (Grollman, A., Ed., *Ann. N. Y. Acad. Sci.*, **88** (4), 771–1020, 1960)
475. *Nierenfunktion und Nervensystem* (Dutz, H., Ed., Veb Verlag Volk und Gesundheit, Berlin, 1959)
476. *Nierensymposion* (Göttingen, 1959, Kramer, K. and Ullrich, K. J., Eds., Georg Thieme, Stuttgart, 1960)
477. *The Parathyroids* (Greep, R. O., and Talmage, R. V., Eds. Charles C Thomas, Springfield, Ill., 1961)
478. *Pathogenese u. Therapie der Ödeme* (Gigon, A., and Ludwig, H., Eds., Benno Schwabe and Co., Basel, 1960)
479. Peters, G., *Nebennierenrinden—Inkretion und Wasser—Elektrolythaushalt* (Georg Thieme, Leipzig, 1960)
480. Pitts, R. F., *The Physiological Basis of Diuretic Therapy* (Charles C Thomas, Springfield, Ill., 1959)
481. *Recent Advances in Renal Disease*, Proc. of a Conf. (Milne, M. D., Ed., Roy. Coll. Physicians, London, 22–23 July, 1960)

482. *Regulation of Inorganic Ion Content of Cells* (CIBA Foundation Study Group #5, Wolstenholme, G. E. W., and O'Connor, C. M., Eds., Little, Brown & Co., Boston, 1960)

483. Reubi, F., *Nierenkrankheiten* (Hans Huber, Bern u. Stuttgart, 758 pp., 1960)

484. Siegenthaler, W., *Klinische Physiologie und Pathologie des Wasser und Salzhaushaltes* (Springer Verlag, 175 pp. Berlin, Göttingen, Heidelberg, 1961)

485. *Water and Electrolyte Metabolism* (Steward, C. P., Strengers, T., Eds., Elsevier Publ. Co., Amsterdam, 1961)

486. White, A. G., *Clinical Disturbances of Renal Function* (W. B. Saunders Co., 1961)

* English translation will be announced in *Technical Translations*, issued by the Office of Technical Services, US Department of Commerce, and will be made available by the Photoduplication Service, Library of Congress, and by the SLA Translation Center at the John Crerar Library, Chicago, Illinois.

RESPIRATION[1,2]

By John W. Severinghaus

Department of Anesthesia, Cardiovascular Research Institute, University of California Medical Center, San Francisco, California

REGULATION OF RESPIRATION

Influences of wakefulness.—Hypocapnia, however produced in anesthetized man or animals, results in apnea. It has been commonly assumed that this phenomenon also occurs in the waking state. However, Fink (177, 178), following the leads of Boothby and Mills, has found no periods of either apnea or periodic breathing in naive experimental subjects after either voluntary or mechanical hyperventilation for five to ten minutes to an average Pco_2 of 21 mm Hg. The respiratory minute volume in the recovery period fell to about two-thirds of control volume and remained at this level for approximately ten minutes while the end-expiratory Pco_2 gradually rose toward the control level. In several instances, subjects fell asleep during this recovery period when the Pco_2 was below normal and exhibited complete apnea until they woke up. Fink concludes that as much as two-thirds of normal resting ventilation when awake is independent of carbon dioxide drive. Mikhailov (389) reported the post-hyperventilation respiratory patterns in a large number of athletes after instructing them to take 10, 25, or 40 deep breaths. Seventy-six per cent of them, after the hyperventilation, had normal or increased ventilation and 24 per cent showed Cheyne-Stokes breathing or apneic periods. He gave them diverting tasks to avoid a conscious attention on breathing. Normal subjects will hyperventilate if forced to breathe with a metronome, no matter what the rate (447). One might conclude that certain patients with neurocirculatory asthenia have an abnormal dependence on the higher centers for the control of respiration (317). Poole (467) statistically noted during which phase of the respiratory cycle other nervous activity, such as arousal, spontaneous blinking, and voluntary tapping movements, most often occurs and found a rather high degree of correlation with inspiration suggesting that the over-all activity of the nervous system and that of the respiratory system are temporally related throughout the respiratory cycle. Bulow & Ingvar (94) observed the close correlation between EEG activity and respiration in the transition from sleep to wakeful state in normal subjects. The possibility that this waking stimulation of respiration may be mediated through the hypothalamus was studied in awake cats by Redgate (479, 480), who found that hypothalamic depression by direct injection of minute doses of thiopental or by electrodesicca-

---

[1] This review terminated with papers published before June 1, 1961 and available by July 1, 1961.

[2] Among the abbreviations used in this chapter are: Pco_2 (partial pressure of carbon dioxide); and Po_2 (partial pressure of oxygen).

tion decreased the electrical excitability of the inspiratory center. Electrical stimulation of nuclei in the thalamus can produce either acceleration of breathing or inhibition (610).

Respiratory center.—Salmoiraghi & von Baumgarten (520) reported the first intracellular recordings from neurons in the respiratory center. The resting potentials observed ranged from 25 to 70 mv with an average of 45, and the amplitude of the action potentials as 20 mv to 55 mv. With inspiratory neurons, they observed synaptic potentials, action potentials, slow repolarizing potentials, and slow depolarizing potentials. They also noted a slow depolarizing shift developing during the burst of action potentials. A striking difference in the records obtained from the expiratory neurons was the presence during inspiration of relatively large hyperpolarizing potentials occurring concomitantly with a shift of the membrane potential towards negativity. Merkulova (383) demonstrated the decussation of spinal fibers carrying impulses from the respiratory center to spinal centers in the cats after longitudinal sections of the spinal cord.

REFLEX CONTROL

Carotid body response to gas tensions.—It now seems established beyond much question that the hypoxic drive of the chemoreceptors contributes toward maintaining ventilation at its normal level even at sea level. One of the major reasons for failure to observe sea-level hypoxic drive was the lack of exercise on the part of the subjects during the studies. Hornbein & Roos (273) found that the respiratory response to mild hypoxia (alveolar Po_2 falling from 100 to 90 mm Hg) was greatly accentuated by moderate exercise, a possibility suggested by Haldane but largely ignored since. Saito, Honda & Hasumura (516), found a linear 6 per cent increase in ventilation per mm Hg fall in alveolar oxygen tension below 95 mm when Pco_2 and pH were held constant in anesthetized dogs. Hornbein, Roos & Griffo (274) were able to detect transient increases in ventilation with reductions of alveolar Po_2 to 93 mm Hg in a normal subject. Milic-Emili & Dejours (390) demonstrated that the reduction in ventilation during increased oxygen breathing was not ascribable to mechanical effects of oxygen on the lung, such as atelectasis or bronchoconstriction.

Reed & Kellogg (481, 482) induced hypoxia and hypercapnia during sleep to determine the interrelationships of the two drives. The carbon dioxide response curve is shifted 5 mm Hg toward higher alveolar Pco_2 by sleep, and 1 mm Hg toward lower alveolar Pco_2 by hypoxia equivalent to 12,000 feet while awake. Hypoxia during sleep shifts the sleeping carbon dioxide response curve again by 1 mm Hg. This lack of hypoxic drive is the more surprising since the hypoventilating sleeper is already somewhat hypoxic by waking standards. Joels *et al.* (296, 297, 298) have used the isolated perfused carotid body of the cat to study the independent effects of Pco_2, pH, and hypoxia on chemoreceptor impulse discharge. They found that the chemoreceptor response to the combination of hypoxia and hypercapnia greatly exceeded that which might have been expected from the arithmetic summation of the effects of either stimulus acting alone. At constant perfusate pH, they also detected a stimulus produced by the rising P_{CO_2}, whether the P_{O_2} of the perfusate was high or low. The pH had a similar independent effect. The response of the chemoreceptors to hypoxia was surprisingly feeble if the pH of the perfusate was very alkaline, for example 7.75.

The usual carotid body response to hypoxia is not present within a few hours after birth, either in rats (4) or in man (214), but develops within a few days of birth.

Kellogg (310) reviewed the interrelationships of altitude and carbon dioxide acclimatization.

Carotid body response to drugs.—Byck (95) reviewed the effects of ganglionic blockade on chemoreceptors, and he reported evidence that hexamethonium blocks the carotid body response to nicotine competitively, abolishing the hyperpnea of 6 μg (intracarotid nicotine), reducing the effect of up to 100 μg, but not blocking larger doses, with sublethal doses of hexamethonium. Hexamethonium did not block the cyanide hyperpnea at all. On the other hand, Cope (118) showed that a high tension of oxygen can block the respiratory gasp reaction after cyanide is given intravenously in man.

Carotid body structure.—Costero & Barroso-Moguel (120) examined carotid body tumors and noted the occurrence of argentaffin cells which are morphologically similar to serotonin-containing cells in the gastrointestinal tract, suggesting a possible role of serotonin in the carotid body. Ladenheim (328) described the similarity of the glomus jugulare to the carotid body and the rete mirabile of the fish, noting that the glomus jugulare really should be regarded as a glomus of the external carotid artery and may be considered the homologue of the rete mirabile. Its function in man is not defined. Muscholl *et al.* (414) chemically identified norepinephrine and practically no epinephrine in glomus cells.

Stretch receptors.—Afferent stretch and proprioreceptor impulses modify the pattern of respiration. Siebens & Puletti (545) demonstrated respiratory afferent impulses in dorsal nerve roots in the thoracic segments of anesthetized cats, suggesting that large numbers of proprioceptors within the thoracic wall are activated during each inspiration and each expiration. Vagotomy abolishes the usual early expiratory diaphragmatic muscle activity in dogs (660). Patients have occasionally been reported in whom a respiratory center disturbance led to synchronization of respiration with the pulse rate. Frye & Braunwald (202) showed in one such subject that this was not caused by direct transmission from the heart to the phrenic nerve but required the participation of the central nervous system. Bucher & Battig (88) were able to produce pulse-synchronized respiration in the rabbit by a suitable combination of pneumothorax and dead space. Gamma-aminobutyric acid, which is known to inhibit stretch receptors, appears to exert its effects on respiration by decreasing the sensitivity of the slowly adapting pulmonary stretch receptors (152).

Passive body movement and acceleration.—The extreme vibration and vertical body movement to which low-altitude jet pilots are subjected has been suggested as a possible cause of the hyperventilation and occasional loss of consciousness occurring in these situations. Dixon *et al.* (144) exposed a group of normal subjects to various forms of passive body motion while measuring ventilation and alveolar Pco_2. Rapid acceleration in the longitudinal axis of the body like that produced by vertical acceleration of the seat of an aircraft was capable of inducing hyperventilation of which the subject was usually unaware and reduced the end-tidal carbon dioxide tension 10 mm Hg or more. Passive leg motion did not reduce the alveolar Pco_2. Steady forward acceleration (pressure against the back) up to levels of 12 G predominantly decreased tidal volume and increased rate of breathing but did not change alveolar ventilation (616).

pH AND Pco_2 CONTROL

Cerebrospinal fluid chemoreceptors for pH and Pco_2.—The location of these receptors, first noted by Leusen, has not been settled. Loeschcke (348) believes them to be in the lateral recesses of the fourth ventricle, whereas Massion *et al.* (374) eliminated the pH response by cauterizing the area postrema but could not obtain respiratory responses to solutions of varying pH applied topically to the area postrema. Loeschcke (348) found that procaine solutions too dilute (0.1 per cent) to affect anything but superficial structures produce apnea when introduced into the lateral recesses of the fourth ventricle. Sergievskii (538) observed slight respiratory responses to varying the Pco_2 of spinal fluid washed through the lateral ventricles. The pH of the cerebrospinal fluid is controlled by (*a*) the surrounding tissue Pco_2 which is influenced by blood flow, which in turn is controlled by arterial Pco_2 (137, 158); and (*b*) the fixed ions (primarily Na^+ and Cl^-) which determine the bicarbonate concentration at that Pco_2. The rate of alteration of these ions, and hence the transfer of bicarbonate between blood and spinal fluid in metabolic acidosis or alkalosis, is relatively slow (268). It is probably this process which is responsible for the slowness of acclimatization to altitude. Acclimatization does not correlate well with blood bicarbonate pH changes (310). Spinal fluid pH of normal subjects averages $7.31 \pm .02$ and has a mean Pco_2 of 43.7, 4 mm above arterial Pco_2 (384). Winterstein (651), reviewing intracranial chemoreceptors, suggests that these pH (and Pco_2) receptors may also play a role in the respiratory response to cerebral anoxia via anaerobic acid production in the receptor cells. However, Leusen & Demeester (339) failed to find cerebrospinal fluid acidosis after acute anoxia in dogs.

Blood pH and Pco_2.—Loeschcke (348), Lambertsen (330, 331), and Kellogg (310) have reviewed aspects of pH-Pco_2 interrelationships in control of respiration. Lambertsen *et al.* (331) used $NaHCO_3$ infusion in man to determine the pH and P_{CO_2} effects separately. At constant P_{CO_2} (50 mm Hg), ventilatory response was half eliminated by returning pH to normal. He points out that the cerebrospinal fluid H^+ alteration could not have been corrected, so that partial P_{CO_2} effect can still come from cerebrospinal fluid pH change. There is no evidence for a molecular effect of carbon dioxide independent of pH change. Katsaros, Loeschcke & co-workers (308) gave human volunteers 0.5 g per kg of sodium bicarbonate and in the postabsorptive period determined the carbon dioxide response curves. The shift of the carbon dioxide response curve because of pH change was only half as much with $NaHCO_3$ alkalosis as that produced by ammonium chloride acidosis, a 0.01 pH elevation decreasing ventilation 0.8 liters per minute (at constant P_{CO_2}) or conversely, at constant ventilation, increasing P_{CO_2} 0.32 mm Hg. Using these data Loeschcke (349) proposed appropriate modifications of the Gray multiple-factor theory equation. Saito, Honda & Hasumura (517) found the partial respiratory response to arterial H^+ ion changes in dogs and rabbits to be considerably less than that found by Loeschcke in man. The variability of these responses may, of course, reflect various permeabilities of the blood-brain barrier to the altered cations and anions used. The depression of respiration produced by metabolic alkalosis in patients may be considerable. Swanson (584), treating three patients with tris(hydroxymethyl)amino methane (THAM) buffer for compensated carbon dioxide retention produced striking anoxemia and further hypoventilation.

Carbon dioxide response curves.—The response to respiratory depressants can be quantitated in several ways. The intercept or apneic threshold and the slope or $\dot{V}/\Delta$ P_{CO_2} of a carbon dioxide response curve are occasionally used. The elevation of P_{CO_2} at any particular ventilation or, conversely, the depression of ventilation at any particular P_{CO_2} may be determined. In contrast to the awaking state, apnea can be easily obtained under anesthesia in man and animals by over-ventilation. The arterial or alveolar P_{CO_2} at which apnea occurs, termed the apneic threshold (247), was 30.7 to 33 mm Hg during halothane anesthesia. This was 6 to 9.5 mm lower than the spontaneously occurring carbon dioxide tension, the difference between the two increasing with the depth of anesthesia. Lambertsen *et al.* (332) have chosen to use a P_{CO_2} of 46 mm Hg as a standard and report the change in respiratory minute volume, tidal volume, and respiratory rate at this P_{CO_2}. Others (57, 161, 227, 348) preferred to report the P_{CO_2} displacement of the carbon dioxide response curve. It is also now generally agreed that the two parameters which should be recorded are the alveolar or arterial P_{CO_2} and a function as closely related to the neural output of the respiratory center as possible. Most investigators have preferred to use minute ventilation rather than alveolar ventilation for this purpose, since the calculations are then not affected by rebreathing or dead space changes. The electrically integrated diaphragmatic electromyogram has also been suggested as a closer approximation to the respiratory center output (451).

The administration of salicylates to normal man was shown to shift the carbon dioxide response curve to the left and increase its slope (523). Froeb (199) was unable to confirm differences in the carbon dioxide response curves of professional SCUBA divers in contrast to the apneustic divers reported by Schaefer (527). Barnett & Peters (43) reported an interesting investigation of dogs with chronic tracheostomy. With 500 ml added dead space, respiratory minute volume and arterial P_{CO_2} were both increased proportionately, reaching about 16 liters per minute at a P_{CO_2} of 50, at which time mean arterial oxygen saturation had dropped to 90 per cent. Carbon dioxide response curves can be obtained equally well with added dead space or added carbon dioxide to the inspired air. Both methods provide more useful information than attempts to measure the respiratory response to airway obstruction. Samet, Fierer & Bernstein (524) attempted to do carbon dioxide response curves on normal subjects breathing through various-sized resistances. Unfortunately, the resistors consisted of holes drilled through rubber stoppers, making them both nonlinear and nonreproducible.

Nunn & Ezi-Ashi (439) also studied the effect of added resistance on ventilation during anesthesia, using both constant-pressure (water trap)—type resistors and narrow diameter tubes. Unfortunately, it is difficult to assess the significance of changes in ventilation when resistances are added unless one measures both the mechanical work done on the resistor and the increase in arterial P_{CO_2}. Gerardy et al. (209) reported a 37-year-old female with absolutely no response to carbon dioxide but normal pulmonary function. She was highly dependent on hypoxic drive. The only known cerebral difficulties were in abnormal EEG and a third nerve palsy, probably caused by a carotid aneurysm. There was no blood in the spinal fluid.

Possibility of carbon dioxide receptors in the venous circulation.—During the past year the possibility of a pulmonary arterial carbon dioxide receptor was suggested by Riley (495) and Armstrong and co-workers (21). The authors have pointed out that the rises in hydrogen ion and P_{CO_2} in venous blood during exercise are directly proportional to the observed hyperpnea of exercise. Yamamoto & Edwards (659) used an extracorporeal pump oxygenator to increase the CO_2 tension in blood which was returned to the venous system of rats. They found they were able to infuse six times the normal carbon dioxide production with essentially no increase in arterial P_{CO_2} since ventilation was increased in proportion to the load of carbon dioxide in the venous blood. However, Cropp & Comroe (126) failed to observe, in chloralose-treated cats, any ventilatory response to increasing the pulmonary artery P_{CO_2} when arterial P_{CO_2} was held constant. Dickinson, Green & Howell (141) reported transient apnea following the injection of 0.1 to 1 ml of carbon dioxide gas into the right ventricle and pulmonary artery of the cat. The apnea appeared to be a reflex originating from receptors in the lungs and was abolished by the intravenous injection of acetazolamide. It was not produced by the equivalent amount of tenth-normal hydrochloric acid or by other gases. In summary, one finds little direct evidence for mixed venous or pulmonary arterial carbon dioxide receptors controlling respiration.

MISCELLANEOUS INFLUENCES

Exercise.—Craig & Cummings (125) and Elbel (169) were able to show that the inhalation of oxygen before brief exercise inhibited ventilation by 24 per cent in the 20-second control periods before and after the end of the run and delayed the rise in pulse rate. At the beginning of a run, a threefold increase in ventilation was accomplished instantaneously with little change in end-expiratory carbon dioxide tension or respiratory quotient, implying a comparable increase in cardiac output. The ventilation reduction produced during exercise by oxygen breathing is mostly ascribable to the reduction in metabolic acidosis (456). Koizumi *et al.* (319) demonstrated respiratory stimulation with repetitive stimuli of monosynaptic reflexes in leg flexor or extensor muscle groups. They suggest that these reflex mechanisms contribute to the immediate augmentation of respiration during exercise or whenever muscle tension increases. Dejours *et al.* (139) find the ventilatory stimulus of muscular exercise to be independent of the oxygen and carbon dioxide stimuli. Psychic factors which play a large role in resting ventilation appear to have no influence on ventilation during exercise (25, 388). Athletes tolerate hypoxia better (206) and increase their ventilation less during exercise than normal individuals (16).

Thermal effects.—It has long been known that cerebral hyperthermia results in hyperventilation. In cats this effect is not dependent on the integrity of either the carotid body or the hypothalamus (436). Keatinge & Evans (309) demonstrated hyperventilation with low Pco_2 during the first few minutes of immersion of unclothed man in water at 5 to 15°C. Neither at rest nor at work was evidence found to corroborate earlier predictions of hypercapnia arising because of cold immersion. During hypothermia in dogs, Terzioglu *et al.* (593, 594) showed that anoxia stimulates ventilation in a relatively normal way via the carotid body down to 27°C. At 24° the response to 10 per cent oxygen is slight. After denervation of the chemoreceptors, hypoxia during hypothermia produces respiratory depression. In anesthetized hypothermic dogs, the ventilatory response to inspired carbon dioxide is approximately normal if consideration is taken of the decreased metabolic rate (521).

Effect of drugs on the control of respiration.—Eckenhoff & Oech (161) and Bellville (58) extensively reviewed the effects of drugs—in particular, narcotics—and their antagonists upon respiration. Lambertsen, Wendel & Longenhagen (332), using the technique of holding arterial Pco_2 at 46 mm, found that the respiratory minute volume decrease following administration of chlorpromazine plus meperidine was considerably greater than that caused by meperidine alone, whereas chlorpromazine had little if any effect of its own. Greisheimer *et al.* (227) compared the respiratory effects of phenazocine and meperidine at a Pco_2 of 50. Both drugs in comparable doses reduced alveolar ventilation about 50 per cent. Berkowitz *et al.* (62) found that phenazocine depressed respiration more than equivalent doses of morphine. Unfortunately respiratory depression cannot be adequately measured without the use of a carbon dioxide stimulus which limits other narcotic studies (265, 266).

Belleville (57) compared morphine and oxymorphone and by careful interpretation of his carbon dioxide response curves computed that the oxymorphone was 14.8 times as potent as morphine in terms of respiratory depressant effects, whereas it had been reported to be only nine times as potent as
an analgesic. The failure of narcotic antagonists to reverse the respiratory
depressant effects of the narcotics completely was again documented (486).
In patients with limited pulmonary reserve and carbon dioxide retention,
the administration of narcotics and antagonists may be dangerous. Ngai
(437) used decerebrate vagotomized cats to study the effects of narcotics on
the response to electrical stimulation of various components of the medulla
and pons. He found the inhibitory vagal reflex to be accentuated while most
centers were depressed, particularly those governing rate. In contrast
Schmidt & Dal Ri (528) found that urethane and barbiturates diminished
the effectiveness of inspiratory and expiratory vagal reflexes. The combination of thiopental and chloralose has been noted to cause periodic breathing
in dogs (530). Simmons et al. (554) noted respiratory alkalosis in each of 11
patients with proved or probable Gram-negative bacteremia in which the
hyperventilation could not be ascribed to fever, drugs, cerebral lesions,
anemia, or hypotension, this alkalosis indicating, apparently, a stimulation
of the respiratory center.

The mild hypoventilation resulting from halothane anesthesia has been
documented by several authors (180, 269). After one and a half hours of
treatment with 1.5 per cent halothane, the mean P_{CO_2} found in patients was
51 mm Hg. However, Hanks et al. (247) report a mean of 41 mm P_{CO_2} on 1.75
per cent halothane (endotracheal tube, non-rebreathing valve).

Valtin & Tenney (617) and Stein et al. (569) investigated regulation of
respiration in hyperthyroidism in man and rat. In contrast to other hyper-
metabolic states such as fever and after salicylate and dinitrophenol administration, alveolar carbon dioxide tension rose in hyperthyroidism, reflecting
a proportionately greater increase in metabolism than in alveolar ventilation.
P_{CO_2} may fall abnormally during exercise in hyperthyroidism. The carbon
dioxide response curve was not altered. The respiratory stimulation, seen
with hyperthyroidism, could be predicted from a knowledge of the increase
in metabolism and the usual carbon dioxide response curve.

MECHANICS

Compliance.—The active field of respiratory mechanics is the subject of
an excellent and comprehensive review by Mead in the April 1961 issue of
Physiological Reviews (375). Since this review to some extent overlaps the
time period of Mead's review, only those papers which did not appear in his
review will be discussed here.

Since most lung compliance studies are done with esophageal or pleural
pressure measurements, it is interesting that intrapleural pressure varies
with gravitational height at 0.2 centimeter of water per centimeter descent,
implying that the lung has a specific gravity of 0.2 (326). Bondurant et al.

(77) also noted that central venous congestion may cause errors in esophageal balloon pressure. Permutt & Martin (453) demonstrated that the pressure volume curve of normal males does not change its slope or shift in position with age. If transpulmonary pressure is plotted against total lung volume, the effect of age is primarily a decrease in vital capacity and increase in residual volume. The compliance of the tracheal bronchial tree decreases progressively with age (130). At $+10$ cm trans-tracheal pressure, human tracheal and bronchial segments were found to increase 46 to 101 per cent in volume *post mortem*. Drorbaugh (154) found the compliance of mice, rats, rabbits, and dogs to be the same if expressed per unit of vital capacity, and each animal requires the same pressure for the intake of one tidal volume. The elastic work per minute, like the rate of oxygen consumption, was found to be proportional to the 0.7 power of body weight. Hyatt (285) used the technique which he and Fry (201) described (see Mead's review) to compare the flow-volume and pressure-flow curves of normal and emphysematous individuals. They particularly call attention to the disproportional reduction of maximal expiratory flow in emphysema, noting that resting expiratory flow is often at the maximum expiratory flow rate. Marshall & Widdicombe (372) examined the phenomenon of stress relaxation of the human lung. When a full inspiration is held, the negative esophageal pressure rises (toward ambient) gradually over 10 or 15 seconds. The most likely explanations for the phenomenon are (*a*) the opening of alveoli which open only when the distending pressure is high and close when pressure falls, (*b*) a gradual fall in the tension of the surface lining material in the lung with held inspiration, and (*c*) a possible stress relaxation in the muscular or connective tissues of the lung, which cannot be ruled in or out by this study. The phenomenon did not appear to be related to changes in blood volume or redistribution of air and was not particularly affected by histamine aerosol. Histamine and epinephrine infusions may decrease the compliance in rabbits (89, 379). Oxygen breathing does not affect pulmonary compliance (391). Bernstein's (67) observation that airway closure in some units occurs above functional residual capacity may explain why after a period of quiet breathing, the compliance of normal adults (535) and dogs (621) can be increased 20 per cent by a deep breath. Severinghaus *et al.* (539) demonstrated that there is an abrupt 25 per cent fall in compliance of one lung when its pulmonary artery is occluded and demonstrated that this is entirely due to the fall in alveolar Pco_2 producing bronchoconstriction. This alkalotic bronchoconstriction probably underlies the compliance changes with death and with cessation of flow during cardio-bypass (340). It also raises serious doubts about studies of excised lung compliance when inflated with air containing no carbon dioxide. Three weeks after cardiac surgery, lung compliance was still reduced (334).

Resistance.—In normal adults, the upper airway accounts for approximately 45 per cent of the total airway resistance; but the actual resistance in the upper airway is extremely variable, being minimal with mouth breathing, in which case the larynx is the major component (286). Airflow resistance in unanesthetized dogs has been studied by exteriorizing the trachea (418). Hull & Long (281), ventilating curarized dogs at their resonant frequency (5.4 cps), computed tissue resistance to be 19 per cent of total resistance. Patients with chronic respiratory disease who note respiratory embarrassment in cold environments reveal marked rises in air flow resistance when breathing cold air but not when their faces or torsos are exposed to cold air (636). Airway resistance in normals was unchanged. This resistance is also increased by cigarette smoking (191, 283). Resistance in emphysema is significantly decreased by breathing helium (226).

Adding expiratory resistance in asthma and emphysema, comparable to lip pursing, aids expiration primarily by increasing mean lung volume (231). At any particular lung volume, expiratory flow rate could not be increased by adding external resistance.

Surface tension.—Surface tension characteristics of the material lining pulmonary alveoli have been recognized rapidly in the past few years as responsible for the stability of the alveolar radius and the maintenance of normal gas distribution. The observation that bubbles of pulmonary edema fluid were stable for many hours had two possible explanations: one, that the surface film, when collapsed to minimal area, became impermeable to gas; and two, that the surface tension fell to zero and pressure inside the bubble fell to ambient. Pattle (452) has continued his experiments with such bubbles, showing that gases can diffuse through the walls of the stable bubbles if a partial pressure difference exists across the bubble wall. He concludes that the surface layer of these bubbles offers no significant resistance to the passage of gas and therefore the surface tension within the bubble must approach zero. He also notes an interesting behavior of shrinking bubbles which he terms "clicking", in which the bubble progressively flattens with gravitational forces and then suddenly sheds a portion of its surface film, increasing its surface tension and becoming round again. The rate of clicking varies with bubble diameter from several clicks per second to less than one click per minute. Clements *et al.* (112) correlated the expandability of human and rat lungs against the surface activity of extracts and used these data to extend the theory of alveolar stability and its contribution to alveolar mechanics. Preliminary evidence (603) suggests surface tension alterations in guinea pigs after vagotomy, dogs after pulmonary artery occlusion, and man after cardiopulmonary bypass. Unfortunately, the interpretation of area-tension diagrams obtained from lung extracts varies, and technique is not standardized. Slight changes, such as were observed with smoke exposure (397), have little meaning by themselves. It is of interest that an attempt to use one lung as an artificial kidney has been limited by post-lavage atelectasis, perhaps ascribable to loss of surface lining (519).

Lung volumes.—Both normal people and polio patients showed increases in functional residual capacity and vital capacity after periods of positive-pressure breathing, perhaps caused by opening of atelectatic areas (86). In the prone position, inspiratory capacity is slightly larger than when sitting, but the functional residual capacity and expiratory reserve volume are considerably reduced (406). Negative-pressure breathing produced snorkel fashion (immersion) is not only more comfortable than equivalent negative pressure on the airway; but, surprisingly, it was found by Hong *et al.* (271) that functional residual capacity averaged 450 ml greater with snorkel type than with negative airway pressure breathing. The only explanation offered is an involuntary increase in inspiratory muscle tonus. Hepper, Fowler & Helmholz (261), testing 39 healthy male physicians and laboratory workers ranging from 21 to 44 years of age, find that lung volume is not a linear function of height. Engstrom's repression curve of functional residual capacity versus height in children has been confirmed (211).

Flow rates.—It has become readily apparent that obstructive airway disease may be most accurately measured by tests of maximum flow rates. The issue this year seems to have been which portion of the expiratory velocity tracing is best correlated with the degree of obstruction. Franklin & Lowell (192) find that the expiratory flow rate during the third quarter of a maximal forced expiration is the most useful index. Anderson (17) compared a host of timed vital capacity and flow rate measurements with the maximal breathing capacity in 500 men, mostly coal miners with some emphysema. He found the best results were obtained by measuring the volume expired in one second after the first 300 ml had been discarded. A number of papers have presented flow rates in normal individuals (20, 320, 341, 363, 609, 645); in children (207, 357) and in various obstructive diseases in children (91, 211, 576, 632); and in adults (92, 106, 155, 231, 244, 293, 392, 449, 457, 475, 536, 665). In view of the widespread use of the maximal breathing capacity as a standard of reference, it is of interest that Zocche, Fritts & Cournand (666) found the volume of ventilation which nine healthy young men could maintain for 15 minutes was only 53 per cent of the maximum breathing capacity. A similar figure was obtained for older patients with chronic pulmonary emphysema. These data suggest that the maximum breathing capacity is not the limiting response to be expected from stimuli such as hypoxia or hypercapnia and that the capacity of a patient for maintaining an augmented minute volume is an important determinant of the responses these stimuli evoke. Capel & Smart (106) observed that the one-second forced expiratory volume usually increased immediately following exercise both before and after inhalation of epinephrine spray in patients with obstructive airway disease, but not in normal people. Similar improvement was found immediately following a forced inspiration or a Müller maneuver. The apparently reduced airway resistance appeared in their study to be related to the increased pulmonary blood volume or blood flow. Stein *et al.* (570) used the techniques of Amdure and Mead for measuring the mechanical properties of the lungs of guinea pigs during experimental asthma produced by histamine aerosol. The experimental disease appears similar to human bronchial asthma in its effect on the mechanics of breathing.

Muscles of respiration.—The contributions of the diaphragm to normal respiration have been studied by means of bipolar electrodes in the esophagus (5, 458). The activity of the diaphragm continues during expiration for varying lengths of time, depending on the type of breathing, but not after vagotomy (660). Electrical activity is well correlated with the trans-diaphragmatic pressure found at relaxation volume. However, at minimum lung volume the electrical activity during maximum inspiratory effort is small, notwithstanding the high trans-diaphragmatic pressure. Agostoni & Rahn (6) report that the trans-diaphragmatic pressure may be as high as 100 cm of water during a maximal inspiratory effort and also during a maximal abdominal contraction, whether the alveolar pressure is zero or whether a high alveolar expiratory pressure is developed. Agostoni & Fenn (7) demonstrated that the rate at which the expiratory muscles can develop intrathoracic positive pressure depends on the expiratory resistance. With no added resistance to expiration, the muscles simply cannot contract fast enough to develop high intrathoracic pressures. Rosenblueth *et al.* (506) have shown persisting electrical activity at the periphery of the diaphragm after phrenic section in cats, dogs, monkeys, and rabbits. The thoracic innervation for the periphery of the diaphragm is not active during normal respiration but contributes to coughing, vomiting, defecation, and parturition. Respiratory action potentials have also been recorded from intrinsic muscles of the larynx and the nostril and scalene muscles in the dog (442). Yin Chi Chang (661) demonstrated a decreased action potential in respiratory muscles on the side of unilateral chest damage in dogs.

Work of breathing and efficiency.—Craig (123), continuing Agostoni's studies, measured the total amount of mechanical work which subjects could do in one respiratory cycle, breathing against the highest possible resistances. The significant observation was that even at very slow flow rates, the maximum pressure developed by the muscles was less than that developed against a complete obstruction so that the total work accomplished during expiration was only 69 per cent, and during inspiration 79 per cent, of that which should have been predicted from the pressures developed against an obstruction at various lung volumes. The decrease in the work of breathing with therapeutic procedures and drugs in patients with cor pulmonale and emphysema is in part related to the recovery from heart failure (246) as well as to the reduced airway resistance (245). Margaria *et al.* (365) report that during the maximal values of ventilation attained with exercise, the mechanical work of breathing amounts to about 100 to 120 cal per minute. Surprisingly, the ventilation observed with maximum voluntary exercise is also the maximum useful ventilation since any further increases in minute ventilation cost consumption of more oxygen than the incremental amount delivered to the body; that is, increasing ventilation beyond this point could not permit a greater external work. Their data indicate that the mechanical efficiency of the respiratory muscles is 25 per cent. Milic-Emili & Petit (393) have again measured this efficiency in terms of the mechanical work related to the additional energy cost. When hyperventilation was produced in subjects in the supine position, by adding dead space these authors obtained efficiency figures of 0.19 to 0.25 in good agreement with other figures on various muscle efficiencies. Cooper (117) reported that during mild exercise the frictional work is greater during inspiration than during expiration, whereas with high levels of work the converse is true. Yorifuji & Sera (662) have attempted to assess the efficiency of breathing by relating resistive and elastic work. The work of breathing during exercise in patients with restrictive and obstructive disease is a large fraction of total work (665).

Work of breathing and control of respiration.—Rohrer's concept that respiration occurs at a frequency where respiratory work is minimal has been re-examined by Mead (376) in light of more recent concepts that the product of muscle tension and contraction time, rather than that of tension and distance, is determinant in work. He suggests that in man and guinea pig, both at rest and during exercise, natural breathing takes place at frequencies approximating the least cost in terms of average force of the muscle rather than in terms of computed respiratory work. He also found that the effects of mechanical changes imposed on the lungs influenced frequency of breathing more than comparable external mechanical changes did. If the adjustments of frequency are mediated reflexly, the pertinent receptors probably cannot be located in the respiratory muscles or, for that matter, in any part of the chest wall. Receptors in these sites could not distinguish between external loads and equivalent changes in the lungs. Receptors in the lungs, on the other hand, would make such a distinction. Mead suggests that receptors in the lung are the principal, if not the only, receptors responsible for frequency adjustment.

Campbell *et al.* (101, 102) have used a series of closed metal drums to apply varying elastances to the external airway of subjects. The smallest load which could be detected half the time in six normal subjects was 2.47 cm of water per liter which represented a 10 to 20 per cent change in the normal elastic load of breathing. These workers then determined the effect of increasing loads up to 46 cm of water per liter during the course of five breaths in nine conscious and three anesthetized human subjects. There was a progressive increase in the tidal volume and by inference in the end-inspiratory muscle tension from the first to the fifth loaded breath. The effect was greater with larger loads and was greater in the conscious subjects. The end-inspiratory muscle tension was probably increased in the first loaded breath in most subjects. The findings are considered to be due to a reflex action and evidence is presented, in disagreement with Mead, that this is a somatic reflex not necessarily involving afferents from the lungs. The work has relevance regarding the mechanism of dyspnea since the sensations are comparable and implies that the sensation of dyspnea is an awareness of the inappropriateness of the inspiratory force required to produce a certain tidal volume.

Obesity.—The association of hypoventilation with obesity in some individuals led Gilbert *et al.* (213) to search for abnormal carbon dioxide responses in 26 obese subjects. Five of the subjects who hypoventilated on room air also hypoventilated in response to carbon dioxide. Naimark & Cherniack demonstrated (427) in a careful study of the mechanics of respiration in twelve obese individuals that the compliance of the total respiratory system is less than half of normal whereas the compliance of the lungs in obese individuals was normal. Compliance of the chest wall alone was reduced by a factor of three. In the supine position, the compliance of the chest wall was reduced another 25 per cent and the functional residual capacity was also reduced (608). Alexander *et al.* (10) reported that in a group of extremely obese individuals of whom 50 per cent were somnolent, only 10 per cent hypoventilated. Said's (515) observation of a low arterial Po_2 is probably related to atelectasis because of a low functional residual capacity.

Mechanics of phonation.—The mechanism by which voice resonances are produced has puzzled many investigators. Because of his interest in the anomalies of the acoustic impedance found in experiments in cadavers, Van Den Berg (618) constructed an electrical analogue of the trachea, lungs, and tissues. The analogue demonstrated that previous results showing unexpected resonances were primarily artifacts and suggest that the respiratory system behaves approximately like a tube opened at the alveolar end. The effective length of this tube decreases with decreasing frequency. Margaria & Cavagna (366, 367) have shown an excellent correlation between sound volume and airway pressure. Draper *et al.* (153) further pointed out that the tracheal pressure which varies from 2 cm of water for quiet speech to 30 cm for parade ground shouting is quite constant and independent of lung volume. This implies an active participation of the diaphragm during quiet phonation at high lung volumes. Gremy (228) has calculated the energy spent by the vocal cords during singing. He believes that it cannot be all provided by transfer from the flowing air stream. However, the influence of a partially resonant open-ended tube on this energy is difficult to calculate.

Acceleration.—The various respiratory effects of acceleration have been extensively investigated (110, 634, 664). With forward acceleration, a doubling of elastic work and an increase in frequency to almost 40 cpm at 12 G are of particular interest. Pulmonary edema may occur in the posterior portions of the lungs.

GAS EXCHANGE

Humidification.—Walker & Wells (631) reviewed heat and water exchange in the respiratory tract. Bargeton (41) carefully developed an apparatus permitting the measurement of mean expired gas temperature and water vapor. He compared measurements with predicted values and with determinations of the performance of a model giving similar values. It is of interest that at a ventilation of 30 liters per minute mixed expired air is 2.5 degrees cooler than body temperature and has a water vapor pressure of only 41 mm Hg. The upper airway is a surprisingly poor heat and water-vapor equilibrating device, these results suggesting a heat dead space of about 50 ml and a slightly smaller water-vapor dead space although Bargeton did not calculate these values. Ingelstedt & Toremalm (287) also constructed a model in which they used the transfer of heat from the walls of a brass tube to a flowing air stream to study boundary conditions and make predictions of the effects of boundary layers of gas on the transfer of heat and water vapor in the airway. Negus (433) concluded that the human nose is an inefficient device for wetting and warming inspired air.

Lower airway.—Jacobs & Papperman (292), measuring the pH of the lining of the airway through a bronchoscope with a tiny glass electrode, observed that the mucous coat in suppurative airway disease appears to be more acid than in the normal airway. It should be noted, however, that the pH of mucus will change more than 1.0 pH if the carbon dioxide in the gas over it changes from room air to alveolar air. Tracheal ciliary activity ceased 5 to 28 minutes after placing the cilia in a saline solution which had been bubbled with the smoke from two cigarettes in an experiment reported by Ballenger (36). One cannot conclude whether the tar or the carbon monoxide was responsible. Hilding (264) compares the ciliary stream and its overlying mucous blanket to a river that begins in the tiny branches of the respiratory bronchioles, joining together in an ever-accelerating stream to the larynx. He has pointed out that interruptions of this stream by squamous cell islands, bronchial openings, and the presence of cigarette smoke may enhance the action of carcinogens.

Bronchoconstriction.—The ability of epinephrine to relieve bronchoconstriction in asthmatics was found by Blumenthal *et al.* (76) to be improved by the intravenous administration of sodium lactate. It is of interest that small doses of acetylsalicylic acid can completely reverse the bronchoconstrictive action of the peptide bradykinin in guinea pigs (114). Kilburn (314), using bronchograms in anesthetized paralyzed dogs, quantitated the dimensional changes of the airway in response to positive and negative pressure, various respiratory gases, and drugs. Five per cent carbon dioxide inhalation with controlled respiration appears to have produced bronchoconstriction.

Alveolar gas exchange.—Nunn (440) contributed an excellent review of the factors relating ventilation and carbon dioxide elimination, particularly in anesthesia. Visser (623) calculated the time course of the changes of oxygen and carbon dioxide pressures and concentrations of blood passing through the pulmonary capillaries. Considering the effect of oxygen on the carbon dioxide dissociation curve, carbon dioxide transfer is limited by the oxygen diffusion. Carbon dioxide does not diffuse as rapidly as has generally been assumed (73). However, the change of pH during passage of the blood through the last 90 per cent of the pulmonary capillaries is not greater than 10 per cent of the arteriovenous pH difference. The blood-gas relationships are described in a new four-quadrant diagram (623). The diffusion of labeled $^{14}CO_2$ is not detectably different from $^{12}CO_2$ in isolated perfused rabbit lungs (37). Attempts to treat the time course of inert gas washin or washout mathematically have considered ventilation to be continuous. Riggs & Goldstein (494) derived appropriate equations for considering the effects of a cyclic ventilation but conclude that this has no practical advantage over the simpler continuous ventilation equations. Dantzig *et al.* (135) attempted to derive a comprehensive mathematical model of alveolar gas exchange suitable for handling in computers. The preliminary mathematical model does not include many of the important problems in gas exchange, many of which have been carefully considered by Fahri & Rahn (173) in preparing an electrical analogue for simulating the dynamic changes of carbon dioxide stores. Apnea, in anesthetized paralyzed patients after hyperventilation with oxygen, is commonly being used for bronchoscopy and other short procedures in which the airway must be examined. During apnea, the Pco_2 of the arterial blood rises to the venous concentration in about 0.5 minutes and then rises at about 3 ml per minute varying in anesthetized subjects from 1.5 to 6 ml per minute (166). Heller & Watson (259) recorded with an oxygen electrode the rate at which arterial Po_2 falls after filling the lungs with various concentrations of oxygen and then leaving the face open to air. After 100 per cent oxygen breathing, the arterial Po_2 remained above 100 mm for more than four minutes. Moll & Bartels (402) computed the errors arising from the nitrogen exchange involved in measurement of basal metabolic rate in the closed and open circuit. They point out that in a closed system, nitrogen elimination exceeds oxygen uptake by the blood stream and tissues so one may read an artifactual fall in the basal metabolic rate of at least 60 ml per minute in the first minute and 23 ml per minute even after 10 minutes. In an open system, nitrogen elimination makes very large errors in the other direction, overestimating oxygen consumption when gas of high oxygen concentration is breathed.

Distribution of ventilation.—Langer, Bornstein & Fishman (333) suggest that the rhythmic oscillation sometimes seen in the plateau of a single-breath nitrogen curve results from a combination of uneven alveolar ventilation and vascular impacts. The poorly ventilated areas seem to be located in the perihilar rather than in the peripheral regions of the lung. By choice of various soluble and insoluble gases for the single breath before the nitrogen plateau was recorded, the location of various gas concentrations in proportion to blood flow was determined. Maloney *et al.* (360) showed in dogs that paradoxical respiration following thoracoplasty does not involve *Pendelluft*. Unilateral distribution abnormalities have been demonstrated by Stahle (566) using the helium dilution method with a bronchospirometry catheter.

Ventilation perfusion relationships and arterial-alveolar gradients.—In the past several years it has become apparent that in the normal animal or man virtually none of the arterial-alveolar oxygen gradient can be ascribed to diffusion gradients. This oxygen gradient was found to increase progressively with oxygen uptake in experiments by Asmussen & Nielsen (22) and Doll (146); the value they found was 17 mm at rest, higher than most reports. With heavy work, the gradient varied from 20 mm when 12 per cent oxygen was breathed to 27 mm when 50 per cent oxygen was breathed. The data suggest a large role of abnormal distribution, a small contribution of shunts, and no contribution at all of diffusion gradient which the authors now believe cannot be directly determined for oxygen. McIlroy & Holmgren (419) also note that if the rise in body temperature with exercise is allowed for, no fall in arterial P_{O_2} occurs with exercise. Finley et al. (179) were able to reduce the calculated shunt from 5 per cent to less than 1 per cent in the anesthetized dog by the simple maneuver of continuous positive-pressure breathing which would be expected to open up all atelectatic areas, confirming the concept that some atelectasis is a normal phenomenon. Unevenness of ventilation perfusion ratios also produces inert gas tension gradients. Klocke & Rahn (318) have shown the distribution difference between normal and emphysematous individuals by measuring the pN_2 of human bladder urine. Edwards & Farhi (164) developed a highly accurate method for nitrogen dissolved in blood using the gas chromatograph which, they say, in addition to alveolar-arterial nitrogen gradients, should permit determination of alveolar temperature! Nitrogen in the alveoli plays a certain role in the prevention of atelectasis that is of interest in the choice of space capsule atmospheres. MacHattie & Rahn (359) found that mice could thrive in an atmosphere of pure oxygen at 197 mm Hg with the exception that several animals died within 48 hours after being subjected to this environment, probably of pulmonary atelectasis. Kreuzer et al. (321) noted a decreased arterial-alveolar oxygen gradient in altitude-acclimatized dogs, possibly because they were hyperventilating and therefore had less atelectasis. Briscoe et al. (85) estimated the degree of nonuniformity of ventilation perfusion relationships in emphysema, showing that the poorly ventilated alveoli are grossly overperfused in relation to their ventilation. Similar differentiation has been obtained with radioactive krypton by Gurtner et al. (234). Atelectasis is probably also responsible for the low arterial oxygen tension observed in obese individuals (515). Several new methods of detecting shunts and uneven ventilation have been described (278, 445). Ross & Farhi (507) found that for accurate theoretical analysis of the ventilation perfusion relationships, it is necessary to estimate the composition of the dead space gas inspired into that alveolus.

Carbon dioxide gradients and dead space.—Anesthetized subjects were again shown (440, 441) to have enlarged alveolar dead space and a difference between arterial and end tidal carbon dioxide tension of about 5 mm Hg, the cause of which has not yet been ascertained. Reichel et al. (484) and Sakamoto (518) have attempted to correlate dead space and carbon dioxide gradients with the perfusion abnormality in emphysema. Abnormally distributed pulmonary blood flow leads to arterial-alveolar carbon dioxide gradients (235, 571) unless local ventilation shifts away from unperfused alveoli (539).

Atelectasis.—The evidence that diffuse airway closure or alveolar collapse is a normal phenomenon is now very convincing. Bernstein (67) showed that some airways close during expiration even above functional residual capacity, depending on expiratory flow rate. The reopening of closed units by a deep breath is reflected in the stress relaxation studied by Marshall & Widdicombe (372); the increases in compliance (490, 535, 621); the increases in functional residual capacity (86, 315); and the decrease in shunt (179).

With the widespread use of cardiopulmonary bypass, a postperfusion pulmonary congestion syndrome consisting primarily of atelectasis has become apparent (33, 603). Interference with the normal pulmonary surface-active lining may play an important role. A lung which has been chronically atelectatic and then re-expanded shows a considerable loss of compliance and increased resistance of the pulmonary vascular bed (350). Postoperative atelectasis still accounts for 13 to 25 per cent of postoperative deaths (208, 253, 381, 450, 474).

Diffusion.—Carbon monoxide methods have almost completely supplanted the direct determination of diffusing capacity with oxygen gradients. However, Briehl & Fishman (82) prepared a more accurate Bohr integral chart to improve the accuracy of the oxygen method. Piiper, Haab & Rahn (460, 461, 462) examined the effect of the unequal distribution of pulmonary diffusing capacity in the determination of arterial-alveolar oxygen gradients. Evidence obtained from study of the dog which is breathing different oxygen tensions can only be explained by assuming the presence of pulmonary blood flow through capillaries which have serious limitations of diffusion but which are capable of being saturated at high oxygen tensions.

On the other hand, Asmussen & Nielsen (23) now believe that the relative contributions of diffusion and distribution to the arterial-alveolar Po_2 difference cannot be calculated since low oxygen breathing reduces the oxygen uptake from hypoventilated areas less than from hyperventilated areas. Blank & Roughton (73) showed that the red cell membrane is about one-twentieth as permeable to carbon dioxide as a comparable layer of water yet still 1000 times more permeable than long-chain alcohol monolayers. The red cell membrane appears to offer no measurable impediment to the diffusion of oxygen (322). The effective pore radius of the red cell determined by a new method is 4.2 A (220). Dyson, Sinclair and West (159) noted that the exchange of $^{15}O_2$ from alveolar gas was considerably greater than that of $^{16}O_2$ because of the absence of back pressure. The disappearance of $^{15}O_2$ should be more comparable to that of carbon monoxide. Dollery & West (148) noticed that when ^{15}O-labeled carbon dioxide is breathed, the disappearance of the radioactivity from the alveolar gas phase is extraordinarily rapid. This extremely interesting observation is accounted for since the oxygen of carbon dioxide is freely exchangeable with the oxygen of water through bicarbonate formation. Staub, Bishop & Forster (568) determined the over-all association rate constant K'_C for the uptake of oxygen by normal human red blood cells, using a membrane-covered oxygen electrode in a modified Hartridge-Roughton apparatus. Dissociation kinetics have been studied for oxygen and carbon monoxide (18, 134, 313). The Roughton and Forster technique for separately calculating pulmonary capillary blood volume and true diffusing capacity of the pulmonary membrane by measuring the pulmonary diffusing capacity for carbon monoxide at several different capillary oxygen tensions has found a number of uses. Lewis *et al.* (342) used both the single-breath and rebreathing methods, obtaining higher values for a diffusing capacity for carbon monoxide and pulmonary capillary blood volume and lower values for the diffusion capacity of the pulmonary membrane with the rebreathing method. Johnson *et al.* (300) found the diffusion capacities of the lung and of the pulmonary membrane and the pulmonary capillary blood volume to be closely correlated with blood flow during exercise. They estimate the average time spent by red cells in the pulmonary capillaries at rest to be 0.79 seconds, falling to 0.5 seconds at levels of exercise tripling cardiac output. Jones & Meade (302) have shown mathematically that anomalies noted in the pulmonary diffusing capacity for carbon monoxide with time of breath holding may be explained by effects on alveolar volume and are not proof of nonuniform distribution. The diffusion capacities of the lung and the pulmonary membrane are increased by hypercapnia (476), by the Mueller maneuver (121), by elevating left atrial pressure (504), by inflation of a pressure suit (508), by the inverted posture (435), and by exercise (39, 52, 248). The lung's diffusion capacity and the pulmonary capillary blood volume decrease with administration of histamine aerosol (79). The diffusing capacity for carbon monoxide is increased when pulmonary blood flow is high, either in patients with atrial septal defect (56) or in experimental animals with left to right shunts (483), and decreased in the postoperative period (142, 147) and in various pulmonary diseases (304, 588). Bates *et al.* (53) reported pulmonary capillary blood volume and diffusion capacity of the pulmonary membrane in a group of cardiorespiratory diseases. The pathomorphology of abnormal diffusion has been reviewed by Meesen (378).

PULMONARY CIRCULATION

Pulmonary Vascular Resistance

Hemodynamics.—The major pulmonary arteries are remarkably distensible with almost linear pressure-volume curves over the physiologic range and exhibit some stress relaxation and hysteresis (193). Sinusoidal flow pumped into excised rabbit pulmonary arteries at various frequencies identified reflections at 8 cps with a minimum input impedance at 4 cps (61). The pulmonary vascular resistance *in vivo* alters in such a way that pulmonary artery pressure is kept almost constant at very high (373) and very low (589) flows, suggesting the presence of elements with the characteristics of a constant back-pressure rather than a constant resistance.

Effects of lung volume.—In no field of physiology are the hydrodynamic relationships so complex or so frequently misinterpreted as in the determination of the effect of lung volume, ventilation, and airway pressure on the pulmonary vascular resistance. Whittenberger *et al.* (643), in a meticulous open-chest experiment on dogs, thoroughly confirmed the increase in pulmonary vascular resistance caused by lung inflation and showed this effect to be due primarily to the relation between pulmonary artery pressure and alveolar pressure. Roos *et al.* (503), having read Whittenberger's paper, over-looked the error introduced by contrasting positive- and negative-pressure inflation when the absolute pressure of the pulmonary artery was kept constant. As Whittenberger pointed out, the pressure outside the right atrium and ventricle and left atrium (intrapleural pressure) is also reduced during normal inspiration. Thomas *et al.* (597, 598) do not reduce perfusion or downstream pressures with negative-pressure lung inflation, in their experiments. Similar work has been done by others (249, 411, 487). In short, it seems established that pulmonary vascular resistance *in vivo* will increase at increasing lung volumes as much with spontaneous respiration, as with positive pressure inflation (at constant blood flow).

If left atrial pressure is lower than airway pressure, a portion of the total pulmonary vascular resistance must exist at the capillary-venular junction. Its behavior is not as a constant resistance but as a constant back-pressure, or pressure drop, independent of flow (38, 453, 454). When lung volume is reduced below functional residual capacity, pulmonary vascular resistance changes very little but in some circumstances may increase (555, 643). The dependence of pulmonary vascular resistance on alveolar pressure is also illustrated in an experiment by Frank, quoted by Whittenberger (643). At comparable volumes, he found airway pressure and vascular resistance in the saline-filled lobe to be less than half that observed in the air-filled lobe. Others, however, find resistance in air- and saline-filled lungs about equal (127, 598). The difference between these experiments probably lies in the relationship of left atrial or pulmonary venous pressure to airway pressure. Lloyd & Wright (346) and Banister & Torrance (38) found no evidence of a critical closing pressure in the lung and presented vital evidence suggesting that the pressure in the alveolar wall around the pulmonary capillaries is somewhat negative to airway pressure presumably caused by the surface tension of the alveolar lining. Howell (277) and Permutt (455) have shown that with inflation of the lung the compliance of the vascular system decreases, the capillaries tending to empty and the larger vessels tending to fill.

Effects of respiratory gases.—The literature on this subject through the spring of 1960 was excellently reviewed by Fishman (183) with 454 references. The greatest interest in this field has resided in the question whether unilateral hypoxia can cause a shift of blood away from the hypoxic lung. Fishman concludes that it can, which is the more remarkable since most of his own evidence failed to show the effect. Arborelius (19), using the careful techniques worked out by himself and Defares and collaborators (138), found that whereas 10 per cent oxygen in the right lung is capable of shunting blood to the opposite lung in man in the supine position, it is not able to produce a shift when the right lung is dependent. Hypoxia does not measurably increase the total thoracic blood volume (194) but does increase the pulmonary vascular resistance considerably more than a comparable rise in cardiac output produced by exercise (184). In patients with ventricular septal defects, pulmonary vascular resistance is considerably reduced by oxygen breathing (370). The report of Moulder *et al.* (410) that elevating the pulmonary artery oxygen saturation above 90 per cent causes pulmonary vasoconstriction should be considered against considerable evidence to the contrary (183).

Pulmonary venoconstriction from saline injection and hypoxia.—Considerable evidence seems to be accumulating that active constriction can occur somewhere between pulmonary capillaries and the left atrium, accounting for pulmonary edema of altitude sickness and after hypertonic saline injections.

Houston (275) reported four cases of pulmonary edema occurring in healthy individuals going suddenly to high altitudes and commented that this syndrome seems to have been noticed by many others and given various explanations. Houston attributes it to left ventricular failure although in the absence of indication that the left auricular pressure is elevated it would seem also possible that the mechanism might be pulmonary venoconstriction. Hultgren & Spickard (282), reviewing medical experiences in Peru, noted considerable evidence for the occurrence of pulmonary edema, particularly with exercise, in people, horses, and mules at high altitude. The disease seen in high-altitude exposure of pigs and cows, however, is right-sided failure without pulmonary edema. They note that the disease called soroche is most commonly associated with pulmonary edema in acclimatized normal individuals who go to the sea coast for five to twenty days and then return to altitude. No evidence of left ventricular failure was elicited, and they also suggest the possible contribution of constriction of pulmonary venules distal to the capillaries. The possibility that the pulmonary hypertension in hypoxia may in part be caused by venoconstriction is also supported by Duke's observation (156) of an increase in lung blood volume during nitrogen ventilation in the isolated perfused cat lung and by Naeye (423), who obtained histological evidence in patients with chronic hypoxemia produced by either altitude or hypoventilation that alveolar capillaries were much more congested in the hypoxemic cases than in the normal controls. This postulate would suggest that the effect of hypoxia on the pulmonary arterioles is a secondary protective response resulting from increased capillary pressure similar to that observed in the lung bases in mitral stenosis.

It has been shown by Eliakim *et al.* (170) and confirmed by Reineck *et al.* (488) and Brutsaert (87) that hypertonic saline injections result in elevations in wedge pressure without elevations in left atrial pressure in the dog. The involvement of a sphincter at the junction between the superior pulmonary vein and left atrium in the dog has been implicated by Eliakim although a contribution of the small pulmonary venules cannot be ruled out.

Nervous influences.—Daly (133) reviewed this field in a symposium dedicated to Professor Jarisch. Pulmonary vasoconstriction was produced by increasing intracranial pressure (29) but not by perfusion of hypoxic blood into vertebral arteries (222). Pulmonary hypertension resulted from bladder distention in patients with cervical cord transections (8). Pulmonary vasoconstriction produced by electrical stimulation of stellate sympathetics no longer occurred 10 to 30 minutes after interruption of the bronchial circulation (13).

Drugs.—Aviado (30) and Fowler (186) reviewed pharmacologic agents active in the pulmonary circulation. The possibility that bronchoconstriction *per se* may influence pulmonary vascular resistance has been investigated with equivocal results (27). Aminophylline, tetraethylammonium, bretylium tosylate, papaverine, and atropine have insignificant effects (238, 250, 502, 647). Tolazoline (Priscoline) is a potent pulmonary vasodilator with insignificant effects on arterial oxygen saturation (232, 572, 644), whereas acetylcholine, also a potent pulmonary vasodilator, may significantly reduce arterial oxygen saturation (71, 111, 525), particularly in patients with chronic pulmonary emphysema. Pretreatment of a rabbit with reserpine results in much better filling of the pulmonary vascular system with contrast media (622) by blocking a vasoconstrictive response to the dye. Harris, Fritts & Cournand (254) have been unable to find a dose of serotonin that influences the pulmonary artery pressure without altering the brachial artery pressure in man, suggesting that serotonin may not be as specific a pulmonary vasoconstrictor as was believed. The decapeptide hypertensin or angiotonin elevates both pulmonary arterial and wedge pressures which, in spite of the conclusion of the authors, precludes the assignment of a pulmonary vasoconstriction to the drug (526, 533).

Reports concerning the pulmonary vasomotor activity of epinephrine and norepinephrine (157) should be considered against the seven reasons adduced by Fowler (186) for errors in determining pulmonary vasoconstriction with epinephrine and norepinephrine.

Total and capillary blood volumes.—Milnor *et al.* (399) and Dock *et al.* (145) determined the pulmonary blood volume from pulmonary artery to left atrium by subtraction. They determined dye-dilution blood volumes by injecting indicators separately in both the pulmonary artery and left atrium and sampling from a brachial artery. Both groups agree on an average volume of about 350 ml.

The pulmonary capillary blood volume has been shown to correlate well with the expected effects on transmural pressure of the capillaries of such influences as exercise, posture, norepinephrine, ganglionic blockade, and respiratory maneuvers (53, 300, 342, 343).

The pulsatility of pulmonary capillary blood flow first shown by Lee & DuBois and confirmed by others has been questioned by Rigatto & Fishman (492) who failed to observe significantly greater pulses with nitrous oxide than with air inspired in the body plethysmograph. One may object, however, that their instrument was much less sensitive than that of Lee & DuBois and they do not appear to have ruled out the possibility that respiratory quotient, temperature, and humidity variations superimposed on their plethysmograph tracings may have obscured the pulsatile uptake of nitrous oxide. Caro & MacDonald (108), confirming the pulsatility of pulmonary capillary flow, also make the interesting observation that the pulmonary and systemic systems are both about one-fourth wavelength long at the normal frequency range (rabbit). The significance is that a one-fourth wavelength system presents the minimum impedance load on the ventricle.

UNEVEN DISTRIBUTION OF PULMONARY CIRCULATION

Measurement of uneven distribution.—Carbon dioxide gradients have been used as an index of the maldistribution of blood flow through the lungs. Stein *et al.* (571) showed the development of carbon dioxide gradients after serum-induced thrombi were embolized to the pulmonary circulation of the dog. They also noted the opening of atriovenous shunts in the lung disclosed by low oxygen tensions while breathing pure oxygen, the fall in arterial Pco_2 indicating a reflex hyperpnea. Haab *et al.* (235) recorded the increase in carbon dioxide gradient caused by reducing pulmonary blood flow in a dog during partial heart-lung bypass. The gradient was almost unaffected until pulmonary blood flow had fallen to half of control values. Hugh-Jones & West (278) used a four-channel mass spectrometer to record the instantaneous gas concentrations present in bronchi resulting from partial obstruction either to bronchi or blood flow. Under certain circumstances, these patterns should be diagnostic of regional variations in gas and blood flow. In a series of papers, West, Dollery, and their collaborators reported the use of radioactive carbon monoxide, carbon dioxide, and oxygen to demonstrate regional variations in blood flow and ventilation (149, 640, 641) and regional variations in diffusing capacity (150). In man in the erect posture, apical pulmonary capillaries do not all appear to be open in the normal individual at rest but are opened by exercise or in high pulmonary flow diseases. The postural variations in blood flow in the apex account for the whole of the ventilation perfusion ratio inequality of the normal lung. Exercise overcomes the postural effect on distribution in the lateral position (107).

Effect on ventilation.—The occlusion by balloon catheter of one pulmonary artery has been found to result in a prompt shift of ventilation away from the occluded lung in both man and dogs. Swenson *et al.* (586) found that unilateral pulmonary artery occlusion produced virtually no change in total ventilation, arterial Pco_2, or physiologic dead space. During bronchospirometry in nine patients, the occlusion of one pulmonary artery reduced the ventilation of that lung from 45 to 29 per cent of the total. Severinghaus *et al.* (539) demonstrated that this same homeostatic mechanism occurred in dogs and was entirely ascribable to bronchoconstriction resulting from the fall in alveolar Pco_2 following occlusion. It was prevented by inhalation of 6 per cent carbon dioxide in air or isoproterenol aerosol or 100 per cent nitrogen but not by atropine or vagotomy. Airway resistance on the occluded side was doubled and compliance fell 25 per cent. When blood flow was restored, shunting was detected and ventilation returned slowly with normal inflation or immediately after hyperinflation of that lung, suggesting that the bronchoconstriction had produced some atelectasis. Cahill *et al.* (97) also observed falls in compliance and increase in resistance with embolization with barium.

Pulmonary embolism.—Tachypnea may be produced by embolizing less than 10 per cent of the pulmonary vascular bed with 75 μ glass beads (68). Homologous blood clot emboli in dogs produce little reflex change, occasional infarcts, some artherosclerotic plaques, but usually are completely reabsorbed within 28 days (14, 291, 639).

The physiologic aspects of clinical embolism have been reviewed by Robin (497) and Dexter (140). Serum lactic dehydrogenase activity (627) and arteriography (574) appear to be more useful than carbon dioxide gradients (497) for diagnosis. Long-term anticoagulant treatment of primary pulmonary hypertension may disclose repeated minute embolism as its cause (45, 646). Embolism plays an important role in sickle cell disease (407, 475), sudden death in obese pilots (581), and toxic reactions to contrast media (66).

Pulmonary shunts.—Niden (438) *et al.*, using right ventricular bypass for constant cardiac output, showed that small changes in arterial oxygen saturation (on air) are caused by epinephrine, histamine, and serotonin. Unfortunately, these cannot be attributed to shunts since 100 per cent oxygen was not used. Fritts *et al.* (195), injecting krypton 85 dissolved in T-1824 dye, found large shunts in patients with Weber-Rendu-Osler's disease but minor shunts in patients with emphysema and cirrhosis. Others report sizable shunts in cirrhosis (51, 500).

Pulmonary edema.—Uhley *et al.* (612, 613) demonstrated small increases in right lymphatic duct flow in dogs after inflation of a balloon in the left atrium. Urabe *et al.* (615) identified an association between the occurrence of pulmonary edema following neurosurgery and lesions in the internal capsule, the lentiform nucleus, and the third ventricle. Wagner (630) *et al.* were unable to prevent the accumulation of pulmonary edema in an isolated perfused lobe by using positive pressure in the airway. Ebert (160) has studied the lung in congestive heart failure. See Section 37 for edema resulting from hypoxia.

Bronchial circulation.—Several dye-dilution techniques for estimating bronchial blood flow have been described (196, 429, 430). Aviado *et al.* (31) have shown that in the absence of pulmonary arterial flow, bronchial blood flow passes pulmonary capillaries and becomes oxygenated before reaching pulmonary veins, but it does not pass the alveoli when pulmonary circulation is intact and therefore constitutes a shunt. Their calculations would appear to attribute all the pulmonary tissue oxygen consumption to bronchial blood, whereas the effect of pulmonary artery occlusion on alveoli and bronchi (539) indicates that the pulmonary circulation and ventilation normally take care of a share of the metabolic needs. Alley *et al.* (12) have shown that the bronchial arterial hypertrophy following pulmonary arterial occlusion can be reversed on reopening the pulmonary artery. Bronchial vascular resistance is increased by positive pressure on the airway and by vagotomy (272).

Morphology of pulmonary vessels.—James, Owen & Thomas (295) injected the pulmonary vascular system with a solution containing radio opaque and radioactive materials to outline the smaller pulmonary vessels. The vasa vasorum of the pulmonary artery arise from the bronchial circulation (602). The normal and abnormal maturation of the pulmonary vascular system has been extensively studied (70, 263, 354, 505, 628, 629).

BLOOD-GAS TRANSPORT

Hemoglobin.—Hemmingsen & Scholander (260) reported that the specific supplemental transfer of oxygen through hemoglobin solutions occurs only at low oxygen pressures when a portion of the hemoglobin may be expected to be desaturated. Mathematical justification has been attempted by three groups (115, 174, 633). The evidence for very low tissue Po_2 suggests that myoglobin facilitates oxygen transport in mammalian muscle (529). Bartels *et al.* (46) have carefully determined oxygen dissociation curves in 14 normal subjects, in some of them over a period of several years. The resultant individual characteristic variations are constant for years. The maximum variation of Po_2 at 50 per cent saturation was 5.4 mm Hg. Their new standard curve is half saturated at 26.8 mm Hg. Saturation is complete at $Po_2 = 370$ mm Hg (356). Hemoglobin deforms at pH 10 and dissociates into equal halves at pH 11 (327). The pH dissociation of human fetal hemoglobin is asymmetric (280). The effect on pH of the fetal hemoglobin dissociation curve is virtually identical to that of adults, although the lamb fetal hemoglobin is half saturated at a Po_2 of only 16 mm compared to the adult value of 32 to 37 mm (385). At 14,900 feet, both sheep and fetal hemoglobin have the same dissociation curves as animals living at sea level (386). Bartels *et al.* (47, 48) made the striking observation that in the weeks following birth the dissociation curve shifts to the right beyond the adult average by 7 mm Hg Po_2 at 50 per cent saturation in infants, 16 mm in kids, and 14 mm in lambs. Hellegers & Schruefer (258) constructed dissociation nomograms based on the Hill equation and their data on maternal and fetal blood. Edwards *et al.* (165) reported a shift of the dissociation curve to the left with age of red cells and also of solutions of their hemoglobins. Increasing cation concentration shifts the curve to the right [Rossi-Fanelli (511, 512, 564)]. Further attempts to define the constants in Adair's equation appear to be limited by the scatter of experimental data and the nonhomogeneity of hemoglobin (64, 176, 221). The source of protons in the Bohr effect appears to be still unexplained. Two groups have found evidence that the reactive SH- groups are not responsible (60, 561). Nor can the effect be attributed to proton displacement by oxygen (368) although Bernard (65) has assumed this in his mathematical model. For kinetics of hemoglobin-oxygen and carbon monoxide reactions, see Diffusion.

Carbon dioxide transport.—The solubility coefficient α for carbon dioxide in plasma at 37°, redetermined by Bartels & Wrbitzky (50), is 0.5134 in man ($S = 0.0303$ mM/mm Hg Pco_2). Harms & Bartels (252) prepared a nomogram for computation of the carbon dioxide dissociation curves at various saturations and temperatures. Methods of determining the hydration rates of carbon dioxide have been reviewed by Kern (312).

Buffering capacity of fluids against carbon dioxide-induced H^+ alterations is independent of the bicarbonate concentration, but depends on other buffer systems such as proteins. For separated human plasma, Δ pH/Δ log Pco_2 is 0.85 (625) compared to 1.0 for bicarbonate solutions from 1–50 mM and about 0.65 for blood. The carbon dioxide dissociation curve and pK of spinal fluid may be assumed to be identical to that of a comparable bicarbonate solution. The cerebral spinal fluid pK' found by Alexander *et al.* (11) is probably 0.02–0.03 too high because of too small a pH range and buffer uncertainty.

The dynamics of carbon dioxide stores have been shown by Farhi & Rahn (173) to depend largely on muscle blood flow, requiring many hours for equilibrium at a new Pco_2.

Leroy *et al.* (338) computed the carbon dioxide body pool in man to be 487 ± 103 millimols per square meter and determined the turnover rates of the pool and of the bone carbonate.

Use of amine buffers.—Nahas and Papper organized a conference on amine buffers such as tris (hydroxymethyl) aminomethane which was published as a 500-page review (426). Since tris (hydroxymethyl) aminomethane leaks through the blood brain barrier (268) and depresses respiration (63, 83), its use in the treatment of carbon dioxide intoxication (84, 361, 584) is open to serious question. During apneic oxygenation it may be infused to keep pH constant and Pco_2 almost constant (270, 394).

Carbonic anhydrase.—After administration of acetazolamide (Diamox), carbon dioxide reacts so slowly with blood water that mixed venous blood on reaching the lungs is still 6 mm Hg above its final equilibrium tension (98) and on leaving the lungs is far below its final equilibrium value even in emphysema (464). The ventilatory increase from acetazolamide (25 to 50 mg/kg) in man is only 15 per cent compared to about 100 per cent in dogs (99). Tissue Pco_2 rises in spite of hyperventilation, contraindicating use of acetazolamide in treatment of carbon dioxide retention (428). Basal metabolic rate is not reduced by acetazolamide (20 mg/kg) in man (117). The kinetics of carbonic anhydrase inhibition are reported by Maren (364).

TISSUE GAS

Capillary geometry.—Thews (595, 596) computed the oxygen diffusion conditions in grey matter using new histological evidence that the tissue cylinder around each capillary in the cortex has a mean radius of 30 μ. He determined the oxygen permeability of thin slices of brain at 20°C to be 2×10^{-5} cm^3 per cm per min per atm, agreeing well with Krogh's figure. The new calculation also includes the influence of oxygen release from blood. Thews predicts a mean Po_2 of 17 mm in the cortex which is considerably lower than other estimates but agrees well with the actually observed values obtained with the Clark-type oxygen electrode. Greven (230) has determined oxygen diffusion coefficients in various tissues but they would appear to be lower than Krogh's and Thew's values. Schmidt-Nielsen & Pennycuik (529) found that the smallest mammals have significantly higher capillary densities than do large ones; these aid the supply of oxygen required by their relatively high metabolic rates.

Po_2 and Pco_2.—A quantitative measurement of gas tensions in the cerebral cortex, made possible by the membrane-covered electrodes (2, 288, 353, 582), showed in general that the cortical Po_2 is considerably lower than venous blood Po_2, averaging about 15 mm Hg. The Po_2 of cisternal fluid in man is intermediate between arterial and venous levels averaging 175 mm while oxygen is being breathed (75). Cerebral cortex Pco_2, measured by several individuals (288, 289, 540), was found to be 4 to 6 mm above jugular venous Pco_2. Joyner, Horwitz & Williams (303) made the interesting observation that tissue oxygen availability to a bare electrode appears to increase with heparin clearing of lipemia.

EFFECTS OF OXYGEN AND CARBON DIOXIDE

Anoxia.—Craig (124) reported loss of consciousness in four underwater swimmers which was apparently associated with preliminary hyperventilation of air. In the absence of a carbon dioxide drive to respiration, some individuals have an insufficient drive from hypoxia to prevent loss of consciousness. Forty-three children who were subject to profound anoxia at birth had an abnormal incidence of low IQ (20 per cent below 70 Stanford-Binet) but no significant differences in neurological or psychiatric studies (59). The ability of the newborn to withstand total oxygen lack has been reviewed by Mott (409). James (294) found metabolic acidosis in the newborn to be the most reliable guide to the severity of pre-existing anoxia. Eckstein & Horsley (163) noted an increase in peripheral venous tone with hypoxia. Hurtado (284) noted a decreased respiratory response to breathing carbon dioxide in acute mountain sickness, the subjects showing a mild respiratory acidosis at rest. The oxygen consumption of subjects residing at 15,000 feet is about 20 per cent above normal in terms of fat-free mass (459). Chronic anoxia increases the cerebral blood volume (626). Chickens have a much lower altitude tolerance than other small but warm-blooded animals (15). Glucose infusion makes men more susceptible to hypoxia, perhaps related to its potassium effect (546). Also see Pulmonary Circulation.

Oxygen toxicity.—The relation of Pco_2 to oxygen toxicity has been restudied (371, 590), confirming the earlier findings that increased carbon dioxide can potentiate convulsions in low concentrations and inhibit in high concentrations. Oxygen toxicity is intensified by thyroxin (559) and reduced by arginine (210). The psychomotor performance of men at three atmospheres of oxygen was not disturbed (190).

Hypercapnia.—The technique of apneic oxygenation (diffusion respiration) has resulted in considerable interest in hypercapnia since it finds clinical use in anesthesia, e.g., bronchoscopy. The primary interest this year, centering on the sympathoadrenal system, was reviewed by Tenney (592). Adrenalectomy in dogs prevents the rise of plasma epinephrine but not of norepinephrine with hypercapnia (395, 396). Depending on the ambient temperature, adrenalectomy also blocked the rise in free fatty acids and glucose with hypercapnia (417, 580). The cardiac irritability seen on withdrawal from hypercapnia cannot be produced by similar pH increases following sodium bicarbonate infusion (663). It is prevented by infusion of epinephrine or norepinephrine during withdrawal (223) and is probably caused by imbalance between vagal and sympathetic effects according to Price (470) who has reviewed the cardiovascular effects of carbon dioxide.

Elevated Pco_2 appears to cause lipid membranes to lose sodium ion, pack more closely, and increase their electrical resistance (531). The pressor response to catecholamines is reduced by hypercapnia (432). The rise of epinephrine, norepinephrine, and 17-hydroxy cortical steroids has also been demonstrated in normal man with the breathing of 7 to 14 per cent carbon dioxide (532). Previous work had suggested that carbon dioxide concentrations above 40 per cent produced apnea. Two reports this year indicate the persistence of spontaneous breathing with 70 per cent carbon dioxide (90, 225). Papilledema has been noted in chronic respiratory acidosis (362). The performance of normal man does not deteriorate with chronic carbon dioxide until the atmosphere contains three per cent or more (527). The effects of Pco_2 above 70 mm Hg on the human cerebral circulation have not been clarified

The role of carbon dioxide in the nervous system was reviewed by Woodbury (655) and its effect on cerebral circulation by Sokoloff (563).

Hypocapnia.—Since hypocapnia reduces cerebral blood flow, one might ascribe some of its effect to ischemia or hypoxia. In fact, Robinson & Gray (498, 499) found elevated pain threshold during passive hyperventilation was at least transiently restored to normal by inhalation of amyl nitrite coincident with the observable retinal dilatation. However, ammonia vapor inhalation also reduced pain threshold. It is thus not clear whether the analgesia is caused by hypoxia.

Chronic hypocapnia is the driving force for the metabolic adjustments to high altitude (310) of which the extrarenal retention of Cl^- and excretion of Na^+ and K^+, and hence of bicarbonate, are the most important (311).

NEWBORN

The lungs.—Excellent reviews appeared on respiration by Cross (128) and on circulation by Dawes (136) and by Lind (345). Naeye (424) has shown reduced pulmonary arterial media in congenital pulmonary stenosis and atresia.

With the first breath the newborn uses virtually all of the muscles of the respiratory system (78), developing negative pressures as high as 77 cm of water (416); dilates the trachea; almost completely aerates both lungs (175);

and develops a normal functional residual capacity within the first hour (212, 305, 306). The negative pressures are sufficient to rupture his own lungs with the first breath if large alveolar ectasias are present (514). Richards & Bachman (490) determined total lung and chest wall compliance in 21 normal infants paralyzed with succinylcholine. As with anesthetized animals, the compliance is increased by a previous deep breath. Gruenwald (233), attempting to inflate newborn lungs at autopsy with saline, apparently failed to carry out the experiments with the lungs immersed under saline and therefore observed large transudations of fluid which made the study worthless.

Placental gas exchange.—The possibility is still being considered that a countercurrent blood flow mechanism in the placenta might permit the umbilical vein oxygen tension to exceed that of the uterine vein (387, 471). In human studies, the umbilical venous Pco_2 is higher (472), and the oxygen tension lower (556), than in intervillous-space blood which is believed to represent uterine venous blood (276, 473, 620). Misrahy (400) implanted oxygen electrodes in fetal and maternal cat, rabbit, and guinea pig brain and found oxygen availability in the fetus equal to the maternal value.

Newborn control of respiration.—The Hering-Breuer reflex, apnea upon lung inflation, has been shown by Cross *et al.* (129) to be active in sleeping newborn babies even though it disappears in the adult. The carotid body response to hypoxia does not develop until several days after birth in man (214) and rats (4). Shortly after birth, a slight metabolic acidosis, pH 7.30, Pco_2 39.1, arterial oxygen saturation 95, was found by Reardon *et al.* (477). Progesterone, which has been shown to be responsible for the hyperventilation of pregnancy, is not responsible for the low Pco_2 usually found in the newborn since doses of 10 to 50 mg given to babies (over 18 days old) did not stimulate respiration (567). In view of the paucity of information on the newborn carbon dioxide response, it is of interest that Stahlman's data (567), when replotted, show a normal carbon dioxide response curve with a mean intercept of approximately 30 mm Hg and a doubling of ventilation with about a 5 mm Pco_2 rise above 35 mm Hg.

Idiopathic respiratory distress of the newborn.—An international symposium organized by Rudolph (513) prefers this title to "hyaline membrane syndrome". The incidence and fatality are increasing (28, 496). Implicated factors include premature rupture of the membranes (100), radiation (182), and caesarean section (72) as well as the previously recognized high incidence in diabetes and prematurity. Electron microscopy has revealed significant and generalized thickening of the endothelium of the pulmonary capillary (105). It is not yet known whether the lack of adequate alveolar surface-active material is the common factor. Sutherland & Ratcliff (583) demonstrated a decreased crying vital capacity in infants with neonatal respiratory distress syndrome, being able to predict the occurrence of this disease from measurements made within the first few minutes of life.

LUNG ANATOMY AND METABOLISM

Anatomy.—McLaughlin, Tyler & Canada (422) have shown that the mammalian lung falls into three separate groups based on subgross anatomy. The lobular structure and bronchial circulation of human and horse lung separate them from monkey-dog-cat, and cow-pig-sheep groups. Broncho-vascular segmental anatomy is beautifully illustrated by Bloomer *et al.* (74) and by the new segmental nomenclature supplied by Boyden (80). Three-dimensional studies of lung elastica have been prepared by Carton *et al.* (109). Electronmicroscopy of the alveolar interstitial tissue (329, 352) disclosed three types of fibrous tissue: collagen, elastic fibers, and a newly described microfibril. The number of alveoli per terminal respiratory unit increases about ninefold from birth and the total number of alveoli may increase as much as 1000 times from birth to puberty (172). Electronmicroscopy and new methods of preparation have added to the morphology of emphysema (257, 485, 577, 578, 579, 585, 657, 658).

Lung metabolism.—Fritts, Richards & Cournand (197) have attempted to measure pulmonary tissue oxygen consumption by the difference between Fick and dye-dilution curve outputs. Normally, the Fick has an overestimation error because of lung tissue oxygen consumption which is too small to be measured. In tuberculosis the difference between the two curve outputs indicated that lung metabolism was 12 per cent of the total basal metabolic rate. Lung tissue *in vitro* is reported to be capable of both producing and metabolizing histamine (344) and of releasing unesterified fatty acids (347). Hamilton *et al.* (241) suggest that erythrocyte destruction in the lungs is the major cause for anemia in primary pulmonary hemosiderosis.

COMPARATIVE PHYSIOLOGY

Comparative anatomy.—Riad (489) reports that desert animals exhibit a number of pulmonary peculiarities. The alveoli of the *Jaculus jaculus* are lined by only two to four cells (10 to 16 in the rat), and the bronchial epithelium has peculiar pits with covers and four or five hair cells at the base which resemble receptors. Using latex injections into the airway, Akester (9) corrected some of the anatomic errors reported from previous studies of the complex respiratory systems of domestic fowl, pigeon, and duck. Multiple air sacs extend throughout the vertebral column, sternum, and humerus. Johansen & Hol (299) have shown by cineradiography in the fish that the gill ducts have sphincters which can reject particulate matter as small as 40 μ in diameter.

Swim bladders.—Wittenberg (652, 654), noting that the toadfish swim bladder preferentially secretes carbon monoxide by a ratio of 5.44 to oxygen, suggests that this is evidence against the Haldane concept of acid secretion liberating oxygen from hemoglobin. It may be objected that the influence of the countercurrent system in the rete mirabile on this ratio cannot be predicted in the present state of knowledge concerning the rete function. He obtained evidence (653) that the Portuguese man-of-war inflates its float with carbon monoxide made from L-serine.

ENVIRONMENTAL FACTORS

Hypothermia.—In dogs the carotid chemoreceptor response to hypoxia is retained at 25 to 27°C (522, 593). The carbon dioxide response is somewhat depressed (236, 521), and vagal impulses (Hering-Breuer) are still functional (237).

Aerosols.—Mitchell (401), reviewing aerosol deposition, finds minimal alveolar retention occurring with particles 0.4 to 0.6 μ diameter. Electrostatic charges affect the deposition of aerosols (351) and may have effects on pulmonary 5-hydroxytryptamine metabolism (325). Shephard (544), studying pulmonary cripples in their homes, correlated the occurrence of smog and bronchoconstriction. Nagelschmidt (425) separates the ultimate pathological changes following inhalation of dusts into two groups, the slightly soluble dusts causing interstitial and disseminated fibrosis and the insoluble dusts causing nodular or focal fibrosis.

CLINICAL PHYSIOLOGY

ARTIFICIAL RESPIRATION

Pulmonary effects.—Negative-pressure breathing was shown to double air flow resistance (600) and reduce oxygen saturation (42). Intermittent positive-pressure breathing has no effect on compliance or distribution of inspired air in normal people (171) or in emphysema (113, 605), whereas continuous positive pressure increases compliance somewhat in normal people but especially in pulmonary edema (543) and decreases shunt caused by atelectasis (179). Jones, MacNamara & Gaensler (301) constructed an artificial resistor simulating the collapsible bronchioles in emphysema. This has helped to clarify some of the difficulty found in the use of intermittent positive-pressure breathing in the treatment of emphysema. They suggest the construction of a patient-cycled respirator capable of delivering very high flow rates at pressures which are decreasing rather than increasing during inspiration. Negative expiratory phase increased the transpulmonary pressure and thus aggravated airway closure. Although the great majority of reports favors the use of some form of intermittent positive-pressure breathing in patients with emphysema (93, 113, 187, 188, 200, 413, 547), Barach (40) and Campbell (103) still promote the use of small amounts of oxygen, hoping to achieve partial relief of hypoxia without developing carbon dioxide narcosis.

Circulatory effects.—Ting, Hong & Rahn (601) have shown that continuous negative-pressure breathing in conscious normal subjects reduces peripheral venous pressure slightly but has no effect on arterial pressure. They note that the veins entering the thoracic cavity must collapse and effectively divide the circulation into the thoracic and nonthoracic components, with the left ventricle maintaining the pressure difference between the two. During positive-pressure breathing, peripheral venous pressures rise parallel to intrapleural pressure (337). Continuous positive-pressure breathing may reduce the cardiac output and central blood volume even in normal awake subjects (316).

Resuscitation.—Mouth-to-mouth breathing continues to be found more satisfactory than the external pressure methods (468), hyperventilation of the resuscitator being unnecessary to provide normal ventilation of the victim (635) even during electro-shock convulsions (168).

Tracheotomy.—The indications in favor of tracheotomy in therapy are broadening (151, 591), even to the point of including its use with the newborn (638). The Scandinavian success with tracheotomy in children has been greatly improved by the use of an ingenious small humidifier (604).

PULMONARY DISEASE

Pulmonary function studies.—This year a plethora of over 200 papers dealt with pulmonary function studies in human disease. The reader is especially referred to papers on: emphysema (131, 185, 219, 307, 408, 491, 573); fibrosis (34, 537, 611); pneumoconiosis (92, 122, 420, 431, 501); asbestosis (32, 336, 649); asthma and chronic bronchitis (55, 444, 463, 637); Hamman-Rich syndrome (267); pulmonary alveolar proteinosis (189, 562); sarcoid (558); renal failure (198); rheumatoid spondylitis (606); and the postoperative period (3, 255, 560).

Aspiration.—Laryngeal protective reflexes have been shown by Pontoppidan & Beecher (466) to decrease progressively with age, the threshold concentration of ammonia gas required to produce a momentary apnea increasing more than sixfold from the second to the eighth and ninth decades of life. Halmagyi & Colebatch (239, 240) demonstrated that blockade of a large number of airways occurs in sheep after aspiration of 1 to 3 ml per kg of either fresh or sea water. Fluid aspiration was also followed by a significant degree of pulmonary hypertension caused by arteriolar constriction, unrelated to the hypoxia, in the lungs. The dramatic effects of these very small amounts of aspirated fluid suggest obstruction at the bronchiolar level caused by the formation of stable bubbles with the alveolar lining material. Seawater aspiration results in hemoconcentration and hypovolemia which may be treatable with plasma infusions (478). Otter *et al.* (448) showed that death after fresh-water aspiration is caused not by hemolysis and increased potassium but by anoxia from airway blockade.

METHODS

Blood and gas sampling and handling.—Gambino (204) & Maas (358) agree that capillary blood taken from a heated ear lobe shows no pH, Pco_2, or Po_2 errors compared to arterial blood. In fact, according to Siggaard-Andersen (549), a 50-microliter drop of blood on a glass slide exposed to air for two minutes before being drawn into a micro capillary pH electrode shows only a 0.01 pH rise because of carbon dioxide loss.

One might even gather that exposure to mineral oil is worse than exposure to air (205). At high Po_2, the self-metabolism of blood results in a fall of Po_2 averaging 3 mm Hg per minute (24). Siggaard-Andersen (549) condemns use of fluoride since it does not stop this oxygen consumption (which is mostly by leukocytes) and it raises pH by causing loss of cation from red cells (or perhaps a fluoride-bicarbonate shift). Percutaneous arterial catheterization is possible with the Massa-type needle if the outer polyethylene jacket is replaced with teflon (44). Mylar coated on one side with polyethylene can be used to make very strong and virtually impermeable Douglas bags (541). Van Liew (619) developed techniques to permit Scholander analysis when the total available gas sample volume was only 0.4 ml.

Blood pH.—Accuracy of blood pH measurement is usually limited by errors in the liquid junction between blood and the calomel reference electrode. Saturated KCl precipitates proteins and hemolyzes red cells at the junction. However, this appears not to be the source of trouble since a 0.15-M NaCl or KCl liquid junction introduces errors of more than 0.1 pH in similar systems (534, 550). Astrup, Siggaard-Andersen, and co-workers (26, 380, 551, 552, 553) developed a capillary pH electrode and micro-tonometer for equilibrating blood with known Pco_2. They prepared a log Pco_2–pH chart on which the sample Pco_2, standard bicarbonate, and base excess can be read, after original pH and pH after equilibration have been determined. In this equipment the liquid junction is formed by dipping a capillary in saturated KCl. They found errors of only 0.01 pH, ascribable to the suspension effect of red cells, and of 0.015 pH if the junction was at room temperature (550).

Oxygen electrodes.—Several modifications of the now widely used Clark membrane-covered polarographic electrode principle have been described. Polgar & Forster (465) found that with a Mylar membrane on the Clark electrode, unstirred blood reads only about 5 per cent less than gas, but equilibration requires three to five minutes.

Response times of 30 seconds with an unstirred blood-gas difference of less than 2 per cent are reported if the platinum cathode diameter is reduced to 0.001 inches or less as in the Beckman needle electrode (2, 75, 582). Satisfactory electrodes were constructed by coating the platinum with polystyrol (49), silicon (400), and collodion (607), the reference electrode being outside the membrane. Tsao & Vadnay (607) and Kreuzer *et al.* (323) made electrodes suitable for introducing in vessels. Gleichmann & Lübbers (216), using a cellophane spacer and a teflon membrane, contrived an electrode with very good long-term stability, fast response, low pressure sensitivity, and a gas-stirred blood difference of 5 per cent. Also, Po_2 electrodes may be used to read blood oxygen content by freeing the hemoglobin oxygen in dilute solution (434). With 6 μ teflon, Kreuzer *et al.* (324) achieved response times of less than one second, suitable for continuous monitoring of airway Po_2. Lübbers (353) and Ingvar (290) devised an ingenious double-cathode tissue oxygen electrode, one platinum cathode being recessed slightly and turned on periodically to provide calibration for the other electrode while in use.

Oximetry.—Mathematical justification of reflectance (69) and transmission (404) oximetry and careful comparisons of the two by Mook & Zijlstra (403) indicate that both methods are potentially equivalent in accuracy.

Carbon dioxide electrode.—Gleichmann & Lübbers (217, 218), Siesjo (548), Hertz (262), and Severinghaus (541) have reported variations of carbon dioxide electrode construction improving stability, linearity, and response time, and reporting tissue P_{CO_2} determinations.

Rebreathing technique for mixed venous P_{CO_2}.—Campbell & Howell (104) simplified the Collier technique, eliminating the rapid carbon dioxide analyzer, by having the subject prepare his own rebreathing mixture in a preliminary 90-second rebreathing. Sykes (587) applied the technique to apneic anesthetized subjects and newborns. It has been found possible also to make the technique much more complicated by eliminating the rebreathing bag and substituting a pneumotachygraph, an eight-channel recorder, an assistant with two flowmeter controls and an infrared carbon dioxide analyzer (446).

Gas chromatography.—The accurate analysis of blood oxygen and carbon dioxide as well as other blood gases by chromatography will apparently require the prior extraction of the gases before injection into the flowing gas stream (355, 415, 650). Hamilton (242, 243) has increased the accuracy of gas chromatography for respiratory gases.

Infrared analyzers.—The infrared carbon dioxide analyzer can be improved by use as a negative-pressure regulator to control pressure in the microcatheter sample cell, with a needle-sampling orifice like that of the nitrogen meter. Operation at low regulated pressure increases linearity, eliminates water condensation, reduces sensitivity to pressure changes in the sampled system, and permits high speed response at very low flow rates as needed for use in babies or small animals (541). The pressure-broadening effect in infrared carbon dioxide analyzers has been shown (542) to be correctable by a factor applied to the measured carbon dioxide concentration dependent only on the concentration of oxygen, nitrogen, nitrous oxide, or cyclopropane. The curious lack of effect of water vapor on the infrared analyzer is explained as a pressure-broadening effect of water vapor (541). A non-microphonic infrared carbon dioxide analyzer (35) and a rapidly responding ultraviolet oxygen analyzer (614) are of interest.

Pulmonary function methods.—Gaensler's (203) review of this field during the year indicates the extent to which techniques have been changing, particularly as new apparatus is developed. In the short time since his review, many other methodology papers have appeared, predominantly in the realm of respiratory mechanics (167, 335, 398, 469) including plethysmography (377, 493) and flow tests (369, 509, 642), and of gas volume measurement (54, 96, 116, 279, 382, 421, 557).

Books and monographs.—During the year, books and monographs were published on clinical cardiopulmonary physiology (224, 565, 648), on factors in pulmonary ventilation and distribution (229, 251), on the pulmonary circulation (132, 412), and on methods in respiratory physiology (403, 624).

Rossier, Bühlmann & Wiesinger's comprehensive monograph on clinical respiratory physiology and Fleisch's on respiratory methods have been translated into English (181, 510). An excellent and comprehensive series of fifteen articles on carbon dioxide and man was edited by Eckenhoff (162). Respiratory problems of the newborn were the subject of a Ross conference (443) and of a monograph by Abramson (1). Bloomer *et al.* (74) published a beautifully illustrated surgical anatomy of the bronchovascular segments. Hayek's monograph was revised and enlarged (256). For the space traveler, a symposium report on closed-circuit respiratory systems was published (656). The Federation Committee on Biological Handbooks has published *Blood and Other Body Fluids* (143). Volume three of Glasser's *Medical Physics* (215) contains sections on decompression sickness and oximetry, and comprehensive reviews of pulmonary physiology, non-uniform ventilation, and respiratory gas analysis methods.

LITERATURE CITED

1. Abramson, H. A., *Resuscitation of the Newborn Infant* (C. V. Mosby Co., St. Louis, Mo., 274 pp., 1960)
2. Adams, J. E., and Severinghaus, J. W., *The Physiologist*, **3**, 5 (1960)
3. Adams, W. E., and Perkins, J. F., Jr., *Clinical Cardiopulmonary Physiology*, p. 689 (Grune & Stratton, Inc., New York, 101 pp., 1960)
4. Adolph, E. F., and Hoy, P. A., *J. Appl. Physiol.*, **15**, 1075 (1960)
5. Agostoni, E., Sant'Ambrogio, G., and Carrasco, H. del Portillo, *J. Appl. Physiol.*, **15**, 1093 (1960)
6. Agostoni, E., and Rahn, H., *J. Appl. Physiol.*, **15**, 1087 (1960)
7. Agostoni, E., and Fenn, W. O., *J. Appl. Physiol.*, **15**, 349 (1960)
8. Agrest, A., and Roncoroni, A. J., *Circulation Research*, **8**, 501 (1960)
9. Akester, A. R., *J. Anat.*, **94**, 487 (1960)
10. Alexander, J. K., Amad, K. H., and Cole, V. W., *J. Lab. Clin. Med.*, **56**, 787 (1960)
11. Alexander, S. C., Gelfand, R., and Lambertsen, C. J., *J. Biol. Chem.*, **236**, 592 (1961)
12. Alley, R. D., Van Mierop, L. H. S., Peck, A. S., Kausel, H. W., and Stranahan, A., *Am. Rev. Respirat. Diseases*, **83**, 31 (1961)
13. Allison, P. R., Daly, I. de B., and Waaler, B. A., *J. Physiol. (London)*, **155**, 44P (1961)
14. Allison, P. R., Dunhill, M. S., and Marshall, R., *Thorax*, **15**, 273 (1960)
15. Altland, P. D., *J. Appl. Physiol.*, **16**, 141 (1961)
16. Andersen, K. L., *Acta Physiol. Scand.*, **48**, Suppl. 168, 5 (1960)
17. Anderson, W. H., *Diseases of Chest*, **38**, 370 (1960)
18. Antonini, E., and Gibson, Q. H., *Biochem. J.*, **76**, 534 (1960)
19. Arborelius, M., Jr., Lundin, G., Svanberg, L., and Defares, J. G., *J. Appl. Physiol.*, **15**, 595 (1960)
20. Arkins, J. A., *Diseases of Chest*, **37**, 496 (1960)
21. Armstrong, B. W., Hunt, H. H., Blyde, R. W., and Workman, J. M., *Science*, **133**, 1897 (1961)
22. Asmussen, E., and Nielsen, M., *Acta Physiol. Scand.*, **50**, 153 (1960)
23. Asmussen, E., and Nielsen, M., *Acta Physiol. Scand.*, **51**, 385 (1961)
24. Asmussen, E., and Nielsen, M., *Scand. J. Clin. Lab. Invest.*, **13**, 297 (1961)
25. Astrand, I., Astrand, P. O., Christensen, E. H., and Hedman, R., *Acta Physiol. Scand.*, **50**, 254 (1960)
26. Astrup, P., *Clin. Chem.*, **7**, 1 (1961)
27. Attinger, E. O., *Arch. intern. pharmacodynamie*, **125**, 463 (1960)
28. Avery, M. E., and Oppenheimer, E. H., *J. Pediat.*, **57**, 553 (1960)
29. Aviado, D. M., *Arch. exptl. Pathol. Pharmakol.*, **240**, 446 (1961)
30. Aviado, D., *Pharmacol. Revs.*, **12**, 159 (1960)
31. Aviado, D. M., Daly, M. de B., Lee, C. Y., and Schmidt, C. F., *J. Physiol. (London)*, **155**, 602 (1961)
32. Bader, M. E., Bader, R. A., and Selikoff, I. J., *Am. J. Med.*, **30**, 235 (1961)
33. Baer, D. M., and Osborne, J. J., *Am. J. Clin. Pathol.*, **34**, 442 (1960)
34. Baglio, C. M., Michel, R. D., and Hunter, W. C., *J. Thoracic Cardiovascular Surg.*, **39**, 695 (1960)
35. Baker, L. E., *IRE Trans. on Bio-Med. Electronics*, **8**, 16 (1961)
36. Ballenger, J. J., *New Engl. J. Med.*, **263**, 832 (1960)
37. Baltzer, V., and Bucher, K., *Helv. Physiol. et Pharmacol. Acta*, **18**, 193 (1960)
38. Banister, J., and Torrance, R. W., *Quart. J. Exptl. Physiol.*, **45**, 352 (1960)
39. Bannister, R. G., Cotes, J. E., Jones, R. S., and Meade, F., *J. Physiol. (London)*, **152**, 66P (1960)
40. Barach, A., *Anesthesiology*, **22**, 367 (1961)
41. Bargeton, D., and Barres, G., *Compt. rend. soc. biol.*, **154**, 46 (1960)
42. Bark, J., Franke, D., and Kronschwitz, H., *Der Anaesthesist*, **9**, 63 (1960)
43. Barnett, T. B., and Peters, R. M., *J. Appl. Physiol.*, **15**, 838 (1960)
44. Barr, P. O., *Acta Physiol. Scand.*, **51**, 343 (1961)
45. Barritt, D. W., and Jordan, S. C., *Lancet*, **1**, 1309 (1960)
46. Bartels, H., Betke, K., Hilpert, P., Niemeyer, G., and Riegel, K., *Arch. ges. Physiol.*, **272**, 372 (1961)
47. Bartels, H., Hilpert, P., and Riegel, K., *Arch. ges. Physiol.*, **271**, 169 (1960)

48. Bartels, H., Hilpert, P., and Riegel, K., *Arch. ges. Physiol.*, **272**, 59 (1960)

49. Bartels, H., and Reinhardt, W., *Arch. ges. Physiol.*, **271**, 105 (1960)

50. Bartels, H., and Wrbitzky, R., *Arch. ges. Physiol.*, **271**, 162 (1960)

51. Bashour, F. A., and Graves, G., *J. Lab. Clin. Med.*, **56**, 790 (1960)

52. Bates, D. V., Christie, R. V., and Varvis, C. J., *J. Physiol. (London)*, **154**, 13P (1960)

53. Bates, D. V., Varvis, C. J., Donevan, R. E., and Christie, R. V., *J. Clin. Invest.*, **39**, 1401 (1960)

54. Bates, D. V., Pare, J. A. P., and Meakins, J. F., *Can. Med. Assoc. J.*, **83**, 192 (1960)

55. Baum, L. O., Murray, J. A., and Oldham, N. H., *Diseases of Chest*, **39**, 28 (1961)

56. Bedell, G. N., *J. Lab. Clin. Med.*, **57**, 269 (1961)

57. Belleville, J. W., Escarraga, L. A., Wallenstein, S. L., Houde, R. W., and Howland, W. S., *Anesthesiology*, **21**, 397 (1960)

58. Belleville, J. W., *Anesthesiology*, **21**, 727 (1960)

59. Benaron, H. B. W., Tucker, B. E., Andrews, J. P., Boshes, B., Cohen, J., Fromm, E., and Yacorzynski, G. K., *Am. J. Obstet. Gynecol.*, **80**, 1129 (1960)

60. Benesch, R., and Benesch, R. E., *J. Biol. Chem.*, **236**, 405 (1961)

61. Bergel, D. H., Caro, C. G., and McDonald, D. A., *J. Physiol. (London)*, **154**, 18P (1960)

62. Berkowitz, R., Rodman, T., and Close, H. P., *J. Am. Med. Assoc.*, **176**, 1092 (1961)

63. Berman, L. B., O'Connor, T. F., and Luchsinger, P. C., *J. Appl. Physiol.*, **15**, 393 (1960)

64. Bernard, S. R., *Bull. Math. Biophys.*, **22**, 391 (1960)

65. Bernard, S. R., *Bull. Math. Biophys.*, **23**, 1 (1961)

66. Bernstein, F. F., and Evans, R. L., *Clin. Sci.*, **174**, 161 (1960)

67. Bernstein, L., *Am. Rev. Respirat. Diseases*, **81**, 744 (1960)

68. Bernthal, T., Horres, A. D., and Taylor, J. T. III, *Am. J. Physiol.* **200**, 279 (1961)

69. Berzon, R., and Schubert, E., *Arch. ges. Physiol.*, **272**, 58 (1960)

70. Best, P. V., and Heath, D., *Circulation Research*, **9**, 288 (1961)

71. Bishop, J. M., Harris, P., Bateman, M., and Davidson, L. A. G., *J. Clin. Invest.*, **40**, 105 (1961)

72. Blanc, W. A., Gwyn, P. P., Jr., and Lynch, M. J., *Lancet*, **I**, 1348 (1960)

73. Blank, N., and Roughton, F. J. W., *Trans. Faraday Soc.*, **56**, 1832 (1960)

74. Bloomer, W. E., Liebow, A. A., and Hales, M. R., *Surgical Anatomy of the Bronchovascular Segments* (Charles C Thomas, Springfield, Ill., 273 pp., 1960)

75. Bloor, B. M., Fricker, J., Hellinger, F., Nishioka, H., and McCutchen, J., *Arch. Neurol.*, **4**, 37 (1961)

76. Blumenthal, J. S., Blumenthal, M. N., Brown, E. B., Campbell, G. S., and Prosad, A., *Diseases of Chest*, **39**, 516 (1961)

77. Bondurant, S., Mead, J., and Cook, C. D., *J. Appl. Physiol.*, **15**, 875 (1960)

78. Bosman, J. F., and Lind, J., *Acta Paediat.*, **49**, Suppl. 123, 18 (1960)

79. Bouhuys, A., Georg, J., Jonsson, R., Lundin, G., and Lindell, S. E., *J. Physiol. (London)*, **152**, 176 (1960)

80. Boyden, E. A., *Diseases of Chest*, **39**, 1 (1961)

82. Briehl, R. W., and Fishman, A. P., *J. Appl. Physiol.*, **15**, 337 (1960)

83. Brinkman, G. L., *Am. J. Med. Sci.*, **239**, 728 (1960)

84. Brinkman, G. L., Remp, D. G., Coates, E. O., Jr., and Priest, E. Mc., *Am. J. Med. Sci.*, **239**, 341 (1960)

85. Briscoe, W. A., Cree, E. M., Filler, J., Houssay, H. E. J., and Cournand, A., *J. Appl. Physiol.*, **15**, 785 (1960)

86. Brody, A. W., O'Halloran, P. S., Wander, H. J., Connolly, J. J., Roley, E. E., and Kobold, E., *J. Appl. Physiol.*, **15**, 561 (1960)

87. Brutsaert, D., Lacroix, E., and Leusen, I., *Acta Cardiol.*, **15**, 273 (1960)

88. Bucher, K., and Battig, P., *Helv. Physiol. et Pharmacol. Acta*, **18**, 219 (1960)

89. Bucher, K., *Helv. Physiol. et Pharmacol. Acta*, **19**, 84 (1961)

90. Bücherl, E. S., *Der Anaesthesist*, **9**, 67 (1961)

91. Bühlmann, A., and Gierhake, W., *Schweiz. med. Wochschr.*, **42**, 1153 (1960)

92. Bühlmann, A., and Schuppli, M., *Deut. med. Wochschr.*, **40**, 1745 (1960)

93. Bühlmann, A., *Helv. Med. Acta*, **27,** 548 (1960)

94. Bulow, K., and Ingvar, D. H., *Acta Physiol. Scand.*, **51,** 230 (1961)

95. Byck, R., *Brit. J. Pharmacol.*, **16,** 15 (1961)

96. Byles, P. H., *Brit. J. Anaesthesia*, **32,** 470 (1960)

97. Cahill, J. M., Attinger, E. O., and Byrne, J. J., *J. Appl. Physiol.*, **16,** 469 (1961)

98. Cain, S. M., and Otis, A. B., *J. Appl. Physiol.*, **15,** 390 (1960)

99. Cain, S. M., *Proc. Soc. Exptl. Biol. Med.*, **106,** 7 (1961)

100. Calkins, L. A., and Miller, H. C., *Am. J. Obstet. Gynecol.*, **78,** 1005 (1959)

101. Campbell, E. J. M., Freedman, S., Smith, P. S., and Taylor, H. E., *Clin. Sci.*, **20,** 223 (1961)

102. Campbell, E. J. M., Dinnick, O. P., and Howell, J. B. L., *J. Physiol.* (*London*), **156,** 260 (1961)

103. Campbell, E. J. M., *Lancet*, **I,** 12 (1960)

104. Campbell, E. J. M., and Howell, J. B. L., *Brit. J. Diseases of Chest*, **54,** 137 (1960)

105. Campiche, M., Prod'hom, S., and Gautier, A., *Ann. Paediat.*, **196,** 81 (1961)

106. Capel, L. H., and Smart, J., *Thorax*, **14,** 161 (1959)

107. Carlens, E., and Dahlstrom, G., *Am. Rev. Respirat. Diseases*, **83,** 202 (1961)

108. Caro, C. G., and McDonald, D. A., *J. Physiol.* (*London*), **153,** 68P (1960)

109. Carton, R. W., Dainauskas, J., Tews, B., and Hass, G. M., *Am. Rev. Respirat. Diseases*, **82,** 186 (1960)

110. Cherniack, N. S., Hyde, A. S., Watson, J. F., and Zechman, F. W., Jr., *Aerospace Med.*, **32,** 113 (1961)

111. Chidsey, C. A. III, Fritts, H. W., Jr., Zocche, G. P., Himmelstein, A., and Cournand, A., *Malattie Cardiovascolari*, **1,** 1 (1960)

112. Clements, J. A., Hustead, R. F., Johnson, R. P., and Griebetz, I., *J. Appl. Physiol.*, **16,** 444 (1961)

113. Cohen, A. A., Hemingway, A., and Hemingway, C., *Am. Rev. Respirat. Diseases*, **83,** 340 (1961)

114. Collier, H. O. J., Holgate, J. A., Schachter, M., and Shorley, P. G., *Brit. J. Pharmacol.*, **15,** 290 (1960)

115. Collins, R. E., *Science*, **133,** 1593 (1961)

116. Conant, J. S., *Diseases of Chest*, **37,** 656 (1960)

117. Cooper, E. A., *Quart. J. Exptl. Physiol.*, **46,** 13 (1961)

118. Cope, C., *J. Am. Med. Assoc.*, **175,** 1061 (1961)

119. Coppen, A. J., and Mezey, A. G., *J. Appl. Physiol.*, **16,** 367 (1961)

120. Costero, I., and Barroso-Moguel, R., *Am. J. Pathol.*, **38,** 127 (1961)

121. Cotes, J. E., Snidal, D. P., and Shepard, R. H., *J. Appl. Physiol.*, **15,** 372 (1960)

122. Cotes, J. E., *Thorax*, **15,** 244 (1960)

123. Craig, A. B., Jr., *J. Appl. Physiol.*, **15,** 1098 (1960)

124. Craig, A. B., Jr., *J. Am. Med. Assoc.*, **176,** 255 (1961)

125. Craig, F. N., and Cummings, E. G., *J. Appl. Physiol.*, **15,** 583 (1960)

126. Cropp, G., and Comroe, J. H., Jr., *The Physiologist*, **3,** 43 (1960)

127. Cross, C. E., Rieben, P. A., and Salisbury, P. F., *Am. J. Physiol.*, **198,** 1029 (1960)

128. Cross, K. W., *Brit. Med. Bull.*, **17,** 160 (1961)

129. Cross, K. W., Klaus, M., Tooley, W. H., and Weisser, K., *J. Physiol.* (*London*), **151,** 551 (1960)

130. Croteau, J. R., and Cook, C. D., *J. Appl. Physiol.*, **16,** 170 (1961)

131. Curtis, J. K., Rasmussen, H. K., Bauer, H., and Cree, E., *Diseases of Chest*, **38,** 285 (1960)

132. Daley, R., *Clinical Disorders of the Pulmonary Circulation* (Little, Brown & Co., Boston, 364 pp., 1960)

133. Daly, I. de B., *Arch. exptl. Pathol. Pharmakol.*, **240,** 431 (1961)

134. Dalziel, K., and O'Brien, J. R. P., *Biochem. J.*, **78,** 236 (1961)

135. Dantzig, G. B., De Haven, J. C., Cooper, I., Johnson, S. M., DeLand, E. C., Kanter, H. E., and Sams, C. F., *Perspectives in Biol. Med.*, **4,** 324 (1961)

136. Dawes, G. S., *Brit. Med. Bull.*, **17,** 148 (1961)

137. Defares, J. G., Derksen, H. E., and Duyff, J. W., *Acta Physiol. et Pharmacol. Néerl.*, **9,** 327 (1960)

138. Defares, J. G., Lundin, G., Arborelius, M., Jr., Stromblad, R., and Svanberg, L., *J. Appl. Physiol.*, **15,** 169 (1960)

139. Dejours, P., Lefrancois, R., Flandrois, R., and Teillac, A., *J. physiol.* (*Paris*), **52,** 63 (1960)

140. Dexter, L., Dock, D. S., McGuire, L. B., Hyland, J. W., and Haynes, F. W., *Med. Clin. North Am.*, **44**, 1251 (1960)

141. Dickinson, G. J., Green, J. H., and Howell, J. B. L., *J. Physiol. (London)*, **155**, 38P (1961)

142. Dietiker, F., Lester, W., and Burrows, B., *Am. Rev. Respirat. Diseases*, **81**, 830 (1960)

143. Dittmer, D. S., *Blood and Other Body Fluids* (Biol. Handbook Committee, Fed. Am. Soc. Exptl. Biol., Washington, D. C., 540 pp., 1961)

144. Dixon, M. E., Stewart, P. B., Mills, F. C., Varvis, C. J., and Bates, D. V., *J. Appl. Physiol.*, **16**, 30 (1961)

145. Dock, D. S., Kraus, W. L., McGuire, L. B., Hyland, J. W., Haynes, F. W., and Dexter, L., *J. Clin. Invest.*, **40**, 317 (1961)

146. Doll, E., Konig, K., and Reindell, H., *Arch. ges. Physiol.*, **271**, 283 (1960)

147. Doll, E., Otterbein, C., Konig, K., and Reindell, H., *Arch. ges. Physiol.*, **272**, 511 (1961)

148. Dollery, C. T., and West, J. B., *J. Physiol. (London)*, **154**, 12P (1960)

149. Dollery, C. T., West, J. B., Wilcken, D. E. L., Goodwin, J. F., and Hugh-Jones, P., *Brit. Heart J.*, **23**, 225 (1961)

150. Dollery, C. T., Dyson, N. A., and Sinclair, J. D., *J. Appl. Physiol.*, **15**, 411 (1960)

151. Donnenfeld, R. S., Greenberg, E. M., Warshaw, J., Casey, F. G., Jr., Adie, G. C., and Bishop, H. F., *N. Y. J. Med.*, **60**, 3243 (1960)

152. Drakontides, A. B., *Am. J. Physiol.*, **199**, 748 (1960)

153. Draper, M. H., Ladefoged, P., and Whitteridge, D. *Brit. Med. J.*, **I**, 1837 (1960)

154. Drorbaugh, J. E., *J. Appl. Physiol.*, **15**, 1069 (1960)

155. Duffield, D. P., and Ashford, J. R., *Brit. J. Ind. Med.*, **17**, 122 (1960)

156. Duke, H. N., Margalhaes, J. R., and Rouse, W., *J. Physiol. (London)*, **155**, 37 (1960)

157. Duke, H. N., and Stedeford, R. D., *Circulation Research*, **8**, 640 (1960)

158. Duyff, J. W., *Arch. ges. Physiol.*, **272**, 60 (1960)

159. Dyson, N. A., Sinclair, J. D., and West, J. B., *J. Physiol. (London)*, **152**, 325 (1960)

160. Ebert, R. V., *Arch. Internal Med.*, **107**, 450 (1961)

161. Eckenhoff, J. E., and Oech, S. R., *Clin. Pharmacol. and Therap.*, **1**, 483 (1960)

162. Eckenhoff, J. E., *Anesthesiology*, **21**, 585 (1960)

163. Eckstein, J. W., and Horsley, A. W., *J. Lab. Clin. Med.*, **56**, 847 (1960)

164. Edwards, A. W. T., and Farhi, L. E., *Federation Proc.*, **20**, 422 (1961)

165. Edwards, M. J., Koler, R. D., Rigas, D. A., and Pitcairn, D. M., *J. Clin. Invest.*, **40**, 636 (1961)

166. Eger, E. I., and Severinghaus, J. W., *Anesthesiology*, **22**, 419 (1961)

167. Ehrner, L., *Acta Med. Scand.*, **167**, Suppl. 353 (1960)

168. Elam, J. O., Ruben, A. M., Greene, D. G., and Bittner, T. J., *J. Am. Med. Assoc.*, **176**, 565 (1961)

169. Elbel, E. R., Ormond, D., and Close, D., *J. Appl. Physiol.*, **16**, 48 (1961)

170. Eliakim, M., Stern, S., and Nathan, H., *Circulation Research*, **9**, 327 (1961)

171. Emerson, P. A., Torres, G. E., and Lyons, H. A., *Thorax*, **15**, 124 (1960)

172. Emery, J. L., and Mithal, A., *Arch. Disease Childhood*, **35**, 544 (1961)

173. Farhi, L. E., and Rahn, H., *Anesthesiology*, **21**, 604 (1960)

174. Fatt, I., and La Force, R. C., *Science*, **133**, 1919 (1961)

175. Fawcitt, J., Lind, J., and Wegelius, C., *Acta Paediat.*, **49**, Suppl. 123, 5 (1960)

176. Fenne, D. W., and Nahas, G. G., *J. Appl. Physiol.*, **15**, 315 (1960)

177. Fink, B. R., *J. Appl. Physiol.*, **16**, 15 (1961)

178. Fink, B. R., *Brit. J. Anesthesia*, **33**, 97 (1961)

179. Finley, T. N., Lenfant, C., Haab, P., Piiper, J., and Rahn, H., *J. Appl. Physiol.*, **15**, 418 (1960)

180. Fisher, W. W., *Am. J. Vet. Research*, **22**, 279 (1961)

181. Fleisch, A., *New Methods of Studying Gaseous Exchange and Pulmonary Function* (Corsi, C., Transl., Charles C Thomas, Springfield, Ill., 116 pp., 1960)

182. Fleming, W. H., Szakcs, J. E., Hartney, T. C., and King, E. R., *Lancet*, **I**, 1010 (1960)

183. Fishman, A. P., *Physiol. Revs.*, **41**, 214 (1961)

184. Fishman, A. P., Fritts, H. W., Jr., and Cournand, A., *Circulation*, **22**, 204 (1960)

185. Fouche, R. F., Spears, J. R., and Ogilvie, C., *Brit. Med. J.*, **I**, 1312 (1960)

186. Fowler, N., *Am. J. Med.*, **28**, 927 (1960)

187. Fraimow, W., Mann, J. J., Flickinger, H., and Cathcart, R. T., *J. Am. Med. Assoc.*, **173**, 1098 (1960)

188. Fraimow, W., Cathcart, R. T., and Goodman, E., *Am. Rev. Respirat. Diseases*, **81**, 815 (1960)

189. Fraimow, W., Cathcart, R. T., and Taylor, R. C., *Ann. Internal Med.*, **52**, 1177 (1961)

190. Frankenhaeuser, M., Graff-Lonnevig, V., and Hesser, C. M., *Acta Physiol. Scand.*, **50**, 1 (1960)

191. Franklin, W., and Lowell, F. C., *Ann. Internal Med.*, **54**, 379 (1961)

192. Franklin, W., and Lowell, F. C., *J. Allergy*, **32**, 162 (1961)

193. Frasher, W. G., and Sobin, S. S., *Am. J. Physiol.*, **199**, 472 (1960)

194. Fritts, H. W., Jr., Odell, J. E., Harris, P., Braunwald, E. W., and Fishman, A. P., *Circulation*, **22**, 216 (1960)

195. Fritts, H. W., Jr., Hardewig, A., Rochester, D. F., Durand, J., and Cournand, A., *J. Clin. Invest.*, **39**, 1841 (1960)

196. Fritts, H. W., Jr., Harris, P., Chidsey, C. A. III, Clauss, R. H., and Cournand, A., *Circulation*, **23**, 390 (1961)

197. Fritts, H. W., Jr., Richards, D. W., and Cournand, A., *Science*, **133**, 1070 (1961)

198. Fritz, H., and Lindqvist, B., *Acta Med. Scand.*, **169**, 181 (1961)

199. Froeb, H. F., *J. Appl. Physiol.*, **16**, 8 (1961)

200. Fruhmann, G., and Bernsmeier, A., *Münch. med. Wochschr.*, **50**, 2493 (1960)

201. Fry, D. L., and Hyatt, R. E., *Am. J. Med.*, **29**, 672 (1960)

202. Frye, R. L., and Braunwald, E., *New Engl. J. Med.*, **263**, 775 (1960)

203. Gaensler, E. A., *Ann. Rev. Med.*, **12**, 385 (1961)

204. Gambino, S. R., *Am. J. Clin. Pathol.*, **35**, 175 (1961)

205. Gambino, S. R., *Am. J. Clin. Pathol.*, **35**, 268 (1961)

206. Gandelsman, A. V., Gracheva, R. P., and Prokopovich, N. V., *Sechenov Physiol. J. USSR (Engl. Transl.)*, **46**, 989 (1960)

207. Gandevia, B., *Arch. Disease Childhood*, **35**, 236 (1960)

208. Gardiner, A. S., *Anaesthesia*, **15**, 246 (1960)

209. Gerardy, W., Herberg, D., and Kuhn, H. M., *Klin. Wochschr.*, **12**, 583 (1960)

210. Gershenovich, Z. S., and Krichevskaya, A. A., *Biochemistry (USSR) (Engl. Transl.)*, **25**, 790 (1960)

211. Geubelle, F., and De Rudder, P., *Acta Paediat.*, **50**, 277 (1961)

212. Geubelle, F., Karlberg, P., Koch, G., Lind, J., Wallgren, G., and Wegelius, C., *Biol. Neonatorum*, **1**, 169 (1959)

213. Gilbert, R., Sipple, J. H., and Auchincloss, J. H., Jr., *J. Appl. Physiol.*, **16**, 21 (1961)

214. Girard, F., Lacaisse, A., and Dejours, P., *J. physiol. (Paris)*, **52**, 108 (1960)

215. Glasser, O., *Medical Physics*, **III** (Year Book Publ., Inc., Chicago, 754 pp., 1960)

216. Gleichmann, U., and Lübbers, D. W., *Arch. ges. Physiol.*, **271**, 431 (1960)

217. Gleichmann, U., *Arch. ges. Physiol.*, **272**, 57 (1960)

218. Gleichmann, U., and Lübbers, D. W., *Arch. ges. Physiol.*, **271**, 346 (1960)

219. Goldsmith, J. R., *Am. Rev. Respirat. Diseases*, **82**, 485 (1960)

220. Goldstein, D. A., and Solomon, A. K., *J. Gen. Physiol.*, **44**, 1 (1960)

221. Gomez, D. M., *J. Appl. Physiol.*, **200**, 135 (1961)

222. Gomori, P., Takacs, L., and Kallay, K., *Acta Med. Acad. Sci. Hung.*, **16**, 75 (1960)

223. Goott, B., Rosenberg, J. C., Lillehei, R. C., and Miller, F. A., *J. Thoracic Cardiovascular Surg.*, **40**, 625 (1960)

224. Gordon, B. L., *Clinical Cardiopulmonary Physiology* (Grune & Stratton, New York, 1001 pp., 1960)

225. Graham, G. R., Hill, D. W., and Nunn, J. F., *Der Anaesthesist*, **9**, 70 (1960)

226. Grape, B., Channen, E., and Tyler, J. M., *Am. Rev. Respirat. Diseases*, **81**, 823 (1960)

227. Greisheimer, E. M., Krumperman, L. W., Rusy, B. F., and Ellis, D. W., *Anesthesiology*, **21**, 370 (1960)

228. Gremy, F., *J. physiol. (Paris)*, **52**, 555 (1960)

229. Greve, L. H., *Unequal Ventilation, a Study with the Aid of the Katapherometer* (Doctoral thesis, Kemink & Zoon, Utrecht, Netherlands, 144 pp., 1960)

230. Greven, K., *Arch. ges. Physiol.*, **271**, 14 (1960)

231. Gronbaek, P., and Skouby, A. P., *Acta Med. Scand.*, **168**, 1 (1960)

232. Grover, R. F., *Am. Heart J.*, **61**, 5 (1961)

233. Gruenwald, P., *Anat. Record*, **139**, 471 (1961)

234. Gurtner, H. P., Briscoe, W. A., and Cournand, A., *J. Clin. Invest.*, **39**, 1080 (1960)

235. Haab, P. E., Galletti, P. M., and Hopf, M. A., *Proc. Am. Soc. Artificial Internal Organs*, **6**, 266 (1960)

236. Hall, F. G., and Salzano, J., *US Govt. Research Rept.*, **34**, (1960)

237. Hall, F. G., and Salzano, J., *Anesthesiology*, **21**, 281 (1961)

238. Halmagyi, D. F. J., and Colebatch, H. J. H., *Circulation Research*, **9**, 136 (1961)

239. Halmagyi, D. F. J., and Colebatch, H. J. H., *J. Appl. Physiol.*, **16**, 35 (1961)

240. Halmagyi, D. F. J., *J. Appl. Physiol.*, **16**, 41 (1961)

241. Hamilton, H. E., Sheets, R. F., and Evans, T. C., *J. Lab. Clin. Med.*, **56**, 823 (1960)

242. Hamilton, L. H., and Kory, R. C., *J. Appl. Physiol.*, **15**, 820 (1960)

243. Hamilton, L. H., *J. Appl. Physiol.*, **16**, 571 (1961)

244. Hamm, J., *Klin. Wochschr.*, **21**, 1093 (1960)

245. Hamm, J., *Klin. Wochschr.*, **21**, 1101 (1960)

246. Hammond, J. D. S., *Clin. Sci.*, **20**, 107 (1961)

247. Hanks, E. C., Ngai, S. H., and Fink, B. R., *Anesthesiology*, **22**, 393 (1961)

248. Hanson, J. S., and Tabakin, B. S., *J. Appl. Physiol.*, **15**, 402 (1960)

249. Harasawa, M., and Rodbard, S., *Am. Heart J.*, **60**, 73 (1960)

250. Harasawa, M., and Rodbard, S., *Am. J. Physiol.*, **200**, 287 (1961)

251. Harbord, R. P., and Woolmer, R., *Symposium on Pulmonary Ventilation* (John Sherratt & Son, Altrincham, Engl., 109 pp., 1959)

252. Harms, H., and Bartels, H., *Arch. ges. Physiol.*, **272**, 384 (1961)

253. Harris, M. S., *Diseases of Chest*, **39**, 539 (1961)

254. Harris, P., Fritts, H. W., Jr., and Cournand, A., *Circulation*, **21**, 1134 (1960)

255. Haupt, G. J., and Camishion, R., *Surg. Clin. North Am.*, **40**, 1477 (1960)

256. Hayek, H. von, *The Human Lung* (Revised ed., Krahl, V. E., Transl., Hafner Publ. Co., New York, 372 pp., 1960)

257. Heard, B. E., *Am. Rev. Respirat. Diseases*, **82**, 792 (1960)

258. Hellegers, A. E., and Schruefer, J. J. P., *Am. J. Obstet. Gynecol.*, **81**, 377 (1961)

259. Heller, M. L., and Watson, T. R., Jr., *New Engl. J. Med.*, **264**, 326 (1961)

260. Hemmingsen, E., and Scholander, P. F., *Science*, **132**, 1379 (1960)

261. Hepper, N. G. G., Fowler, W. S., and Helmholz, H. F., Jr., *Diseases of Chest*, **37**, 314 (1960)

262. Hertz, C. H., and Siesjo, B., *Acta Physiol. Scand.*, **47**, 115 (1959)

263. Herzenberg, H., and Eskelund, V., *Acta Paediat.*, **50**, 263 (1961)

264. Hilding, A. C., *Diseases of Chest*, **39**, 357 (1961)

265. Hirsjarvi, E., and Krusius, F. E., *Scand. J. Clin. Lab. Invest.*, **13**, 126 (1961)

266. Holford, F. D., and Mithoefer, J. C., *Surg. Clin. North Am.*, **40**, 907 (1960)

267. Holland, R. A. B., and Blacket, R. B., *Am. J. Med.*, **29**, 955 (1960)

268. Holmdahl, M. H., Nahas, G. G., Hassam, D., and Verosky, M., *Ann. N. Y. Acad. Sci.*, **92**, 520 (1961)

269. Holmdahl, M. H., and Payne, J. P., *Acta Anaesthesiol. Scand.*, **4**, 173 (1960)

270. Holmdahl, M. H., *Ann. N. Y. Acad. Sci.*, **92**, 794 (1961)

271. Hong, S. K., Ting, E. Y., and Rahn, H., *J. Appl. Physiol.*, **15**, 550 (1960)

272. Horisberger, B., and Rodbard, S., *Circulation Research*, **8**, 1149 (1960)

273. Hornbein, T. F., and Roos, A., *Federation Proc.*, **20**, 430 (1961)

274. Hornbein, T. F., Roos, A., and Griffo, Z. J., *J. Appl. Physiol.*, **16**, 11 (1961)

275. Houston, C. S., *New Engl. J. Med.*, **263**, 478 (1960)

276. Howard, W. F., Hunter, C. A., Jr., and Huber, C. P., *Surg., Gynecol. Obstet.*, **112**, 435 (1961)

277. Howell, J. B. L., Permutt, S., Proctor, D. F., and Riley, R. L., *J. Appl. Physiol.*, **16**, 71 (1961)

278. Hugh-Jones, P., and West, J. B., *Thorax*, **15**, 154 (1960)

279. Hugh-Jones, P., *Industrial Pulmonary Diseases Symposium* (Little, Brown & Co., Boston, 273 pp., 1960)

280. Huisman, T. H. J., *Biochim. et Biophys. Acta*, **46**, 384 (1961)

281. Hull, W. E., and Long, E. C., *J. Appl. Physiol.*, **16**, 439 (1961)

282. Hultgren, H., and Spickard, W., *Stanford Med. Bull.*, **18**, 76 (1960)

283. Hunziker, V. A., and Bühlmann, A., *Allergie Asthma*, **6**, 145 (1960)

284. Hurtado, A., *Ann. Internal Med.*, **53**, 247 (1960)

285. Hyatt, R. E., *Am. Rev. Respirat. Diseases*, **83**, 676 (1961)

286. Hyatt, R. E., and Wilcox, R. E., *J. Appl. Physiol.*, **16**, 326 (1961)

287. Ingelstedt, S., and Toremalm, N. G., *Acta Physiol. Scand.*, **51**, 204 (1961)

288. Ingvar, D. H., *Neurology*, **2**, 68 (1961)

289. Ingvar, D. H., Siesjo, B., and Hertz, C. H., *Experientia*, **15**, 306 (1959)

290. Ingvar, D. H., Lubbers, D. W., and Siesjo, B., *Acta Physiol. Scand.*, **48**, 373 (1960)

291. Inkley, S. R., Gillespie, L., Jr., and Koletsky, S., *J. Lab. Clin. Med.*, **57**, 114 (1961)

292. Jacobs, S., and Papperman, S. M., *Am. Rev. Respirat. Diseases*, **82**, 416 (1960)

293. Jaeger, M., *Schweiz. med. Wochschr.*, **90**, 648 (1960)

294. James, L. S., *Acta Paediat.*, **49**, Suppl. 122 (1960)

295. James, W. R. L., Owen, G. M., and Thomas, A. J., *Brit. Heart J.*, **22**, 695 (1960)

296. Joels, N., Neil, E., and Vaughan Hudson, B., *J. Physiol. (London)*, **155**, 30P (1961)

297. Joels, N., and Neil, E., *J. Physiol. (London)*, **154**, 7P (1960)

298. Joels, N., and Neil, E., *J. Physiol. (London)*, **155**, 45P (1961)

299. Johansen, K., and Hol, R., *J. Exptl. Biol.*, **37**, 474 (1960)

300. Johnson, R. L., Jr., Spicer, W. S., Bishop, J. M., and Forster, R. E., *J. Appl. Physiol.*, **15**, 893 (1960)

301. Jones, R. H., McNamara, J., and Gaensler, E. A., *Am. Rev. Respirat. Diseases*, **82**, 164 (1960)

302. Jones, R. S., and Meade, F., *Quart. J. Exptl. Physiol.*, **46**, 131 (1961)

303. Joyner, C. R., Jr., Horwitz, O., and Williams, P. G., *Circulation*, **22**, 901 (1960)

304. Kanagami, H., Katsura, T., Shiroshi, K., Baba, K., and Ebina, T., *Acta Med. Scand.*, **169**, 583 (1961)

305. Karlberg, P., *J. Pediat.* **56**, 585 (1960)

306. Karlberg, P., Cherry, R. B., Escardo, F., and Koch, G., *Acta Paediat.*, **49**, 345 (1960)

307. Karon, E. H., Koelsche, G. A., and Fowler, W. S., *Proc. Mayo Clinic*, **35**, 307 (1960)

308. Katsaros, B., Loeschcke, H. H., Lerche, D., Schonthal, H., and Hahn, N., *Arch. ges. Physiol.*, **271**, 732 (1960)

309. Keatinge, W. R., and Evans, M., *Quart. J. Exptl. Physiol.*, **46**, 83 (1961)

310. Kellogg, R., *Anesthesiology*, **21**, 634 (1960)

311. Kennedy, T. J., *Anesthesiology*, **21**, 704 (1960)

312. Kern, D. M., *J. Chem. Education*, **37**, 14 (1960)

313. Kernohan, J. C., *J. Physiol. (London)*, **155**, 580 (1961)

314. Kilburn, K. H., *J. Appl. Physiol.*, **15**, 229 (1960)

315. Kilburn, K. H., McDonald, J., and Piccinni, F. P., *J. Appl. Physiol.*, **15**, 801 (1960)

316. Kilburn, K. H., and Sieker, H. O., *Circulation Research*, **8**, 660 (1960)

317. Kimura, E., *Japan. Heart J.*, **1**, 72 (1960)

318. Klocke, F. J., and Rahn, H., *J. Clin. Invest.*, **40**, 286 (1961)

319. Koizumi, K., Ushiyama, J., and Brooks, C. McC., *Am. J. Physiol.*, **200**, 679 (1961)

320. Kory, R. C., Callahan, R., Boren, H. G., and Syner, J. C., *Am. J. Med.*, **30**, 243 (1961)

321. Kreuzer, F., Tenney, S. M., Andresen, D. C., Schreiner, B. F., Hye, R. E., Jr., Mithoefer, J. C., Valtin, H., and Naitove, A., *J. Appl. Physiol.*, **15**, 796 (1960)

322. Kreuzer, F., and Yahr, W. Z., *J. Appl. Physiol.*, **15**, 1117 (1960)

323. Kreuzer, F., Harris, E. D., Jr., and Nessler, C. G., Jr., *J. Appl. Physiol.*, **15**, 77 (1960)

324. Kreuzer, F., Rogeness, G. A., and Bornstein, P., *J. Appl. Physiol.*, **15**, 1157 (1960)

325. Krueger, A. P., and Smith, R. F., *J. Gen. Physiol.*, **44**, 269 (1960)

326. Krueger, J. J., Bain, T., and Patterson, J. L., Jr., *J. Appl. Physiol.*, **16**, 465 (1961)

327. Kurihara, K., and Shibata, K., *Arch. Biochem. Biophys.*, **88**, 298 (1960)

328. Ladenheim, J. C., and Sachs, E., Jr., *Neurology*, **11**, 303 (1961)

329. Laitinen, E. A., *Acta Pathol. Microbiol. Scand.*, **49**, 136 (1960)

330. Lambertsen, C. J., *Anesthesiology*, **21**, 642 (1960)

331. Lambertsen, C. J., Semple, S. J. G., Smyth, M. G., and Gelfand, R., *J. Appl. Physiol.*, **16**, 473 (1961)

332. Lambertsen, C. J., Wendel, H., and Longenhagen, J. B., *J. Pharmacol. Exptl. Therap.*, **131**, 381 (1961)

333. Langer, G. A., Bornstein, D. L., and Fishman, A. P., *J. Appl. Physiol.*, **15**, 855 (1960)

334. Larmi, T. K. I., and Appelqvist, R., *Scand. J. Clin. Lab. Invest.*, **13**, 174 (1961)

335. Larmi, T. K. I., and Appelqvist, R., *Scand. J. Clin. Lab. Invest.*, **13**, 167 (1961)

336. Leathart, G. L., *Brit. J. Ind. Med.*, **17**, 213 (1960)

337. Lenfant, C., and Howell, B. J., *J. Appl. Physiol.*, **15**, 425 (1960)

338. Leroy, G. V., Okita, G. T., and Tocus, E. C., *J. Lab. Clin. Med.*, **56**, 922 (1960)

339. Leusen, I., and Demeester, G., *Arch. ges. Physiol.*, **270**, 390 (1960)

340. Lewin, R. J., Cross, C. E., Rieben, P. A., and Salisbury, P. F., *Am. J. Physiol.*, **198**, 873 (1960)

341. Lewinsohn, H. C., Capel, L. H., and Smart, J., *Brit. Med. J.*, **I**, 462 (1960)

342. Lewis, B. M., McElroy, W. T., Hayford-Welsing, E. J., and Samberg, L. C., *J. Clin. Invest.*, **39**, 1345 (1960)

343. Lewis, B. M., Furusho, A., and Dalton, E., *J. Lab. Clin. Med.*, **56**, 922 (1960)

344. Lilja, B., Lindell, S. E., and Saldeen, T., *J. Allergy*, **31**, 492 (1960)

345. Lind, J., *Acta Paediat.*, **49**, Suppl. 122 (1960)

346. Lloyd, T. C., Jr., and Wright, G. W., *J. Appl. Physiol.*, **15**, 241 (1960)

347. Lochner, W., and Nasseri, M., *Arch. ges. Physiol.*, **272**, 180 (1960)

348. Loeschcke, H. H., *Der Anaesthesist*, **9**, 38 (1960)

349. Loeschcke, H. H., *Klin. Wochschr.*, **15**, 771 (1960)

350. Long, E. T., Adams, W. E., Benfield, J. R., Mikouchi, T., Reimann, A. F., and Nigro, S., *J. Thoracic Cardiovascular Surg.*, **40**, 640 (1960)

351. Longley, M. Y., and Berry, C. M., *Arch. Environmental Health*, **2**, 535 (1961)

352. Low, F. N., *Anat. Record*, **139**, 105 (1961)

353. Lübbers, D. W., *Arch. ges. Physiol.*, **272**, 56 (1960)

354. Lucas, R. V., Jr., St. Geme, J. W., Jr., Anderson, R. C., Adams, P., Jr., and Ferguson, D. J., *Am. J. Diseases Children*, **101**, 467 (1961)

355. Lukas, D. S., and Ayres, S. M., *J. Appl. Physiol.*, **16**, 371 (1961)

356. Lundgren, C. E. G., *Scand. J. Clin. Lab. Invest.*, **13**, 291 (1961)

357. Lyons, H. A., Tanner, R. W., and Picco, T., *Am. J. Diseases Children*, **100**, 196 (1960)

358. Maas, A. H. J., and Heijst, A. N. P. van, *Clin. Chim. Acta*, **6**, 31 (1961)

359. MacHattie, L., and Rahn, H., *Proc. Soc. Exptl. Biol. Med.*, **104**, 772 (1960)

360. Maloney, J. V., Jr., Schmutzer, K. J., and Raschke, E., *J. Thoracic Cardiovascular Surg.*, **41**, 291 (1961)

361. Manfredi, F., Sieker, H. O., Spoto, A. P., and Saltzman, H. A., *J. Am. Med. Assoc.*, **173**, 999 (1960)

362. Manfredi, F., Merwarth, C. R., Buckley, C. E. III, and Sieker, H. O., *Am. J. Med.*, **30**, 175 (1961)

363. March, H. W., and Lyons, H. A., *Diseases of Chest*, **37**, 602 (1960)

364. Maren, T. H., Parcell, A. L., and Malik, M. N., *J. Pharmacol. Exptl. Therap.*, **130**, 389 (1960)

365. Margaria, R., Milic-Emili, G., Petit, J. M., and Cavagna, G., *J. Appl. Physiol.*, **15**, 353 (1960)

366. Margaria, R., and Cavagna, R., *Boll. soc. ital. biol. sper.*, **35**, 2077 (1960)

367. Margaria, R., and Cavagna, R., *Boll. soc. ital. biol. sper.*, **35**, 2075 (1960)

368. Margaria, R., Rossi, S. M. L., and Margaria, S. R., *Accad. nazl. Lincei*, **28**, 304 (1960)

369. Marks, A., and Bocles, J., *Southern Med. J.*, **53**, 1211 (1960)

370. Marshall, H. W., Swan, H. J. C., Burchell, H. B., and Wood, E. H., *Circulation*, **23**, 241 (1961)

371. Marshall, J. R., and Lambertsen, C. J., *J. Appl. Physiol.*, **16**, 1 (1961)

372. Marshall, R., and Widdicombe, J. G., *Clin. Sci.*, **20**, 19 (1961)

373. Marshall, R. J., Wang, Y., Semeer, H. J., and Shepherd, J. T., *Circulation Research*, **9**, 53 (1961)
374. Massion, W. H., Mitchell, R. A., and Severinghaus, J. W., *Anesthesiology*, **22**, 137 (1961)
375. Mead, J., *Physiol. Revs.*, **41**, 281 (1961)
376. Mead, J., *J. Appl. Physiol.*, **15**, 325 (1960)
377. Mead, J., *J. Appl. Physiol.*, **15**, 736 (1960)
378. Meesen, H., *Stanford Med. Bull.*, **19**, 19 (1961)
379. Meier, M., *Helv. Physiol. et Pharmacol. Acta*, **18**, 119 (1960)
380. Mellemgaard, K., and Astrup, P., *Scand. Clin. Lab. Invest.*, **12**, 187 (1960)
381. Meneely, G. R., and Ferguson, J. L., *J. Am. Med. Assoc.*, **175**, 1074 (1961)
382. Meneely, G. R., *Ind. Med. and Surg.*, **29**, 290 (1960)
383. Merkulova, N. A., *Bull. Exptl. Biol. Med. (USSR) (Engl. Transl.)*, **49**, 41 (1960)
384. Merril, C. R., Seipp, H. W., and Luchsinger, P. C., *J. Appl. Physiol.*, **16**, 485 (1961)
385. Meschia, G., Hellegers, A., Blechner, J. N., Wolkoff, A. S., and Barron, D. H., *Quart. J. Exptl. Physiol.*, **46**, 95 (1961)
386. Meschia, G., Hellegers, A., Prystowsky, H., Huckabee, W., Metcalfe, J., and Barron, D. H., *Quart. J. Exptl. Physiol.*, **46**, 156 (1961)
387. Meschia, G., Prystowsky, H., Hellegers, A., Huckabee, W., Metcalfe, J., and Barron, D. H., *Quart. J. Exptl. Physiol.*, **45**, 284 (1960)
388. Mezey, A. G., and Coppen, A. J., *Clin. Sci.*, **20**, 171 (1961)
389. Mikhailov, V. V., *Bull. Exptl. Biol. Med. (USSR) (Engl. Transl.)*, **49**, 31 (1960)
390. Milic-Emili, G., and Dejours, J. R. P., *J. Physiol. (Paris)*, **52**, 177 (1960)
391. Milic-Emili, G., and Petit, J. M., *J. physiol. (Paris)*, **52**, 175 (1960)
392. Milic-Emili, G., and Melon, J., *Boll. soc. ital. biol. sper.*, **36**, 1268 (1960)
393. Milic-Emili, G., and Petit, J. M., *J. Appl. Physiol.*, **15**, 359 (1960)
394. Millar, R. A., Brindle, G. F., and Gilbert, R. G. B., *Brit. J. Anaesthesia*, **32**, 248 (1960)
395. Millar, R. A., and Morris, M. E., *Anesthesiology*, **22**, 433 (1961)
396. Millar, R. A., and Morris, M. E., *Anesthesiology*, **22**, 62 (1961)
397. Miller, D. A., Bondurant, S., Bratton, J., and McIlroy, T., *J. Lab. Clin. Med.*, **56**, 929 (1960)
398. Miller, J. H., and Simmons, D. H., *J. Appl. Physiol.*, **15**, 967 (1960)
399. Milnor, W. R., Jose, A. D., and McGaff, C. J., *Circulation*, **22**, 130 (1960)
400. Misrahy, G. A., Beran, A. V., Spradley, J. F., and Garwood, V. P., *Am. J. Physiol.*, **199**, 959 (1960)
401. Mitchell, R. I., *Am. Rev. Respirat. Diseases*, **82**, 627 (1960)
402. Moll, W., and Bartels, H., *Arch. ges. Physiol.*, **271**, 583 (1960)
403. Møller, B., *Hydrogen Ion Concentration in Arterial Blood (Acta Med. Scand.,* Suppl. 348, 340 pp., 1959)
404. Mook, G. A., and Zijlstra, W. G., *Acta Med. Scand.*, **169**, 149 (1961)
405. Mook, G. A., and Zijlstra, W. G., *Acta Med. Scand.*, **169**, 141 (1961)
406. Moreno, F., and Lyons, H. A., *J. Appl. Physiol.*, **16**, 27 (1961)
407. Moser, K. M., *Diseases of Chest*, **37**, 637 (1960)
408. Motley, H., *Missouri Med.*, **57**, 701 (1960)
409. Mott, J. C., *Brit. Med. Bull.*, **17**, 144 (1961)
410. Moulder, P. V., Lancaster, J. R., Harrison, R. W., Michel, S. L., Snyder, M., and Thompson, R. G., *J. Thoracic Cardiovascular Surg.*, **40**, 588 (1960)
411. Müller, A., and Debrunner, W., *Der Anesthesist*, **9**, 344 (1960)
412. Müller, C., *Cardiopulmonary Hemodynamics in Chronic Lung Disease with Special Reference to Pulmonary Tuberculosis* (Ejnar Munksgaards Forlag, Copenhagen, 371 pp., 1960)
413. Munck, O., Kristensen, H. S., and Lassen, H. C. A., *Lancet*, **I**, 66 (1961)
414. Muscholl, V. E., Rahn, K. H., and Watzka, M., *Naturwissenschaften*, **14**, 325 (1960)
415. Muysers, K., Siehoff, F., and Worth, G., *Klin. Wochschr.*, **39**, 83 (1961)
416. McClure, J. H., and Balagot, R. C., *Obstet. and Gynecol.*, **17**, 243 (1961)
417. McElroy, W. T., Jr., and Spitzer, J. J., *J. Appl. Physiol.*, **16**, 339 (1961)
418. McIlreath, F. J., Jr., Craig, A. B., Jr., and Anzalone, A. J., *J. Appl. Physiol.*, **16**, 463 (1961)

419. McIlroy, M. B., and Holmgren, A., *Federation Proc.*, **20**, 423 (1961)
420. McKerrow, C. B., and Gilson, J. C., *Modern Trends in Occupational Health* (Butterworth and Co., London, 313 pp., 1960)
421. McKerrow, C. B., McDermott, M., and Gilson, J. C., *Lancet*, **I**, 149 (1960)
422. McLaughlin, R. F., Jr., Tyler, W. S., and Canada, R. O., *J. Am. Med. Assoc.*, **175**, 694 (1961)
423. Naeye, R. L., *Arch. Pathol.*, **71**, 447 (1961)
424. Naeye, R. L., *Am. Heart J.*, **61**, 586 (1961)
425. Nagelschmidt, G., *Brit. J. Ind. Med.*, **17**, 247 (1960)
426. Nahas, G. G., *Ann. N. Y. Acad. Sci.*, **92**, 333 (1961)
427. Naimark, A., and Cherniack, R. M., *J. Appl. Physiol.*, **15**, 377 (1960)
428. Naimark, A., Brodovsky, D. M., and Cherniack, R. M., *Am. J. Med.*, **28**, 368 (1960)
429. Nakamura, T., Katori, R., Miyazawa, K., Ohtomo, S., Watanabe, T., Watanabe, T., Miura, Y., and Takizawa, T., *Diseases of Chest*, **39**, 193 (1961)
430. Nakamura, T., Katori, R., Miyazawa, K., Ohtomo, S., Watanabe, T., and Watanabe, T., *Diseases of Chest*, **37**, 680 (1960)
431. Nakamura, T., Takiyawa, T., and Takishima, T., *Tôhoku J. Exptl. Med.*, **73**, 309 (1961)
432. Nash, C. W., and Heath, C., *Am. J. Physiol.*, **200**, 755 (1961)
433. Negus, V., *Ann. Royal Coll. Surg. Engl.*, **27**, 171 (1960)
434. Neville, J. R., *J. Appl. Physiol.*, **15**, 717 (1960)
435. Newman, F., and Thomson, M. L., *J. Physiol. (London)*, **153**, 71P (1960)
436. Newman, P. P., and Wolstencroft, J. H., *J. Physiol. (London)*, **152**, 87 (1960)
437. Ngai, S. H., *J. Pharmacol. Exptl. Therap.*, **131**, 91 (1961)
438. Niden, A. H., Burrows, B., and Barclay, W. R., *Circulation Research*, **8**, 509 (1960)
439. Nunn, J. F., and Ezi-Ashi, T. I., *Anesthesiology*, **22**, 174 (1961)
440. Nunn, J. F., *Anesthesiology*, **21**, 620 (1960)
441. Nunn, J. F., and Hill, D. W., *J. Appl. Physiol.*, **15**, 383 (1960)
442. Ogawa, T., Jefferson, N. C., Toman,
J. E., Chiles, T., Zambetoglou, A., and Necheles, H., *Am. J. Physiol.*, **199**, 569 (1960)
443. Oliver, T. K., *Adaptation to Extrauterine Life* (Ross Labs., Columbus, Ohio, 94 pp., 1959)
444. Olsen, H. C., and Gilson, J. C., *Brit. Med. J.*, **I**, 450 (1960)
445. Olthof, G. K. A., *Acta Physiol. et Pharmacol. Néerl.*, **9**, 137 (1960)
446. Osborn, J. J., and Macey, M. B., *J. Appl. Physiol.*, **15**, 1159 (1960)
447. Osipova, O. V., and Smiraov, K. M., *Sechenov Physiol. J. USSR (Engl. Transl.)*, **46**, 319 (1961)
448. Otter, G. den, Houhuys, F. V., and Bakker, N. J., *Acta Physiol. et Pharmacol. Néerl.*, **9**, 415 (1960)
449. Pabst, H. W., *Helv. Med. Acta.*, **27**, 759 (1960)
450. Palmer, K. N. V., *Lancet*, **I**, 191 (1961)
451. Panchenko, I. A., *Bull. Exptl. Biol. Med. (USSR) (Engl. Transl.)*, **49**, 20 (1960)
452. Pattle, R. E., *Phys. in Med. Biol.*, **5**, 11 (1960)
453. Permutt, S., and Martin, H. B., *J. Appl. Physiol.*, **15**, 819 (1960)
454. Permutt, S., and Bromberger-Barnea, B., *Federation Proc.*, **20**, 105 (1961)
455. Permutt, S., Howell, J. B. L., Proctor, D. F., and Riley, R. L., *J. Appl. Physiol.*, **16**, 64 (1961)
456. Perret, C., *Helv. Physiol. et Pharmacol. Acta*, **18**, 72 (1960)
457. Perret, C., *Schweiz. med. Wochschr.*, **90**, 1129 (1960)
458. Petit, J. M., Milic-Emili, G., and Delhez, L., *J. Appl. Physiol.*, **15**, 1101 (1960)
459. Picon-Reategui, E., *J. Appl. Physiol.*, **16**, 431 (1961)
460. Piiper, J., *J. Appl. Physiol.*, **16**, 493 (1961)
461. Piiper, J., Haab, P., and Rahn, H., *J. Appl. Physiol.*, **16**, 499 (1961)
462. Piiper, J., *J. Appl. Physiol.*, **16**, 507 (1961)
463. Platts, M. M., Hammond, J. D. S., and Stuart-Harris, C. H., *Quart. J. Med.*, **29**, 559 (1960)
464. Pocidalo, J. J., Corcket, F., Amiel, J. L., Lissac, J., Finetti, P., and Blazo, M. C., *Rev. franç. études clin. et biol.*, **5**, 582 (1960)
465. Polgar, G., and Forster, R. E., *J. Appl. Physiol.*, **15**, 706 (1960)
466. Pontoppidan, H., and Beecher, H. K., *J. Am. Med. Assoc.*, **174**, 2209 (1960)
467. Poole, E. W., *Nature*, **189**, 579 (1961)

468. Poulsen, H., *Der Anaesthesist*, **9,** 141 (1961)
469. Pratt, P. C., and Klugh, G. A., *Am. Rev. Respirat. Diseases*, **83,** 690 (1961)
470. Price, H. L., *Anesthesiology*, **21,** 652 (1960)
471. Prystowsky, H., Meschia, G., and Barron, D. H., *Yale J. Biol. Med.*, **32,** 441 (1960)
472. Prystowsky, H., Hellegers, A. E., and Bruns, P., *Am. J. Obstet. Gynecol.*, **81,** 372 (1961)
473. Quilligan, E. J., Vasicka, A., Aznar, R., Lipsitz, P. J., Moore, T., and Bloor, B. M., *Am. J. Obstet. Gynecol.*, **79,** 1048 (1960)
474. Raffensperger, J. G., Diffenbaugh, W. G., and Strohl, E. L., *J. Am. Med. Assoc.*, **174,** 130 (1960)
475. Rahimtoola, S., Good, C. J., and Davies, P. D. B., *Thorax*, **15,** 320 (1960)
476. Rankin, J., McNeill, R. S., and Forster, R. E., *J. Appl. Physiol.*, **15,** 543 (1960)
477. Reardon, H. S., Baumann, M. L., and Haddad, E. J., *J. Pediat.*, **57,** 151 (1960)
478. Redding, J. S., Voigt, G. C., and Safar, P., *J. Appl. Physiol.*, **15,** 1113 (1960)
479. Redgate, E. S., *Am. J. Physiol.*, **198,** 1299 (1960)
480. Redgate, E. S., *Am. J. Physiol.*, **198,** 1304 (1960)
481. Reed, D. J., and Kellogg, R. H., *J. Appl. Physiol.*, **15,** 1130 (1960)
482. Reed, D. J., and Kellogg, R. H., *J. Appl. Physiol.*, **15,** 1135 (1960)
483. Reemtsma, K., Gantt, J. R., Schramel, R. J., Ziskind, M. M., Hyman, A. L., Quiroz, A., and Creech, O., Jr., *Surgery*, **49,** 77 (1961)
484. Reichel, G., Ulmer, W. T., and Harberg, D., *Klin. Wochschr.*, **38,** 683 (1960)
485. Reid, L., *Thorax*, **15,** 132 (1960)
486. Reidt, W. U., Cullen, J. H., and Smith, L. H. E., *Am. Rev. Respirat. Diseases*, **83,** 481 (1961)
487. Reimann, A. F., Long, E. T., Adams, W. E., Ozoa, A. K., and Nigro, S., *Diseases of Chest*, **39,** 56 (1961)
488. Reineck, H., Rapp, R., and Gauer, O. H., *Arch. ges. Physiol.*, **272,** 15 (1960)
489. Riad, Z. M., *Anat. Record*, **137,** 99 (1960)
490. Richards, C. C., and Bachman, L., *J. Clin. Invest.*, **40,** 273 (1961)

491. Richards, D. W., *Ann. Internal Med.*, **53,** 1105 (1960)
492. Rigatto, M., and Fishman, A. P., *J. Clin. Invest.*, **39,** 1626 (1960)
493. Rigatto, M., and Fishman, A. P., *J. Appl. Physiol.*, **16,** 391 (1961)
494. Riggs, D. S., and Goldstein, A., *J. Appl. Physiol.*, **16,** 531 (1961)
495. Riley, R. L., Ross, R. S., and Armstrong, B., *Federation Proc.*, **20,** 431 (1961)
496. Ringrose, C. A. D., and Vant, J. R., *Can. Med. Assoc. J.*, **83,** 1037 (1960)
497. Robin, E. D., *Med. Clin. North Am.*, **44,** 1269 (1960)
498. Robinson, J. S., and Gray, T. C., *Brit. J. Anaesthia*, **33,** 62 (1961)
499. Robinson, J. S., *Brit. J. Anaesthesia*, **33,** 69 (1961)
500. Rodman, T., Sobel, M., and Close, H. P., *New Engl. J. Med.*, **263,** 73 (1960)
501. Rogan, J. M., Ashford, J. R., Chapman, P. J., Duffield, D. P., Fay, J. W. J., and Rae, S., *Brit. Med. J.*, **II,** 1337 (1961)
502. Rokseth, R., Kjorstad, H., Skaga, E., and Storstein, O., *Scand. J. Clin. Lab. Invest.*, **12,** 493 (1960)
503. Roos, A., Thomas, L. J., Jr., Nagel, E. L., and Prommas, D. C., *J. Appl. Physiol.*, **16,** 77 (1961)
504. Rosenberg, E., and Forster, R. E., *J. Appl. Physiol.*, **15,** 883 (1960)
505. Rosenberg, H. S., McNamara, D. G., Leachman, R. A., and Buzzi, R. M., *Arch. Pathol.*, **70,** 141 (1960)
506. Rosenblueth, A., Alanis, J., and Pilar, G., *Arch. intern. physiol. et biochim.*, **69,** 19 (1961)
507. Ross, B. B., and Farhi, L. E., *J. Appl. Physiol.*, **15,** 363 (1960)
508. Ross, J. C., Lord, T. H., and Ley, G. D., *J. Appl. Physiol.*, **15,** 843 (1960)
509. Ross, S. M., and Kao, F. F., *J. Appl. Physiol.*, **16,** 380 (1961)
510. Rossier, P. H., Bühlmann, A., and Wiesinger, K., *Respiration: Physiological Principles and their Clinical Applications* (Mosby, St. Louis, Mo., 505 pp., 1960)
511. Rossi-Fanelli, A., Antonini, E., and Caputo, A., *J. Biol. Chem.*, **236,** 391 (1961)
512. Rossi-Fanelli, A., Antonini, E., and Caputo, A., *J. Biol. Chem.*, **236,** 405 (1961)
513. Rudolph, A. J., and Smith, C. A., *J. Pediat.*, **57,** 905 (1960)

514. Ryssing, E., *Ugesk rift Laeger*, **122**, 31 (1960)

515. Said, S. I., *Ann. Internal Med.*, **53**, 1121 (1960)

516. Saito, K., Honda, Y., and Hasumura, N., *Japan. J. Physiol.*, **10**, 673 (1960)

517. Saito, K., Honda, Y., and Hasumura, N., *Japan. J. Physiol.*, **10**, 634 (1960)

518. Sakamoto, A., and Murao, M., *Japan. Heart J.*, **1**, 37 (1960)

519. Salisbury, P. F., Briggs, J. N., Hamel, N. C., Cross, C. E., and Rieben, P. A., *Trans. Am. Soc. Artificial Internal Organs*, **5**, 32 (1959)

520. Salmoiraghi, G. C., and von Baumgarten, R., *J. Neurophysiol.*, **24**, 203 (1961)

521. Salzano, J., and Hall, F. G., *J. Appl. Physiol.*, **15**, 397 (1960)

522. Salzano, J., and Hall, F. G., *Proc. Soc. Exptl. Biol. Med.*, **106**, 199 (1961)

523. Samet, P., Fierer, E. M., and Bernstein, W. H., *J. Appl. Physiol.*, **15**, 826 (1960)

524. Samet, P., Fierer, E. M., and Bernstein, W. H., *Diseases of Chest*, **39**, 388 (1961)

525. Samet, P., Bernstein, W. H., and Widrich, J., *Am. Heart J.*, **60**, 433 (1960)

526. Sancetta, S. M., *Circulation Research*, **8**, 616 (1960)

527. Schaefer, K. E., *Aerospace Med.*, **32**, 197 (1961)

528. Schmidt, G., and Dal Ri, H., *Arch. exptl. Pathol. Pharmakol.*, **240**, 19 (1960)

529. Schmidt-Nielsen, K., and Pennycuik, P., *Am. J. Physiol.*, **200**, 746 (1961)

530. Schopp, R. T., *Science*, **132**, 957 (1960)

531. Sears, D. F., and Eisenberg, R. M., *J. Gen. Physiol.*, **44**, 869 (1961)

532. Sechzer, P. H., Egbert, L. D., Linde, H. W., Cooper, D. Y., Dripps, R. D., and Price, H. L., *J. Appl. Physiol.*, **15**, 454 (1960)

533. Segel, N., Harris, P., and Bishop, J. M., *Clin. Sci.*, **20**, 49 (1961)

534. Semple, S. J. G., *J. Appl. Physiol.*, **16**, 576 (1961)

535. Senterre, J., and Petit, J. M., *Rev. franç. études clin. et biol.*, **5**, 1007 (1960)

536. Sera, K., *Japan. Circulation J.*, **25**, 222 (1961)

537. Sera, K., *Japan. Heart J.*, **2**, 170 (1961)

538. Sergievskii, M. V., and Okuneva, G. N., *Sechenov Physiol. J. USSR (Engl. Transl.)*, **46**, 1043 (1960)

539. Severinghaus, J. W., Swenson, E. W., Finley, T. N., Lategola, M. T., and Williams, J., *J. Appl. Physiol.*, **16**, 53 (1961)

540. Severinghaus, J. W., *Der Anaesthesist*, **9**, 50 (1960)

541. Severinghaus, J. W., *Anesthesiology*, **21**, 717 (1960)

542. Severinghaus, J. W., Larson, C. P., and Eger, E. I., *Anesthesiology*, **22**, 429 (1961)

543. Sharp, J. T., Bunnell, I. L., Griffith, G. T., and Greene, D. G., *J. Clin. Invest.*, **40**, 665 (1961)

544. Shephard, R. J., Turner, M. E., Carey, G. C. R., and Phair, J. J., *J. Appl. Physiol.*, **15**, 70 (1960)

545. Siebens, A. A., and Puletti, F., *Science*, **133**, 1418 (1961)

546. Sieker, H. O., and Wilson, W. P., *Arch. Neurol.*, **3**, 704 (1960)

547. Sieker, H. O., and Manfredi, F., *Progr. in Cardiovascular Diseases*, **3**, 178 (1960)

548. Siesjo, B. K., *Acta Physiol. Scand.*, **51**, 297 (1961)

549. Siggaard-Andersen, O., *Scand. J. Clin. Lab. Invest.*, **13**, 196 (1961)

550. Siggaard-Andersen, O., *Scand. J. Clin. Lab. Invest.*, **13**, 205 (1961)

551. Siggaard-Andersen, O., Engel, K., Jorgensen, K., and Astrup, P., *Scand. J. Clin. Lab. Invest.*, **12**, 172 (1960)

552. Siggaard-Andersen, O., and Engel, K., *Scand. J. Clin. Lab. Invest.*, **12**, 177 (1960)

553. Siggaard-Andersen, O., *Scand. J. Clin. Lab. Invest.*, **12**, 311 (1960)

554. Simmons, D. H., Nicoloff, J., and Guze, L. B., *J. Am. Med. Assoc.*, **174**, 2196 (1960)

555. Simmons, D. H., Linde, L. M., Miller, J. H., and O'Reilly, R. J., *Circulation Research*, **9**, 465 (1961)

556. Sjostedt, S., Rooth, G., and Caligara, F., *Arch. Disease Childhood*, **35**, 529 (1961)

557. Small, M. J., and Abramowitz, S., *Am. Rev. Respirat. Diseases*, **83**, 124 (1961)

558. Smellie, H., Apthorp, G. H., and Marshall, R., *Thorax*, **16**, 87 (1961)

559. Smith, C. W., Bean, J. W., and Bauer, R., *Am. J. Physiol.*, **199**, 883 (1960)

560. Smith, T. C., Cook, F. D., De Kornfeld, T. J., and Siebecker, K. L., *J. Thoracic and Cardiovascular Surg.*, **39**, 788 (1960)

561. Smyth, D. G., Battaglia, F. C., and Meschia, G., *J. Gen. Physiol*, **44**, 889 (1961)

562. Snider, T. H., Wilner, F. M., and Lewis, B. M., *Ann. Internal Med.*, **52**, 1318 (1961)

563. Sokoloff, L., *Anesthesiology*, **21**, 664 (1960)

564. Sommerkamp, H., Riegel, K., Hilpert, P., and Brecht, K., *Arch. ges. Physiol.*, **272**, 591 (1961)

565. Sottrup, T., *Studies on the Pulmonary Function and the Diaphragmatic Function in Patients Convalescing from Life Threatening Poliomyelitis* (Ejnar Munksgaards Forlag, Copenhagen, 261 pp., 1960)

566. Stahle, I., *Scand. J. Clin. Lab. Invest.*, **13**, 186 (1961)

567. Stahlman, M., *Am. J. Diseases Childhood*, **101**, 216 (1961)

568. Staub, N. C., Bishop, J. M., and Forster, R. E., *J. Appl. Physiol.*, **16**, 511 (1961)

569. Stein, M., Kimbel, P., and Johnson, R. L., Jr., *J. Clin. Invest.*, **40**, 348 (1961)

570. Stein, M., Schiavi, R. C., Ottenberg, P., and Hamilton, C., *J. Allergy*, **32**, 8 (1961)

571. Stein, M., Forkner, C. E., Jr., Robin, E. D., and Wessler, S., *J. Appl. Physiol.*, **16**, 488 (1961)

572. Stern, S., and Braun, K., *Am. J. Cardiol.*, **7**, 188 (1961)

573. Stone, D. J., Schwartz, A., and Feltman, J. A., *Am. Rev. Respirat. Diseases*, **82**, 493 (1960)

574. Stoney, W. S., and Adams, J. E., *Am. Rev. Respirat. Diseases*, **83**, 26 (1961)

576. Strang, L. B., *Arch. Disease Childhood*, **35**, 224 (1960)

577. Strawbridge, H. T. G., *Am. J. Pathol.*, **37**, 161 (1960)

578. Strawbridge, H. T. G., *Am. J. Pathol.*, **37**, 309 (1960)

579. Strawbridge, H. T. G., *Am. J. Pathol.*, **37**, 391 (1960)

580. Stupfel, M., and Roffi, J., *Compt. rend. soc. biol.*, **154**, 1387 (1960)

581. Stutman, L. J., *Aerospace Med.*, **31**, 659 (1960)

582. Sugioka, K., *Anesthesiology*, **21**, 135 (1960)

583. Sutherland, J. M., and Ratcliff, J. W., *Am. J. Diseases Childhood*, **101**, 67 (1961)

584. Swanson, A. G., *Am. J. Med. Sci.*, **240**, 417 (1960)

585. Sweet, H. C., Wyatt, J. P., and Kinsella, P. W., *Am. J. Med.*, **29**, 277 (1960)

586. Swenson, E. W., Finley, T. N., and Guzman, S. V., *J. Clin. Invest.*, **40**, 828 (1961)

587. Sykes, M. K., *Brit. J. Anaesthesia*, **32**, 256 (1960)

588. Tabakin, B. S., Hanson, J. S., Adhikari, P. K., and Naeye, R. L., *Am. Rev. Respirat. Diseases*, **83**, 194 (1961)

590. Taylor, D. W., *J. Physiol. (London)*, **152**, 506 (1960)

591. Tecimer, L. B., Pearse, M. L., and Yamashita, J., *Arch. Internal Med.*, **105**, 891 (1960)

592. Tenney, S. M., *Anesthesiology*, **21**, 674 (1960)

593. Terzioğlu, M., Emiroğlu, F., Gokhan, N., and Özer, F., *Arch. intern. physiol. et biochim.*, **69**, 161 (1961)

594. Terzioğlu, M., Gokhan, N., Emiroğlu, F., and Özer, F., *Arch. intern. physiol. et biochim.*, **69**, 177 (1961)

595. Thews, G., *Arch. ges. Physiol.*, **271**, 197 (1960)

596. Thews, G., *Arch. ges. Physiol.*, **271**, 227 (1960)

597. Thomas, L. J., Jr., Griffo, Z. J., and Roos, A., *J. Appl. Physiol.*, **16**, 451 (1961)

598. Thomas, L. J., Jr., Roos, A., and Griffo, Z. J., *J. Appl. Physiol.*, **16**, 457 (1961)

599. Ting, E. Y., and Lyons, H. A., *J. Appl. Physiol.*, **16**, 517 (1961)

600. Ting, E. Y., Hong, S. K., and Rahn, H., *J. Appl. Physiol.*, **15**, 554 (1960)

601. Ting, E. Y., Hong, S. K., and Rahn, H., *J. Appl. Physiol.*, **15**, 557 (1960)

602. Tobin, C. E., *Surg., Gynecol. Obstet.*, **3**, 297 (1960)

603. Tooley, W., Gardner, R., Thung, N., and Finley, T. N., *Federation Proc.*, **20**, 428 (1961)

604. Toremalm, N. G., *Acta Oto-Laryngol.*, **52**, 6 (1960)

605. Torres, G., Lyons, H. A., and Emerson, P., *Am. J. Med.*, **29**, 946 (1960)

606. Travis, D. M., Cook, C. D., Julian, D. G., Crump, C. H., Helliesen, P., Robin, E. D., Bayles, T. B., and Burwell, C. S., *Am. J. Med.*, **29**, 623 (1960)

607. Tsao, M. U., and Vadnay, A., *J. Appl. Physiol.*, **15**, 712 (1960)

608. Tucker, D. H., and Sieker, H. O., *Am. Rev. Respirat. Diseases*, **82**, 787 (1960)

609. Tulou, P., *Am. J. Med.*, **30**, 243 (1961)

610. Ueda, H., Katayama, S., Goto, H., and Ito, K., *Japan. Heart J.*, **1**, 1 (1960)

611. Uehlinger, A., Fuchs, W. A., Buhlmann, A., and Uehlinger, E., *Deut. med. Wochschr.*, **42**, 1829 (1960)

612. Uhley, H., Leeds, S. E., Sampson, J. J., and Friedman, M., *Circulation Research*, **9**, 688 (1961)

613. Uhley, H. N., *Diseases of Chest*, **37**, 532 (1960)

614. Ulmer, W. T., Prugger, H., and Bruck, A., *Arch. ges. Physiol.*, **270**, 536 (1960)

615. Urabe, M., Segawa, Y., Tsubokawa, T., Yamamoto, K., Araki, K., and Izumi, K., *Japan. Heart J.*, **2**, 147 (1961)

616. *US Govt. Research Repts.*, **33**, 460 (1960)

617. Valtin, H., and Tenney, S. M., *J. Appl. Physiol.*, **15**, 1107 (1960)

618. Van Den Berg, J., *Acta Physiol. et Pharmacol. Néerl.*, **9**, 361 (1960)

619. Van Liew, H. D., *J. Appl. Physiol.*, **16**, 578 (1961)

620. Vasicka, A., Quilligan, E. J., Aznar, R., Lipsitz, P. J., and Bloor, B. M., *Am. J. Obstet. Gynecol.*, **79**, 1041 (1960)

621. Verstraeten, J. M., *Rev. franç. études clin. et biol.*, **5**, 490 (1960)

622. Virtama, P., and Jankala, E., *Angiology*, **12**, 77 (1961)

623. Visser, B. F., *Phys. in Med. Biol.*, **5**, 155 (1960)

624. Visser, B. F., *Clinical Gas Analysis Based on Thermal Conductivity* (Kemink & Utrecht, Netherlands, 183 pp., 1960)

625. Visser, B. F., and Maas, A. H. J., *Clin. Chim. Acta*, **5**, 850 (1960)

626. Voitkevich, V. I., *Sechenov Physiol. J. USSR (Engl. Transl.)*, **46**, 92 (1960)

627. Wacker, W. E. C., and Snodgrass, P. J., *J. Am. Med. Assoc.*, **174**, 2142 (1960)

628. Wagenvoort, C. A., Neufeld, H. N., DuShane, J. W., and Edwards, J. E., *Circulation*, **23**, 740 (1961)

629. Wagenvoort, C. A., Neufeld, H. N., DuShane, J. W., and Edwards, J. E., *Circulation*, **23**, 733 (1961)

630. Wagner, E., Rieben, P. A., Katsuhara, K., and Salisbury, P. F., *Circulation*, **9**, 382 (1961)

631. Walker, J. E. C., and Wells, R. E., Jr., *Am. J. Med.*, **30**, 259 (1961)

632. Wallgren, G., Geubelle, F., and Koch, G., *Acta Paediat.*, **49**, 415 (1960)

633. Wang, J. H., *Science*, **133**, 1770 (1961)

634. Watson, J. F., Cherniack, N. S., and Zechman, F. W., *J. Clin. Invest.*, **39**, 1737 (1960)

635. Weerden, G. J. van, *Der Anaesthesist*, **10**, 85 (1961)

636. Wells, R. E., Jr., Walker, J. E. C., and Hickler, R. B., *New Engl. J. Med.*, **263**, 268 (1960)

637. Wells, R. E., Jr., *Med. Clin. North Am.*, **44**, 1279 (1960)

638. Weseman, C. M., *Am. J. Diseases Childhood*, **100**, 881 (1960)

639. Wessler, S., Freiman, D. G., Ballon, J. D., Katz, J. H., Wolff, R., and Wolf, E., *Am. J. Pathol.*, **38**, 89 (1960)

640. West, J. B., and Dollery, C. T., *J. Appl. Physiol.*, **15**, 405 (1960)

641. West, J. B., Dollery, C. T., and Hugh-Jones, P., *J. Clin. Invest.*, **40**, 1 (1961)

642. West, J. B., *J. Appl. Physiol.*, **15**, 976 (1960)

643. Whittenberger, J. L., McGregor, M., Berglund, E., and Borst, H. G., *J. Appl. Physiol.*, **15**, 878 (1960)

644. Widimsky, J., Kasalicky, J., Valach, A., Dejoar, R., Vyslouzil, Z., and Lukes, M., *Brit. Heart J.*, **22**, 571 (1960)

645. Wigderson, A., and Kohan, M., *Can. Med. Assoc. J.*, **83**, 1068 (1960)

646. Wilcken, D. E. L., MacKenzie, K. M., and Goodwin, J. F., *Lancet*, **I**, 781 (1960)

647. Williams, M. H., Jr., Zohman, L. R., and Bertrand, C. A., *Diseases of Chest*, **37**, 597 (1960)

648. Williams, M. H., *Clinical Applications of Cardiopulmonary Physiology* (Harper & Brothers, New York, 233 pp., 1960)

649. Williams, R., and Hugh-Jones, P., *Thorax*, **15**, 109 (1960)

650. Wilson, R. H., Jay, B., Doty, V., Pingree, H., and Higgins, E., *J. Appl. Physiol.*, **16**, 374 (1961)

651. Winterstein, H., *Pharmacol. Revs.*, **13**, 71 (1961)

652. Wittenberg, J. B., *J. Gen. Physiol.*, **44**, 521 (1961)

653. Wittenberg, J. B., *J. Exptl. Biol.*, **37**, 698 (1960)

654. Wittenberg, J. B., and Wittenberg, B. A., *J. Gen. Physiol.*, **44**, 527 (1961)

655. Woodbury, D. M., *Anesthesiology*, **21**, 686 (1960)

656. Wright Patterson Air Development Division, *Closed Circuit Respiratory System, Symposium* (WADD T.R. 60-574, 475 pp., 1960)

657. Wright, R. R., *Am. J. Pathol.*, **37**, 63 (1960)

658. Wyatt, J. P., Fischer, V. W., and Sweet, H., *Lab. Invest.*, **10**, 159 (1961)

659. Yamamoto, W. S., and Edwards, M. W., Jr., *J. Appl. Physiol.*, **15**, 807 (1960)

660. Yin Chi Chang, *Byull. Eksptl. Biol. Med.*, **50**, 1013 (1960)*

661. Yin Chi Chang, *Byull. Eksptl. Biol. Med.*, **50**, 917 (1961)*

662. Yorifuji, S., and Sera, K., *Japan. Circulation J.*, **24**, 1463 (1960)

663. Young, D. T., Monroe, E. W., and Craige, E., *Am. J. Physiol.*, **759**, 199 (1960)

664. Zechman, F. W., Cherniack, N. S., and Hyde, A. S., *J. Appl. Physiol.*, **15**, 907 (1960)

665. Zeilhofer, R., and Rupprecht, E., *Klin. Wochschr.*, **4**, 184 (1961)

666. Zocche, G. P., Fritts, H. W., Jr., and Cournand, A., *J. Appl. Physiol.*, **15**, 1073 (1960)

* English translation will be announced in *Technical Translations*, issued by the Office of Technical Services, US Department of Commerce, and will be made available by the Photoduplication Service, Library of Congress, and by the SLA Translation Center at the John Crerar Library, Chicago, Illinois.

NEUROENDOCRINE ASPECTS OF BLOOD VOLUME REGULATION[1,2]

By Gordon Farrell[3] and Anna Newman Taylor[4]

Department of Physiology, Western Reserve University, Cleveland, Ohio

Recent reviews by Ravdin, Walker & Rhoads (1), by Brown, Hopper & Wennesland (2), and by Reeve, Allen & Roberts (3), as well as articles by Gregersen & Rawson (4, 5), have dealt in depth with the problems of blood volume determination, the dynamics of the vascular system, and the alterations in blood volume consequent to disease conditions. One of the most interesting current developments is the emergence of the unifying concept that certain elements of blood volume regulation (the control of water and electrolyte balance) may be by systems analogous to those for the maintenance of arterial pressure. The reflexes concerned may be virtually identical in certain instances, though there are adaptations related to the special physical or physiological consequences of changes in volume. We should like to examine the evidence on these points in some detail.

A Brief Review of Arterial Pressure Control

Review of the physiologic mechanism for the regulation of arterial pressure is certainly not necessary for the present readers, but a brief summary may be germane. It will be recalled that the "pressor area" is a diffuse collection of neurons in the lateral reticular formation of the rostral two-thirds of the medulla (6 to 9). Present opinion holds that these cells tonically excite the spinal vasoconstrictor sympathetic neurons via descending pathways in the ventrolateral column (8, 10, 11). This phenomenon appears to be a manifestation of the general role of the brainstem reticular formation, that is, activation of the function of other areas of the central nervous system (12). The tonic activity of the reticular formation is apparently intrinsic to the nature of its cells, in that they discharge spontaneously at a level conditioned by the local metabolic environment and the inflow of afferent impulses (13, 14). In the instance of the components of this system which have to do with vasomotor activity, the ultimate result is, of course, contraction of vascular smooth muscle as a consequence of the release of a sympathetic mediator (presumably norepinephrine) at the terminals of the postganglionic neurons in the periphery. It is now generally accepted that the maintenance of normal vascular tone is by virtue of a balance established between stimulation from the pressor areas and inhibition by impulses set up as a result of deformation of receptors concentrated in the carotid sinus and aortic arch, but present in many other parts of the vascular system. The reflexes arising

---

[1] The survey of literature pertaining to this review was concluded in October 1961.
[2] Among the abbreviations used in this chapter is ADH (antidiuretic hormone).
[3] Established Investigator, The American Heart Association.
[4] Research Fellow, The American Heart Association.

in the atria and ventricles are believed to be qualitatively similar to those in the arterial system, though quantitatively less important (15, 16). If the spontaneous activity inherent in the pressor area is unleashed by removal of inhibition (e.g., denervation of the baroreceptors), profound vasoconstriction results, a phenomenon in certain respects analogous to apneusis and decerebrate rigidity. In both latter instances, removal of normal inhibition results in unrestrained motor activity, in large part the consequence of reticular activation (17, 18).

Unfortunately, in spite of the long and illustrious history of the pressoreceptor reflexes, and the extensive and detailed studies which are available, the precise central connections by which inhibition of vasomotor activity is mediated are still not entirely clear. The nucleus solitarius is almost certainly the first relay for the pressoreceptor impulses. However, a depressor area in the medial reticular formation of the caudal third of the bulb has been documented (7, 8, 9). It is commonly held that inhibition of the activity of the pressor area occurs at the medullary level, and such inhibition is presumably mediated by internuncials arising either in the nucleus solitarius itself or secondarily relayed through the depressor area. Descending depressor fibers are found in the dorsolateral column, and it appears that inhibition of the activity of the preganglionic sympathetic neurons also occurs locally in the cord (7, 8, 19).

In certain respects the vasomotor reflex system may be thought of as fundamentally neuroendocrine in nature. If a neuroendocrine mechanism is defined as one in which nerve cells, in response to appropriate stimuli, secrete a humoral factor which reaches target cells by passage in the blood or by diffusion (20, 21), there seems to be little argument with this point of view. The participation of the adrenal medulla in the general response to hypotension is certainly purely neuroendocrine. Further, the sympathetic transmitter even when released by postganglionic fibers unrelated to the adrenal medulla is not limited to the zone of secretion but overflows into the blood stream to act on distant sites (22).

The authors are fully aware that the foregoing truncated description of the vasomotor-pressoreceptor relationship scarcely does justice to the subject. However, detailed review is not necessary since comprehensive discussions of the subject are available (11, 15, 16). Our present purpose is to view the general organization of this system, in which a vegetative function, driven by the paleontologically ancient brainstem reticular formation, is modulated by reflexes which test the specific performance of that function and adjust its activity by exercising inhibition. In its broad outlines, this type of physiological device may be utilized in the volume-mediated aspects of the regulation of the secretion of antidiuretic hormone and aldosterone.

Antidiuretic Hormone and Blood Volume

That plasma volume is intimately related to total body water is self-evident, since changes in free water are reflected equally throughout the body-water compartments (23). Administration of antidiuretic hormone (ADH) is accompanied by increased plasma volume when water is available; pathological deficiency leads to hypovolemia. The control of the secretion of this neuroendocrine factor is clearly important to the vascular system.

The earliest studies on ADH regulation emphasized the role of osmoreceptors (24 to 27). However, it has been known for some time that ADH secretion is modified by changes in the volume or distribution of body fluids independent of osmolarity. A considerable amount of older experimental data, some of it admittedly indirect and not always in perfect agreement, can be quoted in this regard. Hemorrhage (28, 29, 30), orthostasis (31 to 37), venous occlusion (38, 39), and alterations of extracellular fluid volume by a variety of maneuvers (40 to 46) have all been shown to alter renal water handling or plasma antidiuretic activity in such a way as to indicate that changes in ADH secretion were provoked. The cited references by no means encompass the extensive literature on the subject, and the reader is referred for greater detail to manuscripts by Epstein (47), Smith (48), Welt (49), and Gilbert & Glaser (50). Certain of the above experiments may be open to question because of the reliance on antidiuresis alone as evidence for ADH secretion. Alterations in water excretion have been reported with postural changes in the water-loaded subject, presumably independent of ADH output (51). However, more recent work employing improved methods for determining blood ADH levels has removed any question that changes in vascular or total extracellular fluid volume are potent stimuli to ADH secretion (52, 53, 54).

There was considerable speculation as to how the organism detects changes in volume, and the great pioneer in physiology, J. P. Peters, postulated the existence of specific volume receptors a quarter of a century ago (55). Many reports offering support of the concept have since appeared [see Epstein (47), Smith (48), Welt (49), and Gilbert & Glaser (50)]. Despite extensive experimental work, the location of the receptors remained unknown for many years, and the whole subject seemed clouded in mystery.

There were early suggestions that the "volume receptors" were sensitive not to the total volume of the vascular compartment but rather to specific hemodynamic parameters. Strauss (43) observed that the diuresis induced by isotonic expansion of the extracellular fluid volume was less marked in the sitting than in the recumbent position and pointed out that the distribution of the volume was important. Epstein, Post & McDowell (56), on the basis of experiments in which arteriovenous anastomoses were opened or closed, placed the receptors in the arterial tree. Harrison and his collaborators believed them to be within the cranial cavity (33, 35). Increased ADH secretion was noted by several workers to occur under conditions (syncope, emesis, tilting, etc.) in which the most obvious physiological trigger was an acute fall in arterial pressure (32, 57, 58, 59). This concept was strengthened by the studies of Ginsburg (29, 30, 60), who found that increased ADH secretion during hemorrhage was indeed more directly related to arterial pressure than to the decrease in blood volume. Ginsburg explored the effects of vagotomy and carotid sinus denervation. The response to hemorrhage was not prevented by vagotomy alone, but combined vagotomy and carotid sinus denervation effectively reduced it (60). More recently, Share & Levy (61) found that carotid occlusion results in a profound increase in ADH secretion, providing the vagi are first cut.

It is scarcely necessary to review the elegant work of Henry and his collaborators demonstrating that afferent stimuli for ADH control arise in stretch receptors in the left atrium and pericardial portion of the pulmonary veins (62 to 65). These receptors also act by inhibition of ADH secretion. Atkins & Pearce (66) observed that diuresis following expansion of plasma volume occurs (though to a lesser degree) despite vagotomy. It may well be that the buffering action of one reflex complicates studies aimed at elucidating the other. Share & Levy also found that vagotomy by itself resulted in increased jugular vein ADH levels, in support of the belief that the vagus conducts inhibitory influences (61).

The atrial reflex is initiated by the small pressure changes necessary to distend these thin-walled structures. On the other hand, the carotid receptors probably respond to changes in systolic arterial pressure or pulse pressure of the same order of magnitude as those influencing the carotid sinus vasomotor reflex system. In neither case is there any reason to believe that the receptors are any different from those which mediate the familiar vasomotor responses to changes in venous return or arterial pressure.

It could and probably will be argued that changes in ADH secretory levels occur in many experimental situations involving blood volume redistribution in which no change in arterial pressure is observed. Aside from the explanation based on the atrial reflex, it should be apparent that the simple fact of maintenance of arterial pressure provides no information as to the level of baroreceptor activity. In any experimental procedure which should result in reduced venous return, the existence of normal arterial pressure undoubtedly reflects the participation of the pressoreceptor reflexes.

If the receptors which initiate reflexes for regulation of ADH secretion are analogous to those for arterial pressure control, what can be said of the central integration? That the impulses generated in the atrial and carotid receptors which affect ADH secretion are transmitted via the vagus and glossopharyngeal nerves has either been demonstrated or can be inferred from our knowledge of the innervation of these structures (63, 67). The first relay undoubtedly occurs in the nucleus solitarius. In the instance of arterial pressure regulation, the anatomical juxtaposition of the nucleus solitarius and the medullary reticular formation makes synaptic connections with vasomotor active areas convenient. However, the site of ADH elaboration is clearly at a considerable distance up the brainstem, and the question of medullary-hypothalamic relationships must be considered. That vagal influences are transmitted rostralward through the brainstem is well known. Stimulation of the depressor component of the vagus results in inhibition of cortical EEG activity; conversely, hyperexcitability of the motor cortex results from section of the buffer nerves (68, 69). Dell & Olson recorded evoked potentials in the midbrain and hypothalamus following vagal stimulation (70). Bronk and his collaborators stimulated the sinus nerve and vagus and recorded synchronous activity in the lateral hypothalamus (71).

Remaining to be clarified is the manner in which medullary influences ascend to the hypothalamus. It is not difficult to envision transmission via the reticular formation itself on the basis of the anatomical continuity of this structure into the diencephalon (13, 14, 68, 72). On the other hand, well-defined projections to the hypothalamus are present in the midbrain and may be utilized as part of the cephalad flow. The central gray periventricular system, the dorsal longitudinal fasciculus of Schütz, and the mammillary peduncle with its contribution to the medial forebrain bundle are all possibilities (73, 74, 75), although the exact nature of neural connections between the reticular activating system and the midbrain-hypothalamic system has not been defined (76).

It is, of course, both unnecessary and almost certainly inaccurate to imagine that tonic activation of hypothalamic activity arises solely in the medullary-pontine reticular formation. The spinothalamic connections with the midbrain reticular substance provide an entranceway to the hypothalamus for somatic pain and temperature influences and presumably constitute one of the major pathways for such information (76, 77). A valuable clue is provided by the recent observations of Sharpless & Rothballer (78) that stimulation in the dorsal tegmentum and periaqueductal gray of the midbrain results in profound increases in ADH release. These workers implicate the dorsal bundle of Schütz as the responsible structure. Further evidence for midbrain influence on water metabolism comes from the work of Gilbert who discovered that the subcommissural organ shows marked histological changes in response to dehydration and that ablation of the structure in rats leads to disturbances in water intake (50, 79).

Vagal stimulation enhances neurohypophyseal activity resulting in the release of both ADH and oxytocin (80 to 83). At first glance this phenomenon would seem to conflict with the observations that the vagus conducts impulses which inhibit medullary activity. However, it is common knowledge that whole vagal stimulation does not mimic the effects of the specific inhibitory reflexes known to utilize the nerve. Many readers will recall the difficulties which medical students have in attempting to rediscover the Hering-Breuer reflex by vagal stimulation. Increased afferent inflow from the many different types of fibers in the vagus may serve to enhance reticular activity in a nonspecific fashion, in the same way that spinal afferent inflow does (13, 14).

That the net effect on ADH secretion of ascending influence from the medullary-pontine reticular formation, as well as from the midbrain, is tonic stimulation can be inferred from the work of Henry et al. (63, 64, 65) and of Share & Levy (61). In each instance, the reflex pattern appears to involve inhibition (initiation of inhibition of ADH output by atrial distention, and removal of inhibition by carotid occlusion), which must necessarily act against a background of tonic activity. Additional indirect support for the concept comes from the work of Walker (84) who believes that the increased antidiuretic activity attributable to anesthetic agents reflects removal of inhibition. Walker envisions the inhibitory influences in this instance as being of cortical origin.

The concept of reticular activation of hypothalamic or pituitary function is by no means new. The subject has been discussed in some detail in regard to the control of the secretion of gonadotropins, ACTH, and the thyroid-stimulating hormone (76, 85 to 90). Slusher and co-workers (91, 92) also have evidence for inhibition of pituitary activity as part of the regulatory mechanism.

The foregoing discussion has put particular emphasis on the volume aspect of ADH regulation. Not to be neglected is the osmoreceptor mechanism, which indeed is probably the more sensitive and possibly the more important in day-to-day control of the secretion of the polypeptide. Parenthetically, this point of view is not shared by Holland & Stead (93) who observed hour-to-hour variations in urine volume independent of the osmotic status of their subjects and stated that "during ordinary activity the secretion of antidiuretic hormone is influenced more by reflex than by osmotic stimuli."

The location and central connections of the osmoreceptors are still not entirely clear. Jewell and Verney's classical work (25, 26, 27) places a large component of the system in the hypothalamus; however, the observations of Sawyer and his collaborators (94, 95) of osmoreceptor activity in the olfactory bulb clearly indicate that these receptors are not limited to the hypothalamus. Clemente and his co-workers (96) have evidence for medullary response to changes in plasma osmolarity, and suggest the area postrema as a receptor site.

It should be self evident that under conditions of electrolyte balance the osmoreceptor mechanism serves the function of maintaining fluid volume, since if the total body electrolyte remains constant, changes in osmolarity reflect changes in body water. Thus when the mechanisms for maintaining electrolyte balance function properly, the osmoreceptors work hand-in-hand with the volume receptors. On the other hand, in persistent negative sodium balance (e.g., prolonged sodium deprivation or adrenal insufficiency), the osmoreceptor mechanism fails to function as a protective device for blood volume, but sacrifices volume for osmolarity. In the crisis of critically reduced volume, the volume receptor mechanism is prepotent and induces ADH secretion despite the resultant dilution of plasma electrolyte (45).

In summary, then, on the basis of the information available at this time, it appears likely that the volume aspect of ADH regulation is by a mechanism comparable to that for arterial pressure control, i.e., (a) the secretion of ADH is tonically stimulated by reticular formation activity just as is vasomotor sympathetic activity, and (b) the effect of vascular reflexes on ADH output is by virtue of inhibition either of the medullary-pontine reticular formation via internuncials arising in the nucleus solitarius or by ascending relays to the hypothalamus.

Aldosterone and Blood Volume

No one believes that the adrenal is the only resource available to the organism in its efforts to achieve sodium balance. Certainly survival is possible in some species in the absence of the adrenal, if sufficient sodium is available in the diet. Further, the kidney is able to alter sodium handling in response to such purely physical factors as renal plasma flow (97). However, only the rare renocentric[5] would deny the importance of the adrenals, particularly in mediating the fine adjustments required for modern mammalian life.

Aldosterone doubtless plays the dominant role in the adrenal participation in sodium balance; indeed, it appears to be the principal steroid secretory product in more primitive life forms, for example, in amphibians (98).

The development of our present concepts of aldosterone regulation unfolds an almost startling parallelism with those for ADH control. The earliest discovered and still best-documented stimulus to aldosterone secretion is alteration of electrolyte intake (99 to 105). Deane & Greep (99, 100) expressed the belief that the ratio of dietary sodium to potassium was the critical determinant of the adrenal output of electrolyte active steroids. However, it soon became evident that changes in the extracellular fluid volume or circulating blood volume are important regulators of aldosterone secretion, regardless of sodium balance per se. Expansion of the extracellular fluid compartment in a large variety of experimental situations leads to reduction in the aldosterone secretory rate, either as determined directly or as reflected in urinary electrolyte levels; conversely, contraction of the extracellular fluid results in elevated output of the steroid (106 to 120). Acute or chronic hemorrhage was also found to be a profound stimulus to aldosterone secretion (121, 122). Thus, it is clear that volume receptors are concerned in aldosterone regulation, just as they are in ADH control.

The question of the locus of the receptors has attracted considerable attention. In retrospect, it is not entirely surprising that such receptors were found in the carotid arteries and in the atria. Occlusion of the common carotid induces an immediate marked elevation of secretion of the steroid (123) and sodium retention (124). The response is prevented by prior denervation of the thyrocarotid junction (123). Carotid denervation leads to elevated aldosterone secretion rates (125). Distention of the right atrium prevents the expected rise in aldosterone output in response to hemorrhage (120, 126, 127).

[5] This term is introduced to describe those physiologists to whom the kidney is the hub of the biological universe.

The analogy to the ADH mechanism is apparent, with minor differences. Thus, the right atrium may be more important than the left for aldosterone; the left atrium appears to be dominant for the ADH system. The carotid pressoreceptors for aldosterone control are apparently concentrated in the region of the thyrocarotid junction (123) rather than being dispersed throughout the sinus area as they are for arterial pressure control. When these shades of difference are taken into account, however, the pattern which emerges has a familiar ring; deformation of vascular receptors initiates reflexes which act to inhibit the secretion of the steroid, just as such reflexes act to inhibit vasomotor activity and ADH secretion. Contrariwise, cessation of the flow of inhibitory impulses results in hyperactivity of the system under consideration[6] (128, 129).

The ninth and tenth cranial nerves undoubtedly contain the afferent limbs of these reflexes (67, 125, 127, 132). Vagotomy has not, however, always yielded the anticipated results. Very high or very low aldosterone values are seen in some experiments following acute vagotomy (133). Careful vagal cooling usually depresses the output of the steroid (134), which suggests that the intact vagus supports the activity of the system. By contrast, Mills and his co-workers found that the return of aldosterone secretion to normal following release of caval constriction does not occur in the vagotomized preparation (135, 136), and Baisset and his collaborators (127) reported that vagotomy blocks the atrial stretch phenomenon. The latter observations support the concept that the principal role of the vagus is to conduct inhibitory influences. The probable solution to this apparent dilemma, which seems to arise whenever one attempts to unravel the physiology of this nerve, is that the visceral afferent impulse traffic carried in the vagus supports reticular formation activity as part of the tonic effect of afferent inflow in general. Against this background of steady-state stimulation, the specialized reflexes can exercise inhibition as dictated by the level of operation of the particular physiological process whose function they test.

The manner in which vascular reflexes bring about specific changes in

---

[6] The concept of baroreceptor participation in aldosterone control has been challenged by one group of workers (130). There appears to be an error in experimental logic in some of this latter work, however. Thus, in two out of three experiments in which the inferior vena cava was chronically constricted following carotid denervation, the aldosterone secretion rates were markedly elevated—to levels 200 to 300 per cent higher than in animals subjected to vena cava constriction alone (Table II of that manuscript). This is precisely what would be anticipated if the carotid receptors are the source of inhibitory impulses, and confirms in general the observations of Gann & Bartter that carotid denervation leads to elevated aldosterone output. Carpenter et al. unaccountably interpret the data as denying the importance of the baroreceptors. In another set of experiments, these workers failed to obtain increased aldosterone output after carotid constriction in intact animals, which seems rather odd since we have been able to confirm Gann & Bartter's observations on this point with no difficulty whatsoever (131).

aldosterone secretion is not as yet entirely clear, although there is sufficient experimental evidence to warrant the formulation of a working hypothesis. Aldosterone secretion is known to be subject to stimulation by ACTH, as part of the general action of this hormone on the adrenal (133, 137, 138), and a complete discussion of the factors which regulate aldosterone output must necessarily take into account the role of the pituitary. For the present, however, we should like to limit consideration to those aspects of the problem which have to do with selective changes in the output of aldosterone, excluding the other steroids.

There seemed little doubt that a humoral factor specific for aldosterone secretion existed, and indirect evidence for such a hormone arising in the diencephalon was presented by our group some years ago (139). Bioassay of extracts of diencephalic tissue revealed the presence of the factor, and subsequent studies established that it could be obtained from epiphyseal tissue (133, 140, 141). The preparation of a highly potent fraction was described (142, 143). In addition to inducing marked increases in aldosterone secretion in the hypophysectomized decerebrate dog, the hormone brings about lipid deposition in the zona glomerulosa as well as widening of the subglomerulosa (sudanophobic) zone in the adrenal of the hypophysectomized rat.[7] The name "adrenoglomerulotropin" has been used to designate the factor. Recent studies have demonstrated that the structure of the hormone is very probably 6-methoxy-1-methyl-1,2,3,4-tetrahydro-2-carboline (145), an indole structurally related to melatonin (146). The synthetic compound is very potent, inducing maximal selective stimulation of aldosterone secretion in submicrogram doses (145).

Failure to find adrenoglomerulotropic activity in an extract of pineal tissue has been reported (147). The significance of the latter study is tempered somewhat by the fact that the extract was not prepared according to the methods reported to yield such activity.

Three laboratories, working independently, have since confirmed the existence of adrenoglomerulotropin. Lucis, Dyrenfurth & Venning (148) found stimulation of aldosterone synthesis *in vitro* by a freshly prepared saline extract of hog diencephalon including the pineal gland. They also reported that a commercial pineal preparation was inactive. Kovacs, David & Weisz (149), using acetone extracts of human pineal tissue, demonstrated stimulation of aldosterone output in rat adrenals *in vitro*. The observations of Keller, Piotti & Romani (150) are of particular interest. These workers found a selective action of adrenoglomerulotropin on the carboxylic acid esterase activity of the zona glomerulosa of the rat adrenal, and by the use of this assay method they purified the hormone to such an extent that they were able to assign it a "structure similar to that of melatonin". The findings of this group

---

[7] On examination of the figure that is submitted in evidence on this point, in discussion of a paper by Davis (144), the reader will recognize that the illustration was printed upside down, so that the legends are reversed.

are in remarkably close agreement with our own. It is to be anticipated that the present minor differences in opinion as to structure will shortly be resolved.

The unequivocal demonstration of a diencephalic hormone specific for aldosterone secretion strongly suggests that the role of the central nervous system in aldosterone regulation is by virtue of alterations in the rate of elaboration of that hormone. The most plausible theory, first voiced by Bartter, Mills & Gann (128, 129), is that this substance is secreted under the influence of tonic stimulation and that the vascular reflexes act by inhibition of its secretory rate. This suggested reflex pattern is analogous to the pressoreceptor-vasomotor and ADH-regulating mechanisms discussed above.

At this point in the development of the problem it is difficult to speculate as to the central connections which mediate this phenomenon. First of all, no one is quite sure exactly where adrenoglomerulotropin is elaborated. Its presence in the pineal gland would indicate that it is secreted by this gland; glomerulotropic activity is present in the vein of Galen which drains the pineal area (143). Depletion of pineal lipid as a consequence of sodium restriction is additional evidence for participation of this structure (151). Acute pinealectomy reduces aldosterone secretion. However, the effect is lost within a week after the operation, and it would seem that the hormone must arise elsewhere in the brainstem (143).

We may be confronted with the same kinds of problems which faced Fisher, Ingram, and Ranson in the early days of research on the supraoptic-paraventricular-neurohypophyseal relationship when it was found that removal of the pars nervosa by itself does not result in permanent diabetes insipidus. Sufficient ADH is apparently elaborated and absorbed within the hypothalamus to maintain water balance (152). However, more extensive surgery resulting in degeneration of the cells in the hypothalamic nuclei which are now known to be the site of ADH synthesis gave the anticipated result. Perhaps in the instance of adrenoglomerulotropin, also, it may be necessary to seek out diencephalic nuclei which are the actual site of synthesis of the hormone.

Despite the lack of information as to the site of elaboration of adrenoglomerulotropin, there are clues to the central pathways subserving its control. Bilateral lesions adjacent to the cerebral aqueduct in the rostral midbrain [in almost exactly the same region implicated in ADH regulation by Sharpless & Rothballer (78)] markedly reduce aldosterone secretion (153, 154). Fibers subserving the control of both water and electrolyte metabolism apparently course through this ancient part of the brainstem. Conversely, lesions in other areas (caudal midbrain tegmentum and the habenular region) lead to selective increases in the secretory rate of the steroid, as though inhibition were removed (153, 154). It is of interest in this connection that destruction of the habenulopineal area induces a highly significant elevation in cortisol output, presumably as a result of increased ACTH release. This phenomenon may obscure the specific effects on aldosterone secretion of discrete lesions ventral to this region if pineal damage occurs in the production of such lesions (154).

Taken as a whole, the above experiments suggest that adrenoglomerulotropin is elaborated, at a level somewhere between maximal and minimal, under the influence of tonic excitation on the one hand and inhibition on the other. It is quite possible that sources of both steady-state and phasic inhibition exist. Steady-state inhibition of cerebral origin must certainly be considered. This has been demonstrated in the instance of ACTH secretion; decortication leads to hypercorticism (90). Mason (155) has demonstrated that destruction of elements of the hippocampal circuit leads to a state of hyperreactivity of the pituitary adrenal axis. As mentioned above, descending inhibition is also thought to explain the increased ADH output following anesthetics (84). Not to be forgotten are the observations that psychic influences can alter the secretion of ADH and aldosterone quite independently of the fluid or electrolyte status of the individual at the time (156, 157, 158).

Whatever the role of descending inhibition in aldosterone secretion, it appears clear that ascending phasic inhibition arising in vascular receptors constitutes an important part of the regulatory system and may be the most important "volume receptor" control mechanism.

Possible electrolyte receptors.—Although many workers are inclined to view the changes in aldosterone secretion which accompany alterations in electrolyte intake as being mediated solely by changes in the volume of the extracellular fluid, there is some reason to believe that this is not the case. Luetscher and his co-workers (159) observed some years ago that hyponatremia stimulates aldosterone secretion even though the volume of the extracellular fluid was carefully maintained. More recently it has been found that the intracarotid infusion of potassium stimulates aldosterone secretion, whereas infusion into a peripheral vessel is without effect. The phenomenon was not prevented by carotid denervation; thus carotid body chemoreceptors were excluded as the responsible structures (160). These observations provide evidence for an intracranial electrolyte receptor. The nature of the specific stimulus for such receptors is quite unknown, as is their location within the cranial cavity. It is to be hoped that additional research will soon be forthcoming on this most interesting aspect of the problem.

Role of the kidney in aldosterone regulation.—If the kidney does not have a brain of its own, as some might conclude from the apparently intelligent activity of the organ (161), it certainly has a mind of its own. Under certain conditions this organ can carry out many of the functions normally regarded as the province of the vegetative nervous system. Some may have forgotten that the distal tubule can concentrate urine (granted, to a limited extent) during water deprivation even in the total absence of ADH (152, 162, 163). Certainly the reduction of urine formation *per se* in circulatory failure tends to maintain plasma volume (164, 165). It is a common belief that the renin-angiotensin system can serve to supplement the vasomotor mechanism in shock (166, 167). However, it comes as a surprise that the kidney can also substitute for the pituitary. Angiotensin has steroidogenic properties in man and dog (168 to 174) though, curiously enough, not in the rat (175).[8]

It has been suggested by some workers that aldosterone secretion is normally controlled by the renin-angiotensin system rather than by the neuroendocrine relationship described above, a proposition which the present authors frankly consider somewhat remote. In support of this concept it was claimed that the decapitate dog responds to hemorrhage with increased aldosterone secretion (therefore, the responsible hormone is of extracranial origin) and that the response is prevented by nephrectomy (therefore, the hormone must come from the kidney) (171, 174). These experiments are singularly unconvincing because of the lack of adequate controls. For example, in one study the head was cut off, following which an adrenal venous blood sample was taken for steroid analysis; the bleeding was done, and an hour later a second blood sample collected for steroids. The second blood sample frequently contained more aldosterone than the first, though never very much as compared with what would be expected in an intact animal; and a "response" to bleeding was therefore recorded. The "response" was highly variable, and completely absent in certain cases. Further, the necessary controls, an equal or adequate number of decapitate dogs followed sequentially under similar conditions but without bleeding, were limited to three cases of which the actual data on only one is available. In one of the other two, "corticosterone output increased slightly" (171). One wonders whether the results of the entire study may have represented random fluctuations in steroidogenesis related to the physiological status of the animal (level of oxygenation, body temperature, administration of supportive therapy, etc.) following removal of the head, rather than to any specific response to hemorrhage. Our intransigence on this point is related to the fact that in many hundreds of assay experiments in our laboratory in which decerebrate dogs with brain removed have been bled (sometimes to death) we have found no convincing response to hemorrhage (144).

The experiments which purport to demonstrate that nephrectomy prevents the increase in aldosterone secretion consequent to hemorrhage (indicating that the kidneys are the normal source of the responsible hormone) are similarly inadequate. In the first place, the effects of nephrectomy

---

[8] The latter observation would seem to be in disagreement with the earlier findings of Deane & Masson (176) that renin induces zona glomerulosa widening in the rat. However, Deane & Masson's experiments were carried out in intact animals, and marked zona fasciculata hypertrophy indicative of pituitary stimulation was also noted, a result which raises serious question as to specificity of the response. That renin stimulates ACTH release in the rat has also been demonstrated by Sevy & Ohler (177), who found that administration of the enzyme induces ascorbic acid depletion in the intact but not in the hypophysectomized rat. Heat-inactivated renin was inert in these experiments, and the effect was blocked by antirenin; thus a nonspecific action of the renin preparation was apparently ruled out.

should be entirely reproducible, since removal of the kidneys is such a straightforward surgical procedure. In point of fact, however, every reported experiment of this type includes a few dogs with neither pituitary nor kidneys who respond to hemorrhage, sometimes reaching aldosterone secretion levels as high as those reported for control animals with kidneys intact (171, 174, 178). Secondly, the logical control experiments were not done; i.e., demonstration that the level of responsiveness of the animals to known steroidogenic agents remained the same after nephrectomy. An alternate interpretation of the data is that the adrenal sensitivity (to whatever agent induced the response to hemorrhage in the control animal) was reduced by nephrectomy, the kidneys acting in a permissive role. This possibility has received considerable support from recent experiments concerning the effects of nephrectomy on the 17-hydroxycorticoid secretion rates following burn stress or inferior vena cava constriction. The nephrectomized animal fails to demonstrate the increase in corticoid secretion rates which occurs in the intact animal in these experimental situations (179, 180). The defect is almost certainly not caused by failure of such animals to secrete ACTH, or by the absence of a kidney hormone. Rather, blockade of steroidogenesis occurs at the adrenal level, since the response to exogenous ACTH was found to be markedly impaired in the nephrectomized dogs (180). A possible explanation is the accumulation of toxic metabolites; adrenal sensitivity to ACTH is known to be reduced in cirrhosis and severe hypertension (181, 182).

Thus, the studies which would give the kidney a causal role in the physiological regulation of aldosterone secretion are superficially convincing, but on closer inspection the experimental data and their interpretation leave much to be desired.

On the other hand, there seems little doubt that angiotensin, if given in sufficiently high doses, is a steroidogenic agent. Parenthetically, ADH is also (183 to 186), but to extrapolate to a necessary role for either hormone in the physiological control of adrenal function is another matter. The critical question is: does stimulation of steroidogenesis occur at levels of the polypeptide which are normally found in the blood? Data on blood levels of angiotensin are meager. However, in 1959 Skeggs (187) carried out a series of experiments in which angiotensin was injected into nephrectomized dogs and the resultant blood levels determined by direct analysis. The control values before infusion were 0.02 to 0.05 Goldblatt units per liter (0.0084 to 0.021 μg per liter). Following the infusion of 0.46 units of angiotensin (0.193 μg) per minute, the blood level was 0.16 units (0.067 μg) per liter, 3 to 8 times the control values and well within the range found in dogs with experimental malignant (renal) hypertension (187). The arterial pressure was markedly elevated, as would be expected.

In a recent study, Ganong and his co-workers (188) also infused angiotensin in graded doses into nephrectomized dogs and determined the resultant steroid secretion rates. At an infusion rate (0.167 μg per min) comparable to that used by Skeggs, only a slight increase in aldosterone secretion was observed, to about one-fifth that achieved in the same study with a maximal dose of ACTH (188). At doses $2\frac{1}{2}$ and 10 times as high, the aldosterone secretion rate approached 40 per cent of that obtained with ACTH. Although accurate estimation of the blood levels of the polypeptide achieved with these higher doses is not possible, it is evident that they would be observed only in severe malignant renal hypertension (187). From these data, one would predict that blood levels which are quite sufficient to induce hypertension might at the same time be inadequate to bring about increased steroidogenesis. This indeed appears to be the case: neither experimental nor clinical renal hypertension is uniformly accompanied by increased secretion of either aldosterone or cortisol (189 to 193). These rather simple reflections raise some serious question as to whether this polypeptide plays any role in the normal regulation of adrenal function. That an occasional patient with severe hypertension may owe his elevated steroid secretion rate in part to high levels of angiotensin remains, of course, a possibility.

Hume has suggested that the central nervous system control of aldosterone secretion depends on an action (neural or humoral) of the brainstem on the kidney which induces alterations in renin release. The resultant angiotensin is supposed to stimulate the zona glomerulosa to secrete aldosterone (194). This rather delightful scientific *deus ex machina* seems to resolve at once all the differences in opinion, but appears rather unlikely in view of the lack of evidence for brainstem control of renin secretion and the dubious significance of the angiotensin-aldosterone scheme.

Integration of Vascular Reflexes for Arterial Pressure and Volume

The authors have no desire to oversimplify a complicated subject or to extend a theory far beyond the limits afforded by the experimental evidence. Nevertheless, it is sometimes useful during the development of a field of study to propose a way of thinking about a problem which, even if it subsequently proves incorrect in whole or in part, at least provides a point of departure for further study. In this light, we should like to suggest that the presently available evidence indicates the following.

(*a*) The driving force which maintains a state of tonic nondiscriminatory stimulation of vasomotor activity, ADH secretion, and aldosterone output is the brainstem reticular formation. Against this background of tonic stimulation, the vascular reflexes in turn exercise inhibition. The resultant level of activity in each system is thus maintained in a nicely adjusted balance capable of change in either direction as dictated by the adequacy of the circulation.

(*b*) The receptors which form the afferent limb of reflexes subserving the responses of the vasomotor system, the posterior pituitary system, and the aldosterone-regulating system are fundamentally similar, i.e., vascular proprioceptors. The carotid baroreceptors apparently serve in this capacity for all three systems. On the other hand, the low-pressure atrial receptors, modified to the special physical circumstances of reduced venous return, primarily affect aldosterone and ADH secretion.

(c) In response to contraction of the circulating blood volume, the organism institutes remedial processes of both immediate and long-term nature. In addition to the well-known responses of the vasomotor components of the sympathetic nervous system, increased ADH and aldosterone secretion occur. The latter are aimed at restoring blood volume, though protein synthesis and erythropoiesis obviously are necessary to complete the reparative process if their loss was part of the original problem.

ADDENDUM: Since the preparation of this manuscript it has come to our attention that Krieger, Saito & Krieger (*Lancet*, p. 567, September 9, 1961) have reported two patients with pretectal tumors in the area implicated in aldosterone regulation by Newman *et al.* (153). Urinary aldosterone was low in both cases: one failed to show the expected response to sodium deprivation.

LITERATURE CITED

1. Ravdin, I. S., Walker, J. M., and Rhoads, J. E., *Ann. Rev. Physiol.*, **15**, 165 (1953)
2. Brown, E., Hopper, J., Jr., and Wennesland, R., *Ann. Rev. Physiol.*, **19**, 231 (1957)
3. Reeve, E. B., Allen, T. H., and Roberts, J. E., *Ann. Rev. Physiol.*, **22**, 349 (1960)
4. Gregersen, M. I., *Ann. Rev. Physiol.*, **13**, 397 (1951)
5. Gregersen, M. I., and Rawson, R. H., *Physiol. Revs.*, **39**, 307 (1959)
6. Monnier, M., *Arch. intern. physiol.*, **49**, 455 (1939)
7. Wang, S. C., and Ranson, S. W., *J. Comp. Neurol.*, **71**, 437 (1939)
8. Alexander, R. S., *J. Neurophysiol.*, **9**, 205 (1946)
9. Bach, L. M. N., *Am. J. Physiol.*, **171**, 417 (1952)
10. Wang, S. C., and Ranson, S. W., *J. Comp. Neurol.*, **71**, 457 (1939)
11. Uvnäs, B., *Neurophysiology*, Sect. 1, 1131 (Am. Physiol. Soc., Washington, D. C., 1960)
12. French, J. D., *Neurophysiology*, Sect. 1, 1281 (Am. Physiol. Soc., Washington, D. C., 1960)
13. Moruzzi, G., and Magoun, H. W., *Electroencephal. and Clin. Neurophysiol.*, **1**, 455 (1949)
14. Magoun, H. W. *Physiol. Revs.*, **30**, 459 (1950)
15. Aviado, D. M., and Schmidt, C. F., *Physiol. Revs.*, **35**, 247 (1955)
16. Heymans, C., and Neil E., *Reflexogenic Areas of the Cardiovascular System* (Churchill, London, 1958)
17. Schreiner, L. H., Lindsley, D. B., and Magoun, H. W., *J. Neurophysiol.*, **12**, 207 (1949)
18. Breckenridge, C. G., Hoff, H. E., and Smith, H. T., *Am. J. Physiol.*, **162**, 74 (1950)
19. Lim, R. K. S., Wang, S. C., and Yi, C. L., *Chinese J. Physiol.*, **13**, 61 (1938)
20. Scharrer, E., and Scharrer, B., *Handbuch mikroskop. Anat. Menschen*, **6**, 953 (Springer-Verlag, Berlin, 1954)
21. Rothballer, A. B., *Excerpta Med.*, Sect. III, **11**, iii (1957)
22. Brown, G. L., *CIBA Foundation Symposium: Adrenergic Mechanisms*, 116 (1960)
23. Welt, L. G., *Clinical Disorders of Hydration and Acid Base Equilibration*, 81 (Little, Brown & Co., Boston, 262 pp., 1955)
24. Chambers, G. H., Melville, E. V., Hare, R. S., and Hare, K., *Am. J. Physiol.*, **144**, 311 (1945)
25. Verney, E. B., *Proc. Roy. Soc. (London), B*, **135**, 25 (1947)
26. Jewell, P. A., *J. Physiol. (London)*, **121**, 167 (1953)
27. Jewell, P. A., and Verney, E. B., *Phil. Trans. Roy. Soc. London*, **240**, 197 (1957)
28. Rydin, H., and Verney, E. B., *Quart. J. Exptl. Physiol.*, **27**, 343 (1938)
29. Ginsburg, M., and Heller, H., *J. Endocrinol.*, **9**, 274 (1953)
30. Ginsburg, M., *J. Endocrinol.*, **11**, 165 (1954)
31. Asmussen, E., Christensen, E. H., and Nielsen, M., *Scand. Arch. Physiol.*, **81**, 214 (1939)
32. Brun, C., Knudsen, E. O. E., and Raaschou, F., *J. Clin. Invest.*, **25**, 568 (1946)
33. Lewis, J. M., Jr., Buie, R. M., Sevier, S. M., and Harrisson, T. R., *Circulation*, **2**, 822 (1950)
34. Epstein, F. H., Goodyer, A. V. N., Lawrason, F. D., and Relman, A. S., *J. Clin. Invest.*, **30**, 63 (1951)
35. Viar, W. N., Oliver, B. B., Eisenberg, S., Lambardo, T. A., Willis, K., and Harrisson, T. R., *Circulation*, **3**, 105 (1951)
36. Newman, E. V., *New Engl. J. Med.*, **250**, 347 (1954)
37. Pearce, M. L., and Newman, E. V., *J. Clin. Invest.*, **33**, 1089 (1954)
38. Farber, S. J., Becker, W. H., and Eichna, L. W., *J. Clin. Invest.*, **32**, 1145 (1953)
39. Wilkins, R. W., Tinsley, C. M., Culbertson, J. W., Burrows, B. A., Judson, W. E., and Burnett, C. H., *J. Clin. Invest.*, **32**, 1101 (1953)
40. Blomhert, G., Molhuysen, J. H., Gerbrandy, J., de Vries, L. A., and Borst, J. G. G., *Lancet*, **II**, 1011 (1951)
41. Murphy, R. J. F., and Stead, E. H., Jr., *J. Clin. Invest.*, **30**, 1055 (1951)
42. Orloff, J., and Blake, W. D., *Am. J. Physiol.*, **164**, 167 (1951)
43. Strauss, M. B., Davis, R. K., Rosenbaum, J. D., and Rossmeisl, E. C., *J. Clin. Invest.*, **30**, 862 (1951)
44. Welt, L. G., and Orloff, J., *J. Clin. Invest.*, **30**, 751 (1951)
45. Leaf, A., and Mamby, A. R., *J. Clin. Invest.*, **31**, 60 (1952)
46. Petersdorf, R. G., and Welt, L. G., *J. Clin. Invest.*, **32**, 283 (1953)

47. Epstein, F. H., *Yale J. Biol. and Med.*, 29, 282 (1956)
48. Smith, H. C., *Am. J. Med.*, 23, 623 (1957)
49. Welt, L. G., *Circulation*, 21, 1002 (1960)
50. Gilbert, G. J., and Glaser, G. H., *Arch. Neurol.*, 5, 179 (1961)
51. Surtshin, A., and White, H. L., *J. Clin. Invest.*, 35, 267 (1956)
52. Baratz, A. H., and Ingraham, R. C., *Am. J. Physiol.*, 198, 565 (1960)
53. Weinstein, H., Berne, R. M., and Sachs, H., *Endocrinology*, 66, 712 (1960)
54. Share, L., *Endocrinology*, 69, 925 (1961)
55. Peters, J. P., *Body Water, The Exchange of Fluids in Man*, 288 (Charles C Thomas, Springfield, Ill., 1935)
56. Epstein, F. H., Post, R. S., and McDowell, M., *J. Clin. Invest.*, 32, 233 (1953)
57. Brun, C., Knudsen, E. O. E., and Raaschou, F., *Acta Med. Scand.*, 122, 486 (1945)
58. Noble, R. L., and Taylor, N. B. G., *J. Physiol. (London)*, 122, 220 (1953)
59. Andersson, B., and Larsen, S., *Acta Physiol. Scand.*, 32, 19 (1954)
60. Ginsburg, M., and Brown, L. M., "The Neurohypophysis," *Proc. Symposium Colston Research Soc.*, 8th, 1956, 109 (1957)
61. Share, L., and Levy, M. N., *The Physiologist*, 4, 107 (1961)
62. Gauer, O. H., Henry, J. P., and Sieker, H. O., *Circulation Research*, 4, 79 (1956)
63. Henry, J. P., and Pearce, J. W., *J. Physiol. (London)*, 131, 572 (1956)
64. Henry, J. P., Gauer, O. H., and Reeves, J. L., *Circulation Research*, 4, 85 (1956)
65. Henry, J. P., Gauer, O. H., and Sieker, H. O., *Circulation Research*, 4, 91 (1956)
66. Atkins, E. L., and Pearce, J. W., *Can. J. Biochem. and Physiol.*, 37, 91 (1959)
67. Paintal, A. S., *J. Physiol. (London)*, 120, 596 (1953)
68. Zanchetti, A., Wang, S. C., and Moruzzi, G., *Electroencephal. and Clin. Neurophysiol.*, 4, 357 (1952)
69. Heymans, C. and Bouckaert, J. J., *Presse méd.*, 41, 729 (1933)
70. Dell, P., and Olson, R., *Compt. rend. soc. biol.*, 145, 1088 (1951)
71. Bronk, D. W., Lewy, F. H., and Larrabee, M. G., *Am. J. Physiol.*, 116, 15 (1936)
72. Starzl, T. E., Taylor, C. W., and Magoun, H. W., *J. Neurophysiol.*, 41, 461 (1951)
73. Guillery, R. W., *J. Anat.*, 91, 91 (1957)
74. Nauta, W. J. H., *Brain*, 81, 319 (1958)
75. Nauta, W. J. H., and Kuypers, H. G. J. M., *Henry Ford Intern. Symposium: Reticular Formation of the Brain*, 3 (1958)
76. Anderson, E., Bates, R. W., Hawthorne, E., Haymaker, W., Knowlton, K., Rioch, D. M., Spence, W. T., and Wilson, H., *Recent Progr. in Hormone Research*, 13, 21 (1957)
77. Mehler, W. R., Feferman, M. E., and Nauta, W. J. H., *Anat. Record*, 124, 332 (1956)
78. Sharpless, S. K., and Rothballer, A. B., *Am. J. Physiol.*, 200, 909 (1961)
79. Gilbert, G. J., *Anat. Record*, 126, 253 (1956)
80. Chang, H. C., Chia, K. F., Hsu, C. K., and Lim, R. K. S., *J. Physiol. (London)*, 90, 87P (1937)
81. Chang, H. C., Chia, K. F., Huang, J. J. and Lim, R. K. S., *Chinese J. Physiol.*, 14, 161 (1939)
82. Sattler, D. G., *Proc. Soc. Exptl. Biol. Med.*, 44, 82 (1940)
83. Andersson, B. *Acta Physiol. Scand.*, 23, 24 (1951)
84. Walker, J. M., "The Neurohypophysis," *Proc. Symposium Colston Research Soc.*, 8th, 1956, 221 (1957)
85. Barraclough, C. A., and Sawyer, C. H., *Endocrinology*, 57, 329 (1955)
86. Sawyer, C. H., *Physiological Triggers and Discontinuous Rate Processes*, 164 (Bullock, T. H., Ed., Am. Physiol. Soc., Washington, D. C., 1957)
87. Harris, G. W., *Henry Ford Intern. Symposium: Reticular Formation of the Brain*, 207 (1958)
88. Sawyer, C. H., *Henry Ford Intern. Symposium: Reticular Formation of the Brain*, 223 (1958)
89. Sayers, G., Redgate, E. S., and Royce, P. C., *Ann. Rev. Physiol.*, 20, 243 (1958)
90. Egdahl, R. H., *Endocrinology*, 68, 574 (1961)
91. Slusher, M. A., and Critchlow, V., *Proc. Soc. Exptl. Biol. Med.*, 101, 497 (1959)
92. Slusher M. A., and Hyde, J. E., *Endocrinology*, 68, 773 (1961)

93. Holland, B. C., and Stead, E. A., *Arch. Internal Med.* **88**,, 571 (1951)
94. Holland, R. C., Cross, B. A., and Sawyer, C. H., *Am. J. Physiol.*, **196**, 796 (1959)
95. Sundsten, J. W., and Sawyer, C. H., *Proc. Soc. Exptl. Biol. Med.*, **101**, 524 (1959)
96. Clemente, C. D., Sutin, J., and Silverstone, J. T., *Am. J. Physiol.*, **188**, 193 (1957)
97. Selkurt, E. E., *Ann. Rev. Physiol.*, **21**, 117 (1959)
98. Carstensen, H., Burgers, A. C. J., and Li, C. H., *Gen. and Comp. Endocrinol.*, **1**, 37 (1961)
99. Deane, H. W., and Greep, R. O., *Am. J. Anat.*, **79**, 117 (1946)
100. Deane, H. W., Shaw, J. H., and Greep, R. O., *Endocrinology*, **43**, 133 (1948)
101. Axelrad, B. J., and Luetscher, J. A., Jr., *J. Clin. Invest.*, **33**, 916 (1954)
102. Axelrad, B. J., Johnson, B. B., and Luetscher, J. A., Jr., *J. Clin. Endocrinol.*, **14**, 783 (1954)
103. Singer, B., and Stack-Dunne, M. P., *J. Endocrinol.*, **12**, 130 (1955)
104. Rosnagle, R. S., and Farrell, G. L., *Am. J. Physiol.*, **187**, 7 (1956)
105. Luetscher, J. A., Jr., *Recent Progr. in Hormone Research*, **12**, 175 (1956)
106. Leaf, A., Bartter, F. C., Santos, R. F., and Wrong, O., *J. Clin. Invest.*, **32**, 868 (1953)
107. Weston, R. E., Hanenson, I. B., Grossman, J., Berdasco, G. A., and Wolfman, M., *J. Clin. Invest.*, **32**, 611 (1953)
108. Beck, J. C., Giroud, C. J. P., Dyrenfurth, I., and Venning, E. H., *Can. J. Biochem. and Physiol.*, **33**, 884 (1955)
109. Beck, J. C., Dyrenfurth, I., Giroud, C. J. P., and Venning, E. H., *Arch. Internal Med.*, **96**, 463 (1955)
110. Falbriard, A., Muller, A. F., Crabbé, J., and Duckert-Maultsbech, A., *Helv. Med. Acta*, **22**, 495 (1955)
111. Liddle, G. W., Bartter, F. C., Duncan, L. E., Jr., Barber, J. K., and Delea, C., *J. Clin. Invest.*, **34**, 949 (1955)
112. Streeten, D. H. P., Conn, J. W., Louis, L. H., Fajans, S. S., Seltzer, H. S., Johnson, R. D., Gittler, R. D., and Dube, A. H., *J. Lab. Clin. Med.*, **46**, 957 (1955)
113. Bartter, F. C., *Metabolism, Clin. and Exptl.*, **5**, 369 (1956)
114. Bartter, F. C., Liddle, G. W., Duncan, L. E., Jr., Barber, J. K., and Delea, C., *J. Clin. Invest.*, **35**, 1306 (1956)
115. Duncan, L. E., Jr., Liddle, G. W., and Bartter, F. C., *J. Clin. Invest.*, **35**, 1299 (1956)
116. Muller, A. F., Riondel, A. M., and Mach, R. S., *Lancet*, **I**, 831 (1956)
117. Muller, A. F., Riondel, A. M., and Manning, E. L., *Helv. Med. Acta*, **23**, 610 (1956)
118. Venning, E. H., Dyrenfurth, I., and Giroud, C. J. P., *J. Clin. Endocrinol.*, **16**, 1329 (1956)
119. Venning, E. H., Dyrenfurth, I., Giroud, C. J. P., and Beck, J. C., *Can. Med. Assoc. J.*, **77**, 773 (1957)
120. Bartter, F. C., *Recent Progr. in Hormone Research*, **15**, 305 (1959)
121. Farrell, G. L., Rosnagle, R. S., and Rauschkolb, E. W., *Circulation Research*, **4**, 606 (1956)
122. Goodkind, M. J., Ball, W. C., and Davis, J. O., *Am. J. Physiol.*, **189**, 181 (1957)
123. Bartter, F. C., Mills, I. H., and Gann, D. S., *J. Clin. Invest.*, **39**, 1330 (1960)
124. Barger, A. C., Muldowney, F. P., and Liebowitz, M. R., *Circulation*, **20**, 273 (1959)
125. Gann, D. S., and Bartter, F. C., *Am. J. Physiol.*, **199**, 193 (1960)
126. Anderson, C. H., McCally, M., and Farrell, G. L., *Endocrinology*, **64**, 202 (1959)
127. Baisset, A., Demonte, H., Douste-Blazy, L., and Montastruc, P., *Compt. rend. soc. biol.*, **153**, 1069 (1959)
128. Bartter, F. C., and Gann, D. S., *Circulation*, **21**, 1016 (1960)
129. Gann, D. S., Mills, I. H., and Bartter, F. C., *Federation Proc.*, **19**, 605 (1960)
130. Carpenter, C. C. J., Davis, J. O., and Ayers, C. R., *J. Clin. Invest.*, **40**, 1160 (1961)
131. Anderson, C. H., McCally, M., and Farrell, G. L. (Unpublished observations)
132. Chapman, K. M., and Pearce, J. W., *Nature*, **184**, 1238 (1959)
133. Farrell, G. L., *Recent Progr. in Hormone Research*, **15**, 275 (1959)
134. Anderson, C. H., McCally, M., and Farrell, G. L., *Circulation*, **18**, 688 (1958)
135. Mills, I. H., Casper, A. G. T., and Bartter, F. C., *Science*, **128**, 1140 (1958)
136. Gann, D. S., Mills, I. H., Cruz, J. F., Casper, A. G. T., and Bartter, F. C., *Proc. Soc. Exptl. Biol. Med.*, **105**, 158 (1960)

137. Liddle, G. W., Duncan, L. E., Jr., and Bartter, F. C., *Am. J. Med.* **21**, 380 (1956)

138. Farrell, G., *Physiol. Revs.*, **38**, 709 (1958)

139. Rauschkolb, E. W., and Farrell, G. L., *Endocrinology*, **59**, 526 (1956)

140. Farrell, G. L., *Endocrinology*, **65**, 29 (1959)

141. Farrell, G. L., *Endocrinology*, **65**, 239 (1959)

142. Farrell, G., *Circulation*, **21**, 1009 (1960)

143. Farrell, G. L., *Federation Proc.*, **19**, 601 (1960)

144. Farrell, G. L., *Recent Progr. in Hormone Research*, **17**, 340 (Discussion of paper by Davis, J. O.) (1961)

145. Farrell, G., and McIsaac, W. M., *Arch. Biochem. Biophys.*, **94**, 543 (1961)

146. Lerner, A. B., Case, J. D., and Heinzelman, R. V., *J. Am. Chem. Soc.*, **81**, 6084 (1959)

147. Wurtman, R. J., Altschule, M. D., Greep, R. O., Falk, J. L., and Grave, G., *Am. J. Physiol.*, **199**, 1109 (1960)

148. Lucis, O. J., Dyrenfurth, I., and Venning, E. H., *Can. J. Biochem. and Physiol.*, **39**, 901 (1961)

149. Kovacs, K., David, M. A., and Weisz, P., *Med. Exptl. (Hung.)*, **3**, 113 (1960)

150. Keller, A., Piotti, L. E., and Romani, J. D., *Ann. endocrinol. (Paris)*, **22**, 82 (1961)

151. Panagiotis, N. M., and Hungerford, G. F., *Endocrinology*, **69**, 217 (1961)

152. Fisher, C., Ingram, W. R., and Ranson, S. W., *Diabetes Insipidus and the Neurohormonal Control of Water Balance: A Contribution to the Structure and Function of the Hypothalamico-hypophyseal System* (J. W. Edwards, Ann Arbor, Mich., 1938)

153. Newman, A. E., Redgate, E. S., and Farrell, G. L., *Endocrinology*, **63**, 723 (1958)

154. Taylor, A. N., and Farrell, G., *Endocrinology* (In press)

155. Mason, J. W., *Henry Ford Intern. Symposium: Reticular Formation of the Brain*, 645 (1958)

156. Verney, E. B., *Lancet*, **II**, 739 (1946)

157. Venning, E. H., Dyrenfurth, I., and Beck, J. C., *J. Clin. Endocrinol. and Metabolism*, **17**, 1005 (1957)

158. Lamson, E. T., Elmadjian, F., Hope, J. M., Pincus, G., and Jorjorian, D., *J. Clin. Endocrinol. and Metabolism*, **16**, 954 (1956)

159. Johnson, B. B., Lieberman, A. H., and Mulrow, P. J., *J. Clin. Invest.*, **36**, 757 (1957)

160. Gann, D. S., Cruz, J. F., Casper, A. G. T., and Bartter, F. C., *Abstr., Endocrine Soc., 42nd Meeting*, 14 (Miami, Fla., 1960)

161. Smith, H. W., *From Fish to Philosopher* (Little, Brown & Co., Boston, 1953)

162. White, H. L., and Heinbecker, P., *Am. J. Physiol.*, **123**, 566 (1938)

163. Shannon, J. A., *J. Exptl. Med.*, **76**, 371 (1942)

164. Corcoran, A. C., and Page, I. H., *J. Exptl. Med.*, **78**, 205 (1943)

165. Lauson, H. D., Bradley, S. E., and Cournand, A., *J. Clin. Invest.*, **23**, 381 (1944)

166. Sapirstein, L. A., Jr., Ogden, E., and Southard, F. D., *Proc. Soc. Exptl. Biol. Med.*, **48**, 505 (1941)

167. Huidobro, F., and Braun-Menendez, E., *Am. J. Physiol.*, **137**, 47 (1942)

168. Genest, J., Koiw, E., Nowaczynski, W., and Sandor, T., *Advance Abstr. of Short Communs. Intern. Congr. Endocrinol.*, *1st*, 173 (Fuchs, F., Ed., Periodica, Copenhagen, 1960)

169. Genest, J., Nowaczynski, W., Koiw, E., Sandor, T., and Biron, P., *Essential Hypertension*, 126 (Reubi, F. C., Bock, K. D., and Cottier, P. T., Eds., Springer-Verlag, Berlin, 1960)

170. Laragh, J. H., Angus, M., Kelly, W. G., and Lieberman, S., *J. Am. Med. Assoc.*, **174**, 234 (1960)

171. Davis, J. O., Carpenter, C. C. J., Ayers, C. R., Holman, J. E., and Bahn, R. C., *J. Clin. Invest.*, **40**, 684 (1961)

172. Kaplan, N. M., and Bartter, F. C., *Abstr. Endocrine Soc., 43rd Meeting*, 15 (New York, N. Y., 1961)

173. Mulrow, P. J., and Ganong, W. F., *Yale J. Biol. and Med.*, **33**, 386 (1961)

174. Davis, J. O., *Recent Progr. in Hormone Research*, **17**, 293 (1961)

175. Peterson, R. E. (Personal communication)

176. Deane, H. W., and Masson, G. M. C., *J. Clin. Endocrinol.*, **11**, 193 (1951)

177. Sevy, R. W., and Ohler, E. A., *Am. J. Physiol.*, **174**, 471 (1953)

178. Ganong, W. F., and Mulrow, P. J., *Endocrinology* (In press)

179. Gann, D. S., Kingsbury, B., Drucker, W. R., and Travis, R. H., *Clin. Research*, **9**, 179 (1961)

180. Gann, D. S., Kingsbury, B., Drucker,

W. R., and Travis, R. H., *Proc. Soc. Exptl. Biol. Med.*, **108**, 99 (1961)

181. Samuels, L. T., Brown, H., Eik-Nes, K., Tyler, F. H., and Dominguez, O. V., *CIBA Foundation Colloq. on Endocrinol.: Hormones in Blood*, **II**, 208 (1957)

182. Cooper, D. Y., Touchstone, J. C., Roberts, J. M., Blakemore, W. S., and Rosenthal, O., *J. Clin. Invest.*, **37**, 1524 (1958)

183. Hume, D. M., and Nelson, D. H., *Abstr. Endocrine Soc.*, *39th Meeting*, 98 (New York, N. Y., 1957)

184. Royce, P. C., and Sayers, G., *Proc. Soc. Exptl. Biol. Med.*, **98**, 70 (1958)

185. Hilton, J. G., Scian, L. F., Westermann, C. D., and Kruesi, O. R., *Proc. Soc. Exptl. Biol. Med.*, **100**, 523 (1959)

186. Hilton, J. G., Scian, L. F., Westermann, C. D., Nakano, J., and Kruesi, O. R., *Endocrinology*, **67**, 298 (1960)

187. Skeggs, L. T., Jr., *Intern. Congr. Physiol. Sci.*, *21st*, *Buenos Aires*, *1959*, 1

188. Ganong, W. F., Mulrow, P. J., and Cera, G., *Abstr. Endocrine Soc.*, *43rd Meeting*, 14 (New York, N. Y., 1961)

189. Genest, J., Lemieux, G., Davignon, A., Koiw, E., Nowaczynski, W., and Steyermark, P., *Science*, **123**, 503 (1956)

190. Genest, J., *Can. Med. Assoc. J.*, **77**, 773 (1957)

191. Cottier, P. T., *Essential Hypertension*, 66 (Reubi, F. C., Bock, K. D., and Cottier, P. T., Eds., Springer-Verlag, Berlin, 1960)

192. Laragh, J. H., Ulick, S., Januszewicz, V., Deming, Q. B., Kelly, W. G., and Lieberman, S., *J. Clin. Invest.*, **39**, 1091 (1960)

193. Warter, J., Schwartz, J., and Bloch, R., *Essential Hypertension*, 147 (Reubi, F. C., Bock, K. D., and Cottier, P. T., Eds., Springer-Verlag, Berlin, 1960)

194. Hume, D. M., *Federation Proc.*, **20**, 87 (1961)

COMPARATIVE ENDOCRINOLOGY OF THE INVERTEBRATES[1]

By William G. Van der Kloot

Department of Physiology and Biophysics, New York University School of Mecidine,[2] New York, N. Y.

The years since 1953, when Berta Scharrer (1) reviewed invertebrate endocrinology in this series, saw the vigorous development of the themes then apparent. In addition, new endocrine systems were discovered, several hormones were completely or partially purified, and ambitious attempts were made to find out how some of the hormones act on their target cells. The volume of publication was large and I can discuss only some of the important advances and issues. More detailed discussions will be found in any of the large number of reviews; there are almost as many reviews as major discoveries. The subjects of a few of the reviews include: invertebrate hormones [E. & B. Scharrer (2, 3), Gabe (4), B. Scharrer (5), Scheer (6), Karlson (7, 8), Butenandt (9)]; crustacean endocrinology [Kleinholz (10), Scheer (11), Welsh (12), Knowles & Carlisle (13), Carlisle & Knowles (14), Passano (15, 16)]; and insect endocrinology [Wigglesworth (17, 18, 19), Schneiderman & Gilbert (20), Gilbert & Schneiderman (21), Hinton (22), Joly (23), Lees (24), Bodenstein (25, 26), Pflugfelder (27), Williams (28), Van der Kloot (29, 30, 31)].

There are some disagreements about the best names for the endocrine organs—at one time the crustacean endocrinologists had two distinct "X organs" and two "Y organs" as well. I will use the names which seem best, without further argument, and put some of the alternatives in parentheses.

MOULTING AND GROWTH

Insects

In 1953 it was apparent that the moult of insects is triggered by a hormone synthesized by neurosecretory cells in the brain. The hormone from the brain stimulates the thoracic glands to secrete. The thoracic gland hormone, in turn, acts on the tissues of the body to produce the changes marking the moult. This scheme has been repeatedly confirmed and has received much additional experimental support.

The hormone from the brain.—The hormone which stimulates the thoracic gland is synthesized in neuroendocrine cells in the pars intercerebralis of the brain. The number of neurons which stain like secretory cells varies greatly from species to species; in the *Cecropia* silkmoth there are 26, in locusts

[1] The survey of literature pertaining to this review was concluded in May 1961.

[2] The preparation of this review was assisted by Grant B-1870 from the Institute of Neurological Diseases and Blindness, Public Health Service, and by a grant from the National Science Foundation for travel to the Third International Symposium on Comparative Endocrinology.

there are over 2000 [Highnam (32)]. In some insects there are also lateral groups of neurosecretory cells, which may lie outside of the pars intercerebralis [Williams (33), Cazal (34), Lhoste (35), Nayar (36), Köpf (37)]. Sometimes the lateral cells show a secretory cycle only late in postembryonic life, which suggests that they have a special role to play [Arvy *et al.* (38), Formigoni (39), Kobayashi (40)]. The *Cecropia* pupa needs both lateral and medial cells to release the brain hormone, so either two hormones are involved or two substances combine to form a single hormone [Williams (41), Van der Kloot (30)]. The neurosecretory material is seen in the cell bodies and axons as granules averaging 1500 A in diameter and surrounded by a 70-A-thick limiting membrane [Meyer & Pflugfelder (42), Willey & Chapman (43)]. Nishiitsutsuji-Uwo (44) believes that the secretory granules are formed from mitochondria which are transformed by the action of the Golgi zone. The movement of the secretory granules down the axons was conclusively demonstrated by B. Scharrer (45) and by Thomsen (46), who actually ligatured the axons in a fly and showed that secretory material accumulated on the proximal side of the ligature. Histological evidence suggests that the neurosecretory material is usually released into the blood at the corpora cardiaca, a small organ behind the brain. The corpora cardiaca are made up of the endings of neurosecretory cells and of small intrinsic cells which also show signs of secretion [Willey & Chapman (43)]. Although the corpora cardiaca are usually not essential for the secretion of the brain hormone, it has been assumed that they provide a ready channel for release directly into the main circulatory stream. Therefore, the corpus cardiacum is cited as an example of a neurohemal organ: a structure specialized for the release of neurosecretory material into the blood [Carlisle & Knowles (47)]. On the other hand, the axon endings may actually penetrate into the cytoplasm of the intrinsic cells of the corpora cardiaca and almost touch the nucleus, suggesting that there is a more intimate relationship between the cellular elements than might be assumed [Meyer & Pflugfelder (42)]. The nerve running from the brain to the corpora cardiaca of *Rhodnius* can conduct action potentials [Van der Kloot (30)] and it seems likely that the hormone is released when an action potential invades the axon terminals.

The chemistry of the thoracic gland stimulating hormone is just being explored. L'Hélias (48, 49) believes that the hormone is a derivative of pteroyl glutamic acid, but this idea has received no support. Kobayashi & Kirimura (50) obtained 2 mg of material by extracting 8500 silkworm brains with ether; the injection of 0.1 mg of this material into a brainless pupa led to adult development. This experiment must now be controlled by testing similar extracts of parts of the central nervous system which do not serve as sources of the hormone. Gersch (51) reports that when an unspecified amount of his "neurohormone D_1" was injected into an isolated larval abdomen of the fly *Calliphora*, a "partial pupation" was sometimes obtained. In a "certain" percentage of cases, complete pupation followed the injection of neurohormone D_1 into an isolated abdomen containing an implanted thoracic gland. Neurohormone D_1 is a slightly water-soluble, ether-insoluble extract of the central nervous system or of the blood of the cockroach *Periplaneta;* the extract is purified further by paper chromatography [Gersch & Unger (52), Gersch *et al.* (53)]. Gersch concludes that neurohormone D_1 is a hormone which activates the thoracic glands. Two points must be considered in evaluating these results. First, parts of the central nervous system other than the pars intercerebralis of the brain have never been found to trigger the thoracic gland. Secondly, other physiologically active molecules, in comparatively high concentrations, can trigger endocrine organs. This is a point which appears to have been ignored by a number of invertebrate endocrinologists. To cite one example, Söderberg (54) showed that the release of hormone by the thyroid of the cat is dramatically increased after the injection of only one microgram of acetylcholine. So far there is no conclusive proof that the hormone from the brain has been extracted, and rigid criteria must be met before it can be concluded that an extract capable of stimulating the thoracic glands actually contains brain hormone.

The thoracic glands.—Thoracic glands (prothoracic glands, ventral glands, peritracheal glands) now have been described in many insects, and implantation experiments show that they release the hormone causing moulting. In the most convincing experiments, activated thoracic glands are implanted into surgically isolated pupal abdomens. This preparation is ideal because it contains no known endocrine organs, survives for weeks, and promptly develops into an adult abdomen when the thoracic gland hormone is present. It is more difficult to perform the reverse experiment, removing the thoracic gland without killing the animal. This was accomplished in the locust. The animals deprived of the thoracic gland never moult again (Joly *et al.* (55), Strich-Halbwachs (56)]. Removal of the gland does not stop mitosis in the epidermis. However, Chadwick (57) removed the thoracic glands of the cockroach without interfering with subsequent moults. In some insects the thoracic gland is quite diffuse. It is always possible that thoracic gland cells are present even though they are separated from the major strand of the organ, which would explain Chadwick's results.

Another challenge to the general rule is the report by Ichikawa & Nishiitsutsuji-Uwo (58). They found that some isolated pupal abdomens of *Cynthia* which were implanted with active brains developed into adult abdomens. This suggests that the hormone from the brain of the moth acted on the tissues directly, since the thoracic gland was not present. However, their animals are only prevented from developing by isolating the abdomen at a critical period in the insect's life, and the isolated abdomen probably contains thoracic gland hormone in a titer just below that needed for development. Whatever the explanation for these results may be, they should not be regarded as more than an eccentricity. In *Cecropia,* a closely related species in which thoracic gland secretion stops during the pupal stage, Williams (33) found no development in sixty isolated abdomens implanted with active brains.

A further complication to the general scheme is the finding by Wigglesworth (59) that the injection of substances like India ink, which are picked up by the hemocytes of the blood, prevent the activation of the thoracic gland. Moulting is also delayed by extensive injuries or by limb removal, so the insects may have a mechanism which prevents the activation of the thoracic gland until wounds are healed [O'Farrell & Stock (60), Wigglesworth (19)].

A major achievement was the isolation and crystallization, by Butenandt & Karlson (61), of a compound which acts like the thoracic gland hormone. The active compound was named "ecdyson" [or really it was misnamed; see Snodgrass (62)]. The injection of only 20 μg of ecdyson causes an isolated pupal abdomen of *Cynthia* to develop [Williams (63)]. Ecdyson injections have also caused a number of other insect species to moult. Karlson (7) subsequently found that there are actually two active compounds: α and β ecdyson. Alpha ecdyson is reported to be $C_{18}H_{30}O_4$: the ultraviolet and infrared spectra suggest that it is an unsaturated ketone, with two or more hydroxyl groups, and one ethyl and one methyl group. Probably it is a two-ringed structure [Karlson (64)].

Kobayashi & Burdette (65) investigated the effects on isolated abdomens of *Calliphora* of an extract containing ecdyson and an extract containing the "brain hormone" of Kobayashi & Kirimura (50). The brain hormone by itself has no effect. Ecdyson, as expected, causes pupation. But the brain hormone potentiates the action of ecdyson, so the injection of a normally subthreshold dose of ecdyson causes pupation when the brain hormone is given simultaneously. This finding may help to account for the results of Ichikawa & Nishiitsutsuji-Uwo (58), who were able to get isolated abdomens to develop when implanted with active brains. If the isolated abdomens contained a subthreshold titer of ecdyson, which was then potentiated by the brain hormone, development could occur by the mechanisms commonly found in insects.

Diapause.—Diapause is defined as a developmental standstill which is not enforced by the external world. In insects, diapause can be a spectacular example of the suspension of growth; for months or even years not a single cell divides. Since some insect eggs enter diapause before there is a cell division, the control of diapause is not always an endocrinological problem. At other stages, however, the suspension of activity by one of the endocrine organs is responsible for the cessation of growth, and the study of the control of diapause has been prominent in insect endocrinology. For example, the pupal diapause of the *Cecropia* silkmoth, the larval diapause of the sawfly, the nymphal diapause of the cricket, and the prepupal diapause of *Calliphora* all result from a failure by the brain to release its hormone [Williams (33), Church (66), Sellier (67)]. On the other hand, the diapause of *Sialis* appears to result from the inactivity of the thoracic gland [Rahm (68)].

Some workers believe that diapause is produced by the inhibitory action of other endocrine organs. For example, the larval diapause of the rice stem borer is broken in about 6 per cent of the animals from which the corpora allata and the corpora cardiaca are eliminated by a ligature [Fukaya & Mitsuhashi (69, 70)]; it is not certain whether so few break diapause because of injury produced by the operation or because it is so difficult to form the proper ligature on this tiny insect. So far, there is no overwhelming evidence for a diapause produced by an inhibitory hormone.

Diapause is frequently used as a means of passing the winter; in these cases renewed development follows exposure to low temperatures. In the silkmoth *Cecropia*, low temperatures act on the brain, which becomes endocrinologically active after the animal is returned to room temperatures [Williams (71)]. The loss of endocrine activity by the brain of *Cecropia* is paralleled by the partial depolarization of many of the brain neurons and a pronounced fall in the cholinesterase activity of brain homogenates [Van der Kloot (31, 72, 73)]. During chilling a cholinergic substance accumulates in the brain. It was suggested that this cholinergic substance induces the re-synthesis of cholinesterase when the animal is returned to room temperatures and that the brain neurons then regain excitability and hormone release is resumed.

On the other hand, in the lime hawk moth, the brain hormone seems to be released at low temperatures [Highnam (74)], and the implantation of a chilled brain into an animal kept at room temperatures does not end dia-pause. One group of neurosecretory cells in the brain of the sheep blowfly is continually active during diapause [Fraser (75)], but these cells are probably not involved in the activation of the thoracic gland. It seems clear that the neurosecretory cells of the brain may be shut down in different ways in dif-ferent insects.

Every known instance of a larval or a pupal diapause ultimately results from the absence of the thoracic gland hormone and, therefore, many studies have compared the diapausing with the developing animal in the hope of uncovering the biochemical actions of the thoracic gland hormone.

The action of the thoracic gland hormone.—The oxygen consumption of the diapausing pupa of the *Cecropia* silkmoth is only 5 per cent that of the adult moth [Schneiderman & Williams (76)]. Furhermore, the oxygen con-sumption of the diapausing pupa is scarcely decreased by exposure to carbon monoxide or cyanide and the pupae can live for months in CO to O_2 ratios as high as 33 to 1 [Schneiderman & Williams (77)]. The cellular basis for the changes in respiration is the virtual disappearance from most of the tissues of cytochromes b and c; 95 per cent of both b and c are gone within 24 hours after the onset of diapause. Cytochromes b_5 and $a+a_3$ also decrease, but to a lesser extent [Schappirio & Williams (78, 79)]. The tissues still contain some mitochondria, but they are deficient in cytochromes b and c. Only the intersegmental muscles [Shappirio & Williams (78)] and the central nervous system [Van der Kloot (73)] retain a normal respiration during diapause. The changes in the cytochromes are the basis for the insensitivity to CO and CN. Oxidations are limited by the low titer of cytochrome *c*, but cytochrome oxidase is in great excess. Therefore, even when most of the cytochrome oxidase is combined with CO or with CN, the remainder is sufficient to transfer the electrons from cytochrome *c* [Harvey & Williams (80, 81), Kurland & Schneiderman (82)]. At least some of the tissues of the diapausing anaimal also have a remarkable capacity for anaerobic life; the heart beats for $5\frac{1}{2}$ hours in the complete absence of oxygen [Harvey & Williams (80)].

Other chemical changes during diapause include the accumulation of as much as 5 *M* glycerol in the blood [Wyatt & Kalf (83), Wyatt & Meyer (84)]. There are conspicuous changes in the proteins of the blood and of the tissues [Telfer & Williams (85), Laufer (86)], and there is a marked decrease in the rate of incorporation of ^{14}C amino acids into protein [Telfer & Williams (87)]. The onset of adult development is accompanied by a significant rise of the ratio of the RNA's to the DNA's [Wyatt (88)].

The battery of biochemical changes might reasonably be regarded as sufficient to stop development. Development, once begun, can be blocked by CO or CN, so it seems that the loss of cytochromes *b* and *c* might underlie the suspension of growth. By this interpretation, the action of ecdyson is to promote the resynthesis of the cytochromes.

This logical idea is demolished by the findings that the synthesis of cytochromes *b* and *c*, the return of a CO and CN sensitive respiration, the increase in the rate of ^{14}C amino acid incorporation, the synthesis of specific proteins in the tissues, and probably the synthesis of RNA, are all elicited by simply wounding the animal [Schneiderman & Williams (76), Kurland & Schneiderman (82), Shappirio (89), Telfer & Williams (87), Laufer (86), Wyatt (88)]. Injury produces the chemical changes characteristic of development, but the animal does not develop. Similarly, in the bug *Rhodnius*, there is a pronounced fall in the oxygen consumption between moults [Zwicky & Wigglesworth (90)]. Ecdyson produces cytological changes suggesting an increased protein synthesis—but indistinguishable changes are produced by injury [Wigglesworth (19)].

By hindsight, it is easy to see that these investigations were bound to uncover metabolic changes which may be far removed from the primary action of the thoracic gland hormone. While it is desirable to contrast stages in the insect's life where ecdyson is absent with stages where there is a high hormone titer, we must also recognize that the diapausing pupa is a highly specialized animal. If its metabolism did not decrease drastically, it could live for only a few weeks on the accumulated food reserves. Similarly, *Rhodnius* must sometimes lurk for months until a blood meal comes its way. Both animals must be selected for every possible metabolic economy. For this reason, the spectacular changes produced in these animals by ecdyson, and by injury, may be far removed from the role of the thoracic gland hormone in more conventional insects, which are vigorous and active creatures throughout life.

A different approach to the action of ecdyson is seen in the study by

Clever & Karlson (91), who showed that the injection of ecdyson into *Chironomus* larvae promptly caused changes in the pattern of chromosomal puffing—changes similar to those seen at pupation. It will not be easy to decide whether this observation shows that a primary site of ecdyson's action is on the chromosome, or whether the change in the chromosome is merely one of the host of cytological changes produced by the hormone. Surely the idea that a hormone acts primarily by altering the physiology of the chromosome is worthy of the most intense experimental testing. The problem of the action of ecdyson is particularly difficult because the hormone produces the most diverse influences on different tissues: some grow, some differentiate, some die, all according to the time table of the insect's development. It is hard to believe that this hormone will be found to act by promoting either energy metabolism or a single type of synthesis in the insect.

The corpora allata.—Since the classic studies of Wigglesworth, it has been recognized that the corpora allata, small endocrine organs in the head, secrete a hormone which regulates progress in differentiation. When the hormone is present, the insect scarcely changes, moulting from a larva to a larva, or experimentally from a pupa to a pupa. Under special circumstances, the corpora allata hormone may even promote the return of larval characters to a portion of pupal or adult tissue. [Piepho & Holz (92) extended this observation to endodermal tissues.] The factor from the corpora allata which is responsible for these actions is called the juvenile hormone. Normally, in an insect with complete metamorphosis, the corpora allata secrete at each larval moult, secrete at a reduced rate at the pupal moult, and are inactive at the adult moult.

A really unexpected discovery is that adult males of the *Cecropia* silkmoth contain large amounts of the juvenile hormone [Williams (93)]. The hormone can be extracted with ether. There is no reason to believe that the high titer of hormone in the adult male serves any physiological function, because males deprived of the corpora allata at the time of pupation develop normally, live normally, and father normal offspring—even though they do not contain a trace of hormone. The corpora allata of the adult males are six times larger than those of females, which explains the sex difference in the amount of extractable hormone [Schneiderman & Gilbert (20)].

Further purification of the crude extract can be followed by injecting the fractions into pupae about to embark on adult development, or by local applications to the cuticle. The retention of pupal characters or of a patch of juvenile cuticle shows that the extracts are active [Williams, Moorhead & Pulis (94), Wigglesworth (95), Gilbert & Schneiderman (96)]. Preliminary chemical studies of purified extracts suggest that the active molecule is a water-insoluble lactone which is rich in methyl and in methylene groups [Williams (97)]. Other animals and plants have been tested for the presence of substances which mimic the effects of the juvenile hormone. Active extracts are obtained from every animal phylum tested except the sponges and the flatworms [Schneiderman & Gilbert (98), Gilbert & Schneiderman

(21)]. Particularly rich sources of the juvenile hormone are cow thymus, adrenal cortex, and heavy cream [Williams *et al.* (94)]; it is also found in dried brewer's yeast and in *Escherichia coli* [Schneiderman, Gilbert & Weinstein (99)]. Almost least surprising, considering the above list, is that it is also found in insect feces [Karlson & Schmialek (100)]. So the juvenile hormone— or at least a group of substances mimicking its action—is scattered throughout the living world, just like the estrogens.

Active corpora allata stimulate the thoracic glands to secrete [Williams (101)]. Extracts which are partially purified for juvenile activity still stimulate the thoracic gland, so it seems possible that the action is caused by the juvenile hormone itself [Gilbert & Schneiderman (96)]. The ability of the corpora allata to stimulate the thoracic gland may explain how the milkweed bug manages to moult after the removal of the medial neurosecretory cells from the brain [Johansson (102)].

Pupal corpora allata stimulate the thoracic glands of the *Cynthia* silkworm but do not produce a juvenile effect [Ichikawa & Nishiitsutsuji-Uwo (103)]. Dried corpora allata are also effective in this test system, so it seems that here the thoracic glands are stimulated by brain hormone stored in the allata [Ichikawa (104)].

The progress of an insect from the larva to the adult depends on the inactivity of the corpora allata. In the cockroach *Leucophaea*, if the nerve running from the brain to the corpora allata is transected at the time of the moult to the adult, the corpora allata continue to secrete. Presumably, in this species the corpora allata is shut down by the action of an inhibitory nerve supply [Lüscher & Englemann (105)]. The inhibitory nerve from the brain does not appear to originate in neurosecretory cells. In the silkworm, severing the nerve from the brain to the corpora allata does not prevent normal pupation, so juvenile hormone release is not prevented here by an inhibitory nerve [Bounhiol (106)]. Many older experiments show that implanted corpora allata, free of nerve connections, lose activity with succeeding moults [see Wigglesworth (17)]; so the inhibitory nerve may not be the sole mechanism used by insects to turn off secretion by the allatum. Some evidence suggested that the pericardial cells are important in regulating the activity of the corpora allata, but it now seems that the extensive injury produced during the operations was responsible for the effects [Lüscher & Engelmann (105)].

In considering the way in which the juvenile hormone regulates development, it is hard to see how a single biochemical action, like the regulation of some aspect of energy metabolism, could account for the hormone's actions. When ecdyson and juvenile hormone are present together in the larva of an insect with complete metamorphosis, the growth of the larval tissues is promoted. In the absence of the juvenile hormone, ecdyson is a potent killer of larval tissues; it then favors the growth of the adult organs only. Wigglesworth (18) proposed that the juvenile hormone acts by indirectly fostering the enzymatic reactions underwriting larval development. It seems more likely to me that the hormone acts by supressing the factors controlling the formation of the adult characters [see Williams (97)].

CRUSTACEANS

The moult of crustaceans, like that of insects, is ultimately controlled by neuroendocrine cells. In most crustaceans, however, the moult promptly follows the removal of the neurosecretory cells, showing that the hormone inhibits moulting. The perikaryia of the cells are grouped on the surface of the brain to form the medulla terminalis X organ. The axon terminals are in the sinus gland, which serves as the neurohemal organ in this system [Bliss & Welsh (107), Passano (108)]. Both the medulla terminalis and the sinus gland are in the eyestalks of most crustaceans.

The sinus glands also contain the axon terminals of neurosecretory cells whose perikaryia are in other parts of the central nervous system [Bliss & Welsh (107), Bliss et al. (109, 110), Knowles (111)]. The axon terminals contain two distinct sizes of secretory granules [Hodge & Chapman (112)]. Selective staining shows that there are six distinct types of neurosecretory terminals in the sinus gland of the crab *Callinectes* [Potter (113)]. Quite possibly, a number of hormones are released by this endocrine system [Durand (114)]. The secretory granules are transported down the axons from the cell bodies [Passano (115), Enami (116), Matsumoto (117), Fingerman & Aota (118)].

The Y organ.—At first the hormone from the medulla terminalis X organ was thought to act directly on the tissues to prevent the moult. However, Gabe (119, 120) ascribed an endocrine function to a paired, bilateral tissue lying beneath the external adductor muscles of the mandibles. This gland is called the Y organ (ventral gland). Echalier (121, 122, 123) then showed that the bilateral removal of the Y organ permanently blocks moulting (if the glands are removed after the first steps in the moult are undertaken, the moult is completed, but than further moulting is prevented). Moulting resumes once again if Y organs are re-implanted [Echalier (122), Carlisle (124)]. It is clear from these experiments that the hormone from the Y organ is needed to trigger the first stages of moulting (the pre-moult). But either the hormone is unnecessary for the completion of the moult, or sufficient hormone accumulates in the blood and tissues to see the moult carried through. In animals deprived of the Y organ, the removal of the medulla terminalis X organ does not produce a moult; so it seems that the hormone released at the sinus gland acts by inhibiting the secretion of the Y organ. Cutting the nerve which runs directly to the Y organ does not interfere with the moulting cycle [Echalier (123)]. The interaction between the medulla terminalis X organ and the Y organ is seen nicely in the crayfish *Orconectes* [Durand (125)]. The type 11 neurosecretory cells stop secreting just before the moult, at about the time the Y organ becomes activated. Y-organ secretion stops four to five days after the moult, just when the neurosecretory cells resume secretion.

The Y organ strikingly resembles the thoracic gland of insects both in histology and in embryonic development. Moreover, in some animals, like the spider crab *Maja*, the Y organs atrophy in the mature animal. In *Carcinus*, on the other hand, the Y organ of the mature crab remains functional; further moulting is prevented by continued secretion from the medulla terminalis X organ [Carlisle (124)]. The resemblance between the thoracic gland and the Y organ was enhanced by the discovery of Karlson (7) that ecdyson prepared from silkmoths can cause crustaceans to moult. Moreover, a substance similar to ecdyson can be prepared from the prawn *Cragon*. An attempt to extract ecdyson from Y organs was unsuccessful, probably because the inactive glands do not store significant quantities of the hormone [Karlson & Skinner (126)]. The injection of an extract of Y organs causes a threefold rise in the calcium of the blood within 24 hours [Carlisle (124)]. This result is not easy to interpret in terms of the mobilization of calcium found during the moult, but it does show that an active substance can be obtained from the Y organ.

Moult-accelerating hormone.—Some workers believe that there is also a moult-accelerating hormone in the Crustacea [Carlisle & Dohrn (127)]. This hormone is supposed to act by shortening the pre-moult period. The evidence for the moult-accelerating principle is that removal of the eyestalks delays moulting in some populations of the prawn *Palaemon* [Carlisle (128)] and that extracts of the central nervous system sometimes speed moulting. It is obviously difficult to separate the possible effects of injury and of the injection of a rich brew of substrates and coenzymes from a true hormonal action, and this claim has been vigorously debated. It is now important to know whether the factor from the central nervous system acts on the Y organ, or whether the injection of the extracts also hastens the moult of a prawn whose Y organs are removed after the critical period for the initiation of the moult.

Action of the Y-organ hormone.—So far there is little direct evidence about the effects of the crustacean-moulting hormone on the target cells. The removal of the eyestalks raises oxygen consumption and decreases the respiratory quotient [Bliss (129)], but the same changes also occur in the absence of the Y organ [Passano (16)].

Juvenile hormone.—The strong analogy between the control of growth in insects and in crustacea obviously raises the question of whether the crustaceans also produce a juvenile hormone. The question remains unanswered because all crustacean endocrinology so far has been done on postmetamorphic animals in which juvenile hormone would scarcely be expected.

THE CONTROL OF REPRODUCTION

INSECTS

The corpora allata.—Some insects develop normal eggs when the corpora allata are removed [Williams (101)]; but in a number of other species, the corpora allata are essential for egg maturation. [The list was extended by

Johansson (130), DeWilde & Stegwee (131), Larsen & Bodenstein (132).]
The classic studies of Pfeiffer (133) suggest that a hormone from the corpora
allata is needed to mobilize the materials for egg growth. Bodenstein (134)
and L'Hélias (135) showed that removal of the corpora allata increases the
amount of fat stored in the fat body. Allatectomy decreases the oxygen
consumption of adults of *Calliphora* and of the Colorado beetle. The oxygen
consumption is not decreased by castration, so the change comes from
corpora allata removal and not simply from the lack of ovarian development
[Thomsen & Hamburger (136), DeWilde & Stegwee (131)]. Wang & Dixon
(137) find that allatectomy decreases the transaminase activity in the
muscles of cockroaches; this finding agrees with the general feeling of all the
workers in this field that the corpora allata hormone promotes protein
synthesis so that when the hormone is absent fat accumulates. This idea is
easily tested with isotope techniques and should be followed up.

We now know of three distinct actions produced by the allatum: the
juvenile effect, the triggering of the thoracic gland, and the effect on egg
maturation. The evidence cited before suggests that the thoracic gland
stimulating factor is the same as the juvenile hormone. Extracts containing
juvenile hormone stimulate the respiration of beetle homogenates [DeWilde
& Stegwee, quoted in (21)] but not of isolated pupal abdomens [Gilbert &
Schneiderman (21)]. Larsen & Bodenstein (132) report that juvenile hormone
extracts, made from cockroaches, promote ovarian development in mosquitoes. However, cockroach extracts have little juvenile hormone activity
[Wigglesworth (95)], and the mineral oil used as a solvent might have its
own metabolic effects [Gilbert & Schneiderman (21)]. From the information
now available, it seems best to take the conservative position that only a
single hormone is secreted by the corpora allata [for a contrary opinion see
Lüscher (138) and Sägesser (139)].

Egg development is an excellent situation for studying the regulation of
activity of the corpora allata. The cockroaches *Leucophaea* and *Diploptera*
and the milkweed bug have inhibitory nerves running from the brain to the
corpora allata; when the nerve is cut, egg maturation begins [Scharrer (45),
Engelmann & Lüscher (140), Engelmann (141, 142, 143), Johansson (130)].
Since the corpora allata are under direct nervous control, various sensory
stimuli can provoke or inhibit hormone secretion. In some insects the corpora
allata are inhibited during starvation or when the animal is fed on a glucose
diet [Johansson (130), Von Harnack (144), Scharrer & Von Harnack (145)];
in mosquitoes the corpora allata are activated when the gut is distended
[Larsen & Bodenstein (132)]. The stimuli of mating release the allata from
inhibition in virgin cockroaches, so that egg maturation begins. Once the
embryos begin to develop, the allata are inhibited by mechanical stimuli
arising from the expansion of the brood sack [Roth & Stay (146), Engelmann
(143)] and perhaps also by a chemical released into the blood [Engelmann
(141)]. If a chemical stimulus is involved, it is quite nonspecific, since muscle
homogenates inhibit the corpora allata as readily as egg case extracts

[Engelmann (143)]. The injection of ecdyson is also reported to inhibit secretion by the corpora allata [Engelmann (147)].

When isolated allata are implanted in the cockroaches, they continue to undergo a cyclic activation [Engelmann (143)] so a nervous control may usually be superimposed on an intrinsic secretory cycle.

Medial neurosecretory cells.—In some flies the medial neurosecretory cells of the brain are important for egg maturation [Thomsen (148)]. An effect similar to the removal of the neurosecretory cells is produced by feeding the flies on a protein-free diet. It now seems that a neurosecretory material acts by stimulating the synthesis of proteinase in the gut and thereby providing for the digestion of proteins [Thomsen & Møller (149)]. In *I. limbata* the implantation of medial neurosecretory cells into a gravid female almost immediately stimulates oviposition, even when the eggs are immature [Nayar (150)].

The gonads.—Despite extensive investigation, there is no evidence that either the ovary or the testis secretes a hormone in any insect.

Egg diapause.—The insect endocrine system not only regulates the development of the eggs, but may also determine their fate after fertilization and laying. In some races of the silkworm, the females can lay either eggs which promptly pass through embryonic development or eggs which enter diapause. The diapausing eggs are produced by a hormone circulating in the blood of the mother; the hormone is released by neurosecretory cells in the subesophageal ganglion [Fukuda (151, 152), Hasegawa (153)]. This ganglion can always produce the hormone; but in females laying nondiapausing eggs, hormone production is suppressed by an inhibitory action of the brain. Morohoshi (154) concludes that a secretion from the corpora allata is also needed for the production of nondiapausing eggs. Hasegawa (155) extracted the brains and subesophageal ganglia of 15,000 silkworms with methanol and chloroform. The injection of this extract causes normal females to lay diapausing eggs.

CRUSTACEA

Our knowledge of the reproductive physiology of the crustacea was revolutionized by the discovery of the androgenic gland by Charniaux-Cotton (156, 157). The androgenic gland (vas deferens gland) is found only in males. It consists of a solid strand of cells which usually extends between the muscles of the coxopodite of the last walking leg and the vas deferens. The gland is widespread among the crustacea [Legrand (158), Duveau (159), Charniaux-Cotton (160, 161), Balesdent-Marquet (162)].

The most dramatic experiment is to dissect the androgenic gland from a male and implant it into a female. The ovary of the female is then transformed into a testis, and the male secondary sexual characteristics are progressively acquired over the next few moults [Charniaux-Cotton (157, 161)]. However, the operated females do not usually become functional males, because the sperm ducts which they develop do not form a lumen. Functional males are produced when two glands are implanted into young females [Charniaux-Cotton (163)]. Males deprived of their androgenic glands do not become females. They do stop further differentiation of male secondary sexual characters; and if an ovary is implanted, it survives without modification.

The activity of the androgenic gland seems to be controlled by endocrine centers in the eyestalk. Removal of the eyestalks from immature males of *Carcinus* causes hypertrophy of the androgenic gland and stimulation of testicular development [Demeusy (164, 165), Demeusy & Veillet (166)]. In fact, the hypertrophied genital tract may be larger than that of a normal adult animal. The location of the endocrine center in the eyestalk is uncertain.

The removal of the eyestalks from immatured female crustaceans is followed by the rapid development of the ovaries [Vernet-Conubert *et al.* (167), Vernet-Cornubert & Demeusy (168)]. The source of the ovary-inhibiting factor appears to be the medulla terminalis X organ [Carlisle (169), Matsumoto (117)]. In these experiments it is worth noting that external secondary sexual characters may not be developed. Carlisle & Butler (170) report that extracts made from mated queen bees inhibit the development of the ovaries when injected into eyestalkless females of *Leander* (see below).

Female isopods have modified appendages, called oöstegites, which are held to form a pouch for carrying developing eggs. The oöstegites develop markedly at the moult before egg laying begins. When a castrated male is implanted with an ovary, and the eggs in the ovary form yolk, the operated male develops oöstegites [Charniaux-Cotton (171, 172, 173), Legrand (174)]. Castration of a female causes the egg-bearing hairs on the oöstegites to regress at the next moult.

In summary, the crustacea seem to have a hormone favoring the development of male sexual characters, secreted by the androgenic gland. The gland, in turn, is inhibited in the immature males by a factor secreted by some structure in the eyestalks. The growth of the ovary is likewise inhibited by a hormone from the medulla terminalis X organ of the eyestalks. There is also evidence for a factor secreted by the ovary which promotes the acquisition of the female secondary sexual characters.

MOLLUSCS

Neurosecretory cells are well known in molluscs, and secretory cycles have been described which appear to correlate with reproductive ability [Lubet (175), Herlant-Meewis & Van Mol (176), Van Mol (177), Kraus (178)]. Lubet (175) presents evidence that a neurosecretory product readies the animal so that it sheds its gametes following an appropriate external stimulus.

The optic gland.—Wells & Wells (179) studied the control of gonad growth in *Octopus*. In both males and females, cutting the optic nerves or removing certain parts of the brain leads to the tenfold enlargement of the optic gland and to the maturation of the gonads. The optic glands are small clusters of cells sitting on the optic stalk. If the optic glands are removed before the brain operation, the gonads do not enlarge. Cutting the nerve from the brain to the optic glands causes secretion by the glands and maturation of the gonads. So the optic glands appear to be regulated by an inhibitory nerve coming from the brain. The inhibitory center in the brain is normally driven by visual stimuli; perhaps the diurnal light-dark cycle is important.

ANNELIDS

Polychetes.—Bobin & Durchon (180) concluded, from histological studies, that secretory granules which accumulate at the base of the brain of *Nereis* reflect the secretion of a hormone which inhibits the development of the gonads. This correlation was doubted by Defretin (181). More recently, Hauenschild (182, 183) presented experimental evidence that secretory cells in the brain of *Platynereis* do indeed produce a hormone which inhibits the development of sexual individuals.

Oligochetes.—Herlant-Meewis (184) found that removing the anterior part of the central nervous system from *Eisenia* stops egg development and leads to the regression of sexual characters. Egg laying is resumed when the type A neurosecretory cells of the cerebral ganglion regenerate.

REGENERATION

CRUSTACEA

If a limb is removed from a decapod crustacean, a stump is rapidly grown. Then growth either stops or is greatly slowed until just before the next moult, when the regenerate grows extremely rapidly [Bliss (185), Durand (125)]. The rapid growth can be produced at any time by implanting an active Y organ [Echalier (186)] or by removing the eyestalks so that the Y organ is activated. The effect on regeneration may be a sensitive test for assaying extracts of Y organ.

INSECTS

Regeneration in insects depends on the presence of the hormone from the thoracic gland [Bodenstein (187), O'Farrell & Stock (60), Stock & O'Farrell (188)]. If a leg is amputated early in the intermoult cycle, the leg regenerates completely. The next moult is delayed by a time equal to the interval between the preceding moult and the amputation. When the amputation is performed after a critical period in the intermoult cycle, only a stump is formed and complete regeneration is postponed until the next intermoult cycle.

ANNELIDS

When some of the posterior segments of an annelid are amputated, they usually regenerate promptly. If the region containing the brain is also removed, regeneration is retarded [Durchon (189), Casanova (190)]. If the brain is removed a few days before the amputation, regeneration is prevented [Hubl (191), Clark & Bonney (192)]. Regeneration by headless worms can be promoted by implanting the segment containing the brain into the coelom [Hauenschild (193)]. Within six hours after the amputation of some of the posterior segments, there are histological signs of increased activity by neurosecretory cells of the brain [Hubl (191), Clark & Clark (194)]. So the evidence is quite good that regeneration depends on the presence of a hormone which is secreted by some of the neurosecretory cells of the brain. Whether the hormone is acting directly on the tissues, or is activating a second endocrine organ, remains a question.

WATER METABOLISM

CRUSTACEA

An important event in the moult cycle is the increase in body size which is achieved by the uptake of large amounts of water. Robertson (195) showed that, at the moult, the crab *Carcinus* takes in sea water through the foregut and hepatopancreas until its weight is increased by 66 per cent. After eyestalk removal much more sea water is taken up [Carlisle (196)]. The increased water uptake can be counteracted by injecting extracts of the sinus gland or of the medulla terminalis X organ. Carlisle (196) believes that the hormone responsible for the increase in water uptake is distinct from the hormone which normally inhibits the Y organs, because eyestalk extracts can be made which restrain water uptake without delaying moulting. The detailed evidence supporting this conclusion is unpublished.

The land crab *Gecarcinus* takes up water from damp soil by means of the pericardial sacks [Bliss (185)]. Eyestalk removal also promotes water uptake by this route.

INSECTS

If the bug *Iphita* is forced to drink salt water, the medial neurosecretory cells become choked with granules [Nayar (197, 198)]. This may merely reflect the increased neurosecretory activity which is produced by a non-specific "stress" [Hodgson & Geldiay (199)]. There is more direct evidence for the importance of the dorsal part of the brain in the regulation of water content in the beetle *Anisotarsus* [Nuñez (200)]. And Altmann (201) finds that corpora cardiaca extracts promote water retention in honeybees; corpora allata extracts and epinephrine cause diuresis.

MOLLUSCS

Hekstra & Lever (202) report that the removal of both pleural ganglia causes the snail *Limnaea* to swell, presumably by taking up water. They suppose that the ganglion secretes a water-balance hormone. However, reimplantation of pleural ganglia has not yet been shown to restore water balance, so an endocrine interpretation seems premature.

From the available evidence it seems possible that water content may be

controlled by neurosecretory cells in several of the major groups of the animal
kingdom. But this is obviously a field which will profit from much further
comparative study.

THE CONTROL OF BODY COLOR

INSECTS

The color of the pupa of some butterflies depends on the color of the
environment in which they pupate. Hidaka (203) showed that the control is
by a substance or substances secreted by the prothoracic ganglion of *Papilio
exuthus*. In *Pieris rapae*, the prothoracic region is also implicated [Ohtaki
(204)]. The color change which is normally seen in *Cerura* at pupation is,
reasonably enough, produced by the thoracic gland hormone. Injections of
α ecdyson in doses too small to produce morphogenetic change do produce the
pupal coloration [Büchmann (205, 206)].

The diurnal color changes of the stick insect depend on the brain: if the
brain is removed, the insects become permanently light. Darkening is
produced by extracts of the tritocerebrum of the brain (which contains a
group of neurosecretory cells) and of the corpora cardiaca [Dupont-Raabe
(207, 208)]. The two factors are chemically distinct; the corpora cardiaca
factor appears to be a dipeptide similar to one of the color change hormones
of the shrimp [Knowles, Carlisle & Dupont-Raabe (209)].

CRUSTACEA

In the crustacea both color change and retinal pigment movements are
under hormonal control. The details of the control which are now known
make up a long and difficult story because: (*a*) much work can be done with
extracts partially purified by paper chromatography or electrophoresis;
(*b*) the extracts are often tested by injection into intact animals, which
always raises the possibility that the extract is simply triggering hormone
release by the true endocrine organ; (*c*) the glands are difficult to deal with
surgically and the classic methods of extirpation and implantation are little
used; (*d*) each type of chromatophore has a distinct response pattern;
(*e*) assays are performed on different animals by different workers. Therefore,
only a single example will be cited, the concentration of the red-yellow
pigment in large and small chromatophores. Extracts which concentrate the
pigment are obtained from the sinus glands and the postcommissure organs
of the shrimp *Leander*, the brain and connectives of the crayfish *Cambarella*,
and the corpora cardiaca of the stick insect [Knowles (210); Knowles,
Carlisle & Dupont-Raabe (209); DeLerma, Dupont-Raabe & Knowles (211);
Fingerman & Lowe (212)]. The active principle from *Leander* and the stick
insect is slowly dialyzable, electropositive at pH 7.5–7.8, and is called the A
substance. When a crude extract is allowed to stand, the A substance
disappears and two new substances, which are also active, appear. The
breakdown of the A substance is prevented by boiling the extract, so that
transformation is probably enzymatic [Knowles *et al.* (213)]. The A sub-

stance was further purified by column chromatography on alumina, followed by countercurrent extraction [Ostland & Fänge (214), Edman *et al.* (215)]. The biological activity of this highly purified extract is eliminated by incubation with trypsin or with chymotrypsin, so the A substance is most probably a polypeptide.

ENDOCRINE INFLUENCES ON THE HEART BEAT

The pericardial organs were discovered by Alexandrowicz (216, 217) in decapod crustaceans. The pericardial organs consist of a group of fine, multibranched nerve endings lying in the pericardial cavity, ideally sited for releasing chemicals into the blood about to enter the heart. The median connective and dorsal trunks of stomatopoda are analogous organs. The nerve terminals are filled with electron-dense granules averaging 12,000 A in diameter [Maynard, Maynard & Potter quoted by Welsh (218)]. The location of the perikaryia of the nerve cells is unknown. Extracts of the pericardial organs increase the amplitude of the heart beat, but the frequency either increases or decreases depending on the species (Alexandrowicz & Carlisle (219)]. Carlisle (220) concluded that the active substance is an ortho dihydroxytryptamine. Maynard & Welsh (221) found that the material is dialyzable, heat stable, and inactivated by trypsin and chymotrypsin; it is likely that the active molecule is a polypeptide.

In insects, extracts which act on the heart can be prepared from the corpora cardiaca, corpora allata, and the central nervous system [Cameron (222), Gersch & Unger (52)]. The relation of these chemicals to the endocrine system remains uncertain.

ACTIVITY RHYTHMS

INSECTS

The cockroach is normally active during the hours of darkness, and this activity rhythm persists even when the animal is kept in constant darkness. In a brilliant series of investigations, Harker (223, 224) showed, by parabiosis experiments, that activity is produced by a hormone. The hormone is released by neurosecretory cells in the subesophageal ganglion; the activity rhythm can be shifted from animal to animal by merely transplanting the ganglion. The transplantation experiments suggest that subesophageal ganglia without afferent input can maintain a 24-hour cycle of hormone secretion. However, the secretory cycle is influenced by a nerve running from the corpora allata to the subesophageal ganglion; if this nerve is transected, the activity rhythm disappears in about a week. The nerve is a route for the transport of neurosecretory material which moves from the corpus cardiacum, through the corporus allatum, and then to the subesophageal ganglion. The amount of neurosecretory material in the allatum-subesophageal ganglion nerve is greatly increased if the recurrent nerve is cut, and the activity rhythm then becomes erratic. Therefore, the rhythm of activities seems to be controlled by a hormone released by neurosecretory cells, and the hormone sources in turn are regulated by a second neurosecretory system.

Ozbas & Hodgson (225) found that an extract of the corpora cardiaca of *Periplaneta* can decrease the spontaneous electrical activity of isolated nerve cords. Injection of the extract into an intact cockroach produces incoordination and stereotyped locomotion for 24 to 96 hours. The evidence suggests that the active material is produced in the neurosecretory cells of the brain and is transported down the axons to the corpora cardiaca. According to Milburn *et al.* (226), only high concentrations of the extract of the cardiaca decrease activity in the nerve cord. Lower doses increase the efferent activity in the phallic nerve. Almost identical effects are found about 15 minutes after the subesophageal ganglion is removed. Roeder *et al.* (227) believe that there is an inhibitory system, originating in the subesophageal ganglion, which affects neurons in the cord. The extract from the cardiaca is thought to block the descending inhibitory system. It seems possible that the two approaches, the study of activity rhythms and that of corpora cardiaca extracts, are moving towards a common resolution.

CRUSTACEA

The land crab *Gecarcinus* shows predictable changes in activity in the days just before the moult. The activity changes in the same way when the moult occurs naturally and when the moult is provoked by removing the eyestalks [Bliss (228)]. Perhaps the activity rhythm is influenced by the hormone from the Y organ.

Annelids.—The sexual swarming of the polychaete *Platynereis* takes place at 30-day intervals. Laboratory cultures can be synchronized by appropriate light-dark cycles so that all of the individuals swarm at the same time. Hauenschild (183) reports that the swarming is controlled by neurosecretory cells in the brain.

INTERACTIONS BETWEEN INDIVIDUALS

Hormone secretion is sometimes regulated by chemicals which are passed from one animal to another. These chemicals have been called social hormones or pheromones [Karlson & Lüscher (229)]. An excellent example comes from studies of the migratory locust. When male locusts become sexually mature, they simultaneously become gregarious in habit and are colored bright yellow [Norris (230)]. On the approach of a mature, yellow male, an immature male responds by trembling his antennae, palpi, and femura [Loher (231)]. This "vibration" response is elicited by a volatile substance secreted from the epidermis of the yellow males. Loher (232) showed that continued exposure to the volatile substance has a stimulating effect on the corpora allata of the young males. The activation of the corpora allata then speeds their sexual development. The presence of an active corpus allatum is a prerequisite for the maintenance of the yellow color, sexual maturity, and the secretion of the volatile substance. The corpora allata are also needed by females of the cockroach *Byrsotria* for the production of a substance which stimulates the male precopulatory behavior [Barth (233)].

Queen bees secrete a "queen substance" from their mandibular glands. When the queen substance is no longer released in the hive, the ovaries of the workers begin to develop, and the workers start to construct brood cells for the development of new queens [Butler (234), Butler *et al.* (235)]. Barbier & Lederer (236) showed that the chemical which inhibits the construction of the queen cells is 9-oxo-2-decenoic acid

$$CH_3—CO\cdot(CH_2)_5—CH{=}CH—COOH.$$

It is interesting that this molecule is closely related to 10-hydroxy-2-decenoic acid which is produced by the nurse bees and is a constituent of royal jelly.

When reproducing adults are removed from a termite colony, some of the hitherto immature termites develop within six days into "supplementary reproductives". The reproducing adults secrete a substance which inhibits the development of the supplementary reproductives [Lüscher (237)]. Lüscher (138) has now presented a complete hypothesis for the hormonal control of caste differentiation in termites. To choose one of the best documented examples, a termite soldier can be produced experimentally by taking a corporus allatum from a newly moulted supplementary reproductive and implanting it into a full grown larva [Lüscher (238)]. Only corpora allata from reproductively competent individuals are effective, so Lüscher suggests that a gonadotropic hormone, not the juvenile hormone, is responsible for soldier development.

CONCLUSIONS

The endocrine organs which were discussed are listed in Table I. The table emphasizes the importance of neurosecretory cells in the endocrine systems of all of the invertebrate groups which have been studied in any detail. On the other hand, there is little unity in the function served by neurosecretion in the different groups. Obviously, in the long evolutionary history of the invertebrates, secretory neurons have been incorporated into the service of diverse physiological systems.

It should also be emphasized that, even in the classes well studied, most of the neurosecretory cells are not known to be hormone sources. For example, in the silkworm *B. mori* there are about 30 neurons of the brain showing cytological signs of secretion [Kobayashi (40)]. Many of these cells must be producing the hormone which stimulates the thoracic glands. In the subesophageal ganglion there are 80 neurosecretory cells; some must produce the egg diapause hormone. There are about 1100 neurosecretory cells in the thoracic and abdominal ganglia; none of these are as yet implicated as hormone sources. And, indeed, there is no compelling reason to assume, from cytological study, that true hormones are produced by all of these cells. For this reason, I prefer to call neurosecretory cells which are known to

TABLE I
INVERTEBRATE ENDOCRINE ORGANS

ARTHROPODS

Insects:
Neurosecretory cells of the protocerebrum—corpora cardiaca—corpora allatum complex
Thoracic glands
Corpora allata
Neurosecretory cells of the subesophageal ganglion
Neurosecretory cells of the tritocerebrum

Crustacea:
Neurosecretory cells of the medulla terminalis X organ—sinus gland complex
Y organs
Androgenic glands
Ovaries
Pericardial glands

MOLLUSCS

Neurosecretory cells of the brain
Optic glands

ANNELIDS

Neurosecretory cells of the brain

release a hormone neuroendocrine cells, to keep the lines clear between cytological and physiological evidence.

So far we have little idea of how many chemicals are secreted by any of these endocrine organs. The neurosecretory cells of the protocerebrum of the insect brain, for example, are implicated in the control of at least four diverse physiological functions, and we have no idea of how many distinct hormones are involved. This emphasizes the need, not only for increased chemical work on the extracts, but also for the testing of active fractions on a number of different systems.

Similarly, the insect corpora allata are involved in both the control of development and in the sexual endocrinology of adult females. While one hormone may be involved in both functions, we will not be certain until highly purified hormone preparations are available and properly tested.

The progress of crustacean endocrinology has undoubtedly been slowed because some of the principal organs are located in the eyestalks. This arrangement makes it all too easy to snip off the eyestalks as the first step in a "endocrinological" investigation. The problem here is that the operation eliminates one of the animals' most important sense organs, a considerable portion of the brain, and a number of suspected endocrine organs—all in one blow. There is a large body of information about the effects of this operation on metabolism, blood concentrations of various substances, and even on activity rhythms. These data are hard to evaluate because of the difficulty in devising an adequate control for so traumatic an operation. Experiments of this type are most valuable if they are accompanied by the implantation of the isolated, suspected endocrine organ.

The unifying theme in arthropod endocrinology appears to be the thoracic gland and the Y organ. Both are developed from ectodermal invaginations in either the maxillary or antennary segment, are histologically similar, and release the same or a similar hormone. And arthropod classes which have not been investigated experimentally contain organs which resemble the thoracic glands [Gabe (4)]. In short, the presence of this endocrine organ in the arthropods may be as characteristic a feature as the jointed legs. Obviously, the development of a phylum based on a rigid exoskeleton must have depended on the evolution of a system for the control of moulting.

From this common base the arthropod endocrine system has undoubtedly diverged in several directions. There is, for example, no reason to believe that insects have an organ even analogous to the androgenic gland. And even systems which are somewhat similar, like the neuroendocrine cells regulating moulting, may be unrelated in their evolutionary history.

The focal point of arthropod endocrinology appears to be the moult along with the attendant control of growth and differentiation. This is an opportunity for studying growth which is almost without a peer and promises the richest rewards for future investigators. The other invertebrate phyla remain almost unexplored from the standpoint of comparative endocrinology, in spite of the excellent work of a handful of pioneers. We need many more studies before an over-all view can be taken of the evolution of endocrine systems.

In all of the invertebrate groups, we know far more about the endocrine control of the dramatic, infrequent events in an animal's life—moulting, swarming, egg laying—than in any day-by-day adjustments for preserving homeostasis. But then comparative endocrinology is still in a phase of rapid growth. Few problems are settled, so the next years offer as many opportunities as the years just past.

LITERATURE CITED

1. Scharrer, B., *Ann. Rev. Physiol.*, **15**, 457–72 (1953)
2. Scharrer, E., and Scharrer, B., *Recent Progr. in Hormone Research*, **10**, 183 240 (1954)
3. Scharrer, E., and Scharrer, B., *Handbuch der Mikroskopischen Anatomie des Menschen*, **6**, 953–1006 (Springer, Berlin, Germany, 1954)
4. Gabe, M., *Ann. biol.*, **30**, 5–62 (1954)
5. Scharrer, B., *Hormones*, **3**, 57–95 (1955)
6. Scheer, B. T., *Vitamins and Hormones*, **18**, 141–204 (1960)
7. Karlson, P., *Ann. sci. nat. Zool. et biol. animale*, **18**, 125–38 (1956)
8. Karlson, P., *Vitamins and Hormones*, **14**, 227–66 (1956)
9. Butenandt, A., *Naturwissenschaften*, **46**, 461–71 (1959)
10. Klcinholz, L. H., *Recent Advances in Invertebrate Physiology*, 173–96 (Univ. of Oregon, Eugene, Ore., 1957)
11. Scheer, B. T., *Recent Advances in Invertebrate Physiology*, 213–27 (Univ. of Oregon, Eugene, Ore., 1957)
12. Welsh, J. H., *Recent Advances in Invertebrate Physiology*, 161–70 (Univ. of Oregon, Eugene, Ore., 1957)
13. Knowles, F. G. W., and Carlisle, D. B., *Biol. Revs. Cambridge Phil. Soc.*, **31**, 396–473 (1956)

14. Carlisle, D. B., and Knowles, F. G. W., *Endocrine Control in Crustaceans* (Cambridge Univ. Press, London, Engl., 150 pp., 1959)
15. Passano, L. M., *The Physiology of Crustacea*, **1**, 433–536 (Academic Press, New York, N. Y., 670 pp., 1960)
16. Passano, L. M., *Am. Zoologist*, **1**, 89–95 (1961)
17. Wigglesworth, V. B., *The Physiology of Insect Metamorphosis* (Cambridge Univ. Press, Cambridge, Engl., 152 pp., 1954)
18. Wigglesworth, V. B., *Symposia Soc. Exptl. Biol.*, **11**, 204–7 (1957)
19. Wigglesworth, V. B., *The Control of Growth and Form* (Cornell Univ. Press, Ithaca, N. Y., 131 pp., 1959)
20. Schneiderman, H. A., and Gilbert, L. I., *Cell, Organism and Milieu*, 157–84 (Ronald Press, New York, N. Y., 1959)
21. Gilbert, L. I., and Schneiderman, H. A., *Am. Zoologist*, **1**, 11–51 (1961)
22. Hinton, H. E., *Sci. Progr.*, **45**, 307–20 (1957)
23. Joly, P., *Ann. biol.*, **34**, 97–118 (1958)
24. Lees, A. D., *The Physiology of Diapause in Arthropods* (Cambridge Univ. Press, Cambridge, Engl., 151 pp., 1955)
25. Bodenstein, D., *Aspects of Synthesis and Order in Growth*, 257–68 (Thirteenth Growth Symposium, Princeton Univ. Press, Princeton, N. J., 1955)
26. Bodenstein, D., *Recent Advances in Invertebrate Physiology*, 197–211 (Univ. of Oregon, Eugene, Ore., 1957)
27. Pflugfelder, O., *Entwicklungsphysiologie der Insecten* (Akademische Verlagsgesellschaft Geest und Portig, K. G., Leipzig, Germany, 490 pp., 1958)
28. Williams, C. M., *A Symposium on the Chemical Basis of Development*, 794–806 (Johns Hopkins Press, Baltimore, Md., 1958)
29. Van der Kloot, W. G., *Ann. Rev. Entomol.*, **5**, 35–52 (1960)
30. Van der Kloot, W. G., *Am. Zoologist*, **1**, 3–9 (1961)
31. Van der Kloot, W. G., *Inhibition in the Nervous System* (Pergamon Press, New York, N. Y., in press, 1961)
32. Highnam, K. C., *Quart. J. Microscop. Sci.*, **102**, 27–38 (1961)
33. Williams, C. M., *Biol. Bull.*, **93**, 89–98 (1947)
34. Cazal, P., *Bull. biol. France et Belg.*, Suppl. 32, 1–227 (1948)
35. Lhoste, J., *Arch. zool. exptl. et gén.*, **89**, 169–83 (1952)
36. Nayar, K. K., *Biol. Bull.*, **108**, 296–307 (1955)
37. Köpf, H., *Biol. Zentr.*, **76**, 28–42 (1957)
38. Arvy, L., Bounhiol, J. J., and Gabe, M., *Compt. rend. acad. sci.*, **236**, 627–29 (1953)
39. Formigoni, A., *Ann. sci. nat. Zool. et biol. animale*, **18**, 283–91 (1956)
40. Kobayashi, M., *Sanshi Shikenjo Hôkoku*, **15**, 181–273 (1957)
41. Williams, C. M., *Growth*, **12**, 61–74 (1948)
42. Meyer, G. F., and Pflugfelder, O., *Z. Zellforsch. u. mikroskop. Anat.*, **48**, 556–64 (1958)
43. Willey, R. B., and Chapman, G. B., *J. Ultrastruct. Research*, **4**, 1–14 (1960)
44. Nishiitsutsuji-Uwo, J., *Nature*, **188**, 953–45 (1960)
45. Scharrer, B., *Biol. Bull.*, **102**, 261–72 (1952)
46. Thomsen, E., *J. Exptl. Biol.*, **31**, 322–30 (1954)
47. Carlisle, D. B., and Knowles, F. G. W., *Nature*, **172**, 404–5 (1953)
48. L'Hélias, C., *Ann. sci. nat. Zool. et biol. animale*, **18**, 276–81 (1956)
49. L'Hélias, C., *Bull. biol. France et Belg.*, **91**, 241–63 (1957)
50. Kobayashi, M., and Kirimura, J., *Nature*, **181**, 1217 (1958)
51. Gersch, M., *Am. Zoologist*, **1**, 53–57 (1961)
52. Gersch, M., and Unger, H., *Naturwissenschaften*, **44**, 117 (1957)
53. Gersch, M., Fischer, F., Unger, H., and Koch, H., *Z. Naturforsch.*, **15b**, 319–22 (1960)
54. Söderberg, U., *Acta Physiol. Scand.*, Suppl. 147, 113 pp. (1958)
55. Joly, P., Joly, L., and Halbwachs, M., *Ann. sci. nat. Zool. et biol. animale*, **18**, 257–61 (1956)
56. Strich-Halbwachs, M. C., *Ann. sci. nat. Zool.*, Ser. 12, **1**, 483–570 (1959)
57. Chadwick, L. E., *J. Exptl. Zool.*, **131**, 291–306 (1956)
58. Ichikawa, M., and Nishiitsutsuji-Uwo, J., *Mem. Coll. Sci., Univ. Kyoto, B*, **27**, 9–15 (1960)
59. Wigglesworth, V. B., *J. Exptl. Biol.*, **32**, 649–63 (1955)
60. O'Farrell, A. F., and Stock, A., *Australian J. Biol. Sci.*, **7**, 525–36 (1954)
61. Butendandt, A., and Karlson, P., *Z. Naturforsch.*, **9b**, 389–91 (1954)

62. Snodgrass, R. E., *Proc. Entomol. Soc. Wash.*, **62**, 265–70 (1960)

63. Williams, C. M., *Anat. Record*, **120**, 743 (1954)

64. Karlson, P., *Proc. Intern. Congr. Biochem.*, *4th, Vienna*, **12**, 37–48 (1959)

65. Kobayashi, M., and Burdette, W. J., *Proc. Soc. Exptl. Biol. Med.* (In press)

66. Church, N. S., *Can. J. Zool.*, **33**, 339–69 (1955)

67. Sellier, R., *Compt. rend. acad. sci.* **228**, 2055 (1949)

68. Rahm, U. H., *Rev. suisse zool.*, **59**, 173–237 (1952)

69. Fukaya, M., and Mitsuhashi, J., *Japan. J. Appl. Entomol. Zool.*, **1**, 145–54 (1957)

70. Mitsuhashi, J., and Fukaya, M., *Japan. J. Appl. Entomol. Zool.*, **4**, 127–34 (1960)

71. Williams, C. M., *Biol. Bull.*, **110**, 201–18 (1956)

72. Van der Kloot, W. G., *Biol. Bull.*, **109**, 276–94 (1955)

73. Van der Kloot, W. G., *J. Cellular Comp. Physiol.*, **46**, 359 (1955)

74. Highnam, K. C., *Quart. J. Microscop. Sci.*, **99**, 73–88 (1958)

75. Fraser, A., *Proc. Roy. Soc. Edinburgh*, LXVII, 127–40 (1960)

76. Schneiderman, H. A., and Williams, C. M., *Biol. Bull.*, **105**, 320–34 (1953)

77. Schneiderman, H. A., and Williams, C. M., *Biol. Bull.*, **106**, 238–52 (1954)

78. Shappirio, D. G., and Williams, C. M., *Proc. Roy. Soc. (London)*, B, **147**, 218–32 (1957)

79. Shappirio, D. G., and Williams, C. M., *Proc. Roy. Soc. (London)*, B, **147**, 233–46 (1957)

80. Harvey, W. R., and Williams, C. M., *Biol. Bull.*, **114**, 23–35 (1958)

81. Harvey, W. R., and Williams, C. M., *Biol. Bull.*, **114**, 36–53 (1958)

82. Kurland, C. G., and Schneiderman, H. A., *Biol. Bull.*, **116**, 136–61, (1959)

83. Wyatt, G. R., and Kalf, G. F., *J. Gen. Physiol.*, **40**, 833–47 (1957)

84. Wyatt, G. R., and Meyer, W. L., *J. Gen. Physiol.*, **42**, 1005–11 (1959)

85. Telfer, W. H., and Williams, C. M., *J. Gen. Physiol.*, **36**, 389–413 (1953)

86. Laufer, H., *Ann. N. Y. Acad. Sci.*, **89**, 490–515 (1960)

87. Telfer, W. H., and Williams, C. M., *J. Insect Physiol.*, **5**, 61–72 (1960)

88. Wyatt, G. R., *Proc. Intern. Congr. Biochem.*, *4th, Vienna*, **12**, 161–78 (1959)

89. Shappirio, D. G., *Ann. N. Y. Acad. Sci.*, **89**, 537–48 (1960)

90. Zwicky, K., and Wigglesworth, V. B., *Proc. Roy. Entomol. Soc. London*, **31**, 153–60 (1956)

91. Clever, U., and Karlson, P., *Exptl. Cell Research*, **20**, 623–26 (1960)

92. Piepho, H., and Holz, I., *Biol. Zentr.*, **78**, 417–24 (1959)

93. Williams, C. M., *Nature*, **178**, 212–13 (1956)

94. Williams, C. M., Moorhead, L. V., and Pulis, J. F., *Nature*, **183**, 405 (1959)

95. Wigglesworth, V. B., *J. Insect Physiol.* **2**, 73–84 (1958)

96. Gilbert, L. I., and Schneiderman, H. A., *Trans. Am. Microscop. Soc.*, **79**, 38–67 (1960)

97. Williams, C. M., *Science*, **133**, 1370 (1961)

98. Schneiderman, H. A., and Gilbert, L. I., *Biol. Bull.*, **115**, 530–35 (1958)

99. Schneiderman, H. A., Gilbert, L. I., and Weinstein, M., *Nature*, **188**, 1041–42 (1960)

100. Karlson, P., and Schmialek, H., *Z. Naturforsch.*, 146, 821 (1959)

101. Williams, C. M., *Biol. Bull.*, **116**, 323–38 (1959)

102. Johansson, A. S., *Nytt Mag. for Zoologi*, **7**, 1–132 (1959)

103. Ichikawa, M., and Nishiitsutsuji-Uwo, J., *Biol. Bull.*, **116**, 88–94 (1959)

104. Ichikawa, M. (Personal communications, June 1961)

105. Lüscher, M., and Engelmann, F., *J. Insect. Physiol.*, **5**, 240–58 (1960)

106. Bounhiol, J. J., *Compt. rend. acad. sci.*, **245**, 1087–89 (1957)

107. Bliss, D. E., and Welsh, J. H., *Biol. Bull.*, **103**, 157–69 (1952)

108. Passano, L. M., *Physiol. Comp. et Oecol.*, **3**, 155–89, (1953)

109. Bliss, D. E., Durand, J. B., and Welsh, J. H., *Z. Zellforsch.*, **39**, 520–36 (1954)

110. Bliss, D. E., Durand, J. B., and Welsh, J. H., *Pubbl. staz. zool. Napoli*, **24**, 68–69 (1954)

111. Knowles, F. G. W., *Pubbl. staz. zool. Napoli*, **24**, 74–78 (1954)

112. Hodge, M. H., and Chapman, G. B., *J. Biophys. Biochem. Cytol.*, **4**, 571–74 (1958)

113. Potter, D. M., *Zweites Internationales Symposium über Neurosekretion*, *Lund*, 113–18 (Springer, Berlin, Germany, 1958)

114. Durand, J. B., *Biol. Bull.*, 111, 62–76 (1956)
115. Passano, L. M., *Pubbl. staz. zool. Napoli*, 24, 72–73 (1954)
116. Enami, M., *Pubbl. staz. zool. Napoli*, 24, 70–71 (1954)
117. Matsumoto, K., *Biol. J. Okayama Univ.*, 4, 103–76 (1958)
118. Fingerman, M., and Aota, T., *Anat. Record*, 131, 552 (1958)
119. Gabe, M., *Compt. rend. acad. sci.*, 237, 1111–13 (1953)
120. Gabe, M., *Ann. sci. nat. Zool. et biol. animale*, 18, 145–52 (1956)
121. Echalier, G., *Compt. rend. acad. sci.*, 238, 523–25 (1954)
122. Echalier, G., *Compt. rend. acad. sci.*, 240, 1581–83 (1955)
123. Echalier, G., *Ann. sci. nat. Zool.*, Ser. 12, 1, 1–57 (1959)
124. Carlisle, D. B., *J. Marine Biol. Assoc. United Kingdom*, 36, 291–307 (1957)
125. Durand, J. B., *Biol. Bull.*, 118, 250–61 (1960)
126. Karlson, P., and Skinner, D. M., *Nature*, 185, 543–44 (1960)
127. Carlisle, D. B., and Dohrn, P. F. R., *Publ. staz. zool. Napoli*, 24, 69–83 (1953)
128. Carlisle, D. B., *J. Marine Biol. Assoc. United Kingdom*, 38, 351–59 (1959)
129. Bliss, D. E., *Biol. Bull.*, 104, 275–96 (1953)
130. Johansson, A. S., *Nature*, 181, 198–99 (1958)
131. DeWilde, J., and Stegwee, D., *Arch. néerl. zool.*, 13, 277–89 (1958)
132. Larsen, J. R., and Bodenstein, D., *J. Exptl. Zool.*, 140, 343–81 (1959)
133. Pfeiffer, I. W., *J. Exptl. Zool.*, 99, 183–233 (1945)
134. Bodenstein, D., *Biol. Bull.*, 124, 105–15 (1953)
135. L'Hélias, C., *Compt. rend. acad. sci.*, 236, 2164–66 (1953)
136. Thomsen, E., and Hamburger, K., *J. Exptl. Biol.*, 32, 692–99 (1955)
137. Wang, S., and Dixon, S. E., *Can. J. Zool.*, 38, 275–83 (1960)
138. Lüscher, M., *Ann. N. Y. Acad. Sci.*, 89, 549–63 (1960)
139. Sägesser, H., *J. Insect Physiol.*, 5, 264–85 (1961)
140. Engelmann, F., and Lüscher, M., *Verhandl. deut. zool. Ges. (Hamburg)*, 215–20 (1956)
141. Engelmann, F., *J. Insect Physiol.*, 1, 257–58 (1957)
142. Engelmann, F., *Biol. Bull.*, 116, 406–19 (1959)
143. Engelmann, F., *Ann. N. Y. Acad. Sci.*, 89, 516–36 (1960)
144. Von Harnack, M., *Biol. Bull.*, 115, 521–29 (1958)
145. Scharrer, B., and Von Harnack, M., *Biol. Bull.*, 115, 508–20 (1958)
146. Roth. L. M., and Stay, B., *Science*, 130, 271–72 (1959)
147. Engelmann, F., *Z. vergleich. Physiol.*, 41, 456–70 (1959)
148. Thomsen, E., *J. Exptl. Biol.*, 29, 137–172 (1952)
149. Thomsen, E., and Møller, I., *Nature*, 183, 1401–2 (1959)
150. Nayar, K. K., *Proc. Indian Acad. Sci.*, XLVII, 233–51 (1958)
151. Fukuda, S., *Annotationes Zool. Japon.*, 25, 149–44 (1952)
152. Fukuda, S., *Proc. Japan Acad.*, 29, 381–84 (1953)
153. Hasegawa, K., *J. Fac. Agr.*, *Tottori Univ.*, 1, 83–124 (1952)
154. Morohoshi, S., *J. Insect Physiol.*, 3, 28–40 (1959)
155. Hasegawa, K., *Nature*, 179, 1300–1 (1957)
156. Charniaux-Cotton, H., *Compt. rend. acad. sci.*, 238, 953–55 (1954)
157. Charniaux-Cotton, H., *Compt. rend. acad. sci.*, 239, 780–82 (1954)
158. Legrand, J. J., *Compt. rend. acad. sci.*, 243, 1363–65 (1956)
159. Duveau, J., *Arch. anat. microscop. et morphol. exptl.*, 46, 179–209 (1957)
160. Charniaux-Cotton, H., *Ann. biol. clin. (Paris)*, 32, 371–98 (1956)
161. Charniaux-Cotton, H., *The Physiology of Crustacea*, I, 411–47 (Academic Press, New York, N. Y., 670 pp., 1960)
162. Balesdent-Marquet, M.-L., *Compt. rend. acad. sci.*, 247, 534–36 (1958)
163. Charniaux-Cotton, H., *Bull. soc. zool.*, *France*, 83, 314–31 (1958)
164. Demeusy, N., *Arch. zool. exptl. et gén.*, 95, 253–402 (1957)
165. Demeusy, N., *Cahiers biol. marine*, 1, 257–77 (1960)
166. Demeusy, N., and Veillet, A., *Compt. rend. acad. sci.*, 246, 1104–7 (1958)
167. Vernet-Cornubert, G., Demeusy, N., and Veillet, A., *Compt. rend. acad. sci.*, 234, 1405–7 (1952)
168. Vernet-Cornubert, G., and Demeusy, N., *Compt. rend. acad. sci.*, 240, 360–61 (1955)
169. Carlisle, D. B., *Pubbl. staz. zool. Napoli*, 24, 355–72 (1953)
170. Carlisle, D. B., and Butler, C. G., *Nature*, 177, 276–77 (1956)
171. Charniaux-Cotton, H., *Compt. rend. acad. sci.*, 234, 2570–72 (1952)
172. Charniaux-Cotton, H., *Compt. rend. acad. sci.*, 236, 141–42 (1953)

173. Charniaux-Cotton, H., *Ann. sci. nat. Zool. et biol. animale*, **19**, 411–560 (1957)

174. Legrand, J. J., *Compt. rend. acad. sci.*, **241**, 1083–85 (1955)

175. Lubet, P., *Compt. rend. acad. sci.*, **241**, 254–56 (1955)

176. Herlant-Meewis, H., and Van Mol, J.-J., *Compt. rend. acad. sci.*, **249**, 321–22 (1959)

177. Van Mol, J.-J., *Compt. rend. acad. sci.*, **250**, 2280–81 (1960)

178. Kraus, E., *Z. Zellforsch.*, **51**, 748–76 (1960)

179. Wells, M. J., and Wells, J., *J. Exptl. Biol.*, **36**, 1–33 (1959)

180. Bobin, G., and Durchon, M., *Arch. anat. microscop. et morphol. exptl.*, **42**, 112–26 (1953)

181. Defretin, R., *Arch. zool. exptl. et gén.*, **92**, 73–140. (1955)

182. Hauenschild, C., *Z. Naturforsch.*, **14b**, 81–86 (1959)

183. Hauenschild, C., *Z. Naturforsch.*, **14b**, 87–89 (1959)

184. Herlant-Meewis, H., *Compt. rend. acad. sci.*, **243**, 823–25 (1956)

185. Bliss, D. E., *Bertil Hanström, Zoological papers in honour of his 65th birthday* (Zool. Inst., Lund., Sweden, 56–75, 1956)

186. Echalier, G., *Compt. rend. acad. sci.*, **242**, 2179–80 (1956)

187. Bodenstein, D., *J. Exptl. Zool.*, **129**, 209–24 (1955)

188. Stock, A., and O'Farrell, A. F., *Australian J. Biol. Sci.*, **7**, 302–7 (1954)

189. Durchon, M., *Arch. zool. exptl. et gén.*, **94**, 1–9 (1956)

190. Casanova, G., *Compt. rend. acad. sci.*, **240**, 1814–16 (1955)

191. Hubl, H., *Wilhelm Roux' Arch. für Entwicklungsmech. Organ.*, **149**, 73–87 (1956)

192. Clark, R. B., and Bonney, D. F., *J. Embryol. Exptl. Morphol.*, **8**, 112–18 (1960)

193. Hauenschild, C., *Z. Naturforsch.*, **15b**, 52–55 (1960)

194. Clark, R. G., and Clark, M. E., *Nature*, **183**, 1834–35 (1959)

195. Robertson, J. D., *Comp. Biochem. Physiol.*, **1**, 183–212 (1960)

196. Carlisle, D. B., *Pubbl. staz. zool. Napoli*, **27**, 227–31 (1956)

197. Nayar, K. K., *Current Sci. (India)* **25**, 192–93 (1956)

198. Nayar, K. K., *Z. Zellforsch. u. mikroskop. anat.*, **51**, 320–24 (1960)

199. Hodgson, E. S., and Geldiay, S., *Biol. Bull.*, **117**, 275–83 (1959)

200. Nuñez, J. A., *Z. vergleich. Physiol.*, **38**, 341–54 (1956)

201. Altmann, G., *Insectes sociaux*, **3**, 33–40 (1956)

202. Hekstra, G. P., and Lever, J., *Proc. Koninklijke Nederlandse Akad. van Wetenshrappen*, Ser. C, **63**, 217–82 (1960)

203. Hidaka, J., *Annotationes Zool. Japon.*, **29**, 69–74 (1956)

204. Ohtaki, T., *Annotationes Zool. Japon.*, **33**, 97–103 (1960)

205. Büchmann, D., *Biol. Zentr.*, **72**, 276–311 (1953)

206. Büchmann, D., *J. Insect Physiol.*, **3**, 159–89 (1959)

207. Dupont-Raabe, M., *Ann. sci. nat. Zool. et biol. animale*, **18**, 293–303 (1956)

208. Dupont-Raabe, M., *Arch. zool. exptl. et gén.*, **94**, 61–294 (1957)

209. Knowles, F. G. W., Carlisle, D. B., and Dupont-Raabe, M., *J. Marine Biol. Assoc. United Kingdom*, **34**, 611–35 (1955)

210. Knowles, F. G. W., *Endeavour*, **14**, 95–104 (1955)

211. DeLerma, B., Dupont-Raabe, M., and Knowles, F. G. W., *Compt. rend. acad. sci.*, **241**, 995–98 (1955)

212. Fingerman, M., and Lowe, M. E., *Physiol. Zoöl.*, **30**, 216–31 (1957)

213. Knowles, F. G. W., Carlisle, D. B., and Dupont-Raabe, M., *Compt. rend. acad. sci.*, **242**, 825 (1956)

214. Ostlund, E., and Fänge, R., *Ann. sci. nat. Zool. et biol. animale*, **18**, 325–34 (1956)

215. Edman, P., Fänge, R., and Ostlund, E., *Zweites Internationales Symposium über Neurosekretion, Lund*, 119–23 (Springer, Berlin, Germany, 1958)

216. Alexandrowicz, J. S., *J. Marine Biol. Assoc. United Kingdom*, **31**, 563–80 (1953)

217. Alexandrowicz, J. S., *Pubbl. staz. zool. Napoli*, **24**, 29–45 (1953)

218. Welsh, J. H., *The Physiology of Crustacea*, **2**, 281–305 (Academic Press, New York, N. Y., 681 pp., 1960)

219. Alexandrowicz, J. S., and Carlisle, D. B., *J. Marine Biol. Assoc. United Kingdom*, **32**, 175–92 (1953)

220. Carlisle, D. B., *Biochem. J.*, **63**, 32–33P (1956)

221. Maynard, D. M., and Welsh, J. H., *J. Physiol. (London)*, **149**, 215–27 (1959)

222. Cameron, M. L., *Nature*, **172**, 349–50 (1953)

223. Harker, J. E., *J. Exptl. Biol.*, **33**, 224–34 (1956)

224. Harker, J. E., *Cold Spring Harbor Symposia Quant. Biol.*, **25**, 279–87 (1960)

225. Ozbas, S., and Hodgson, E. S., *Proc. Natl. Acad. Sci. US*, **44**, 825–30 (1958)

226. Milburn, N., Weiant, E. A., and Roeder, K. D., *Biol. Bull.*, **118**, 111–19 (1960)

227. Roeder, K. D., Tozian, L., and Weiant E. A., *J. Insect Physiol.*, **4**, 45–62 (1960)

228. Bliss, D. E., *Science*, **132**, 145–47 (1960)

229. Karlson, P., and Lüscher, M., *Nature*, **183**, 55–56 (1959)

230. Norris, M. G., *Anti-Locust Bull. #18*, 1–44 (1954)

231. Loher, W., *Proc. Roy. Entomol. Soc. London*, **34**, 49–56 (1959)

232. Loher, W., *Proc. Roy. Soc. (London)*, **153**, 380–97 (1960)

233. Barth, R. H., Jr., *Science*, **13**, 1598–99 (1961)

234. Butler, C. G., *Experientia*, **13**, 256–57 (1957)

235. Butler, C. G., Callow, R. K., and Johnston, N. C., *Nature*, **184**, 1871 (1959)

236. Barbier, M., and Lederer, E., *Compt. rend. acad. sci.*, **250**, 4467–69 (1960)

237. Lüscher, M., *Rev. suisse zool.*, **63**, 261–67 (1956)

238. Lüscher, M., *Rev. suisse zool.*, **65**, 372–77 (1959)

COMPARATIVE PHYSIOLOGY: LATITUDINAL EFFECTS ON PHYSIOLOGICAL PROPERTIES OF ANIMAL POPULATIONS[1],[2]

By F. John Vernberg

*Duke University Marine Laboratory, Beaufort, North Carolina, and
Department of Zoology, Duke University, Durham, North Carolina*

In the last 25 years an ever-increasing interest has been shown in studying the physiological differences of animal populations, especially those which are latitudinally separated. Although these studies have taken diverse paths and encompass various physiological processes, two fundamental problems are involved. One is the question whether a physiological variation is genotypic or phenotypic; the second is the demonstration of the physiological mechanism involved in these variations. Frequently, when differences are noted in the physiological performance of organisms from different geographical areas, it is enticing to assume that these differences reflect inherent physiological patterns. However, the role of environmental forces in determining the physiological response needs to be carefully analyzed.

Although it would be highly desirable to review completely all of the papers relating to this topic, for obvious reasons this review will be limited to include review articles which have extensive lists of literature on the different topics included in this article, and recent studies not discussed in previous reviews. In addition to papers dealing with the physiological response of widely separated populations, studies on the response of these populations at their area of geographical overlap are included. Any omission of important or interesting work is unintentional.

Excellent general discussion of taxonomic, genetical, and ecological considerations can be found in various publications (1, 4, 28, 45, 52, 69, 83, 99, 103, 104, 138, 212, 266, 293, 308). The 1955 review papers of Prosser (193), dealing with physiological variation, and Bullock's (21) paper on temperature compensation in poikilotherms summarize much of the earlier work relating to latitudinal effects on physiological response (see also 22). Temperature influences on animals have been discussed in numerous recent books and reviews (64, 111, 192, 195); recent papers on latitudinal adaptation in plants have also been published (27, 146, 158, 205, 228, 235).

Topics of special interest to be considered here are general considerations of latitudinal distribution, historical review of significant earlier papers, the influence of various environmental factors on different physiological func-

[1] The information in this article covers the literature as far back as deemed feasible to go and includes references up to July 1961.

[2] I am indebted to my fellow workers at the Laboratory for their help. I am especially indebted to Dr. Winona B. Vernberg without whose help this article would have been impossible.

tions of various groups of multicellular animals, and possible mechanisms involved in physiological adaptation.

GENERAL CONSIDERATIONS

It was recognized early in the history of biology that tropical animals and arctic animals displayed similar rates of activity, although their respective habitat temperatures were dissimilar. This fact was especially difficult to interpret in poikilothermic animals in which the rate of a physiological function usually increases with elevated temperature until the organism is injured. It was assumed that these latitudinally separated populations of animals must have become climatically adapted to their environmental stresses. In the evolution of the study of this problem, the first phase, and one that is actively being pursued today, deals with the description of physiological races. The second phase attempts to deal with an understanding of the physiological mechanisms involved in the process of climatic adaptation. This classification is arbitrary and all studies cannot be put easily into these categories.

One of the most obvious variable environmental factors associated with latitude is temperature. However, as northern species become distributed in lower latitudes they may not be subjected to a different and higher temperature regime. Some inshore northern marine species seek deeper and cooler waters in the southern part of their distributional range, equatorial submergence (52), whereas some terrestrial species are found at higher altitudes at lower latitudes (83, 209). Because of peculiar ocean currents, some organisms are exposed to higher temperatures at higher latitudes than more southernly distributed populations (98). Also, some habitats in southern mountains have lower temperatures than more northern, low-altitude areas (296).

A number of recent papers deal with the general problem of the distribution of organisms in reference to latitude and temperature and are included merely to demonstrate the tremendous number of animals and problems available for physiological adaptation studies: elasmobranchs and chimeras (155); fish (98); barnacles (9, 37, 298); fiddler crabs (42, 262, 284); many phyla (57, 98). Also, numerous problems need investigation in the polar regions. Some physiological responses in the antarctic (179) and the arctic (227 to 234) have been studied; also, the existence of physiological races of animals, especially birds, in the southern cold temperate zones has been stressed (167). A special plea has been made for work on plankton physiology, reproductive physiology, and tolerance physiological studies in the arctic and subarctic regions (49). Marked changes within recent times in the abundance and range of many animals have been observed: marine invertebrates in South Australia (33); Norwegian avifauna (73); fishes of western North America (98); numerous species of plants and animals, especially European forms (36); and marine animals in New England (264). Seasonal shifts in distributional limits have been observed (297).

Recently Fischer reviewed and re-emphasized the well-known principle that in the tropics there is a greater diversity of plant and animal life than is found in more northern latitudes (57). The same relationship within one group (Calanoida) was noted (17). Thorson (269) found the infauna along arctic shores as rich and diverse as in the tropics, but most groups of animals and plants are better represented in lower latitudes. Fischer suggested that "the tropical environment is receptive to wider latitudes of physiologic variation—to a wider range of mutations—than is the temperate and polar environment." The basis for this hypothesis is that temperature fluctuations are slight in the tropics and tropical temperatures are nearer the optimum for protoplasm than are high-latitude temperatures. Subsequent papers in the present review tend to suggest that, in respect to compensation to temperature, species from the temperate zone have the greater degree of thermal lability which might be associated with a more complex genetic system, especially if most physiological factors are polygenic in nature.

Hutchins discussed the bases for temperature zonation in the geographical distribution of shallow-water marine species (101). In general, he felt that four types of zonation could explain the distribution of many species. Type 1. Thermal lethal limits of a species during winter limit its northward distribution, while summer temperature limits equatorward distribution. Type 2. North-south limits are determined by thermal limits required for repopulation. Type 3. In summer, the poleward limit is determined by the thermal requirement for repopulation while the equatorward limit is determined by the maximum temperature for survival. Type 4. In winter, the poleward limit is determined by the minimum temperature for survival; the southward limit, by the temperature limiting repopulation.

Numerous specific examples based on field observations show the usefulness of this technique in determining geographic limits of animals. In addition to correlations with field studies, an experimental and statistical approach to zoogeography has been stressed (12, 97, 129, 265).

Although temperature is probably the primary cause of latitudinal zonation, work in the China Seas does not support the concept that there is a gradual lowering of upper boundaries of the entire littoral population into the lower littoral zone and even into the sublittoral zone as one moves from temperate latitudes to the equator. The role of moisture in this zonation has been stressed (157). Other workers also have pointed out the importance of the interaction of temperature and moisture in zoogeography (51, 87, 211). This distribution pattern of an animal in reference to latitude might also be influenced by a combination of temperature and salinity. Many euryhalinic species which settle in the upper littoral zone in the high-salinity water of the North Sea Coast are present in the high-salinity deep water of the stratified Baltic Sea; this phenomenon is called brackish-water submergence (202).

The marked seasonal change in the duration of light at different latitudes has been shown to exert a marked influence on animal distribution (1, 4,

83, 303). Since light exerts a profound influence on many phases of the biology of animals (303), it has been found that light influences differentially the physiology of organisms at various latitudes (8, 55, 140, 270).

Recently the importance to organisms of geophysical factors not extensively studied in the past has been stressed (19, 20, 128, 181, 216, 295). Although it is to be expected that variation in these factors with latitude will result in different physiological expressions by separated populations, detailed studies are not now available. However, their role in the migration and orientation of various species is becoming better understood. Recently Hasler & Schwassmann reported on the sun orientation of fish at different latitudes (80). The present review will not attempt to cover this broad subject of migration and orientation as the papers cited above contain many references in this field.

A number of rules have been proposed as a natural outgrowth of the numerous observations and comparisons on animals from widely separated latitudinal areas. It should be noted that the physiological significance of these principles is not clearly understood and needs more experimental evidence. This subject is too voluminous to be dealt with in detail in this review; therefore, only a few of the more obvious rules will be briefly discussed.

Bergmann's Rule.—Generally, the smaller-sized geographic races of a species are found in the warmer part of the species range, while the larger-sized races are found in the cooler regions (143).

Allen's Rule.—Protruding portions of the body are relatively shorter in the cooler parts of the range of a species than in the warmer regions (143).

Both of these rules have been demonstrated to apply to an overwhelming majority of birds and mammals (199). However, the usefulness of these rules in terms of heat conservation has been strongly questioned (105, 226). An equally strong reply to this possible invalidation of these rules clearly defined their scope in broad evolutionary terms (144).

Numerous studies involving poikilothermic animals have not given a clear understanding of the applicability of these rules (21, 34, 61, 83, 141, 182, 196, 257, 267, 301). As recently discussed by Ray (199), three categories of comments have been made: (*a*) those in agreement with Bergmann's Rule; (*b*) those observing an inverse relationship since tropical poikilotherms are larger than northern species; and (*c*) those contending that these rules are meaningless for poikilotherms since these animals produce no significant metabolic heat. Ray grew 12 species of cold-blooded organisms at different temperatures in the laboratory, studied four additional forms in the field, and observed *Bufo boreas* both in the field and the laboratory; he found that 76.5 per cent conformed to Bergmann's Rule and that Allen's Rule was applicable to 70 per cent of the species studied. These figures were higher when the results of other studies were included.

Gloger's Rule.—"In general, animals in cool dry climates are lighter in color, have less melanin pigment . . . than races of the same species living in humid warm climates" (83). Tropical insects tend to be lighter in color than species from colder regions (113). Recently, the application on this rule was extended to *Dermacentor* ticks (203), and Hamilton reported another example for birds (74). Low temperature favors melanin formation in insects but the role of humidity is not clear (310). It was suggested that differences in coloration in beetles are genetic rather than environmentally controlled (44, 310). Perhaps this phenomenon is more clearly related to protective coloration than to a classical view of physiological adaptation.

Schmidt's Rule (as modified by Taning).—The number of vertebrae of fish is lowest at about 6°C., with the number increasing with both lower and higher temperature (260). A more detailed discussion of this rule will be dealt with under the general subject of growth studies at various latitudes.

The concept of a physiological race and the criteria of testing physiological variation used in this paper are based on the discussion in the review paper of Prosser (193).

With this brief introduction to some general considerations, the remainder of this paper will deal specifically with various physiological responses in relation to latitude and geographical races.

HISTORICAL STUDIES

Davenport (38) amassed much of the earlier literature on the influence of various environmental factors on animals and plants. Although I was not able to find specific reference to any systematic investigation of populations that are widely separated latitudinally, many earlier workers recognized the problems involved in this type of study. In Davenport's section on the temperature limits of life, he presented charts which summarized data on the lethal thermal limits of many species, ranging from animals associated with warm springs to species commonly collected from snow-covered mountains in the Alps. At this time he stated, "The interpretation of the differences in sensitiveness to cold of the honey bee (*Apis melifica*) and the red ant (*Formica rufa*), . . . , must wait for further knowledge." This statement is still apropos 65 years later even though much more is known about the influence of temperature on organisms. Davenport emphasized that certain "elements ought always to be regarded in experiments on the ultraminimum temperature." These included: (*a*) history of the temperature conditions in which the individual or its race had lived before experimentation; (*b*) duration of application of thermal stress and the kind of medium in which the organism is exposed; and (*c*) thermal acclimatization. Thus, it would appear from his discussion that early biologists were well aware that protoplasm may become modified through the action of environmental forces and that physiological adaptation is a fundamental characteristic of organisms.

One of the earliest and most cited papers demonstrating the difference in a physiological rate function with latitude is that of Mayer (142). When comparing the rate of pulsation of *Aurellia aurita*, a scyphomedusan collected in Halifax, Nova Scotia, with that of a population sample from Tortugas,

Florida, he noted that the northern form reached a similar maximum rate at lower temperatures than did the southern group. Although there was a region of overlap in response, the northern form beat at a much lower temperature range (about 0 to 28°C.) than the species from a lower latitude (about 12 to 36°C.). The summer habitat temperature in Nova Scotia was 14°C. while the summer temperature in Florida was 29°C. In another set of experiments the rate of heartbeat of oysters from Japan was compared with that of a species inhabiting tropical waters (259). At any temperature within the range of species viability, the temperate-zone forms exhibited a higher rate. When plotting the rate against temperature, the resultant curve for the high-latitude species was displaced to the left of that of the tropical species. However, no mention was made of the size of the animals studied.

Another physiological function which received some attention during this early period of study dealt with the relative growth rates of various species from different parts of its geographical range. Sea urchins from Plymouth, England, and Spitzbergen had comparable growth rates although their habitat temperatures were different, i.e., 14 and 4°C., respectively (178). However, it was observed that barnacles from high latitudes grew more rapidly at their particular habitat temperature than did individuals of the same species from southern waters at their own temperatures (159). Another variation in growth patterns was observed in work with the razor clam where individuals from southern areas grew much faster initially, but northern populations had a longer more sustained period of growth (300). Differences in the breeding season of animals from different latitudes were reported. The breeding season begins earlier in warmer parts of the range of the species, according to Orton (177). He also reported that temperature was the most important factor regulating breeding in marine invertebrates and that a definite temperature for breeding is a physiological constant for each marine species. A few years later, it was reported that the critical temperature for spawning of oysters was 20°C. and that this temperature held for all parts of its range with no adjustment to the extremes of its distribution (170).

As early as 1916, Krogh suggested that the respiratory exchange in cold-blooded animals from warm and cold waters would show differences which could be correlated with their respective habitats (122). However, this correlation was first demonstrated in terrestrial forms. The rates of oxygen consumption of fruit flies from a warm climate and a cold climate were correlated with temperatures corresponding to the two habitats (25 and 14°): both populations consumed oxygen at the same rate at 14°, but at 25° the northern form had the higher rate. At the time this work was published, both populations were thought to belong to one species, *Drosophila pseudo-obscura;* subsequently, the two races were separated into two sibling species (46).

In 1936, three papers appeared which represented important contributions to the problem of latitudinal effects on animals. A brief review of these papers will serve as background for subsequent detailed discussion of recent papers.

Thorson compared the larval development, growth, and metabolism of lamellibranchs from arctic water and warmer seas (267). In general, he found that species with a northerly distribution have a higher metabolic rate than southerly distributed species of the same genus at the same temperature. When comparing systematic groups which have a high oxygen consumption rate in the Mediterranean and in boreal waters with arctic species, it was noted that high-latitude species also have a high rate, but groups from southern waters with low levels of oxygen consumption have a relatively low metabolic rate. Epifaunal forms, like *Pecten* and *Modiolaria*, have a high rate of oxygen consumption, especially at higher temperatures, while digging species and level-bottom forms have not only a somewhat lower rate of oxygen uptake but also have a slower rate of increase with temperature. Thus, the rate of oxygen consumption seems to be correlated with the mode of life of the individual species within a given geographical area and, also, this rate represents a form of metabolic adaptation to differences in temperature as found in southern and northern waters. Thorson was aware that his results could be influenced by size differences in species, that seasonal differences might be observed, and that spawning and nonspawning animals might respond differently. Although the degree of response varied with species, usually the young of a species consumed more oxygen per unit weight and time than larger-sized specimens; the smaller-sized individuals had higher rates during spawning season and also appeared to be more sensitive to temperature changes. During the spawning season most species had an increased rate of oxygen consumption. He noted that deep-water forms, where the water temperature was below 0°C., were more temperature sensitive than shallow-water forms. No mention was made of Q_{10} values by this author but calculations from his data show values ranging from 1.34 to 21.1.

Working on molluscan species from marine waters of Denmark and the Mediterranean Sea, Sparck reported results similar, in general, to those of Thorson (245). In addition to the relation of oxygen consumption to habitat he reported that a relatively high rate of oxygen uptake was characteristic of arctic species, while relatively low rates were found in Mediterranean species. If northern species moved to warm waters, the increased metabolic rate would cause the animal to starve to death, thus limiting its southern distribution. On the other hand, the northern distribution of southern forms would be limited by thermal influences on larval development and reproduction. Although he mentioned the influence of size and season on metabolic rate, a detailed description of physiological state of the animals he studied was not given. It is difficult to interpret some of his graphs as only a few data points are given.

Fox reported on the activity and metabolism of cold-blooded animals in different latitudes (59). Unlike Sparck and Thorson, when comparing the oxygen consumption rate of animals of the same genus found in Sweden and

England, he found the English (warm-water forms) species to have a higher rate at any temperature than the corresponding northern species. This difference was thought to be ascribable to nonlocomotory (cellular) metabolism. However, the rate of respiratory movements and the heart rate of northern animals at about 6°C. were similar to those of southern species when determined at about 16°C. Within one species (*Pandalus montagui*) which is found in both localities, he noted that the rate of beating of the scaphognathite showed definite adaptation to temperature. Intraspecifically, no correlation was found between body size and oxygen consumption; no mention was made of interspecific comparisons although the northern forms tended to be much larger. These studies were made at different seasons of the year.

Later when determining the rate of oxygen consumption at different temperatures of muscle tissue from *Pandalus montagui*, Fox & Wingfield found the metabolic-temperature curve for northern animals to be parallel and to be to the right of the curve for the southern animals (62). This would bear out Fox's earlier hypothesis that the differences in oxygen consumption of the whole organism were caused by cellular (nonlocomotory) differences. In a later paper, the importance of body size in making comparisons was pointed out (302). The metabolic rate of the polychaete worm *Pectinaria auricoma* (average weight, 0.04 g) was much higher than that of another worm *P. koreni* (average weight, 0.40 g); both species are from England. However, the metabolic-temperature curve of *P. granulata* from Greenland (average weight, 0.54 g) was intermediate between the two English species. Thus metabolic adaptation to latitude is best seen when comparing similar-sized species.

In the last in this series of papers by Fox & Wingfield, additional data showed that the northern species will function at a faster rate than a closely related southern species when compared at a similar temperature (60, 61, 302). The fundamental question was raised as to whether these differences in physiological function were individual modifications (phenotypic variation) or were reflected genetic differences (genotypic variation). However, during this period some insight was gained into the relationship of phenotypic and genotypic variation to physiological processes of geographically isolated populations. Strains of *Lymantria dispar*, the gypsy moth, from localities in Europe, Asia, and North America were studied and reared under laboratory conditions (72). Therefore, strain differences could be attributed to genotype rather than to the differential effect of environment. Geographical gradients, which agreed in a general way to climatic changes from north to south, were observed in respect to pigmentation of larvae, "strength" of sex races, incubation period of eggs, etc. North-south clines in morphological traits of the honey bee were observed (2). When colonies were transplanted to various areas, it was concluded that these differences were genetic, rather than influenced directly by the environment. Other work on strains of *Drosophila funebris* showed that southern strains have a relatively high resistance to high temperatures and a decreased viability at low temperatures when compared with northern strains (271). Studies on the influence of temperature on meristic characters of fish showed that the number of rays in the dorsal fin rose with higher temperature (222 to 225). Thus geographical differences in physiological function manifested in the growth pattern might be phenotypic in nature.

Physiological differences between populations of one species have been observed where the populations are not widely separated by latitude (microgeographic variation). In many cases these differences appear to be a phenotypic expression of a compensatory phenomenon to a particular environmental stress (3, 21, 41, 236, 237). However, a genotypic basis for variation has been reported in other studies (7, 66, 88, 117, 126, 208, 209, 247).

One method of determining the existence of inherent differences between latitudinally separated populations is by transplantation studies. In some cases, the physiological differences persisted (2, 72, 112, 132), while in others differences were phenotypic (30, 40, 197).

LETHAL LIMITS

The range of temperature which is compatible with the life of an organism is commonly called the zone of tolerance; the maximal or minimal point of a temperature gradient at which death will result is termed the zone of resistance. The exact lethal thermal point is difficult to define in some cases and it appears to be dependent upon many factors (15, 16, 63, 64, 102, 195, 274). Fry and his co-workers have developed excellent techniques for graphically representing this zone of resistance by a polygon which represents high and low lethal-temperature points plotted against acclimation temperature. This type of representation gives a better picture of the relationship of genotypic to phenotypic variation. As has been shown in the lobster, the shape of this polygon may be altered by various combinations of temperature, salinity, and oxygen (137). Many data are available on the thermal death limits of various species (4, 11, 63, 64, 118, 119, 176, 188, 195). However, many of these studies are of limited value for comparative purposes as the techniques were poorly described, the thermal history of the animals was not mentioned, or other important variables were not controlled. The studies described below represent examples of some different facets of the problem of the response of geographically separated animal populations and do not represent a complete review of this field.

Early workers demonstrated latitudinal differences in marine animals. *Aurelia* from Nova Scotia died at water temperatures of 29 to 30°C., while Florida species survived temperatures up to 38.5°C. (142). *Limulus* from Woods Hole died at 41°C. but Florida species were not killed until 46.2°C. was reached (142). The prawn *Pandalus montagui* from Sweden could not survive aquarium temperature above 11°C., whereas individuals of this species from England could be maintained at 17°C. (62). It should be pointed out that marked differences in thermal limits can be observed in one geographical area by species occupying different habitats (18, 56, 176). Therefore, it is important in assessing the role of latitude to compare the same species or closely related forms having similar habitat requirements.

Physiological races of a periwinkle found in Japan on the Pacific Ocean coast (cold climate) and the Japan Sea coast (warm climate) showed marked seasonal differences in temperature tolerance. Results were in accord with the general adaptational concept; cold-adapted animals can withstand low temperatures better than warm-adapted forms. However, unexpectedly, the cold-adapted forms are much more heat tolerant than the animals from the Japan Sea coast (173, 174, 175).

Tropical- and temperate-zone species of *Uca* (fiddler crabs) have markedly different thermal death limits, especially at low temperatures (284). All the animals used in this study had similar recent thermal histories in the field; thus it was felt that differences did not reflect seasonal or different degrees of thermal acclimation shown to be operative in some animals (15). When temperate-zone species were acclimated to reduced temperature (15°C.), their lower lethal limit was markedly reduced, but cold-acclimation had little influence on tropical species. Phenotypically, temperate-zone crabs were thermally labile, whereas tropical species were stenothermal. Being thermally labile would have marked survival value to crabs in the temperate zone where the annual fluctuation of temperature is great.

The critical thermal maxima in 26 species of salamanders have been correlated with season, acclimation, photoperiod, dehydration, and latitude (102). This detailed study revealed that southern races could withstand higher temperatures better than northern races. Stuart correlated differences in the critical minimum threshold for toads with their altitudinal distribution (252). Marked differences in the ability of two closely related species to withstand low temperature near their distribution limits were demonstrated in *Tilapia* from Israel (309). However, morphologically similar populations of a single species of minnow from various latitudes did not show significant differences in thermal resistance times; but in other species, differences in lethal temperatures were observed when a morphological basis for subspecies existed (77, 136).

After investigating many phases of the energy metabolism of birds of the genus *Emberiza* extensively, Wallgren found the species with the more southern distribution to have a zone of thermal neutrality about 32 to 38°C., the range for the northern form being 25 to 33°C. (294). Critical temperatures for each species showed a similar relationship, the values being 38 to 39°C. for the southern form, 33 to 34°C. for the northern form. He suggested that the southern limit of distribution is determined largely by limit of heat tolerance. The southern form migrates during the winter but the northern form can withstand lower temperatures and remains over much of its breeding grounds throughout the year. The importance of temperature and moisture to the distribution of finches in western United States was studied by Salt (211). Each of the three morphologically similar species he studied was adapted in physiological and psychological mechanisms so that it could breed in an area of discrete climatic and vegetational character more efficiently than either of its sister species which occupy adjacent but different areas. Climate, vegetation, and behavior patterns all played a part in defining the individual breeding ranges.

Strains of *Drosophila funebris* from southern localities exhibited a higher level of viability at high temperature and lowered viability at low temperature than strains from northern localities (271). Results of studies on hybrids between geographical populations of *Drosophila pseudoobscura* showed that at low temperature (16°), viability of hybrids was longer than either the F_2 generation or the parents, whereas at 25° the F_1 gave similar values to those of the adults but better than those of the F_2 generation. This suggested that heterosis *per se* furnishes a physiological stimulus resulting in higher fitness (286). Although no correlation in latitude was studied, unusual thermal adaptations in discontinuously distributed genera of thermophilous water mites which were widely separated geographically suggested that these species either arose by polyphyletic acquisition of water margin adaptations or by dispersal and subsequent extinction of some monophyletic ancestral group (156).

In relation to geographical limits the degree of temperature tolerance of various intertidal animals was correlated with geographical limits (243). The least tolerant species had southern affinities while the most tolerant were northern forms. Since field and laboratory experiments showed that the temperatures experienced in nature are well within the tolerance limits of most of the animals, Southward felt that the causal relation between temperature and distribution must be sought in nonlethal terms, such as debilitating effects or interspecific competition. This view has been expressed concerning the distribution of other groups (8, 16, 110, 171, 246, 256, 257).

At the tissue level, observations on the rate of ciliary activity in isolated sections of gill of a lamellibranch indicate a marked correlation of temperature and habitat. Tissue from deep-water species was more thermally sensitive than tissue from shallow-water and intertidal organisms (220, 283), and tissue from a northern species of *Modiolus* is much more sensitive than a southern species (282). Thermal acclimation studies show that gill tissue from intertidal (warm-water forms) species are more temperature labile than deep-sea (cold-water forms) animals which tend to be stenothermal.

For cold-blooded animals it has been suggested that the thermal resistance of the tissues is a species characteristic which is independent of the environmental conditions of the species in the individual portions of its habitat. In closely related but different species, the thermal resistance of the tissues differs and is directly related to the temperature of the environment (275, 276). The subspecies of the polytypic species represent the result of a conservative formation of new varieties, in which the protein structure of the organism is practically unchanged. There appears to be a progressive formation of new varieties in nature, leading to the appearance of subspecies which differ cytophysiologically and give rise to new species.

As mentioned earlier, thermal lethal limits are influenced by a number of environmental factors. Some studies have shown that photoperiod is important. Goldfish exposed to long periods of illumination and short periods of darkness exhibited greater resistance to high temperature than did fish exposed to the reverse cycle of illumination (91). Seasonal variations in death limits in salamanders would be partially explained by photoperiod (102). It is conceivable that the interaction of these two factors might have pronounced influence on latitudinal distribution of some species.

Numerous studies have demonstrated that various combinations of temperature and salinity exert profound influence on the survival and distribution of various species (63, 64, 68, 84, 118, 119, 166, 189, 202, 218, 256, 273, 285). Panikkar long ago suggested that crustaceans with feeble powers of regulation can penetrate into brackish water far more easily at higher than at lower temperatures (180). Apparently certain marine species are limited to brackish water in the northern range of their distribution while fresh-water species exist only in lower latitudes. High temperatures reduce the optimum osmotic pressure of animals in diluted media and increase their range of tolerance to lower salinities; this would seem to be a physiological reason for adaptation to brackish and fresh water to take place more actively in warm sea than in cold. Serious questions concerning this generalization were raised by Schlieper (219). Verwey (285) reviewed papers relating to this general problem and pointed out the apparent disagreement in the results of various workers; some species appear to survive low temperatures better in high than low salinities, some respond in a reverse manner, and some withstand low salinities at low temperature and high salinities at high temperature. Results of recent studies on the influence of temperature on sodium metabolism suggest that high temperature may assist some brackish-water species in the invasion of more dilute media (131).

BREEDING

The recent review article on the annual reproductive cycles of marine invertebrates by Giese (70) cites many valuable papers relating to latitudinal differences in breeding. A few of the more important older papers dealing with invertebrates and vertebrates will be discussed here, along with recent work.

Very early it was suggested that each species had a definite temperature for breeding and that this temperature was constant over the entire range of the animal (170, 177). However, physiological races appear to exist, and this view does not apply to all species. The southern races breed at the higher temperatures (92, 120, 132, 161, 210, 214, 291). Even within one geographical area, local races of lugworms have distinctly different times of spawning, which might suggest that temperature is not of prime importance (50). Other studies suggest that temperature *per se* is not entirely responsible for breeding. In *Calanus* the first egg-laying of the year depends on the production of phytoplankton rather than temperature acting directly on the adult copepod. In general, this egg-laying occurs earlier in lower latitudes (140). The release of nauplii from the mantle cavity of barnacles is synchronized with the outburst of diatoms (8).

In general, animals from northern latitudes have fewer number of broods of young per year than more southern species (48, 70, 134, 140, 186). Also, the number of young per brood appears to increase with latitude. Birds from the northern and eastern parts of Europe tend to have larger clutches than those species from the southern and western regions (123, 124, 125). It was suggested that the increased daylight during the nesting season allowed a longer period for feeding the developing young. Turtles from lower latitudes have longer reproductive seasons but lay fewer egges per clutch than more northern species (272). Although it might be suspected that because marked fluctuations of mammal populations seldom occur in lower latitudes, northern populations would have a high reproductive rate, short breeding cycle, and an increased litter size. However, Lord found that only nonhibernating prey species show a correlation between litter and latitude; hibernators, fossorial-prey species, and predators (with the possible exception of foxes) appear to be unaffected by latitude with reference to litter size (134).

The length of the breeding season varies with latitude (70, 79, 214, 272). The breeding cycles of two species of barnacles, genus *Mitella*, one from north (California) and the other south (New Zealand) of the tropics, were mirror images of each other; in both cases breeding took place during the warm months of the year (90).

Differences between spermatogenetic cycles of the house sparrow *Passer domesticus* from various localities does not appear to be correlated with latitude (270). Hence, it was proposed that daylength was not the overriding influence in the timing of the cycle, but temperature and sunshine were of great importance.

Engels studied the influence of photoperiod on the testicular cycle of a species of bird which experiences transequatorial migration contrasted to a typical temperate-zone migrant's cycle (55). Although the bobolink would be exposed to two daylength cycles during its migration across the tropics, this species has only one reproductive cycle per year as is typical of birds which breed above tropical and subtropical latitudes. The bobolinks appear to have the necessary photoperiodic mechanism to enable them to establish a wintering population in the northern hemisphere, but juncos and white-throated sparrows could not extend their wintering range into the southern hemisphere without readjustment of this mechanism.

EMBRYOLOGY

Many of the studies comparing the physiological differences between latitudinally separated populations of animals have dealt primarily with the adult organism. However, it is well known that the developing embryologic stages are greatly influenced by environmental factors. Hence, selection of physiologically adapted races might be related more to responses by young stages than by the adult. Although the physiological mechanism of the adult may have been determined by a process of "canalization" during embryonic development (292, 293), in many temperate-zone species the adult will face a greater variation in environmental stresses than the larvae; and therefore some of these mechanisms are found to be operative only in adult forms.

Embryological studies of interspecific and intraspecific comparison of animals from different latitudes have involved numerous measurements: size of eggs, rates of cleavage and development, oxygen consumption rates at different temperatures, formation of meristic characteristics, and survival and longevity.

Eggs of northern races or species are generally larger than those of southern ones (139, 161). Physiological differences in rate of development have been reported for eggs of widely distributed populations of certain marine invertebrates (40, 221, 267, 268, 304, 305, 306). In colder waters, morphogenesis in relation to cleavage will proceed more slowly than in warmer waters. A race from a warm region reaches a specific stage of differentiation in the 8-cell or 16-cell stage, but in a race from a colder region this stage of development will be reached only in the morula or blastula stage. Apparently temperature and photoperiod play a role in conditioning the rate of cleavage in eggs of littoral surface organisms (306). Distinct differences in the behavior of races of nemertine embryos were noted in that the ingestion of dead embryos occurred in earlier stages in the forms from Murmansk than in the forms from Roscoff (221).

For the purpose of determining the influence of temperature and latitude on larval development of gastropod mollusks, Dehnel (40) found embryos and larvae from northern population grew two to nine times as fast as southern populations of the same species at a given, comparable temperature. Rearing studies in the laboratory demonstrated that growth was apparently temperature independent over the physiological temperature range. The growth curve of the northern form (growth measured in length of embryo of veliger larvae) was displaced to the left of the curve of the southern form when the rate of relative growth was plotted against temperature.

However, in *Calanus finmarchicus*, no adaptation of development of eggs to temperature was observed; eggs from arctic populations took the same length of time to develop as eggs from the temperate-water females whether at 0 or 20°C. (140). Similar results were obtained when rearing embryos of various species of barnacles with the notable exception that the upper lethal temperature was lower in northern species than in southern ones (186). Additional references on earlier work were cited in the historical section of this review (see also 57).

In general, differences in the developmental pattern of geographical insect strains as influenced by temperature show a similar picture (1, 172, 190, 215, 261). However, more detailed studies on the relationship of phenotypic and genotypic variations between races are possible for many insects as a result of the relative ease of rearing them in the laboratory (72, 94, 117, 126, 127, 261).

Recently it was demonstrated that phenotypic variation in mice was affected by the level of a uniformly acting environmental influence; i.e., low temperature increased phenotypic variation (5).

Heuts (84, 85, 86, 88) studied the influence of temperature and salinity on races of the three-spined stickleback from Scandinavia to France. Although two distinct morphological and ecological races were found, at their area of overlap morphological intermediate forms were found. However, Heuts found that these intermediate forms are not necessarily intermediate in their physiological properties and in their ecological requirements.

Latitudinal differences in meristic characters have served as a basis for distinguishing subspecies or populations of various animals, especially fish. The number of vertebrae in fish in relation to temperature has been most extensively studied (67, 130, 222 to 225, 260, 296). In many species, population differences are not genetic but result from phenotypic effects—the number of vertebrae is lowest at about 6°C. and the value rises with both lower and higher temperatures. By studying the embryology of various species, a thermal-sensitive period for determining the number of vertebrae (pheno-critical period) was observed during gastrulation. It was postulated that all phenotypical variations in meristic characters are undoubtedly determined by metabolism within certain genetically restricted limits. The excellent work of Heuts (84, 85, 86, 88) on physiological races of sticklebacks (*Gasterosteus aculeatus*) showed that the number of lateral plates is genetically fixed in each race but the number of fin-rays is modified by salinity and temperature. The temperature lability varied from low to high according to the salinity, and both races showed different temperature variation patterns.

Extensive studies on the mechanism of physiological isolation in fishes (Cobitidae) have been reported by Minamori (147 to 154). The temperature tolerance and rates of growth, differentiation, and oxygen consumption in embryos of local races of fish and their hybrids clearly demonstrated physiological differences. He suggested that the hypo- or hypertrophic development and the inviability of hybrids may result from temperature adaptation in two kinds of systems: the first system is concerned with the increment in activity of respiratory enzymes of embryos and is controlled by nuclear factors; the second system concerns the amount of energy necessary to sustain the normal development of the embryo and is controlled by cytoplasmic or maternal factors. Similar results were obtained for European salmonid fish (244).

Classic work by Moore, using various species of frogs (genus *Rana*), showed that embryonic adaptations were marked on a north-south cline. Not only did northern species breed earlier at a given latitude, develop faster at lower temperatures, and exhibit a lower lethal temperature range than did southern species; but latitudinally separated populations of one species *R. pipiens* exhibited similar responses (160 to 164). Differences in embryonic development of *R. pipiens* from different altitudes in Mexico were correlated with temperature. Similar embryonic adaptations, have been shown in toads (287, 288, 290). Interestingly, crosses between animals from Vermont and the highlands of Mexico produced viable embryos, whereas crosses between Vermont and lowland animals produced abnormal embryos (209). However, a recent study of embryology of *R. pipiens* from Wisconsin and high-altitude regions of Costa Rica revealed that the low-latitude embryos exhibit a slower rate of development at any given temperature, are less resistant to low temperatures, and have a narrower range of temperature tolerance than embryos from the more northern latitude (289).

The rate of oxygen consumption of pupae of a population of *Drosophila melanogaster* from Oregon was higher than that of individuals from central Java. However, only one temperature was used in this preliminary study (307).

Growth and Morphological Studies

One of the earliest approaches to studying physiological differences in geographically separated animals (physiological races) was to observe their growth rates and morphological comparisons of various body measurements. The growth rates of animals in response to temperature have been studied for years, but relatively few papers have dealt with latitudinally separated animals.

Variation in growth patterns of populations of one species from latitudinally separated populations has been reported. Sea urchins from Spitzbergen (4°C.) grew at about the same rate as members of the same species found at Plymouth where the mean water temperature is about 14°C. (178), which is the reverse situation noted by Thorson for certain mollusks (267). However, Moore found that *Balanus balanoides* from cold waters grew more rapidly at their own temperatures than did specimens from warm waters (159). Another variation was observed for populations of the razor clam in which growth in southern clams was initially more rapid but less sustained than in northern forms (300). The clam *Mya arenaria* grows more rapidly in southern waters than in northern latitudes (255). Dehnel (41) concluded that, when measuring the rate of shell growth in *Mytilus californianus* from Alaska and California, it was necessary to consider the depth of submergence from which the population samples were taken. Samples from California grew faster than those from Alaska when comparing populations living at the 3-ft level of submergence. Within any one latitudinal area there was a positive effect of submergence upon rate of increase of shell dimensions: the longer the period of submergence, the longer the period of feeding. Taking many factors into consideration, Dehnel felt that actual discrepancy in intrinsic growth rate was small or absent. Seasonal differences in the growth of copepods from one population were less than those observed in latitudinally separated populations of the same species (10).

Interaction of temperature and salinity altered the mode of growth of two regional populations of the fish *Gobius minutus*, and Swedish populations showed a more pronounced seasonal rhythm than those from France (258).

Salinity was shown to influence the growth of *Artemia salina* from different localities. A differential effect was shown on growth of parthenogenetic females and females from bisexual populations, and females and males did not respond similarity (71).

Variations in diverse morphological characteristics of geographically separated populations are extremely numerous. These differences are important, as they reflect the interaction of environmental forces on the genetic composition of populations and this is manifested in the physiological expression of body form. The formulation of certain ecogeographical laws and recent discussions concerning them were cited earlier.

Color differences in latitudinally separated populations of animals have been reported in insects (2, 39, 44, 72, 113, 310), lugworms (50), ticks (203), and birds (74). In some cases, these differences have been shown to be genotypic (2, 39, 44, 72). Differences have also been reported for relationship of various parts of the body, excluding total body length (54, 208, 209, 248). Morphological gradients in *Drosophila robusta* paralleled in a general way similar north-south gradients of inversion frequencies found in this species (248). Latitudinal clines in length of wings of birds (74) and *Drosophila* (201, 248) have been reported; in fruit flies, the northern forms had the longer wings, whereas the reverse was observed in birds. The starfish (*Asterias rubens*) from the western Baltic Sea is smaller and the integument is softer and more weakly sclerotized than that found in populations of this species in the North Sea (218). Variations in the shells of *Siphonaria*, a mollusk, could be correlated with latitude (100). A genetic basis for the correlation between trunk segmentation in a salamander and latitude has been suggested (89).

Behavior

Differences in the behavior of closely related species and subspecies from various latitudes have been reported. Oyster drills from Virginia stop drilling at temperatures below 15°C., whereas individuals from Delaware Bay do not drill below 10°C. (249). The innate dance tempos of six different geographical-ecological races of bees were found to be distinct (13). Certain subspecies of insects have not only different methods of ovipositing but have distinctly different preferences for sites (66, 126). Although physiological races of fish have been observed in respect to thermal limits (166), temperature did not influence their cruising speed differentially (136). The cloacal temperature and respiratory rate of a Brazilian breed of chicken showed different reactions to temperature and humidity from those of a New Hampshire breed (29). A marine copepod showed variation in behavior to vertical migration with latitude. It was suggested that this species has an optimum light intensity within which it stays, and perhaps it uses this light sensitivity and vertical movements as a means of sampling different layers of sea water (140). Although not emphasizing latitudinal variation, Kerkut & Taylor found that the spontaneous activity of isolated ganglia of the cockroach, crayfish, and slug varies with temperature. Differences in response to immediate exposure to temperature and after a period of thermal acclimation were noted (116). The ability of animals to control their body temperature by behaviorial means is well known (14, 21, 228).

The rate of pumping by latitudinally separated populations of mollusks has been reported (196, 197). Also, physiological races of mollusks have been described in respect to their ability to pump effectively in waters containing great amounts of suspended material (133).

Oxygen Consumption of Whole Organisms

Earlier results suggest that latitudinal compensation in metabolism has occurred in many species. In general, northern animals consume oxygen at a faster rate than southern animals when determined over a wide temperature spectrum. Scholander *et al.* measured the rate of oxygen consumption at various temperatures of 38 species of tropical and arctic poikilotherms, including fishes, crustaceans, insects, and spiders. They concluded that there is considerable, but incomplete, metabolic adaptation in aquatic arctic forms relative to aquatic tropical species, while terrestrial insects revealed slight adaptation if any. Scholander *et al.* thought no evidence had been found to show that organisms are adapted to temperature fluctuation by metabolic insensitivity to temperature changes (229); however, their work dealt with various tropical- and arctic-zone species which occupied different habitats, and it has been found that marked metabolic differences have been reported for species occupying different habitats within one geographical area (195, 278; see also 217). Also, the influence of laboratory thermal acclimation on metabolism was not determined.

In 1955, Bullock (21) and Prosser (193) reviewed papers relating to the metabolic adaptations of latitudinally separated animal populations. Since then a number of papers have indicated the importance of a number of factors which influence metabolism in comparing the response of different populations.

When comparing similar-sized species of fiddler crabs (genus *Uca*) from temperate and tropical zones, which have similar thermal histories, no consistent difference in metabolism correlated with latitude was observed except at low temperatures; but an intraspecific comparison of *Uca rapax* from northern Florida and Jamaica shows the classical type of response, especially at low and high temperatures (279). Tashian (262) demonstrated that crabs weighing three grams from Trinidad and southern Florida had similar metabolic rates when determined at 24°C., while the New York species was slightly lower. But at 14°C. animals from New York had a higher metabolic rate than the more southern forms. Working at still lower temperatures (1.4 and 15°C.), it was reported that *Uca pugilator* from Massachusetts had a significantly higher rate of metabolism than specimens from Florida only at the lower temperature (42). However, it is possible that these results might be influenced by seasonal temperature changes. Seasonal studies on *U. pugnax* indicated that "winter" animals from North Carolina had higher metabolic rates in the temperature range of 7 to 25°C. than "summer" animals, while the tropical species *U. rapax* did not show any seasonal fluctuation. This absence of any seasonal variation in metabolism may be correlated with the thermal constancy of the tropics, whereas fluctuating yearly temperatures of more northern latitudes have resulted in a labile metabolic pattern in temperate-zone species which can be correlated with thermal acclimation (280). Marked seasonal changes in rates of oxygen uptake were observed in an arctic species of amphipod (121). Although no seasonal acclimation in the metabolism of the striped shore crab (a temperate-zone species) was observed when determined at 16°C., respiratory rates did bear some relationship to local seasonal temperature changes when intertidal sea-water temperatures were below the environmental mean of 16° (207).

Metabolic rate determinations made at a number of temperature levels give a better insight into the influence of temperature on metabolism than generalizations from a few widely separated thermal points. Certain points along a temperature gradient appear to be of a more critical nature for the organism than others. This type of metabolic response when graphed gives a "staircase" appearance. In general, tropical- and temperate-zone fiddler crabs responded similarly at intermediate and elevated temperatures, but at low temperatures tropical species were metabolically activated at a higher temperature than more northern species. Similar responses have been observed in bees and fruit flies and in the heart rate of oysters (279). However, it has been found in some animals that the influence of temperature on metabolism is a regular one and the respiratory rate increases with rising temperature. When results are plotted, the resultant metabolism-temperature curve is regular without dips or peaks except at the optimum temperature (65).

In general this marked influence of a relatively narrow temperature increase may be expressed in terms of a high Q_{10}. After reviewing and re-evaluating many papers, Rao & Bullock concluded that Q_{10} was dependent on size and temperature of adaptation (198). With fiddler crabs, the highest Q_{10} values for temperate-zone species tended to occur at lower temperatures than for tropical-zone species. Values ranging from 3.73 to 15.9 were reported for tropical crabs with a temperature increase from 12 to 15°C., while a high Q_{10} was observed in a temperate-zone species between 7 to 12°C. (279). A lamellibranch living in the cold waters of Greenland exhibited a Q_{10} of 21 over the temperature range of −1 to 1°C. (207). Work on tropical invertebrates shows that in some animals Q_{10} decreases with increasing temperature while in other organisms no systematic variation in Q_{10} with temperature was observed (183, 184, 213).

When making inter- and intraspecific comparisons, it is important to consider body size (195). The slope of the linear regression curve obtained when plotting body weight against metabolic rate (weight-specific) varies with temperature: the steepest slope is at a higher temperature for the tropical species of fiddler crabs than for northern species (279), while in the striped shore crab the curve obtained was significantly less steep at 23.5°C. than at lower temperatures (206, see also 198). Thus with the change in slope the Q_{10} values of different-sized organisms will be changed. Within certain temperature ranges, the smaller-sized organism might appear to be more temperature sensitive than a larger-sized animal, but this relationship may be altered at another thermal point. Therefore, apparent differences between populations may be related to body size differences rather than to inherent metabolic variation.

Recent work on decapod crustaceans has further demonstrated that thermal acclimation has a pronounced influence on metabolism. Populations of the striped shore crab from southern California and Oregon show a close correlation between compensatory respiration levels and habitat temperature during the winter. Northern crabs consumed oxygen at a faster rate than southern forms when this consumption was determined at an acclimation temperature higher than the field temperature at the time of collection (207). The same general tendency was noted when temperate- and tropical-zone fiddler crabs were compared, in that individuals of the northern population exhibit higher metabolic rates at low and intermediate temperatures than southern members of the same species (280). Working with *Uca pugilator* from Massachusetts and Florida, Demeusy measured their respiratory rates at 1.4 and 15°C. when they had been maintained at 20°C. for various time intervals. The northern forms showed higher rates throughout a seven-week period when these rates were determined at 1.4°C. Although no statistically significant difference was noted between the respiratory activity of the two groups of fiddler crabs at 15°C., it should be noted that determinations were not made at this temperature over an extended period of time (42). The recent review paper on acclimation in mollusks describes general tendencies similar to those observed in crustaceans (237).

An apparent difference was reported in respiration of populations of the copepod *Acartina clausi*, from England and Long Island, when results were based on dry weight. The forms from English waters had a statistically higher metabolic rate during the cooler months of the year. It was suggested that the American form has a greater capacity for control of its metabolism under varying conditions of temperature (31). However, work on other species of copepods did not show dissimilar metabolic rates for populations from England and America (200).

A number of papers have appeared recently which deal only with the respiratory metabolism of tropical invertebrate animals, but as yet comparisons with data from other geographical areas have not been made (145, 183, 184, 213).

Morris measured the metabolic rate of fishes of the same species from California and Oregon at two temperatures (15 and 25°C.). He concluded that in the Cottidae there were two mechanisms correlated with latitudinal differences; the southern individuals had lower Q_{10} values and they showed a lateral translation of their metabolic rate-temperature curve to the right

(165). Thermal acclimation studies on goldfish show similar results (114). An earlier paper by Sumner & Laniham, in which the metabolic response of warm and cold spring fishes was compared, has a bearing upon climatic adaptation but did not stress latitudinal effects (254).

Determination of the respiratory rates of amphibians from the tropics and more northern latitudes at two temperature levels (14 and 24°C.) showed that the respiratory metabolism for the northern forms averaged higher than that of the tropical species at both temperatures. In contrast to the results of Morris, these workers did not find a significant variation in the Q_{10} values of northern and southern forms except in *Bufo boreas* (263).

Metabolic rates of birds in relation to distribution have been studied (211, 250, 294, 299). Wallgren reported that two species of *Emberiza* differed in their metabolic response and thermal limits. One species is more cold tolerant than the other. In both species, metabolism in cold was lower in specimens acclimated to winter temperatures than in those acclimated to room temperature (294, for earlier work see 230). In finches, it has been shown that if all other factors remain constant through a season, the metabolic rate remains fairly constant. Changes in the rate are chiefly caused by environmental factors. During low temperature these species use surplus energy for existence activities. Thus the distribution of these birds is dependent upon a favorable climate to support their energy needs (211).

Tissue Metabolism

Differences have been reported in the Q_{O_2} values of tissues of animals from different latitudes. In general, tissues from animals from a northern latitude consume more oxygen when determined at intermediate or elevated temperatures than tissues in those from a more southern latitude. Gill tissue from the clam *Mercenaria mercenaria* living in New York consumed oxygen at a much higher rate than North Carolina clams when this rate was determined at 25°C. (93). Clams were collected in New York when the water temperature was below 20°C., while the sea water temperature in North Carolina was about 27°C. Similar results were obtained for brain tissue of the toadfish from North Carolina and Massachusetts (277). Interspecific differences have been reported as well: Q_{O_2} values of brain and liver tissue of an arctic fish were higher than for a species from lower latitudes when determined over a wide range of temperature (187). However, Fox & Wingfield (62) reported the reverse tendency in that muscle tissue of a prawn from England consumed more oxygen than a more northern form when the rate was determined at a comparable temperature. None of the above studies involved laboratory thermal acclimation; they were based on field acclimation effects and therefore may reflect phenotypic variation.

Studies of the influence of thermal acclimation on respiratory tissue metabolism of animals from one population indicate that some tissues show marked compensatory adaptations whereas others are less sensitive (21, 192, 194). In goldfish, one worker found that brain tissue from cold-acclimated animals had higher metabolic rates than warm-acclimated ones, whereas another found no difference in Qo_2 of brain and liver preparations from cold- and warm-acclimated organisms; but the Qo_2 of gill tissue from cold-acclimated animals was significantly higher (21, 194). Roberts found that muscle tissue from the striped shore crab showed compensatory adaptation but brain cells did not (207).

When measuring the oxygen consumption rate of tissues from two closely related species of fiddler crabs from the temperate and tropical zones, Vernberg found differences in the rates of cold- and warm-acclimated gill tissue (281). Interestingly, the pattern of response of gill tissue from the temperate-zone species was similar to that exhibited by the response of the whole organism. The different patterns of response have been described by Prosser (194). At high temperature (36°), gill tissue from the tropical species had a higher rate than that of the temperate-zone species, but at low temperature (15°) the reverse was observed. Although these differences were minimized as a result of temperature acclimation, the genotypic limits of these two species appear to be different. The results in the mid-gut gland were less clear but suggested that this tissue not only is less thermally labile than gill tissue but does not respond in the same manner as the whole organism. It is proposed that certain tissues are more important than others in regulating the metabolic response of the organism.

Much recent work has been reported on tissue response to temperature and consequently has a bearing on the understanding of possible mechanisms involved in climatic adaptation of latitudinally separated animal populations. When the oxygen consumption of tissues near the lethal limits of the whole animal is determined, brain tissue is more influenced than other tissues (16, 169). Recent papers on the influence of cold and heat on respiration of tissues, especially mammals (108), stressed that this is a special case in the general problem of regulation of cell metabolism (43). Acclimation studies serve as a useful tool for the study of regulatory processes associated with increased energy release. It should also be noted that an additional tool in this general study is to use animals which show special physiological adaptations to a warm or cold climate. For example, Precht (191) reported on the resistance adaptation of some functions or organs of tropical fish to extreme temperatures, while other workers have studied the influence of elevated temperatures on tissue chemistry of an arctic fish (168) and tissue respiration of the arctic ground squirrel (75). Recent papers have dealt with cellular adaptation and cellular injury and death as a result of environmental stress (81, 109). Although the role of enzymes in temperature acclimation has been stressed (21, 107, 115, 192, 194, 251), a comprehensive study of the role of enzymes in determining metabolism of animals from different latitudes is lacking.

Florkin emphasized the necessity of the biochemical approach in studying climatic adaptation by pointing out the wide spectrum of biochemical phenomena as yet unexplained (58). The external environment not only exerts a direct effect on the metabolism of organisms, but influences the internal modifications relative to activating biochemical mechanisms of the homeostatic characteristic of each form of stress. It is an important consideration that metabolic homeostasis does not necessarily lie in the parameter corresponding to the environment, i.e., the homeostasis put into play during osmotic stress influences not only osmoregulation of the internal environment but also certain aspects of nitrogen metabolism.

Biochemical tools, such as chromatography and serological methods, have been used in detecting biochemical differences between races of one species and between closely related species of one genus (23, 24, 32, 204).

HORMONES

Inherent differences in the behavior of molting hormones of populations of *Palaemon* (decapod crustacean) from Plymouth, England, and Roscoff have been reported (26). Earlier papers reported what appeared to be contradictory results: in one area eyestalk removal initiated proecdysis and accelerated molting and in the second area molting was slower (25, 47). Presumably, the eyestalks contain a molt-inhibiting hormone and a molt-accelerating hormone, and the relative rate of secretion of these two hormones by the two populations is genotypically different. Another study reported that molting in *Uca pugnax* is temperature sensitive and that it is blocked at 15°C. or below. Thus, the northern limits of distribution of this species are established by the inability of larvae to molt at low temperature (185).

Although no strict correlation with latitude was observed, strains of *Schistosoma japonicum* varied in their virulence (95, 96).

OSMOREGULATION

A population of *Nereis diversicolor*, a polychaete from Roscoff, France, exhibited distinctive differences from populations from Wales and England in that it could regulate its weight in dilute sea water at a faster rate (53). These differences were felt to be racial and not environmental. However, after a rather complete laboratory and field study of this species from different parts of its geographical range, Smith felt this species showed a uniform pattern and level of chloride regulation regardless of the region in which it was found (239 to 242). He suggested that the differences in response and distribution may be caused by environmental rather than racial factors.

The existence of separate physiological races of differing osmotic resistance for populations of crabs from the Black Sea and the Mediterranean has been suggested (189). However, extended experiments on acclimation and breeding are lacking. Also, Shewan reported that arctic species of teleosts tend to have higher concentrations of trimethylamine oxide than species from the North Sea (238); it is possible that this difference is associated with osmotic stress. The study of the interrelation of supercooling and osmoregulation in arctic fishes and invertebrates revealed that shallow-water fish double their osmoconcentration during winter and are thereby protected against freezing. Marine invertebrates are nearly isosmotic with sea water (233).

<h2>THERMOREGULATION</h2>

The problem of thermoregulation in arctic and tropical birds and mammals has received much attention, with special attention being given to body temperature, body insulation, and metabolic adaptations. Irving & Krog measured the body temperatures of 22 species of mammals and 30 species of birds from the arctic and subarctic regions. The mean body temperature of the northern birds was 0.5°C. lower than the mean value of many temperate-zone species; however, the mean body temperature of the northern mammals was 0.5° higher than the mean for temperate-zone species. These differences were felt to be not indicative of climatic adaptation but rather the result of sampling from a limited number of species (106).

Body temperature does not appear to be significantly different in populations of animals from various latitudes, but additional studies have demonstrated that the degree of body insulation is much more important than metabolic response in climatic adaptation (230, 231, 235, see also 6). The color of the pelage appeared to be important in response to low temperature, in that heat control is less efficient with dark hair than with white hair (253). Seasonal changes in insulation of the fur of arctic- and temperate-zone mammals have been described with the relative change ranging from 12 to 52 per cent; the greatest fluctuation was noted in the larger species (78).

Recent review papers cite many references relative to problems of thermoregulation and hibernation (135); Hardy reviewed over 3000 references on the influence of heat and cold on thermoregulation (76). Results of studies on thermoregulation by behavior in reptiles indicate that large reptiles are restricted to the tropics or aquatic environments because of the expense in time that would be required to control the body temperature by behavioral methods. However, with smaller-sized species, body temperature seems to be fairly uniform within a genus, even though its members live in different habitats or climatic regions (14).

The energy balance of a species has significance in determining its latitudinal limits. This problem has been discussed for cold environments (82), seasonal variation in energy balance and its relation to migration (299), and the role of energy balance in limiting the northward distribution of tropical finches (35).

<h2>LITERATURE CITED</h2>

1. Allee, W. C., Emerson, A. E., Park, O., Park, T., and Schmidt, K. P., *Principles of Animal Ecology* (W. B. Saunders Co., Philadelphia, Pa., 837 pp., 1949)

2. Alpatov, W. W., *Quart. Rev. Biol.*, **4**, 1–58 (1929)

3. Anderson, J. D., and Prosser, C. L., *Biol. Bull.*, **105**, 369 (1953)

4. Andrewartha, H. G., and Birch, L. C.,

The Distribution and Abundance of Animals (Univ. of Chicago Press, Chicago, Ill., 782 pp., 1954)

5. Ashoub, M. R., Biggers, J. D., McLaren, A., and Michie, D., *Proc. Roy. Soc. (London), B,* **149,** 192–203 (1958)

6. Babenyscheff, V. P., *Zool. J.,* **17,** 540 (1938)

7. Barigozzi, C., *Année biol.,* **33,** 241–250 (1957)

8. Barnes, H., *Année biol.,* **33,** 67–85 (1957)

9. Barnes, H., *Oikos,* **9,** 139–57 (1958)

10. Battaglia, B., *Année biol.,* **33,** 259–68 (1957)

11. Beckman, C., and Menzies, R., *Biol. Bull.,* **118,** 9–16 (1960)

12. Birch, L. C., *Evolution,* **7,** 136–49 (1953)

13. Boch, R., *Z. vergleich. Physiol.,* **40,** 289–320 (1957)

14. Bogert, C. M., *Evolution,* **3,** 195–211 (1949)

15. Brett, J. R., *Univ. Toronto Studies,* **52,** 1–49 (1944)

16. Brett, J. R., *Quart. Rev. Biol.,* **31,** 75–87 (1956)

17. Brodsky, K. A., *Doklady Akad. Nauk SSSR,* **106,** 1103–6 (1956)

18. Broekhuysen, G. J., *Trans. Roy. Soc. S. Africa,* **28,** 255–92 (1941)

19. Brown, F. A., Jr., *Cold Spring Harbor Symposia Quant. Biol.,* **25,** 57–72 (1960)

20. Brown, F. A., Jr., Brett, W. J., Bennett, M. F., and Barnwell, F. H., *Biol. Bull.,* **118,** 367–81 (1960)

21. Bullock, T. H., *Biol. Revs. Cambridge Phil. Soc.,* **30,** 311–42 (1955)

22. Bullock, T. H., *Année biol.,* **33,** 199–203 (1957)

23. Capurro, S. L., and Francisco, S. G., *Invest. zool. chileanas,* **5,** 31–39 (1959)

24. Capurro, S. L., and Francisco, S. G., *Invest. zool. chileanas,* **5,** 97–101 (1959)

25. Carlisle, D. B., *J. Marine Biol. Assoc. U. K.,* **32,** 289–95 (1953)

26. Carlisle, D. B., *J. Marine Biol. Assoc. U. K.,* **38,** 351–59 (1959)

27. Carnegie Inst. Wash. Year Book, *Annual Rept. Director Dept. Plant Biol.,* **59,** 313–24 (1960)

28. Carter, G. S., *Animal Evolution, A Study of Recent Views of Its Causes* (Sidgwick and Jackson, London, 368 pp., 1951)

29. Cesnik, R., *Rev. agr. (São Paulo),* **33,** 193–98 (1958)

30. Choe, S., and Ohshima, Y., *Bull. Japan. Soc. Sci. Fisheries,* **24,** 616–19 (1958)

31. Conover, J., *Limnol. Oceanog.,* **4,** 259–68 (1959)

32. Cordeiro, A. R., Lewgoy, F., and Tondo, C. V., *Rev. brasil. biol.,* **20,** 69–78 (1960)

33. Cotton, B. C., *West Australian Naturalist,* **7,** 137–41 (1960)

34. Cowles, R. B., *Am. Naturalist,* **79,** 561–67 (1945)

35. Cox, G. W., *Ecology,* **42,** 253–65 (1961)

36. Crisp, D. J., *Geograph. J.,* **125,** 1–19 (1959)

37. Crisp, D. J., *Nature,* **188,** 681 (1960)

38. Davenport, C. B., *Experimental Morphology,* Part I & II (The Macmillan Co., New York and London, 509 pp., 1897)

39. Dean, Sister Mary Baptista, *Wasmann J. Biol.,* **14,** 1–57 (1956)

40. Dehnel, P. A., *Physiol. Zoöl.,* **28,** 115–44 (1955)

41. Dehnel, P. A., *Biol. Bull.,* **110,** 43–53 (1956)

42. Demeusy, N., *Biol. Bull.,* **113,** 245–53 (1957)

43. Depocas, F., *Brit. Med. Bull.,* **17,** 25–31 (1961)

44. Dobzhansky, T., *Am. Naturalist,* **67,** 97–126 (1933)

45. Dobzhansky, T., *Genetics and the Origin of Species* (Columbia Univ. Press, New York, 364 pp., 1951)

46. Dobzhansky, T., and Poulson, D. F., *Z. vergleich. Physiol.,* **22,** 473–78 (1935)

47. Drach, P., *Bull. Biol.,* **78,** 4062 (1944)

48. Dunbar, M. J., *Can. J. Research,* **19,** 258–66 (1941)

49. Dunbar, M. J., *Arctic,* **6,** 75–90 (1953)

50. Duncan, A., *Nature,* **184,** 71–72 (1959)

51. Edney, E. B., *Water Relations of Terrestrial Arthropods* (Cambridge Univ. Press, Cambridge, 108 pp., 1957)

52. Ekman, S., *Zoogeography of the Sea* (Sidgwick and Jackson, London, 417 pp., 1953)

53. Ellis, W. G., *J. Exptl. Biol.,* **14,** 340–50 (1937)

54. Emerson, A. E., *Ann. Entomol. Soc. Am.,* **28,** 369–95 (1935)

55. Engels, W. L., *Biol. Bull.,* **120,** 140–47 (1961)

56. Evans, R. G., *J. Animal Ecol.,* **17,** 165–73 (1948)

57. Fischer, A. G., *Evolution,* **14,** 64–81 (1960)

58. Florkin, M., *Ann. soc. roy. zool. Belg.*, **89**, 105–18 (1958–1959)
59. Fox, H. M., *Proc. Zool. Soc. (London)*, 945–55 (1936)
60. Fox, H. M., *Proc. Zool. Soc. (London)*, *A*, **108**, 501–5 (1938)
61. Fox H. M., *Proc. Zool. Soc. (London)*, *A*, **109**, 141–56 (1939)
62. Fox, H. M., and Wingfield, C. A., *Proc. Zool. Soc. (London)*, *A*, **107**, 275–82 (1937)
63. Fry, F. E. J., *Année biol.*, **33**, 205–19 (1957)
64. Fry, F. E. J., *Ann. Rev. Physiol.* **20**, 207–24 (1958)
65. Fuhrman, G. J., and Fuhrman, F. A., *J. Gen. Physiol.*, **42**, 711–22 (1959)
66. Fulton, B. B., *Ann. Entomol. Soc. Am.*, **18**, 363–83 (1925)
67. Gabriel, M. L., *J. Exptl. Zool.*, **95**, 105–48 (1944)
68. Gause, G. F., *J. Exptl. Zool.*, **87**, 85–100 (1941)
69. Gause, G. F., *Quart. Rev. Biol.*, **17**, 99–114 (1942)
70. Giese, A. C., *Ann. Rev. Physiol.*, **21**, 547–76 (1959)
71. Gilchrist, B. M., *Proc. Zool. Soc. (London)*, **134**, 221–35 (1960)
72. Goldschmidt, R., *Bibliog. Genet.*, **11**, 1–186 (1934)
73. Haftorn, S., *Sterna* (Stavanger Museum), **3**, 105–37 (1958)
74. Hamilton, T. H., *Wilson Bull.*, **70**, 307–46 (1958)
75. Hannon, J. P., Vaughan, D. A., and Hock, R. J., *J. Cellular Comp. Physiol.*, **57**, 5–10 (1961)
76. Hardy, J. D., *US Naval Air Develop. Center Aviat. Med. Accel. Lab. Rept. NADC-MA-6015*, **3**, 1–296 (1960)
77. Hart, J. S., *Publ. Ontario Fisheries Research Lab.*, **72**, 1–79 (1952)
78. Hart, J. S., *Can. J. Zool.*, **34**, 53–57 (1956)
79. Harvey, E. B., *The American Arbacia and other Sea Urchins* (Princeton Univ. Press, Princeton, N. J., 298 pp., 1956)
80. Hasler, A. D., and Schwassmann, H. O., *Cold Spring Harbor Symposia Quant. Biol.*, **25**, 429–42 (1960)
81. Heinmets, F., *Intern. J. Radiation Biol.*, **2**, 341–52 (1960)
82. Henschel, A., *Conf. on Cold Injury, Trans.*, **6**, 303–16 (1958)
83. Hesse, R., Allee, W. C., and Schmidt, K. P., *Ecological Animal Geography* (John Wiley & Sons, Inc., New York, 715 pp., 1951)
84. Heuts, M. J., *Nature*, **158**, 839–40 (1946)
85. Heuts, M. J., *Evolution*, **1**, 89–102 (1947)
86. Heuts, M. J., *Mededel. Koninkl. Vlaam. Acad. Wetenschappen, Belg.*, **9**, 5–63 (1947)
87. Heuts, M. J., *Heredity*, **2**, 63–75 (1948)
88. Heuts, M. J., *J. Genet.*, **49**, 183–91 (1949)
89. Highton, R., *Evolution*, **14**, 351–60 (1960)
90. Hilgard, G. H., *Biol. Bull.*, **119**, 169–88 (1960)
91. Hoar, W. S., and Robertson, G. B., *Can. J. Zool.*, **37**, 419–28 (1959)
92. Hopkins, A. E., *Bull. US Bur. Fisheries*, **47**, 57–83 (1931)
93. Hopkins, H. S., *J. Exptl. Zool.*, **102**, 143–58 (1946)
94. Hovanitz, W., *Biol. Bull.*, **85**, 44–51 (1943)
95. Hsu, H. F., and Hsu, S. Y. Li, *J. Parasitol.*, **46**, 228 (1960)
96. Hsu, S. Y. Li, and Hsu, H. F., *Am. J. Trop. Med. Hyg.*, **9**, 195–98 (1960)
97. Hubbs, C. L., *Am. Naturalist*, **68**, 115–28 (1934)
98. Hubbs, C. L., *J. Marine Research*, **7**, 459–82 (1948)
99. Hubbs, C. L., Ed., *Zoogeography a Symposium* (Am. Assoc. Advance Sci., Washington 5, D. C., 420 pp., 1959)
100. Hubendick, B., *Atlantide Rept.*, **1**, 151–66 (1950)
101. Hutchins, L. W., *Ecol. Monographs*, **17**, 325–35 (1947)
102. Hutchison, V. H., *Physiol. Zoöl.*, **34**, 92–125 (1961)
103. Huxley, J., Ed., *The New Systematics* (Clarendon Press, Oxford, 583 pp., 1940)
104. Huxley, J. S., *Evolution, The Modern Synthesis* (Allen and Unwin, London, 645 pp., 1942)
105. Irving, L., *Evolution*, **11**, 257–59 (1957)
106. Irving, L., and Krog, J., *J. Appl. Physiol.*, **6**, 667–80 (1954)
107. Jacobsohn, K. P., and Tapadinhas, J., *Bull. soc. portugaise sci. natl.*, **13**, 181–83 (1941)
108. Jasper, R. L., Denison, M. E., Zarrow, M. X., and Hiestand, W. A., *Am. J. Physiol.*, **195**, 285–87 (1958)
109. Johnson, B. F., and James, T. W., *J. Protozool.*, **7**(Suppl.), 21 (1960)
110. Johnson, D. S., *J. Animal Ecol.*, **21**, 118–19 (1952)

111. Johnson, F. A., Eyring, H., and Polissar, M. J., *Kinetic Basis of Molecular Biology* (John Wiley and Sons, Inc., New York, 874 pp., 1954)
112. Kalabuchov, N. J., *J. Animal Ecol.*, **6**, 254–75 (1937)
113. Kalmus, H., *Nature*, **148**, 428–31 (1941)
114. Kanungo, M. S., and Prosser, C. L., *J. Cellular Comp. Physiol.*, **54**, 259–63 (1959)
115. Kanungo, M. S., and Prosser, C. L., *J. Cellular Comp. Physiol.*, **54**, 265–74 (1959)
116. Kerkut, G. A., and Taylor, B. J. R., *Behavior*, **13**, 259–79 (1958)
117. King, J. C., *Am. Naturalist*, **93**, 171–80 (1959)
118. Kinne, O., *In Physiological Adaptation* (Am. Physiol. Soc., Washington, D. C., 195 pp., 1958)
119. Kinne, O., *Veröffentl. Inst. Meeresforsch. in Bremerhaven*, **6**, 177–202 (1959)
120. Korringa, P., *Année biol.*, **33**, 1–17 (1957)
121. Krog, J., *Biol. Bull.*, **107**, 397–410 (1954)
122. Krogh, A., *Respiratory Exchange of Animals and Man* (Longmans, Green, London, 1916)
123. Lack, D., *Ibis*, **89**, 302–52 (1947)
124. Lack, D., *Ibis*, **90**, 25–45 (1948)
125. Lack, D., *The Natural Regulation of Animal Numbers* (Clarendon Press, Oxford, 343 pp., 1954)
126. Lal, K. B., *Nature*, **132**, 934 (1933)
127. Le Clercq, J., *Bull. Soc. Roy. Sci. Liège*, **2–3**, 52–59 (1955)
128. Lindauer, M., *Cold Spring Harbor Symposia Quant. Biol.*, **25**, 371–78 (1960)
129. Lindroth, C. H., *Ecology*, **34**, 657–66 (1953)
130. Lindsey, C. C., *Can. J. Zool.*, **31**, 211–25 (1953)
131. Lockwood, A. P. M., *J. Exptl. Biol.*, **37**, 614–30 (1960)
132. Loosanoff, V. L., and Nomejko, C. A., *Biol. Bull.*, **101**, 151 56 (1951)
133. Loosanoff, V. L. and Tommers, F. D., *Science*, **107**, 69–70 (1948)
134. Lord, R. D., *Am. Midland Naturalist*, **64**, 488–99 (1960)
135. Lyman, C. P., *Conf. on Cold Injury, Trans.*, **6**, 57–87 (1960)
136. McCauley, R. W., *Can. J. Zool.*, **36**, 655–62 (1958)
137. McLeese, D. W., *J. Fisheries Research Bd. Can.*, **13**, 247–72 (1956)
138. Macan T. T., *Biol. Revs.*, **36**, 151–98 (1961)

139. Marshall, N. B., *Evolution*, **7**, 328–41 (1953)
140. Marshall, S. M., and Orr, A. P., *Année biol.*, **33**, 43–47 (1957)
141. Martof, B. S., and Humphries, R. L., *Am. Midland Naturalist*, **6**, 350–89 (1959)
142. Mayer, A. G., *Papers from Tortugas Lab. Carnegie Inst.*, **6**, 3–24 (1914)
143. Mayr, E., *Evolution*, **1**, 263–88 (1947)
144. Mayr, E., *Evolution*, **10**, 105–8 (1956)
145. Mendes, E. G., and Nonato, E. F., *Univ. São Paulo, Fac. filosof., ciênc. e letras, Bol. zool.*, **21**, 153–66 (1957)
146. Menzel, D. W., and Ryther, J. H., *Deep-Sea Research*, **6**, 351–67 (1960)
147. Minamori, S., *J. Sci. Hiroshima Univ., Ser. B*, **11**, 55–59 (1950)
148. Minamori, S., *J. Sci. Hiroshima Univ., Ser. B*, **13**, 199–212 (1952)
149. Minamori, S., *J. Sci. Hiroshima Univ., Ser. B*, **14**, 125–49 (1953)
150. Minamori, S., *Japan. J. Ecol.*, **4**, 66–68 (1954)
151. Minamori, S., *Japan. J. Genet.*, **30**, 243–51 (1955)
152. Minamori, S., *Japan. J. Zool.*, **12**, 89–104 (1956)
153. Minamori, S., *J. Sci. Hiroshima Univ., Ser. B*, **17**, 55–65 (1957)
154. Minamori, S., *J. Sci. Hiroshima Univ., Ser. B*, **17**, 65–119 (1957)
155. Misra, K. S., and Menon, M. A. S., *Records Indian Museum*, **53**, 73–86 (1955)
156. Mitchell, R., *Evolution*, **14**, 361–77 (1960)
157. Mokyevsky, O. B., *Limnol. Oceanog.*, **5**, 389–96 (1960)
158. Mooney, H. A., and Billings, W. D., *Ecol. Monographs*, **31**, 1–29 (1961)
159. Moore, H. B., *J. Marine Biol. Assoc. U. K.*, **19**, 851–68 (1934)
160. Moore, J. A., *Biol. Bull.*, **83**, 375–88 (1942)
161. Moore, J. A., *Evolution*, **3**, 1–24 (1949)
162. Moore, J. A., *Am. Naturalist*, **86**, 247–54 (1950)
163. Moore, J. A., *Proc. Natl. Acad. Sci. US*, **37**, 862–66 (1951)
164. Moore, J. A., *Am. Naturalist*, **96**, 1–22 (1952)
165. Morris, R. W., *Limnol. Oceanog.*, **5**, 175–79 (1960)
166. Morris, R. W., *Physiol. Zoöl.*, **34**, 217–27 (1961)
167. Murphy, R. C., *Proc. Roy. Soc. (London), B*, **152**, 642–54 (1960).
168. Musacchia X. J., and Clark, M. R., *Physiol. Zoöl.*, **30**, 12–17 (1957)
169. Nardone, R. M., and Caravaggio,

L. L., *J. Exptl. Zool.*, **131**, 163–71 (1956)

170. Nelson, T. C., *Ecology*, **9**, 145–54 (1928)

171. Newman, W. A., *Veliger*, **2**, 89–94 (1960)

172. Nishigaki, J., *Nippon Ôyô Dobutsu Konchu Gaku Zasshi*, **2**, 264–70 (1958)

173. Ohsawa, W., *J. Inst. Polytech., Osaka City Univ., Ser. D*, **7**, 197–217 (1956)

174. Ohsawa, W., and Tsukuda, H., *J. Inst. Polytech., Osaka City Univ., Ser. D*, **7**, 173–88 (1956)

175. Ohsawa, W., and Tsukuda, H., *J. Inst. Polytech., Osaka City Univ., Ser. D*, **7**, 189–96 (1956)

176. Orr, P. R., *Physiol. Zoöl.*, **28**, 290–94 (1955)

177. Orton, J. H., *J. Marine Biol. Assoc. U. K.*, **12**, 339–66 (1920)

178. Orton, J. H., *Nature*, **111**, 144–48 (1923)

179. Pace, N., *Conf. on Cold Injury, Trans.*, **6**, 141–74 (1960)

180. Panikkar, N. K., *Nature*, **146**, 366–67 (1940)

181. Papi, F., *Cold Spring Harbor Symposia Quant. Biol.*, **25**, 475–80 (1960)

182. Park, O., *Physiol. Zoöl.*, **22**, 359–72 (1949)

183. Parvatheswararao, V., *Proc. Natl. Inst. Sci. India*, **26**, 64–72 (1960)

184. Parvatheswararao, V., *J. Animal Morphol. and Physiol.*, **6**, 34–47 (1959)

185. Passano, L. M., *Biol. Bull.*, **118**, 129–36 (1960)

186. Patel, B., and Crisp, D. J., *Physiol. Zoöl.*, **33**, 104–19 (1960)

187. Peiss, C. N., and Field, J., *Biol. Bull.*, **99**, 213–24 (1950)

188. Pitkow, R. B., *Biol. Bull.*, **119**, 231–45 (1960)

189. Pora, E. A., *Bull. inst. Oceanog. (Monaco) 903*, 1–43 (1946)

190. Poulson, D. F., *J. Exptl. Zoöl.*, **68**, 237–46 (1934)

191. Precht, H., *Z. vergleich. Physiol.*, **42**, 365–82 (1959)

192. Precht, H., Christophersen, J., and Hensel, H., *Temperatur und Leben* (Springer, Berlin, 514 pp., 1955)

193. Prosser, C. L., *Biol. Revs.*, **30**, 229–62 (1955)

194. Prosser, C. L., Ed., *Physiological Adaptation* (Am. Physiol. Soc., Washington, D. C., 185 pp., 1958)

195. Prosser, C. L., and Brown, F. A., Jr.,

Comparative Animal Physiology (W. B. Saunders Co., Philadelphia, Pa., 688 pp., 1961)

196. Rao, K. P., *Biol. Bull.*, **104**, 171–81 (1953)

197. Rao, K. P., *Biol. Bull.*, **106**, 353–59 (1954)

198. Rao, K. P., and Bullock, T. H., *Am. Naturalist*, **88**, 33–44 (1954)

199. Ray, C., *J. Morphol.*, **106**, 85–108 (1960)

200. Raymont, J. E. G., *Limnol. Oceanog.*, **4**, 479–91 (1959)

201. Reed, S. C., and Reed, E. W., *Evolution*, **2**, 41–48 (1948)

202. Remane, A., and Schlieper, C., *Die Biologie Des Brackwassers* (E. Schweizerbart'sche Verlagsbuch-Handlung, Stuttgart, 348 pp., 1958)

203. Resnik, P. A., *Materialy Poznan. Fauny i Flory SSSR, Otdel. Zool.*, **34**, 107–12 (1956)

204. Ridgway, G. J., Cushing, J. E., and Durall, G. L., *U. S. Fish and Wildlife Serv. Spec. Sci. Rept.*, **257**, 1–9 (1958)

205. Ritchie, D., *Bull. Torrey Botan. Club*, **86**, 367–73 (1959)

206. Roberts, J. L., *Physiol. Zoöl.*, **30**, 232–42 (1957)

207. Roberts, J. L., *Physiol. Zoöl.* **30**, 242–55 (1957)

208. Ruibal, R., *Evolution*, **9**, 322–38 (1955)

209. Ruibal, R., *Copeia*, 212–21 (1957)

210. Runnstrom, S., *Bergens Museums Aarbok. Naturo. Rekhe*, **3**, 1–36 (1936)

211. Salt, G. W., *Ecol. Monographs*, **22**, 121–52 (1952)

212. Sara, M., *Attualità zool.*, **9**, 273–379 (1957)

213. Saroja, K., *Proc. Indian Acad. Sci.*, **49**, 183–93 (1959)

214. Sastry, A. N., *Studies on the Bay Scallop*, Aequipecten irradians concentricus *Say, in Alligator Harbor, Florida* (Doctoral thesis, Florida State Univ., Tallahassee, Fla., 1961)

215. Satomi, H., *Nippon Ôyô Dobutsu Konchu Gaku Zasshi*, **1**, 106–12 (1957)

216. Sauer, F., and Sauer, E., *Cold Spring Harbor Quant. Biol.*, **25**, 463–74 (1960)

217. Schlieper, C., *Biol. Zentr.*, **69**, 216–26 (1950)

218. Schlieper, C., *Année biol.*, **33**, 117–27 (1957)

219. Schlieper, C., Flugel, H., and Rudolf, J., *Experientia*, **16**, 1–8 (1960)

220. Schlieper, C., Kowalski, R., and Ermann, P., *Kiel. Meeresforsch.*, **14**, 3–10 (1958)
221. Schmidt, G. A., *Folia Biol.* (*Warsaw*), **6**, 265–85 (1958)
222. Schmidt, J., *Compt. rend. lab., Carlsberg*, **14**, 11–17 (1917)
223. Schmidt, J., *Compt. rend. lab., Carlsberg*, **14**, 1–7 (1919)
224 Schmidt, J., *Compt. rend. lab., Carlsberg*, **14**, 1–14 (1920)
225. Schmidt, J., *Compt. rend. lab., Carlsberg*, **14**, 19–23 (1921)
226. Scholander, P. F., *Evolution*, **9**, 15–26 (1955)
227. Scholander, P. F., Flagg, W., Hock, R. J., and Irving, L., *J. Cellular Comp. Physiol.*, **42**, 1–56 (1953)
228. Scholander, P. F., Flagg, W., Walters, V., and Irving, L., *Am. J. Botany*, **39**, 707–13 (1952)
229. Scholander, P. F., Flagg, W., Walters, V., and Irving, L., *Physiol. Zoöl.*, **26**, 67–92 (1953)
230. Scholander, P. F., Hock, R., Walters, V., and Irving L., *Biol. Bull.*, **99**, 225–36 (1950)
231. Scholander, P. F., Hock, R., Walters, V., Johnson, F., and Irving, L., *Biol. Bull.*, **99**, 237–58 (1950)
232. Scholander, P. F., and Vandam, L., *J. Cellular Comp. Physiol.*, **49**, 1–4 (1957)
233. Scholander, P. F., Vandam, L., Kanwisher, J. W., Hammel, H. T., and Gordon, M. S., *J. Cellular Comp. Physiol.*, **49**, 5–24 (1957)
234. Scholander, P. F., Walters, V., Hock, R., and Irving, L., *Biol. Bull.*, **99**, 259–71 (1950)
235. Scholander, S., and Kanwisher, J., *Plant Physiol.*, **34**, 574–76 (1959)
236. Segal, E., *Biol. Bull.*, **111**, 129–52 (1956)
237. Segal, E., *Am. Zool.*, **1**, 235–44 (1961)
238. Shewan, J. M., *Biochem. Soc. Symposia* (*Cambridge, Engl.*), **6**, 28 (1951)
239. Smith, R. I., *Biol. Bull.*, **108**, 326–45 (1955)
240. Smith, R. I., *Biol. Bull.*, **109**, 453–74 (1955)
241. Smith, R. I., *J. Marine Biol. Assoc. U. K.*, **34**, 33–46 (1955)
242. Smith, R. I., *Année biol.*, **33**, 93–107 (1957)
243. Southward, A. J., *J. Marine Biol. Assoc. U. K.*, **37**, 49–66 (1958)
244. Spaas, J. T., and Heuts, M. J., *Hydrobiologia*, **12**, 1–26 (1958)
245. Sparck, R., *Biol. Medd.*, **13**, 1–27 (1936)
246. Sparck, R., *Année biol.*, **33**, 233–39 (1957)
247. Staiger, H., *Année biol.*, **33**, 251–58 (1957)
248. Stalker, H. D., and Carson, H. L., *Evolution*, **1**, 237–48 (1947)
249. Stauber, L. A., *Ecology*, **31**, 107–18 (1950)
250. Steen, J., *Ecology*, **39**, 625–30 (1958)
251. Steinbach, H. B., *J. Cellular Comp. Physiol.*, **33**, 123–31 (1949)
252. Stuart, L. C., *Copeia*, 220–29 (1951)
253. Stullken, D. E., and Hiestand, W. A., *Ecology*, **34**, 610–13 (1953)
254. Sumner, F. B., and Laniham, U. N., *Biol. Bull.*, **82**, 313–27 (1942)
255. Swan, E. F., *Ecology*, **33**, 365–74 (1952)
256. Swedmark, B. *Année biol.*, **33**, 183–89 (1956)
257. Swedmark, M., *Année biol.*, **33**, 163–70 (1956)
258. Swedmark, M., *Arch. zool. exptl. et gén. Notes et Rev.*, **95**, 32–51 (1958)
259. Takatsuki, S., *Records Oceanog. Works Japan*, **1**, 102 (1928)
260. Taning, A. V., *Biol. Revs.*, **27**, 169–93 (1952)
261. Tantawy, A. O., and Vetukhiv, M. O., *Am. Naturalist*, **94**, 395–403 (1960)
262. Tashian, R. E., *Zoologica*, **41**, 39–47 (1956)
263. Tashian, R. E., and Ray, C., *Zoologica*, **42**, 63–68 (1957)
264. Taylor, C. C., Bigelow, H. B., and Graham, H. W., *U. S. Fish and Wildlife Serv. Fish. Bull.*, **57**, 293–345 (1957)
265. Teissier, G., *Année biol.*, **33**, 151–57 (1956)
266. Thorpe, W. H., *Biol. Revs.*, **3**, 177–212 (1930)
267. Thorson, G., *Medd. Grønland*, **100**, 1–155 (1936)
268. Thorson, G., *Année biol.*, **27**, 249–57 (1950)
269. Thorson, G., in *Treatise on Marine Ecology and Paleoecology*, 461–534 (Hedgpeth, J. W., Ed., Geol. Soc. Am., New York, **1**, 1296 pp. (1957)
270. Threadgold, L. T., *Condor*, **62**, 190–201 (1960)
271. Timofeeff-Ressovsky, N. W., in Stalker, H. D., and Carson, H. L., *Evolution*, **1**, 237–48 (1947)
272. Tinkle, D. W., *Ecology*, **42**, 68–76 (1961)
273. Todd, M., and Dehnel, P. A., *Biol. Bull.*, **118**, 150–72 (1960)

274. Tsukuda, H., and Ohsawa, W., *J. Inst. Polytech., Osaka City Univ., Ser. D*, **9**, 69–72 (1958)

275. Ushakov, B., *Intern. Congr. Zool., 25th*, Paper 37, 1–6 (1958)

276. Ushakov, B., *Zool. Zhur.*, **37**(5), 693–702 (1958)

277. Vernberg, F. J., *Biol. Bull.*, **106**, 360–70 (1954)

278. Vernberg, F. J., *Physiol. Zoöl.*, **20**, 227–34 (1956)

279. Vernberg, F. J., *Biol. Bull.*, **117**, 163–84 (1959)

280. Vernberg, F. J., *Biol. Bull.*, **117**, 582–93 (1959)

281. Vernberg, F. J., *Anat. Record*, **137**, 399 (1960)

282. Vernberg, F. J., Schlieper, C., and Schneider, D. E. (Unpublished)

283. Vernberg, F. J., Schneider, D. E., and Schlieper, C., *J. Elisha Mitchell Sci. Soc.* (In press, 1961)

284. Vernberg, F. J., and Tashian, R. E., *Ecology*, **40**, 589–93 (1959)

285. Verwey, H., *Année biol.*, **33**, 129–49 (1956)

286. Vetukhiv, M., *Evolution*, **11**, 348–60 (1957)

287. Volpe, E. P., *Evolution*, **6**, 393–406 (1952)

288. Volpe, E. P., *Physiol. Zoöl.*, **26**, 344–54 (1953)

289. Volpe, P., *Am. Naturalist*, **91**, 303–9 (1957)

290. Volpe, P., *Physiol. Zoöl.*, **30**, 164–76 (1957)

291. Voss, N. A., *Bull. Marine Sci. Gulf and Caribbean*, **9**, 84–99 (1959)

292. Waddington, C. H., *Nature*, **150**, 563–65 (1942)

293. Waddington, C. H., *Perspectives in Biol. Med.*, **2**, 379–401 (1959)

294. Wallgren, H., *Acta Zool. Fennica*, **84**, 1–110 (1954)

295. Wallraff, H. G., *Cold Spring Harbor Symposia Quant. Biol.*, **25**, 451–62 (1960)

296. Weisel, G. F., *Ecology*, **36**, 1–6 (1955)

297. Wells, H. W., and Gray, I. E., *Biol. Bull.*, **119**, 550–59 (1960)

298. Wells, H. W., Wells, M., and Gray, I. E., *Ecology*, **41**, 578–80 (1960)

299. West, G. C., *Auk*, **77**, 306–29 (1960)

300. Weymouth, F. W. McMillan, H. C., and Rich, W. H., *J. Exptl. Biol.*, **8**, 228–49 (1931)

301. Wimpenny, R. S., *Quart. Rev. Biol.* **16**, 389–425 (1941)

302. Wingfield, C. A., *Proc. Zool. Soc. (London)*, A, **109**, 103–8 (1939)

303. Withrow, R. B., Ed., *Photoperiodism and Related Phenomena in Plants and Animals* (Am. Assoc. Advance. Sci., Washington, D. C., 903 pp., 1959)

304. Wolsky, A., *Proc. Pac. Sci. Congr., 8th*, **3**, 505–10 (1958)

305. Wolsky, A., *Intern. Oceanog. Congr.-Preprints*, 360–61 (1959)

306. Wolsky, M., and Wolsky, A., *Anat. Record*, **131**, 611 (1958)

307. Wolsky, M., and Wolsky, A., *Anat. Record*, **134**, 657–58 (1959)

308. Wright, W., *Perspectives in Biol. Med.*, **3**, 107–51 (1959)

309. Yashouv, A., *Bamidgeh*, **12**, 62–66 (1960)

310. Young, F. N., *Evolution*, **14**, 277–83 (1960)

AUTHOR INDEX

SUBJECT INDEX

A

Acceleration
circulatory effects of, 177
Acetylcholine
binding of, 334
botulinum toxin and, 336, 337
cardiac output and, 153
catecholamine activity and, 113
cell enzymes and, 44
cell growth and, 43, 44
esophageal motility and, 115
intestinal motility and, 113, 114
mammary development and, 70
muscle excitation and, 335-37
nerve conduction and, 333
nerve excitation and, 326, 333, 334
potassium fluxes and, 114
pulmonary circulation and, 442
synaptic transmission and, 340, 341
thyrotropin secretion and, 492
transmitter role of, 162
vascular responses to, 147, 152, 153
Acid
gastric secretion of, 119-21
see also Hydrogen ion concentration
Acid-base regulation
disorders of, 398
kidney role in, 390-98
titrable acid excretion, 396, 397
Acrasin
cell aggregation and, 12
Actin
embryonic appearance of, 42
Activity rhythms
invertebrate
endocrine control of, 507, 508
Adenohypophysis
ACTH content of, 225, 228
adrenal cortex and, 223-51
aldosterone secretion and, 248
cortisone effects on, 224
Fraction H of, 236
insulin and, 224

metabolism of, 224, 233
protein synthesis in, 224
transplantation of, 226-28
Adenosine monophosphate
ACTH action and, 233-35
Adipose tissue
ACTH action on, 235-36
corticosteroid action on, 245-46
heat insulation by, 94
see also Fatty tissue
Adrenal cortex
ACTH effects on, 232-42, 483
adenohypophysis and, 223-51
adrenoglomerulotropic effects on, 479
atrophy of, 73
cholesterol in, 228, 234
enzymes of, 233-39
estrogen effects on, 73
functions of
development of, 19
histochemistry of, 42, 43
5-hydroxytryptamine and, 239
hyperplasia of, 73
involution of, 226
metabolism of, 233-39
progesterone effects on, 73, 241
regeneration of, 228
steroid hormones of
ACTH secretion and, 227, 228, 241
blood content of, 238, 240-42
carbohydrate metabolism and, 244, 245
catabolism of, 237, 242-44
degradation of, 226, 237
electrolyte excretion and, 377-84, 390, 400
electrolyte metabolism and, 358
enzyme activity and, 247
fat metabolism and, 246
metabolic effects of, 244-47
metabolism of, 75
protein binding of, 75
protein metabolism and, 242, 245-46
secretion of, 75, 232-42
stomach secretion and, 121
tissue enzymes and, 44, 45

urinary excretion of, 244
vasopressins and, 232
water excretion and, 379, 383, 384
steroidogenesis in, 232-42
temperature regulation and, 95
thyroid hormone and, 241
X zone of, 42, 43
zona glomerulosa of, 73, 250, 479, 482
Adrenal gland
adrenal-weight factor, 224
Adrenal medulla
cold effects on, 96
metabolism of, 237
Adrenocorticotropin (ACTH)
adrenal effects of, 226
adrenal-weight factor of, 224
aldosterone secretion and, 248, 249, 479
amino acid metabolism and, 237
biochemistry of, 223-25
biogenesis of, 224, 225, 228
corticoidogenesis and, 233-32, 240, 249
adenosine monophosphate and, 233-35
adrenal steroids and, 241, 242
ascorbic acid and, 239, 240
calcium and, 234
thyroid hormones and, 241
vitamin-A deficiency and, 238
extra-adrenal effects of, 235-37
fat metabolism and, 235, 236
inactivation of, 240, 241
lactation and, 70
pituitary content of, 225, 228
secretion of, 225-33
anesthetics and, 231
antidiuretic hormone and, 232
basal, 226, 227
brain field for, 226
brainstem and, 230, 231
cerebral cortex and, 230, 231
cold and, 225, 226
conditioned responses and, 225
corticotropin-releasing

581

androgen effects on, 76
metabolism of, 76
Sensations, cutaneous
see Skin, sensations from
Serotonin
see 5-Hydroxytryptamine
Shivering
hypoxia and, 88
metabolism and, 93, 94,
97
temperature regulation
and, 87, 94, 95
Shock
capillary permeability in,
160
cholinergic vasomotor
nerves and, 146
kidney function in, 366
see also Endotoxins
Skin
androgen action on, 73
circulation in, 148-50
bradykinin and, 149
carbon dioxide and, 154,
155
nervous control of, 90,
148
reactive hyperemia and,
150
regional differences in,
148, 149
sweating and, 149
temperature and, 90, 93
temperature regulation
and, 144
thermovascular reflexes,
144, 145, 149, 150
vasodilator mechanisms
in, 148, 149, 150
cold effects on, 96
connective tissue of, 73
embryology of, 20, 23, 24
estrogen action on, 73
heat transfer through, 98
nerve endings in, 200, 201
nerve fiber distribution in,
202-4
nerve stimulation in, 203
pigmentation of, 73
progesterone action on, 73
sebaceous glands of, 68,
73
sensations from, 199-210
central feedback on, 212
clinical observations on,
212-16
cold exposure and, 93, 97
discrimination in, 288
dysesthesia, 214, 215
free nerve endings and,
217, 288
human sensory studies,
216-18
latency of, 207, 209
leprosy and, 212, 213
modality specificity and,
210

nerve lesions and, 213
protopathic, 290
punctate theory of, 216,
217
sensory input alteration
and, 214-16
spatial summation in,
218
spinal cord lesions and,
213, 214
tactile discrimination,
97
thermal, 213, 214, 217,
218
see also Pain; Receptors,
cutaneous; Temper-
ature; Touch; etc.
temperature of
cold exposure and, 93
fitness and, 93
regional differences in,
94, 148
sensations and, 97
temperature regulation
and, 86, 87
thermal insulation by, 94,
98
thermal receptors in, 88,
89
Sleep
"activated", 313, 314
behavior during, 315
brainstem role in, 311,
312
catecholamine secretion
and, 94
cold exposure and, 93
cortisone role in, 314
dreaming and, 314
EEG changes in, 311, 313,
314
hypoxia in, 422
respiratory changes in,
422
reviews on, 300
Sodium
active transport of, 325-
28
aldosterone secretion and,
248, 250, 477
blood volume regulation
and, 477-84
brain receptor for, 390
corticosteroid catabolism
and, 243
coupled pump for, 371-73,
375, 385
depletion of, 386
fibrillation and, 188
field equation for, 330
heart excitation and, 182-
84, 188
intestinal absorption of,
127
ionic transfer of, 182-84,
188, 189
kidney exchanges of,

363-98
microelectrodes for, 192
muscle membranes and,
328, 329, 332
nerve excitation and, 325-
32
nerve membranes and,
330, 331
permeability to, 183
receptors sensitive to,
481
regulation of, 250
salivary content of, 111,
118
salt gland and, 326
salt wasting syndrome,
391
stomach secretion of, 119,
120
sugar absorption and, 130
taste preference for, 111
taste threshold for, 111
tissue clearance of, 150
tissue exchanges of, 357,
373, 374
transport of, 126, 127
Somatotropin
see Growth hormone
Spermatozoa
capacitation of, 63, 64
fertilization by, 63, 64
sex of, 57, 64
spermatogenesis, 57, 58
temperature effects on, 91
transport of, 63
types of, 64
Spinal cord
afferent neurons in, 209,
210, 291, 292
afferent paths in, 205,
209-13, 216, 292, 294
anterolateral columns of,
201, 211, 214, 294
chordotomy, 213, 215
clinical disorders of, 213,
214
dorsal columns of, 210,
211, 213
electrical activity of
temperature and, 100
motoneurons of
see Nerve cells
spinothalamic system,
290, 292-94
Spirolactones
aldosterone actions and,
382
kidney function and, 382
uterine effects of, 66
Spleen
antibody formation and,
48
circulation in, 153
tissue grafting and, 47
Stomach
central control of, 116
circulation in, 153

CUMULATIVE INDEX

VOLUMES 20 TO 24

INDEX OF CONTRIBUTING AUTHORS

602

INDEX OF CHAPTER TITLES